Van Roalte Institute
¥5

Historical Directory
of the
Christian Reformed Church in
North America

2005

D1260054

Historical Directory
of the
Christian Reformed Church
in North America

Compiled and Edited by

Richard H. Harms

Historical Commmittee of the Christian Reformed Church
in North America.
Grand Rapids, Michigan

© 2004 by Historical Committee of the Christian Reformed Church in North America
All rights reserved
Grand Rapids, Michigan

ISBN 0-9748422-1-4

Illustrated on the cover:

Rev. Douwe J. Van der Werp, 1811-1876
Rev. Dr. Henry Beets, 1869-1947
Rev. Marinus Goote, 1912-1999
Rev. Dante A. Venegas
Chaplain InSoon Gho
Rev. Nathan Visker

Contents

ABBREVIATIONS USED

CRC	Christian Reformed Church in North America
E	Evangelist
GKN	Gerformeerde Kerken in Nederland
I	Interim pastor
L	Lay worker
M	Missionary
OPC	Orthodox Presbyterian Church
PC	Presbyterian Church
PCA	Presbyterian Church in America
PCC	Presbyterian Church in Canada
PCUSA	Presbyterian Church (USA)
PRC	Protestant Reformed Churches
RCA	Reformed Church in America
S	Specialized minister
SS	Stated Supply
UPC	United Presbyterian Church
URC	United Reformed Churches

Name of the Denomination

For the two years following 1857, the congregations used no corporate name. In 1859 Holland Reformed Church (Hollandsche Gerformeerde Kerk) was adopted, which was changed to Free Dutch Reformed Church (no record of a Dutch translation used) in 1861. Two years later True Dutch Reformed Church (Ware Hollandsche Gerformeerde Kerk) was approved which was changed to Holland Christian Reformed Church (Hollandsche Christelijke Gerformeerde Kerk) in 1880. In 1894 churches were permitted to use Christian Reformed Church (Christelijke Gerformeerde Kerk) as well. The full adoption of Christian Reformed Church came in 1904. Christian Reformed Church in North America was adopted in 1974.

PREFACE

This is the first effort to compile a single directory of historical information of the Christian Reformed Church in North America (www.crcna.org), a denomination of 280,000 members with congregations in the United States and Canada, but particularly numerous in Michigan, Ontario, California, and Iowa. The denomination was founded by approximately 1,200 Dutch immigrants (about 300 families) in Michigan who left the Reformed Church in America in 1857. Initially determined to remain Dutch in character, following World War I English came to be commonly spoken in the churches. Since the 1960s the denomination has worked to become more multiethnic. Currently the denomination has ministries in more than 30 countries and its North American services are conducted in 14 languages.

The beliefs and doctrine of the Christian Reformed Church in North America are based on the Holy Bible, God's infallible written Word contained in the 66 books of the Old and New Testaments. We believe that it was uniquely, verbally and fully inspired by the Holy Spirit and that it was written without error (inerrant) in the original manuscripts. It is the supreme and final authority in all matters on which it speaks. With many other Christians, the denomination subscribes to the Apostles' Creed, the Athanasian Creed, and the Nicene Creed. We are part of the Christian church that follows the teachings of sixteenth-century reformer John Calvin and are rooted in the Reformed churches in the Netherlands that subscribe to the Belgic Confession, the Canons of Dort, and the Heidelberg Catechism.

The denomination's ecclesiastical structure involves local, regional, and bi-national (Canada and USA) levels. The local congregations, providing a variety of ministries, are administered by a council, a meeting of the elders, deacons and minister(s), which has responsibilities detailed in the Church Order. Classis, a regional group of congregations within a geographical area, has the authority to deal with matters that concern its congregations in common. A minister and an elder from each congregation are delegated to attend each classis meeting. Classical decisions are binding on the congregations in its region. There are 47 classes in the denomination, 12 in Canada and 35 in the United States. The annual synod is a bi-national gathering, which represents all the congregations with delegates from each classis. The tasks of synod include adopting creeds, the church order, liturgical forms, hymnals, principles of worship, and moral/ethical positions. Synod also provides general oversight for the joint ministries undertaken among congregations.

Much effort has been expended to make this directory as accurate and complete as possible. Work on this directory began when the denomination was approaching its golden anniversary and Dr. Henry Beets (1869-1947) began recording information about ministers and ministries on slips of paper. These slips of paper have survived and are now available in the CRC Archives. Although we do not have a record of all who helped gather subsequent data, Rev. John Leugs (1929-1988) and Rev. Henry Baak (1916-2001) each contributed much as volunteers. Various staff members of the CRC Archives and the denominational headquarters in Grand Rapids, Michigan have also done much.

I took up the task four years ago and began collating the various data sets into a single set and attempted to fill some of the many gaps. In an effort to provide listings as thorough as possible, all yearbooks and major denominational publications were reviewed. Biographical data was gathered from a number of archival records and secondary sources, including sources now available on the internet, such as the social security death index and various directories. We further attempted to contact each person still living. The data on the nearly 2,800 ministers and 1,500 ministries were keyed into an electronic database, which, along with the source documents, are housed in the archives at Calvin College. During the summer of 2002 the information on ministers was made available via the internet at http://www.calvin.edu/library/database/crcmd/index.htm, which is updated and corrected weekly and also contains images of most of those who served in the ordained ministry.

To provide an indication of the wide-ranging service of denomination members, also included are unordained people who served as missionaries, evangelists, in specialized ministry capacities, or taught at the denomination's institutions of higher learning, Calvin Theological Seminary and Calvin College. Because I was not able to find consistent source material, not included are those who served in administrative or support positions, or on the many committees, boards and other advisory bodies that have served the denomination.

Ministries (congregations, chapels, mission stations, etc.) are listed alphabetically by location under the current name. We attempted to list the first year of activity, which may, or may not be the year of organization. If a congregation's status changed, the year of that event is indicated. Former names were all referenced to the current name, not an intermediate name. Status descriptors of ministries (in parentheses) have changed over time and are not always identical, so this directory uses the descriptor used at the time the ministry was/is active. No descriptor indicates that the ministry is an organized congregation.

The section on ministers contains full names, birth information, graduate education, charges served, retirement, and death information. If an individual left the ordained ministry in the denomination, our record keeping ends, but when possible we have attempted to provide suggestions on where to look for subsequent information. Last names are alphabetized without regard to blank spaces or case so that Van der, Vander, VanDer are all treated as the same. Unless otherwise indicated, individuals served as ordained pastors. Appointments as stated supply, missionary, interim, evangelist, or lay leader are indicated in parentheses with the appropriate abbreviation.

The data on chaplains, seminary faculty, and college faculty were confirmed with sources from the respective agencies. Although we attempted to confirm all other data with original sources, such sources were not always extant. As a result, years of service were drawn from the best surrogate available — yearbook listings, which are not as specific as actual employment data would have been.

In addition to Revs. Leugs and Baak, I owe an inestimable debt to Hendrina Van Spronsen, who carefully copy edited the manuscript for consistency. In addition, archival staff members such as H.J. Brinks, Wendy Blankespoor, Boukje Leegwater, and Zwanet Janssens, and many others whose names I do not know, contributed their labor to this product. I thank the Historical Committee of the CRC (currently Dr. Harry Boonstra, Rev. Michael De Vries, Dr. Robert Swierenga, and Mrs. Janet Sheeres) for their support of this project, and their willingness to publish this as the inaugural volume.

In spite of diligent effort there are omissions and errors and these are mine. Please communicate these to me at crcarchives@calvin.edu or Archives, Calvin College, 1855 Knollcrest Circle SE, Grand Rapids,

MI 49546, so that future editions and the online directory of ministers will be improved. Data in this directory are current as of December 2002.

RICHARD HARMS,
ARCHIVIST, GRAND RAPIDS, MICHIGAN

Ministries

Abbotsford, BC — Abbotsford
see: Abbotsford, BC — First

Abbotsford, BC — Back to God Chapel
1969-1977
former name: Abbotsford, BC — Gifford Chapel,
1969-72
staff: H. Jansen (L), 1970-71; S. Hoogendoorn
(L), 1971-72; D. Groothuis (L), 1972-77

Abbotsford, BC — First
see: Abbotsford, BC — Gateway Community

Abbotsford, BC — Gateway Community
1950-
former names: Abbotsford, BC — Abbotsford,
1950-1969; Abbotsford, BC — First, 1969-2001
pastors: P. De Koekkoek (M), 1949-51; J. Betten,
(M), 1951-53; J. Roorda, 1953-57; T. Heyboer,
1958-69; P. Van Egmond, 1969-80; H. De Moor,
Sr., 1975-78; A. Beukema, 1981-95; B. Slofstra,
1990-; H.F. Steenbergen, 1996-

Abbotsford, BC — Gifford Chapel
see: Abbotsford, BC — Back to God Chapel

Abbotsford, BC — Hillside (emerging)
1996-
organized: 2001
pastor: M. Rylaarsdam, 2000-

Abbotsford, BC — Living Hope
1969-
former name: Abbotsford, BC — Second, 1969-
2002
pastors: M.W. Heyboer, 1969-73; H. Mennega,
1973-79; H.A. Van Hoff, 1980-89; T. Venema (L),
1989-90; H.C. Salomons, 1990-99; H.G. DeRuyter
(L), 1990-94; C.D. Korver, 1995-2001; C. Vander
Ploeg, 2002-

Abbotsford, BC — New Life
1986-
pastors: J. Poortenga, 1988-; B. Gritter, 1994-

Abbotsford, BC — Second
see: Abbotsford, BC — Living Hope

Abbotsford, BC — Trinity
1977-
pastors: R. Stienstra, 1978-85; H. Numan, Jr.,
1986-91; G.J. Veeneman, 1992-97; S. Couperus,
1994-

Abbotsford, BC — Zion Chinese
1979-
organized: 1987
pastors: S.M. Jung, 1979-83; L. Chen, 1981-88;
P.S. Lam, 1991-95

Aberdeen, WA — Gethsemane (emerging)
1996-
former name: Olympia, WA — Gethsemane,
1996-2000
pastor: Y.S. Shin, 1996-

Ackley, IA — Ackley
1868-1998, discontinued
pastors: J. Schepers, 1876-82; J.C. Groeneveld,
1882-84; H. Huizingh, 1886-90; C. Bode, 1891-
1903; H. Ahuis, 1904-13; D.H. Kromminga, 1914-
16; D. Plesscher, 1919-25; A.D. Folkema, 1926-
35; B.E. Visscher, 1935-40; C. Greenfield, 1940-
44; P. Dekker, 1945-47; I.W. Meuzelaar, 1948-51;
W.R. Witte, 1951-54; E.C. Marlink, 1955-59; L.C.
Bergsma, 1960-64; H. Salomons, 1964-69; W.M.
Elgersma, 1970-73; K.D. Van De Griend, 1974-77;
A.J. DeVries, 1977-82; F.R. De Boer, 1983-92;
A.J. Van Schouwen, 1992-95; J.J. Reardon, 1996-
97

Acquackanonk, NJ
see: Clifton, NJ — Richfield

Acton, ON — Acton
see: Acton, ON — Bethel

Acton, ON — Bethel
1953–
former name: Acton, ON — Acton, 1953–73
pastors: R. Groeneboer, 1955–59; J. Nutma,
1959–63; W. Van Dyk, 1964–67; P. Brouwer,
1967–72; J. Corvers, 1973–77; J. Cooper, 1978–
83; D. Miedema, 1985–90; A.G. Van Giessen,
1991–94; S.R. Brix, 1995–2002

Ada, MI — Ada
1909–
pastors: M.M. Schans, 1911–15; J.K. Van Baalen,
1916–20; H. Dekker, 1921–42; A.E. Rozendal,
1942–48; W.K. Reinsma, 1948–51; B.A. Van
Someren, 1952–55; A.J. Verburg, 1956–65; R.A.
Bruxvoort, 1965–73; A.M. MacLeod, 1974–83; B.P.
Bosscher, 1984–89; D.R. Fauble, 1990–96; J. Cooper, 1998–

Adrian, MI — Community
1975–1979
pastor: C. Libolt (E), 1975–79

Aetna, MI — Aetna
1921–
pastors: R.J. Karsen, 1924–27; J. Vande Kieft,
1927–31; R.H. Haan, 1931–39; M. Goote, 1939–
43; J.F. Hollebeek, 1943–47; G.P. Holwerda, 1947–
50; P.C. Zylstra, 1952–56; P. Honderd 1956–63;
F.D. Steen, 1963–67; J.A. Monsma, 1967–72; S.J.
Sietsema, 1972–78; D.M. Lieverdink, 1978–86;
L.M. Korf, 1986–95; B. Center (E), 1996–

Afton, CA — Afton
1913–1919, discontinued

Agassiz, BC — Agassiz
1961–
pastors: B. Den Herder, 1964–67; C. De Bree,
1968–69; J.H. Kits, 1969–74; J. Vander Schaaf,
1975–77; W. Geerts, 1977–83; J. Corvers, 1983–
91; J.M. De Koekkoek, 1991–92; R.W. Ouwehand,
1994–

**Ajax, ON — Crossroads Community
(emerging)**
1994–
organized: 2000
pastors: A.G. Van Giessen, 1994–

Ajax, ON — New Life Community
see: Pickering, ON — New Life Community

Ajax, ON — Real Life (emerging)
2001–
pastor: J. Wildeboer (E), 2001–

Akron, OH — Akron
1963–
organized: 1967
pastors: H.T. Karsten, 1963–73; C.E. Bajema,
1973–77; B.J. Becksvoort, 1978–85; B.N.
Huizenga, 1986–90; H.R. Winters, 1992–

**Akron, OH — Kent State University
(campus ministry)**
1970–
staff: H.R. Post, 1970–72; K. Hermann (L), 1980–
91; M. Roeda (E), 1995–96

Alameda, CA (mission)
1926–1926; 1936–1937
staff: P.J. Hoekenga, 1925–27

Alameda, CA (service home)
1944–1946; 1952–1953
staff: A. Mulder (L), 1952–53

Alameda, CA — Alameda
1924–
former names: San Francisco, CA — San Francisco, 1924–25; Alameda, CA — First, 1981–1997
pastors: P.J. Hoekenga (M), 1923–27; N. De Vries
(M), 1928–37; E. Tanis, 1937–46; C.R. Veenstra,
1946–51; H. Petroelje, 1953–82; J.A. Huttinga,
1982–92; R.R. Broekema, 1994–99; D.J.
Nederhood, 1997–

Alameda, CA — First
see: Alameda, CA — Alameda

Alamosa, CO — Alamosa
1904–
pastors: G. Zylstra, 1925–41; A.W. Hoogstrate,
1941–44; E. Ubels, 1945–49; P.A. Boertje, 1950–
54; J.L. Meppelink, 1954–58; R.A. Bruxvoort,
1958–61; L.K. Tanis, 1962–65; B.E. Visscher,
1965–72; M.H. Bierma, 1972–79; S.J. Van Heest,
1979–83; K.H. Eiten, 1984–92; C. Vander Neut,
1993–2000; M. Rylaarsdam, 2001–

Albany, CA — Korean
see: El Cerrito, CA — East Bay Korean

Alberni, BC — Alberni
see: Port Alberni, BC — First

Albuquerque, NM — Albuquerque
see: Albuquerque, NM — Chelwood Community

Albuquerque, NM — Chelwood Community
1953-
organized: 1956
former names: Albuquerque, NM — Albuquerque,
1953-58; Albuquerque, NM — First, 1958-1967
pastors: H. Hoekstra, 1953-57; B.N. Huizenga
(M), 1958-65; A.J. Haan, 1965-68; K.D. Koeman,
1968-74; C. Vander Neut, 1974-80; R.H. Cok,
1981-92; D.J. Hunderman, 1993-96; R.A.
Bouwman, 1998-

Albuquerque, NM — Fellowship
1962-
organized: 1978, began as a chapel
former name: Albuquerque, NM — Valley, 1978-
85
pastors: S.K. Redhouse (M), 1962-65; H.A. Van
Dam (M), 1965-69; A.J. Veltkamp, 1970-90; J.W.
Dykhuis, 1991-

Albuquerque, NM — First
see: Albuquerque, NM — Chelwood Community

**Albuquerque, NM — Government School
(mission)**
1921-1928
staff: M. Vander Beek (L), 1921-25; S.A. Lay (L),
1925-26

**Albuquerque, NM — Korean Presbyterian
Galilee**
1996-
organized: 1997
pastors: S.H. Chung, 1994-97; R.Y. Ryu, 1997-
2001; W. Lee, 1999-

**Albuquerque, NM — Southwest Campus
Christian Fellowship (campus ministry)**
1982-
pastor: A. Begay, 1982-2001

Albuquerque, NM — Valley
see: Albuquerque, NM — Fellowship

Alexandria, VA (service home)
1943-1945

Alger, WA — Alger
see: Alger, WA — Alger Community

Alger, WA — Alger Community
1956-
organized: 1980
former name: Alger, WA — Alger, 1980-98
pastors: J. Klunder (L), 1956-64, 1965-66; G.
Veenstra (L), 1964-65; R. Bouwkamp (L), 1966-
71; S. De Vries, 1971-75; E.R. Hommes, 1975-81;
H.T. Karsten, 1982-89; R.A. Sizemore, 1990-94;
R.J. De Ruiter, 1996-

Allegan, MI — Allegan
1960-1987, merged into Allegan, MI — Unity
pastors: S. Siebersma (E), 1960-65; F. Bakker
(E), 1965-71; H. Hoekstra (E), 1971-76; A. Sluis
(L), 1976-81; S.M. Merz, 1981-86

Allegan, MI — Millgrove
1941-1987, merged into Allegan, MI — Unity
organized: 1978
pastor: M. Tanis (L), 1941-44, 1946-50; A.
Timmerman (L), 1942-44; T. Venema (L), 1942-
43; D. Disselkoen (L), 1943-47; A. Groeneveld (L),
1946-47; A. Geerts (L), 1946-47; K. Postma (L),
1949-51; T. Smit (L), 1949-50; A. De Wys (L),
1949-50; L. Dams (E), 1951-58; A. Sluiter (L),
1951-52; T. Aardsma (L), 1951-52; A. Johnson
(L), 1951-52; O. Aardsma (L), 1958-60; A. Marcus
(E), 1959-60; M. Groenendyk (L), 1963-66; W.
Willink (E), 1966-77; P.N. Battjes (E), 1978-87

Allegan, MI — Monterey (mission)
1941-1944
staff: B. Brouwer (L), 1941-44

Allegan, MI — Moore School (mission)
1948
staff: N. Tanis (L), 1948

Allegan, MI — Spec Lake Chapel
1953-1974
staff: R.S. Meyer (L), 1959-60; J. De Vries (L),
1960-61; J. Turkstra (L), 1958-65; M. Veltkamp
(L), 1965-68

Allegan, MI — Unity
1982-
organized: 1982
absorbed: Allegan, MI — Allegan and Allegan, MI
— Millgrove
pastors: B.J. Niemeyer, 1988-91; D.S. Dykstra,
1992-97; D. Pewee, 1998-

**Allen, TX — All Nations Grace Fellowship
(classical ministry)**
1994-1998, discontinued

Allendale, MI — Allendale
see: Allendale, MI — First

Allendale, MI — First
1880–
organized: 1881
former name: Allendale, MI — Allendale, 1880–1952; occasionally also referred to as Pearline, MI — Pearline which was a post office about one mile east of Allendale
pastors: W. Heyns, 1885–91; J.B. Van der Werp, 1893–94; J.W. Brink, 1896–1900; L. Berkhof, 1900–1902; H. Keegstra, 1903–08; J.A. Gerritsen, 1909–12; J.C. Schaap, 1913–21; A. Bliek, 1921–24; W.D. Vander Werp, 1925–27; H. Keegstra, 1928–41; M. Bolt, 1942–47; D.J. Drost, 1948–52; F.M. Huizenga, 1954–68; J.T. Holwerda, 1969–72; S. Newhouse, 1973–87; G.G. Heyboer, 1988–; P.K.C. Yu, 1999–

Allendale, MI — Friendship Chapel (emerging)
1995–
pastors: S. Wunderink (E), 1995–98

Allendale, MI — Grand Valley State University (campus ministry)
1968–
pastors: R.W. Westveer, 1968–78; J. De Boer, 1979–

Allendale, MI — Second
1952–
pastors: C.M. Schemper, 1952–57; E.H Oostendorp, 1958–71; R.D. Ritsema, 1972–78; A.L. Van Wyhe, 1978–86; D.W. Royall, 1986–91; J.E. De Vries, 1992–

Allison, IA — Bethel
1920–1967, discontinued
former name: Coster, IA — Coster, 1920–1940
pastors: K.A. Koning, 1925–29; R.H. Wezeman, 1933–36; D.J. Drost, 1936–40; F. Handlogten, 1940–43; P.B. Huisman, 1944–48; C.G. Ter Maat, 1949–54; J.A. Bultman, 1956–60; I.W. Meuzelaar, 1961–65

Alliston, ON — Alliston
1953–
pastors: H. Hollander, 1957–62; G. Bieze, 1962–67; S. Terpstra, 1967–75; J.W. Hielkema, 1975–78; G.J. Van Arragon, 1979–83; J. De Vries, 1983–87; S. Cooper, 1987–93; H.D. Zantingh, 1994–

Alpaugh, CA (mission)
1916

Alto, MI — Lakeside Community
1968–
organized: 1977
former name: Alto, MI — Campau Lake Chapel, 1968–69
pastors: W.B. Ipema (L), 1968–69; R.J. Kuiper (L), 1968–69; M. Barber (E), 1969–74; M. Keuning (E), 1974–79; J.J. Berends, 1979–81; B.W. Mulder, 1981–97; R.D. Bultman, 1998–

Alto, WI — Alto
1881–
divided into: Alto WI, — First and Alto, WI — Second, 1881–1886
pastors: J.C. Groeneveld, 1884–93; M.J. Marcusse, 1894–96; P. Kosten, 1897–98; H.M. Vander Ploeg, 1899–1901; M. De Boer, 1900–03; P. Bloem, 1904–07; J. Homan, 1907–10; J. De Jonge, 1911–13; R. Vande Kieft, 1914–15; P. Van Dyk, 1915–18; R. Diephuis, 1919–25; W. Borgman, 1925–32; K.W. Fortuin, 1933–37; T. Heyboer, 1938–43; M. Huizenga, 1943–47; W. Alkema, 1948–57; C.M. Schoolland, 1958–62; W.J. Dykstra, 1962–65; J. Geels, 1966–69; G.E. De Vries, 1971–79; J. Kroon, 1980–91; R.L. Gelwicks, 1992–96; J.C. Tousley, 1997–99

Alto, WI — First
see: Alto, WI — Alto

Alto, WI — Second
see: Alto, WI — Alto

Ames, IA — Ames
see: Ames, IA — Trinity

Ames, IA — Iowa State (campus ministry)
1966–
staff: A. Menninga, 1966–68; F.J. Walhof, 1968–86; S.A. Young (RCA), 1988–92; B. Strait (L), 1992–

Ames, IA — Iowa State Korean Campus (campus ministry)
1993–
pastor: M.S. Kim, 1993–

Ames, IA — Korean
1988–
affiliated with CRC in 1988, was Korean Bansuk Presbyterian Church
pastors: J.D Lee, 1989–93; M.S. Kim, 1993–

4

Ames, IA — Trinity
1964-
organized: 1971
former names: Ames, IA — Ames, 1971-72;
Ames, IA — University, 1972-1990; Ames, IA —
Unity, 1990-1997
pastors: A.D. Menninga (M), 1964-68; F.J.
Walhof, 1968-81; A.J. Stienstra, 1981-90; J.E.
Kok, 1991-96; T.J. Niehof, 1997-

Ames, IA — Unity
see: Ames, IA — Trinity

Ames, IA — University
see: Ames, IA — Trinity

Amsterdam, ID — Amsterdam
1912-1919, discontinued
pastor: W. Meyer, 1914-17

Anacortes, WA — Anacortes
1964-
organized: 1992
pastors: L. Dams (E), 1964-70; C.G. Roelofs (M),
1970-74; A. Poot (E), 1974-75; D.B. Muir, 1977-
83; F. Lantinga (E), 1985-93; C.A. Reyneveld,
1993-97; D. Fakkema (E), 1997-

Anaheim, CA — Anaheim
1956-
pastors: F. De Jong, 1956-57; I.J. Apol. 1958-65;
H.R. Roelofs, 1965-75; D.W. Van Gent, 1976-81;
R.D. De Young, 1982-93; D.L. Piers, 1989-93;
D.R. Koll, 1994-; A.W. Chun, 1999-2001

Anaheim, CA — Dae II Korean
1987-1996, merged into Anaheim, CA — Neung
Ryuk
pastors: D.R. Chung, 1987-94; W.S. Chung,
1992-96; J.J. Kim, 1993-94

Anaheim, CA — Garden Grove Korean
1993-
former name: Anaheim, CA — Korean, 1993-1994
pastor: Y.O. Kim, 1988-2001; S.J. Kang, 1997-
2000; S.E. Nam, 2001-

Anaheim, CA — Korean
see: Anaheim, CA — Garden Grove Korean

Anaheim, CA — Latin American
1969-
organized: 1983
pastors: C.J. Nyenhuis (M), 1969-90; G. Ortiz,
1991-95; Francisco Golon (E), 1996-

Anaheim, CA — Neung Ryuk
1987-
former name: Norwalk, CA — Rok Won, 1993-
1997; absorbed Anaheim, CA — So Mang Korean,
1987-1996; Anaheim, CA — Dae II Korean, 1997-
1998, which was Garden Grove, CA — So Mang
Korean, 1990-1997
pastors: D.R. Chung, 1987-94; M.W. Bay, 1991-
92; P.H. Kim, 1992-; W.S. Chung, 1995-96; J.I.
Hyun, 1996-97
pastor of Tyrannus Korean: J.I. Hyun, 1989-96

Anaheim, CA — So Mang Korean
see Anaheim, CA — Neung-Ryuk

Ancaster, ON — Ancaster
1976-
pastors: M.J. Contant, 1976-80; C. Van
Niejenhuis, 1981-85; B.H. De Jonge, 1986-99;
G.H. Pols, 2000-

Ancaster, ON — Fellowship
1989-
pastors: P.A. Hoytema, 1990-98; B.H. De Jonge
(I), 1999-2000; J.H. Bouwers, 2000-

Anchorage, AK (service home)
1963-1976
staff: W. Heynen, 1963-64; W.A. Verwolf, 1969-
72; D. Recker, 1973-75

Anchorage, AK — Alaska Korean
1994-
organized: 1997
pastors: J.J. Kim, 1996-; K.S. Jho, 1994-

Anchorage, AK — Anchorage
see: Anchorage, AK — Trinity

Anchorage, AK — Crosspoint (emerging)
1998-
pastor: D. Kuiper, 1998-

Anchorage, AK — Trinity
1957-
organized: 1959
former name: Anchorage, AK — Anchorage,
1959-1970
pastors: W. Heynen (M), 1953-71; D.L. Recker,
1973-82; B.J. Van Ee, 1983-92; D.J. Kruis, 1993-
98; J.E. Powell, 2000-

Andover, SD — Andover
1909-1915, branch of Bemis, SD — Bemis

Ann Arbor, MI — Ann Arbor
1955-
organized: 1955
pastors: E.H. Palmer, 1957-60; A.L. Hoksbergen, 1961-66; S. Draayer, 1967-72; G. Haagsma (L), 1968-69; W.C. De Vries, 1973-76; R.W. Klingenberg, 1977-79; W.L. De Jong, 1979-95; J.D. Suk, 1990-93; P.W. Brink, 1995-; H.A. Stob, 1996-

Ann Arbor, MI — Campus Chapel (campus ministry)
1941-
pastors: L. Verduin, 1941-62; D.H. Postema, 1963-98; S. Draayer, 1969-70; R. Palsrok (I), 1969-70; A.J. Benckhuysen, 1998-2001; R. McKenzie (I), 2001;T. Wolthuis, 2001-

Ann Arbor, MI — Korean Hope (emerging)
1991, withdrew
pastors: D.D.Y. Kim, 1991

Ann Arbor, MI — The Lighthouse Community (emerging)
2000-
pastor: D.K. Sung, 2000-

Appleton, WI — Covenant
1977-
organized: 1982
pastors: N.J. Gebben, Sr., 1977-78; D.J. Steenhoek, 1980-87; C.G. Van Halsema, 1987-91; E.J. Laarman, 1992-

Apple Valley, CA — Church of the Way (emerging)
1993-
emerging, 1995
former name: Victorville, CA — Church of the Way, 1993-99
pastor: R. Lewis (E), 1993-

Arcadia, CA — Arcadia
see: Arcadia, CA — Hope Community

Arcadia, CA — Hope Community
1939-
organized: 1941
former name: Arcadia, CA — Arcadia, 1939-2000
pastors: F. De Jong, 1939-43; W. Heynen, 1943-49; J.B. Ibershoff, 1949-57, 1990-98; K. Rietema, 1958-64; F. Diemer, 1965-68; J.S. Meyer, 1969-75; M. De Vries, 1976-80; R.D. Kramer, 1981-95; S. Sybenga, 1997-

Arcadia, CA — Indonesian (emerging)
1993-
pastors: H.L. Lie, 1993-97; P.A. Manuhutu, 1998-

Arlene, MI — Arlene
1894-1968, discontinued
former name: Caldwell, MI — Caldwell, 1898-1926
pastors: E. Van Korlaar, 1902-05; M.J. Marcusse, 1906-13; J. Kolkman, 1914-20; S. Fopma, 1920-26; M. Keuning, 1934-36; S. Werkema, 1936-40; P. Van Tuinen, 1940-44; W. Dubois, 1944-48

Arleta, CA — Valley
1988-1993, withdrew
organized: 1988
former name: North Hollywood, CA — Valley, 1988-1989
pastor: J.Y. Kim, 1987-93

Arlington, TX — Trinity Oaks
1985-1995, discontinued
organized: 1987
pastors: D.R. Tigchelaar, 1985-86; C.G. Kromminga, Jr., 1987-93; D.J. Vrieland, 1993-95

Arlington, WA (mission)
1912

Arlington Heights, IL — Our Shepherd Korean (emerging)
1988-2001, discontinued
pastors: J.S. Gho, 1988-95; E. Shin, 1995-2000

Arroyo Grande, CA — Central Coast
1982-1996, discontinued
organized: 1982
former name: Arroyo Grande, CA — Rivershore Korean, 1984-95
pastors: C. Vander Plate, 1983-85; A.A. Mulder, 1985-87; T.P. Hoekstra, 1988-90; K.J. Voss, 1991-96

Arroyo Grande, CA — Rivershore Korean
see: Arroyo Grande, CA — Central Coast

Artesia, CA — Artesia
see: Artesia, CA — First

Artesia, CA — Artesia Hispanic
see: Artesia, CA — Iglesia Berea

Artesia, CA — Cerritos Central
1983-1993, discontinued
former names: Artesia, CA — Dae Sin Korean

Presbyterian, 1983-1984; Artesia, CA – Na Sung Korean, 1984-1985
merged: Long Beach, CA – Korean, 1985-1989
pastors: S.H. Park, 1983-84; P.S. Hahn, 1985-92; Y.S. Kang, 1985-86; J. Choi, 1986-89

Artesia, CA — Dae Sin Korean Presbyterian
see: Artesia, CA – Cerritos Central

Artesia, CA — First
1938-
organized: 1938
former name: Artesia, CA – Artesia, 1938-54
pastors: L. Bouma, 1938-43; K.E. de Waal Malefyt, 1944-65; C. Vander Plate, 1965-81; D.A. Warners, 1982-94; R.D. Goudzwaard, 1995-

Artesia, CA — Iglesia Berea (emerging)
1993-1998, discontinued
pastor: F.G. Golon, (E), 1993-98

Artesia, CA — Na Sung Korean
see: Artesia, CA – Cerritos Central

Artesia, CA — Rivershore Korean
see: Artesia, CA – The Spirit Filled

Artesia, CA — The Spirit Filled
1992-
organized: 1993
former name: Cypress, CA – Rivershore Korean, 1992-93; Artesia, CA – Rivershore Korean, 1994-95
pastors: H. Chei, 1992-94; K.S. So, 1995-96; J.H. Park, 1996-

Artesia, CA — Trinity
1954-
pastors: P. Van Tuinen, 1954-70; A. De Jager, 1970-73; S. Cooper, 1973-78; L.G. Christoffels, 1979-90; Andrew Vanden Akker, 1991-

Athens, ON — Athens
1954-
pastors: P. Kranenburg, 1957-60; H. Eshuis, 1962-66; J.S. Mantel, 1967-71; F. Heslinga, 1972-77; G. Bieze, 1977-92; J. Roke, 1992-97; G.T. van Leeuwen, 1999-

Atlanta, GA — Atlanta
see: Atlanta, GA – New Hope Church of Dunwoody

Atlanta, GA — Christ Community
1989-2002, discontinued

organized: 1990
pastors: J. Nash, 1986-2002; G. Boyd, 1998-2002

Atlanta, GA — Comunidad San Pablo
2000-
pastor: P. Toledo, 2000-

Atlanta, GA — New Hope
see: Atlanta, GA – New Hope Church of Dunwoody

Atlanta, GA — New Hope Church of Dunwoody
1983-
organized: 1985
former names: Atlanta, GA – Atlanta, 1983-85; Atlanta, GA – New Hope, 1993-2000
pastors: F.J. Mac Leod (M), 1975-80; W.W. Leys, 1983-89; C.J. De Vos, 1990-97; D.G. Buis, 1997-

Atlanta, GA — Shalom Korean (emerging)
1995-
pastor: C.Y. Jeon, 1995-

Atlanta, GA — Vision One (emerging)
1998
pastor: G. Boyd

Atwood, MI — Atwood
1896-
pastors: G.G. Haan (M), 1901-03; J.A. Rottier, 1908-11; J.D. Pikaart, 1914-21; S. Bouma, 1921-27; M. Dornbush, 1929-43; H. Goodyke, 1945-53; N. Punt, 1954-58; D.W. Van Gent, 1958-62; A.J. Vander Griend, 1963-66; G.L. Van Enk, 1966-69; S.J. Bultman, 1969-74; H.J. Weidenaar, 1975-80; A.T. Spriensma, 1981-84; J.M. Evenhouse, 1985-99

Aurora, CO — Crestview
see: Aurora, CO – Eastern Hills Community

Aurora, CO — Eastern Hills Community
1984-
former name: Aurora, CO – Crestview, 1984-1988
pastors: D.J. Deters (M), 1983-88; S. Sikkema, 1989-

Aurora, CO — Khmer
see: Denver, CO – Khmer

Aurora, CO — New Life Korean (emerging)
1999-2000, discontinued

pastor: W. Lee, 1999-2000

Austin, TX (service home)
1943-1945
staff: J. Vande Kieft, 1943-45

Austin, TX — Chapel of the Hills (emerging)
1995-1998, withdrew from denomination
pastor: P.W. Deckinga, 1985-89; M. Brouwer,
1991-92; J.I. Koopman, 1995-98

Austin, TX — Christ's Fellowship (emerging)
1985-1989, discontinued
pastors: P.W. Deckinga, 1985-89; J.I. Koopman,
1986-87

Austin, TX — North Austin Community
see: Round Rock, TX — North Austin Community

Austin, TX — Sunrise Community
1987-
organized: 1990
pastors: J.I. Koopman, 1987-97; M. Brouwer (S),
1991-92; J.W. Zuidema, 1992-93; T.E. Dykman,
1993-

Austinville, IA — Austinville
1917-
pastors: E. Kooistra, 1921-26; E. Joling, 1926-
34; J.J. Pott, 1935-37; R.S. De Haan, 1937-43;
C.O. Buus, 1943-46; W.H. Ackerman, 1947-50;
G.D. Pars, 1951-56; R.H. Tjapkes, 1956-60; W.S.
Gritter, 1960-64; A. Walma, 1964-68; A. Van
Heyst, 1969-73; J.D. Stoel, 1973-79; P.D.
Sikkema, 1979-83; J.A. Houseward, 1984-88;
D.E. Kats, 1989-95; G.M. McGuire, 1996-

Avon, SD — Avon
1890-1911, discontinued

Aylmer, ON — Aylmer
1949-
pastors: J. Gritter (M), 1948-54; J. Vande Kieft,
1951-58; J. Koopmans, 1958-61; C.D. Tuyl, 1962-
66; C.C. Spoor, 1967-73; W. Renkema, 1974-79;
H.J. Boekhoven, 1980-90; R.A. Wynia, 1987-91;
J.D. Hellinga, 1994-2000; R.J. de Lange, 2000-

Bakersfield, CA — Bakersfield
see: Bakersfield, CA — White Lane Bible Way

Bakersfield, CA — Cornerstone Community (emerging)
1991-1998, discontinued

pastor: H.G. Faber, 1991-98

Bakersfield, CA — White Lane Bible Way
1970-1996, discontinued
former name: Bakersfield, CA — Bakersfield,
1970-1993
pastors: J.E. Versluys, 1967-75; N. Vanderzee,
1976-80; R.B. Vermeer, 1981-85; C.W. Bergman,
1986-89 N.B. Haan, 1991-95

Baldwin, WI — Baldwin
1888-
pastors: A.W. Meyer, 1894-1905; E. Van Korlaar,
1905-12; H.J. De Vries, 1913-18; S.A. Dykstra,
1919-22; S.G. Brondsema, 1922-26; N. Jansen,
1927-48; R. Evenhuis, 1948-51; P. Ouwinga,
1951-56; P. Vander Weide, 1956-63; G.H. Vande
Riet, 1964-76; R.L. Scheuers, 1977-81; D.A.
Zylstra, 1981-92; P.S. Leo, 1994-99; L.B.
Mensink, 2000-

Baldwinsville, NY — Community
see: Syracuse, NY — Community

Barrhead, AB — Barrhead
1950-
pastors: G.H. Polman, 1955-57; W.G. Dubois,
1962-66; W. Dryfhout, 1968-72; J. Visser, 1972-
79; D. Van der Wekken, 1979-83; G.J. Heersink,
1984-91; C. Vriend, 1991-97; W.A. Ten Harmsel,
1998-2000; D.A. Meinema, 2003-

Barrie, ON — Barrie
see: Barrie, ON — First

Barrie, ON — Covenant
1980-
pastors: J. de Winter, 1981-84; J. Van Dyk,
1985-89; H.A. Van Hoff, 1989-97; Philip Apoll,
1998-

Barrie, ON — First
1950-
former name: Barrie, ON — Barrie, 1950-75
pastors: R.J. Bos (M), 1948-52; S.G. Brondsema
(M), 1952-55; J. Vander Meer, 1955-58; J.
Geuzebroek, 1959-64; J. Van Dyk, 1965-69; H.
Eshuis, 1970-77; H.J. Bierman, 1977-83; P.D.
Stadt, 1984-89; J. Tuininga, 1990-93; J.W. Luth,
1990-98; J.B. Vos, 1994-99; J. Kerkhof, 2000-

Barrow, AK — Barrow (emerging)
1996-
former name: Barrow, AK — Barrow Korean Presbyterian, 1997

8

pastor: G.J. Park, 1996–2002

Barrow, AK — Barrow Korean Presbyterian
see: Barrow, AK – Barrow

Barstow, CA — Hi-Desert (unorganized)
1984–1992
pastors: J.F. Holleman, 1983–85; V.G. Van Ee, 1986–88; J.P. DiMaggio (PCA), 1991–92

Bartlett, IL — West Wind Community (classical ministry)
1994–1997, discontinued
pastor: M.D. Timmer, 1994–97

Battle Creek, MI — Battle Creek
1933–
pastors: J.O. Schuring, 1935–39; L. Oostendorp, 1939–42; H. Exoo, 1942–48; J.M. Dykstra, 1949–52; S. Vander Jagt, 1952–56; J.C. Ribbens, 1956–61; E.C. Dykstra, 1962–69; H.A. Brink, 1969–78; O.W. Duistermars, 1979–84; H. Minnema, 1985–91; G.D. Nieuwsma, 1991–2002

Battle Creek, MI — Hillcrest Chapel
1952–1964
staff: J.C. Buffinga (L), 1952–53, 1954–57, 1961–62; W. Willink (L), 1953–54; W. Timmer (L), 1955–59

Battle Creek, MI — Urbandale (mission)
1922

Bauer, MI — Bauer
see: Hudsonville, MI – Bauer

Bayonne, NJ — Bayonne (emerging)
1998–
pastor: D.R. Calix (E), 1998–

Beamsville, ON — Beamsville
see: Beamsville, ON – Providence

Beamsville, ON — Providence
1985–
former name: Beamsville, ON – Beamsville, 1985
pastors: H. Vander Plaat, 1985–93; J. Van Marion, 1995–

Beautiful Mountain, NM (mission)
1956–1962
staff: E. Henry (L), 1956–63

Beaverdam, MI — Beaverdam
1882–

formed by members who left the Reformed Church in America
pastors: H.H. Dieperink-Langereis, 1890–93; H, Huizingh, 1893–1901; S.S. Vander Heide, 1902–04; S. Volbeda, 1904–05; S.P. Eldersveld, 1906–09; A. Keizer, 1910–16; H.J. Heynen, 1916–18; T. De Boer, 1918–20; J.A. Rottier, 1920–26; H.J. Heynen, 1926–29; J. Geels, 1929–43; H. Kooistra, 1943–53; F.R. DeBoer, 1954–59; W. Hekman, 1959–72; A.E. Rozendal, 1973–78; J. Van Groningen, 1979–85; D.J. Weemhoff, 1985–88; J.W. Uitvlugt, 1990–94; D.E. Kats, 1995–99; T.J. Wagenmaker, 2000–

Beaver Dam, WI — Faith Community
1960–
organized: 1977
pastors: M. Veltkamp (L), 1960–65; J. Geels (L), 1966–69; J.H. Van Schepen, 1972–78 (M); D.A. Kamper, 1978–87; L.L. Meyer, 1988–2000; D. Katsma (E), 1993–98; D.J. Dykstra, 2001–

Beaverton, OR — Oak Hills
see: Portland, OR – Oak Hills

Beaverton, OR — Zion Korean
see: Portland, OR – Zion Korean
1994–

Beclabito, NM (mission)
1975–1992
pastor: J. Talley (E), 1975–92

Bejou, MN — Bejou
1915–1993, discontinued
pastors: J.M. Dykstra, 1925–28; R.A. Rozeboom, 1928–35; W.K. Reinsma, 1935–41; G.H. Vande Riet, 1941–46; C. Maring, 1946–49; P. Vos, 1950–53; L.F. Baker, 1954–59; A.W. Koolhaas, 1961–64; G.D. Mouw, 1970–73

Belding, MI — Oakwood
1958–
organized: 1976
pastors: P. Doot (L), 1958–64; G. Yff (M), 1966–67; H. Buikema (L), 1968–69; R. Koornneef (M), 1970–76; D.G. Belanus, 1976–79; J.A. Ritsema, 1980–84; A. Gelder, 1985–95; J.M. Meyer, 1995–

Belleville, ON — Maranatha
1953
pastors: P.M. Jonker, 1955–58; J. Dresselhuis, 1959–62; G. Ringnalda, 1963–66; E. Gritter, 1966–72; H. Katerberg, 1973–77; H. Getkate, 1978–84; J. Visser, 1985–

Bellevue, AB — Bellevue
1953-1985, discontinued
pastor: E.O. Holkeboer, 1974-76

Bellevue, WA — Bellevue
1967-
pastors: P.J. Hoekstra (M), 1960-62; J. Batts
(M), 1967-71; F.D. Rietema, 1971-76; N.
Vogelzang, 1976-81; O.J. Hogan, 1981-86; H.A.
Brink, 1986-99; D.C. Roorda, 1999-

Bellflower, CA — Belen (emerging)
1993-
pastor: I.B. Alvarez, 1994-

Bellflower, CA — Bellflower
see: Bellflower, CA – First

Bellflower, CA — Bethany
1943-
former name: Bellflower, CA – Second, 1943-
1952
pastors: F. De Jong (M), 1943-44; F. De Jong,
1944-49; M. Vander Zwaag, 1949-53; B.N.
Huizenga, 1954-58; W.H. Rutgers, 1958-64; O.W.
Duistermars, 1964-70; J. Hasper, 1970-76; H.
Hiemstra, 1977-91; T.R. Hull, 1989-91; D.W.
Vander Veen, 1992-2001; D.J. Jeltema, 1998-

Bellflower, CA — Calvin
see: Los Alamitos, CA – Calvin

Bellflower, CA — First
1927-
former name: Bellflower, CA – Bellflower, 1927-
43
pastors: J.J. Werkman, 1928-35; G.S. Kok, 1935-
46; H. De Mots, 1947-54; W. Terpsma, 1947-49;
J.T. Holwerda, 1954-63; W.H. Ackerman, 1964-
73; J.C. Ribbens, 1974-80; D.G. Draayer, 1980-89;
J. Van Schepen, 1990-2002; M. Chung, 1999-

Bellflower, CA — Grace
1946-1974; discontinued
organized: 1961
former name: Bellflower, CA – Way of Life Gospel Chapel, 1950-54
pastors: A. Hanstra (L), 1946-51; T. Afman (L),
1950-51; B. De Boer (L), 1950-55; M. Tanis (L),
1955-61; P. Dekker, 1961-67; D.W. Oostendorp,
1968-74

Bellflower, CA — Grace Filipino
1994-
organized: 1997

former name: Long Beach, CA – Grace Filipino,
1994-97
pastor: E. Tandayu, 1994-

Bellflower, CA — New Life (emerging)
1998-
pastor: J. Choi, 1998-

Bellflower, CA — Rehoboth
1957-1985, discontinued
pastors: J. Rook, 1957-64; B. Nederlof, 1964-69;
R. Evenhuis, 1969-72; J. Koopmans, 1973-81;
J.K. Tuinstra, 1982-85

Bellflower, CA — Rosewood
1950-
former name: Bellflower, CA – Third, 1950-1980
pastors: J.F. Hollebeek, 1951-58; W. Van
Peursem, 1958-67; J.J. Wiegers, 1967-71; D.J.
Negen, 1972-80; E.G. Cooke, 1980-85; T.D.
Kauffman, 1991-95; D.J. Brink, 1986-; W. Ward
(E), 1995-

Bellflower, CA — Second
see: Bellflower, CA – Bethany

Bellflower, CA — Sheep Gate (emerging)
1984-1990
remnant merged into: Bellflower, CA – Calvin,
now Los Alamitos, CA – Calvin
former name: Bellflower, CA – Yang Moon Korean, 1984-88
pastor: P.W. Won, 1984-89

Bellflower, CA — Third
see: Bellflower, CA – Rosewood

Bellflower, CA — Way of Life Gospel Chapel
see: Bellflower, CA – Grace

Bellflower, CA — Yang Moon Korean
see: Bellflower, CA – Sheep Gate

Bellingham, WA — Alger Community
see: Alger, WA – Alger Community

Bellingham, WA — Bellingham
see: Bellingham, WA – Hope in Christ

Bellingham, WA — Hope in Christ
1960-
former name: Bellingham, WA – Bellingham,
1960-2001
pastors: P.E. Vermaat (M), 1960-64; J.H. Paauw,
1965-67; G. Holkeboer, 1967-70; A.L. Louwerse,

1970-75; R. Koornneef, 1976-89; J.T. Petersen, 1990-95; D.L. Kotzebue, 1990-93; G.A. Terpstra, 1997-

Bellingham, WA — Western Washington (campus ministry)
1970-1981
staff: J. Osterhouse (L), 1970-71; A. Louwerse, 1970-71: W.K. Bulthuis, 1971-74; A.D Bosscher, 1975-81

Bellwood, IL — Bellwood
see: Elmhurst, IL – Elmhurst

Belmont, MI (mission)
1924
staff: J.R. Brink (M), 1924

Belmont, NS — Belmont
see: Truro, NS – John Calvin

Bemis, SD — Bemis
1898-
former name: Palmer, SD – Palmer, 1898-1906
pastors: A.J. Brink, 1901-04; J.C. Schaap, 1904-06; L. Ypma, 1907-09; P. Van Vliet, 1910-14; S. Bouma, 1915-18; A.B. Voss, 1919-23; G. Andre, 1923-42; R. Star, 1943-50; B. Vanden Brink, 1950-53; A.A. Arkema, 1954-57; R. Star, 1958-67; W.P. Green, Jr., 1968-72; H.A. Sponholz, 1972-76; B.F. Tol, 1976-80; J. Riemersma, 1980-85; R.L. Bierenga, 1985-89; W. Vanden Bos, 1990-93; J. Kroon, 1994-97; D.R. Smith, 1998-2001

Bennion, UT — Cambodian
see: West Valley, UT – Cambodian

Bergenfield, NJ — Bergenfield
1906-08, withdrew to True Reformed Dutch Church
pastor: C.V. Van Houten, 1906-08

Berwyn, IL — Berwyn
see: Elmhurst, IL – Faith

Berwyn, IL — Ebenezer
1867-
former names: Chicago, IL – Fourteenth Street, 1867-1904; Chicago, IL – First, 1904-1946
pastors: J. Schepers, 1868-71; F. Hulst, 1871-73; W. Greve, 1875-78; K. Vanden Bosch, 1878-81; T.M. Vanden Bosch, 1882-83; W. Greve, 1886-90; H. Douwstra, 1890-92; J. Riemersma, 1893-99; W. Heyns, 1900-02; E. Breen, 1903-09; S.S.

Vander Heide, 1909-18; J. Van Lonkhuyzen, 1918-28; B. Essenburg, 1929-45; A.D. Folkema, 1945-52; L.J. Dykstra, 1953-57; H. Hoekstra, 1957-62; D.E. Bradford, 1963-69; E.L. Shuart, 1970-80; F.F. Gunnink, 1982-85; D.J. Timmermans, 1986-92; L.L. Schemper, 1993-2000; M. Den Bleyker, 2001-

Beverly, AB — Beverly
see: Edmonton, AB – Maranatha

Bigelow, MN — Asian American (emerging)
1915-
former name: Bigelow, MN – Bigelow, 1915-1990; Bigelow, MN – Community, 1990-1992
organized: 1915-92; classical ministry, 1992-99; emerging 1999-
pastors: C. Van Reenen (M), 1922-26; J.G. Van Dyke, 1927-31; W.L. Van Rees, 1932-39; W. Vande Kieft, 1939-43; H.S. Koning, 1943-49; G. Vander Plaats, 1949-52; J. Riemersma, 1954-61; P. Sluys, 1962-65; P.F. Dahm, 1966-69; J.L. Vanderlaan, 1971-76; R.J. Lammers, 1977-2001

Bigelow, MN — Bigelow
see: Bigelow, MN – Asian American

Bigelow, MN — Community
see: Bigelow, MN – Asian American

Big Horn, MT (mission)
1910

Big Rapids, MI — Fellowship
1964-
organized: 1971
pastors: J. Van Til (M), 1964-70; R.C. De Vries (M), 1970-77; G.D. Postema, 1978-85; J.G. Van Ryn, 1987-94; E.C. Visser, 1995-

Big Rapids, MI — Ferris State (campus ministry)
1966-
staff: J. Van Til, 1966-70; R. DeVries, 1970-77; K. Zorgdrager, 1979-82; L. Ausema (RCA), 1983-89; J. Karsten (RCA), 1989-94; M. Wissink (E), 1995-

Big Timber, MT — Big Timber
1908-1910 (discontinued)

Billings, MT (mission)
1924-1930 (branch of Shepherd, MT)

Binghamton, NY — Valley
1964-
organized: 1971
pastors: P.E. Vermaat (M), 1964-84; L.L. Schemper, 1984-93; A. Gelder, 1994-

Birnamwood, WI — Birnamwood
1909-1971, discontinued
organized: 1910
former name: Plover, WI – Marathon County, 1909-1930
pastors: D. Weidenaar (M), 1920-26; J. Guichelaar, 1931-35; E.H. Oostendorp, 1935-39; A. Baker, 1939-43; C.J. Toeset, 1944-48; N. Jansen, 1948-57; H.A. Ouwinga, 1957-62; J. Vugteveen, 1962-66

Bishop, MI — Bishop
1908-1927, discontinued, members joined Fremont and Reeman, MI
pastors: N. Gelderloos, 1910-12; N.J. Burggraf, 1912-16; R. Posthumus, 1917-25

Blackfalds, AB — Woodynook
see: Lacombe, AB – Woodynook

Black Rock, NM (mission)
1927-1930
staff: H. Fryling, 1927-29; C. Hayenga, 1929-30

Blackstock, ON — Blackstock
see: Bowmanville, ON – Rehoboth

Blackwell, ON (mission)
1928-1932
staff: W. Meyer, 1930-32

Blackwell, ON — Blackwell
see: Sarnia, ON – First

Blaine, WA — Christ's Community (congregational ministry)
1988-95

Blanco Canyon, NM (mission)
1915-1920
staff: H. Heyns, 1915-20

Blenheim, ON — Blenheim
1952-
pastors: G.J. Spykman, 1955-59; A Huls, 1959-62; A.A. Van Geest, 1963-66; G.J. Heersink, 1967-77; J. Tenyenhuis, 1977-82; K.J. Vanderwal, 1984-92; M.W. Bootsma, 1993-2002

Bloomfield, ON — Bethany
1949-
former name: Bloomfield, ON – Bloomfield, 1949-70
absorbed: Picton, ON – Picton, 1954
pastors: J. Betten, 1954-61; J. Zantingh, 1961-65; P. Breedveld, 1965-70; Praamsma, 1971-76; J. Kuipers, 1977-81; P.J. De Vries, 1981-89; H. Salomons, 1990-95; H.A. Newhouse, 1996-2000

Bloomfield, ON — Bloomfield
see: Bloomfield, ON – Bethany

Bloomington, MN — Calvary
see: Minneapolis, MN – Calvary

Blyth, ON — Blyth
1962-
pastors: R.J. Sikkema, 1963-66; H.W. Kroeze, 1967-73; T. Hoogsteen, 1973-79; A. Dieleman, 1979-1983; R.L. Gelwicks, 1984-87; W.H. Lammers, 1989-92; A.A. Van Geest, 1994-2001

Boca Raton, FL — Bethel Korean
see: Boca Raton, FL – Boca Raton Korean

Boca Raton, FL — Boca Raton
1963-1983, discontinued
organized: 1972
pastors: J.O. Schuring (M), 1963-68; R.C. De Vries, 1968-70; R.H. Tjapkes, (M), 1971-76; R.D Goudzwaard, 1976-80

Boca Raton, FL — Boca Raton Korean
1987-
organized: 1999
former name: Boca Raton, FL – Bethel Korean, 1994-97; Boca Raton, FL – Korean, 1987-94
merged with Fort Lauderdale, FL – New Life Korean, 1997
pastors: J.D. Cho, 1987-93; S.T. Yun, 1993-96; K.S. Kim, 1991-92, 1997-; J.J.K. Lee, 1999-
pastor of New Life Korean: K.S. Kim, 1992-97

Boca Raton, FL — Florida Atlantic University (campus ministry)
1966-1971
staff: J.O. Schuring, 1966-68; R.O. DeVries, 1968-69; R. Tjapkes, 1970-71

Boca Raton, FL — Korean
see: Boca Raton, FL – Boca Raton Korean

Boise, ID — Boise
see: Boise, ID – Cloverdale

Boise, ID — Cloverdale
1970-1997, withdrew, joined United Reformed
Churches, 1997; became: Boise, ID — Cloverdale
Reformed Christian Church
former name: Boise, ID — Boise, 1970-83
pastors: W. Vande Kieft, 1973-74; D.W.
Lagerwey, 1978-82; J.P. Vosteen, 1983-89; J.J.
Stastny, 1986-87; E.J. Marcusse, 1991-97

Boonton, NJ (mission)
1901-1908
staff: E.O. Van Duyne, 1901-08

Borculo, MI — Borculo
1883-
pastors: W. Greve, 1890-93; G.G. Haan, 1893-
96; T. Vander Ark, 1897-1900; W. De Groot,
1901-03; P. Kosten, 1904-07; J.B. Jonkman,
1908-12; E.J. Krohne, 1912-21; K.W. Fortuin,
1922-28; A. De Vries, 1929-45; C. Vanden Heuvel,
1945-49; R. Evenhuis, 1951-55; G. Van Groningen,
Sr., 1955-58; C. De Haan, 1958-68; E.C. Dykstra,
1969-70; T.L. Brouwer, 1971-86; H.G. Vanden
Einde, 1988-2001

Boston, MA — Hope
see: Framingham, MA — Hope

**Boston, MA — Iglesia Cristiana Reformada
Emanuel (emerging)**
1984-1997, discontinued
former name: Boston, MA — Iglesia Cristiana
Reformada Hispaña, 1984-96
pastors: J.E. Vanga (E), 1984-89; G.A Koning,
1989-91

**Boston-Jamaica Plain, MA — Iglesia
Cristiana Reformada Hispaña Emanuel**
see: Boston, MA — Iglesia Cristiana Reformada
Emanuel

Boulder, CO — Boulder
see: Boulder, CO — Crestview

Boulder, CO — Boulder Korean (emerging)
1996-
congregational ministry, 1996-97
pastor: R. Yeo, 1997-

Boulder, CO — Crestview
1961-
organized: 1963
former name: Boulder, CO — Boulder, 1961-67
pastors: J.J. Vanden Hoek (M), 1961-65; J.C.

Vander Ark (M), 1966-74; R.L. Westenbroek,
1975-80; J. Terpstra, 1980-90; M.L. Tidd, 1991-

**Boulder, CO — University of Colorado
(campus ministry)**
1966-1990
staff: J.C. Vander Ark, 1966-69, 1970-71; C.
Bajema, 1969-73; S.E. Ver Heul, 1973-80; A. De
Jong (L), 1980-84; C.J. DeVos, 1985-90

Bowmanville, ON — Bowmanville
see: Bowmanville, ON — Rehoboth

Bowmanville, ON — Maranatha
1964-
pastors: H. Van Andel, 1965;J. Nutma, 1966-71;
G. Corvers, 1972-81; H.J. Bout, 1981-82; J.
Zantingh, 1983-90; J. Binnema, 1991-94; M.F.
Miedema, 1997-

Bowmanville, ON — Rehoboth
1950-
former name: Bowmanville, ON — Bowmanville,
1957
absorbed: Blackstock, ON — Blackstock, 1950
pastors: H. Moes (M), 1949-52; A.W. Schaafsma,
1954-59; J.C. Verbrugge, 1960-66; A. Vanden
Berg, 1966-72; A. De Jager, 1973-87; C.T.
Fennema, 1989-94; M.F. Abma, 1989-98; H.C.
Salomons, 1999-

**Bowness-Montgomery, AB — Bowness-
Montgomery**
see: Calgary, AB — Maranatha

Boynton Beach, FL — Faith (emerging)
1983-1989, discontinued
pastor: J.H. Van Hemert (M), 1985-89

Bozeman, MT — Bozeman
1945-
pastors: J. Medendorp, 1945-51; T.E. Hofman,
1951-55; J. Geels, 1956-66; R.J. Buining, 1967-
71; J.A. Petersen, 1971-76; O.J. Hogan, 1978-81;
J.M. Evenhouse, 1982-85; A.A. Arkema, 1986-91;
J. Wanders, 1992-99; W.A. Knight, 2000-

**Bozeman, MT — Gallatin Gateway
Community**
1955-
organized: 1970
began as an evangelism program, Back to God
Chapel a chapel in 1962-67
former name: Gallatin Gateway, MT — Gallatin
Gateway, 1967-87

pastors: H. Westra (L), 1955-59, 1964-65; N.P. Baylor (L), 1959-64; D.C Bouma, (M), 1965-68; D.L. Recker, 1968-73; R.D. Steen, 1973-77; T.F. Thole, 1978-81; D.W. Van Gent, 1981-83; W.D. Vis, 1984-91; B.J. Van Ee, 1992-

Bradenton, FL — Bradenton
1956-
pastors: W.P. DeBoer, 1956-58; H.J. Baas, 1958-63; E. Heerema, 1964-77; R.D. Ritsema, 1978-81; H.A. Ouwinga, 1981-92; R.G. Baker, 1982-97, D.L. Aldrink, 1993-; M.J. Klingenberg, 2002-

Bradford, ON — Springdale
1952-
former name: Springdale, ON — Springdale, 1951-1981, 1983-2000
pastors: R. Wildschut, 1953-59; P. Kranenburg, 1960-63; J.W. Van Stempvoort, 1963-69; L.W. Van Dellen, 1969-73; T.J. Ouwehand, 1974-76; J.M. Evenhouse, 1977-82; L.T. Schalkwyk, 1982-92; H. McPhee, 1993-

Bradley, MI — Bradley
1916-1926, discontinued
pastor: K. Poppen, 1923-25

Brampton, ON — Brampton
see: Brampton, ON — Immanuel

Brampton, ON — Immanuel
1949-
former name: Brampton, ON — Brampton, 1949-65
pastors: C. Spoelhof (M), 1948-49; S.G. Brondsema (M), 1949-51; G. Andre, 1951-53; J. Van Harmelen, 1953-58; P.M. Jonker, 1958-74; H.R. DeBolster, 1962-65; M.N. Greidanus, 1974-80; J. Kuipers, 1981-89; A. Vanden Ende, 1985-91; H.D. Praamsma, 1990-98; A.D. Evans (I), 1998; A.D. Evans, 1998-2001; E.J. Schuringa, 2002-

Brampton, ON — Living Hope
1987-1996, discontinued
former name: Heart Lake, ON, — Living Hope, 1987
pastor: D.A. Gritter, 1985-83

Brampton, ON — Second
1965-
pastors: H.R. DeBolster, 1965-66; C.T. Fennema, 1968-79; P.W. De Bruyne, 1979-87; P. Nicolai, 1982-91; J. Van Dyk, 1983-85; W. Suk, 1985-86; H.G. Samplonius, 1989-95; H.D. Praamsma,

1990-98; C.N. Overduin, 1996-2002; D.A. Evans, 1999-

Brandon, MB — Brandon
see: Brandon, MB — First

Brandon, MB — First
1951-
former name: Brandon, MB — Brandon, 1951-79
pastors: M. Dornbush (M), 1950-55; J. De Jong, 1955-56; M. Dornbush, 1958-62; J. Boonstra, 1962-65; J. Dresselhuis, 1966-70; A. Schweitzer, 1970-74; J. Huizenga, 1975-81; W. Smit, 1982-88; E.S.H. Busink, 1988-

Brantford, ON — Brantford
see: Brantford, ON — Hope

Brantford, ON — First
1951-1994, merged into Brantford, ON — Hope
see: Brantford, ON — Hope
pastors: A. Persenaire (M), 1951-54; H.J. Triezenberg, 1954-58; D.J. Scholten, 1958-66; R. Praamsma, 1967-71; A.H. Venema, 1972-76; J.R. Poelman, 1978-83; T. Hoogsteen, 1983-90; J. Klazinga, 1991-93

Brantford, ON — Hope
1994-
former name: Brantford, ON — Brantford, 1951-74, then Brantford, ON — First, 1973-94 which was merged with Brantford, ON — Shalom, 1978-94 into Brantford, ON — Hope
pastors: R.E. Grift, 1996-

Brantford, ON — Shalom
1978-1994, merged into Brantford, ON — Hope
pastors: A.H. Venema, 1978; J.W. Jongsma, 1979-87; L.H. Batterink, 1987-94

Brigham City, UT — Brigham City
see: Brigham City, UT — Living Hope Christian Fellowship

Brigham City, UT — Intermountain Christian Mission
see: Brigham City, UT — Living Hope Christian Fellowship

Brigham City, UT — Living Hope
see: Brigham City, UT — Living Hope Christian Fellowship

Brigham City, UT — Living Hope Christian Fellowship

1954–

organized: 1984

former name: Brigham City, UT – Intermountain Christian Mission, 1954-63; Brigham City, UT – Brigham City, 1963-88; Brigham City, UT – Living Hope, 1988-96

pastors: C. Kuipers, 1954-63; L. Benally (L), 1959-64; L. Baas (L), 1959-63; C. Kuipers, 1964; A.E. Mulder, 1964-66; G. Klumpenhouwer (L), 1964-66; E. Vos (L), 1964-69; E. Boer, 1968-85; I. Mulder (L), 1967-70; J. Lineweaver (L), 1970-73; L. Haak (L), 1974-75; D.J. Hunderman, 1986-93

Brighton, ON — Fellowship

1979–

pastors: C. Vink, 1980-83; C.A. Persenaire, 1984-89; H.F. Steenbergen, 1990-96; R. Praamsma, 1997-2001

Brinston, ON — Community of Matilda Township

see: Dixon's Corners, ON – Community of Matilda Township

Britt, IA (mission)

1910-1911

Britt, IA — Britt

1957–

pastors: T. Medema, 1958-61; J. Riemersma, 1961-68; R.J. Lammers, 1970-77; T.J. Niehof, 1977-82; V.D. Vander Top, 1982-88; B. Wassink, 1989-96; S.J. Mulder, 1997-2002

Brockville, ON — Bethel

1950–

pastors: A.H. Smit (M), 1950-52; L. Van Laar, 1952-56; A. De Jager, 1957-61; J. Koopmans, 1961-66; J.G. Klomps, 1967-71; H. Numan, 1971-76; L. Mulder, 1976-80; P.J. Boodt, 1982-86; H.P. Kranenburg, 1987-2000; N. Cornelisse, 2002–

Brookfield, WI — Brookfield

1939–

former names: Milwaukee, WI – Milwaukee, 1939-73; Brookfield, WI – Milwaukee, 1973-80

pastors: J. DeJong, 1929-42 (M); W. Verwolf, 1942-46; E. Boer, 1952-56; M.G. Zylstra, 1956-63; T.C. Vanden Heuvel, 1964-67; A.A. Cammenga, 1970-76; D.J. Steenhoek, 1977-80; R.A. Bouwman, 1981-87; J. Bylsma, 1987-96; P.T. Verhulst, 1998–

Brookfield, WI — Milwaukee

see: Brookfield, WI – Brookfield

Brooklyn, NY — Messiah's

1986-1993, withdrew became Independent was Messiah's Baptist

pastor: S. Schlissel, 1986-92

Brooks, AB — Brooks

1952–

absorbed: Duchess, AB – Duchess, 1950-52

pastors: M. Dornbush (M), 1950-55; W.L. Vander Beek, 1955-58; A. Vanden Ende, 1959-63; C. De Bree, 1965-68; R.G. Fisher, 1969-73; D. Velthuizen, 1973-78; J. Veltman, 1979-86; T. Maan, 1986-91; J. Corvers, 1991-2000; C.A. Fluit, 2002–

Broomall, PA — Trinity

1957–

former name: Philadelphia, PA – Trinity, 1957-93; Philadelphia/Broomall, PA – Trinity, 1974-77; Broomall, PA – Trinity, 1978-80; Philaelphia, PA - Trinity, 1980-94

pastors: A.J. Haan (M), 1954-58; S. Draayer, 1958-62; E.J. Piersma, 1963-68; D.G. Zandstra, 1969-76; J. Vugteveen, 1976-94; J.E. Kok, 1996–

Brooten, MN — Brooten

1916–

pastors: A. Wassink, 1920-22; C. Groot, 1928-35; J. Guichelaar, 1935-41; G.J. Haan, 1941-45; J.D. Pikaart, 1945-52; C. Terpstra, 1953-58; W.H. De Vries, 1958-62; C. Bishop, 1963-67; G.L. Kramer, 1967-70; L. Roossien, 1971-74; T. Genzink, 1974-79; T.J. Kikkert, 1979-82; A. Hannink, 1983-85; J.D. Zondervan, 1986-91; R.R. Sprik, 1991-99; D.J. Swinney, 2001–

Buena Park, CA (mission)

1936-1937

Buena Park, CA — Buena Park

1933-1939, discontinued, members joined Artesia, CA

pastor: J.J. De Jonge (M), 1933-39

Buena Park, CA — Calvin

see: Los Alamitos, CA – Calvin

Buena Park, CA — Korean CRC of Orange County

see: Westminster, CA – Korean CRC of Orange County

Buena Park, CA — Messiah Korean
see: La Mirada, CA — Messiah Korean

Buena Park, CA — Morning Star
see: Los Angeles, CA — Okto Glory

Bunde, MN — Bunde
1887-
former name: Clara City, MN — Bunde, 1988-89
pastors: J.H. Schultz, 1892-94; H.J. Potgeter,
1896-1900; H. Ahuis, 1901-04; H. Niehaus, 1904-
06; D.H. Kromminga (M), 1908-11; J. Plesscher,
Sr., 1912-16; F. Schuurmann, 1918-26; W. Bode,
1930-41; P.F. Dahm, 1942-54; J.C. Lont, 1955-
59; R.H. Haan, 1959-64; R.R. Graves, 1965-72;
R.D. Boertje, 1972-76; J.T. Petersen, 1976-80; J.
Vander Lugt, 1981-91; T.K. Groelsema, 1992-98;
A.J. Van Wolde, 1998-

**Burbank, CA — Bethany Korean Community
(emerging)**
1999-
organized: 2000
pastors: S.M. Bang, 1999-; D.K. Kong, 2002-

Burbank, IL — Immanuel
1973-
pastors: G.P. Hutt, 1974-82; L.L. Meyer, 1979-81;
L.W. Van Essen, 1982-93; A.J. Machiela, 1993-
96; S.K. Rhoda, 1996-2002

Burdett, AB — Burdett
1911-
organized with families from the Nyverdal, AB —
Nyverdal which dissolved; families from the western portion organized as Granum, AB — Granum
and families from the eastern portion organized
as Burdett, AB — Burdett
pastors: R. Wildschut, 1945-47; A.H. Selles,
1955-60; J.W. Jongsma, 1961-64; F.J. Van Dyk,
1965-69; M.J. Lise, 1970-75; G.H. Polman, 1975-
79; C.J. Tuininga, 1979-83; B. Beukema, 1984-
88; T.W. Bomhof, 1989-93; J.C. Fraser, 1995-

Burke, VA — Grace
1975-
organized: 1976
former name: Springfield, VA — Northern Virginia,
1974-76; Northern Virginia, VA — Grace, 1977-78
pastors: W.D. Ribbens, 1975-81; V.F. Geurkink,
1982-93; C.L. Geschiere, 1993-2002

Burlington, ON — Aldershot
see: Waterdown, ON — Bethel

Burlington, ON — Bethel
see: Waterdown, ON — Bethel

Burlington, ON — Burlington
1953-
pastors: J. Van Dyk, 1956-59; A.W. Schaafsma,
1959-65; L. Mulder, 1965-70; G. Ringnalda, 1971-
77; J.J. Hoytema, 1978-89; J. Kerkhof, 1989-
2000; S.R. Brix, 2002-

Burlington, ON — Faith
1984-
pastors: J.A. Quartel, 1984-92; P. Veltman,
1994-97; K.P. De Raaf, 1999-

Burnaby, BC — Burnaby
see: Burnaby, BC — Nelson Avenue Community

Burnaby, BC — First
see: New Westminster, BC — First

Burnaby, BC — Nelson Avenue Community
1957-
former name: Burnaby, BC — Burnaby, 1957-
2000
pastors: B. Den Herder, 1960-63; J. Zwaanstra,
1964-68; D. Pierik, 1968-79; J.G. Groen, 1980-
90; O.J. Hogan, 1991-94; P.F. Reinders, 1992-97;
M.H. Van Hofwegen, 1999-

Burnips, MI — Burnips
1923-29, discontinued, members joined Oakland,
MI
pastor: J.L. Koerts, 1924-25

Burnips Corners, MI (mission)
1911

Butler Center, IA (mission)
1912

Butte City, ID (mission)
1914

Byron Center, MI — Byron Center
see: Byron Center, MI — First

Byron Center, MI — First
1902-
former name: Byron Center, MI — Byron Center,
1903-54
pastors: F.J. Drost, 1905-10; A.J. Rus, 1910-14;
J.J. Holwerda, 1914-19; H. Guikema, 1921-29;
A.J. Rus, 1930-51; W. Hendriksen, 1952-61; H. De
Wolf, 1961-77; R.J. Noorman, 1977-84; T.C.

16

Vanden Heuvel, 1985-97; T.K. Groelsema, 1998-; J.C. Klompien, 2001-

Byron Center, MI — Friendship
1987-
pastors: C.D. Compagner, 1988-

Byron Center, MI — Heritage
1970-
pastors: J.R. Pruim, 1971-76; S. Mast, 1978-87; D.L. Slings, 1987-99; P.R Byma, 1990-98; L.K. Stieva, 2001-

Byron Center, MI — Pathway Ministries
1993-
organized 2001
pastors: T.R. Wolthuis, 1992-2000; J.R. Stam (I), 2000-

Byron Center, MI — Second
1953-
pastors: A. Jabaay, 1954-64; J. Vander Lugt, 1965-70; J. De Vries, 1970-78; P.E. Bakker, 1979-84; H.J. Wigboldy, 1984-91; J.P. Gorter, 1993-; T.A. Kuperus, 1996-

Cadillac, MI — Cadillac
1944-
mission, 1926-30;
organized: 1946
pastors: E.J. Holtrop (M), 1926-30; M. Huizenga, 1947-53; E. Boeve, 1954-58; C. Bolt, 1958-61; F. Kaemingk, 1961-64; A. Poel, 1966-72; B. Van Antwerpen, 1973-78; R.R. Graves, 1978-84; K.J. Nydam, 1984-97; J.C. Vanderhooft, 1996-98; P.R. Byma, 1998-

Caldwell, ID (emerging)
1975-1976

Caldwell, MI — Caldwell
see: Arlene, MI — Arlene

Caledonia, MI — Caledonia
1954-
organized: 1962
pastors: A.W. Bytwork (E), 1954-62; R.J. Buining, 1963-67; R. Stienstra, 1967-71; H.G. Entingh, 1972-82; M.N. Buwalda, 1982-91; G.F. Van Oyen, 1993-94; R.S. Greenway, 1995-

Caledonia, ON — Maranatha
see: York, ON — Maranatha

Calgary, AB — Calgary
see: Calgary, AB — First

Calgary, AB — Covenant
1988-
pastors: B.A. Amsing, 1989-92; J. Kerssies, 1993-2000; C.D. Korver, 2001-

Calgary, AB — Emmanuel
1956-
former name: Calgary, AB — Second, 1956-57
pastors: M. Vrieze, 1958-61; L.T. Schalkwyk, 1962-66; H.R. De Bolster, 1966-71; N. Vander Kwaak, 1971-76; J. Joosse, 1976-86; K. De Koning, 1982-90; M.S. Jorritsma, 1987-91; P. Nicolai, 1991-96; A.G. Vander Leek, 1995-; E. Jager, 2001-

Calgary, AB — First
1952-
former name: Calgary, AB — Calgary, 1952-56
pastors: P.J. Hoekstra (M), 1952-55; T.E. Hofman, 1955-62; C.M. Schemper, 1962-65; A.G. Van Eek, 1966-70; H. Wildeboer, 1971-84; F.D. Breisch, Jr., 1974-81; W. Dyk, 1979-84; J. Ypma. 1982; D.J. Tigchelaar, 1984-89; J. Poortenga, 1985-88; M. Reitsma, 1989-; P.F. Reinders, 1997-

Calgary, AB — Hillside Community (emerging)
2001-
pastor: G.A Vandermolen, 2001-

Calgary, AB — Maranatha
1956-
former name: Bowness-Montgomery, AB — Bowness, 1956-64
pastors: P.J. Hoekstra (M), 1956-60; C. Padmos, 1960-65; A.A. Van Geest, 1966-72; E. Den Haan, 1973-77; J.S. Hielema, 1978-86; K. de Koning, 1982-84; J.S. Gangar, 1986-90; R.A. Wynia, 1991-92; P.C. Stellingwerff, 1995-2002

Calgary, AB — New Hope (emerging)
1996-
pastor: J. Van Sloten (E), 1996-

Calgary, AB — Peace Community
1978-1989, discontinued
organized: 1981
pastors: K.J. Verhulst, 1978-85; C.H. Claus, 1986-88

Calgary, AB — Second
see: Calgary, AB — Emmanuel

Camarillo, CA — Camarillo Hispanic
see: Camarillo, CA — Iglesia Cristiana Ref. De
Camarillo

**Camarillo, CA — Iglesia Cristiana Ref. De
Camarillo**
1993-
pastor: R. Aragon, 1993-

Camarillo, CA — New Harvest
see: Camarillo, CA — Paseo Community

**Camarillo, CA — Paseo Community
(emerging)**
1990-
organized: 2001
former name: Camarillo, CA — New Harvest,
1990-97
pastors: G.A. Smith, 1991-95; M.H. Bierma,
1996-

Cambridge, ON — Maranatha
1958-
former name: Galt, ON — Maranatha, 1958-73
pastors: J.G. Kunst, 1958-61; A. Persenaire,
1961-64; J.H. Binnema, 1965-69; J. Koole, 1970-
78; H.J. Bout, 1978-81; R. Koops, 1983-2002

Campbellford, ON — Campbellford
1949-1961, discontinued

**Campbell River, BC — Hope Community
(emerging)**
1989-1995, withdrew, became Vineyard Church,
Campbell River, BC
pastor: C.H. Claus, 1989-95

Camrose, AB — Camrose (unorganized)
1979-1982

Canoncito (Canyon Cito), NM (mission)
1933-1942
staff: C. Kuipers (L), 1933-39; J.R. Brinks, 1939-
40; J.W. Brink, 1940-42

Cape Coral, FL — Cape Coral
1974-1993, withdrew, became Trinity United Reformed Church
organized: 1978
pastors: R.J. Pontier, 1977-86; F.J. MacLeod,
1986-91; D.W. Royall, 1991-93

Carisso, AZ (mission)
see: Teec Nos Pos, AZ — Four Corners

Carlstat, AB (mission)
1912

Carnes, IA — Carnes
1904-1943, discontinued, members joined Orange
City, IA
pastors: J.B. Vanden Hoek, 1908-14; J. Gulker,
1915-17; A. Wassink, 1917-20; H.J. Heynen, 1920-
23; W. Meyer, 1924-29; J.G. Vande Lune, 1930-
37; J.E. Brink, 1938-42

Carp Lake, MI (mission)
1914

Carson, CA — Grace Filipino (emerging)
1993-
emerging, 1998
pastors: E. Tandayu, 1993-

Castlewood, SD — Castlewood
1968-1970, discontinued

**Cave Creek, AZ — Celebration Community
at Cave Creek (emerging)**
2001
pastor: A. Lindemulder, 2000-

Cawker City, KS — Dispatch
see: Dispatch, KS — Dispatch

Cedar, IA — Cedar
1941-
pastors: W. Meyer, 1941-43; H. Petroelje, 1943-
49; J. Mulder, 1949-52; R.R. Graves, 1952-56; C.
Van Essen, 1956-60; B.B. Blankers, 1961-65; O.
Holtrop, 1965-69; W. Van Dyk, 1970-74; R.L.
Jipping, 1974-78; T.G. Soerens, 1978-83; A.
Zylstra, 1983-88; W.D. Hubers, 1989-96; D.L.
Jabaay (E), 1997-

Cedar Falls, IA — Cedar Falls
1961-
former name: Waterloo, IA — Waterloo, 1961-66
pastors: T. Vanden Bosch (M), 1958-61; L.J.
Wolters, 1962-65; A.L. Louwerse, 1966-70; A.E.
Likkel, 1970-74; C.G. Roelofs, 1974-79; A.L.
Kuiper, 1981-88; H.F. Hharnden, 1988-92; P.W.
Townsend, 1994-99; D.K. Harrison, 2001-

**Cedar Falls, IA — Northern Iowa
(campus ministry)**
1967-1971
staff: A.L. Louwerse, 1967-69; E. Gabrielse (L),
1969-70; A. Helder, 1970-71; A. Likkel, 1970-71

Cedar Hill, TX — Hope Fellowship (emerging)
1992-
organized 1998
former name: De Soto, TX — Hope Fellowship, 1992-95
pastor: T.E. Pettinga, 1991-

Cedar Rapids, IA — Peace
1970-
organized: 1972
pastors: E.D. Dykema (M), 1970-77; K.D. Van De Griend, 1977-83; G.L. Hoek, 1983-92; D.M. MacLeod, 1993-

Cedar Springs, MI — Pioneer
1955-
organized: 1961
pastors: W. Willink (E), 1955-62; C.M. Schoolland, 1962-63; A. Zwart, 1964-67; D.M. Doyle, 1969-74; B. Vermeer, 1974-76; H.J. Baas, 1977-94; F.J. Van Dyk, 1995-98; D.R. Van Harten, 2000-

Celeryville, OH — Calvary Chapel
see: Willard, OH — Calvary Chapel

Cerritos, CA — Heaven Bound Ministry (emerging)
1994-
emerging, 1995
pastor: A.H. Choh (E), 1994-

Champaign, IL — Champaign
see: Champaign, IL — Hessel Park

Champaign, IL — Champaign-Hessel Park
see: Champaign, IL — Hessel Park

Champaign, IL — Hessel Park
1952-
organized: 1983
former names: Champaign, IL — Champaign, 1959-64; Champaign, IL — Champaign-Hessel Park, 1964-78
pastors: F.H. Klooster (M), 1952-53; H.A. Koops (M), 1956-60; L. Sweetman, Jr. (M), 1962-64; B. Boelens (M), 1964-69; M.P. Hoogland, 1969-74; A.D. Menninga, 1975-80; J. Reiffer, 1981-96; N.P. Jasperse, 1996-2001; T.S. Bossenbroek, 2001-

Champaign, IL — University of Illinois Campus Ministry
1964-1977

staff: B. Boelens, 1964-69; M. Hoogland, 1969-74; A. Menninga, 1975-77

Chandler, AZ — Christ's Community
1985-
pastors: A. Lindemulder, 1984-98; N.D. Rozenboom, 1989-92; H.G. Faber, 1998-2001; R. Walter, 2001-2002

Chandler, MN — Chandler
1916-
pastors: B. Nagel, 1920-29; A. Disselkoen, 1930-39; A. Bliek, 1940-46; G. Van Laar, 1947-50; J.E. Brink, 1951-55; C.S. Steenstra, 1955-59; T.M. Monsma, 1959-62; A.J. Van Schouwen, 1963-68; T. Heyboer, 1969-77; C. Negen, 1977-78; R. Zomermaand, 1978-84; D.J. Boogerd, 1985-89; J.H. Engbers, 1990-94; K.J. Vryhof, 1995-2002

Charlotte, MI — Charlotte (emerging)
1962-
pastors: A.W. Bytwork (E), 1962-73; R.A. DeLange (M), 1973-77; N. Roorda, 1979-82; C.E. Keegstra, 1982-89; E. Visscher (E), 1989-93; B. McAtee (E), 1995-

Charlottetown, PE — Charlottetown
1955-
pastors: M. Dornbush (M), 1962-68; E. Den Haan, 1968-73; H.H. Boer, 1973-78; T.J. Ouwehand, 1976-80; G.V. Martin, 1981-85; C. Geleynse, 1985-93; N.A. Sennema, 1993-98; B. Van Eyk, 1999-

Chatham, ON — Calvary
1975-
pastors: R.G. Fisher, 1976-83; J. Tuininga, 1984-90; S. Sybenga, 1990-97; S.G. Baarda, 1998-

Chatham, ON — Chatham
see: Chatham, ON — First

Chatham, ON — First
1926-
former name: Chatham, ON — Chatham, 1926-64
pastors: S.A. Dykstra (M), 1924-26; J.R. Brink (M), 1926-27; T. DeBoer, 1928-37; L. Trap, 1938-45; D. Zwier, 1946; G.J. Vander Ziel, 1947-53; J.C. Verbrugge, 1955-60; L. Mulder, 1961-65; J.W. Van Weelden, 1966-73; L. Slofstra, 1975-81; W. Dykstra, 1982-90; J.W. Postman, 1991-95; P.D. Stadt, 1996-

Chatham, ON — Grace
1965-

former name: Chatham, ON — Second, 1965
pastors: J.B. Vos, 1965–71; R. Koops, 1971–83; P. Kranenburg, 1984–86; H.P. Bruinsma, 1988–93; P. Nicolai, 1996–

Chatham, ON — Second
see: Chatham, ON — Grace

Chesapeake, VA — Chesapeake (emerging)
1986–1989, discontinued
pastor. D.C. Sherow, 1986–89

Chicago, IL — 127th/Ridgeland Ave. (mission)
1937–1937

Chicago, IL — American Indian Chapel (unorganized)
1960–86, discontinued
pastors: A.E. Jongsma (L), 1960–64; H. Bielema (L), 1964–82; R.J. Van Antwerpen (M), 1982–86

Chicago, IL — Archer Avenue
1911–1997, discontinued
former name: Summit, IL — Summit, 1911–18
pastors: J.O. Vos, 1912–17; J.C. Monsma, 1917–19; P. Jonker, Sr., 1920–30; C.J. Van Schouwen, 1931–37; T.P. Verhulst, 1938–43; W.P. Brink, 1944–48; H.J. Triezenberg, 1949–54; I.J. Apol, 1954–58; G. Haan, 1959–64; B. Ver Meer, 1965–69; C.J. Klompien, 1970–73; D.A. Zylstra, 1974–81; W.G. Vis, 1983–87; C.L. Geschiere, 1987–93; D.J. Griffioen, 1993–97

Chicago, IL — Auburn Park
see: Oak Lawn, IL — Kedvale Avenue

Chicago, IL — Back to God Church
1964–
emerging, 1981
organized: 1993
pastors: R. Huizenga (L), 1964–80; D.A. Crushshon, Sr., 1981–

Chicago, IL — Bethel (mission)
1918

Chicago, IL — Burr Oak School (mission)
1937

Chicago, IL — Chinese Gospel Mission
see: Chicago, IL — Hyde Park

Chicago, IL — Christ's Vineyard (diaconal ministry)
1990–
emerging, 1990–98
pastor: J. Flores, 1990–

Chicago, IL — Douglas Park
see: Elmhurst, IL — Faith

Chicago, IL — Englewood Community (mission)
1950–1953
staff: A.C. Dreyer (L), 1950–53

Chicago, IL — Englewood First
see: Oak Lawn, IL — Calvin

Chicago, IL — Englewood Second
see: Oak Lawn, IL — Kedvale Avenue

Chicago, IL — First
see: Berwyn, IL — Ebenezer

Chicago, IL — Fourteenth Street (mission)
1927

Chicago, IL — Fourteenth Street
see: Berwyn, IL — Ebenezer

Chicago, IL — Fourth
1923–1945, discontinued, members merged into Oak Park, IL — Oak Park (see: Elmhurst, IL — Faith)
pastors: H. Bel, 1923–28; J. Putt, 1929–40; R.O. De Groot, 1941–45

Chicago, IL — Garfield
1963–1988, discontinued
organized: 1971
pastors: J. Wassenaar (L), 1963–64; J. Klunder (L), 1964–66; J. LeGrand, Jr. (M), 1969–74; J.J. Reiffer, 1975–81; D.J. Sieplinga, 1982–84

Chicago, IL — Grace and Peace Fellowship (emerging)
1985–
pastors: J.M. Matias, 1983–85; P. Aviles, 1985–

Chicago, IL — Helping Hand Mission
1901–1985
also known as: Chicago, IL — City Mission
staff: A J. Van de Water (L), 1915–29;.J. Rus, 1917–19; G. Steenstra (L), 1929–35; G. Plum (L), 1936–38; I. Vande Weide (L), 1935–37; G. Weeber, 1936–39; N. Youngsma (L), 1939–48; H.G. Jager

(L), 1948-49; J. Nauta (L), 1949-53; C. Laning (E), 1952-80; R.E. Grevengoed, 1981-84; K.A. Bielema, 1984-85

Chicago, IL — Hope Christian Fellowship (emerging)
1985-1996, discontinued
pastors: R. Maldonado, Jr., 1985-92; P. Windsor (RCA) (I), 1993-96

Chicago, IL — Hyde Park
1955-
organized: 1974
former name: Chicago, IL – Chinese Gospel Mission, 1955-58
pastors: I.C. Jen (M), 1955-58; P. Han (M), 1959-83; K. Wong, 1988-98; P.C. Wu, 1999-

Chicago, IL — Jewish Mission/ Nathaneal Institute (mission)
1918-1965
staff: J.H. Beld, 1919-21; A. Huisjen (E), 1920-58; J. Rottenberg/E. Newman (S), 1921-23; E. Vander Meulen/J.S. Tibma (L), 1923-24; W. Yonker (L), 1925-53; T. Delis, 1928-42; E. Vander Meulen (L), 1933-60; J. Zandstra, 1943-49; W. Tuit (L), 1943-47; B. Kok (L), 1947-49; J.R. Rozendal, 1952-64; N. Van Mersbergen (L), 195457; E. Vander Meulen (L), 1958-71; G. Koedoot, 1963-65

Chicago, IL — Korean
see: Wheeling, IL – Korean

Chicago, IL — Lawndale
1926-1927; 1950-
organized: 1963
pastors: W. Yonker (L), 1926-27; N. Van Mersbergen (L), 1946-54; J. Overzet (L), 1952-53; A. Reitsma (L), 1950-53; C. Buist (E), 1953-63; H.D. Bultje (M), 1961-62; P. Huiner, 1962-65; D.E. VanderBrug, 1966-69; J. Steigenga (L), 1968; R.O. Grevengoed, 1971-81; J.E. Wolff, 1981-

Chicago, IL — Living Spring Community
2000-
pastor: M. Kim, 2000-

Chicago, IL — Loop Christian Ministries (emerging)
1987-
classical ministry, 1987-98
pastor: T.H. Douma, 1987-

Chicago, IL — Madison Street (mission)
1939-1946
staff: M. Spiers (L), 1939-42; N. Paulina (L), 1940-41; N. Youngsma (L), 1945-46

Chicago, IL — Mustard Seed Fellowship
1988-1989
pastor: A. Gonzales (E), 1988-89

Chicago, IL — Pullman
1942-
ermerging, 1972;
organized: 1980
former name: Chicago, IL – Pullman Gospel Center, 1942-72
pastors: E. Dykstra (E), 1950-51; W. Aardsma (E), 1955-63; A. Huisman (E), 1963-69; S. Van Klompenberg (L), 1970-71; H.E. Botts, 1972-80; C.G. Kromminga, Jr., 1978-86; R.E. Williams, 1981-

Chicago, IL — Pullman Gospel Center
see: Chicago, IL – Pullman

Chicago, IL — Roseland
1975-
organized: 1987
former name: Chicago, IL – Roseland Christian Ministries Center, 1985-98
pastors: A. Van Zanten, 1976-; E.A. Harrison, 1985-90

Chicago, IL — Roseland Christian Ministries Center
see: Chicago, IL – Roseland

Chicago, IL — Roseland Community Gospel (mission)
1932-1954
staff: H. De Boer (L), 1932-41; G. Bos (L), 1940-49, 1952-53; M.E. Dykstra (L), 1946-49; W. Aardsma (E), 1950-55; H. Aardsma (L), 1951-53

Chicago, IL — Roseland/Cottage Grove (mission)
1947-1952

Chicago, IL — Roseland First
see: Lynwood, IL – Lynwood

Chicago, IL — Roseland Fourth
see: Orland Park, IL – Orland Park

Chicago, IL — Roseland Second
1893-1969, merged into Orland Park, IL — Orland Park
pastors: H. Van Hoogen, 1894-1895; K. Kuiper, 1896-1911; W. Borgman, 1911-19; H. Baker, 1919-26; L. Trap, 1926-38; W. Haverkamp, 1937-43; W.L. Van Rees, 1944-51; B. Van Someren, 1952-58; J. Bylsma, 1960-65; C. Terpstra, 1965-70

Chicago, IL — Roseland Third
1907-1971, members merged with Oak Lawn, IL — Kedvale Avenue
pastors: W. Stuart, 1908-15; W.M. Trap, 1916-17; G.W. Hylkema, 1918-25; G. Hoeksema, 1926-58; J. Pott, 1959-64; J. Bylsma, 1965-71

Chicago, IL — South End (mission)
1918

Chicago, IL — South Side Mission
1939-1956
staff: I. Vander Weide (L), 1939-46; Mr./Mrs. C. Plug (L), 1949-51; D. Hesselink (L), 1951-55

Chicago, IL — Spirit and Truth Fellowship (emerging)
1977-1998, withdrew
emerging: 1983
pastors: E. Lugo, 1977-87; R. Baker, 1977-87; M. Oriz, 1983-86; R.M. Crawford, 1983-87; J. Rivera (S), 1987-98

Chicago, IL — Summit
see: Chicago, IL — Archer Avenue

Chicago, IL — Third
see: Lombard, IL — Lombard

Chicago, IL — Twelfth Street
see: Lombard, IL — Lombard

Chicago, IL — Western Springs (mission)
1937

Chicago, OH — Chicago
see: Willard, OH — Willard

Chicago Heights, IL — Mexican Mission
1960-1964
staff: J. Berlanga (L), 1960-64

Chicago Junction, OH — Chicago Junction
see: Willard, OH — Willard

Chilliwack, BC — Chilliwack
see: Chilliwack, BC — First

Chilliwack, BC — First
1952-
former name: Chilliwack, BC — Chilliwack, 1952-73
pastors: G.H. Polman, 1957-61; B. Den Herder, 1964-67; J. Dykstra, 1968-72; G.J. Hogeterp, 1972-78; A. Schweitzer, 1979-86; A.C. Leegwater, 1987-95; P.J. Janssens, 1996-98; H.G. De Ruyter, 1994-

Chilliwack, BC — Heartland Fellowship (emerging)
1994-
pastors: K. Byl (E), 1994-

Chinle, AZ — Chinle (classical ministry)
1992
staff: C. Grey, Jr. (E)

Chino, CA — Calvary
1961-
organized: 1969
pastors: M. Tanis (L), 1961-69; A.J. Schoonveld, 1971-77; A.A. Mulder, 1977-85; B.T. Ballast, 1983-; D.J. Klop, 1985-; J.E. Hoekema, 2000-

Chino, CA — First
see: Chino, CA — First/Primera Iglesia

Chino, CA — First/Primera Iglesia
1958-1997, withdrew, affiliated with United Reformed Church
former name: Chino, CA — First, 1958-69
pastors: P.W. Brouwer, 1959-67; L.J. Dykstra, 1967-75; G.W. Frens, 1968-72; T.J. Van't Land, 1973-75; T.C. Vanden Heuvel, 1975-79; R.J. Venema, 1980-86; R.J. Blauw, 1986-92; R.L. Scheurs, 1993-97

Chino, CA — Primera Iglesia Cristiana Reformada
see: Chino, CA — First/Primera Iglesia

Choteau, MT — Choteau
1905-1921, discontinued, became a branch of Conrad, MT; mission station, 1936-37

Chula Vista, CA — First
see: San Diego, CA — Trinity Fellowship

Chula Vista, CA — Iglesia Cristiana Siervo del Señor (classical ministry)
1987-1995, discontinued
pastors: F.J. Machado(S), 1987-91; J.V. Ruiz (S), 1992-95

Chula Vista, CA — Trinity
1961-1993, merged into San Diego, CA — Trinity Fellowship
pastors: A.P. Veenstra (M), 1960-78; J. Zandstra, 1973-78; D.M. Doyle, 1978-80; W.D. Dirksen, 1980-87; A. Rumph, 1988-93

Church Rock, NM — Church Rock
1969-
organized: 1983
pastors: M. Chavez (L), 1969; J. Tso (L), 1969-70; J. Yazzie (L), 1970-71; P. DeJong (M), 1971-73; A. Begay, 1974-78; B. Garnanez (E), 1979-88; C.J. Brummel (E), 1988-96; J. Kostelyk (E), 1996-

Cicero, IL — Beverly View Mission (mission)
1952-1953
staff: W. Baar (L), 1952-53

Cicero, IL — First
see: Lombard, IL — Lombard

Cicero, IL — First Cicero Evangelism (mission)
1950-1952

Cicero, IL — Second
see: Cicero, IL — Warren Park

Cicero, IL — Warren Park
1899-1973, discontinued, members merged into Cicero, IL — West Suburban (see: Elmhurst, IL — Faith)
former names: Chicago, IL — Douglas Park, 1899-1927; Cicero, IL — Second, 1927-56
pastors: F. Welandt, 1899-1905; C. De Leeuw, 1905-10; J. Manni, 1910-16; J.O. Vos, 1917-26; P.A. Hoelstra, 1927-40; C.M. Schoolland, 1940-43; M.J. Vander Werp, 1944-48; E.L. Haan, 1949-56; D.P. Bergsma, 1958-62; F.W. Van Houten, 1962-70; A.A. Mulder, 1970-73

Cicero, IL — Warren Park Evangelism (mission)
1949-1956

Cicero, IL — West Suburban
1973-1977, merged into Elmhurst, IL — Faith

pastors: O. Breen, 1973-75; A.A. Mulder, 1973-77

Cincinnati, OH — Cincinnati
merged into: Cincinnati, OH — Crosspoint,

Cincinnati, OH — Crosspoint
1997-
formed by the merger of Cincinnati OH — Cincinnati and Cincinnati, OH — New Community
former names: Cincinnati, OH — Cincinnati, 1857-1951 and 1987-97; Cincinnati OH — Parkview Heights, 1952-87; joined CRC 1866
pastors: W. Greve, 1869-74; J.R. Schepers, 1875-78; W.H. Frieling, 1881-82; W. Greve, 1883-86; O. Stuit, 1886-88; M. Van Vessem (M), 1890-95; J. Timmerman, 1895-96; J. Vander Mey, 1896-98; H. Vander Werp, 1899-1905; A.W. Meyer, 1905-07; J.B. Vander Werp, 1909-11; A. Dekker, 1912-16; H. Dekker, 1916-21; W. Goudberg, 1921-26; A. Jabaay, 1926-31; J.J. Kenbeek, 1931-41; R.J. Karsen, 1942-43; C. Abbas, 1944-49; H. Bajema, 1949-54; S.M. Voortman, 1954-57; H.J. Sprik, 1958-65; H.D. Clark, Jr., 1966-72; E.J. Dykstra, 1972-75; W. Verhoef, 1977-82; H.A. Stob, 1984-89; J.G. Zevalking, 1990-98; P.D. Sikkema, 1996-; T.J. Van Milligen, 1999-; T.N. Leunk, 2001-

Cincinnati, OH — New Community (emerging)
1991-1996
merged into: Cincinnati, OH — Crosspoint, 1996
pastor: P.S. Sikkema, 1991-96

Cincinnati, OH — Parkview Heights
see: Cincinnati, OH — Crosspoint

Clam Union, MI — Clam Union
see: Vogel Center, MI - Vogel Center

Clara City, MN — Bunde
see: Bunde, MN — Bunde

Clara City, MN — Clara City
1951-1972, discontinued
pastors: M.G. Zylstra, 1952-56; J.E. Jeffers, 1957-61; W.H. Kooienga, 1963-67; H.A. Sponholtz, 1967-72

Claremont, CA — Indonesian (emerging)
2000-
pastor: L. Siregar, 2000-

Clarkson, ON — Clarkson
see: Mississauga, ON — Clarkson

Clearbrook, BC — Trinity
see: Abbotsford, BC — Trinity

Clear Lake, MT — Clear Lake
1917-1921, discontinued

Clear Lake, SD — Bemis
see: Bemis, SD — Bemis

Cleveland, OH — East Side
1872-
pastors: J. Stadt, 1872-77; T.M. Vanden Bosch, 1891-94; A.J. Vanden Heuvel, 1895-1901; J.W. Wiebenga (I), 1901-02; B. Nagel, 1903-06; J.R. Brink, 1907-11; G.J. Van De Riet, 1911-20; G. Westenberg, 1921-27; O. Holtrop, 1927-39; D.J. Drost, 1940-48; O. DeGroot, 1948-52; A.E. Pontier, 1952-55; G.D. Pars, 1956-62; G.L. Dahnke, 1963-71; G.F. Vander Weit, 1971-89; J.D. Westra, 1988-93; E.A. Harrison, 1990-

Cleveland, OH — Maple Heights
1944-1993, discontinued
organized: 1958
began as a branch of Cleveland, OH — East Side
pastors: J.H. Brink, 1944-54; J.H. Houseward, 1955-61; S. Draayer, 1962-67; W.R. Lenters, 1968-73; R.C. Vredeveld, 1973-79; C. Van Essen, 1980-84; G.P. Veenstra, 1985-92

Cleveland, OH — Maple Heights Chapel
1955-1956
staff: J. Elffers (L), 1955-56

Cleveland, OH — West Park
1872-
former name: Cleveland, OH — West Side, 1872-1961
pastors: J. Stadt, 1872-77; F. Welandt, 1883-85; H. Tempel, 1888-93; A.J. Vanden Heuvel, 1895-1901; J. Bolt, 1904-08; J.J. Weersing, 1909-12; J. Mulder, 1912-15; A. Dekker, 1916-18; M. Botbyl, 1918-28; E.J. Holtrop, 1928-43; J.E. Meeter, 1945-51; R.D. Baker, 1952-53; H.B. Spaan, 1953-59; J.H. Primus, 1960-63; D.M. Stravers, 1963-67; C.E. Keegstra, 1967-75; R.A. Meyering, 1976-79; D.M. Stravers, 1980-92; P.E. Bakker, 1993-2001; G.D. Daley, 2002-

Cleveland, OH — West Side
see: Cleveland, OH — West Park

Clifton, NJ — Clifton
see: Clifton, NJ — Richfield

Clifton, NJ — Eastside Gospel Hall (mission)
1949-1954
staff: L. Ver Maas (L), 1949-64

Clifton, NJ — Joy, Peace and Love
1994-1996, discontinued
pastor: E.N. Romero, 1994-96

Clifton, NJ — Northside
1905-2002, discontinued
former name: Passaic, NJ — North Side, 1905-64
pastors: A.J. Vanden Heuvel, 1907-12; J.J. Hiemenga, 1913-18; S.S. Vander Heide, 1918-29; E.F.J. Van Halsema, 1930-48; S. Van Dyken, 1949-52; S.J. De Vries, 1953-56; W. Van Antwerpen, 1957-66; S. Ten Brink, 1967-74; J.D. Van Regenmorter, 1974-79; R.W. De Vries, 1979-93; T.G. Klaasen, 1997-2002

Clifton, NJ — Richfield
1825-
joined CRC, 1890, was a member of True Protestant Dutch Reformed Church
former names: Acquackanonk, NJ — Acquackanonk, 1890-1908, Passaic, NJ — Hope Avenue, 1908-26; Prospect Street, 1926-1956; Clifton, NJ — Clifton, 1956-65
absorbed via merger in 1975: Lodi, NJ — Lodi, 1876-1975; Passaic, NJ — Summer Street, 1876-1975 (was: Passaic, NJ — Passaic, 1875-1894, 1896-1908; Passaic/Patterson, NJ — Passaic/Patterson, 1895)
pastors: S.J. Vander Beek, 1892; A. Van Houten, 1892-95; J.A. Westervelt, 1896; J.F. Van Houten, 1896-1906; J.M. Gyhsels, 1909-13; D. De Beer, 1913-46; C. Van Ens, 1947-52; G. Stob, 1953-62; J.T. Malestein, 1962-68; A.J. Haan, 1969-73; A.R. Rienstra, 1973-83; I.J. Apol, 1983-87; R.W. Loerop, 1988-94; T.H. Huizenga, 1997-99; P.J. Mans (I), 1999-2000; P.L. Padro, 2002-

Clinton, ON — Clinton
1949-
pastors: C. Spoelhof (M), 1948; R.J. Bos, 1948-52; G.J. Hoytema, 1952-59; L. Slofstra, 1960-64; G.J. Heersink, 1964-67; A. Beukema, 1969-75; J.K. Boersma, 1975-78; A. Vanden Berg, 1976-83; H.G. Samplonius, 1985-89; D. Miedema, 1990-96; W. De Jong, 1996-2001

Clymer, NY — Clymer
1883-1896, withdrew
joined CRC in 1890

pastor: M. Van Vessum (M), 1887-88

Cobden-Pembrook, ON — Cobden-Pembrook
see: Pembroke, ON — Zion

Cobourg, ON — Cobourg
see: Cobourg, ON — Grace

Cobourg, ON — Grace
1955-
former name: Cobourg, ON — Cobourg, 1955-70
pastors: A.H. Smit (M), 1955-57; A. Rumph, 1957-60; G.J. Heersink, 1961-64; J.J. Hoytema, 1964-68; W. De Jong, 1969-72; A.J. Vanden Pol, 1973-79; R.W. Ouwehand, 1979-84; H. Getkate, 1985-88; E. Gritter, 1988-97; J.E. Vander Veer, 1999-

Cochrane, ON — Cochrane
1950-
pastors: J. Vander Meer, 1951-55; B. Bruxvoort (M), 1959-60; B. Kok (M), 1961-64; J. Tebsen (E), 1967-68; J.H. Binnema, 1973-78; H. Boehm (E), 1988-97, P. Veltman, 1997-2000

Coffee Creek, MT — Coffee Creek
1914-1921, discontinued, became a branch of Conrad, MT; was a mission station, 1936-1937

Collendoorn, MI — Collendoorn
see: Holland, MI — East Saugatuck

Collingwood, ON — Collingwood
1953-
pastors: S.G. Brondsema, 1953-56; G. Andre, 1956-60; L. Vander Heide, 1960-62; R. Praamsma, 1963-67; H. Numan, Sr., 1967-71; L. Praamsma, 1972-74; L.J. Howerzyl, 1975-78; N.J. Peters, 1978-80; L.T. Schalkwyk, 1980-82; J.E. Top, 1984-87; K.M. Gehrels, 1987-94; W. De Ruiter, 1996-2000; J. Kerssies, 2000-

Colorado Springs, CO — Colorado Community (emerging)
1993-1997, discontinued
emerging, 1995
pastor: D.S. Huizenga, 1993-97

Colorado Springs, CO — Colorado Springs
see: Colorado Springs, CO — Cragmor

Colorado Springs, CO — Cragmor
1960-
former name: Colorado Springs, CO — Colorado Springs, 1960-66

pastors: A.J. Haan (M), 1958-62; W.A. Bierling, 1962-66; C.E. Bajema, 1966-69; W.W. Leys, 1869-74; S. Mast, 1974-78; J.J. Wiegers, 1979-84; M.H. Bierma, 1985-96; S.J. Alsum, 1998-

Colton, SD — Colton
1915-
pastors: S.G. Brondsema (M), 1917-19; S.G. Brondsema, 1919-22; C.J. Scholten, 1923-35; J.G. Vande Lune, 1937-45; A. De Vries, 1945-50; W. Vande Kieft, 1951-54; D.P. Bergsma, 1954-58; L.F. Stockmeier, 1958-63; W. Swets, 1964-69; B. Vermeer, 1969-72; L.J. Kuiper, 1973-76; J.A. Bultman, 1976-82; A.L. Vander Hart, 1984-88; N.J. Visser, 1989-97; T.H. Vander Ziel, 1997-2001

Columbia, MO — Immanuel Community
1979-1995, discontinued
pastors: R.D. Steen, 1977-82; T.E. Pettinga, 1983-91; D.J. Einfeld, 1992-95

Columbus, MT — Columbus
1916-1939, discontinued, became a branch of Manhattan, MT

Columbus, OH — Ohio State Campus Ministry
1966-1993
staff: R. Van Harn, 1966-68; E. Schipper, 1968-69; E. Schipper, 1969-70; R. Van Harn, 1970-76; E.T. Lewis, 1976-93

Columbus, OH — Olentangy
1957-
began as a branch of Willard, OH
pastors: H.J. Sprik, 1954-57 (M); J. Zandstra (M), 1957-58; H.D. Bultje (M), 1958-60; G. De Young, 1960-64; R.E. Van Harn, 1966-70; G.J. Postma, 1971-73; R. Opperwall, 1973-86; R.J. Hamstra, 1987-98; R.A. Arbogast, 1999-

Compton, CA — Compton
1927-1928; 1939-1951, discontinued
organized: 1940
pastors: H.J. De Vries, (M), 1927-28; H. Dusseljee (M), 1940-41, 1939-41; J.B. Swierenga, 1941-44; S.G. Brondsema, 1946-48; R. Star, 1950-51

Compton, CA — Nueva Comunidad (emerging)
1998-
pastors: O.A. Alfaro (E), 1998-

Comstock, MI (mission)
1945-1946
staff: E. Postma (E), 1945-46

Comstock, MI — Bethel
see: Kalamazoo, MI — Comstock

Comstock, MI — Comstock
see: Kalamazoo, MI — Comstock

Comstock Park, MI — Comstock Park
1930-
organized: 1957
pastors: G. Youngs (L), 1934-35; J. Vande Water (L), 1936-37; G. Veenstra (L), 1937-45; H. Barber (L), 1944-48; L. Dams (L), 1945-49; W. Swierenga, 1949-60; P.J. Veenstra, 1961-75; J.H. Looman, 1975-84; M.J. Meekhof, 1984-89; G.A. Koning, 1991-

Conrad, MT — Conrad
1909-
pastors: M. Borduin (M), 1911-15; J.A. Gerritsen, 1918-21; M. Borduin (M), 1925-34; W.C. Steenland, 1934-37; J.B. Swierenga, 1938-42; J.R. Brink, 1943-46; P. Van Dyk, 1947-49; L. Sweetman, Jr., 1951-53; J. Morren, 1953-56; J.W. Postman, 1956-59; J.A. Bonnema, 1960-62; H.T. De Jong, 1965-68; J.M. Moes, 1971-78; P. DeJong, 1979-83; J.H. Elenbaas, 1983-87; J.M. De Koekkoek, 1987-91; J.T. Ebbers, 1992-96

Coopersville, MI — Coopersville
see also: Polkton, MI — Polkton

Coopersville, MI — Coopersville
1920-
pastors: J.R. Brink (M), 1923-25; H.D. Vande Kieft, 1927-43; W.H. Ackerman, 1943-47; P. Jonker, Jr., 1948-52; A.A. Koning, 1953-59; A.E. Pontier, 1960-64; C.N. Van Dalfsen, 1965-69; R.O. De Groot, 1969-75; F.F. Gunnink, 1975-82; G.H. Stoutmeyer, 1983-90; W. Renkema, 1991-98; L.A. Lobdell, Jr., 1999-

Coopersville, MI — Lamont
see: Lamont, MI — Lamont

Coopersville, MI — Little Farms (emerging)
1952-1997, withdrew to Orthodox Presbyterian Church
organized: 1971-75
pastors: H. Meekhof (L), 1952-54; R. Doornbos (L), 1954-57; R. Ericks (E), 1955-56; H. Van Til (L), 1957-58; H. Hamburg (L), 1958-66; J. De

Vries (L), 1966-72; H.R. Post, Jr., 1973-77; G.J. Rozenboom, 1978-81; W.D. Vis (L), 1981-82

Coquille, OR — Hope (emerging)
1989-1996, discontinued
pastor: R. Joling (E), 1989-96

Coquitlam, BC — Coquitlam
see: Coquitlam, BC — Mundy Park Christian Fellowship

Coquitlam, BC — Mundy Park Christian Fellowship
1969-
organized: 1976
former names: Coquitlam, BC — Coquitlam, 1969-88
pastors: E.H. Busink, 1976-88; K.A. Baker, 1989-92; T.W. Bomhof, 1993-2002

Cornwall, ON — Cornwall
see: Cornwall, ON — Immanuel

Cornwall, ON — Immanuel
1950-
former names: Martintown, ON — Martintown, 1950; Cornwall, ON — Cornwall, 1950-72
pastors: A.H. Smit (M), 1950-54; R.H. Hooker, 1954-59; P.F. Dahm, 1963-66; A. Driese, 1968-72; D.J. Tigchelaar, 1972-76; S.J. Sietsema, 1978-88; A. Van Muyen, 1989-93; A.C. Groen, 1994-2000; H.A. Vanderbeek, 2001-

Corona, CA — Garden Grove Korean
see: Anaheim, CA — Garden Grove Korean

Corsica, SD — Corsica
1906-
pastors: C. Maring, 1909-13; K. Bergsma, 1914-16; J.G. Vande Lune, 1916-20; S.P. Eldersveld, 1920-24; J.R. Van Dyke, 1925-29; L. Verduin, 1929-41; J. Guichelaar, 1941-45; E.H. Oostendorp, 1946-50; P. Huisman, 1951-57; S.M. Voortman, 1957-61; J.T. Ebbers, 1961-69; G.G. Heyboer, 1970-74; W. Verhoef, 1973-77; L.F. Stockmeier, 1977-83; D.J. Vrieland, 1983-89; A.J. Van Dellen, 1989-96; J.D. Buwalda, 1998-

Corvallis, OR — Church of the Savior
see: Corvallis, OR — Knollbrook

Corvallis, OR — Corvallis
see: Corvallis, OR — Knollbrook

Corvallis, OR — Knollbrook
1969-
organized: 1973
former name: Corvallis, OR – Corvallis, 1969-73; Corvallis, OR – Church of the Savior, 1973-87
pastors: F.D. Breisch, Jr. (M), 1969-73; H.T. DeJong, 1975-76; H.B. Spaan, 1976-85; C.J. Aardsma, 1986-97; K.M.B. Van Schelven, 1998-

Corvallis, OR — Oregon State (campus ministry)
1966-1974
staff: J. Vander Beek (L), 1966-69; F. Breisch, 1969-73; A.D. Bosscher, 1973-74

Coster, IA — Coster
see: Allison, IA – Bethel

Courtenay-Campbell River, BC — Courtenay-Campbell River
1952-1960, discontinued

Cramersburg, SK — Cramersburg
1912-1923, discontinued

Crookston, MN — Crookston
see: Crookston, MN – First

Crookston, MN — First
1917-
former name: Crookston, MN – Crookston, 1917-88
pastors: W. Meyer (M), 1917-27; J.M. Dykstra, 1925-29; R.A. Rozeboom, 1929-43; N. De Vries, 1944-48; M. Keuning, 1950-62; G.D. Mouw, 1970-73; M. Stegink, 1982-89; R.J. Rozema, 1990-93; D.L. Jabaay (E), 1993-97; J. Baldwin (E)1990-

Crown Point, IN — Crown Point
see: Crown Point, IN – First

Crown Point, IN — First
1961-
former name: Crown Point, IN – Crown Point, 1961-71
pastors: R.L. Peterson, 1961-64; H.J. Sprik, 1965-69; A. Petroelje, 1970-74; L.R. Smits, 1974-79; W.H. Kooienga, 1980-94; G.S. Janke, 1994-2001; J.J. Sheeres, 2002-

Crownpoint, NM — Crownpoint
1912-
organized: 1929-1947, 1971-

includes: Whitehorse Lake Mission and Becabito Mission
pastors: D.H. Muyskens, 1912-13 (M); J. Bolt (M), 1914-40; J. Van Bruggen (M), 1938-58; E.D. Dykema, (M), 1958-64; L. Largo (L), 1958-59; C. Tsosie (L), 1959-62; E. Benally (L), 1960-62; J. Toledo (L), 1960-66; J. Charles (L), 1963-64, 1967-68; P. Belin (L), 1964-66; D.M. Doyle (M), 1966-69; J. Yazzie (L), 1967-68;A. Gelder (M), 1969-74; L. Benally (L), 1970-72; A. Becenti (L), 1970-72; G.T. Stuit, 1974-88; M.A. Harberts, 1990-93; R.L. Jipping, 1993-; B. Garnanez (E), 1989-90

Crownpoint, NM — Toyee Mission and Whitehorse Lake Mission
see: Crownpoint, NM – Crownpoint

Crystal Lake, IL — Fox Valley
1982-
pastors: D.J. Einfeld, 1982-92; J.J. Wiegers, 1992-99; G. Cooper, 2000-

Cutlerville, MI — Covenant
1962-
pastors: H.L. Bergsma, 1963-66; M.S. Jorritsma, 1967-73; G.F. Van Oyen, 1973-88; D.J. Van Essen, 1980-84; A. Petroelje, 1985-96; H.L. Bergsma, 1991-94; E.P. Heerema, 1995-2001; C.A. Walters, 1997-

Cutlerville, MI — Cutlerville
see: Cutlerville, MI – First

Cutlerville, MI — Cutlerville East
1954-
pastors: R.W. Westveer, 1955-60; S. Kramer, 1960-69; G.P. Holwerda, 1969-77; J.H. Engbers, 1978-90; C.D. Vander Meyden, 1990-97; W.R. Sytsma, 1998-

Cutlerville, MI — Cutlerville Hills
see: Cutlerville, MI – Hillside Community

Cutlerville, MI — First
1893-
former names: Fisher Station, MI – Fisher Station, 1903-07; Cutlerville, MI – Cutlerville, 1907-54
pastors: S.S. Vander Heide, 1899-1902; E. Vander Vries, 1903-07; T. Jongbloed, 1908-11; J. Post, 1914-20; H. Vander Woude, 1921-23; L. Van Haitsma, 1924-29; Z.J. Sherda, 1930-53; D.J. Hoitenga, Sr., 1954-62; J.L. Vander Laan, 1962-

67; H. Bossenbroek, 1968-72; W. Swets, 1973-97, K.E. Van Wyk, 1996-; D.A. Gritter, 2001-

Cutlerville, MI — Fourth
see: Cutlerville, MI — Hillside Community

Cutlerville, MI — Hillside Community
1968-
former names: Cutlerville, MI — Fourth, 1968; Cutlerville, MI — Cutlerville Hills, 1968-90
pastors: H.T. De Jong, 1968-75; M.J. Vander Vliet, 1976-85; G.R. Mossel, 1986-; R.G. Kool, 1990-; J.G. Zevalking, 1998-2000; R.A. Blacketer, 1998-2000; G.L. Zandstra, 2001-

Cutlerville, MI — Pinegate Community
1967-1998, discontinued
organized: 1990
pastors: K. Tebben (E), 1967-79; A.W. Bytwork (E), 1979-84; H. Boehm (E), 1985-88; G.F. Van Oyen, 1988-93; D.M. Doyle, 1995-98

Cutlerville, MI — Providence
1976-
pastors: C.D. Compagner, 1979-84; R.J. Noorman, 1984-90; L.T. Riemersma, 1991-94; J.G. Van Ryn, 1994-96; J. Vanden Akker, 1996-

Cypress, CA — Messiah Korean
1988-
organized: 1991
former name: Buena Park, CA — Messiah Korean, 1991-93; Norwalk, CA — Messiah Korean, 1994-97
pastor: W.S. Yeo, 1988-95

Cypress, CA — Rivershore Korean
see: Artesia, CA — The Spirit Filled

Cypress Gardens, FL — Cypress Gardens
1975-1983, discontinued
former name: Winter Haven, FL — Cypress Garden, 1975-76
pastors: F. Bakker (E), 1975-76; J. Van Ens, 1977-80

Dallas, TX — Bethel
1973-
organized: 1978
pastors: A. Vander Veen (E), 1973-74; D.G. Zandstra, 1976-83; D.L. Slings, 1983-87, C.A. Heuss, 1992-95; J.R. Sittema, 1989-

Darien, IL — Rhythm Ministries (emerging)
1998-2000, discontinued

pastor: D. Maat, 1998-2000

Darien, IL — Suburban Life Community
1991-
organized: 1998
pastor: T.P. Hoekstra, 1990-

Davenport, IA — Kimberly Village
1965-2000, discontinued
organized: 1970
former name: Davenport, IA — Quint Cities, 1965-68
pastors: S. Vander Jagt (M), 1965-79; R.D. Goudzwaard, 1980-84; M.B. Fynaardt, 1986-96; T. Grotenhuis, 1998-2000

Davenport, IA — Quint Cities
see: Davenport, IA — Kimberly Village

Dayton, OH — Calvary Community
1960-1986, discontinued
organized: 1961
former name: Dayton, OH — Kettering, 1964-83
pastors: J. Batts (L), 1960; T.L. Brouwer (M), 1961-65; J.W. Dykstra (M), 1965-68; J. Zandstra (M), 1969; N.J. Gebben, Sr., 1969-73; J.F. Hollebeek, 1973-80; A.A. Arkema, 1980-86

Dayton, OH — Kettering
see: Dayton, OH — Calvary Community

Dearborn, MI — Dearborn
1936-
organized: 1938
pastors: J. Entingh, 1936-43; J.D. Eppinga, 1944-51; G.D. Vanderhill, 1951-68; R.L. Peterson, 1969-76; J.R. Boot, 1976-84; T.J. Brown, 1985-95; T.D. Slachter, 1996-2002

Dearborn, MI — Harvest Fellowship (emerging)
2001-

Dearborn, MI — Peace Arab-American Ministries (emerging)
1989-1996, discontinued
pastor: S.J. Kelley, 1989-96

Decatur, GA — Christ Community
see: Atlanta, GA — Christ Community

Decatur, GA — Vision One (emerging)
1998-
pastor: G. Boyd, 1998-

Decatur, MI — Decatur
1917-1993, discontinued
organized: 1927
pastors: J.R. Brink (M), 1927; P.J. Steen, 1928-
30; J. Hoogland, 1930-36; J.H. Steenwyk, 1937-
46; P.A. Boertje, 1947-50; S.A. Dykstra, 1950-57;
R.L. Wiebenga, 1958-61; A.W. Koolhaas, 1964-
69; J.A. Bultman, 1969-75; H. Dykema, 1977-81;
J. Hekman, 1982-86; S.M. Metz, 1986-89; A.J.
De Vries, 1990-94

Delavan, WI — Delavan
1931-
pastors: J.P. Smith, 1933-38; Henry DeMots,
1938-43; L.J. Lamberts, 1943-48; E. Ubels,
1949-53; R.B. Vermeer, 1953-58; M.J. Vander
Werp, 1958-62; C. Vander Ark, 1962-66; G.G.
Hofland, 1967-71; T. Medema, 1971-77; G.G.
Heyboer, 1977-81; P. Van Drunen, 1982-85; T.L.
Brouwer, 1986-94; D.J. Roeda, 1995-

Delta, BC — First Ladner
see: Delta, BC–Ladner

Delta, BC — Ladner
1950-
former names: Ladner, BC — Ladner, 1950-71;
Ladner/Delta, BC — Ladner/Delta, 1971-75; Delta,
BC — First Ladner, 1975-2000
pastors: P. De Koekkoek, 1951-53; J.R. Van Dyke,
1954-57; C.W. Tuininga, 1958-64; A.P. Geisterfer,
1965-69; P. Kranenburg, 1970-74; S. Greidanus,
1975-78; H. Salomons, 1978-90; J.R. Berry,
1990-98; H. Jonker, 1999-

Delta, BC — West Coast Community (emerging)
1999-
pastor: J.R. Berry, 1999-

De Motte, IN (mission)
1932

De Motte, IN — Bethel
1968-
pastors: M.N. Buwalda, 1969-74; J.A. Botting,
1975-80; G.G. Heyboer, 1981-88; H. De Groot,
1988-92; T.D. Wetselaar, 1994-95; E.P. Meyer,
1996-98; E. Schering, 1998-

De Motte, IN — Community
see: Roselawn, IN — Community

De Motte, IN — De Motte
see: De Motte, IN — First

De Motte, IN — First
1932-
former name: De Motte, IN — De Motte, 1932-68
pastors: W. Haverkamp, 1933-37; C.J. Van
Schouwen, 1937-42; H. DeMots, 1943-47; P.F.
Holtrop, 1947-52; C.W. Flietstra, 1953-57; B. Van
Someren, 1958-65; A.E. Rozendal, 1965-73; E.G.
Cooke, 1973-80; A.H. Jongsma, 1981-88; B.J.
Haan, Jr., 1989-98; E.R. Tigchelaar, 2000-

Denver, CO — Center of Hope
1957-1981, discontinued
organized: 1960
former name: Denver, CO — Fairview, 1957-76
pastors: E.S. Holkeboer, 1957-61; E. Los, 1961-
68; K.J. Vander Wall, 1968-72; A.J. Haan, 1973-
81; J.J. Berends, 1980-81

Denver, CO — Christian Indian Center (emerging)
1964-1999, discontinued
1971, emerging
pastors: P. Bakker (L), 1964-71; J. Yazzie (E),
1971-76; H.A Van Dam, 1977-84; M. Deckinga
(E), 1985-89

Denver, CO — Denver
see: Denver, CO — First

Denver, CO — Fairview
see: Denver, CO — Center of Hope

Denver, CO — Family in Christ Community
1981-
pastors: J.J. Berends, 1981-90; E. Schering,
1991-94; P. Jorden, 1997-

Denver, CO — First
1907-
former name: Denver, CO — Denver, 1907-36
pastors: I. Van Dellen, 1907-40; D.D. Bonnema,
1924-27; K. Bergsma, 1928-36; W. Van Peursem,
1940-45; J Guichelaar, 1945-50; H.J. Evenhouse,
1951; H.N. Erffmeyer, 1953-57; E.S. Holkeboer,
1957-61; R.B. Vermeer, 1958-66; J.L. Vander
Laan, 1967-75; M.L. De Young, 1974-76; J.
Gunnink, 1976-87; J.D. Van Regenmorter, 1988-
97; M.R. Van't Hof, 1998-

Denver, CO — Gospel Chapel/South Clayton (mission)
1946-1958
staff: G. Veenstra (L), 1946-53; L.R. Haan (L),
1949-50; G. Veen (L), 1949-50; J. Bol (E), 1950-
58; R. Eriks (L), 1955-57

Denver, CO — Highlands Ranch Ministries
1969-1995, discontinued
former name: Denver, CO — Ridgeview Hills, 1969-95
pastors: D.H. Aardsma, 1968-72; J. Hofman, Jr., 1973-77; R.A. Hertel, 1977-83; D.K. Kelderman, 1983-88; K.J. Van Harn, 1986-89; W. Leys, 1989-94; J.A. De Boer (I), 1995

Denver, CO — Hillcrest
1962-
pastors: T. Verseput, 1962-68; J.P. Boonstra, 1968-77; T.E. Dykman, 1977-86; J.L. Alferink, 1987-94; M.D. Timmer, 1998-

Denver, CO — Horizon Community
see: Highlands Ranch, CO — Horizon Community

Denver, CO — Khmer (emerging)
1992-
congregational ministry, 1992-98
pastors: J. Kim (E), 1994-

Denver, CO — New Life Fellowship
1976-1979, discontinued
pastors: J.L. Vander Laan, 1975-76; M.G. Vande Steeg, 1976-79

Denver, CO — New Life Korean (emerging)
1999-2000, discontinued
pastor: W. Lee, 1999-2000

Denver, CO — Ridgeview Hills
see: Denver, CO — Highlands Ranch Ministries

Denver, CO — Rivendell
see: Denver, CO — The Outpost

Denver, CO — Second
1936-
pastors: R.H. Hooker, 1937-48; M. Ouwinga, 1949-56; L.A. Bazuin, 1958-63; A.C. De Jong, 1964-66; G.P. Holwerda, 1966-69; B. Byma, 1970-75; G.R. Erffmeyer, 1976-82; C.D. Compagner, 1984-88; W. Verhoef, 1990-2002

Denver, CO — Sun Valley Community Church (emerging)
1966-
emerging, 1967
pastors: M. Suwyn (L), 1966-68; G.D. Negen (M), 1969-74; L. Roossien, Jr., 1974-81; J. Vande Lune, 1981-88; N.A. Negrete, 1988-95; E. Burgos, 1997-

Denver, CO — The Outpost (emerging)
1997-
former name: Denver, CO — Rivendell, 1997-99
pastor: J. Van Kooten, 1998-99

Denver, CO — Third
1952-
pastors: J. Zwaanstra, 1953-64; K. Rietema, 1964-71; J.R. Kok, 1972-91; R.J. Nydam, 1974-84; W.L. Meyer, 1984-88; T.D. Draayer, 1988-

Denver, CO — Trinity
1958-1993, discontinued
pastors: J. Fondse, 1958-62; L. Kerkstra, 1962-66; J.A. Bultman, 1966-69; H. De Young, 1969-74; J.E. Versluys, 1975-83; E.R. Hommes, 1984-93

Denver, CO — Way of Life Gospel Center (mission)
1946-1957
staff: B. Bruxvoort (L), 1946-49; J. Bol (E), 1952-57

Des Moines, IA — Crossroads Fellowship
1950-
former name: Des Moines, IA — Des Moines, 1950-2002
pastors: W. Verwolf, (M), 1946-49; J.C. Medendorp, 1951-54; E.F. Hills, 1954-62; J.E. Versluys, 1963-67; T.L. Smith, 1968-71; L.J. Vander Zee, 1970-73; L.D. Meyer, 1974-81; A.S. Luke, 1981-87; J. Van Marion, 1988-95; C.A. Heuss, 1995-98; A.L. Kuiper, 1999-; A. Veenstra, 2000-

Des Moines, IA — Des Moines
See: Des Moines, IA — Crossroads Fellowship

De Soto, TX — Hope Fellowship
see: Cedar Hill, TX — Hope Fellowship

Des Plaines, IL — Des Plaines
see: Des Plaines, IL — First

Des Plaines, IL — First
1927-1993, discontinued
organized: 1929
former name: Des Plaines, IL — Des Plaines, 1927-69
pastors: R.H. Hooker, 1930-37; W.H. Steenland, 1937-38; H. Kooistra, 1938-43; A.H. Selles, 1943-46; J.H. Kromminga, 1946-49; G. Zylstra, 1949-62; J.H. Draisma, 1962-68; L.J. Wolters,

1969-79; K.J. Wiersum, 1980-83; R.J. Vander Roest, 1984-93

Detroit, MI (mission)
1923
staff: J.R. Brink (M), 1923

Detroit, MI — Community
see: Detroit, MI – Nardin Park Community

Detroit, MI — Detroit
see: Detroit, MI – First

Detroit, MI — First
1914-
former name: Detroit, MI – Detroit, 1914-71
pastors: H. Bel, 1918-21; H. Verduin, 1921-26; M. Monsma, 1928-34; G.W. Hylkema, 1934-38; J.O. Schuring, 1939-44; M. Ouwinga, 1944-49; V.C. Licatesi, 1950-54; S. Vander Jagt, 1956-60; J.H. Groenewold, 1961-67; F.D. Steen, 1967-75; D.A. Warners, 1976-82; W.J. Moxey, 1982-87; W.C. De Vries, 1987-

Detroit, MI — Nardin Park Community
1966-1981, discontinued
organized: 1971
former name: Detroit, MI – Community, 1976
pastors: H.E. Botts (M), 1966-72; H. De Bruyn (M), 1973-74; J.J. Steigenga, 1974-78

Detroit, MI — Wayne State Inter Varsity Christian Fellowship
1970-
staff: W. De Vries (L), 1970-72; R. Kok (I), 1972-73; J.D. Natelborg, 1975-2001

Dexter, NM — Dexter
1912-1920, discontinued

Diamond Bar, CA — Body of the Lord (emerging)
2000-
pastor: M.S. Lee, 2000-

Diamond Springs, MI — Diamond Springs
1921-1929, discontinued, became a branch of Oakland, MI
pastor: J.L. Koerts, 1924-25

Dispatch, KS — Dispatch
1880-
former name: Rotterdam, KS – Rotterdam, 1880-1940
pastors: W.R. Smidt, 1887-89; A.J. Vanden

Heuvel, 1893-95; E. Bos, 1896-1902; E. Vanden Berge, 1903-04; E. Bos, 1906-09; G.W. Hylkema, 1909-15; H.J. Ruys, 1916-21; H.J. De Vries, 1922-27; J.M. Byleveld, 1927-29; R.S. De Haan, 1929-37; F.M. Huizenga, 1938-43; R.R. DeRidder, 1946-49; J. Paauw, 1951-55; H. Visscher, 1955-59; H.P. Baak, 1959-65; L. Bouma, 1965-69; S.E. Ver Heul, 1970-73; P. De Jong, 1973-79; C.H. Bruxvoort, 1979-84; R.R. DeVries, 1984-90; J.A. Vermeer, 1990-95; H. De Jong, 1995-

Dixie, ON — Dixie
see: Mississauga, ON – Clarkson

Dixon's Corners, ON — Community of Matilda Township
1989-
pastor: S.J. Gerrits, 1989-98; C.H. Witten, 2001-

Dollard Des Ormeaux, QC — First
see: Montreal, QC – First

Doon, IA — Doon
1902-1997, withdrew, affiliated with United Reformed Churches
pastors: P. Van Vliet (M), 1906-08; N.J. Burggraaf, 1908-12; M. De Boer, 1912-17; B. De Jonge, 1917-22; M. Monsma, 1924-28; J. Betten, 1928-36; E.F. Visser, 1938-42; W. Hekman, 1941-48; A.H. Bratt, 1949-52; C.J. Toeset, 1952-57; C. Vander Plate, 1957-60; J.H. Elenbaas, 1960-66; G.A. Oosterveen, 1966-71; W. Dryfhout, 1972-77; H. Vander Kam, 1979-82; P.R. Hoekstra, 1982-85; P. Van Drunen, 1985-92

Doornspijk, MI — Doornspijk
see: Oakland, MI – Oakland

Doraville, GA — Shalom Korean
see: Atlanta, GA – Shalom Korean

Dorr, MI — Dorr
1938-
mission, 1924-25
pastors: J.R. Brink (M), 1924-25; L.E. Veltkamp, 1938-42; J.H. Bratt, 1942-46; J.H. Steenwyk, 1946-51; H. Bel, 1951-57; A. Dusseljee, 1957-59; R.J. Vande Kieft; 1959-65; B.W. Mulder, 1966-69; P. De Boer, 1970-73; R. J. Vander Borgh, 1973-76; S.M. Voortman, 1976-89; A.L. Van Whye, 1990-2000; M.A. Scheffers (I), 2000-2002; G.D. Nieuwsma, 2002-

Douglas, IA — Douglas
1883, discontinued

Douglas, MI (mission)
1939–1940

Douglas, SD — Douglas
see: New Holland, SD — New Holland

Downers Grove, IL — Horizon Community
see: Lisle, IL — Horizon Community

Downsview, ON — Friendship Community
see: Toronto, ON — Friendship Community

Drayton, ON — Drayton
1950–
former name: Drayton, ON — First, 1973–98
pastors: A.D. Folkema, 1952–57; C. Spoelhof, 1954–55; A.J. Vanden Pol, 1957–61; L. Doezema, 1961–66; H. Lunshof, 1967–71; A.A. Van Geest, 1972–77; D. Velthuizen, 1978–88; D.J. Tigchelaar, 1989–96; G.J. Bomhof, 1998–

Drayton, ON — First
see: Drayton, ON — Drayton

Drenthe, MI — Drenthe
1847–
former name: Drenthe, MI — Drenthe (RCA), 1847–82; joined the denomination as South Blendon, MI — South Blendon, 1882; members of Drenthe, MI — Presbyterian, 1853–1886 merged in 1886
pastors: W.R. Smit, 1851–53; W.R. Smit, 1853–1886; R. Pieters, 1861–65; J. Huyssoon, 1865–66; W. Moerdyke, 1869–72; C. Van Der Veen, 1875–82; H. Vander Werp, 1883–86; E. Broene, 1886–95; A. Keizer, 1896–98; D.R. Drukker, 1898–1902; M. Van Vessum, 1903–10; T. Vander Ark, 1910–16; W.D. Vander Werp, 1916–25; B. Essenburg, 1925–29; B.J. Danhof, 1930–37; L. Veltkamp, 1937–42; N.L. Veltman, 1944–47; M. Bolt, 1947–52; J.J. Kenbeek, 1952–64; S.T. Cammenga, Sr., 1965–71; H.C. Van Wyk, Jr., 1971–79; C.D. Vander Meyden, 1979–86; H.F. Vlaardingerbroek, 1986–97; R.J. Meyer, 1997–

Dresden, ON — Dresden
1951–
pastors: R. Bronkema, Sr. (stated supply), 1956–58; J. Joosse, 1960–63; H. Mennega, 1964–67; A.C. Groen, 1968–71; H.L. Downs, 1972–78; D. Miedema, 1981–85; J.H. Binnema, Jr., 1986–91; J.H. Noordhof, 1992–97; D.E. Miedema, 1999–

Duchess, AB — Duchess
see: Brooks, AB — Brooks

Duncan, BC — Duncan
see: Duncan, BC — First

Duncan, BC — First
1952–
former name: Duncan, BC — Duncan, 1952–88
pastors: L.T. Schalkwyk, 1958–62; J. Van Dyk, 1962–65; J. Boonstra, 1965–71; H. De Moor, Jr., 1971–74; A. Schweitzer, 1974–79; J. dePater, 1978–83; J.H. Kits, 1984–92; L.H. Batterink, 1994–2001; G.G. Colyn, 2002–

Dundas, ON — Calvary
see: Flamborough, ON — Calvary

Dundas, ON — Calvin
1954–
former name: Greensville, ON — Greensville, 1954–58
pastors: A. Persenaire, 1956–61; J. Nutma, 1963–66; W. Renkema, 1970–74; J. Zantingh, 1973–83; R. Steinstra, 1985–90; M.L. Van Donselaar, 1990–

Dunnville, ON — Bethel
1958–
pastors: G.J. Hoytema, 1959–64; A.J. Vanden Pol, 1963–67; J. Kerssies, 1968–72; W. De Jong, 1972–76; G.V. Martin, 1977–81; H.A. Vander Windt, 1982–89; R. Stienstra, 1990–92; M.J. Vandyk, 1993–98; G.P. Van Smeerdyk, 2001–

Dunwoody, GA — Comunidad Cristiana San Pablo (emerging)
2001–
pastor: P. Toledo, 2001–

Durango, CO — Grace Fellowship
see: Durango, CO — Sunrise Community

Durango, CO — Sunrise Community (emerging)
1996–2000, discontinued
former name: Durango, CO — Grace Fellowship, 1996–97
pastor: D.J. Hunderman, 1996–2000

Durham, NC — The River (emerging)
1998–
pastor: C.S. Moore, 1997– ; N.A. Visker, 2003–

Dutton, MI — Dutton
1915–1993, organized as the first English-speaking rural church; withdrew to become Independent Reformed

pastors: J. Medendorp, 1921-26; M. Arnoys, 1927-30; J. Vande Kieft, 1931-43; F. Handlogten, 1943-52; R. Leetsma, 1954-58; C.S. Steenstra, 1959-64; B. Kok, 1964-69; P. De Jong, 1980-90; W.H. Lammers, 1981-89; P.T. Murphy, 1992-93

Duvall, WA — Duvall
1934-1951, merged with Sultan, WA — Sultan to form Monroe, WA — Monroe
pastors: P.J. Hoekstra, 1936-43; S.A. Dykstra, 1943-45; A. Wassink, 1946-50
members and records transferred to the newly established church at Monroe, WA — Monroe

Eagle Butte, SD — Pleasant Valley
1934-1947, discontinued
pastor: H.J. Schripsema (stated supply), 1933-37

East Grand Forks, MN — Community
1963-
organized: 1971
former name: Grand Forks, ND — Community, 1971-98
pastors: P. Lagerwey (M), 1963-74; L.D. Slings, 1975-79; J.D. Lion, 1981-84; R.J. Rozema, 1990-93; D.L. Jabaay (E). 1993-97; J.L. Baldwin (E), 1998-

East Islip, NY — Christ Community
1957-
organized: 1964
former name: East Islip, NY — East Islip, 1964-87
pastors: F. Bultman (M), 1957-66; A.A. Arkema, 1966-71; R.C. Vredeveld, 1971-72; A.E. Likkel (M), 1974-80; P.C. Kelder, 1978-80; M.A. Davies, 1980-84; K.J. Verhulst, 1985-

East Islip, NY — East Islip
see: East Islip, NY — Christ Community

East Jordan, MI (mission)
1910

East Jordan, MI — Vance Chapel
1961-1983
staff: G.J. Drenth (L), 1961-72; M. Essenberg (L), 1961-67; W. Vander Ark (E), 1974-75; M. Van Vliet (M), 1975-76; H. Drenth (E), 1977-80

East Lansing, MI — East Lansing
see: East Lansing, MI — River Terrace

East Lansing, MI — Michigan State Univ. (campus ministry)
1966-
staff. A.L. Hoksbergen, 1966-72; T. Limburg, 1972-77; J. Terpstra, 1977-80; C.G. Libolt (E), 1983-86; T. Spoores (E), 1989-90; D.J. Kool, 1992-93; G.J. Kett, 2000-

East Lansing, MI — River Terrace
1935-
former names: Lansing, MI — First, 1934-1969; East Lansing, MI — East Lansing, 1969-79
pastors: G.R. Youngs, 1936-40; Dr. J.E. Luchies, 1942-46; H. Dykhouse, 1947-56; J.M. Hofman, 1957-67; J.H. Brink, 1968-72; A. Hoksbergen, 1966-90; T.C. Limburg, 1972-77; J. Terpstra, 1977-80; C. Libolt, 1986-; D.J. Kool, 1992-93

Eastmanville, MI — Eastmanville
1884-1994, withdrew, affiliated with United Reformed Churches
pastors: J. Post, 1895-1900; F.J. Drost, 1902-05; L.J. Hulst, 1906-10; H.E. Oostendorp, 1911-14; J. Wyngaarden, 1915-18; G. Goris, 1919-21; B.H. Spalink, 1921-24; H. Dykhouse, 1924-29; A. Persenaire, 1929-48; P. Huisman, 1948-51; L. Van Drunen, Jr., 1952-58; N. Punt, 1958-64; M. Toonstra, Jr., 1965-79; R.C. Heerspink, 1979-84; M.C. Groenendyke, 1984-90; D.J. Vander Meulen, 1991-93

East Maple Ridge, BC (church plant)
2000-

East Martin, MI — East Martin
1921-
former name: Gun River, MI — Gun River, 1921-23; Martin, MI — East Martin, 1923-98
pastors: J.R. Brink(M), 1923-24 A. Dusseljee, 1924-28; W. Alkema, 1928-48; J. Entingh, 1948-53; E. Joling, 1953-59; G. Yff, 1960-65; A.J. Schoonveld, 1966-71; J.L. Witvliet, 1971-76; G. Compaan, 1976-83; H.R. Roelofs, 1985-92; S.R. Van Eck, 1995-2001

East McBain, MI (mission)
1910-1915

East Overisel, MI — East Overisel
see: Overisel, MI — East Overisel

East Palmyra, NY — East Palmyra
1907-
pastors: M. Botbyl (M), 1908-12; C. Maring, 1913-18; J.S. Balt, 1918-28; J.L. Koert, 1928-34;

R. Rienstra, 1935–45; A. Baker, 1945–50; W. Van
Antwerpen, 1951–57; H.G. Arnold, 1957–62; C.
Witt, 1963–68; J. Cooper, 1968–70; R.J. Van der
Borgh, 1971–73; P. Huisman, 1974–81; H.F.
Vlaardingerbroek, 1981–86; S.R. Scripps, 1986–
91; K.H. Bratt, 1991–

East Paris, MI — East Paris
see: Kentwood, MI – East Paris

East Saugatuck, MI — East Saugatuck
see: Holland, MI – East Saugatuck

East Vancouver, WA (emerging)
2001–

East Vriesland, NE — East Vriesland
see: Oost Friesland, NE – Oost Friesland

Eau Gallie, FL — Eau Gallie
see: Indian Harbour Beach, FL – Grace

Ebenezer, SD — Ebenezer
1892–1914, discontinued
pastors: A.B. Vander Velde Vander Bok, 1904–05;
B. Nagel, 1906–08; H. Dekker, 1909–13

Edam, SK — Edam
1917–1923, discontinued

Eddyville, IA — Eddyville
1913–1926, discontinued, members merged with
Oskaloosa, IA
pastors: A.H. Bratt, 1919–21; J.S. Dykstra, 1921–
26

Edgerton, MN — Bethel
1947–
pastors: W.F. Vander Hoven, 1948–52; J.A.
Hoeksema, 1953–58; J. Leugs, 1959–67; E.F.
Visser, 1968–71; W.P. Green, Jr., 1972–76; H.
Lamsma, 1976–85; D.W. De Groot, 1986–93; D.E.
Den Haan, 1994–99; G. Besteman, 2001–

Edgerton, MN — Edgerton
see: Edgerton, MN – First

Edgerton, MN — First
1902–
former name: Edgerton, MN – Edgerton, 1902–
47
pastors: J.M. Byleveld, 1906–09; J.H. Schultz,
1909–12; A. Bliek, 1913–21; T. Vander Ark, 1922–
30; J.C. Ehlers, 1930–48; S. Kramer, 1949–54;

G.S. Kok, 1954–60; C.O. Buus, 1960–66; P.W.
Brouwer, 1967–94; T.J. Brown, 1995–

Edina, MN — First
see: Minneapolis, MN – First

Edmonton, AB (mission)
1926–1928

**Edmonton, AB — Back to God Chapel
(mission)**
1947–1954
staff: M. Veltkamp (E), 1947–50; J. Kruis (L),
1951–52; G. Veenstra (L), 1952–53; H.J.
Schripsema, 1953–54; C. Anderson (L), 1953–54

Edmonton, AB — Bethel
see: Edmonton, AB – Bethel Community

Edmonton, AB — Bethel Community
1979–
former name: Edmonton, AB – Bethel
pastors: C.T. Fennema, 1979–89; T. Maan, 1991–
2001; J. Schouten, 1997–

Edmonton, AB — Beverly
see: Edmonton, AB – Maranatha

**Edmonton, AB — Campus Ministry,
University of Alberta (campus ministry)**
1976–
pastor: T.J. Oosterhuis, 1976–

Edmonton, AB — Covenant
1979–
pastors: A.H. Venema, 1979–86; J.C. Dekker,
1986–94; J. Pasma, 1995–

Edmonton, AB — Edmonton
see: Edmonton, AB – First

Edmonton, AB — Edmonton Korean
see: Edmonton, AB – Edmonton So-Mang

**Edmonton, AB — Edmonton So-Mang
(emerging)**
1997–
former name: Edmonton, AB – Edmonton Korean, 1997–1998
pastors: W.C. Joung, 1996–99; C.J. Jung, 1999–

Edmonton, AB — Fellowship
1983–

Edmonton, AB — First

1910-

former name: Edmonton, AB — Edmonton, 1910-51

pastors: T. Jongbloed, 1911-19; H.J. Ruys (M), 1921-22; H. Vander Woude, 1923-27; A.H. Selles (M), 1927-29; K.E. de Waal Malefyt, 1930-38; G. Weeber, 1938-40; A.H. Bratt, 1941-43; P. De Koekkoek, 1945-49; J.K. Van Baalen, 1950-55; G.H. Vande Riet, 1956-60; W.C. Boelkins, 1960-66; J.J. Matheis, 1966-69; J. Vriend, 1970-74; H. De Moor, Jr., 1974-80; H.G. Samplonius, 1980-85; H. Vander Beek, 1985-92; C. Van Niejenhuis, 1993-

Edmonton, AB — Glad Tidings

1967-

organized: 1976

pastors: F. DeVries (L), 1970-77; J.K. Jansen, 1977-84; M. Pool, 1984-90; T.M. Corey, 1991-94; R.E. Klok, 1995-

Edmonton, AB — Inglewood

1952-

former name: Edmonton, AB — Third, 1952-92

pastors: M.H. Woudstra, 1953-55; B. Nederlof, 1956-64; F. Guillaume, 1965-69; J. Joosse, 1971-76; S.C. DeWaal, 1976-78; R. De Moor, 1978-84; S.C. DeWaal, 1984-88; J. Westerhof, 1988-93; J.A. Ooms, 1994-

Edmonton, AB — Jasper Place

see: Edmonton, AB — West End

Edmonton, AB — Maranatha

1953-

former name: Beverly, AB — Beverly, 1953-56

pastors: N.B. Knoppers, 1955-60; L.M. Tamminga, 1960-65; C. Padmos, 1965-69; J.W. Jongsma, 1969-73; H. Salomons, 1969-78; H. Jonker, 1974-81; H.D. Praamsma, 1979-83; A. Vanden Berg, 1983-89; N. Cornelisse, 1989-96; A.L. Verboon, 1997-

Edmonton, AB — Ottewell

1962-

pastors: J. Dresselhuis, 1962-66; P.W. De Bruyne, 1966-71; J. Boonstra, 1971-80; P. Breedveld, 1982-92; C. Vink, 1992-95; F. Heslinga, 1998-2002

Edmonton, AB — Second

1951-1984, discontinued

pastors: J.C. Verbrugge, 1951-55; J.H. Piersma, 1956-60; T.C. Van Kooten, 1960-62; J.W.

Uitvlugt, 1963-66; G. Ringnalda, 1966-71; R. Steinstra, 1971-78; J.H. Kits, 1978-84

Edmonton, AB — So Mang

see: Edmonton, AB — Edmonton So-Mang

Edmonton, AB — Third

see: Edmonton, AB — Inglewood

Edmonton, AB — Trinity

1968-

pastors: J.D. Pereboom, 1969-76; M. Pool, 1977-84; A.C. Groen, 1985-94; C. Vander Ploeg, 1997-2002; F.M. Bultman, 2002-

Edmonton, AB — University of Edmonton (campus ministry)

1978-

pastor: T.J. Oosterhuis, 1978-

Edmonton, AB — West End

1954-

former name: Edmonton, AB — Jasper Place, 1954-63

pastors: A. De Jager, 1954-57; G. Nonnekes, 1958-64; H.A. Venema, 1964-68; J.W. Postman, 1968-73; G.H. Pols, 1974-93; A.H. Venema, 1978-79; J.E. Pot, 1992-97; H.G. Samplonius, 1995-

Edson, AB — Edson

1955-1983, merged into Edson-Peers, AB — Edson-Peers

pastors: L. Van Staalduinen, Jr., 1957-60; A.P. Ver Burg, 1961-64; J. Van Hemert, 1965-68; J. Huizenga, 1968-75; R. De Moor, 1975-78; E. Vander Woude, 1978-83

Edson, AB — Edson-Peers

see: Edson-Peers, AB — Edson-Peers

Edson-Peers, AB — Edson-Peers

1983-

created by the merger of Edson, AB — Edson, 1955-83; Peers, AB — Peers, 1950-83

pastors: E. Vander Woude, 1984-85; A.G. Vander Leek, 1986-91; W.H. Vanderwerf, 1991-96; E. Gritter, 1997-2000

El Cerrito, CA — East Bay Korean

1984-2001, discontinued

organized: 1991

former name: Albany, CA — Korean, 1984-93

pastors: H.K. Hwang, 1984-94; J.D. Lee, 1995-2001; E. Kim, 1999-2001

Ellsworth, MI — Atwood
see: Atwood, MI — Atwood

Ellsworth, MI — Ellsworth
1901-
pastors: G.G. Haan (M), 1901-03; P.D. Van Vliet, 1904-07; J.J. De Jonge, 1908-11; G. Hoeksema, 1912-13; R. Posthumus, 1914-17; H. Beute, 1919-24; B.H. Einink, 1925-34; J.T. Holwerda, 1935-41; H.J. Rikkers, 1941-45; G.A. Lyzenga, 1945-50; E. Boeve, 1951-54; H. Zwaanstra, 1954-62; V.F. Geurkink, 1964-68; R.J. Greydanus, 1968-72; M.J. Vander Vliet, 1973-76; W.H. Lammers, 1977-81; B.A. Persenaire, 1982-86; L.T. Riemersma, 1986-91; D.J. Weemhoff, 1992-2001

Elmhurst, IL — Elmhurst
1949-
former name: Bellwood, IL — Bellwood, 1949-63
pastors: B. Byma, 1953-60; J. De Vries, 1961-66; G.H. Stoutmeyer, 1967-72; W.W. Leys, 1974-83; B. DeJong, 1983-; D.R. Armstrong, 1987-; T.L. Rietkerk, 1995-96;

Elmhurst, IL — Faith
1973-
former names: Cicero, IL — West Suburban, 1973-77, which was formed by the merger of Cicero, IL — Warren Park and Oak Park, IL — Oak Park; name changed to Elmhurst, IL — Faith, 1978 Chicago, IL — Douglas Park, 1899-1927, whose name was changed to Cicero, IL — Second, 1927-56, whose name was changed to Cicero, IL — Warren Park, 1956-73, which was merged into Cicero, IL — West Suburban, 1973 Berwyn, IL — Berwyn, 1938-45, whose name was changed to Oak Park, IL — Oak Park, 1945-73, (which also absorbed Chicago, IL — Fourth, 1923-45 at the time of the name change), which was merged into Cicero, IL — West Suburban, 1973
pastors: O. Breen, 1973-75; A.A. Mulder, 1973-77; K. Rietema, 1978-86; L.A. Koning, 1987-; D.L. Jongsma, 1988-91; S.D. Los, 1992-95; J.J. Sheeres, 1995-2002; G. Schuringa, 2002-

Elmhurst, IL — Horizon Community (emerging)
1998-
former names: Lisle, IL — Horizon Community, 1998-99; Woodbridge, IL — Horizon Community, 1999-2001
pastor: D.L. Jongsma, 1997-

El Monte, CA — Amor Viviente
1989-

organized: 1997
pastors: G. Schipper, 1989-92; G. Muller (E), 1989-99; M. Lopez (E), 1999-

El Paso, TX (service home)
1971-1974
staff: O.J. Hogan, 1971-74

El Paso, TX — Christ's Community
see: El Paso, TX — Sunshine Community

El Paso, TX — Paso del Norte (emerging)
1995-1997, discontinued
pastor: J.M. Matias, 1994-97

El Paso, TX — Scottsdale Community
see: El Paso, TX — Sunshine Community

El Paso, TX — Sunshine Community
1960-
organized: 1976, began as an urban ministry
former name: El Paso, TX — Scottsdale Community, 1976-86; El Paso, TX — Christ's Community, 1986-89
pastors: F.J. Van Dyk (M), 1960-63; R. Boeskool, Jr. (M), 1964-67; N.N. Knoppers (M), 1968-71; O.J. Hogan, 1971-74; J.J. Berends, 1974-79; W.C. De Vries, 1981-87; J.A. Dykema, 1989-; J.M. Matias, 1992-94;

Emden, MN — Emden
see: Renville, MN — Emden

Emmons, ND — Emmons
see: Hull, ND — Hull

Emo, ON — Emo
1953-
pastors: J.E. Brink, 1955-57; J.P. Vosteen, 1959-62; C. Vriend, 1962-65; R. Duifhuis, 1967-75; G. Nonnekes, 1975-85; P. Veltman, 1985-94; G.P. Van Smeerdyk, 1995-2001

Englewood, NJ — Englewood
1875-1970, discontinued
joined the CRC from the True Reformed Protestant Dutch Church in 1890
pastors: J.G. Voorhis, 1875-87; A. Van Houten, 1888-92; C.D. Mott, 1892-96; E. Vanden Berge, 1896-99; K. Poppen, 1900-02; J. Dolfin, 1904-09; L.S. Huizenga, 1909-13 and 1916-17; J.C. De Korne, 1917-19; L.S. Huizenga, 1919-20; J., H. Monsma, 1921-24; B.K. Kuiper (stated supply), 1924-26; G. Goris, 1927-30; J.T. Hoogstra, 1930-40; H. Radius, 1940-46; H. Dekker, 1947-50; A.

De Kruiter (stated supply), 1950-51; J.E. Meeter, 1951-66; A.D. Evans, 1967-70

Enumclaw, WA — Enumclaw
1979-1996, discontinued
pastors: W.H. Ackerman, 1978-82; K.J. Wiersum, 1983-86; H. Leetsma, 1986-91; W.D. Vis, 1991-95

Erie, ON — Erie
see: Jarvis, ON — Jarvis

Escalon, CA — Escalon
1949-
pastors: J.J. Weersing (stated supply), 1949-51; J.T. Malestein, 1951-54; L.F. Voskuil, 1955-71; H.D. Clark, Jr., 1972-74; J. dePater, 1975-78; M.H. Bierma, 1979-85; B.A. Persenaire, 1986-; R.J. Ebbers, 1995-99;

Escondido, CA — Escondido
1953-1997, majority withdrew to United Reformed Church; remaining members joined San Marcos, CA — Crossroads, 1998
pastors: J. Roorda, 1957-63; J. Howerzyl, 1964-84; A.A. Cammenga, 1985-97

Escondido, CA — Mexican Migrant Mission
1963-1966
pastor: R.D. Ruis, 1963-66

Essex, ON — Essex
1926-1927, 1928-
organized: 1939
began as Windsor, ON mission
former name: Windsor, ON — Windsor, 1926-1950
pastors: J.R. Brink (M), 1926-27; S.A. Dykstra, 1928-29; W. Meyer (M), 1930-32; M. Van Dyke (M), 1950-51; G. Bouma, 1952-58; J. Vander Meer, 1958-62; H. Numan, Sr., 1963-67; J. De Jong, 1968-72; A. Vanden Berg, 1972-76; W. De Jong, 1976-82; L.H. Batterink, 1983-87; B.B. Bakker, 1988-92; D.R. Tigchelaar, 1994-2001; F. Heslinga, 2002-

Estelline, SD — Estelline
1918-1970, discontinued
pastors; A.D. Folkema, 1919-26; P. Honderd, 1936-39; J. Mulder, 1942-44; C.G. Ter Maat, 1946-49; R. Veldman, 1949-58; M. Keuning, 1962-67

Etobicoke, ON — Rehoboth Fellowship
see: Toronto, ON — Rehoboth Fellowship

Etobicoke, ON — Room for Joy (mission)
1976-1980
staff: L. Vander Spek (E), 1976-79

Eugene, OR — Lasting Connections (emerging)
1994-2001, discontinued
former names: Eugene, OR — Oregon Community, 1994-96; Eugene, OR — Oregon Community Fellowship, 1996-2000
pastor: M.G. Clement (E), 1996-2001

Eugene, OR — Oregon Community Fellowship
see: Eugene, OR — Lasting Connections

Everett, WA — First
1911-
pastors: K. Poppen, 1910-11; A. Guikema (M), 1911-16; C. Vriesman (M), 1916-20; C. Vriesman, 1920-24; J. Mulder, 1925-28; J. Vanden Hoek, 1929-43; H.J. Triezenberg, 1944-49; C. Vander Ark, 1950-55; B.T. Haan, 1954-61; J.W. Maas, 1963-72; W.H. Ackerman, 1973-78; M.S. Jorritsma, 1979-87; J.C. Wiersum, 1988-

Evergreen Park, IL — Beverly Mission
1953-1954
staff: W. Baar (L), 1953-56

Evergreen Park, IL — Evergreen Park
1915-
pastors: Z.J. Sherda, 1916-30; B.H. Spalink, 1930-37; J.P. Smith, 1938-44; A. Jabaay, 1944-52; M. Goote, 1954-62; H.J. Baas, 1963-69; N. Punt, 1969-94; P.A. Hansen, 1994-98; T. Howerzyl, 1999-

Evergreen Park, IL — Park Lane
1953-
pastors: T. Verseput, 1953-57; W. Verwolf, 1957-66; A..M. MacLeod, 1966-74; W.C. Boelkins, 1974-79; D.J. Brink, 1978-86; R.W. DeYoung, 1981-86; G.P. Hutt, 1987-96; C.J. Aardsma, 1997-

Evergreen Park, IL — West Evergreen
1946-1974, discontinued, members merged with Oak Lawn, IL — Kedvale
former name: Chicago, IL — Auburn Park, 1946-62
pastors: H. Baker, 1946-53; W.H. Ackerman, 1954-59; R.J. Tjapkes, 1960-66; C.O. Buus, 1966-69; R.G. Timmerman, 1970-73; L.W. Van Dellen, 1973-74

Everson, WA — Everson
see: Everson, WA – Faith Christian Fellowship

Everson, WA — Faith Christian Fellowship
1943-
former name: Everson, WA – Everson, 1943-2002
pastors: S.G. Brondsema, 1943-46; M. Keuning, 1946-50; J.J. Steigenga, 1951-52; R. Tadema, 1952-55; J.J. Matheis, 1955-61; W.K. Reinsma, 1962-65; H.J. Wigboldy, 1966-70; D.E. Tinklenberg, 1971-80; C.J. Leep, 1980-87; P.J. DeVries, 1989-91; S.D. Frieswick, 1993-2001

Ewa Beach, HI — Anuenue (emerging)
1967-
emerging, 1996
former names: Honolulu, HI – Honolulu, 1969-85; Honolulu, HI – Pacific Community, 1985-98,
organized: 1968-98
pastors: M.D. Hugen, 1967-70; C.K. Van Winkle, 1971-75; R.L. Palsrok, 1977-83; W.D. Dyk, 1984-90; A. Helder, 1991-96; H. Venegas, 1998-

Ewa Beach, HI — Hope Metro (emerging)
1999-
pastor: H. Venegas, 1999-

Exeter, ON — Exeter
1951-
pastors: G.J. Hoytema, 1952-56; A.G. Van Eek, 1958-62; A.J. Stienstra, 1962-65; D.J. Scholten, 1966-70; J. Roeda, 1971-75; C. Bishop, 1976-80; B.H. DeJonge, 1981-86; R.A. Arbogast, 1987-90; S. Vander Meer, 1991-94; P. Tuininga, 1995-

Fairbanks, AK (service home)
1963-1972
staff: R. Wezeman, 1963-66; W. Verwolf (M), 1969-72

Fairbanks, AK — Fairbanks (emerging)
1956-1966, discontinued
pastors: J.J. Vanden Hoek (M), 1957-61; R. Wezeman (M), 1961-66

Fairfield, CA — Fairfield
1979-
organized: 1983
pastors: G.G. Hofland, 1979-89; D.G. Zandstra, 1990-

Fair Oaks, IN (mission)
1934-1936

Fairview, AB — Fairview
see: Fairview, AB – Faith Fellowship

Fairview, AB — Faith Fellowship (emerging)
1983-
organized: 1955-94
former name: Fairview, AB – Fairview, 1983-90
pastors: M.D. Vander Hart, 1981-83; P.L. Hendriks, 1984-92; B. Weenink (E), 1991-

Falmouth, MI — Aetna
see: Aetna, MI – Aetna

Falmouth, MI — Prosper
1894-
former names: North Clam, MI – North Clam, 1894-1902; Prosper, MI – Prosper, 1902-55
pastors: M. DeBoer, 1898-1900; J.B. Van der Werp, 1902-09; J. Haveman, 1910-15; J. Homan, 1915-19; A.J. Rus, 1919-24; J. Gritter, 1924-29; R.J. Bos, 1929-44; H. Vander Kam, 1945-50; R. Wildschut, 1950-53; W.A. Huyser, 1953-57; P. Lagerwey, 1959-63; G.W. Sheeres, 1963-66; J.H. Steenwyk, 1967-72; M. Stegink, 1972-81; D.J. Weemhoff, 1981-85; R. Klimp, 1986-99; R.D. Drenten, 2001-

Farmington, MI — University Hills
1967-1981, discontinued
pastor: J.H. Ellens, 1968-79

Farmington, MT — Chateau
1905-1921, discontinued
former name: Farmington, MT – Farmington, 1905-12, 1914-16

Farmington, MT — Farmington
see: Farmington, MT – Chateau

Farmington, NM — Farmington
see: Farmington, NM – Maranatha Fellowship

Farmington, NM — Kimbeto Chapel
see: Farmington, NM – Maranatha Fellowship

Farmington, NM — Maranatha Fellowship
1925-
organized: 1962
former names: began as a mission station; Farmington, NM – Farmington, 1962-94; operated as a single church with Toadlena, NM, 1927-47; was a mission church, 1927-49
pastors: L.P. Brink, 1925-36; J.C. Morgan (L), 1932-38; N. DeVries (M), 1937-39; B. Pousma (E), 1939-41; H.J. Schripsema (M), 1945-65; C.

Dykema (L), 1947–48; C. Anderson (L), 1950–52, 1954–56; B. Hogue (L), 1956–57; J. Talley (L), 1957–59; K. De Haan (L), 1959–61; F. Begay (L), 1959–60; A. Becenti (L), 1960–61; T. Bitsilli (L), 1960–61; H. Begay (L), 1962–69; C. Tsosie (L), 1963–66;S.T. Yazzie, 1965–86; B. Whitehorse (L), 1968–72T.J. Niehof, 1982–87; J. Vande Lune, 1988–96; G.G. Van Dam, 1997–

Faulkner, IA (mission)
1912

Fennville, MI (mission)
1914–1915; 1940–1955
staff: G. Dykman (L), 1940–44, 1950–55; J. Slager (L), 1941–45; F. Plaggemars (L), 1945–46; J. Tucker (E), 1950–54

Fennville, MI — Bravo Community (emerging)
1935–
pastors: G. Dykman (E), 1937–52; W. Boer (L), 1941–43; R. Vander Meulen (L), 1943–46, 1948–49, 1953–54; A. Bratt (L), 1946–47; J. Ten Harmsel (L), 1949–50; D. Boyd (E), 1952–55; F. Brummel (E), 1956–63; R. Ericks, (E), 1963–66; L.V. Haas (E), 1966–70; G. Mannes (E), 1971–77; G.A. Geurink (E), 1977–81; R.D. Baker, 1981–90; H. Dykema, 1990–96; A.J. Roon, 1996–2001

Fennville, MI — Chapel
1962–1971
staff: H. Langejans (L). 1965–71

Fennville, MI — Mack's Landing Mission (mission)
1933–1954
staff: J. Knoll, Sr.(L), 1941–44; M. Tinholt (L), 1943–47; G. Schreur (L), 1946–49

Fenwick, ON — Bethany
1982–
pastors: A. Dieleman, 1983–88; H. Eshuis, 1988–97; R.J. Loerts, 1997–

Ferrisburg, VT — Ferrisburg
see: Vergennes, VT – Champlain Valley

Ferrysburg, MI — Ferrysburg
see: Ferrysburg, MI – Ferrysburg Community

Ferrysburg, MI — Ferrysburg Community
1953–
former name Ferrysburg, MI – Ferrysburg, 1953–1998

pastors: H.J. Teitsma, 1954–59; G.B. Dokter, 1960–64; J.F. Schuurman, 1964–69; P.C. Zylstra, 1970–76; C.E. Bajema, 1977–83; K.W. Tanis, 1983–90; A.L. Hoksbergen, 1990–94; S.J. Nauta, 1993–

Fife, WA — Hebron (emerging)
1994–
congregational ministry, 1994–99
pastors: J. Cho, 1986–95; A.Y. Yi, 1994–; W.C. Lee, 1995–

Firth, NE — Firth
1890–1918, discontinued, members joined RCA congregation
pastors: E. Breen (M), 1891–93; J. Wyngaarden, 1893–98; T.W.R. Van Loo, 1901–03; E. Vanden Berge, 1906–07; J. Noordewier, 1907–12; J.G. Vande Lune, 1913–16

Fisher Station, MI — Fisher Station
see: Cutlerville, MI – First

Flagstaff, AZ — Arizona State (campus ministry)
1966–1971
staff: W.J. Rozema (L), 1966–68; A.W. Heersink, 1968–71

Flagstaff, AZ — Flagstaff
see: Flagstaff, AZ – Hope Community

Flagstaff, AZ — Hope Community
1968–
organized: 1975
former name: Flagstaff, AZ – Flagstaff, 1968–89
pastors: A.W. Heersink (M), 1968–75; S.J. De Vries, 1975–79; D.J. Klop, 1980–85; F.J. Walhof, 1986–

Flamborough, ON — Calvary
1985–
pastors: A. Driese, 1986–88; J.M. Julien, 1989–91; A.C. Geleynse, 1993–2002

Flanders, NJ — Crossroads Community (emerging)
1965–
emerging, 1997
former name: Flanders, NJ – Flanders Valley, 1968–97
pastors: D.G. Zandstra (M), 1965–69; C.D. Vander Meyden (M), 1969–74; J.C. Vander Ark, 1974–81; D.L. Recker, 1982–95; P. Ingeneri, 1997–

Flanders, NJ — Flanders Valley
see: Flanders, NJ – Crossroads Community

Flat Creek, NY — Flat Creek
see: Flat River, NY – Flat River

Flat River, NY — Flat River
1883-1920, discontinued
was a member of the True Protestant Dutch
Reformed Church, joined the CRC in 1890

Flint, MI (mission; branch of Detroit, MI)
1930

Flint, MI — First
see: Flushing, MI – Good Shepherd

Flint, MI — Good Shepherd
see: Flushing, MI – Good Shepherd

Flushing, MI — Good Shepherd
1931-
former name: Flint, MI – First, 1931-76; Flint, MI
– Good Shepherd, 1976-81
pastors: J.E. Meeter (C), 1933-34; H. Radius,
1934-40; G.B. Boerfyn, 1940-43; A. Baker, 1943-
45; M. Moes, 1946-49; D.E. Bradford, 1951-54; S.
Newhouse, 1954-58; C. Witt, 1958-63; N.B.
Haan, 1964-69; D. Baak, 1970-72; A.J. Machiela,
1975-81; D.R. Koll, 1981-94; T.L. Koster, 1994-
2001

Folsom, CA — River Rock (emerging)
1998-
pastor: T.D. Blackmon, 1998-

Fontana, CA — Friendship Community
1992-
former name: Rancho Cucamonga, CA –
Friendship Community, 1992-94
pastor: R.K. Young, 1992-

**Foothill Ranch, CA — South Orange County
(emerging)**
2000-
pastor: H.G. Bischof, 2000-

Forest, ON — Forest
1953-
pastors: J. Cooper, 1959-62; J.S. Hielema, 1963-
66; P.R. Schoon, 1968-71; S.A. Van Daalen, 1972-
77; R. Vanden Berg, 1978-82; J.M.
Klumpenhouwer, 1984-92; P.L. Vander Beek,
1996-

Forest Grove, MI — Forest Grove
1972-
pastors: D.J. Boogerd, 1973-78; D.D. Ellens,
1979-83; E.J. Knott, 1983-88; B.A. Pennings,
1989-94; D.J. Boogerd, 1996-2000; L.S. Slings
(I), 2001-

**Fort Collins, CO — Colorado State
University (campus ministry)**
1966-1969
staff: G.B. Boerfyn, 1966-69

Fort Collins, CO — Fort Collins
see: Fort Collins, CO – Immanuel

Fort Collins, CO — Immanuel
1912-
joined CRC in 1963
former names: Fort Collins, CO – Evangelische
Immanuels-Gemeinde, 1912-13; Fort Collins, CO –
Immanuel Evangelical, 1913-34; Fort Collins, CO –
Immanuel Evangelical and Reformed, 1934-60;
Fort Collins, CO – Immanuel United Church of
Christ, 1960-63
pastors: W. Reitzer, 1937-59; J. Zandstra (M),
1963; G.B. Boerfyn (M), 1964-68; L.E. Van Essen,
1969-77; A. Helder, 1978-89; P. Jorden, 1983-97;
A.J. Stienstra, 1990-92; J. Terpstra, 1997-

Fort Defiance, AZ — Fort Defiance
1899-1905, discontinued, mission moved to
Rehoboth, NM
pastor: H. Fryling (M), 1896-1905

Fort Lauderdale, FL — Fort Lauderdale
1956-
organized: 1958
pastors: M.C. Baarman (M), 1956-60; W.K. Stob,
1960-63; S.C.J. DeWaal, 1963-67; J.P. Heerema,
1968-71; G.H. Stoutmeyer, 1972-75; J.L. Vander
Laan, 1976-81; H.F. Harnden, 1981-85; W.G. Vis,
1987-93; R.E. Van Hofwegen, 1995-

**Fort Lauderdale, FL — New Life Korean
(emerging)**
1999-
pastor: K.S. Kim, 1999-

Fort McMurray, AB — Evergreen (emerging)
1975-
former name: Fort McMurray, AB – Fort
McMurray, 1975-85
pastors: W. Smit, 1976-82; C. Vink, 1983-90; H.
Valstar (E), 1992-

Fort McMurray, AB — Fort McMurray
see: Fort McMurray, AB — Evergreen

Fort Wayne, IN — Community
1969–
organized: 1974
former name: Fort Wayne, IN — Fort Wayne,
1974–81
pastors: E.S. Holkeboer (M), 1969–87; R.L.
Gelwicks, 1987–92; P.J. Boender, 1993–2000; P.J.
De Vries, 2001–

Fort Wayne, IN — Fort Wayne
see: Fort Wayne, IN — Community

Fort Wayne, IN — Laotian
1999–
pastor: P. Sinbondit, 1999–

Fort William, ON — Fort William
see: Thunder Bay, ON — First

Fort Wingate, NM School (mission)
1932–1946
staff: J.R. Kamps, 1932–33; G. Yff (L), 1933–36;
C. Hayenga, 1936–46

Fort Wingate, NM — Fort Wingate
1965–
organized: 1982
pastors: J. Hofman, Jr. (M), 1965–68; S.
Siebersma (E), 1968–75; G.K. Haagsma, 1977–86;
D.J. Kruis, 1990–93; J. Kostelyk (E), 1994–95; J.
Harvey (E), 1995–

Forth Creek, AB — Chapel
1965–1968
staff: H. Klok (E), 1965–66

Fountain Valley, CA — Community
1965–
organized: 1967
former name: Fountain Valley, CA — Fountain Valley, 1967–88
pastors: R.G. Timmerman (M), 1965–70; R.
Tadema (M), 1970–73; L.K. Tanis, 1973–82; J.M.
Wanders, 1982–92; R.B. Harris, 1992–98

Fountain Valley, CA — Fountain Valley
see: Fountain Valley, CA — Community

**Fountain Valley, CA — Korean American of
Orange County**
1986–

former name: Orange County, CA — Korean
American, 1986–89
pastors: J.T. Kim, 1984–88; S.W. Yoon, 1989–93;
J.S. Oh, 1998–

Fountain Valley, CA — Orange Korean
see: Fullerton, CA — Orange Korean

Fox Lake, WI — Living Hope Community
see: Randolph, WI — Living Hope Community

Framingham, MA — Framingham
see: Boston-Framingham, MA — Hope

Framingham, MA — Hope
1957–
former names: Framingham, MA — Framingham,
1957–83; Boston, MA — Hope, 1990–2000
pastors: N. Vanderzee, 1960–63; R.W. De Vries,
1963–70; E. Walhout, 1971–76; R.M. Hartwell, Jr.,
1977–81; R.A. DeLange, 1982–88; N.J. Gebben,
Sr., 1988–93; G.J. Bekker, 1994–95; R.T. Bouma,
1996–

Frankford, ON — Community
1986–
former name: Frankford, ON — Frankford, 1986–
95
pastors: R.J. Graff, 1987–94; H.C. Kooger, 1995–
2000; M.W. Bootsma, 2002–

Frankford, ON — Frankford
see: Frankford, ON — Community

**Frankfort, IL — The Bridge Community
Church (emerging)**
2000–
pastor: N. Ahrens (E), 2001–

**Franklin, MA — New England Chapel
(emerging)**
1998–
pastor: C.P. Mitchell, 1997–; G.J. Kett, 1999–

Franklin Lakes, NJ — Franklin Lakes
1958–1996, withdrew, became Franklin Lakes
Reformed Bible Fellowship
pastors: R.W. DeVries (M), 1956–63; W.J. Boer,
1963–68; D.E. Bradford, 1969–74; C.E. Keegstra,
1975–78; R.D. Boertje, 1980–83; D.L. Bratt, 1983–
96

Franklin Lakes, NJ — New Life Ministries
see: Midland Park, NJ — New Life Ministries

Fredericton, NB — Fredericton
1961–
pastors: D.M. Lieverdink (M), 1961–65; H. De
Bruyn (M), 1965–69; A. Vanden Ende, 1969–77;
J.M. Klumpenhouwer, 1978–84; G. Nonnekes,
1985–92; M. Veenema, 1992–95; R.D. Boertje,
1998–

**Fredericton, NB — University of New
Brunswick (campus ministry)**
1987–
campus pastor: J. Valk (L), 1987–

Freeman, SD — Bethlehem
1892–1999, withdrew to Reformed Church in the
United States
former names: Freeman, SD — Bethlehem Evangelical and Reformed, 1934–60; Freeman, SD —
Bethlehem United Church of Christ, 1960–71,
joined the CRC, 1971
pastors: J. Orth, 1879–83; L.H. Teichrieb, 1892–
94; F.A. Rittershaus, 1895–1917, 1919–24; J.
Bodenman, 1925–39; W. Korn, 1939–48; H.
Hartman, 1948–52; H. Bartell, 1954–72; R.D. De
Young, 1971–76; R.J. Blauw, 1975–80; R.D. Ruis,
1980–88; L.J. Swier, 1988–92; F.A. Harms, 1994–
98

Fremont, MI — First
1882–
former names: Fremont Centre, MI — Fremont
Centre, 1882–83, Fremont Centre, MI — Fremont,
1884–1914
pastors: J. Noordewier, 1885–91; H. Vander Werp,
1892–99; H. Walkotten, 1899–1907; H. Keegstra,
1908–19; L.J. Lamberts, 1919–43; J.O. Schuring,
1944–48; H. Exoo, 1948–54; G.P. Holwerda, 1954–
61; H.G. Vander Ark, 1962–69; J.L. Meppelink,
1970–77; H.J. Wigboldy, 1977–84; L.P. Troast,
1985–95; A. Petroelje, 1996–; M.D. Bennink.
2002–

**Fremont, MI — Goodwell Community
Sunday School (mission)**
1941–1942
staff: D. Mellema, 1941–42; G. Jordan (L), 1941–
42

**Fremont, MI — Kimball Lake Mission
(mission)**
1940–1943

Fremont, MI — McCallum Chapel
1965–1979
staff: P. Mulder (L), 1965–67, 1968–70; E. Deur

(E), 1967–68, 1974–75; L. De Vries (E), 1971–74;
J. and C. Zuidema (E), 1975–76

Fremont, MI — Reeman
see: Reeman, MI — Reeman

Fremont, MI — Second
1914–
pastors: W. Kuipers, 1914–19; H.J. Mokma, 1919–
26; C. Holtrop, 1926–43; J.H. Schaal, 1943–48;
M.J. Vander Werp, 1948–52; J.P. Smith, 1953–56;
J.C. Medendorp, 1958–64; W.P. Brink, 1964–70;
A.W. Hoogstrate, 1971–80; C.J. De Ridder, 1980–
90; S.E. Hoezee, 1990–93; R.T. Vanderwal, 1995–

**Fremont, MI — South Fremont Missions
(mission)**
1938–1943
staff: J.B. Swierenga (L), 1938

Fremont, MI — Trinity
1954–
pastors: W.K. Stob, 1955–60; O.W. Duistermars,
1961–64; C. Vanden Heuvel, 1964–70; J.J. Vanden
Hoek, 1971–78; K.W. Vis, 1979–84; H.G. Faber,
1984–88; J. Vander Plate, 1988–2000; R.A. Pohler,
2002–

Fremont, MI — Woodville Mission (mission)
see: White Cloud, MI — Woodville Mission

Fremont Centre, MI — Fremont
see: Fremont, MI — First

Fremont Centre, MI — Fremont Centre
see: Fremont, MI — First

Fresno, CA (mission)
1916

Fresno, CA — Fresno
1961–
organized: 1964
pastors: J.J. Steigenga, 1961–62 (M); F. DeJong
(M), 1962–66; D.A. Visser, 1966–70; J. Vigh,
1970–78; M. Reitsma, 1979–89; A. Schaap, 1982–
84; C. Pool, 1989–94; L.J. Kotman, 1990–99; D.L.
Smit, 1995–

Fresno, CA — Hmong (emerging)
1995–
pastor: D.D. Moua (E), 1995–

Fresno, CA — Love Song Community
1995–

pastor: W. Redondo (L), 1995–

Friesland, MN — Friesland
1896–1900, discontinued

Friesland, SD — Friesland
1884–1921, discontinued, members merged with Platte, SD
pastors: S. Bouma, 1903–05; H. Dekker, 1906–09

Fruitland, ON — Fruitland
see: Stoney Creek, ON – Fruitland

Fruitport, MI — Fruitport
1943–
organized: 1955
pastors: J. Zuidema (L), 1944–51; A. Poel (M), 1957–66; F.L. Christensen, 1966–71; G.D. Postema, 1972–78; J.A. Dykema, 1978–89; D.H. Bratt, 1992–98; G.D. Postema, 1999–

Fullerton, CA — Orange Korean
1978–
former name: Fountain Valley, CA – Orange Korean, 1978–80
pastors: J.T. Lee, 1977–81; J.T. Kim, 1978–82; W.S. Yeo, 1983–85; J. Choi, 1985–86; J.U.C. Lee, 1986–2000; E.N. Pyun, 1986–90; P.C. Yang, 1992–97; T. Park, 1997–98; I.Y. Kang, 1998–; C.C. Oh, 1999–; D.Y. Chong, 2000–2001

Fullerton, CA — Shema Presbyterian (emerging)
2000–
pastor: B.S. Lee, 2000–

Fulton, IL — Bethel
1961–
pastors: B. Vermeer, 1962–64; L.J. Wolters, 1965–69; J.J. Berends, 1970–74; C. Admiraal, 1974–81; W. Van Antwerpen, 1981–91; D.L. Jongsma, 1991–97; T.D. Kauffman, 1998

Fulton, IL — First
1886–
former name: Fulton, IL – Fulton, 1886–1961
pastors: H. Huizingh, 1890–93; M. Van Vessem, 1895–97; T.W. Van Loo, 1898–1901; W. Borgman, 1901–03; E.J. Krohne, 1903–09; J.O. Vos, 1909–12; J.B. Jonkman, 1912–19; J. Masselink, 1920–24; A. Bliek, 1924–40; J. Putt, 1940–53; L.A. Bazuin, 1954–58; J.L. Meppelink, 1958–63; T. Van Eerden, 1964–66; J.H. Groenewold, 1967–71; C. Van Essen, 1972–80; F. Bultman, 1981–86; R.A.

Bouwman, 1987–92; A.J. DeVries, 1994–97; W.D. Davelaar, 2000–

Fulton, IL — Fulton
see: Fulton, IL – First

Gainesville, FL (service home)
1943–45
staff: H. Moes, 1943–45

Galesburg, IA — Galesburg
1898–1926, discontinued, members merged with Sully, IA
pastors: J.B. Vanden Hoek, 1905–08; S. Bouma, 1909–11; W. Meyer, 1911–14; M. Borduin, 1915–25

Gallatin Gateway, MT — Gallatin Gateway
see: Bozeman, MT – Gallatin Gateway Community

Gallup, NM — Bethany
1929–
organized: 1956
former name: Gallup, NM – Gallup, 1956–71
pastors: D J.R. Kamps, 1929–30, 1934–35; B. Sprik (L), 1930–34; C. Hayenga, 1935–45;.E. Houseman (M), 1948–60; S. Barton (L), 1950–63;T. Tibboel (L), 1955–57; R.D. Posthuma, 1962–65; A.E. Mulder, 1968–84; W.K. Bulthuis, 1984–

Gallup, NM — Bethlehem Chapel
1970–1971
staff: J. George (L), 1970–71

Gallup, NM — Friendship House
1973–1975
staff: J. Jacobs (L), 1973–74; A. Mulder, 1974–75

Gallup, NM — Gallup
see: Gallup, NM – Bethany

Galt, ON — Maranatha
see: Cambridge, ON – Maranatha

Gardena, CA — Elim of South Bay
1994–2001, discontinued
former names: Torrance, CA – Torrance Glory, 1994–96; Gardena, CA – South Bay Elim
pastors: J.J. 1987–93; H.S. Hong, 1991–98; Lee, S.H. Nam, 1990–99

Gardena, CA — South Bay Elim
see: Gardena, CA – Elim of South Bay

Gardena, CA — The Lord's Church of Love
1993–

former names: Los Angeles, CA — Beverly Hills Korean Presbyterian, 1993; Los Angeles, CA — Beverly Hills Korean, 1993-95; Los Angeles, CA — California Cho Won, 1995-2000
pastors: D.S. Shin, 1993-98; J.D. Lee, 1999-

Garden Grove, CA — Elim
see: Westminster, CA — Garden of Grace

Garden Grove, CA — Elim Dongsan
see: Westminster, CA — Garden of Grace

Garden Grove, CA — Garden of Grace
see: Westminster, CA — Garden of Grace

Garden Grove, CA — Korean American Central Presbyterian (emerging)
1997-
former names: Garden Grove, CA — Orange County Choong Hyun Presbyterian, 1997-99; Los Angeles, CA — Korean American Central Presbyterian, 1999-2000
pastors: J.Y. Kim, 1994-; Y.M. Kim, 1997-; K.P. Chang, 1999-

Garden Grove, CA — Orange County Calvary (emerging)
1998-
pastor: B.I. Lee, 1998-

Garden Grove, CA — Orange County Choong Hyun Presbyterian
see: Garden Grove, CA — Korean-American Central Presbyterian

Garden Grove, CA — Orange Dongsan
see: Westminster, CA — Garden of Grace

Garden Grove, CA — Orange Han Min
see: La Palma, CA — Orange Han Min

Garden Grove, CA — So Mang Korean
see: Anaheim, CA — Neung Ryuk

Gary, IN — Beacon Light
1959-
pastors: G.B. Boerfyn (M), 1958-64; E.D. Dykema, 1964-70; B. DeJong, 1970-74; C.E. Fennema, 1975-78; H.H. Boer, 1978-91; J. LaGrand, 1993-

Gaylord, MI — Friendship
1975-
organized: 1992
former name: Gaylord, MI — Gaylord, 1978-92

pastors: I.E. VerHage (E), 1976-77; J.J. Vanden Hoek (M), 1978-81; V. Schaap (E), 1982-93; S.D. Los, 1995-2000; R.G, Oberg, 2002-

Gaylord, MI — Gaylord
see: Gaylord, MI — Friendship

George, IA — George
1894-1910, discontinued
pastor: J. Gulker, 1897-1901

Georgetown, ON — Georgetown
1956-
pastors: D.C. Los, 1959-62; J. Joosse, 1963-67; A.J. Vanden Pol, 1967-73; J.W. Postman, 1973-77; J. De Jong, 1978-88; W. Suk, 1980-81; B. Slofstra, 1984-90; P.D. Stadt, 1989-96; M.N. Verbruggen, 1995-

German Valley, IL — German Valley
1866-
former names: Ridott, IL — Ridott, 1889-1969; German Valley, IL — Ridott, 1969-86
pastors: K. Wieland, 1868-70; W.H. Frieling, 1871-74; W. Coelingh, 1877-81; W.R. Smidt, 1882-84; J. Stadt, 1885-87; H.J. Potgeter, 1889-92; G.L. Hoefker, 1894-1906; H.C. Bode, 1908-17; J. Masselink, 1918-19; H. Ahuis, 1921-25; J.G. Plesscher, 1926-27; K. Tebben, 1929-35; R. Wezeman, 1936-42; B.J. Haan, 1942-45; J.H. De Haan, 1946-48; C. Abbas, 1949-76; J.D. Buwalda, 1977-82; T.J. Kikkert, 1982-85; K.D. Boonstra, 1985-88; P. De Jong, 1989-2000; J. Ritzema, 2001-

German Valley, IL — Ridott
see: German Valley, IL — German Valley

Gibbsville, WI — Gibbsville
see: Oostburg, WI — First

Glastonbury, CT — Christ Church of Glastonbury
see: Glastonbury, CT — Christ Community

Glastonbury, CT — Christ Community (emerging)
2001-
former name: Glastonbury, CT — Christ Church of Glastonbury, 2001
pastor: W. Gardner, 2001-

Glendale, CA (mission)
1937

Glendale, CA — Glendale
see: Sun Valley, CA — Bethel

Glenham, SD (mission)
1912

Glenn Valley, CA (mission)
1936-1937

Glenview, IL — Living Spring Community (emerging)
2000-
pastor: M. Kim, 1999-

Gloucester, ON — Calvary
see: Ottawa, ON — Calvary

Goderich, ON — Goderich
see: Goderich, ON — Trinity

Goderich, ON — Trinity
1977-
former name: Goderich, ON — Goderich, 1977-91
pastors: W.A. Ludwig, 1978-80; H. Vriend, 1981-91; J.A. Quartel, 1992-2000; S.D. Tamming, 2001-

Goshen, IN — Goshen
1904-
pastors: W. Kole, 1914-23; R. Diephuis, 1925-36; E.L. Haan, 1937-40; W.P. Brink, 1941-44; H. Vander Klay, 1944-49; W.D. Ribbens, 1949-55; R.D. Baker, 1953; B.J. Niemeyer, 1953-56; H.L. De Weerd, 1957-64; R.L. Peterson, 1964-69; W.F. Holleman, 1971-74; R.D. De Young, 1976-82; R.L. Jipping, 1982-93; C.R. Bolt, 1995-2002

Goshen, NY — Goshen
1934-
pastors: O. Breen, 1938-42; T. Heyboer, 1943-49; J.P. Smith, 1950-53; W. Tolsma, 1953-65; R. Wildschut, 1966-80; R.J. Meyer, 1981-88; W. Timmer, 1988-97; Z.G. Anderson, 1998-

Gowen, MI — Community Chapel
1962-1963
staff: R. Cooper (E), 1962-63

Graafschap, MI — Graafschap
1847-
RCA, 1847-57; joined CRC, 1857; Holland, MI — Prospect Park merged in, 2002
pastors: RCA: H.G. Klyn, 1847-51; M.A. Ypma, 1852-55; vacant; CRC: 1855-64; D.J. Van der Werp, 1864-72; W.H. Frieling, 1874-78; R.T.

Kuiper. 1879-89; J. Keizer, 1890-98; A, Keizer, 1898-1902; W. DeGroot, 1903-09; M. Van Vessem, 1910-15; R. Bolt, 1915-22; J.L. Heeres, 1922-27; J.O. Bouwsma, 1927-31; H. Blystra, 1932-47; T.P. Verhulst, 1948-52; L. Oostendorp, 1953-57; J.C. Lont, 1959-62; G.H. Rientjes, 1963-66; B. Den Ouden, 1967-80; L.J. Dykstra, 1981-88; M.J. Hofman, 1989-2000; S.R. Scripps, 2003-

Grande Prairie, AB — Grande Prairie
1955-1997, merged into LaGlace, AB — La Glace
former names: Grande Prairie, AB — La Glace, 1955-60; Grande Prairie, AB — La Glace-Grand Prairie, 1960-62; Grande Prairie, AB — La Glace/Fairview, 1990-93
pastors: J. Hanenburg, 1955-59; D.C. Bouma (M), 1962-65; J. Tuininga, 1966-70; H. Vriend, 1970-76; C.W. Tuininga, 1976-80; M.D. Vander Hart, 1980-83; P.L. Hendricks, 1984-92; S.A. Speelman, 1993-95

Grande Prairie, AB — La Glace
see: Grande Prairie, AB — Grande Prairie

Grande Prairie, AB — La Glace/Fairview
see: Grande Prairie, AB — Grande Prairie

Grande Prairie, AB — La Glace-Grande Prairie
see: Grande Prairie, AB — Grande Prairie

Grand Forks, ND — Community
see: East Grand Forks, MN — Community

Grand Forks, ND — Grand Forks
1910-1915, discontinued

Grand Haven, MI — Chapel of Christ
see: Grand Haven, MI — Oak Grove Fellowship

Grand Haven, MI — Covenant Life
1992-
emerging, 1992-96
pastor: A. De Jong, 1989-

Grand Haven, MI — First
1866-
former name: Grand Haven, MI — Grand Haven, 1866-1881
pastors: K. Vanden Bosch, 1869-78; E. Vander Vries, 1879-83; A. Keizer, 1886-88; K. Kuiper, 1891-96; M.J. Marcusse, 1896-98; W.D. Vander Werp, 1899-1903; S.S. Vander Heide, 1904-09; J. Bruinooge, 1911-16; W. Groen, 1918-24; J.J.

Steigenga, 1924-27; B.J. Danhof, 1927-30; J.G.
Van Dyke, 1931-40; J.C. Verbrugge, 1940-43; J.
Masselink, 1943-49; J.H. Kromminga, 1949-52; B.
Ypma, 1954-61; J. Gunnink, 1962-69; J. Morren,
1970-78; J.H. Scholten, 1980-88; J. Terpstra,
1990-97; P.E. Brink, 1992-93; R.J. Hamstra,
1998-

Grand Haven, MI — Grand Haven
see: Grand Haven, MI — First

Grand Haven, MI — Oak Grove Fellowship
(emerging)
1977-1991, discontinued
former name: Grand Haven, MI — Chapel of
Christ, 1977-1990
pastors: W.R. Willink (E), 1977-85; P.E. Brink,
1985-91

Grand Haven, MI — Second
1882-
pastors: R. Duiker, 1881-87; G.D. De Jong, 1888-
1903; L. Veltkamp, 1904-06; P.D. Van Vliet, 1907-
12; J.M. Ghysels, 1913-19; G. Goris, 1921-27; R.J.
Karsen, 1927-42; E. Tanis, 1943-56; J.A.
Petersen, 1958-64; J. Pott, 1964-74; E.W. Los,
1974-90; A. Breems, 1985-89; J.D. Hellinga,
1991-94; E.J. Tamminga, 1995-; R.J. Byker,
1998-2001

Grand Junction, CO — New Life
1997-
emerging, 1997-2000
pastor: K.J. Nydam, 1997-

Grand Junction, MI — Horseshoe Chapel
(mission)
1942-1982
staff: J. Ten Harmsel (L), 1942; G. De Vries (L),
1942-43; C. Stremeler (L), 1943-46; H. Jager (L),
1946-47; J.C. Dykstra (L), 1946-50; M. Habers
(L), 1946-47; O. Aardsma (E), 1947-58: C.
Overwyk, (L), 1951-52; E. Karsten (L), 1951-52; J.
Koning (L), 1951-52; S. Siebersma (E), 1960-62;
J. De Vries (L), 1963-66; N.P. Baylor (L), 1966-
70; G. Cappendyk (L), 1970-72; P. Vanderkamp
(E), 1973-76, 1982-1983; W. Willink (E), 1975-77,
W. Ridley (E), 1977-82

Grand Ledge, MI — Covenant
see: Lansing, MI — Covenant

Grand Ledge, MI — Hmong Community
see: Lansing, MI — Hmong, Community

Grand Rapids, MI (mission)
1905-1928
staff: J.R Brink, 1905-08, 1913-28; D. Van der
Wagen (E), 1908-14

Grand Rapids, MI — Abundant Life
(emerging)
2000-
pastor: A. Bailey, 2000-

Grand Rapids, MI — Alger Park
1952-
pastors: A.A. Hoekema, 1954-56; L.J. Dykstra,
1957-62; P.Y. De Jong, 1963-64; G. Gritter, 1965-
73; A.J. Vander Griend, 1974-82; R. De Young,
1977-81; G.R. Erffmeyer, 1982-88; L.M. Fryling,
1989-92; E. De Vries, 1987-; D.J. Deters, 1994-

Grand Rapids, MI — Allen Road (mission)
see: Grand Rapids, MI — Haven/36th Street (mission)

Grand Rapids, MI — Alpine Avenue
1881-1990, merged with Grand Rapids, MI —
Highland Hills (which was reorganized as Grand
Rapids, MI — Westend)
pastors: W.H. Frieling, 1882-86; P. Ekster, 1886-
1905; S. Volbeda, 1905-11; J. Van Lonkhuyzen,
1911-18; P.A. Hoekstra, 1919-27; W. Masselink,
1928-42; P.Y. De Jong, 1942-48; J.T. Holwerda,
1948-54; A.W. Hoogstrate, 1954-61; G.P.
Holwerda, 1961-66; J.H. Bergsma, 1966-90

Grand Rapids, MI — Alpine Avenue (mis-
sion)
1976-1977
staff: F.A. Bakker, 1976-77

Grand Rapids, MI — Arcadia
1947-1985, merged into Grand Rapids, MI —
Arcadia-Plainfield
organized: 1958
pastors: H. Buikema (E), 1947-58; P.F. Holtrop,
1959-62; M.G. Zylstra, 1963-70; C.L. Bremer,
1972-78; J. De Vries, 1978-85

Grand Rapids, MI — Arcadia-Plainfield
1985-1989, merged into Grand Rapids, MI —
Blythefield
pastors: J. De Vries, 1985-89

Grand Rapids, MI — Bates Street
see: Grand Rapids, MI — First

Grand Rapids, MI — Baxter Street Mission (mission)
1935-1939
staff: W. De Hoog (L), 1935-37; H. Hoeksema (L), 1938-39

Grand Rapids, MI — Beacon Light Mission (mission)
1927-1964
staff: C. Van't Riet (L), 1937-41; M. Ribbens (L), 1940-41; B. Bruxvoort (L), 1941-43; Miss Dykstra, 1942-43; J. Griffin (L), 1943-48; K. Hellema, 1944-45; K. Brower, 1944-46; J. Hulst (L), 1944-48; J. Last (L), 1947-52; C. Disselkoen (L), 1952-54; G. Stam (L), 1955-58; M. Rieffer (L), 1959-62; R. Noorman (L), 1962-63; R. Van Laar (L), 1962-63; F. Syswerda (L), 1963-64

Grand Rapids, MI — Beckwith Hills
1875-
joined CRC, 1881
former name: Grand Rapids, MI — Legrand Street, 1873-1906; Grand Rapids, MI — Coldbrook, 1906-63
pastors: L.J. Hulst, 1876-1906; J.J. Hiemenga, 1907-13; Y.P. De Jong, 1913-17; L. Veltkamp, 1918-25; E.B. Pekelder, 1925-35; T. Yff, 1936-43; E.L. Haan, 1944-49; R.R. De Ridder, 1949-53; R. Rienstra, 1954-69; O.W. Duistermars, 1970-74; J. Joldersma, 1976-87; L.B. Mensink, 1989-95; E.J. Blankespoor, 1995-

Grand Rapids, MI — Belmont Gospel Mission (mission)
1932-1937; became part of Sunshine Gospel Mission
staff: J. Swierenga (L), 1935-36; Mrs. J.S. Vander Veer (L), 1936-37; W. Scamehorn (L), 1936-37

Grand Rapids, MI — Bethel
1913-1994, merged with Grand Rapids, MI — Granville Ave. and organized as Grand Rapids, MI — Roosevelt Park Community
pastors: G. Hoeksema, 1913-26; G. Hofmeyer, 1926-45; R.L. Veenstra, 1946-52; T. Yff, 1952-56; L. Greenway, 1957-63; W.D Buursma, 1963-73; N.R. Prins, 1974-79; R.B. Lanning, 1982-87; R.J. Buining, 1988-93

Grand Rapids, MI — Bethel Mission
1920-1956
staff: A. Cook (L), 1934-40; J. Vander Veer (L), 1937; A. Veen (L), 1940-49; W. Tuit (L), 1940-43; M. Van Doorne (L), 1944-45; P. Doot (L), 1949-56

Grand Rapids, MI — Bethel Parish
1973-1976
staff: H. Buikema (L), 1973-76

Grand Rapids, MI — Beverly
see: Wyoming, MI — Beverly

Grand Rapids, MI — Blodgett Home
see: Grand Rapids, MI — Mary Free Bed Guild Home

Grand Rapids, MI — Blythefield
see: Rockford, MI — Blythefield

Grand Rapids, MI — Boston Square
1931-
organized: 1942
former name: Grand Rapids, MI — Boston Square Mission, 1931-42
pastors: F. DeVos (L), 1934-35; V.C. Licatesi, 1943-50; A.C. De Jong, 1951-52; N.L. Veltman, 1953-62; M. Goote, 1962-72; W.M. Gebben, 1974-85; A.S. Luke, 1987-95; F.M. Bultman, 1997-2002

Grand Rapids, MI — Boston Square (mission)
1948-1955
staff: H. Faber (L), 1948-52; A. Veen (L), 1952-53

Grand Rapids, MI — Bridge Street Mission
1945-1951
staff: L. Bode (L), 1945-47; H. Wierenga, 1946-49; A. Vander Zwaag (L), 1948-51; E. Dykstra (L), 1951

Grand Rapids, MI — Bristolwood
1956-1985, discontinued
organized: 1966
pastors: G. Malda (E), 1956-66; M.C. Groenendyk, 1966-84

Grand Rapids, MI — Broadway
see: Grand Rapids, MI — Westview

Grand Rapids, MI — Brookmark Sunday School
1962-1963
staff: W. Zylstra (L), 1962-63

Grand Rapids, MI — Brookside
1959-
pastors: D.J. Drost, 1960-68; R.A. Hertel, 1969-77; B.A. Averill, 1975-77; D.W. Vander Veen,

47

1978-92; B.J. Becksvoort, 1985-97; R.W. Vance, 1986-97; N.L. Meyer, 1993-2002; P.R. DeVries, 2001-

Grand Rapids, MI — Buckley Street Chapel
see: Grand Rapids, MI – Grace

Grand Rapids, MI — Burton Heights
1905-
pastors: W. Bode, 1906-10; K. Poppen, 1911-13; H. Beets, 1915-20; H.J. Mulder, 1921-29; E.J. Masselink, 1929-40; G. Stob, 1940-43; H.J. Evenhouse, 1944-51; L. Greenway, 1952-57; A. Brink, 1958-78; R.S. Greenway, 1978-82; D.M. MacLeod, 1985-93; R.D. Bolt, 1996-

Grand Rapids, MI — Burton Heights Mission
1945-1953
staff: B. Vander Pol (L), 1945-46; H. Brummels (L), 1945-50; M. Van Tol (L), 1951-53

Grand Rapids, MI — Calvin
1946-
pastors: C. Boomsma, 1948-83; W.J. Boer, 1970-73; J.P. Heerema, 1974-80; J.R. Boot, 1984-92; H. Kiekover, 1985-94; E.J. Laarman, 1986-92; S.E. Hoezee; 1993-; R. Koornneef, 1997-

Grand Rapids, MI — Cascade
see: Grand Rapids, MI – Cascade Fellowship

Grand Rapids, MI — Cascade Fellowship
1952-
former name: Grand Rapids, MI – Cascade, 1952-93
pastors: J.P. Boonstra, 1953-57; R. Boeskool, Jr., 1958-64; J. Guichelaar, 1964-72; W. Timmer, 1972-79; D.T. Van Oyen, 1980-88; V.G. Van Ee, 1984-86; G.L. Dykstra, 1990-96; T.E. Van Zalen, 1998-

Grand Rapids, MI — Children's Services/ Juvenile Home (mission)
1910-1960
began as a Sunday School
staff: P. Vander Meer (L), 1937-47, 1951-58; P.J. Haan (L), 1940-47; D. Hamming (L), 1947-51; D. Zylstra (L), 1958-60

Grand Rapids, MI — Christ's Community
1976-1989, discontinued
organized: 1978
pastors: A.G. Beerens, 1976-87; D.B. Deppe, 1978-82; J.A. Lucas, 1985-89

Grand Rapids, MI — Church of the Servant
1973-
pastors: J. Vriend, 1974-82; J. Roeda, 1983-; J. Kooreman, 2001-

Grand Rapids, MI — City Hope Ministries (emerging, joint ministry with RCA)
1999-
pastor: D. Venegas, 1999-

Grand Rapids, MI — Coit Community (emerging)
1977-
pastors: P. Kooreman (E), 1977-85, 1988-90; L.V. Haas (E), 1980, 1986-87; H. Perez (E), 1991-94; J. Burton (E), 1994-

Grand Rapids, MI — Coit Hills (mission)
1948-1952
staff: M. Tanis (L), 1948-52

Grand Rapids, MI — Coldbrook
see: Grand Rapids, MI – Beckwith Hills

Grand Rapids, MI — Commerce Street
see: Grand Rapids, MI – First

Grand Rapids, MI — Community
see: Wyoming, MI – Community

Grand Rapids, MI — Comstock Park
see: Comstock Park, MI – Comstock Park

Grand Rapids, MI — Covenant
see: Cutlerville, MI – Covenant

Grand Rapids, MI — Creston
1915-
pastors: K. Bergsma, 1916-23; W. Groen, 1924-26; H. Verduin, 1926-46; W.P. Brink, 1948-52; R. De Groot, 1953-59; W. Hendriksen, 1961-65; J.W. Uitvlugt, 1966-71; J. Dykstra, 1972-82; D.A. Kamper, 1974-78; D.J. Van Beek, 1983-98; J.L. Blom, 1999-

Grand Rapids, MI — Creston Evangelism (mission)
1950-1960, 1986-1989
staff: R. Kruize (L), 1950-51; G. Wiers (L), 1953-55; A. Brott, 1986-89

Grand Rapids, MI — Criminal Justice Chaplaincy
1980-1985, became self-sustaining
pastor: J. Vander Schaaf, 1980-85

Grand Rapids, MI — Crosby Street
see: Grand Rapids, MI — West Leonard Street

Grand Rapids, MI — Cuban Ministry
1962–1972, work taken over by Wyoming, MI — Emanuel Hispanic
pastors: J.S. Boonstra, 1962–65; C.M. Cortina, 1966–72

Grand Rapids, MI — Dennis Avenue
see: Grand Rapids, MI — Mayfair

Grand Rapids, MI — Downtown Campus Ministries
1973–1987
former name: Grand Rapids, MI — Grand Rapids Junior College, 1979–84
chaplains: J. Ouwinga, 1973–78; H.W. Lew, 1979–

Grand Rapids, MI — East
see: Grand Rapids, MI — Eastern Avenue

Grand Rapids, MI — East Leonard
1925–
pastors: B.H. Spalink, 1926–30; M. Arnoys, 1930–39; J.G. Van Dyke, 1940–51; B.E. Pekelder, 1951–55; J.W. Visser, 1955–61; J. Hofman, Jr., 1962–65; W. Haverkamp, 1966–73; H.A. Ouwinga, 1974–81; P.J. Kok, 1982–87; T.D. Slachter, 1989–93; D.A. Warners, 1995–2001; W.S. Wilton, 1999–2000; T.D. Slachter, 2002–

Grand Rapids, MI — East Paris
see: Kentwood, MI — East Paris

Grand Rapids, MI — East Street
see: Grand Rapids, MI — Eastern Avenue

Grand Rapids, MI — Eastern Avenue
1879–
former name: Grand Rapids, MI — East Street, 1879–1912
pastors: J. Post, 1881–87; S.B. Sevensma, 1887–1900; J. Groen, 1900–19; H. Hoeksema, 1920–24; W.P. Van Wyk, 1925–41; C. Huissen, 1941–52; W. Haverkamp, 1955–60; M.D. Hugen, 1962–67; J.R. Kok, 1967–72; P.J. Niewiek, 1972–75; N. Vanderzee, 1972–76; G.D. Negen, 1976–86; V.F. Geurkink, 1977–82; L.J. Vander Zee, 1983–90; R.T. Bouma, 1987–96; R.A. Berkenbosch, 1992–95; M.S.H. Antonides, 1996–

Grand Rapids, MI — Faith
1961–1979, discontinued

Grand Rapids, MI — Faith, Hope, and Love (emerging)
1988–1994, discontinued
pastor: L.A. Pellecer, 1988–94

Grand Rapids, MI — Fifth Avenue
see: Grand Rapids, MI — Franklin Street

Grand Rapids, MI — First
1857–
former names: Grand Rapids, MI — Grand Rapids, 157–79; Grand Rapids, MI — Spring Street, 1879–1900; Grand Rapids, MI — Commerce Street, 1900–12; Grand Rapids, MI — First Grand Rapids, 1912–18; Grand Rapids, MI — Bates Street, 1918–20;
pastors: H.G. Klyn, 1857; W.H. Van Leeuwen, 1863–67; R. Duiker, 1867–72; G.E. Boer, 1873–76; J. Kremer, 1877–79; J.H. Vos, 1881–1900; T. Vander Ark, 1900–05; G.J. Haan, 1906–08; P. Ekster, 1908–18; E. Tanis, 1919–27; D.D. Bonnema, 1927–41; E.F. Visser, 1942–51; W.L. Van Rees, 1951–60; M. Beelen, 1961–70; C. Terpstra, 1970–82; D.J. Klop, 1973–80; R.E. Alexander, 1982–84; D.G. Bos, 1983–84; M.N. Greidanus, 1985–; K.S. Hofman Smith, 2001–2002

Grand Rapids, MI — First Grand Rapids
see: Grand Rapids, MI — First

Grand Rapids, MI — Fourth
see: Grand Rapids, MI — LaGrave Avenue

Grand Rapids, MI — Franklin Street
1887–1966, merged into Wyoming, MI — Rogers Heights
former name: Grand Rapids, MI — Fifth Avenue, 1887–1912
pastors: W.R. Smidt, 1888–1902; W.D. Vander Werp, 1903–06; L. Veltkamp, 1906–18; A.W. De Jonge, 1918–21; B. Essenburg, 1921–25; H. Baker, 1926–37; J. Gritter, 1938–48; J.H. Piersma, 1949–53; R.H. Haan, 1953–59; H. Sonnema, 1959–63; J.M. Julien, 1963–66

Grand Rapids, MI — Front Street Mission (mission)
1948–1962
staff: J. Gronski (L), 1948–49; E. Postma (L), 1949–52; P. Vander Kamp (L), 1952–53; H. Van Wyk, Jr., 1952–57; M. Groenendyke (L), 1957–62

pastors: A.A. Cammenga, Sr., 1961–62; P.E. Bakker, 1963–68; J.M. Julien, 1968–75; G.H. Stoutmeyer, 1975–79

49

Grand Rapids, MI — Fuller Avenue
1925-
pastors: E.J. Van Halsema, 1925-30; G. Goris, 1930-41; J. Weidenaar, 1942-49; G. Gritter, 1950-62; W.F. Vander Hoven, 1962-71; G.L. Dahnke, 1971-74; V.C. Patterson, 1973-74; L.A. Koning, 1976-86; A.L. Vander Hart, 1988-98; G.F. Vander Weit, 2000-

Grand Rapids, MI — Godwin Gospel Chapel
1946-1970
former name: Grand Rapids, MI — Godwin Heights Mission, 1946-61
staff: J. Vredevoogd (L), 1946-49; A.H. Selles, 1949-50; H. Brinks (L), 1950-54; A. Mulder (L)., 1955-61; W. Timmer (L), 1961-69

Grand Rapids, MI — Godwin Heights
see: Wyoming, MI — Godwin Heights

Grand Rapids, MI — Godwin Heights Mission
see: Grand Rapids, MI — Godwin Gospel Chapel

Grand Rapids, MI — Gold Avenue (emerging)
1929-
absorbed Grand Rapids, MI — West Fulton Street Gospel Mission, 1953
pastors: J. Vander Water (E), 1929-43; A. Vander Veer (E), 1944-51; E. Dykstra (E), 1951-64; A. Vander Zwaag (L), 1954-59; A. Vander Veer (L), 1960-61; P. Doot (E), 1964-74; M.D. Knierim (E), 1975-86; W.M. Ridley (E), 1982-91; R.L. Offringa, 1992-99

Grand Rapids, MI — Grace
1947-
organized: 1962
former name: Grand Rapids, MI — Buckley Street Chapel, 1947-62
pastors: A. Veen (E), 1949-62; M. Toonstra, Jr., 1962-65; P. Huiner, 1966-69; P.W. Brink, 1968-74; R.E. Van Harn, 1976-98; D.C. Sherow, 1982-83; J. Nash, 1984-85; V. Anderson, 1987-90; L.D. Slings (I), 1999; R.M. Hofman, 1999-2002; S.W. Venhuizen, 1999-2002

Grand Rapids, MI — Grand Rapids
see: Grand Rapids, MI — First

Grand Rapids, MI — Grand Rapids Junior College
see: Grand Rapids, MI — Downtown Campus Ministries

Grand Rapids, MI — Grandville Avenue
1891-1994, merged with Grand Rapids, MI — Bethel and organized as Grand Rapids, MI — Roosevelt Park Community
pastors: W. Greve, 1893-96; E.R. Haan, 1896-98; J.W. Brink, 1900-04; J. Timmerman, 1905-08; E. Breen, 1909-14; R.L. Haan, 1914-16; Y.P. De Jong, 1917-45; M. Monsma, 1943-53; M. Vander Zwaag, 1953-59; J.H. Piersma, 1960-64; E.H. Palmer, 1964-68; J.D. Hellinga, 1968-72; A.E. Pontier, 1973-81; R. Praamsma, 1982-90; P.W. Townsend, 1991-93

Grand Rapids, MI — Grant Street (mission)
1909-1921, begun by Franklin Street church; merged into Grand Rapids, MI — Way of Life Gospel Chapel
staff: C.J. Jaarsma (L), 1917-19

Grand Rapids, MI — Griggs Street Chapel
1953-1977, joined Orthodox Presbyterian Church
staff: P. Vander Kamp (L), 1955-58; H. Hyma (L), 1958-65; H. Kramer (L), 1958-75

Grand Rapids, MI — Guiding Light Mission
1957-1987, became self-sustaining
staff: A. Van Der Veer (L), 1957-65; A. Ickes (L), 1957-58; W. Bruinsma (L), 1959-60; L. Haas (L), 1964-66; J. Maliepaard, 1966-68; J. Vredevoogd (L), 1969-72; E.W. Oosterhouse (L), 1973-83; H. Koning (L), 1984-87

Grand Rapids, MI — Haven/36th Street (mission)
1929-1959
former name: Grand Rapids, MI — Allen Road
staff: D. Lotterman (L), 1934-36; J. Brinks, (L), 1936-1937; S. Helder (L), 1937-40; J.S. Vander Veer (L), 1940-42; W. Warners (L), 1942-43; G. Oppenhuizen (L), 1943-53; K. Baarman (L), 1944-49

Grand Rapids, MI — Hazen Street (mission)
see: Grand Rapids, MI — Seymour

Grand Rapids, MI — Highland Hills
1950-1992, reorganized as Grand Rapids, MI — Westend
merged with Grand Rapids, MI — Alpine Avenue, 1990
pastors: J.D. Eppinga, 1951-54; A.C. De Jong, 1954-60; N.L. Veltman, 1962-67; M.R. Doornbos, 1968-77; J.F. De Vries, 1977-83; K.J. Nydam, 1981-84; J. Hofman, Jr., 1984-90

Grand Rapids, MI — Hillcrest Community (emerging)

1935–

pastors: J. Pott (L), 1935; A. Hulst (L), 1936–37; 1938–39; J. Smeelink (L), 1936–37; P. Doot (E), 1942–46; M. Tanis (E), 1946–55; R. Holwerda (E), 1956–63; H. Bergsma (E), 1960–61; H. Vander Bilt (E), 1960–63; R. Fisher (E), 1963–64; N. Baylor (E), 1964–66; G. Vander Lugt (E), 1966–75; L.K. Toering (E), 1976–96; M. Van Ess (E), 1996–

Grand Rapids, MI — Ideal Park

1926–

organized: 1961

former name: Grand Rapids, MI – Lamar Plat Gospel Mission

pastors: S. Fennema (L), 1936–39; H. Scholten (L), 1940–41; M. Tanis (L), 1942–46, 1954–55; S. Tiggchelaar, 1945–47; J. Brock (L), 1947–49; B. Ebbelink (L), 1949–52; E. Postma (L), 1952–58; B. Spalink (I), 1959–60; V.C. Licatesi, 1960–62; S.A Werkema, 1962–67; J.M. Hofman, 1967–90; Z.G. Anderson, 1990–93; R.R. Mueller, 1995–2000

Grand Rapids, MI — Immanuel

see: Wyoming, MI – Immanuel

Grand Rapids, MI — Ionia Avenue Gospel Chapel (mission)

1920–1964

staff: M.J. van Dyken (L), 1934–45; J. Westra (L), 1937–44; A. Elve, 1943–44; A. Kaemingk, 1944–45; R. Scholten (L), 1945–46; B. De Korte (L), 1945–55; S. Terpstra, 1953–54; W. Alderink, 1954–55; K. Navis (L), 1955–58; S. Siebersma (L), 1958–60; R. Knaack (L), 1960–62; M. Vugteveen (L), 1962–63; J. DiMaggio (L), 1963–64

Grand Rapids, MI — Kelloggsville (mission)

1936–1937

staff: C. Van't Riet (L), 1936–37

Grand Rapids, MI — Kelloggsville

see: Kentwood, MI – Kelloggsville

Grand Rapids, MI — Kent County Home

see: Grand Rapids, MI – Maple Grove

Grand Rapids, MI — Kent County Jail (mission)

1936–1960

staff: C. Quist, Sr. (L), 1944–51, 1952–60; G. Wiersum (L), 1951–52; B. Ondersma (L), 1953–54

Grand Rapids, MI — Keystone Community (emerging)

1995–

classical ministry, 1995–99

pastor: G. De Jong, 1994–

Grand Rapids, MI — Korean

see: Wyoming, MI – Hahn-In

Grand Rapids, MI — LaGrave Avenue

1887–

former name: Grand Rapids, MI – Fourth, 1888

pastors: J.Y DeBaun, 1887–92; S.J. Vander Beek, 1892–98; H. Beets, 1899–1915; W. Stuart, 1915–25; R.B. Kuiper, 1925–29; H. Bel, 1932–40; E.J. Masselink, 1940–44; G. Goris, 1945–53; J.D. Eppinga, 1954–87; W.S. Gritter, 1968–71; P.D. Winkle, 1973–77; J.J. Steigenga, 1978–; S. Mast, 1990–; W. Stroo, 1999–; P.D. Winkle, 2000–; H.J. Schenkel, 2001–

Grand Rapids, MI — LaGrave Avenue Mission

1948–1953

staff: G. Wiers (L), 1948–53

Grand Rapids, MI — Lamar Plat Gospel Mission

see: Grand Rapids, MI – Ideal Park

Grand Rapids, MI — Lee Street

see: Wyoming, MI – Lee Street

Grand Rapids, MI — Legrand Street

see: Grand Rapids, MI – Beckwith Hills

Grand Rapids, MI — Livingston Chapel

1966–1979

staff: H. Spalink (L), 1966–67, 1969–70; C. Dykema (L), 1967–69; G. Berghoef (E), 1967–68, 1971–79; I. Van Dyke, (L), 1970–71

Grand Rapids, MI — Madison Square

1914–

organized: 1970

former name: Grand Rapids, MI – Madison Square Chapel, 1948–70

pastors: E. Smitter (L), 1918; H. Flokstra (L), 1934–40; A. Vellenga, 1937–39 (L), 1937–39; T. Afman (L), 1940–48; G. Holkeboer (L), 1945–59; W.G. Dubois (M), 1948–62; W. Navis (L), 1962–67; V.F. Geurkink (M), 1967–74; V.C. Patterson, 1974–77; D.J. Sieplinga, 1977–82; D.A. Venegas, 1981–96; D.H. Beelen, 1982–; G.L. Cumberland, 1993–95; S.B. Reeves, Jr., 1998–

Grand Rapids, MI — Madison Square Chapel

see: Grand Rapids, MI — Madison Square

Grand Rapids, MI — Maple Grove (evangelism)

1941–1960

former name: Grand Rapids, MI — Kent County Home

staff: P.J. Haan (L), 1941–48; C. Quist (L), 1948–49, 1952–53; W. DuBois, 1949–50

Grand Rapids, MI — Mary Free Bed Guild Home (mission)

1929–1960

former name: Grand Rapids, MI — Blodgett Home

staff: E. Smitter (L), 1935; T. Afman (L), 1944–48; W. DuBois, 1948–51; B. Ondersma (L), 1951–55; R. Baas (L), 1955–60

Grand Rapids, MI — Mayfair

1893–

former name: Grand Rapids, MI — Dennis Avenue, 1893–1954

pastors: E. Vander Vries, 1896–1903; J.B. Hoekstra, 1903–09; J.A. Kett, 1910–14; H. Danhof, 1914–18; P. Jonker, Jr., 1919–22; W. Kuipers, 1923–27; J.L. Heeres, 1927–32; H.J. Rikkers, 1933–26; J. Weidenaar, 1936–42; L. Oostendorp, 1942–52; H. DeMots, 1954–69; M.R. Doornbos, 1969–74; W.R. Witte, 1976–93; P.T. Verhulst, 1991–98; T.M. Zuidema, 1999–

Grand Rapids, MI (mission)

1905–1928

staff: J.R. Brink, 1905–08, 1913–28; D. Van der Wagen (E), 1908–14

Grand Rapids, MI — Michigan Street Mission (mission)

1932–1937

staff: W. Schamehorn (L), 1935–37

Grand Rapids, MI — Millbrook

1954–

pastors: J. Gunnink, 1956–62; H.N. Erffmeyer, 1963–68; H.G. Vander Ark, 1969–74; J.E. De Vries, 1976–92; M.J. Vellekoop, 1994–2001; W.C. Hensen, 2003–

Grand Rapids, MI — Mission Thrift (Industrial) Store

1929–1987

staff: J. Vande Water (L), 1929–44; J. Systsma (L), 1943–50; P. Winters (L), 1945–72; B. De

Korte (L), 1947–48; A. Van der Veer (L), 1955–66; M. Meekhof (L), 1972–84; G. Huissen (E), 1984–87

Grand Rapids, MI — Monroe Mall Ministries (emerging)

2001

pastor: H. Schenkel, 2001

Grand Rapids, MI — Neland Avenue

1915–

pastors: H.H. Meeter, 1917–26; D.H. Kromminga, 1926–28; H.J. Kuiper, 1929–44; R.J. Danhof, 1945–56; J.O. Schuring, 1957–63; S. Van Dyken, 1964–70; T.E. Hofman, 1972–81; R.J. Hamstra, 1983–86; C.L. Kammeraad, 1982–2002; D.K. Kelderman, 1988–2001; L.A. Kuyvenhoven, 2002–

Grand Rapids, MI — North Park Chapel

1955–1968

staff: J. Fikkert (L), 1955–56; R. Cooper (L), 1956–60; H. Bielema (L), 1960–64; R. Kamrath (L), 1966–68

Grand Rapids, MI — Oakdale Park

1890–

pastors: G.A. De Haan, 1891–95; F.M. Ten Hoor, 1896–1900; H.M. Vander Ploeg, 1901–03; L. Berkhof, 1904–06; Y.P. De Jong, 1907–11; W.P. Van Wyk, 1911–22; H. Kuiper, 1923–25; J.M. Vande Kieft, 1925–32; J.J. Zeeuw, 1932–35; W. Hendriksen, 1935–42; J. Griffioen, 1943–48; P.Y. De Jong, 1948–52; J.H. Piersma, 1953–56; J. Guichelaar, 1956–64; C. Bolt, 1966–71; W. Heynen, 1971–73; H.G. Vanden Einde, 1974–79; W. Vanden Bosch, 1979–; D. Deppe, 1984–85; R. Benton, Jr., 1995–97

Grand Rapids, MI — Oakdale Park Mission

1948–1975

staff: H. Van Eerden (L), 1948–54; H. Flokstra (L), 1952–53; Mrs. F. Diemer (L), 1954–58; S. Hubers (L), 1958–60; S. Siebersma (L), 1958–59; F. Bakker (L), 1959–60; L. Haas (L), 1964–66; R. Brouwer (L), 1967–68; G. Geurink (L), 1974–75

Grand Rapids, MI — Plainfield

see: Plainfield, MI — Plainfield

Grand Rapids, MI — Plainfield Avenue Mission

1904–1906

Grand Rapids, MI — Plymouth Heights

1951–

pastors: E. Heerema, 1953-64; W.M. Van Dyk, 1964-86; L.A. Koning, 1973-76; R. Klimp, 1977-80; P. Van Elderen, Jr., 1988-97; R.L. Palsrok, 1989-2002; J.A. Molenbeek, 1998-

Grand Rapids, MI — Princeton
see: Kentwood, MI — Princeton

Grand Rapids, MI — Riverside
1953-
pastors: W.C. Boelkins, 1955-60; J. Maliepaard, 1961-67; L. Greenway, 1969-77; H.G. Vanden Einde, 1979-87; M.A. Palsrok, 1989-2000; C.L. Geschiere, 2002-

Grand Rapids, MI — Rogers Heights Chapel (mission)
1955-1958
staff: P. Doot (L), 1955-58

Grand Rapids, MI — Roosevelt Park Community
1994-
merger of Grand Rapids, MI — Grandville Avenue (1891-1994) and Grand Rapids, MI — Bethel (1913-1994)
pastors: R. Smith, 1994- ; J.T. Aasman, 1998-

Grand Rapids, MI — Seymour
1932
organized: 1939
former name: Grand Rapids, MI — Hazen Street Mission, 1932-39
pastors: J.J. Pott (L), 1934-35; A. Hulst (L), 1935-36, 1937-39; J. Smeelink (L), 1936-37; R.J. Frens, 1940-53; J. Hasper, 1953-62; J.A. De Kruyter, 1964-75; H. Admiraal, 1973-92; H. Guikema, 1985-89; C.R. Cornelisse, 1989-91; A.A. Arkema, 1991-94; G.L. Zandstra, 1993-2000; L.B. Mensink, 1995-98; J.A. Vanderstoep, 2000-; C.L. Kammeraad, 2002-

Grand Rapids, MI — Shawnee Park
1961-
pastors: L. Veltkamp, 1962-74; D.R. Vander Wall, 1975-81; N. De Nooyer (E), 1977-80; K.D. Van De Griend, 1983-89; R.A. Kok, 1990-2000; E.J. Vander Horst, 2001-

Grand Rapids, MI — Sherman Street
1907-
pastors: J.L. VanTielen, 1908-11; J.J. Weersing, 1912-16; R.B. Kuiper, 1917-23; H. Schultze, 1924-26; M. Van Dyke, 1927-31; W. Van Peursem, 1932-40; G. Goris, 1941-44; L. Veltkamp, 1946-

49; F.W. Van Houten, 1950-53; J.A. Mulder, 1956-67; A. Veen (E), 1962-66; M. Toonstra, Jr., 1961-62; I.J. Apol, 1967-71; W.L. De Jong, 1972-79; H.E. Botts, 1980-87; M.D. Vermaire, 1984-99; D.H. Kromminga, 2000-

Grand Rapids, MI — Sixth Street Gospel Mission (mission)
1940-1945
staff: E. Postema (L), 1940-41; P.B. Peterson (L), 1941-45; L. Bode, 1944-45

Grand Rapids, MI — Spanish Christian Bookstore
1977-1979
staff: D. Lago (E), 1977-79

Grand Rapids, MI — Spring Street
see: Grand Rapids, MI — First

Grand Rapids, MI — Sunshine
see: Grand Rapids, MI — Sunshine Community

Grand Rapids, MI — Sunshine Chapel
see: Grand Rapids, MI — Sunshine Community

Grand Rapids, MI — Sunshine Community
1919-
organized: 1971
begun by Dennis Avenue CRC
former names: Grand Rapids, MI — Sunshine Gospel Hall, 1938-1961; Grand Rapids, MI — Sunshine Chapel, 1961-71; Grand Rapids, MI — Sunshine, 1972-93
pastors: J. Swierenga (L), 1934-36; Mrs. J. Vander Veer (L), 1936-37; H. Bruinekool (L), 1937-40; A. Aldering (L), 1940-45; H. Flokstra (L), 1945-53; H. Brinks, 1955-56; A. Tucker (L), 1957-60; E. Visscher (L), 1960-65; S. Siebersma (L), 1965-68; L.R. Vander Meer, 1970-91; H.J. Teitsma, 1979-82; T.J. Berends, 1986-87; M. Heard, 1993-98; T.E. Mayo, Jr., 1995-99; J. Wilczewski, 1997-98; D.S. Huizenga, 1997-; B.P. Bosscher, 2000-

Grand Rapids, MI — Sunshine Gospel Hall
See: Grand Rapids, MI — Sunshine Community

Grand Rapids, MI — Twelfth Street
1917-1995, merged with Grand Rapids, MI — West Leonard Street
pastors: W.M. Trap, 1918-29; Q. Breen, 1921-24; J.M. Ghysels, 1925-28; J.K. Van Baalen, 1929-43; A.A. Hoekema, 1944-50; E.J. Masselink, 1950-55;

J.P. Boonstra, 1957-63; G.F. Van Oyen, 1964-70; J.W. Dykstra, 1972-85; H.G. Entingh, 1987-94

Grand Rapids, MI — Unity Chapel
1961-1963
staff: M. Toonstra, 1961-62; A. Veen (L), 1962-63

Grand Rapids, MI — Walker
1910-1997, withdrew to United Reformed Church
organized: 1912
former name: Kinney Station, MI — Kinney Station, 1910-12; Grand Rapids, MI — Walker Station, 1913-14
pastors: P.J. Hoekenga, 1916-18; J. Wyngaarden, 1918-28; P. Vos, 1928-47; C.O. Buus, 1949-54; W.R. Witte, 1954-58; R.S. De Haan, 1960-66; S.M. Voortman, 1966-71; C.G. Werkema, Sr., 1971-78; J.R. Jackson, 1979-85; J.A. Wesseling, 1986-91; J.A. Vander Kooi, 1992-97

Grand Rapids, MI — Walker Station
see: Grand Rapids, MI — Walker

Grand Rapids, MI — Way of Life Gospel Chapel
1916-1954
begun by Grand Rapids, MI — Eastern Avenue CRC; absorbed Grand Rapids, MI — Grant Street Mission, 1921
staff: J. Veenstra (L), 1916-17; A. Del Vechio (L), 1917-20; G. Holkeboer (L), 1928-40; W. Geelhoed (L), 1928-46; O.E. Heinrich (L), 1941-48; L. Bode (L), 1941-44; P. Doot (L), 1944-48; M. Tanis (L), 1946-54

Grand Rapids, MI — Westend
1992-
reorganized from Grand Rapids, MI — Highland Hills, 1992
pastor: H. Admiraal, 1992-

Grand Rapids, MI — West Fulton Street Gospel Mission
1929-1953, merged into Grand Rapids, MI — Gold Avenue
staff: J. Van de Water (L), 1930-47; M. De Boer (L), 1945-46; E. Goosen (L), 1946-49; A. Vander Veer (L), 1949-50; E. Goosen (L), 1950-52; E. Dykstra (L), 1952-53; A. Vander Zwaan (L), 1952-53

Grand Rapids, MI — West Leonard Street
1889-
former names: Grand Rapids, MI — Crosby

Street, 1989-1909; merger with Grand Rapids, MI — Twelfth Street, 1994
pastors: G. Broene, 1889-1904; F. Doezema, 1905-14; R.B. Kuiper, 1914-17; S.P. Eldersveld, 1918-20; J.P. De Vries, 1921-26; R. Veldman, 1927-48; C. Vanden Heuvel, 1949-58; R. Leetsma, 1958-64; A.A. Mulder, 1965-70; E.J. Knott, 1971-78; D.J. Deters, 1979-84; H.J. Weidenaar, 1984-88; A.W. Koppendrayer, 1898-93; J.L. Hoekwater, 1994-99; L.D. Slings (I), 1999-2000; N.P. Jasperse, 2001-

Grand Rapids, MI — West Leonard Street Gospel Mission
1942-1948
staff: J. Gronski (L), 1942-48

Grand Rapids, MI — Westview
1893-
former name: Grand Rapids, MI — Broadway, 1893-1961
pastors: C.D. De Mott, 1895-99; M.J. Bosma, 1900-07; J.W. Brink, 1909-12; E. Tanis, 1912-19; H.J. Kuiper, 1919-29; J. De Haan, 1929-45; T. Van Eerden, 1946-51; G.J. Rozenboom, 1953-62; P.L. Vermaire, 1963-73; W.F. Vander Hoven, 1974-82; C. Steenstra, 1983-95; R.B. Groenboom, 1994-; R.G. Baker, 1997-

Grand Rapids, MI — Woodlawn
1968-
pastors: W.K. Stob, 1969-70; D.M. Stravers, 1971-80; J. Timmer, 1980-95; P.M. Jonker, 1993-; M.F. Abma, 1998-

Grand Rapids, MI — Wyoming Park
see: Wyoming, MI — Faith Community

Grand View, SD — Ebenezer
1892-1914, discontinued, members transferred to Corsica, SD — Corsica
former name: Grand View, SD — Grand View, 1892-1903
pastor: T. Smits, 1901-03

Grand View, SD — Grand View
see: Grand View, SD — Ebenezer

Grandville, MI — Fellowship
1975-
pastors: D.G. Bos, 1976-83; D.W. Boonstra, 1984-87; G.D. Postema, 1988-99; L.P. Troast (I), 1999-2000; P.J. Boender, 2000-

Grandville, MI — Hanley

1925-
organized: 1962
pastors: F. Plagemeyer (L), 1938-43; L. Vander Till (L), 1940-44, 1947-48; G. Oppenhuizen (L), 1943-46; L. Vander Til (L), 1946-52; W. De Weerd (L), 1952-53; H. Hoekstra (L), 1953-62; H.D. Bultje, 1963-69; A.J. Bultman, 1970-77; W. Timmer, 1979-88; C.W. Bergman, 1989-95; C.R. Cunningham, 1998-2000; L.P. Troast (I), 2000-2001; D.L. Jolman, 2001-

Grandville, MI — Hope

1915-
former name: Tallmadge, MI — Tallmadge, 1915-18
pastors: G.M. Ophoff, 1922-25; H.D. Vande Kieft, 1927-34; R.L. Veenstra, 1939-41; W.C. Steenland, 1942-45; J.O. Bouwsma, 1946-52; G. Goris, 1953-63; J.F. De Vries, 1964-69; S.T. Cammenga, 1971-83; A.J. Bultman, 1984-92; C.A. Walters, 1991-97; A.L. Vander Hart, 1998-

Grandville, MI — Ivanrest

1927-
organized: 1964
pastors: T. Bouwkamp (L), 1934-43; A. Grothuis (L), 1936-37; G. Oppenhuizen (L), 1943-48; H. Brinks (L), 1948-50; H. Westerfield (L), 1950-51; C. Lanning (L), 1951-52; W. Trimmer (L), 1952-61; W. Prince, 1963-64; L.C. Bergsma, 1964-72; G. Gritter, 1973-76; C.S. Steenstra, 1977-83; G.L. Rutgers, 1981-83; G.G. Vink, 1986-93; D.L. Van Der Wiele, 1987-92; A.J. Schoonveld, 1994-2000; A.J. Meyer, 2001-

Grandville, MI — South Grandville

1954-
pastors: P.C. Zylstra, 1956-64; J.C. Medendorp, 1964-72; L. Van Drunen, 1972-90; R.D. Ritsema, 1990-94; D.B. Mouw, 1995-

Grangeville, ID (mission)

1910-1912

Grangeville, ID — Grangeville

1927-
began as a branch of Zillah, WA, 1926
pastors: J. Zwaanstra, 1933-38; G.D. Pars, 1939-43; J. Vanden Hoek, 1944-46; C.J. Toeset, 1948-52; J.M. Hofman, 1952-57; J.R. Van Dyke, 1957-61; J.E. Jeffers, 1961-67; H.H. Boer, 1968-73; J.D. Buwalda, 1973-77; F. Einfeld, 1977-82; B.M. Anderson, 1982-87; W.D. Zeilstra, 1987-91; T. Vander Ziel, 1991-97; J.J. Reardon, 1997-

Grant, MI — Evergreen Haven

1959-1960
staff: A. Landheer (L), 1959-60

Grant, MI — Grant

1896-
former name: Sun, MI — Sun, 1896-1906
pastors: R. Vande Kieft, 1907-11; J.C. De Bruyn, 1911-14; H.E. Oostendorp, 1914-19; J. Kolkman, 1920-23; H. Beute, 1924-39; C.R. Veenstra, 1940-46; F.L. Netz, 1947-52; E. Bossenbroek, 1952-56; P. Ouwinga, 1956-66; G.J. Rozenboom, 1967-74; R.J. Timmer, 1975-83; S.R. Steenstra, 1984-87; J. Vanden Akker, 1988-96; C.G. Van Wyk, 1998-

Grant, MI — Windfall Chapel

1955-1979
staff: W. Willink (L), 1955-62; D. De Vries (L), 1958-60; M. Koster (L), 1962-64; H. Boehm (E), 1965-70; L. Haas (E), 1970-71, 1973-74; L. Schut (E), 1971-73; P. Doot (E), 1975-76; G. Berghoef (E), 1976-77

Grant Park, IL — Grant Park

see: Momence, IL — Momence

Granum, AB — Granum

1905-
organized with families from the Nyverdal, AB — Nyverdal which dissolved; families from the western portion organized as Granum, AB — Granum and families from the eastern portion organized as Burdett, AB — Burdett
pastors: N. Gelderloos, 1916-21; J. Mulder, 1928-40; H. Petersen, 1942-45; R. Wildschut, 1945-50; R. Star, 1951-59; H. Bouma, 1959-63; G.J. Vander Ziel, 1964-69; P. Van Tuinen, 1970-74; L. Dekens, 1974-78; J. Heidinga, 1978-82; J. Weeda, 1983-91; G.W. Van Den Berg, 1991-94; W.D. Vis, 1995-; J.D. Zondervan, 2002-

Grass Lake, CA (mission)

1981-1982
pastor: D. Berkompas (E), 1981-82

Grassy Lake, AB (mission)

1911

Greeley, CO — Fellowship

1970-
former name: Greeley, CO — Greeley, 1970-73
pastors: G.B. Boerfyn, 1968-69; H.J. Sprik, 1969-72; D.T. Van Oyen (M), 1972-80; J.L.

Hoogeveen, 1980-86; D.A. Kamper, 1987-99;
Claire Vander Neut, 2000-2002

Greeley, CO — Greeley
see: Greeley, CO — Fellowship

Greensboro, NC — Sung Eun Presbyterian
1995-2001, left the denomination
pastor: S. Hur, 1999-2001

Greensville, ON — Greensville
see: Dundas, ON — Calvin

Greenville, MI (mission)
1925
staff: J.R. Brink (M), 1925

Grimsby, ON — Grimsby
see: Grimsby, ON — Mountainview

Grimsby, ON — Mountainview
1962-
former name: Grimsby, ON — Grimsby, 1962-67
pastors: D.C. Los, 1962-67; J.J. Hoytema, 1968-
73; J.W. Van Weelden, 1973-84; H. Vander Plaat,
1973-85; A.A. Van Geest, 1984-94; P.W.
DeBruyne, 1987-92; F.J. Koning, 1993-95; J.J.
Hoytema, 1996-

Grundy Center, IA — College
see: Grundy Center, IA — Grundy Center

Grundy Center, IA — College Church
see: Grundy Center, IA — Grundy Center

Grundy Center, IA — Grundy Center
1916-1941, discontinued
former names: Grundy Center, IA — College
Church, 1916-21, 1936-40; Grundy Center, IA —
College, 1921-36
pastors: W.W. De Groot, 1919-20; F.H. Wezeman,
1925-27; W.H. Rutgers, 1930-33; L.M. Voskuil,
1933-36; F.M. Huizenga (stated supply), 1938

Grundy Center, IA — Lincoln Center
1884-
former names: Lincoln Center, IA — Lincoln Center, 1884-1968; Grundy Center, IA — Grundy Center, 1968-71
pastors: J. Plesscher, Sr., 1885-97; J.H. Schultz,
1897-1909; W. Bode, 1912-16; J.H. Gruessing,
1916-19; M. Weeldreyer, 1919-27; H.N. Gerdes,
1928-29, 1930-31; J.F. Schuurmann, 1931-40; H.
Zwaanstra, 1940-54; A.J. Bandstra, 1955-57; .R.
Slager, 1957-62; M. Stegink, 1964-72; D.W. Van

Gent, 1972-76; A. Poot, 1976-78; A. Hannink,
978-83; R.K. Geelhoed, 1983-87; D.H. Bratt,
1987-92; D.J. Dykstra, 1993-2001; M.D. Ooms,
2001-

Guelph, ON — First
1953-
former name: Guelph, ON — Guelph, 1953-68
pastors: C. Spoelhof, 1953-55; J.C. Derksen,
1957-76; J.D. Hellinga, 1977-82; H. Eshuis, 1983-
88; S. Couperus, 1986-88; J.J. Hoytema, 1989-
96; J.M. Van de Hoef, 1999-

Guelph, ON — Guelph
see: Guelph, ON — First

**Guelph, ON — Huron Campus Ministry
(campus ministry)**
1977-
pastor: E. Den Haan, 1977-

Guelph, ON — New Life
1988-
pastors: S. Couperus, 1988-94; H. Lunshof,
1995-

Gun River, MI — Gun River
see: East Martin, MI — East Martin

Hacienda Heights, CA — Community
see: La Puente, CA — Joy of Jesus

**Hacienda Heights, CA — Eastern United
Korean (emerging)**
1992-1998, discontinued
former names: Hacienda, Heights, CA — United
Korean, 1992; Rowland Heights, CA — Eastern
United Korean, 1993
pastor: Y.T. Kim, 1986-94

Hacienda Heights, CA — Immanuel
see: Rowland Heights, CA — Immanuel

Hacienda Heights, CA — United Korean
see; Hacienda Heights, CA — Eastern United
Korean

**Hackensack, NJ — The Old Church on
the Green**
1686-1908, joined the True Reformed Dutch
Church, 1908 then Presbyterian church, 1918
joined Christian Reformed Church, 1890
former names: Hackensack Reformed Church,
1686-1822; Hackensack True Reformed Protestant
Dutch, 1822-1890

pastors: P.D. Froeligh, 1825-28; C.Z. Paulism, 1831-32; C.T. Demarest, 1839-52; C.J. Blauvelt, 1852-59; J.Y. De Baun, 1860-87; J.C. Voorhis, 1887-1906; J.L Van Tielen, 1906-08

Hagersville, ON — Hagersville Community
1990-
pastor: B.P. Velthuizen, 1992-

Haledon, NJ — Bridgeway Community (emerging)
1999-
pastor: A.R. Sytsma, 1999-

Halifax, NS — All Nations
1958-
former name: Halifax, NS — Halifax, 1958-78
pastors: R.J. Bos (M), 1953-59; G. Andre, 1960; H. Mennega, 1961-64; J. Dykstra, 1964-71; W.S. Gritter, 1971-76; J. La Grand, 1977-87; D.H. Kromminga, 1988-2000; D.A. Vroege, 2001-

Halifax, NS — Dalhousie University (campus ministry)
2001-
staff: S. Martin (L), 2001-

Halifax, NS — Halifax
see: Halifax, NS — All Nations

Halifax, NS — North End Mission
1985-1988
pastor: J.W. Van Donk, 1987-88

Hamilton, MI — Bentheim Spanish Mission (congregational ministry)
1973-1993, discontinued
staff: R.M. Gimenez (E), 1974-75; L. Cordillo (E), 1975-82; S.R. Steenstra, 1982-83; J. Esparza (E), 1983-93

Hamilton, MI — Diamond Gospel Center
1947-1961
staff: H.G. Jager (L), 1947-48; H. Hamberg (E), 1948-49; M.J. Kruis (L), 1949-50; J. Dyk (L), 1950-52; L. Dams (E), 1950-59; O. Aardsma (E), 1958-59; S. Siebersma (E), 1960-61

Hamilton, MI — Diamond Springs (mission)
1921-1929, discontinued

Hamilton, MI — Hamilton
1950-
pastors: I.J. Apol, 1951-54; A.P. Veenstra, 1955-60; S.W. Van Drunen, 1960-64; W. Hofman,

1965-73; W. Van Dyk, 1974-83; M.A. Davies, 1984-91; R.D. De Young, 1993-99

Hamilton, ON — Calvary Chapel
1960-1969
staff: H. Boehm (L), 1960-65; C. Vriend, 1967-69

Hamilton, ON — First
1927-
organized: 1928; began as a mission
former name: Hamilton, ON — Hamilton, 1929-59
pastors: J.S. Balt, 1928-39; W. Meyer, 1939-41; D. Grasman, 1942-44; S.A. Dykstra, 1945-50; T.C. Van Kooten, 1951-60; P.Y. De Jong, 1960-63; A. Kuyvenhoven, 1964-70; C. Vriend, 1965-68; J.G. Klomps, 1971-80; J.W. Postman, 1980-87; F. Heslinga, 1989-98; M. Goheen, 1999-; A. Zantingh, 2000-

Hamilton, ON — Hamilton
see: Hamilton, ON — First

Hamilton, ON — Hamilton Asian Christian (emerging)
2000-
pastor: S. Arthur (E), 2000-

Hamilton, ON — Immanuel
1959-
pastors: J.A. Quartel, 1961-68; W.L. Vander Beek, 1969-75; B. Nederlof, 1975-81; K.A. Baker, 1982-89; J. Zantingh, 1990-98; H.P. Kranenburg, 2000-

Hamilton, ON — Laotian Worshipping Community (emerging)
1990-
pastor: S. Saythavy, 1991-2002

Hamilton, ON — McMaster University Chaplaincy Centre (campus ministry)
1972-
was part of Toronto, ON — University of Toronto/ McMaster University, 1970-73
staff: E. Grittter, 1972-80; A.P. Geisterfer (L), 1980-98; M.D. Fallon (L), 1998-

Hamilton, ON — Mount Hamilton
1952-
former name: Mount Hamilton, ON — Mount Hamilton, 1952-58
pastors: J.C. Ehlers, 1953-64; A. Rumph, 1964-66; H. Mennega, 1967-73; J.W. Jongsma, 1973-79; R.J. Sikkema, 1981-92; J.P. Janssen, 1999-

Hammond, IN — City Mission (mission)
1922-1958
staff: G.J. Ellens (L), 1922-47; D. Aardsma (E), 1946-58; S. Walstra (L), 1950-51; J.O. Kuipers (L), 1956-58

Hammond, IN — Hammond
1959-
pastors: J.H. Paauw, 1957-61; T. Vanden Bosch, 1961-63; L.W. Van Dellen, 1964-69; R. Vander Ley, 1969-73; C.E. Zylstra, 1973-79; H. Bouma, 1980-85; C.J. Afman, 1986-96; R.L. Gelwicks, 1996-

Hammond, IN — New Community Fellowship (emerging)
1995-
former name: South Holland, IL – Mision Hispaña Paz, 1995-98; South Holland, IL – New Community Fellowship, 1998-2000
pastor: I. Torres, 1995-

Hamshire, TX — Hamshire
1929-1946, discontinued
pastors: D. Mellema (M), 1931-37; P. De Jong, 1939-42

Hancock, MN — Hancock
1912-
pastors: J. Cupido, 1916-20; J. Paauw (M), 1920-21; J. Paauw, 1921-27; D.J. Hoitenga, Sr., 1928-37; C. Vanden Heuvel, 1937-40; H. Vander Klay, 1940-44; C.L. Van Zee, 1946-60; N. Roorda, 1961-65; L. Vande Creek, 1965-69; C.J. Afman, 1970-75; C.W. Flietstra, 1975-84; J. Vander Akker, 1984-88; G.A. De Vries, 1989-92; R.D. Ruis, 1992-97; G.L. Essenburg, 1997-2002; W. Versluys, II, 2003-

Haney, BC — First
see: Maple Ridge, BC – Maple Ridge

Haney, BC — Haney
see: Maple Ridge, BC – Maple Ridge

Haney, BC — Maple Ridge
see: Maple Ridge, BC – Maple Ridge

Hanford, CA — First
1912-
former name: Hanford, CA – Hanford, 1912-88
pastors: J. Bolt, 1912; L.P. Brink (M), 1913-15; F.W. Stuart, 1915-19; J.J. De Jonge, 1921-29; R.J. Frens, 1930-40; P.A. Hoekstra, 1940-49; W. Dryfhout, 1949-59; G.S. Kok, 1960-69; H.

Bajema, 1969-80; R.E. Van Hofwegen, 1980-85; K. Rietema, 1986-91; J.A. Huttinga, 1992-2002; L.J. Sikkema, 2002-

Hanford, CA — Hanford
see: Hanford, CA – First

Hanover, ON — Hanover
1985-1995
pastors: W. De Ruiter, 1990-95

Harderwyk, MI — Harderwyk
see: Holland, MI – Harderwyk Ministries

Harrisburg, SD — Harrisburg
1915-1918, discontinued

Harrison, SD — Harrison
1884-
pastors: T.M. Vanden Bosch, 1885-86; C. Bode, 1887-91; W. Heyns, 1891-98; J. Wyngaarden, 1898-1904; H. Vander Werp, 1905-08; K. Poppen, 1908-10; J. Beld, 1911-15; A. Guikema, 1916-26; J. Cupido, 1927-31; C.H. Oldenburg, 1932-40; J. Hanenburg, 1941-44; J. Van Beek, 1945-52; L.C. Bossenbroek, 1952-56; H.N. De Rooy, 1956-59; S. Ten Brink, 1959-63; J. Huizenga, 1964-68; G.L. Essenburg, 1970-75; H. Hollander, 1976-83; C. Van Essen, 1984-92; L.A. Lobdell, Jr., 1993-99; P. De Jong, 2000-

Hartford, CT — Chapel
1962

Hartford, CT — Hartford Hispanic (emerging)
1997-
pastor: C. Aranguiz, 1997-

Hartley, IA — Hartley
1951-1993, discontinued
pastors: A.J. Verburg, 1952-56; J. Leugs, 1956-59; W. Swets, 1959-64; H.L. Downs, 1965-67; L.G. Christoffels, 1970-74; T.H. Vander Ziel, 1974-81; A.J. Van Schouwen, 1983-92

Harvey, IA — Harvey
see: Tracy, IA – Tracy

Hawarden, IA (mission)
1912

Hawarden, IA — Hawarden
1917-
pastors: D.H. Muyskens, 1919-20; N. Jansen,

1920-27; J.R. Rozendal, 1927-34; A.D. Folkema, 1935-45; J. Cupido, 1946-53; B. Vanden Brink, 1953-58; A.J. Van Schouwen, 1958-63; J.J. Wiegers, 1963-67; K.W. Vis, 1967-71; A.J. Stienstra, 1971-75; R.E. Van Hofwegen, 1975-80; J.W. Van Der Heide, 1980-84; M.J. Vander Vliet, 1985-94; T.E. Van Zalen, 1995-98; N. de Vries, 2000-

Hayward, CA — Christ's Community
1963-
former name: Hayward, CA — Hayward, 1963-96
pastors: J.C. Vander Ark (M), 1960-66; J. Hekman (M), 1966-72; V. Vander Zee, 1973-89; J.W. Van Donk, 1981-84; P.A. Hansen, 1991-94; L.M. Fryling, 1995-

Hayward, CA — Hayward
see: Hayward, CA — Christ's Community

Heart Lake, ON — Living Hope
see: Brampton, ON — Living Hope

Hebron, IL (mission)
1928

Hebron, IN (mission)
1932-1936

Helena, MT — First
see: Helena, MT — Green Meadow

Helena, MT — Green Meadow (emerging)
1980-
organized: 1980-1992
former names: Helena, MT — First, 1980-82; Helena, MT — Green Meadow Community, 1982-85
pastors: J.M. Moes, 1978-82; C. Pool, 1983-89; K.K. Volbeda, 1989-90

Helena, MT — Green Meadow Community
see: Helena, MT — Green Meadow

Henderson, NV — Grace Valley (emerging)
1998-
pastor: S. Wunderink (E), 1998-

Hesperia, MI — Newman Chapel (emerging)
1953-
pastors: E. Sikkenga (L), 1965-67; P. Staal (L), 1967-71; J. Zuidema (E), 1972-79; G.R. Mossel, 1980-86; C. Uken, 1986-

Hialeah, FL — Comunidad Christiana
1983-

merger of North Miami Beach, FL — Comunidad Christiana and Hialeah, FL — Iglesia el Redentor, 1986-1999
pastors: J.M. Sanchez, 1983-94; E. Burgos, 1996-97; Milton Villanueva, 1999-2001

Hialeah, FL — Hialeah Gardens
2002-
pastor: J.P. Sanchez, 2002

Hialeah, FL — Iglesia el Redentor (emerging)
see: Hialeah, FL — Comunidad Christiana

Highland, IN — City Mission (mission)
1948-1954
staff: P. Van Der Kamp (E), 1948-54

Highland, IN — Community Evangelism
1960-1964
staff: R. Huizenga (L), 1960-64

Highland, IN — Community Sunday School
1963-1964
staff: M. Botma (L), 1963-64

Highland, IN — First
1908-
former name: Highland, IN — Highland, 1908-53
pastors: J.M Byleveld, 1909-13; Z.J. Sherda, 1913-16; M. DeBoer, 1917-20; G.D. De Jong, 1920-25; J.A. Rottier, 1926-31; M. Van Dyke, 1931-50; E.F. Visser, 1951-56; J.C. Scholten, 1957-75; I.J. Apol, 1976-83; L.G. Zoerhof, 1984-98; R.R. Bergsma, 1998-

Highland, IN — Highland
see: Highland, IN — First

Highland, IN — Second
1953-
pastors: C.O. Buus, 1954-60; A.C. De Jong, 1960-64; W.H. Rutgers, 1964-69; J.E. De Vries, 1969-76; G.P. Holwerda, 1977-87; R.J. Meyer, 1988-96; M.J. Jonkman, 1997-2000; S.R. Van Eck, 2001-

Highland, MI — Highland
1914-
pastors: B. Zwaagman, 1917-24; J.J. Holwerda, 1925-31; C.M. Schoolland, 1932-36; J. Betten, 1936-47; J.J. Kenbeek, 1948-53; R. Boeskool, Jr., 1954-58; S. Newhouse, 1958-62; M. Bolt, 1963-67; F.J. Van Dyk, 1969-78; F.T. Wevers, 1978-82;

S.C. Elzinga, 1982-87; J.W. Van Der Heide, 1988-94; J. Rop, Jr., 1995-98; K.A. Mannes, 1998-

Highlands Ranch, CO — Horizon Community
1995-
former name: Denver, CO — Horizon Community
pastors: J.A. De Boer, 1995-96; P. Van Elderen, Jr., 1997-

High River, AB — High River
1952-
pastors: P.J. Hoekstra (M), 1952-62; D. Kwantes (M), 1963-66; G.J. Hogeterp, 1969-72; J. Versfelt, 1974-75; G.J. Kamps, 1977-82; J.C. Wiersum, 1983-88; N.H. Prenger, 1988-91; H.F. Harnden, 1992-96; J.D. Zondervan, 1997-2002; K.J. Vryhof, 2002-

Hills, MN — Hills
1914-1998, withdrew to United Reformed Churches
pastors: J.B. Vanden Hoek, 1920-24; M.H. Van Dyk, 1925-29; G.S. Kok, 1930-35; E.F. Visser, 1936-38; P. De Koekkoek, 1938-45; J.G. Vande Lune, 1945-53; G.B. Dokter, 1953-56; G.F. Van Oyen, 1957-60; J.G. Kruis, 1962-66; D.W. Boonstra, 1966-69; J.H. Scholten, 1971-75; H.P. Baak, 1975-81; W.D. Vis, 1982-84; S. Ten Brink, 1986-87; T.C. Turngren, 1988-91; A.L. Camarigg, 1991-97

Hinckley, MN — Hinckley
1899-1903, discontinued

Hitchcock, MI — Hitchcock
1908-1913, discontinued

Hoboken, NJ — Hoboken
1913-1987, discontinued
emerging, 1970-87
former name: Hoboken, NJ — Hoboken Spanish, 1970-76
pastors: H. Dekker, 1913-16; T. Jongbloed, 1919-26; H. Vander Woude, 1927-29; J.L. Van Tielen, 1930-34; A.H. Kort, 1934-44; D. Grassman, 1944-48; A.H Oussouren, 1953-55; J. Maliepaard, 1955-61; E.F. Lewis, Jr. (M), 1964-76; M. Santana (L), 1965-66; R.C. Borrego, 1967-73

Hoboken, NJ — Hoboken Spanish
see: Hoboken, NJ — Hoboken

Hoboken, NJ — Seamen's/Immigrants' Home
1911-1962

formally opened, 1915
staff: Mr./Mrs. Mark (L), 1910-11; T. Jongbloed, 1919-23; M.J. Broekhuizen (L), 1923, 1927-32; A.J. Visser (L), 1923-27; E. Apol (L), 1932-42; A.H. Kort, 1936-45; J.J. Dahm (L), 1942-62; D. Grosman (L), 1948-50; A.H. Oussorren, 1951-53; D. Grassman, 1954-56

Hohokus, NJ — Hohokus
1873-1885, discontinued

Holland, IA — Holland
1902-1904, discontinued

Holland, IA — Holland
1920-
pastors: C.G. Hayenga (M), 1918-20; G. Westenberg (M), 1927-28; W.H. Rutgers, 1930-33; L.F. Voskuil, 1933-37; P.H. Eldersveld, 1938-43; P.F. Holtrop, 1943-47; H. Petersen, 1948-53; J.A. Wesseling, 1953-57; J. De Vries, 1957-61; C.K. Van Winkle, 1963-66; J.S. Meyer, 1966-69; J. Entingh, 1970-76; K.J Wiersum, 1976-80; W.G. Van Hal, 1980-84; I.W. Meuzelaar, 1984-88; L.J. Kotman, 1988-90; J. Kroon, 1991-94 G. Nibbelink (E), 1998-

Holland, MI — Beechwood (Lakewood) (mission)
1941-1948
staff: A. Vander Veer (L), 1941-42; C. Grevengoed (L), 1942-46

Holland, MI — Bethany
1946-
pastors: O. Breen, 1947-52; W.P. Brink, 1952-64; H.C. Van Deelen, 1966-68; H.J. Baas, 1969-77; L.J. Hofman, 1977-82; P. Borgdorff, 1983-90; J.P. Heerema, 1991-94; H.D. Schuringa, 1996-99; B.D. Van Kley, 2000-2001; Interim, L.P. Troast, 2001-

Holland, MI — Calvary
1933-
organized: 1959
began as a Sunday School in 1925
former name: Holland, MI — North River (End) Mission (mission), 1933-1952
pastors: G. Lageveen (L), 1934-35; H. Lam (L), 1941-42; A. Vander Veer (E), 1942-44; B. De Boer (L), 1945-47, 1949-50; C. Grevengoed (L), 1947-49; L. Altena (L), 1952-53; H. De Koster (L), 1953-54; A. Walcott, 1958-59; W. Timmer, 1963-68; C.N. Van Dalfsen, 1969-75; J. Roeda, 1975-

83; K.M. Doornbos, 1983-93; F.T. Wevers, 1990-;
R.J. Brouwer, 1994-

Holland, MI — Calvin

1956-
pastors: G. Vander Plaats, 1957-62; G.H.
Stoutmeyer, 1963-67; A. Zwart, 1967-70; R.R.
Graves, 1972-78; J. Fondse, 1979-87; J.S. Meyer,
1988-2000

Holland, MI — Cambodian Fellowship (emerging)

1988-
former name: Holland, MI — Cambodian Ministry,
1988-95
pastor: S. Na (E), 1991-

Holland, MI — Cambodian Ministry

see: Holland, MI — Cambodian Fellowship

Holland, MI — Celebration (emerging)

2001-

Holland, MI — Central Avenue

1865-
former names: Holland, MI — Holland, 1865-88;
Holland, MI — Market Street, 1888-97; Holland, MI
— First, 1902-03
organized: 1865
pastors: J. De Beer, 1867; F. Hulst, 1868-71; J.
Noordewier, 1873-78; G.H. Hoeksema, 1879-81;
J.A. De Bruyn, 1883-85; E. Vander Vries, 1886-
95; H. Van Hoogen, 1895-1903; R.L. Haan, 1904-
14; B.H. Einink, 1915-25; L. Veltkamp, 1925-37;
D.H. Walters, 1938-43; M. Vander Zwaag, 1943-
49; W. Haverkamp, 1949-55; E.J. Masselink,
1955-62; D.L. Van Halsema, 1963-66; T.C.
Vanden Heuvel, 1967-75; J.L. Witvliet, 1976-81;
J.W. Uitvlugt, 1981-90; R.J. Noorman, 1990-97;
J.H. Scholten, 1998-

Holland, MI — Comunidad Cristiana: Vida Nueva

1956-
organized: 1991
former name: Holland, MI — Emmanuel Spanish
Chapel/Iglesia Evangelica Espanola; 1956-91; Holland, MI — Iglesia Hispaña, 1991-96
pastors: E. Vanden Brink (L), 1958-64; Carlos
Tapia-Ruano, 1964-69; F.E. Pott, 1973-76; C.A.
Persenaire, 1976-82; J.C. Hutt, 1985-: E. Gomez,
2001-

Holland, MI — East End (mission)

see: Holland, MI — Spruce Ave. Chapel

Holland, MI — East Saugatuck

1869-
former name: Collendoorn, MI — Collendoorn,
1869-1902; East Saugatuck, MI — East
Saugatuck, 1902-94
pastors: J. Stadt, 1869-70; J.R. Schepers, 1870-
75; W.H. Van Leeuwen, 1875-80; H. Douwstra,
1881-91; A. Keizer, 1891-96; J.B. Hoekstra,
1896-1903; J. Manni, 1903-10; W.D. Vander
Werp, 1911-13; L.J. Lamberts, 1914-19; J.H.
Geerlings, 1919-23; H.M. Vander Ploeg, 1923-34;
S.P. Miersma, 1934-48; P. De Jong, 1949-52; S.
Vroon, 1952-59; J.H. Bergsma, 1960-66; J.
Leugs, 1967-80; J. Vander Plate, 1981-88; R. De
Young, 1989-97; G.L. Luurtsema, 1998-

Holland, MI — Faith

1956-
pastors: J.A. Botting, 1957-63; C.S. Steenstra,
1964-77; C. Bolt, 1977-82; H.A. Brink, 1982-86;
R.A. Pohler, 1986-2002; A.J. Schoonveld, 1987-
94; J.M. Boer, 1995-

Holland, MI — First

see: Holland, MI — Central Avenue

Holland, MI — Fourteenth Street

1902-
pastors: D.R. Drukker, 1902-11; P.A. Hoekstra,
1911-15; H. Hoeksema, 1915-20; J.M. Vande Kieft,
1921-25; W. Masselink, 1925-28; H. Bouma, Sr.,
1928-34; R.J. Danhof, 1934-45; W. Van Peursem,
1945-51; J.F. Schuurmann, 1951-56; S.J. De
Vries, 1958-61; T.C. Van Kooten, 1962-73; R.O.
Broekhuizen, 1973-83; C.E. Bajema, 1983-88;
N.B. Steen, 1988-99; M.J. Hofman, 2000-

Holland, MI — Fusion (emerging)

2001-

Holland, MI — Gibson

1960-
Wesleyan Methodist background, 1885
organized: 1976
pastors: W. Vander Berg (L), 1960-62; R. Knaack
(L), 1962-68; H. Van Til (L), 1968-69; A. Huisman
(E), 1969-74; R. Walter, Jr., 1975-79; T.H. Douma,
1979-87; R.D. Boertje, 1988-98; V.D. Swieringa,
2000-

Holland, MI — Harderwyk

see: Holland, MI — Harderwyk Ministries

Holland, MI — Harderwyk Ministries

1882-

former name: Lake Shore, MI — Lake Shore, 1882-83; Harderwyk, MI — Harderwyk, 1883-1964; Holland, MI — Harderwyk, 1965-2001
pastors: J.B. Jonkman, 1906-08; R. Diephuis, 1908-11; K.W. Fortuin, 1911-14; H. Beute, 1916-19; A. Keizer, 1919-25; J.P. De Vries, 1927-29; T. Vander Ark, 1930-35; C.M. Schoolland, 1936-40; C. Witt, 1941-50; C.G. Kromminga, 1951-53; H. Baker, 1953-57; M. Bolt, 1957-63; R.J. Venema, 1964-66; R.J. Holwerda, 1967-73; G.L. Kramer, 1974-76; P.V. De Jonge, 1976-79; L. Veltkamp, 1977-79; M. De Vries, 1980-93; L.L. Schemper, 1982-84; T.D. Walker, 1991-99 ; J. Stulp, 1994-95; W.A. Brouwer, 1994-; A.A. Gorter, 1995-; S.D. Pearson, 1999-

Holland, MI — Holland
see: Holland, MI — Central Avenue

Holland, MI — Holland Heights
1951-
pastors: H.G. Vander Ark, 1952-62; R.W. Westveer, 1962-66; J.H. Draisma, 1968-75; E.P. Meyer, 1976-85; R.A. Kok, 1986-90; G. De Jong, 1990-

Holland, MI — Iglesia Hispaña
see: Holland, MI — Comunidad Cristiana: Vida Nueva

Holland, MI — Lakewood/Waukazoo (mission)
1942-1949
staff: A. Vander Veer (E), 1942-43; H. Heetderks (L), 1943-45; J. Breuker (L), 1945-49

Holland, MI — Lao Community (emerging)
1991-
pastors: R. Silakhom (E), 1991-96; R.J. Rasasak (E), 1997-

Holland, MI — Lighthouse Community
1987-1993, merged into Holland, MI — Victory Point Ministries
pastor: D.J. Deters, 1988-93

Holland, MI — Maple Avenue
1913-1999, merged into Holland, MI — Maple Avenue Ministries
pastors: W.D. Vander Werp, 1913-16; J.P. Battema, 1917-20; D. Zwier, 1920-46; G.S. Kok, 1946-54; J.A. De Kruyter, 1954-60; G. Gritter, 1962-65; R.B. Vermeer, 1966-73; D.E. Bradford, 1974-80; H. Dykema, 1981-90; P.W. De Haan, 1991-99; E. Gray, 1998-99

Holland, MI — Maple Avenue Ministries (CRC/RCA union congregation)
1999-
pastors: P.W. De Haan, 1999-; D.J. Sieplinga, 1999-

Holland, MI — Maranatha
1957-
pastors: E.G. Cooke, 1958-63; G.J. Postma, 1963-71; K. Rietema, 1972-78; L.D. Slings, 1979-94; D.R. Ackerman, 1995-99; J.R. De Vries, 2000-

Holland, MI — Market Street
see: Holland, MI — Central Avenue

Holland, MI — Mision del Rey de Israel
1997-
former name: Holland, MI — Mision del Rey Jesus, 1997-2000; Holland, MI — Discipular del Rey, 2000-2001
pastor: F. Lopez, 1997-

Holland, MI — Mision del Rey Jesus
see; Holland, MI — Mision del Rey de Israel

Holland, MI — Mision Discipular del Rey
see: Holland, MI — Mision del Rey de Israel

Holland, MI — Montello Park
1940-
pastors: L. Veltkamp, 1942-46; L.F. Voskuil, 1946-52; F. Handlogten, 1952-63; G. Haan, 1964-74; H.R. Roelofs, 1975-85; J.C. Busscher, 1985-94; T.S. Kauffman, 1995-98; A.L. Van Wyhe, 2000-

Holland, MI — Niekerk
1866-
former name: Niekerk, MI — Niekerk, 1866-1968
pastors: J. De Beer, 1966-67; S. Baron, 1869-76; C. Bode, 1879-87; F. Welandt, 1889-99; J. Post, 1900-04; J. Homan, 1905-07; J. Robbert, 1908-11; K. Kuiper, 1911-19; A. De Vries, 1920-25; N. Gelderloos, 1926-29; M. Bolt, , 1930-37; R. Heynen, 1938-43; J. Beebe, 1943-57; D.J. Negen, 1957-65; J.G. Kruis, 1966-73; R.J. Noorman, 1973-77; J.M. Ouwinga, 1978-88; J.H. Scholten, 1988-98; J.W. Van Der Heide, 2000-

Holland, MI — Ninth Street
see: Holland, MI — Pillar

Holland, MI — North River (End) Mission (mission)
see: Holland, MI – Calvary

Holland, MI — North Shore Community (mission)
1947–1951
staff: J. Breuker (L), 1949–50

Holland, MI — Park
1953–
pastors: V.C. Licatesi, 1954–60; D.E. Houseman, 1960–66; J.A. Houseward, 1967–78; D.R. Fauble, 1979–83; E.J. Blankespoor, 1984–95; J.B. Dik, 1996–

Holland, MI — Pigeon Creek Sunday School (mission)
1947–1952
staff: E. Vanden Brink (L), 1949–50

Holland, MI — Pillar
1847–
joined CRC, 1885
former names: Holland, MI – First, 1847–1885 (RCA, 1850–1885); Holland, MI – Ninth Street, 1885–1984
pastors: A.C. Van Raalte, 1847–67; R. Pieters, 1969–80; E. Bos, 1886–92; K. Van Goor, 1893–1902; A. Keizer, 1902–10; E.J. Tuuk, 1911–19; J.M. Ghysels, 1919–25; J. De Haan, Jr., 1925–29; N.J. Monsma, 1929–40; G. Gritter, 1940–47; T. Yff, 1947–52; M.J. Vander Werp, 1952–58; W.R. Witte, 1958–65; L. Greenway, 1966–69; F.W. Van Houten, 1970–74; J. Hasper, 1976–86; C.D. Vander Meyden, 1986–90; C.A. Reyneveld, 1991–93; M. De Vries, 1993–2000; S.J. De Vries, 2002–

Holland, MI — Pine Creek
1895–
former name: West Olive, MI – West Olive, 1895–1913; West Harlem, MI – West Harlem, 1913–26; Pine Creek, MI – Pine Creek, 1926–76
pastors: T.L. De Lange, 1906–09; R. Vande Kieft, 1911–14; B. Nagel, 1914–20; R. Posthumus, 1927–36; H.J. Schripsema, 1937–43; P. Van Tuinen, 1944–49; L.J. Dykstra, 1949–53; G.W. Van Den Berg, 1953–58; L. Van Drunen, Jr., 1958–65; P. Huisman, 1966–74; J. Blankespoor, 1975–79; N.F. Brown, 1980–83; A.M. MacLeod, 1983–85; A.L. Louwerse, 1986–89; R.A. Heerema, 1989–92; Z.G. Anderson, 1993–98; J.D. Voorhees, 2000–

Holland, MI — Prospect Park
1907–2002, merged into Graafschap, MI – Graafschap
pastors: J. Bolt, 1908–10; H.J. Kuiper, 1910–13; A.J. Rus, 1913–17; R. Veldman, 1918–20; J.C. Schaap, 1921–25; L. Van Laar, 1926–39; J.T. Hoogstra, 1940–65; 1940–65; G.D. Klouw, 1966–70; W. Vander Haak, 1972–79; L.R. Smits, 1979–90; P.D. Winkle, 1991–2000

Holland, MI — Providence
1907–
former name: Holland, MI – Sixteenth Street, 1907–66
pastors: W. De Groot, 1909–13; J. Walkotten, 1914–19; H. Keegstra, 1919–28; P. Jonker, Jr., 1929–45; A. Dusseljee, 1946–48; A.W. Hoogstrate, 1948–54; J.H. Brink, 1954–68; J. Gunnink, 1969–76; T.J. Lapinsky, 1977–84; P.D. Winkle, 1986–88; R.O. Broekhuizen, 1991–93; K.M. Doornbos, 1993–

Holland, MI — Sixteenth Street
see: Holland, MI – Providence

Holland, MI — Spruce Avenue Chapel (mission)
1942–1964
former name: Holland, MI – East End (mission), 1942–46
staff: G. Holkeboer (L), 1942–46; B. Altena (L), 1946–48B. Altena (L), 1949–52; E. Vanden Brink (E), 1952–53; F. Brummel (E), 1953–58; B. Helmus (L), 1960–62; W. De Waard (E), 1962–64

Holland, MI — Sunrise
1988–1993, merged into Holland, MI – Victory Point Ministries
pastor: G. De Jong, 1989–93

Holland, MI — Victory Point Ministries
1993–
merger of Holland, MI – Lighthouse Community and Holland, MI – Sunrise
pastors: G. De Jong, 1993–94; D.J. Deters, 1993–94; G.A. Smith, 1995–; S.R. Rusticus, 1997–

Holland, MI — Watershed (emerging)
1999–
pastor: T.D. Walker, 1999–

Holland, MN — Holland
1910–
organized: 1913
pastors: M. De Boer, 1920–21; J.A. Gerritsen, 1921–26; J. Paauw, 1927–44; J. Mulder, 1944–49;

J. Roorda, 1949-53; J. Gunnink, 1953-56; T.L. Smith, 1956-60; E. Walhout, 1961-65; J.L Witvliet, 1967-71; L.D. Meyer, 1971-74; A.P. Vander Pol. 1980-86; H.R. Winters, Jr., 1987-92; N.D. Rozenboom, 1993-97; J.H. Westra (I), 1998-2000; J.H. Westra, 2000-

Hollandale, MN — Hollandale
1934-
began as a branch of Worthington, MN, 1930
pastors: T.P. Verhulst, 1934-38; J. Vander Meer, 1938-41; G.J. Rozenboom, 1941-45; A.H. Bratt, 1945-49; A.A. Koning, 1949-53; S.P. Miersma, 1953-58; A.A. Koning, 1959-65; E.J. Blankespoor, 1967-71; M.A. Davies, 1972-77; R.L. Van Zomeren, 1977-83; G. Compaan, 1983-89; F.J. Van Dyk, 1990-95; H. Dykema, 1996-2001; G.W. Brouwers, 2002-

Holland Center, SD — Holland Center
see: Lodge Pole, SD — Holland Center

Holland Marsh, ON — Holland Marsh
1938-
began as a branch of Hamilton, ON — Hamilton, 1936
former name: Newmarket, ON — Holland, Marsh, 1975-90
pastors: M.M. Schans, 1940-45; J. Vander Meer, 1946-51; P. Lagerwey, 1954-59; J. Hanenburg, 1959-66; J. de Pater, 1966-70; P. Breedveld, 1970-73; M.J. Lise, 1975-81; H.P. Bruinsma, 1982-88; S.A. Van Daalen, 1989-

Honolulu, HI — Honolulu
see: Honolulu, HI — Pacific Community

Honolulu, HI — Hope Metro (emerging)
1999-

Honolulu, HI — Pacific Community
1967-1998, discontinued
organized: 1969
former name: Honolulu, HI — Honolulu, 1969-85; Service Home, 1967-69
pastors: M.D. Hugen (M), 1967-70; C.K. Van Winkle, 1971-75; R.L. Palsrok, 1977-83; W.D. Dyk, 1984-90; A. Helder, 1991-96

Honolulu, HI — Pyung Kang
see: Honolulu, HI — True Light Church of Hawaii

Honolulu, HI — Service Home
see: Honolulu, HI — Pacific Community

Honolulu, HI — True Light Church of Hawaii (emerging)
1991-
former name: Honolulu, HI — Pyung Kang, 1991-2001
joined CRC, 1994
pastor: W.M. Yang, 1991-

Hopkins, MI (mission)
1937, 1941-1942
staff: J. Ten Harmsel (L), 1941-44

Horicon, WI — Marsh View Ministries (emerging)
1998-
pastor: D. Katsma, (E), 1998-

Hornick, IA — Hornick
1897-1907, discontinued

Hospers, IA — First
1894-
former name: Hospers, IA — Hospers, 1894-1979
pastors: W. De Groot, 1898-1901; A.J. Vanden Heuvel, 1902-03; J. Vander Mey, 1904-08; M. Vander Heide, 1910-25; A.B. Voss, 1927-36; J.H. Geerlings, 1936-46; J.F. Hollebeek, 1947-51; D.D. Bonnema, 1951-56; C.R. Veenstra, 1957-65; G.W. Van Den Berg, 1965-71; P.W. De Haan, 1972-77; J.P. Groenewold, 1978-84; J.M. Beach, 1985-89; F.F. Gunnink, 1990-93; M.S. Mc Donald, 1995-96; D.E. Tinklenberg, 1998-

Hospers, IA — Hospers
see: Hospers, IA — First

Houston, BC — Houston
1939-
pastors: H.S. Koning, 1949-51; B. Nederlof, 1953-56; W.L De Jong, 1957-62; S. Viss, Jr., 1962-67; M. Pool, 1976-71; P. Nicolai, 1972-76; H.F. Harnden, 1977-81; K. Pomykala, 1982-84; D.R. Smith, 1985-98; H. Van de Heide, 2000-

Houston, TX — Canaan
1984-1993, discontinued
former name: Houston, TX — Greater Houston Korean, 1984-89
pastors: J.S. Kim, 1984-86; E.W. Park, 1987-92

Houston, TX — Community Life
1992-
pastor: M.S. Johnson, 1990-

64

Houston, TX — Glory Community
1994-1998, discontinued
pastor: E.W. Park, 1992-98

Houston, TX — Greater Houston Korean
see: Houston, TX — Canaan

Houston, TX — Hope
1988-
pastor: R. De Young, 1985-

Houston, TX — New Life
1981-
pastors: K.W. Tanis, 1979-83; J.A. Holleman,
1979-93; R.A. Lyzenga, 1994-2002; D.J.
Wyenberg, 1999-

Houston, TX — Peace Community
1991-
pastors: R.L. Westenbroek, 1990-; G. Schipper,
1999-

Howard City, MI — Pine Grove
1955-
organized: 1981
pastors: W. Willink (E), 1955-57, 1960-62; H.
Geerdes (L), 1957-59; J. Peuler (L), 1959-60; M.
Koster (L), 1962-64; H. Boehm (E), 1965-70; L.V.
Haas (E), 1971-82; J.A. Molenbeek, 1982-92;
G.W. Vander Hoek, 1993-98; P. Troast (I), 1988-
99; J.J. Wiegers, 1999-

Hudsonville, MI — Bauer
1902-
former name: Bauer, MI — Bauer, 1902-93
pastors: W.R. Smidt, 1906-12; B. Zwaagman,
1924-27; J.H. De Haan, 1928-46; S. Van Dyken,
1946-49; E.A. Van Baak, 1950-51; H.J. Teitsma,
1951-54; J.W. Uitvlugt, 1955-59; C. Huissen,
1960-64; B. Ypma, 1965-72; C.J. Klompien,
1973-79; A.J. Bultman, 1980-84; J.L. Meppelink,
1984-86; N.R. Rylaarsdam, 1987-93; A.H.
Jongsma, 1996-99; G.S. Janke, 2001-

Hudsonville, MI — Cornerstone
1987-1993; withdrew, affiliated with United Reformed Churches
pastor: S.M. Arrick, 1988-93

Hudsonville, MI — EverGreen Ministries
1993-
organized: 1997
pastor: L.J. Doornbos, 1993-

Hudsonville, MI — First
1902-
former name: Hudsonville, MI — Hudsonville,
1902-48
pastors: J. Bruinooge, 1906-11; H. Walkotten,
1911-21; E.J. Krohne, 1921-43; T. Yff, 1943-47;
E.F.J. Van Halsema, 1948-55; E.F. Visser, 1956-
62; J. Blankespoor, 1962-75; B. Byma, 1975-88;
D.E. Tinklenberg, 1989-98; S.R. Sytsma, 1999-

Hudsonville, MI — Georgetown
1975-
pastors: E.J. Tamminga, 1977-95; G. De Jong,
1986-90; D.R. Ackerman, 1991-95; J.C. Busscher,
1998-2001; P.C. Hogeterp, 2000-; D.W. Vander
Veen, 2002-

Hudsonville, MI — Hillcrest
1956-
pastors: L. Oostendorp, 1957-64; H.C. Van Wyk,
Jr., 1964-71; M.S. Jorritsma, 1973-77; K.L.
Schepel, 1980-83; M. Stephenson, 1989-96; H.D.
Vanderwell, 1978-2002; R.W. Vance, 1997- ; L.D.
Slings (I), 2002-

Hudsonville, MI — Hudsonville
see: Hudsonville, MI — First

Hudsonville, MI — Immanuel
1948-
pastors: H.N. Erffmeyer, 1948-53; H. Bajema,
1954-59; M.R. Doornbos, 1960-69; B. Van
Antwerpen, 1969-73; H.J. Vugteveen, 1975-81; J.
Stulp, 1983-94; R. Huisman, 1995-

Hudsonville, MI — Messiah
1964-
pastors: A. Besteman, 1964-72; K.L. Havert,
1972-83; D.J. Van Loo, 1983-93; TG. Genzink,
1995-

Hudsonville, MI — North Blendon
1910-
former name: North Blendon, MI — North
Blendon, 1910-93
pastors: J.A. Rottier, 1916-20; J.D. Pikaart,
1921-29; T. Yff, 1930-36; G. Gritter, 1936-40;
F.L. Netz, 1941-47; H. Sonnema, 1947-50; N.
Beute, 1952-60; J.M. Moes, 1962-66; M.L. Van
Donselaar, 1966-70; E.L. Haan, 1971-75; R.J.
Meyer, 1976-81; J. Van Marion, 1982-88; D.R.
Zimmerman, 1989-95; P.R. Hoekstra, 1997-

Hull, IA — First
1893-

former name: Hull, IA – Hull, 1893-1960
pastors: J. Gulker, 1894-97; W. Greve, 1897-
1903; F. Fortuin, 1903-07; H.J. Heynen, 1908-11;
P. Jonker, Sr., 1911-18; J.J. Weersing, 1918-24; C.
Huissen, 1925-29; R.L. Haan, 1930-43; J.
Hanenburg, 1944-50; H.C. Van Deelen, 1952-60;
G.J. Rozenboom, 1962-67; W.H. De Vries, 1967-
72; J. Fondse, 1973-79; M.W. Heyboer, 1979-84;
W. Renkema, 1986-91; R.A. Bouwman, 1992-96;
C.J. Klompien, 1997-

Hull, IA — Hope
1961-
pastors: J.D. De Jong, 1961; J.J. Matheis, 1961-
66; D.J. Klompeen, 1966-70; A.H. Dykstra, 1970-
73; J. Cooper, 1973-80; B.J. Van Ee, 1980-83;
W.D. Van Dyken, 1983-87; A.L. Kuiper, 1987-99;
M.D. Koetje, 2000-

Hull, IA — Hull
see: Hull, IA – First

Hull, ND — Hull
1887-
former name: Emmons, ND – Emmons, 1887-89
pastors: H. Ahuis, 1899-1901; M. Botbyl, 1902-
05; M. Borduin, 1905-07; H. Huizingh, 1908-13;
J.C. De Bruyn, 1914-21; N.J. Monsma, 1922-24;
B.Van Someren, 1925-30; E. Tanis, 1931-37; C.
Witt, 1937-41; J.E. Brink, 1942-46; W. Tolsma,
1946-48; W. Vande Kieft, 1949-51; H. De Groot,
1952-55; A. Walma, 1956-59; M.P. Van Houten,
1960-65; J. Kroon, 1967-72; J. Riemersma,
1972-80; D.J. Wyenberg, 1980-85; L.F. Baker,
1985-90; E.B. Verhulst, 1991-95

Huntington, BC — Back to God Chapel
1960-1971
staff: J. Elenbaas, 1960-64; D. Groothuis (L),
1965-71

Huntington Beach, CA (mission)
1965-1966
pastor: R. Timmerman (M), 1965-66

Huntley, MT (mission)
1916

Ida, MT (mission)
1909-1910

Ilderton, ON — Ilderton
see: London, ON – First

Imlay City, MI — Imlay City
1928-
began as a mission, 1926
pastors: J.R. Brink (M), 1926-27; D. Grasman,
1934-42; C. Boomsma, 1943-48; C. Groot, 1948-
51; D.J. Negen, 1953-57; D.B. Muir, 1958-77;
R.A. De Lange, 1977-82; R.L. Fynewever, 1983-
88; D.D. Poolman, 1988-93; R.W. Loerop, 1994-
2000; K.M. Vander Horst, 2002-

Indianapolis, IN — Devington
see: Indianapolis, IN – Hope Community

Indianapolis, IN — Discovery (emerging)
1995-1998, discontinued
pastor: R.A. Sizemore, 1994-98

Indianapolis, IN — Hope Community
1958-
organized: 1961
former names: Indianapolis, IN – Indianapolis,
1961-66, 1994; Indianapolis, IN – Devington,
1966-78
pastors: J. Zandstra (M), 1958-62; J.C. Ribbens,
1963-65; T. Van Eerden, 1966-71; J. Joldersma,
1971-76; W.S. Gritter, 1976-81; J.A. Holwerda,
1981-92; T.D. Slachter, 1994-96; F. Varga, 1996-
2001

Indianapolis, IN — Indianapolis
see: Indianapolis, IN – Hope Community

Indian Harbour Beach, FL — Grace
1965-
former name: Eau Gallie, FL – Eau Gallie, 1965-
68
pastors: R.E. Van Harn (M), 1961-66; G. Hubers,
1966-71; J.D. Oosterhouse, 1971-75; J.G.
Aupperlee, 1977-85; C. Van Ens, 1985-89; S.C.
Murrell, 1991-92; G.D. Belcher, III, 1999-

Ingersoll, ON — Ingersoll
1953-
pastors: W. Vande Kolk, 1956-59; H.J. Kwantes,
1959-66; K. Hart, 1967-72; H.J. Bierman, 1972-
77; W.C. Veenstra, 1977-82; D.W. Royall, 1983-
86; J. Koole, 1987-95; D. Miedema, 1996-

Inkster, MI — Cherry Hill
1962-1978, discontinued
former name: Inkster, MI – Inkster, 1962-67
pastors: H.E. Botts (M), 1956-64; W.S. Gritter,
1964-68; J.J. Steigenga, 1968-74; A.J.
Hoogewind, 1975-78

Inkster, MI — Inkster
see: Inkster, MI — Cherry Hill

Inver Grove Heights, MN — Grace
1961–
former name: South St. Paul, MN — South Grove,
1961–75
pastors: A. Van Andel, 1959–66; D.J. Van Beek,
1966–72; N.J. Gebben, Sr., 1973–77; P.W.
Deckinga, 1977–85; J.G. Busscher, 1985–

Inwood, IA — Inwood
1912–
pastors: H.J.Heynen, 1914–16; P. Van Vliet, 1917–
18; J.J. Dyk, 1919–24; M. Van Dyke, 1924–27; J.
Haveman, 1927–28; A. Wassink, 1929–46; N.
Beute, 1946–52; L. Bouma, 1953–57; B.W.
Mulder, 1958–63; M.E. Gritters, 1965–71; F.L.
Netz, 1971–73; D.L. Smit, 1974–80; T.J. Ouwinga,
1981–87; W.J. Moxey, 1987–92; D.L. Heilman,
1993–

Ionia, MI — Dildine Community
see: Ionia, MI — New Life

Ionia, MI — New Life
1962–1993, withdrawn to become Living Hope
Community Church
organized: 1984–1992, emerging, 1992–1993
former name: Ionia, MI — Dildine Community,
1968–84; was a Methodist church, 1895–1932,
Dildine Community (independent) Church, 1933–
1962
absorbed Portland, MI — Portland, 1915–84
pastors: R. Bouwman (E), 1975–76; J. Adema (E),
1976–77; R.H. Tjapkes, 1977–78; C.E. Keegstra,
1979–81; J. Vigh, 1981–91

Iowa City, IA — Chinese Church
1986–
organized: 1993
former name: Iowa City, IA — Geneva Community,
1986–88
pastor: J. Chen, 1986–98

Iowa City, IA — Geneva Community
see: Iowa City, IA — Chinese Church

**Iowa City, IA — Iowa State University
(campus ministry)**
1966–
staff: J. Kok, 1966–69; D.W. Nibbelink (L), 1969–
70; J. Chen, 1970–2001

Iowa City, IA — Trinity
1965–1999, discontinued
pastors: R.J. Palma (M), 1960–64; J. Kok (M),
1964–69; A. Helder (M), 1970–78; L.J. Vander
Zee, 1978–83; W. Van Dyk, 1983–91; J.A.
Holwerda, 1992–97

**Iowa City, IA — University of Iowa
(campus ministry)**
1971–
pastor: J. Chen, 1971–

Iowa Falls, IA — Iowa Falls
1947–1993, discontinued
pastors: S.A. Werkema (M), 1947–50; K. Tebben,
1950–56; R.R. Graves, 1956–60; J.A. Bultman,
1960–66; M. Keuning, 1967–71; J. Vander Plate,
1971–75; R.W. De Young, 1976–81; T.R. Dykstra,
1981–87; S.R. Van Eck, 1988–91

Ireton, IA — Ireton
1908–
pastors: P. Van Vliet, 1910; D. Hollebeek, 1910–15;
F., Schuurmann, 1915–18; W. Terpsma, 1918–25;
E.R. Van Farowe, 1926–28; J.R. Van Dyke, 1929–
45; P. Ouwinga, 1946–51; J.B. Hulst, 1954–58; A.
Hannink, 1959–65; J.H. Rubingh, 1966–75; M.B.
Fynaardt, 1975–86; W.H. Oord, 1986–91; G.L.
Luurtsema, 1992–98; R.R. Sprik, 1999–

Iron Springs, AB — Iron Springs
1949–
pastors: J. De Jong, 1949–55; P. Van Egmond,
1957–60; J. De Jong, 1961–65; R. Koops, 1967–
71; H.G Samplonius, 1971–75; P.D. Stadt, 1975–
80; W.A. Brouwer, 1980–85; J.M. Van de Hoef,
1985–91; H. Vander Beek, 1992–96; J.H.
Noordhof, 1997–

**Irvine, CA — Southern California Hope
(emerging)**
1989–1992, discontinued
pastor: P.H. Kim, 1989–92

Irving Park, NJ — Irving Park
see: Midland Park, NJ — Irving Park

Jackson, MI — Cascades Fellowship
1959–
former name: Jackson, MI — Jackson, 1959–93
pastors: J.E. Versluys (M), 1957–63; J. Batts (M),
1963–67; W.J. Dykstra, 1968–78; R. Vander Roest,
1980–84; E. Walhout (stated supply), 1984–85; W.
Versluys, II, 1985–90; R.W. De Vries, 1992–2000

Jackson, MI — Jackson
see: Jackson, MI – Cascades Fellowship

Jackson, MS — Jackson
1978-1985, discontinued
pastor: C.G. Van Halsema (M), 1981-84

Jacksonville, FL — Atlantic Community
1991-
pastors: J.L. Huizenga, 1987-99; J.A. Byker,
2000-

Jacksonville, FL — Baymeadows
see: Jacksonville, FL – Baymeadows Community

**Jacksonville, FL — Baymeadows
Community**
1972-
organized: 1983
former name: Jacksonville, FL – Baymeadows,
1983-84
pastors: H.T.Karsten (E), 1972-82; F.T. Wevers,
1982-90; T.J. Walcott, 1991-96; J.A. De Boer,
1996-98

Jamaica, NY — Queens
1958-
organized: 1960
pastor: P.H. Szto, 1958-86

Jamestown, MI — Jamestown
see also: Zutphen, MI – Zutphen

Jamestown, MI — Jamestown
1894-
former names: Jamestown Center, MI – Jamestown Center, 1894-95; Jamestown, MI – Second,
1895-1903
pastors: P. Jonker, Sr., 1897-99; J. Bolt, 1901-
04; J. Post, 1904-09; H. Baker, 1910-15; P.W. De
Jonge, 1915-18; H. Wierenga, 1920-25; J. Putt,
1925-29; H. Dykhouse, 1929-47; B.E. Pekelder,
1947-51; F. Bultman, 1953-57; J. Gritter, 1958-
64; A.J. Verburg, 1965-71; P.R. Schoon, 1972-73;
C.D. Vander Meyden, 1974-79; J.A. Brinks, 1979-
85; R.S. Lankheet, 1985-89; E.W. Los, 1990-96;
T.J. Lapinsky, 1996-2002

Jamestown, MI — Searchlight Ministries
1998-
organized: 1999
pastor: S.A. Drenth, 1999-

Jamestown, MI — Second
see: Jamestown, MI – Jamestown

**Jamestown Center, MI — Jamestown
Center**
see: Jamestown, MI – Jamestown

Jarvis, ON — Ebenezer
1948-
former name: Jarvis, ON – Jarvis, 1950-71
pastors: G.A. Lyzenga, 1950; J.M. Dykstra, 1952-
59; A. Haalboom, 1960-62; P. Kranenburg, 1963-
66; D.C. Los, 1967-72; P. Brouwer, 1972-79; J.
Tuininga, 1980-84; N. Cornelisse, 1985-89; R.
Praamsma, 1990-97; K.F. Benjamins, 1999-

Jarvis, ON — Jarvis
see: Jarvis, ON – Ebenezer

Jeffers, MN (mission)
1910-1911

Jenison, MI — Baldwin Street
1960-
pastors: J.A. Wesseling, 1961-70; H. Hoekstra,
1970-84; J.A. Holleman, 1975-79; R. De Young,
1979-83; J.R. Pruim, 1985-2000; G. Van
Groningen, Jr., 2001-

Jenison, MI — Cottonwood Heights
1970-
pastors: J.J. Wiegers, 1971-79; J.S. Meyer, 1979-
88; R.C. Heerspink, 1989-99; M.A. Palsrok, 2000-

Jenison, MI — Fairway
1989-
pastors: J.L. Sajdak, 1992-97; D.E. Den Haan,
1999-

Jenison, MI — First
1875-
former names: Jenisonville, MI – Jenisonville,
1875-98; Jenison, MI – Jenison 1898-1949
pastors: T.M. Vanden Bosch, 1886-88; B.H.
Einink, 1893-95; J. Noordewier, 1896-1907; D. De
Beer, 1908-13; G. Westenberg, 1914-21; J.O.
Bouwsma, 1921-27; A. Dusseljee, 1928-40; M.J.
Vander Werp, 1940-44; B. Essenburg, 1945-61;
A.H. Jongsma, 1962-68; P. Vander Weide, 1969-
80; J.L. Witvliet, 1981-93; M.J. Vander Vliet,
1994-

Jenison, MI — Friendship Chapel
1981-
organized: 1998
pastors: M. Keuning (E), 1981-87; P.V. De Jonge,
1987-94; R.H. Verkaik, 1995-2002; J. Stam,
1995-2000

Jenison, MI — Jenison
see: Jenison, MI — First

Jenison, MI — Ridgewood
1965-
pastors: L.J. Hofman, 1965-77; M.R. Doornbos, 1978-89; T.E. Pettinga, 1978-83; T.B. Swieringa, 1983-86; J.R. Boot, 1992-

Jenison, MI — Trinity
1949-
pastors: J. Hasper, 1950-53; M. Arnoys, 1954-65; H.D. Vanderwell, 1966-72; M.W. Heyboer, 1973-76; E.J. Blankespoor, 1977-84; J.T. Petersen, 1985-90; D.L. Heilman, 1987-93; J.C. Busscher, 1994-98; M.W. Heyboer, 1991-

Jenison, MI — Twelfth Avenue
1954-
pastors: H. Vander Kam, 1955-65; J.B. Hulst, 1965-68; H.N. Erffmeyer, 1968-81; C. Bolt, 1982-97; L.G. Zoerhof, 1998-

Jenisonville, MI — Jenisonville
see: Jenison, MI — First

Jersey City, NJ — Filipino (emerging)
1998-
pastor: A. Sideco, 1998-

Jersey City, NJ — Jersey City Mission
1989-
organized: 1997
pastor: E.R. Arevalo, 1989-2001; R. Orostizaga, 2002-

Jersey City, NJ — New City Church (emerging)
1994-
pastor: T. Rubingh, 1995-

Kalamazoo, MI (mission)
1934-1940
staff: A. Spoelstra (L), 1938-39

Kalamazoo, MI — Alamo Avenue
1927-1987, merged into Kalamazoo, MI — Heritage
pastors: W. Verhill, 1932-35; J.G. Kooistra, 1935-40; H. Veldman, 1941-50; E.J. Knott, 1950-59; W. Hofman, 1961-65; R.J. Vande Kieft, 1965-76; C.J. De Ridder, 1976-80; K.H. Bratt, 1981-87

Kalamazoo, MI — Bronco Campus Ministry WMU (campus ministry)
1951-1952, 1966-

staff: M. Keuning (L), 1951-52; C. Van Ens, 1966-74; S. Draayer, 1975-78; W.A. Huyser, 1981-87; G.A. De Vries, 1987-89; S.M. Merz, 1989-93; R. De Young, 1997-

Kalamazoo, MI — Burdick Street
1889-1903, joined the Netherlands Reformed Church in 1909, joined CRC in 1893 as an independent congregation
former name: Kalamazoo, MI — Second, 1893-96
pastors: K. Kreulen, 1889-92; H.H. Dieperink Langereis, 1893-1903

Kalamazoo, MI — Comstock
1913-
pastors: J. Keizer, 1916-23; P. De Koekkoek, 1923-26; M. Van Vessem, 1926-28; J. Beld, 1928-32; P.A. Spoelstra, 1932-44; J.H. Olthoff, 1944-50; J.O. Bouwsma, 1952-58; H. Minnema, 1959-64; H. Bouma, Jr., 1964-79; J. Leugs, 1980-88; R.A. Arbogast, 1990-98; J.R. Pruim, 1999-

Kalamazoo, MI — Comstock Chapel
1945-1946; 1956-1968
staff: E. Postma (E), 1945-46; R. Slager (L), 1956-59; L. Vermaas (E), 1958-59; R. Slager (L), 1960-62; J. De Vries (L), 1961-63; R.C. De Vries (L), 1964-65; R. Brummel (L), 1964-65; J. Steigenga (L), 1965-66; H. Pott (L), 1965-66; A. De Haan (L), 1966-68

Kalamazoo, MI — County Infirmary
1952-1954
staff: B. Dykehouse (L), 1952-56

Kalamazoo, MI — Eastern Hills
1969-1982, discontinued
pastor: R.D. Baker, 1971-81

Kalamazoo, MI — Fairmont Hospital
1952-1954
staff: L. De Kruyter (L), 1952-53; J. Hendikson (L), 1953-54

Kalamazoo, MI — Faith
1962-2002, discontinued
organized: 1965
pastors: G. Geurink (E), 1962-63; R.L. Westenbroek, 1964-65, 1966-69; R.W. Klingenberg, 1969-74; G.J. Rozenboom, 1974-78; G.E. De Vries, 1979-88; S.R. Sytsma, 1989-94; A.J. De Vries, 1997-2002

Kalamazoo, MI — First

1869-1987, merged into Kalamazoo, MI —
Heritage
former names: Kalamazoo, MI, 1869-93;
Kalamazoo, MI — First, 1893-97; Kalamazoo, MI
— Walnut Street, 1897-1913
pastors: J. Noordewier, 1871-73; E. Vander Vries,
1874-79; J. Noordewier, 1880-85; F. Welandt,
1885-89; J. Post, 1889-95; E. Broene, 1895-
1900; J. Robbert, 1901-08; S.P. Eldersveld, 1909-
18; H. Danhof, 1918-24; J.J. Zeeuw, 1925-32; J.J.
Weersing, 1932-38; J.O. Bouwsma, 1938-46; E.B.
Pekelder, 1947-53; G.H. Rientjes, 1955-59; R.O.
De Groot, 1959-69; A. Zylstra, 1970-74; H.J.
Boekhoven, 1976-80; S. Ten Brink, 1980-86

Kalamazoo, MI — Grace

1925-
joined denomination, 1946; was First Protesting
Christian Reformed Church, 1925-45
pastors: H. Danhof, 1925-46; G. Gritter, 1947-50;
J. Vander Ploeg, 1950-56; T. Yff, 1956-64; H.
Vander Kam, 1965-78; A.J. Van Schouwen, 1979-
83; H.G. Arnold, 1983-91; J.A. Brinks, 1991-

Kalamazoo, MI — Heritage

1987-
merger of: Kalamazoo, MI — Alamo Ave.;
Kalamazoo, MI — First; Kalamazoo, MI —
Knollwood, 1987
pastors: A.H. Jongsma, 1988-96; G.M. Stevens,
1996-2002; S.A. Tuin, 1999-

Kalamazoo, MI — Immanuel

1962-
organized: 1988
former name: Kalamazoo, MI — Immanuel
Chapel, 1962-70
pastors: P. Laning (E), 1962-65; J. Medendorp,
1965-67; R. Kooistra (L), 1967-68; V. Luchies
(M), 1969-78; G.R. Young, 1979-82; D.J.
Sieplinga, 1984-89; G.D. Negen, 1991; M.A.
Scheffers, 1991-2000; D.L. Posie, 1999-

Kalamazoo, MI — Immanuel Chapel

see: Kalamazoo, MI — Immanuel

Kalamazoo, MI — Judyville (mission)

1952-1954
staff: M. Boden (L), 1951-52; J. Noordam (L),
1952-54

Kalamazoo, MI — Juvenile Home

1951-1956
staff: B. Dykehouse (L), 1951-56

Kalamazoo, MI — Kalamazoo

see: Kalamazoo, MI — First

Kalamazoo, MI — Knollwood

1941-1987, merged into Kalamazoo, MI — Heritage
organized: 1955
pastors: A. Spoelstra (L), 1941-44; E. Postma (E),
1944-48; M. Keuning (E), 1949-50; C. Zichterman
(L), 1950-54; H. Guikema, 1953-57; F. Diemer,
1958-65; G.G. Vanderlip, 1970-73; S. Draayer,
1973-78; W.G. Van Hal, 1978-80; W.A. Huyser,
1981-87; G.A. De Vries, 1985-87

Kalamazoo, MI — Korean

see: Vicksburg, MI — Korean

Kalamazoo, MI — Lawndale Chapel

1936-1971
staff: A. Spoelstra (L), 1938-44; E. Postma (E),
1944-48; G. Meiste (L), 1950-57, 1959-60; N. De
Jong (L), 1953-60; G. Yff (M), 1959-60; H.D.
Bultje (M), 1960-63; H. Vander Bilt (L), 1965-69;
K. Westerhof (L), 1970-71

Kalamazoo, MI — Lexington Green Community

see: Portage, MI — Lexington Green Community

Kalamazoo, MI — Milwood

1931-
pastors: J. Schaal, 1933-43; J. Entingh, 1943-
48; A. Dusseljee, 1948-52; G. Vander Kooi, 1953-
57; P.G. Holwerda, 1958-65; L. Kerkstra, 1966-
71; F.R. DeBoer, 1971-83; R. Walter, Jr., 1984-93;
K.L. Dwyer, 1994-98; L.D. Slings (I), 1997-98;
L.J. Kotman, 1999-

Kalamazoo, MI — North Christian Mission

1960-1962
staff: W. Navis (L), 1960-62

Kalamazoo, MI — Northern Heights

1965-
pastors: R.J. Sikkema, 1966-69; S.J. Workman,
1969-74; S.J. Bultman, 1974-83; J.G. Aupperlee,
1985-90; D.A. Bosch, 1993-96; R.D. Ritsema,
1996-

Kalamazoo, MI — Northwest

see: Kalamazoo, MI — Westwood

Kalamazoo, MI — North Westnedge Street

see: Kalamazoo, MI — Second

Kalamazoo, MI — Northwood Chapel
1960-1965
staff: N. De Jonge, 1960-63; H. Vander Bilt (L),
1963-65

Kalamazoo, MI — Parchment
1935-
former name: Parchment, MI — Parchment,
1935-69
pastors: A. Poel (M), 1935-44; E. Boer, 1945-49;
G.H. Vande Riet, 1949-56; O. Holtrop, 1956-65; L.
Doezema, 1966-77; D.L. Aldrink, 1978-83; J.L.
Vanderlaan, 1984-91; R.L. Boersma, 1992-

Kalamazoo, MI — Pine Crest State Hospital
1952-1954
staff: L. De Kruyter (L), 1952-53; H. Guikema,
1953-54; N. De Jonge (L), 1953-54; H. Ten Brink
(L), 1955-56

Kalamazoo, MI — Prairie Edge
see: Portage, MI — Prairie Edge

Kalamazoo, MI — Second
1893-
former name: Kalamazoo, MI — North Westnedge
Street, 1893-1914
pastors: S. Koster, 1893-96; F. Fortuin, 1898-
1901; J. Keizer, 1902-11; R. Diephuis, 1911-19;
G.J. Haan, 1920-38; B. Van Someren, 1938-45; L.
Van Laar, 1945-52; C. Greenfield, 1952-59; W.
Haverkamp, 1960-66; J.A. Mulder, 1967-79; J.
Admiraal, 1980-87; R.L. Scheuers, 1987-93; H.A.
Ouwinga, 1994-97; W.H. Lammers, 1998-

Kalamazoo, MI — Southern Heights
1961-
pastors: A.J. Bultman, 1962-66; D.M. Stravers,
1967-71; V.D. Verbrugge, 1972-85; E.P. Meyer,
1985-89; R.D. Vanderwell, 1990-2000 ; D.S.
Sarkipato, 1997-

Kalamazoo, MI — State Hospital
1952-1959
staff: T. Vanden Berg (L), 1952-53; E. Koning (L),
1955-59

Kalamazoo, MI — State Hospital, Fair Oaks
1957-1960
staff: H. Ten Brink (L), 1957-58; H. Hybels (L),
1959-60

Kalamazoo, MI — Third
1907-
pastors: M.J. Bosma, 1907-10; J.C. Schaap,

1911-13; D.R. Drukker, 1914-18; J.P. Battema,
1920-26; J. Masselink, 1927-43; C.H. Oldenburg,
1944-50; J.O. Schuring, 1952-54; W. Vander
Haak, 1954-62; L. Greenway, 1963-66; N.L.
Veltman, 1967-73; W.D. Buursma, 1973-91; J.B.
Dik, 1983-96; K.A. Baker, 1992-; V. Ko, 1999-

Kalamazoo, MI — Walnut Street
see: Kalamazoo, MI — First

Kalamazoo, MI — Way of Life Chapel
1951-1952
staff: A. Vanden Berge (L), 1951-52

**Kalamazoo, MI — Western Michigan
University**
see: Kalamazoo, MI — Bronco Campus Ministry,
WMU

Kalamazoo, MI — Westwood
1952-
former name: Kalamazoo, MI — Northwest,
1952-53
pastors: J. Entingh, 1953-58; H. Visscher, 1959-
64; W.A. Huyser, 1964-77; G. Veenstra, 1978-85;
E.G. Cooke, 1985-89; M.R. Van't Hof, 1989-98;
S.J. Van Heest, 1992-99 ; D.L. Slings (I), 1999-

Kamloops, BC — Kamloops
see: Kamloops, BC — Sahali Fellowship

Kamloops, BC — Sahali Fellowship
1990-
emerging, 1990-2000
pastor: H. Devries, 1990-

Kamloops, BC — Summit
1976-1990
organized: 1979
pastors: D.J. Tigchelaar (M), 1976-84; S.K.
Sikkema, 1984-89

Kanata, ON — Kanata
see: Ottawa, ON — Kanata Community

Kanata, ON — Kanata Community
see: Ottawa, ON — Kanata Community

Kanawha, IA — Kanawha
1900-
pastors: C. Bode, 1903-17; G.L. Hoefker, 1917-
25; D.H. Plesscher, 1925-50; L.A. Bazuin, 1950-
54; P.F. Holtrop, 1956-59; H. Bode, 1959-62; C.A.
Persenaire, 1962-65; M.P. Hoogland, 1967-69;
M.L. Van Donselaar, 1970-76; J.A. Ritsema, 1976-

80; B. Den Herder, 1980-89; R.M. Brenton, 1989-93; G.D. Daley, 1994-2002

Kanawha, IA — Wright
1891-
former name: Wright, IA — Wright, 1891-1955
pastors: H. Van Wesep, 1896-1907; B. Nagel, 1908-14; H.H. Kamps, 1915-17; B. Post, 1919-20; E.R. Van Farowe, 1922-26; H. Wierenga, 1927-30; J.M. Voortman, 1930-42; B. Vanden Brink, 1943-50; L.J. Hofman, 1951-54; E.D. Dykema, 1954-58; V. Luchies, 1958-60; P.H. Vruwink, 1961-64; F. Einfeld, 1965-77; H.J. Westra, 1978-84; R.B. Vermeer, 1985-93; W.G. Brouwers, Jr., 1994-98; C. Walton, 2000-

Kansas City, MO — Lane Avenue
1971-1997, withdrew to United Reformed Churches
pastors: A.L. Van Wyhe, 1968-73; P. Lagerwey, 1974-77; A. Gelder, 1979-85; E. Schering, 1986-91; S.C. Pastine, 1992-97

Keener, IN (mission)
1881-1883
branch of Lansing, IL

Kelloggsville, MI — Kelloggsville
see: Kentwood, MI — Kelloggsville

Kelowna, BC — Kelowna
1972-
pastors: J. Bolt, 1973-76; F. Heslinga, 1977-82; J.S. Mantel, 1983-89; K.S. Gangar, 1989-90; J. Boonstra, 1991-98; S.J. Gerrits, 1998-

Kemptville, ON — First
1957-
pastors: A.H. Smit, 1957; C. Spoelhof, 1958-62; J.M. Klumpenhouwer, 1968-72; J.H. Lamsma, 1972-76; J.C. Derksen, 1976-83; D.C. Los, 1983-88; D. Velthuizen, 1988-95; J.A. Broekema, 1996-2000; B.J. Ponsen, 2002-

Kennewick, WA — Family of Faith
1968-
organized: 1976
former name: Kennewick, WA — Tri-Cities, 1976-2000
pastors: H. Bouma (M), 1968-80; A.J. Machiela, 1981-90; J.D. Lion, 1990-

Kennewick, WA — Tri-Cities
see: Kennewick, WA — Family of Faith

Kenora, ON — Kenora
1955-1963, discontinued
pastor: A. Disselkoen, 1954-57

Kenosha, WI — Kenosha
1902-
pastors: E. Tanis, 1911-12; J.A. Gerritsen, 1912-18; P.W. De Jonge, 1918-26; J.O. Vos, 1926-34; E. Joling, 1934-50; B.N. Huizenga, 1950-54; L.J. Hofman, 1954-59; E.C. Dykstra, 1959-62; C.E. Keegstra, 1963-67; L.F. Baker, 1968-79; P.C. Kelder, 1980-87; M.J. Jonkman, 1987-97; T.R. Hull, 1999-2002

Kent, WA — Good News Community
1990-
organized: 1996
pastors: A.J. Machiela, 1990-93; J. Van Hemert, 1999-2001; D.K. Watson, 2002-

Kent, WA — Kent First Korean
1993-
pastor: H.C. Song, 1994-;Y.R. Yeum, 1996; G. Kim, 2000; S. Kim, 2001-

Kent City, MI — Pioneer Chapel
1955-1960
staff: W. Willink (L), 1955-57, 1960-61; P.L. Brink (L), 1957-60

Kentville, NS — Kentville
1955-
former name: Port William, NS — Port William, 1955-58
pastors: J. Van Dyk, 1959-62; J.G. Groen, 1964-68; H. Vander Plaat, 1969-73; H. Kuperus, 1974-78; J. Visser, 1979-85; J. Joosse. 1986-91; P.C. Stellingwerff, 1991-94; N.J. Visser, 1997-

Kentwood, MI — Centre Pointe
1996-
emerging, 1996
former name: Kentwood, Mi — Centre Pointe Community, 1996-2001
pastors: G. Carney, 1996-97; A. Daley, 1998-2002

Kentwood, MI — Discovery
1991-
organized: 1994
pastors: J.L. Hoogeveen, 1991-95; T.B. Swieringa, 1996-

Kentwood, MI — East Paris
1902-

former name: East Paris, MI – East Paris, 1902-58; Grand Rapids, MI – East Paris, 1958-2000
pastors: Y.P. De Jong, 1905-07; C. Vriesman, 1908-11; J. Robbert, 1912-16; J. De Haan, Sr., 1917-19; H. Heyns, 1920-21; E.F.J. Van Halsema, 1921-25; A. Van Dyken, 1926-30; J. Vander Ploeg, 1930-39; M. Ouwinga, 1939-44; M.H. Faber, 1944-52; J. Bylsma, 1955-60; W.L. Van Reese, 1960-70; G. Bouma, 1972-85; V.L. Michael, 1985-89; G.W. Sheeres, 1990-97; D.A. Brouwer, 1998-

Kentwood, MI — Kelloggsville (mission)
1932-1937

Kentwood, MI — Kelloggsville
1875-
former names: Kelloggsville, MI – Kelloggsville, 1875-1955; Grand Rapids, MI – Kelloggsville, 1955-91
pastors: P. Schut, 1881-87; R. Drukker, 1888-91; S. Koster, 1892-93; J. Noordewier, 1893-96; R.L. Haan, 1898-1900; E. Broene, 1900-07; J.A. Kett, 1908-10; D. Vander Ploeg, 1911-15; M.M. Schans, 1917-24; H.J. Triezenberg, 1925-30; P.G. Holwerda, 1930-33; E. Boeve, 1933-45; C. Holtrop, 1945-52; W.H. Rutgers, 1952-58; G.J. Postma, 1959-63; T. Yff, 1964-72; T.J. Lapinsky, 1972-77; L. Kerkstra, 1978-86; R.W. Vance, 1982-86; R.L. Fynewever, 1988-; M.L. De Young, 1990-

Kentwood, MI — Princeton
1963-
former name: Grand Rapids, MI – Princeton, 1963-93
pastors: H.B. Vanden Heuvel, 1965-70; J.C. Medendorp, 1972-91; T.R. Wolthuis, 1987-92; S. Woudstra, 1991-93; B. Van Antwerpen, 1993-2002

Kentwood, MI — Vietnamese Reformed Christian Church (emerging)
1978-
former name: Grand Rapids, MI – Vietnamese Evangelical Church, 1978-90, part of the group joined the United Methodist Church in 1986
pastors: K.T. Truong (L), 1978-82; V.Q. Tran (L), 1982-85; N.T. Kieu (E), 1988-90; D.J. Griffioen and H.D. Schipper (RCA), 1990-96; L. Duong, 1997-

Kibbie, MI — Kibbie
see: South Haven, MI – Kibbie

Kincardine, ON — Kincardine
1978-
pastors: J.W. Hielkema, 1980-86; T. Baird, 1986-91; N. Elgersma, 1992-98; E. Tenyenhuis, 1999-

Kincheloe, MI — New Hope Community
1981-
organized: 1990
pastors: N.J. Thomasma, 1981-91; G.S. Miller, 1993-98; D.R. Wolters, 2000-

Kingston, ON — First
1950-
former name: Kingston, ON – Kingston, 1952-71
pastors: D. Mellema, 1954-59; H. Uittenbosch, 1960-65; P. Van Egmond, 1965-69; J. Geuzebroek, 1970-74; H.C. Salomons, 1974-82; H. Van Niejenhuis, 1979-84; C.D. Tuyl, 1985-90; H. Mennega, 1991-95; C.J. De Vos, 1997-

Kingston, ON — Kingston
see: Kingston, ON – First

Kingston, ON — Queen's University, Geneva Fellowship (campus ministry)
1974-
pastors: W. Dykstra, 1974-82; W. Van Groningen, 1982-98; P.A. Apol, 1998-

Kingston, ON — Westside Fellowship
1984-
pastors: C.R. Cornelisse, 1984-89; J.G. Groen, 1990-95; E.W. Visser, 1996-

Kinney Station, MI — Kinney Station
see: Grand Rapids, MI – Walker

Kitchener, ON — Community
1948-
former name: Kitchener, ON – Kitchener, 1949-69; Kitchener, ON – First, 1969-95
pastors: C. Spoelhof (M), 1948-54; A.H. Venema, 1955-58; W. Vande Kolk, 1959-61; H.W. Kroeze, 1962-67; P.L. Van Katwyk, 1968-73; P. Breedveld, 1973-82; J. Kuntz, 1983-91; C. Van Niejenhuis, 1991-93; H.J. Bierman, 1994-; B.H. DeJonge, 2000-

Kitchener, ON — First
see: Kitchener, ON – Community

Kitchener, ON — Kitchener
see: Kitchener, ON – Community

Kuner, CO — Kuner
1909-1918, discontinued
pastors: J. Bolt (M), 1910-11; A.J Brink (M),
1911-13

Lacombe, AB — Bethel
1953-
former name: Lacombe, AB — Second, 1953-54
pastors: B. Den Herder, 1955-60; N. Beute,
1960-68; C. Vriend, 1968-74; P. Sluys, 1974-79;
E. Gritter, 1980-88; E. Jager, 1989-93; K.
MacNeil, 1995-

Lacombe, AB — First
see: Lacombe, AB — Woodynook

Lacombe, AB — Lacomb
see: Lacombe, AB — Woodynook

Lacombe, AB — Second
see: Lacombe, AB — Bethel

Lacombe, AB — Woodynook
1935-
began as a branch of Edmonton, AB — Edmonton,
1931-35
former names: Lacombe, AB — Lacombe, 1935-
54; Lacombe, AB — First, 1954-87
pastors: S.G. Brondsema, 1940-43; J. Roorda,
1944-49; E.H. Oostendorp, 1950-55; B.J.
Boerkoel, 1956-59; H. Bajema, 1959-64; A.C.
Leegwater, 1965-70; J. Westerhof, 1971-76; G.J.
Heersink, 1977-84; C. Van Niejenhuis, 1985-91;
M.T. Mobach, 1992-2000; K. deKoning, 2001-

La Crosse, WI — Hope
see: Onalaska, WI — Hope

Ladner, BC — Ladner
see: Delta, BC — First Ladner

Ladner/Delta, BC — Ladner/Delta
see: Delta, BC — First Ladner

**Ladner, BC — Westcoast Community
(emerging)**
2000-

**Lafayette, IN — Christian Ministry Center
(emerging)**
1973-1980
pastor: D. Bos, 1973-75; T. Van't Land, 1975-80;
K. MacDonald, 1975-76

Lafayette, IN — Lafayette
1865-
joined Christian Reformed Church in 1869, from
Presbyterian Church
pastors: J.R. Schepers, 1864-70; J. Schepers,
1871-76; J. Noordewier, 1877-79; B. Mollema,
1882-88; M.J. Marcusse, 1989-94; B.H. Einink,
1895-1902; H.M. Vander Ploeg, 1903-11; D.H.
Kromminga, 1911-14; M.M. Schans, 1915-17; H.J.
Mulder, 1917-21; W. Masselink, 1922-25; J.J.
Hiemenga, 1925-28; J.M Ghysels, 1928-44; J.
Daane, 1945-49; D.J. Hoitenga, Sr., 1949-54; J.T.
Malestein, 1954-58; S. Van Dyken, 1960-64; J.C.
Ribbens, 1965-74; S. Ten Brink, 1974-80; L.B.
Mensink, 1982-89; R. Zomermaand, 1990-96;
A.D. Bosscher, 1990-95; G.E. De Vries, 1996-

Lafayette, IN — Sunrise
1995-
organized: 1995
pastors: R.D. Zomermaand, 1996-2001; R.A.
Lyzenga, 2002-

Lage Prairie, IL — Lage Prairie
see: South Holland, IL — First

La Glace, AB — La Glace
1955-
absorbed, Grande Prairie, AB — Grande Prairie,
1997
pastors: D.C. Bouma (M), 1962-75; J. Tuininga,
1966-70; H. Vriend, 1970-76; C.W. Tuininga,
1976-80; M.D. Vander Hart, 1980-83; P.L.
Hendriks, 1984-92; S.A. Speelman, 1993-99

La Grange, IL (mission)
1936-1936

Laguna Niguel, CA — South Orange Korean
see: Mission Viejo, CA — Urim

Laguna Niguel, CA — Urim
see: Mission Viejo, CA — Urim

Lake Andes, SD (mission)
1950-1958
staff: H. Hamberg (L), 1950-53; M. Veltkamp (E),
1953-58

Lake City, MI — Lake City
1956-
organized: 1966
pastors: C. Holtrop (M), 1956-60; W. De Waard,
1960-62; D.E. den Dulk, 1965-71; W. Vanden

Bosch, 1972-79; P. Veltman, 1981-83; J. Morren, 1984-91; M.N. Buwalda, 1992-

Lake Odessa, MI — Harvest Community
1962-
organized: 1977
former name: Lake Odessa, MI – Lake Odessa (1962-2002)
pastors: H. Brinks (L), 1962-63; W.D. Ribbens (M), 1963-69; H.J. Vugteveen (M), 1970-75; F. Bultman, 1976-81; B.J. Ridder, 1982-

Lake Odessa, MI — Lake Odessa
see: Lake Odessa, MI – Harvest Community

Lake Shore, MI — Lake Shore
see: Holland, MI – Harderwyk Ministries

Lakeview, SD — Lakeview
see: Valentine, NE – Lakeview

Lakewood, CA — Lakewood
see: Long Beach, CA – Long Beach

Lake Worth, FL — Comunidad de Fe ICR (emerging)
1993-
former name: Lake Worth, FL – Iglesia El Buen Samaritano, 1993-2000
pastor: G. Moreno, 1992-; X. Suarez, 1999-

Lake Worth, FL — Iglesia El Buen Samaritano
see: Lake Worth, FL – Comunidad de Fe ICR

Lake Worth, FL — Lake Worth
1955-
pastors: H. Sonnema, 1957-59; W.M. Van Dyk, 1959-64; D.P. Wisse, 1965-70; E.J. Tamminga, 1971-77; H. Vander Kam, 1978-79; R.L. Westenbroek, 1980-90; M.A. Davies, 1991-2000; T.R. Dykstra, 2002-

Lamont, MI — Lamont
1879-
pastors: R. Drukker, 1983-86; W.H. Frieling, 1986-91; J. Post, 1895-1900; L. Veltkamp, 1901-04; L. Ypma, 1904-07; J. Beld, 1907-08; J.L Van Tielen, 1911-15; S. Fopma, 1918-20; J. De Haan, Jr., 1921-25; J. Breuker, 1925-28; J. De Haan, Sr., 1929-38; M. Vander Zwaag, 1938-43; A.W. Hoogstrate, 1944-48; E. Boer, 1949-52; E.B. Pekelder, 1953-56; B.J. Niemeyer, 1956-61; H.B. Vanden Heuvel, 1962-65; R.W. Klingenberg, 1966-69; C. Vanden Heuvel, 1970-72; G. Veenstra,

1973-78; L.J. Wolters, 1979-86; R.B. Lanning, 1987-93; R.A. Terpstra, Jr., 1996-

Langley, BC — Bridge Community (emerging)
1994-
pastor: J. Heuving, 1997-2001; J.A. De Boer, 1999-2001

Langley, BC — First
1950-
former names: Langley Prairie, BC – Langley Prairie, 1950-52; Langley, BC – Langley, 1952-72
pastors: P. De Koekkoek, 1950-54; J.R. Van Dyke, 1954-57; J. Hoogland, 1958-62; J.G. Kunst, 1965-68; J. Van Hemert, 1968-80; M.J. Contant, 1980-94; R. De Moor, 1984-95; K.D. Boonstra, 1995-; M. Pool, 1995-2000

Langley, BC — Immanuel
1986-
pastors: R.W. Hogendoorn, 1987-92; E. Jager, 1993-2001; W. Versteeg, 2002-

Langley, BC — Langley
see: Langley, BC – First

Langley Prairie, BC — Langley Prairie
see: Langley, BC – First

Lansing, IL — Bethel
1958-
pastors: R. Wildschut, 1959-66; A.W. Hoogstrate, 1976-71; H.D. Vanderwell, 1972-78; C.L. Bremer, 1978-96; W.A. Huyser, 1987-91; H.J. Wigboldy, 1992-98; C. Hoogendoorn, 1996-

Lansing, IL — Community Chapel
1949-1971
Sunday school, 1949-65
staff: M. Meeter (L), 1949-53; M. Botma (L), 1953-71

Lansing, IL — First
1919-
former name: Lansing, IL – Lansing, 1919-56
pastors: J. Smitter, 1919-23; C. De Leeuw, 1924-44; J. Vander Ploeg, 1945-50; P.G. Holwerda, 1950-58; J.T. Malestein, 1958-62; N. Vogelzang, 1964-70; H.G. Arnold, 1970-83; L.J. Howerzyl, 1984-92; L.W. Van Essen, 1993-

Lansing, IL — Lansing
see: Munster, IN – First

Lansing, IL — Lansing
see: Lansing, IL – First

Lansing, IL — Mexican Mission
see: Chicago Heights, IL – Mexican Mission

Lansing, IL — Oak Glen
1948-1996, discontinued, majority withdrew to
United Reformed Churches
pastors: C. Greenfield, 1948-52; C. De Haan,
1953-58; M. Vander Zwaag, 1959; E.L. Haan,
1960-71; A.J. Verburg, 1971-93; P.R. Ipema,
1994-96

Lansing, IN — Lansing
see: Munster, IN – First

Lansing, MI (mission)
1924-1925
staff: J.R. Brink (M), 1924-25

Lansing, MI — Covenant
1980-
former name: Lansing, MI – Second, 1980
pastors: J.P. Heerema, 1982-88; J.W. Van Donk,
1988-89; R.R. Broekema, 1989-94; R.D. Baker,
1995-99; S.M. Tuttle, 2001-

Lansing, MI — First
see: East Lansing, MI – River Terrace

Lansing, MI — Hmong (emerging)
1987-
emerging, 1991
former name: Lansing, MI – Hmong Community,
1991-2001
pastors: C.P. Yang (E), 1987-; D. Moua (E), 1991-
95

Lansing, MI — Hmong Community
see: Lansing, MI – Hmong

Lansing, MI — Lansing
see: East Lansing, MI – River Terrace

Lansing, MI — Second
see: Lansing, MI – Covenant

La Palma, CA — Orange Han Min
1994-
organized: 1997
former names: Garden Grove, CA – Orange
Han Min, 1994-96; Westminster, CA – Orange
Han Min, 1996-2000
pastors: S.W. Yoon, 1993- ; J.I. Hyun, 1997-98

La Puente, CA — Hacienda Immanuel
see: La Puente, CA – Joy of Jesus

La Puente, CA — Joy of Jesus
1982-
organized: 1988
former names: Los Angeles, CA – Hacienda
Community, 1982-88; Hacienda Heights, CA –
Immanuel, 1988-91 Rowland Heights, CA –
Immanuel, 1991-99
pastor: K.K. Cho, 1982-2001; L.C Jeong, 2002-

Lark, ND (mission)
1939

Lark, ND — Lark
1910-1929, discontinued, members became a
branch of Holland Center, SD

Las Vegas, NV — Desert Harbor (emerging)
2000-
pastor: J.M. Wanders, 1999-

**Las Vegas, NV — Desert Streams
(emerging)**
2001-
pastor: R.L. Pollema, Jr. (E), 2001-

Las Vegas, NV — Korean Joong-Ang
see: Las Vegas, NV – So Mang Podowon

Las Vegas, NV — Las Vegas Central
see: Las Vegas, NV – So Mang Podowon

Las Vegas, NV — So Mang Podowon
1989-
former name: Las Vegas, NV – Korean Joon-Ang,
1989-91; Las Vegas, NV – Las Vegas Central,
1991; Las Vegas, NV – So Mang Presbyterian,
1991-2002
pastor: C.C. Cho, 1985-

Las Vegas, NV — So Mang Presbyterian
see: Las Vegas, NV – So Mang Podowon

Las Vegas, NV — Yung Kwang
1994-
pastor: M.S. Lee, 1994-

**Lawrenceville, GA — Comunidad Cristiana
San Pablo (emerging)**
2001-
pastor: P. Toledo, 2001-

Leamington, ON — Leamington
1953-1963, discontinued
pastor: P.F. Dahm, 1957-63

Lebanon, IA — Lebanon
see: Sioux Center, IA — Lebanon

Leduc, AB — Ebenezer
1978-
pastors: K.A. Baker, 1978-82; J.P. Groenewold, 1984-91; H. Vriend, 1991-2001; M. Pool (I), 2000-

Leighton, IA — Leighton
1893-
pastors: H. Bode, 1893-1900; H. Keegstra, 1900-03; J.A. Gerritsen, 1904-09; F.J. Drost, 1910-13; G.D. De Jong, 1914-20; J.M. Voortman, 1921-25; A. De Vries, 1925-29; C. Witt, 1929-37; D. Flietstra, 1938-44; C. Greenfield, 1944-48; H. Vander Klay, 1949-52; W.T. De Vries, 1954-58; J.L. Vander Laan, 1958-62; L. Van Staalduinen, Jr., 1963-68; V.D. Verbrugge, 1968-72; H. Bossenbroek, 1972-78; D.J. Boogerd, 1978-85; M.J. Kooy, 1985-91; D.W. Stevenson, 1992-99

Le Mars, IA (mission)
1884-1887, discontinued
pastor: J. Stadt, Jr., 1884-85

Le Mars, IA — Calvin
1950-
began as a branch of Ireton, IA, 1949
organized: 1954
former name: Le Mars, IA — Le Mars, 1950-62
pastors: B.N. Huizenga, 1947-50; P. Honderd (M), 1952-56; C.W. Niewenhuis, 1956-61; C.C. Spoor, 1963-67; J.R. Pruim, 1967-71; J.R. Boot, 1972-76; R.A. Bouwman, 1977-81; M. Den Bleyker, 1982-87; E.C. Visser, 1987-95; W.D. Hubers, 1996-

Le Mars, IA — Le Mars
1892-1915, discontinued
pastors: H. Van Wesep, 1894-96; A.J. Vanden Heuvel, 1904

Le Mars, IA — Le Mars
see also: Le Mars, IA — Calvin

Leonia, NJ — Leonia
1878-1908, withdrew to True Reformed Dutch Church
joined CRC, 1890, when True Protestant Dutch Reformed Church joined

pastors: H. Iserman, 1878-92; J.Y. De Baun, 1892-95; J. Wyckoff, 1896-98;J. Bolt, 1899-1901; S.J. Vander Beek, 1906-08

Leonia, NY (mission)
1926-1927

Leota, MN — Ebenezer
1895-
former name: Leota, MN — Leota, 1894-1961
pastors: W. Kole, 1900-03; J. Gulker, 1904-14; W. De Groot, 1914-16; N. Jansen, 1916-20; G. Bosch, 1920-22; L. Van Laar, 1923-26; G.A. Lyzenga, 1927-45; P. Jonker, Jr., 1945-48; P. Van Tuinen, 1949-54; O. De Groot, 1954-58; A. Besteman, 1959-64; H.G. Entingh, 1964-72; P.J. Koster, 1972-73; J.W. Van Stempvoort, 1975-80; E.R. Tigchelaar, 1980-86; K.H. Bratt, 1987-91; J.D. Buwalda, 1992-98; G.P. Hutt, 2000-

Leota, MN — Leota
see: Leota, MN — Ebenezer

Lethbridge, AB (mission)
1912

Lethbridge, AB — First
1950-
former name: Lethbridge, AB — Lethbridge, 1950-75
pastors: P.J. Hoekstra (M), 1950-53; D.J. Scholten, 1953-58; A. Kuyvenhoven, 1958-64; J. Vriend, 1964-70; L. Mulder, 1970-76; J. Tuininga, 1977-91; A. Joosse, 1994-

Lethbridge, AB — Lethbridge
see: Lethbridge AB — First

Lethbridge, AB — Maranatha
1975-
pastors: H. Van Niejenhuis, 1975-79; G.J. Bomhof, 1980-87; H.J. Bierman, 1988-94; J.R. Huizinga, 1991-; H. Salomons, 1995-99

Lincoln, NE — Northern Lighthouse (emerging) 1997-
pastor: S.J. Keyzer, 1997-

Lincoln Center, IA — Lincoln Center
see: Grundy Center, IA — Lincoln Center

Lindsay, ON — Lindsay
1952-
pastors: H. Moes, 1951-57; G. Ringnalda, 1958-63; J.G. Klomps, 1964-67; J. Westerhof, 1967-71;

J.M. Klumpenhouwer, 1972-78; H.A. Vander Windt, 1978-82; J. Heidinga, 1982-89; K. MacNeil, 1990-95; R.V. Luchies, 1997-

Lisle, IL — Horizon Community
see: Elmhurst, IL — Horizon Community

Listowel, ON — Bethel
1951-
former name: Listowel, ON — Listowel, 1951-72
pastors: R.J. Bos, 1950-52; C. Spoelhof, 1952-59; S. Terpstra, 1960-67; J.A. Quartel, 1968-73; J. Van Dyk, 1973-77; H. Van Dyken, 1977-79; G. Veeneman, 1980-86; J.A. Vander Kooi, 1986-92; J. De Vries, 1995-

Listowel, ON — Listowel
see: Listowel, ON — Bethel

Little Water, AZ (mission)
1899-1900
branch of Ft. Defiance, AZ

Lockport, IL — Community Life
1991-
pastors: D.S. Huizenga, 1988-93; H. Reyenga, Jr., 1988-93; W.W. Leys, 1994-

Lodge Pole, SD — Holland Center
1910-
former name: Holland Center, SD — Holland Center, 1910-87
pastors: J. Rubingh, 1927-35; M. Huizenga, 1935-40; H. Petroelje, 1941-43 ; P. Vos, 1947-50; J.H. Elenbaas, 1952-55; J. Paauw, 1955-57; C.G. Werkema, Sr., 1959-63; L.F. Baker, 1964-68; J.D. Buwalda, 1969-73; K. Vander Heide, 1973-78; H. Bajema, 1980-84; R.R. Mueller, 1984-89; W.H. De Vries, 1990-98; B. Dykstra, 1998-

Lodi, NJ — Lodi
1876-1975, merged into Clifton, NJ — Richfield
joined CRC, 1883, was independent
pastors: W.C. Wust, 1876-78, 1881-83; C. Vorst, 1891-95; I. Contant, 1886-99; R. Diephuis, 1900-03; S. Bouma, 1905-09; F. Welandt, 1910-23; P.J. Yff, 1923-25; C. Spoelhof, 1926-48; C.G. Kromminga, 1948-51; M.C. Baarman, 1951-56; G.D. Negen, 1957-59; R.W. Westveer, 1960-62; S. Ten Brink, 1963-67; L. Van Staalduinen, Jr., 1968-75

Lombard, IL — Lombard
1912-
former names: Chicago, IL — Twelfth Street,

1912-13; Chicago, IL — Third, 1913-27; Cicero, IL — First, 1927-75
pastors: H.J. Mokma, 1914-19; H. Moes, 1920-23; J.J. Weersing, 1924-32; W.H. Rutgers, 1933-43; E.J. Masselink, 1944-50; R.L. Veenstra, 1952-57; H.N. Erffmeyer, 1957-63; J.P. Boonstra, 1963-68; J.T. Ebbers, 1969-78; D.J. Negen, 1980-88; V.G. Vander Zee, 1989-2000; D.G. Buis, 1992-97; N. Elgersma, 1998-

Lombard, IL — Our Shepherd Korean
see: Arlington Heights, IL — Our Shepherd Korean

London, ON — Bethel
1968-
pastors: J. Van Harmelen, 1969-73; A. Beukema, 1975-81; P. Stel, 1982-91; G.K. Haagsma, 1994-2000; E.J. Groot-Nibbelink, 2001-

London, ON — Fanshaw College (campus ministry)
2001-
pastor: G. Miedema, 2001-

London, ON — First
1950-
former name: Ilderton, ON — Ilderton, 1950-51; London, ON — London, 1951-68
pastors: J. Gritter, 1954-58; G. Bouma, 1958-72; D.J. Hart, 1974-80; M.N. Greidanus, 1980-85; W.A. Brouwer, 1986-94; G.J. Van Arragon, 1987-88; P.C. Hogeterp, 1988-2000; G.A. Vandermolen, 1996-2000; A.C. Groen (I), 2000-; P. Pereboom, 2001-

London, ON — Forest City Community (emerging)
1993-
pastor: R.W. Hogendoorn, 1992-

London, ON — Good News
1989-
pastor: R.J. Haven, 1990-

London, ON — London
see: London, ON — First

London, ON — University of Western Ontario (campus ministry)
1976-
pastors: J. Van Til, 1970-75; J. Westerhof, 1976-81; P. Slofstra, 1981-88; K.D. Boonstra, 1988-94; M. Veenema, 1995-

Long Beach, CA (mission)
1932; 1954-1956
staff: F. De Jong , 1954-56

Long Beach, CA — Grace Filipino
see: Bellflower, CA — Grace Filipino

Long Beach, CA — Hispanic
see: Compton, CA — Nueva Comunidad

Long Beach, CA — Journey of Christian Fellowship (emerging)
2000-
pastor: C. Kim (E), 2000-

Long Beach, CA — Korean
see: Artesia, CA — Cerritos Central

Long Beach, CA — Lakewood-Long Beach
see: Long Beach, CA — Long Beach

Long Beach, CA — Long Beach
1953-
former names: Lakewood, CA — Lakewood 1953-68; Long Beach, CA — Lakewood-Long Beach, 1968-71
pastors: F. DeJong (M), 1946-49; F. DeJong, 1949-56; J.G. Van Ryn, 1956-61; J.H. Paauw, 1961-65; H. Leetsma, 1964-70; D.E. den Dulk, 1971-75; M.J. Flikkema, 1975-82; H.J. Schutt, 1983-94; B. Wassink, 1996-

Long Beach, CA — New City (emerging)
1993-
pastor: C.G. Kromminga, Jr., 1993-

Long Beach, CA — Nueva Comunidad (emerging)
1998-
former name: Compton, CA — Nueva Comunidad, 1998-2000
pastor: O.A. Alfaro (E), 1988-

Long Beach, CA — Seaway Ministry
1981-1992
pastor: J. Koopmans, 1981-1992

Longmont, CO — Pleasant Valley
1974-1997, withdrew
pastors: R.H. Cok, 1974-81; J.C. Vander Ark, 1981-93

Longmont, CO — The Journey (emerging)
1999-
pastor: R.J. Ebbers, 1999-

Los Alamitos, CA — Calvin
1991-2001, merged into Garden Grove, CA — Garden of Grace
former name: Bellflower, CA — Calvin, 1991-93
pastors: J.T. Kim, 1990-94; J.J. Kim, 1994-95; N.C. Paek, 1995-96; S.C. Choi, 1999-2001

Los Angeles, CA — American Indian Center
1971-1981
staff: F. Bakker (E), 1971-75; J. Westerhof, 1977-81

Los Angeles, CA — Bell Gardens (mission)
1940-1955
staff: J.J. Werkman (L), 1950-52

Los Angeles, CA — Beverly Hills Korean
see: Gardena, CA — The Lord's Church of Love

Los Angeles, CA — California Cho Won
see: Gardena, CA — The Lord's Church of Love

Los Angeles, CA — Chinese (Chinatown)
see: Monterey Park, CA — Chinese

Los Angeles, CA — Chosen People
1993-
organized: 1994
former name: Los Angeles, CA — Chosen People Korean, 1993
pastor: I.C. Kim, 1993-

Los Angeles, CA — Church of Love
1992-
organized: 1993
former name: Sun Valley, CA — Church of Love, 1998-2000
pastor: J.C. Kim, 1992-

Los Angeles, CA — Church of One Heart
2000-
organized: 2002
pastor: J. Choi, 2000-

Los Angeles, CA — Community
1988-
pastors: S.E. Ver Heul, 1980-; T.P. Doorn, 1981-

Los Angeles, CA — Crenshaw
1963-1995, discontinued
organized: 1966
pastors: G.J. Lau (M), 1963-66; P. Yang (M), 1963-64; J.F. Hollebeek (M), 1968-73; S.M. Jung, 1973-79; G.L. Van Enk, 1979-91; M.T. Brands, 1992-95

Los Angeles, CA — First
1914–1980, discontinued
former name: Los Angeles, CA — Los Angeles, 1914–66
pastors: F.J. Drost (M), 1914–17; P.J. Hoekenga, 1918–19; J. Groen, 1920–24; G.J. Holwerda, 1924–26; W. Groen, 1927–34; S. Struyk, 1934–48; J. Daane, 1949–61; T.E. Hofman, 1962–68; J. Van Ens, 1968–73; V. Vander Zee, 1968–73; B.J. Niemeyer, 1974–80

Los Angeles, CA — Galilee
1992–
former name: Los Angeles, CA — Galilee Presbyterian, 1981–94, joined CRC 1992
pastor: D.W. Yang, 1992–

Los Angeles, CA — Glory
see: Los Angeles, CA — Okto Glory

Los Angeles, CA — Hacienda Community
see: La Puente, CA — Joy of Jesus

Los Angeles — Home Korean (church plant)
2001–
pastor: K.K. Cho, 2001–

Los Angeles, CA — Journey Christian Fellowship (church plant)
2001–
pastor: C. Kim (E), 2001–

Los Angeles, CA — Korean
1976–1993, withdrew to Korean Christian Presbyterian Church
pastors: K.K. Cho, 1982; E.J. Choy, 1982–85; J.Y. Chang, 1983–85; J.T. Kim, 1984–89; J.Y.Y. Kim, 1985–87; J.E. Kim, 1987–93; J.S.S. Kim, 1986–89; S.I. Hyun, 1987–89; D.Y. Park, 1989–92; H.G. Park, 1989–93; Y.G. Jang, 1990–93

Los Angeles, CA — Korean-American Central Presbyterian
see: Garden Grove, CA — Korean American Central Presbyterian

Los Angeles, CA — Korean Peace
1998–
pastor: H.S. Kang, 1997–

Los Angeles, CA — Los Angeles
see: Los Angeles, CA — First

Los Angeles, CA — Los Angeles Home (emerging)
2000–
pastor: K.T. Choe, 2000–; P. Cha, 2002–

Los Angeles, CA — Mt. Sinai Korean
see: Los Angeles, CA — Pilgrim Chapel

Los Angeles, CA — New Ground Harvest (emerging)
2000–
staff: R.P. Black, 2000–

Los Angeles, CA — Okto Glory
1991–2000, discontinued
organized: 1994
absorberd: Los Angeles, CA — Glory Presbyterian, 1991–93; Los Angeles, CA — Glory, 1993–96
pastor: S. Park, 1995–2000

Los Angeles, CA — Pilgrim Chapel (emerging)
1993–
former name: Los Angeles, CA — Mt. Sinai Korean, 1993–97
pastor: S.K. Park, 1992–

Los Angeles, CA — Rehoboth Korean
1990–1993, withdrew
pastor: Y.T. Kim, 1990–93

Los Angeles, CA — The Gracious Ark
1997–
organized: 2002
pastor: J.H. Oh, 1997–2002

Los Angeles, CA — Tyrannus Korean (emerging)
1989–1996, discontinued
pastor: S.I. Hyun, 1989–1996

Los Angeles, CA — U.C.L.A. Inter Varsity (campus ministry)
1968–1980
staff: H. Pott (L), 1968–74; H. De Young, 1974–79

Los Angeles, CA — West Bethel Korean
1984–1993, withdrew
pastor: Y.K. Kim, 1984–93

Loveland, CO — Calvary
1979–1997, withdrew to United Reformed Church
pastors: H. De Young, 1979–87; V.D. Vander Toop, 1988–90; D.L. Piers, 1993–97

Lowell, MI — Calvary
1953–
organized: 1968
pastors: H. Boersma (L), 1953–56; M. Harberts (E), 1956–58; H. Buikema (E), 1958–68; M.B. Fynaardt, 1969–75; R.J. Vande Kieft, 1976–84; S.M. Arrick, 1985–88; C.J. Reitsma, 1990–94; W.J. Renkema, 1994–

Low Prairie, IL — Low Prairie
see: South Holland, IL – First

Lucas, MI — Lucas
1883–
former name: Richland, MI – Richland, 1887–1905
pastors: P. Van Vliet, 1888–92; H. Tempel, 1893–94; J. Vander Mey, 1894–96; M.J. Marcusse, 1898–1906; R. Bolt, 1906–12; P.D. Van Vliet, 1912–19; W. Borgman, 1919–25; J.C. Schaap, 1925–31; J.L. Schaver, 1932–45; R. Wezeman, 1946–51; H. Vanderaa, 1955–60; G.G. Vanderlip, 1960–65; F.L. Netz, 1965–71; G.G. Heyboer, 1974–77; T.J. Brown, 1978–85; M.A. Palsrok, 1985–89; T.A. De Does, 1990–

Lucknow, ON — Lucknow
1952–
pastors: R.J. Bos, 1950–52; C. Spoelhof, 1952–59; S. Terpstra, 1960–64; D.M. Lieverdink, 1965–68; J.W. Van Stempvoort, 1969–75; L. Van Staalduinen, Jr., 1975–80; B. Slofstra, 1980–84; D.F. Thielke, 1985–90; R.V. Luchies, 1991–97; P.J. Janssens, 1998–

Luctor, KS — Luctor
1885–
former name: Luctor-Prairie View, KS – Luctor-Prairie View, 1900–93
pastors: E. Bos, 1892–96; R. Smits, 1899–1901; I. Van Dellen, 1902–03; R. Bolt, 1903–06; H.J. Kuiper, 1907–10; J.B. Vander Werp, 1911–14; J. Mulder, 1915–21; P. Bloem, 1922–30; F. De Jong, 1930–34; M. Vander Zwaag, 1935–38; E.H. Oostendorp, 1939–46; S. Viss, Jr., 1947–50; A.J. Veltkamp, 1951–55; H.R. Roelofs, 1955–58; A.E. Mulder, 1960–64; I.W. Meuzelaar, 1965–75; J.A. Molenbeek, 1975–79; T.J. Vos, 1979–87; L.D. Baar, 1987–94; P. Copeland (RCA), 1998–99 J. Van Der Weele (RCA), 1999–

Luctor-Prairie View, KS — Luctor-Prairie View
see: Luctor, KS – Luctor

Luverne, MN — Luverne
1944–
pastors: J.E. Brink, 1946–48; J. Vanden Hoek, 1949–57; H.C. Van Wyk, Jr., 1957–61; J.F. De Vries, 1961–64; G. Corvers, 1964–67; B. Den Herder, 1967–80; R.L. Scheuers, 1981–87; P.E. Bakker, 1988–94; B. Leiter, 1995–98; G. Koopmans, 2000–

Lynden, WA — Bethel
1951–
pastors: T.P. Verhulst, 1952–55; A. Hannink, 1955–58; A. Zylstra, 1958–65; F.J. MacLeod, 1965–68; J. Hofman, Jr., 1968–73; R.B. Vermeer, 1973–81; K.L. Havert, 1983–90; G. Van Groningen, Jr., 1991–2001; J. Van Schepen, 2002–

Lynden, WA — First
1900–
former name: Lynden, WA – Lynden, 1900–20
pastors: A.J. Brink (M), 1899–1900; A.J. Brink, 1900–01; E. Bos, 1902–06; P.J. Hoekenga, 1907–14; E. Breen, 1914–21; P. Jonker, Jr., 1922–29; I. Westra, 1929–34; D. Hollebeek, 1933–45; J.C. Verbrugge, 1946–51; L.F. Voskuil, 1952–55; W.K. Reinsma, 1956–59; B. Byma, 1960–70; A.C. Leegwater, 1970–82; J. Dykstra, 1982–87; P.J. Kok, 1987–97; L.E. Kok, 1989–91; P.A.Hansen, 1998–

Lynden, WA — Lynden
see: Lynden, WA – First

Lynden, WA — Mountain View
1971–
pastors: M.J. Flikkema, 1972–75; D.C. Bouma, 1975–79; K.R. Rip, 1979–88; J.A. De Boer, 1989–94; E. R. Tigchelaar, 1995–2000; W.A. Ten Harmsel, 2000–

Lynden, WA — Second
1920–
pastors: E. Joling, 1921–26; D.H. Muyskens, 1926–34; W. Groen, 1934–43; J.F. Schuurmann, 1944–51; M. Goote, 1951–54; E.L. Haan, 1956–60; J.D. De Jong, 1961–68; J. Batts, 1971–72; R.L. Slater, 1973–76; A.A. Cammenga, 1976–85; L. Kerkstra, 1986–94; R.L. Offringa, 1989–92; T.L. Haan, 1994–2000; P.J. Mans (I), 2000–2001

Lynden, WA — Sonlight Community
1978–
pastor: K.D. Koeman, 1980–

Lynden, WA — Third
1938-
pastors: A. Van Dyken, 1939-48; R.H. Haan, 1949-53; F.W. Van Houten, 1953-57; W.H. Ackerman, 1959-64; D.J. Negen, 1965-72; O.W. Duistermars, 1974-79; G.W. Sheeres, 1979-90; H. Numan, 1991-99; .G. Hewitt, 1992-95; K.R. Ritsema, 1996-; J.M. Gray, 2001-2002

Lynden, WA — Wiser Lake Chapel (emerging)
1960-1999, withdrew from denomination
pastors: M.D. Vander Griend (L), 1960-72; H. Harnden (L), 1967-68; P. Meyers (L), 1972-73; K. Haagsma, 1973-77; B.C. Hemple, 1977-91

Lyndhurst, NJ — Rutherford
1926-1928, discontinued
mission, 1926-27

Lynnwood, WA — Lynnwood
see: Lynnwood, WA — New Life Fellowship Community

Lynnwood, WA — Lynnwood Korean
1990-
pastors: I.S. Kim, 1989-99; S. Kim, 2001-

Lynnwood, WA — New Life Fellowship Community
1968-1993, withdrew, Lynnwood Independent
former name: Lynnwood, WA — Lynnwood, 1968-90
pastors: S.C. Pastine, 1970-78; R.R. Broekema, 1978-89; J.P. Vosteen, 1989-93

Lynwood, IL — Lynwood
1877-1992, withdrew, affiliated with United Reformed Church
former names: Chicago, IL — Roseland, 1877-92; Chicago, IL — First Roseland, 1892-1971
pastors: G. Broene, 1879-84; H. Vander Werp, 1886-92; J. Robbert, 1893-1901; B.H. Einink, 1902-09; J. Walkotten, 1910-14; F. Doezema, 1914-44; M. Arnoys, 1945-54; T. Van Eerden, 1955-64; R. Leetsma, 1964-92; K. Eiten, 1992

Lytle, MT (mission)
1912-1913

Madison, WI — Crossroads
1959-
former name: Madison, WI — Madison, 1959-92
pastors: W.A. Huyser (M), 1957-64; R.A. Hertel, 1964-69; G. Van Enk, 1969-79; G.W. Frens,

1980-84; T.L. Haan, 1984-88; L.E. Van Essen, 1989-2001; B. Bauman, 1999-

Madison, WI — Geneva Campus
1966-
organized: 1991
former name: Madison, WI — Geneva Campus Chapel, 1968-
pastor: R.A. Hertel, 1966-68; T. Limburg (L), 1968-69; C.E. Bajema, 1968-69; R. Westenbroek, 1969-75; C. Roelofs (L), 1969-70; R.L. Palsrok, 1975-77; W.K. Bulthuis, 1977-84; A. De Jong (E), 1985-87; C.E. Bajema, 1988-

Madison, WI — Geneva Campus Chapel
see: Madison, WI — Geneva Campus

Madison, WI — Madison
see: Madison, WI — Crossroads

Manhattan, MT — Bethel
1960-
pastors: J.R. Kok, 1961-64; T. Medema, 1964-71; G.W. Van Den Berg, 1971-78; A. Petroelje, 1978-85; T.B. Swieringa, 1986-90; J. Weeda, 1991-

Manhattan, MT — First
see: Manhattan, MT — Manhattan

Manhattan, MT — Manhattan
1903-
former name: Manhattan, MT — First, 1960-91
pastors: J.J. Holwerda, 1904-08; J. Vander Mey, 1908-13; T. Vander Ark, 1916-22; A.B. Voss, 1923-27; A.H. Bratt, 1928-41; J. De Jong, 1942-48; P.A. Spoelstra, 1949-58; R. Tadema, 1958-62; J. Fondse, 1962-67; A.H. Venema, 1969-72; R.A. Bruxvoort, 1973-80; G.G. Vink, 1980-86; J. Gunnink, 1987-94; J.W. Van Der Heide, 1995-2000; J.A. Huttinga, 2002-

Maple Grove, MN — Family of Christ
see: Maple Grove, MN — Woodland Creek Community

Maple Grove, MN — Woodland Creek Community
1990-1998, discontinued
former name: Maple Grove, MN — Family of Christ, 1993-97
pastors: T.B. Swieringa, 1990-96; S.A Zwart, 1996-98

Maple Ridge, BC — Maple Ridge
1951-
former name: Pitt Meadows, BC — Pitt Meadows, 1951-52; Haney, BC — Haney, 1952-73; Haney, BC — First, 1973-75; Haney, BC — Maple Ridge, 1975-78
organized: 1951
pastors: W. Feenstra, 1955-69; J.W. Postman, 1959-64; J.W. Jongsma, 1964-69; W. Dykstra, 1969-74; H.G. Samplonius, 1975-80; J. Boonstra, 1980-91; W.C. Veenstra, 1992-2001; M.J. Vellekoop, 2001-

Mariaville, NY — Mariaville
1882-1908, withdrew to Presbyterian Church united with CRC, 1890
former name: Mariaville, NY — Mariaville True Protestant Dutch Reformed

Marion, IA — Cedar Rapids Chapel
1966-1970
staff: C. Van Engelhoven (L), 1966-67; R. Kuiper (L), 1967-68

Marion, MI — Back to God Chapel
1958-1977
former name: Marion, MI — Harding Chapel, 1964-73
staff: W.D. Ribbens (M), 1958-63; M. Barber (L), 1963-65; R. Kuiper (L), 1966-67; H. Boehm (E), 1970-75, 1976-77; G. VanderLugt (L), 1975-76

Marion, SD — Bethel
1893-
joined CRC, 1973
former names: Marion, SD — Bethel Reformed, 1893-1934; Marion, SD — Bethel Evangelical and Reformed, 1934-73
pastors: M. Hofer, 1883-1900; G. Treick, 1900-05; A. Kurtz, 1920-41; K. Krueger, 1943-44; H. Hartman, 1944-52; H. Bartell, 1954-72; R.D. De Young, 1972-73; R.E. Van Hofwegen (intern), 1974-75; N.D. Kloosterman, 1975-78; W.G. Vis, 1979-83; J.W. Maas, 1983-91

Marquette, MI — Faith in Christ Fellowship (emerging)
1993-
pastor: W.R. De Young, 1993-

Marshall, MN — Sonshine Fellowship (classical ministry)
1984-1985
pastor: D. Nieuwsma (E), 1984-85

Marshalltown, IA (unorganized)
1982-1983
pastor: P.K. Uzel (E), 1982-83

Martin, MI — East Martin
see: East Martin, MI — East Martin

Martin, SD — Martin
1929-1937, discontinued
pastor: M. Huizenga (stated supply), 1933-35

Martintown, ON — Martintown
see: Cornwall, ON — Immanuel

Marysville, WA — Cascade
1968-
pastors: H.A. Ouwinga, 1969-74; A. Petroelje, 1974-78; J.M. Wanders, 1978-82; G.A. Terpstra, 1983-89; K.L. Schepel, 1989-94; T.B. Toeset, 1997-

Mason City, IA — Rolling Acres
1962-
organized: 1971
pastors: W.N. Gebben (M), 1962-67; K. Bakker, 1967-70; W.A. Stroo (M), 1970-75; M.L. De Young, 1976-84; J. Vanden Heuvel, 1982-

Matsqui, BC — Gifford Community Chapel
1972-1987
began as Glenmore Road Sunday School
staff: H. Jansen (L), 1972-76; R. Lodewyk (E), 1983-86

Maxwell City, NM — Maxwell City
1893-1908, discontinued
pastor: I. Van Dellen, 1895-1902

McBain, MI — Calvin
1912-
former name: West Branch, MI — West Branch, 1912-45
pastors: E. Van Korlaar, 1916-20; C. Maring, 1922-43; M.M. Schans, 1945-48; F. Einfeld, 1950-65; R.L. Wiebenga, 1966-78; R.J. de Groot, 1978-82; H.J. Westra, 1984-89; R.T. Vanderwall, 1990-95; K.D. Koning, 1996-

McBain, MI — McBain
1917-
pastors: H. Goodyke, 1918-22; G. Hofmeyer, 1923-26; J.C. Kruithof, 1926-29; I.D. Couwenhoven, 1931-59; C. Van Essen, 1960-65; W.J. Dykstra, 1965-68; R.D. Ritsema, 1969-72; K.E. Van Wyk, 1972-79; R. Walter, Jr., 1979-84;

C.H. Bruxvoort, 1984–93; J.W. Zuidema, 1994–98; J.S. Meyer, 2000–

McMinnville, OR — Sunrise
1991–
pastors: M.D. Timmer, 1988–94; G.P. Hutt, 1996–2000; W.S. Wilton, 2001–

Medicine Hat, AB — First
see: Medicine Hat, AB — Medicine Hat

Medicine Hat, AB — Medicine Hat
1953–
former name: Medicine Hat, AB — First, 1980–98
pastors: A.H. Selles, 1955–57; M.D. Geleynse, 1960–64; M.N. Greidanus, 1964–68; H. De Moor, Sr., 1970–75; P. Meyer, 1975–82; M.R. Ten Pass, 1982–85; R.W. Sparks, 1986–91; L.T. Schalkwyk, 1992–93; A. Beukema, 1995–2000; H.A. Newhouse, 2000–

Menno, SD — Peace
1979–
pastors: S.J. De Vries, 1979–86; B. Dykstra, 1986–95; T.R. Hull, 1996–99; W.D. Weber, 1999–

Merced, CA — Gateway Community
1984–
organized: 1989
pastors: A. Schaap, 1984–; A.J. Meyer, 1996–2001; C. Louvau, 1989–99

Mesa, AZ — Maranatha Community (emerging)
1999–
pastor: S. Siebersma (E), 1999–

Meservey, IA — Meservey
1891–1901, discontinued

Miami, FL (mission)
1956–1957
staff: D.L. Van Halsema, 1956–57

Miami, FL — First
see: Miami, FL — South Kendall Community

Miami, FL — Good News
see: Miami, FL — Iglesia Buenas Nuevas

Miami, FL — Good Samaritan
see: Miami, FL — Iglesia El Buen Samaritano

Miami, FL — Iglesia Buenas Nuevas
1991–

organized: 1992
pastors: R.C. Borrego, 1989–95; G. Gracia, 1995–2000, 2001– ; X.L. Suarez, 2000–

Miami, FL — Iglesia El Buen Samaritano
1964–
pastors: C.J. Nyenhuis, 1960–69; B. Bruxvoort (M), 1963–66; J. Grotenhuis (L), 1962–65; G. Hernandez (L), 1963–69; A.J. De Berdt, 1965–67; C. Boersma (L), 1965–69; S. Belin (L), 1967–69; F. Diemer, 1968–79; A. Francken (L), 1968–69; R.C. Borrego, 1978–89; G.A. Serrano, 1988–91; J. Abreu, 1991–94; L.A. Pellecer, 1994–

Miami, FL — Iglesia Piedras Vivas (emerging)
2001–
pastor: M. Bersach, 2001–

Miami, FL — Miami
see: Miami, FL — South Kendall Community

Miami, FL — South Kendall Community
1955–
former names: Miami, FL — Miami, 1955–80; Miami, FL — First, 1980–90
pastors: D.I. Van Halsema, 1956–57; T. Verseput, 1957–62; A.R. Rienstra, 1962–73; M.C. Baarman, 1974–75; J. Vander Plate, 1957–81; J.H. Looman, 1984–88; M.H. Van Hofwegen, 1988–99; D.R. Wolters (I), 1999–2000; V.G. Vander Zee, 2000–

Middleburg, IA — Middleburg
1899–1959, discontinued
pastors: D. Vander Ploeg, 1899–1902; N., Burggraaf, 1902–04; P.J. Hoekenga, 1905–07; L. Van Dellen, 1907–08; J.M. Voortman, 1909–12; J.H. Schultz, 1912–14; J.H. Beld, 1915–19; I. Westra, 1919–23; H.J. Heynen, 1923–26; F. Schuurmann, 1926–34; C. Groot, 1935–40; G. Zylstra, 1941–49; A. Baker, 1950–59

Middlesboro, KY (mission)
1977–1984
pastor: T.C. Limburg, 1977–84

Middleville, MI — Bowen Mills
1954–1974
staff: A. Van Der Veer (E), 1954–55; W. Alderink (E), 1955–59; H. Van Til (L), 1960–64, 1966–68, 1970–72; P. Hogeterp, 1964–66; H. Schutt (L), 1968–72

Middleville, MI — Middleville
1962–

organized: 1965
pastors: L. Vander Til (L), 1952-56; E. Holkeboer (L), 1956-57; J. Poel (E), 1957-62; E.L. Schipper, 1963-68; W. Timmer, 1968-72; R.G. Timmerman, 1973-2001; T.J. DeVries, 2002-

Midland Park, NJ — Irving Park
1955-1998, merged with Wyckoff, NJ — Cedar Hill
former name: Irving Park, NJ — Irving Park, 1955-61
pastors: A.M. Mac Leod, 1955-58; A.J. Bultman, 1959-62; L.J.Dykstra, 1962-67; A.H. Jongsma, 1968-71; I.J. Apol, 1971-76; B.A. Averill, 1977-82; S.J. Van Heest, 1983-90; R.S. Greenway, 1991-95; R.D. Steen, 1996-98

Midland Park, NJ — Love Korean (emerging)
1997-
former name: Ridgewood, NJ — Love Korean, 1997-99
pastor: S.H. Chung, 1997-

Midland Park, NJ — Midland Park
1872-
joined CRC, 1892
pastors: E.R. Haan, 1891-96; D.R. Drukker, 1897-98; F. Doezema, 1899-1905; P. Ekster, 1905-08; J.B. Hoekstra, 1909-26; R.L. Haan, 1923-30; E. Kooistra, 1930-41; J.T. Holwerda, 1941-48; W. Vander Haak, 1949-54; S.H. Rooy, 1954-61; B.E. Pekelder, 1955-62; J. Hasper, 1962-70; D.P. Wisse, 1970-96; J.G. Aupperlee, 1973-77; R. Vander Laan, 1983-90; J.J. Hoogland, 1989-2002; G.L. Zandstra, 1991-93; P.A. Hoytema, 1998-

Midland Park, NJ — New Life Ministries (emerging)
1995-
former name: Franklin Lakes, NJ — New Life Ministries, 1995-1998
pastor: H.J. Vugteveen, 1995-

Midlothian, IL (mission)
1938-1939
staff: J.R. Brink (M), 1938

Mildfordsquare, PA — Trumbauerville
1915-1917, discontinued

Milford, NS — Faith
see: Milford, NS — Faith Community

Milford, NS — Faith Community
1975-

organized: 1986
former name: Milford, NS — Faith, 1986; Shubenacadie, NS — Faith, 1975-87
pastor: C.H. Witten, 1985-2001; P.R. Vanderkooy, 2001-

Mill Creek, WA — Garden of Grace (emerging)
2000-
pastor: G. Kim, 2000-

Mill Creek, WA — Hope Community
see: Mill Creek, WA — Mill Creek Community

Mill Creek, WA — Mill Creek Community
1990-
former name: Mill Creek, WA — Hope Community, 1990-93
pastors: K.R. Rip, 1988-97; E.M. Rietkerk, 1997-; L.A. Likkel, 2000-

Milwaukee, WI (mission)
1942-1955
staff: W. Verwolf, 1942-46; E. Boer, 1953-55

Milwaukee, WI — Milwaukee
1862-1863, joined the Presbyterian Church
see also: Brookfield, WI — Brookfield

Minneapolis, MN — Calvary
1961-
former name: Bloomington, MN — Calvary, 1961-93
absorbed, Minneapolis, MN — First, 1999
pastors: D.H. Aardsma, 1963-68; S. Newhouse, 1968-73; M. Reitsma, 1974-79; J. Bylsma, 1980-87; W.L. Meyer, 1988-94; R.D. Engle, 1992-2001; R. D. Kramer, 1995-

Minneapolis, MN — First
1945-1999, merged with Minneapolis, MN — Calvary
former name: Minneapolis, MN — Minneapolis, 1945-61
mission, 1939-45
pastors: H. Wierenga (M), 1938-39; H. Rikkers, 1945-51; S.A. Werkema, 1952-54; H.G. Arnold, 1953-57; E.L. Shuart, 1957-62; J.P. Vosteen, 1962-66; E. De Vries, 1967-74; J.K. Tuinstra, 1975-82; N. Shepherd, 1983-89; A.P. Vander Pol, 1990-97

Minneapolis, MN — Great Love Mission (emerging)
1991-

pastor: S.M. Kim (E), 1991-

Minneapolis, MN — Minneapolis
see: Minneapolis, MN — First

Minneapolis, MN — University of Minnesota Campus Ministry
1969-1983
staff: J.O. Schuring, 1969-72; B.J. Becksvoort, 1972-77; W. Monsma (L), 1979-80; R.R. Drake (OPC), 1980-83

Mission, BC — Mission Hills Community (emerging)
1997-
pastors: A.P. Turkstra, 1996-

Mission Hills, CA — Korean Peace of Los Angeles
1997-
organized: 1998
pastor: H. Kang, 1997-2000; J.N. Jun, 2001-

Mission Viejo, CA — Urim
1996-
organized: 1998
former names: Laguna Niguel, CA — South Orange Korean, 1996-98; Laguna Niguel, CA — Urim, 1998-99
pastors: J.Y. Chang, 1986; S.J. Kang, 1987-89; S.H. Lee, 1996-97; B.I. Song, 1997-

Mississauga, ON — Bethel Chinese (emerging)
1989-2001, discontinued
pastor: D.Y. Leung, 1989-98

Mississauga, ON — Clarkson
1950-
former names: Dixie, ON — Dixie, 1950-53; Clarkson, ON — Clarkson, 1953-76
pastors: H.W. Kroeze, 1953-62; H. De Moor., Sr., 1962-70; S. Greidanus, 1970-75; A. Kuyvenhoven, 1976-79; J.G. Klomps, 1980-82; W.C. Veenstra, 1982-92; G.H. Pols, 1993-2000; J.G. De Vries, 2001-

Mississauga, ON — Community of Meadowvale
1976-
organized: 1977
former name: Mississauga, ON — Meadowvale Community, 1977-85
pastors: H. Lunshof, 1976-92; R.G. Fisher (I), 1992-93; S. Cooper, 1994-

Mississauga, ON — Meadowvale Community
see: Mississauga, ON — Community of Meadowvale

Missouri City, TX — Community Life
see: Houston, TX — Community Life

Modesto, CA (mission)
1914

Modesto, CA — First
1937-
began as a mission, 1936
former name: Modesto, CA — Modesto, 1938-80
pastors: H.J. De Vries, 1935-37; A.H. Selles (M), 1937-38; J. Zwaanstra, 1938-42; W. Vande Kieft, 1943-49; B. Den Ouden, 1951-67; D.R. Vander Wall, 1967-75; L.J. Dykstra, 1975-81; B. Van Eyk, 1982-85; C. Vander Neut, 1986-93; H. Hiemstra, 1994-2001

Modesto, CA — Modesto
see: Modesto, CA — First

Moline, IL (mission)
1964-1965

Moline, MI — Moline
1908-
pastors: P.A. Hoekstra, 1910-11; J.M. Voortman, 1912-13; J.J. De Jonge, 1913-17; D. Flietstra, 1918-23; J. Bruinooge, 1923-43; J.L. Bult, 1944-49; J.A. Mulder, 1950-56; J.F. Schuurmann, 1956-64; L.C. Bossenbroek, 1964-71; W.H. De Vries, 1972-90; W.C. Hensen, 1993-2003

Momence, IL — Momence
1930-
former name: Grant Park, IL — Grant Park, 1930-34
pastors: R.O. De Groot, 1935-41; S.P. Eldersveld, 1941-42; C. Maring, 1943-46; R.R. Recker, 1947-49; J.A. Hoeksema, 1950-53; P.W. Brouwer, 1953-59; J.M. Dykstra, 1959-64; C.J. Toeset, 1964-72; A. Lindemulder, 1972-78; G. Vander Plaats, 1978-81; C.P. Van Reken, 1982-86; C.A. Reyneveld, 1987-91; T.C. Turngren, 1992-97; R.J. Van der Borgh, 1998-2001

Monarch, AB — Monarch
see: Nobleford, AB — Nobleford

Monee, IL — Family of Faith
2001-

pastor: H. Reyenga, 2001–

Monroe, WA — Monroe
see: Monroe, WA – New Hope Fellowship

Monroe, WA — New Hope Fellowship
1914–
former names: Duvall, WA – Duvall, 1934–51;
Sultan, WA – Sultan, 1914–51 (was a merger of
the two congregations); Monroe, WA – Monroe,
1951–2001
pastors: C.J. Vos, 1951–54; N.R. Prins, 1955–58;
H.T. Karsten, 1958–63; C.G. Werkema, Sr., 1963–
66; J. Stulp, 1967–73; K.R. Slager, 1974–88; D.J.
Negen, 1988–90; T. Medema, 1991–95; R.W.
Jansons, 1995–

Monrovia, CA — Eternal Covenant (emerging)
1993–1995, discontinued
pastor: R. Brooks, 1991–95

Monsey, NY — Monsey
see: Monsey, NY – New Hope

Monsey, NY — New Hope
1825–1908, 1925–
joined CRC from True Protestant Dutch Reformed,
1890; joined True Dutch Reformed Church, 1908–
25
pastors: J.D. Demarest, 1825–55; J.Y. De Baun,
1855–60; A. Van Houten, 1861; J.R. Cooper,
1865–86; J. Trompen, 1890; H. Iserman, 1890;
C.D. De Mott, 1891–92; J. Van Houten, 1892–93;
W.D. Vander Werp, 1897–99; K. Poppen, 1902–04;
J.C. Voorhis, 1906–09; J. Beebe, 1925–28; M.
Botbyl, 1928–40; D.L. Van Halsema (M), 1940–56;
E.T. Lewis, Jr., 1956–64; C.D. Vander Meyden,
1966–69; R. Walter, Jr., 1970–75; L.P. Troast,
1975–80; M.J. Lucas, 1981–85; G.S. Miller, 1991–
93; T. Elliott (stated supply), 2000–

Montague, CA — Big Springs (emerging)
1985–
classical ministry, 1985–1998
pastors: J. DeWitt (E), 1985–88; V. Schaap (E),
1993–2000; M.A. Hofland. 2001–

Montague, MI — Montague
1881–1928, discontinued, members merged into
New Era, MI

Monterey Park, CA — Chinese
1991–

former name: Los Angeles, CA – Chinese, 1991–
92
pastor: J.T.C. Tong, 1997–

Monterey Park, CA — Monterey Park Indonesian (emerging)
1993–1997, discontinued
pastor: H.L. Lie, 1993–97

Montreal, QC (mission)
1964–1965
staff: J. Van Veen (L), 1964–65

Montreal, QC — Communaute de la Rive-Sud
see: Montreal, QC – South Shore

Montreal, QC — First
1954–
former name: Montreal, QC – Montreal, 1954–79
pastors: G. Andre (M), 1953–56; J. Vriend, 1956–
60; N.B. Knoppers, 1960–68; D.J. Hart, 1970–74;
M.D. Geleynse, 1974–81; J. Tenyenhuis, 1982–88;
W.J. Kuurstra, 1988–95; F.C. Guter, 1996–

Montreal, QC — Ministry to Seafarers (emerging)
1965–
classical ministry, 1965–1998
pastors: H. Uittenbosch, 1965–92; M. Winnowski,
1993–97; H.L. Burghart, 1999–

Montreal, QC — Montreal
see: Montreal, QC – First

Montreal, QC — Montreal Island (ministry)
1992–1993
staff: P. Michaud, 1992–93

Montreal, QC — South Shore (classical ministry)
1989–1992
staff: J. Marlowe (E), 1989–92

Montville, NJ — Montville
1824–1908, left the denomination
joined CRC from True Protestant Dutch Reformed
Church, 1890
pastors: J.G. Brinkerhoff, 1824–30; I. De Baun,
1861–65

Moreno Valley, CA — Laotian Vientiane (emerging)
1994–

former name: Riverside CA – Laotian Vientiane, 1994-97
pastor: S. Vilaylack, 1989-

Moreno Valley, CA — Oasis Community (emerging)
1990-
organized: 1999
pastors: A. Breems, 1990-; T.D. Blackmon, 1995-98

Moreno Valley, CA — Yung Kwang (church plant)
2000-

Morrison, IL — Morrison
1935-
pastors: M.H. Faber, 1936-44; P. Honderd, 1945-52; H. Leetsma, 1952-57; E.W. Los, 1957-61; G.D. Pars, 1962-68; A. Walma, 1968-80; H.J. Weidenaar, 1980-84; S.J. Alsum, 1985-89; B. Leiter, 1990-95; B.J. Vaandrager, 1996-

Mountain Lake, MN — Mountain Lake
1913-2001, discontinued
pastors: C.G. Hayenga (M), 1918-25; C.H. Bode (M), 1929-33; G.J. Vander Ziel, 1933-38; C. Abbas, 1938-44; J. Vanden Hoek, 1946-49; H. Vanderaa, 1949-55; J.H. Elenbaas, 1955-60; A.D. Menninga, 1961-64; W.G. DuBois, 1966-73; N. Roorda, 1974-79; D.N. Snapper, 1980-84; M.J. Leese, 1985-93; G. Besteman, 1998-2001

Mount Brydges, ON — Mount Brydges
1976-
pastors: G.J. Bomhof, 1976-80; M.J. Lise, 1981-85; J.E. Top, 1987-96; V. Vandermolen, 1999-

Mount Hamilton, ON — Mount Hamilton
see: Hamilton, ON – Mount Hamilton

Mount Pleasant, MI — Mount Pleasant
see: Mount Pleasant, MI – University Church

Mount Pleasant, MI — Trinity
see: Mount Pleasant, MI – University Church

Mount Pleasant, MI — University Church (campus ministry)
1966-
organized: 1977
former name: Mount Pleasant, MI – Mount Pleasant, MI, 1977-85; Mount Pleasant, MI – Trinity, 1985-2002
pastors: S.J. Bultman (M), 1966-69; J.H.

Ringelberg (L), 1969-70; M.C. Nieboer (M), 1970-75; K.W. Tanis, 1975-79; R.L. Bouwkamp, 1980-83; J.E. Versluys, 1983-93; M. Bouma, 1997-

Mount Vernon, WA — Faith Community Fellowship
1988-
pastor: J.A. Byker, 1989-2000; J.D. Westra, 2002-

Mount Vernon, WA — First
1942-
former name: Mount Vernon, WA – Mount Vernon, 1942-70
pastors: J.K. Van Baalen, 1943-50; C.M. Schoolland, 1950-53; J.A. Petersen, 1953-58; J.A. Hoeksema, 1958-67; J. Fondse, 1967-73; H. Van Dyken, 1973-77; A. Poot, 1979-84; R.J. Holwerda, 1984-89; M.J. Kooy, 1991-

Mount Vernon, WA — Mount Vernon
see: Mount Vernon, WA – First

Mukilteo, WA — Garden of Grace (emerging)
2000-
pastor: G. Kim, 2000-

Munster, IN — Community Sunday School (mission)
1949-1956
staff: P. Vander Vaart (L), 1952-56

Munster, IN — First
1870-
former names: Lansing, IL – Lansing, 1870-76; North Town, IN, 1876-1877; North Township, IN, 1877-1878; Lansing, IN, 1879-1908; Munster, IN – Munster, 1908-71
pastors: B. Mollema, 1879-82; H. Tempel, 1883-86; P. Van Vliet, 1892-1906; W. Borgman, 1907-11; H.J. Mokma, 1912-13; D. Zwier, 1914-20; J.K. Van Baalen, 1920-26; J.H. Monsma, 1926-48; J.L. Bult, 1949-55; W.D. Buursma, 1955-63; L.A. Bazuin, 1963-92; D.J. Van Loo, 1973-76; H.J. Schutt, 1994-; J.J. Brower, 1996-99

Munster, IN — Munster
see: Munster, IN – First

Muskegon, MI — Allen Avenue
1889-
former name: Muskegon, MI – Third, 1889-1929
pastors: P. Kosten, 1889-92; H. Beuker, 1893-94; H. Walkotten, 1895-99; P. Jonker, Sr., 1899-1901;

J. Manni, 1901–03; J. Smitter, 1904–08; H. Tuls, 1908–12; J.L. Van Tielen, 1915–21; D. Flietstra, 1923–31; W. Hendriksen, 1931–35; J. Hoogland, 1936–45; M. Goote, 1946–51; D.J. Drost, 1952–60; E.L. Shuart, 1962–68; T.E. Hofman, 1968–72; D.J. Van Beek, 1972–83; G.B. Dokter, 1985–94; R.L. Bierenga, 1996–

Muskegon, MI — Angell Community (emerging)
former name: Muskegon, MI — Applewood Community Ministires, 1999–2002
1999–
pastor: J. Hough, 1999–

Muskegon, MI — Applewood Community Ministries
See: Muskegon, MI — Angell Community

Muskegon, MI — Bethany
1903–
former names: Muskegon, MI — Fourth, 1903–15; absorbed Muskegon, MI — Green Ridge, 1978
pastors: J.W. Brink, 1904–09; J. Dolfin, 1909–43; A. Brink, 1943–47; L. Veltkamp, 1949–62; W.K. Stob, 1963–69; M. Beelen, 1970–80; L. Roossien, Jr., 1981–; D.J. Van Essen, 1984–

Muskegon, MI — Bluffton
1931–1964, merged into Muskegon, MI — Calvin
organized: 1952
pastors: A. Brink, 1938–43; G.D. VanderHill, 1945–51; C.J. De Bruin (L), 1948–49; H.G. Vander Ark (L), 1949–50; E. Jabay, 1952–55; S. Ten Brink, 1956–69; C. Holtrop, 1960–64

Muskegon, MI — Calvin
1965–
merger of: Muskegon, MI — Bluffton and Muskegon, MI — Hope; absorbed Muskegon Heights, MI — Muskegon Heights, 1981
pastors: N.L. Meyer, 1966–90; G.D. Postema, 1985–88; K.A. Mannes, 1989–94; J.A. Boersma, 1990–; L.P. Troast, 1995–98

Muskegon, MI — Celebration Community (emerging)
1999–
pastor: D. Ridder, 1999–

Muskegon, MI — Christ Community Chapel
1979–1980
pastors: J.A. and C. Zuidema (L), 1979–80

Muskegon, MI — Churchill Mission (mission)
1941–1944

Muskegon, MI — City Mission (mission)
1930–1938
staff: H. Overzett (L), 1930–38

Muskegon, MI — East
1925–1998, discontinued
pastors: J.H. Bruinooge, 1926–41; R.L. Veenstra, 1941–46; G. Vander Kooi, 1946–53; G.J. Postma, 1953–59; W. Smedes, 1959–64; D.P. Bergsma, 1965–67; T. Verseput, 1968–85; J.L. Hoogeveen, 1986–91; J.A. Molenbeek, 1992–98

Muskegon, MI — First
1867–
former name: Muskegon, MI — Muskegon, 1867–1887
absorbed Muskegon, MI — Immanuel, 1974
pastors: L. Rietdyk, 1870–72; D.J. Vander Werp, 1872–75; W.H. Frieling, 1878–81; G.H. Hoeksema, 1881–87; L. Rietdyk, 1888–89; J.I. Fles, 1890–98; B.H. Einink, 1909–15; H. Bultema, 1916–20; H. Bel, 1921–23; S.P. Eldersveld, 1924–41; T. Van Eerden, 1942–46; J.E. Luchies, 1946–50; O. De Groot, 1952–54; E.E. Zetterholm, 1954–58; R.R. De Ridder, 1960–64; W. Tolsma, 1965–74; E. De Vries, 1974–87; A. Vanden Akker, 1988–91; C.H. Bruxvoort, 1993–2001

Muskegon, MI — Fourth
see: Muskegon, MI — Bethany

Muskegon, MI — Grace
1953–
pastors: H.E. Botts, 1954–56; J.T. Ebbers, 1956–61; J. Cooper, 1962–68; H.D. Bultje, 1969–86; K.J. Voss, 1986–91

Muskegon, MI — Green Creek
1953–1956
staff: E. Walcott (L), 1953–56; W. Boelkins (L), 1953–54

Muskegon, MI — Green Ridge
1954–1978
organized: 1964, merged into Muskegon, MI — Bethany, 1978
pastors: R.W. Bronkema (M), 1954–59; H.M. DeRooy (M), 1959–63; E. Boer, 1963–68; P.J. Koster, 1968–72; D.M. Lieverdink, 1973–78

Muskegon, MI — Hope
1950-1970, merged into Muskegon, MI – Calvin
pastors: H.G. Vander Ark (M), 1948-52; N.
Vanderzee, 1952-55; D.H. Aardsma, 1955-58; J.
Breuker, 1959-63; J. Vander Lugt, 1963-65

Muskegon, MI — Immanuel
1887-1974, merged into Muskegon, MI – First
former name: Muskegon, MI – Second, 1887-31
pastors: A. Keizer, 1888-91; J.B. Hoekstra, 1891-
96; G.G. Haan, 1896-98; R.L. Haan, 1898-1904;
J. Walkotten, 1905-10; H.J. Mulder, 1910-17; H.M.
Vander Ploeg, 1918-23; J. Masselink, 1924-27; J.
Breuker, 1928-47; J.C. Scholten, 1948-57; H.
Leetsma, 1957-64; R. Boeskool, Jr., 1967-71; T.
Van Eerden, 1971-73

Muskegon, MI — Mona Lake Mission (mission)
1941-1956
staff: W. De Young (L), 1941-51; R. Huizinga (E),
1950-53; R. Kunnen (L), 1953-54; E. Borgerding
(L), 1955-56; H. Vlasma (L), 1955-56

Muskegon, MI — Muskegon
see: Muskegon, MI – First

Muskegon, MI — Muskegon Community College (campus ministry)
1970-1971
staff: J. DeBoer (E), 1970-71

Muskegon, MI — Ryerson Heights Mission (mission)
1952-1954
staff: J. Tanis (L). 1952-54

Muskegon, MI — Second
see: Muskegon, MI – Immanuel

Muskegon, MI — Third
see: Muskegon, MI – Allen Avenue

Muskegon Heights, MI (mission)
1923-1924

Muskegon Heights, MI — Muskegon Heights
1909-1981, merged into Muskegon, MI – Calvin
organized: 1910
pastors: J.A. Rottier (M), 1911-16; N. Burggraaf,
1916-23; S.A. Dykstra, 1922-24; B.H. Spalink,
1924-26; S.G. Brondsema, 1926-40; E.L. Haan,
1940-44; R. Rienstra, 1945-50; J.H. Steenwyk,

1951-67; W.M. Gebben, 1967-74; K.R. Wezeman,
1974-81

Nahaschitty, NM (mission)
1929-1945, 1948-1962
staff: G. Oppenhuizen (L), 1931-38; B. De Boer
(L), 1937-44; L. Henry (L), 1944-50; E. Henry,
1950-56; J.B. Swierenga, 1956-58; B. Henry (L),
1956-62; M. Harberts (L), 1960-62

Nanaimo, BC — Christ Community
1980-
organized: 1982
former name: Nanaimo, BC – Nanaimo, 1980-87
pastors: A.E. Likkel, 1980-91; W. Brouwer, 1992-
; L.H. Batterink, 2001-

Nanaimo, BC — Nanaimo
see: Nanaimo, BC – Christ Community

Nanuet, NY — Nanuet
1824-1895, discontinued
joined CRC from True Protestant Dutch Reformed
Church, 1890
pastors: J.V.S. Lansing, 1826; J.G. Brinkerhoff,
1830-40; J.D. Demarest, 1843-52; A. Van Houten,
1852-61; J.R. Cooper, 1865-78; H. Iserman,
1886-1890; J. Poppen, 1892

Napa, CA — Napa Valley
see: Napa, CA – Valley Community

Napa, CA — Valley Community
1985-
former name: Napa, CA – Napa Valley, 1986-95
pastors: C.E. Fennema, 1983-88; B. Van
Antwerpen, 1989-93; P.V. De Jonge, 1994-2001;
R.J. Visker, 2002-

Naperville, IL — Christ Community
see: Plainfield, IL – Christ Community

Naschitti, NM — Naschitti
1982-
pastors: J.B. Swierenga (M), 1956-58; M.A.
Harberts (E), 1960-77; C.J. Brummel (E), 1977-
88; J. Sandoval (E), 1988-93; R. Slim, 1994-2000

Nashville, TN — Faith
1983-
former name: Nashville, TN – First, 1983-85
pastors: R.J. Brouwer, 1982-91; G.L. Hoek,
1992-

Nashville, TN — First
see: Nashville, TN – Faith

Navajo, NM — Navajo (emerging)
1992-2000, discontinued
pastor: T. Tso (E), 1982-90

Navan, ON — Navan
1958-1965, members joined Ottawa, ON – Calvary
pastors: C. Spoelhof (M), 1958-62; J.C. De Moor, 1962-65

Nederland, TX (mission)
1936-1937

Nederland, TX — Nederland
1898-1905, discontinued

Neerlandia, AB — Neerlandia
1915-
pastors: A.H. Selles, 1927-29; H. Vander Woude, 1929-41; M. Keuning, 1942-46; J. Rubingh, 1946-48; L. Mulder, 1952-57; H. Van Dyken, 1957-62; H. Hollander, 1962-66; P. Van Drunen, 1970-73; C. Vriend, 1974-91; J.S. Mantel, 1993-2000; R.A. Blacketer, 2000-

Nepean, ON — Barrhaven Fellowship
see: Ottawa, ON – Barrhaven Fellowship

New Amsterdam, WI — New Amsterdam
1911-1916, discontinued

New Brighton, MN — Faith
1966-
former name: South St. Paul, MN – Faith, 1973-75
pastors: A.J. Stienstra (M), 1965-70; G.L. Kramer, 1970-74; R.J. Buining, 1976-82; J.D. Osterhouse, 1982-90; R.J. Brouwer, 1991-94; E.C. Marlink (I), 1994-95; J.T. Petersen, 1995-

New Brighton, MN — Laotian (emerging)
2000-
pastor: R.J. Lammers, 2000-

New Brighton, MN — Pinewood Chapel
1962-1965
staff: R. Olson (L), 1963-64; K. Vander Ark (L), 1964-65

Newcomb, NM (mission)
1942-1945

staff: J. Maring (L), 1942-43; A. Nieuwsma (L), 1943-45

New Era, MI — Migrant Mission
1957-1967
staff: D. Villa (L), 1957-59; Mr./Mrs. A. Rubio (L), 1961-64; Noberto Wolf (L), 1964-65, 1966-67; E. Sikkenga (L), 1965-66

New Era, MI — New Era
1884-
pastors: J.B. Van der Werp, 1895-98; W. Kole, 1898-1900; G. Westenberg, 1901-04; J. Wyngaarden, 1904-11; W.P. Heeres, 1912-17; J.P. De Vries, 1917-21; G.A. Lyzenga, 1922-27; J.L. Schaver, 1927-32; W.D. Vander Werp, 1932-37; M. Bolt, 1937-42; G. Van Laar, 1943-47; J. Hasper, 1947-50; J.A. Botting, 1952-57; S. Viss, Jr., 1957-62; S. Newhouse, 1962-68; R.J. Noorman, 1969-73; J. Weeda, 1974-83; R.J. Vande Kieft, 1984-94; L.D. Baar, 1994-

New Glasgow, NS — Emmanuel
1958-1993, discontinued
former name: New Glasgow, ON – New Glasgow, 1958-72
pastors: J.H. Binnema, Sr., 1969-73; M. Doornbos, 1968; A. Driese, 1975-80; A.J. De Vries, 1982-87; H. Eising, 1987-90

New Glasgow, NS — New Glasgow
see: New Glasgow, NS – Emmanuel

New Holland, SD — New Holland
1883-
former name: Douglas, SD – Douglas, 1883-84
pastors: T.M. Vanden Bosch, 1883-85; H. Tempel, 1886-88; A.W. Meyer, 1889-94; J.C. Groeneveld, 1894-95; H.H. Kamps, 1897-01; W.P. Van Wyk, 1902-04; J.E. De Groot, 1904-07; M. De Boer, 1907-12; J.M. Byleveld, 1913-21; J. Haveman, 1921-27; J.H. Geerlings, 1928-36; B.H. Spalink, 1937-40; C. Vanden Heuvel, 1940-45; T.C. Van Kooten, 1947-51; G. Vander Plaats, 1952-57; P.E. Bakker, 1958-63; J. De Jong, 1965-68; J.A. Botting, 1968-75; W.G. Brouwers, Jr., 1975-81; J.D. Buwalda, 1982-92; D.J. Boogerd, 1992-96; D.W. Cowart, 2000-

New Lenox, IL — New Life (emerging)
1996-
pastor: J.T. Medenblik, 1995-

New Liskeard, ON — New Liskeard
1957-1965, discontinued

pastor: B. Bruxvoort (M), 1959-63

Newmarket, ON — Bethel
1955-
former name: Newmarket, ON — Newmarket, 1955-72
pastors: D.N. Habermehl, 1959-64; J.C. Vander Stelt, 1965-67; J. Joose, 1967-71; A. Driese, 1972-75; S. Vander Meer, 1975-82; H.C. Salomons, 1982-90; M. Veenema, 1989-92; W. Dykstra, 1990-98; M.A. Davies, 2000-

Newmarket, ON — Holland Marsh
see: Holland Marsh, ON — Holland Marsh

Newmarket, ON — Newmarket
see: Newmarket, ON — Bethel

New Richmond, MI — Bethel Chapel
see: New Richmond, MI — New Richmond

New Richmond, MI — New Richmond
1936-1964, discontinued
organized: 1958
former name: New Richmond, MI — Bethel Chapel, 1936-58
pastors: A. Bratt (L), 1941-54; J.O. Handley, 1955-60; P.A. Spoelstra, 1961-62; A. Walcott (M), 1963-64

Newton, IA — Newton
1935-
pastors: F.M. Huizenga, 1943-44; B.H. Spalink(M), 1944-48; D. Grasman, 1948-51; K. Rietema, 1953-58; K.L. Havert, 1958-63; H.G. Vanden Einde, 1964-68; J.W. Dykstra, 1968-72; G.R. Erffmeyer, 1972-76; D.G. Draayer, 1976-80; N. Vogelzang, 1981-84; W. Vanden Bos, 1984-90; D.J. Roeda, 1990-95; M.D. Bennink, 1997-2002

Newton, NJ — Newton
1943-1997, withdrew to United Reformed Churches
pastors: J.H. Kromminga, 1943-46; D.J. Oostenink, Jr., 1946-47; J.J. Holwerda, 1948-56; E. Kooistra, 1956-60; J.H. Ellens, 1961-65; F.R. De Boer, 1965-71; G.W. Frens, 1972-80; R.W. Loerop, 1981-88; C.D. Freswick, 1989-97

New Westminster, BC — First
1952-
pastors: H. Van Andel, 1954-65; J. Kuntz, 1965-72; L. Slofstra, 1970-75; C.C. Spoor, 1973-78; W.L. Vander Beek, 1975-83; P. Brouwer, 1979-95;

W.C. Tuininga, 1984-96; A. Helder, 1996-2002; D.M. Devadatta, 2000-2002

New Westminister, BC — New West Community (emerging)
1997-1999, discontinued
pastor: W.C. Tuininga, 1997-99

New York, NY (mission)
1926-1927

New York, NY — Bank Street
1823-1908, 1925-1934, discontinued
joined CRC from True Protestant Dutch Reformed Church, 1890; withdrew to True Reformed Dutch Church, 1908-22
pastors: H. Iserman, 1895-99; S. Froeligh, 1923-24; C.T. Demarest, 1924-39; S.D. Westervelt, 1940-51; C.T. Demarest, 1852-62; A. Van Houten, 1866-78; J.A. Westervelt, 1880-88; H. Iserman, 1892-98; S.I. Vander Beek, 1898-1901; J.C. Voorhis, 1909-22

New York, NY — Manhattan
1954-1991, discontinued
organized: 1960, began as an evangelism program
former name: New York, NY — New York, 1975-76
pastors: E.S. Callender, 1954-59; M. Visser (L), 1955-58; E. Vander Ploeg (L), 1956-57; B. Greenfield (L), 1958-60; D. Dixon (L), 1958-60; T. Kenbeck (L), 1958-60; P. Huiner (L), 1959-60; G.D. Negen (M), 1959-65; G.D. Negen, 1965-69; J.B. White, 1969-78; J.K. Boersma, 1979-83; M.E. Van Houten, 1990-91

New York, NY — New York
see: New York, NY — Manhattan

New York Mills, NY — Whitesboro
1912-1918, discontinued

Niagara Falls, ON — Niagara Falls
see: Niagara Falls, ON — Rehoboth

Niagara Falls, ON — Rehoboth
1951-
former names: Stamford, ON — Stamford, 1951-55; Niagara Falls, ON — Stamford 1955-56; Niagara Falls, ON — Niagara Falls, 1957-67
pastors: H. Numan, Sr., 1956-63; P. Mantel, 1963-66; G.H. Polman, 1967-73; J. Geuzebroek, 1974-78; L. Tenyenhuis, 1979-82; J.D. Pereboom, 1982-88; J. Pasma, 1988-95; A. Basson, 1999-

Niagara Falls, ON — Stamford
see: Niagara Falls, ON — Rehoboth

Niekerk, MI — Niekerk
see: Holland, MI — Niekerk

Nobleford, AB — Nobleford
1905-
organized with families from the eastern portion
of Nyverdal, AB — Nyverdal, which dissolved; families from the western portion organized as
Ganum, AB — Ganum; and a third group organized
as Burdett, AB — Burdett
former names: Monarch, AB — Monarch, 1911-48
pastors: N. Gelderloos (M), 1916-21; J. Mulder,
1928-42; P.J. Hoekstra, 1944-49; P. Van Dyk,
1949-52; J.W. Van Stempvoort, 1953-57; G.W.
Van Den Berg, 1958-62; J. Hoogland, 1962-66;
K.J. Verhulst, 1966-71; J.S. Mantel, 1971-78; S.A.
Drenth, 1978-82; J.H. Binnema, 1983-87; A.J. De
Vries, 1987-90; J.D. Zondervan, 1991-97; T.G.
Albaugh, 1999-

Noordeloos, MI — Noordeloos
1857-
pastors: K. Vanden Bosch, 1857-69; G. Broene,
1877-79; H. Vander Werp, 1882-83; S. Venema
(Elder), 1887-88; K. Kruelen, 1898-1900; J.
Molhoek (Elder), 1902-06; H. Van Wesep, 1907-
18; H. Heyns, 1919-20; J.J. Zeeuw, 1922-25; S.
Fopma, 1926-44; W.F. Vander Hoven, 1945-48; A.
Walcott, 1948-51; J. Hekman, 1951-55; J.C. Rick-
ers, 1955-60; H.G. Entingh, 1960-64; W.
Masselink, Jr., 1965-69; J. Hanegraaff, 1970-75;
J.A. Brinks, 1975-79; J.A. Botting, 1980-83; C.W.
Niewenhuis, 1984-89; R.J. Timmer, 1990-95; J.
Stulp, 1995-98; M.A. Vande Zande, 2000-

Norfolk, VA (service home)
1958-1996
staff: Mr./Mrs. G. De Vries. Jr., 1959-60; J.C.
Rickers, 1960-65, 1966-68, 1970-71; B.
Grassman (L), 1963-65; Mr./Mrs. R. Klunder (L),
1965-78; Mr./Mrs. B. Frens (L), 1978-82; D.
Mulder (L), 1985-95; B. Nikkel (E), 1995-96

Norfolk, VA — Norfolk
see: Norfolk, VA — Ocean View

Norfolk, VA — Ocean View
1965-
organized: 1975
former name: Norfolk, VA — Norfolk, 1975-77
pastors: J.C. Rickers (M), 1965-91; A.J. Nikkel,
1993-96; D. Mulder (E), 1996-

North Blendon, MI — North Blendon
see: Hudsonville, MI — North Blendon

North Clam, MI — North Clam
see: Falmouth, MI — Prosper

North Haledon, NJ — Covenant
1882-
joined CRC from True Protestant Dutch Reformed
Church, 1890
former names: Paterson, NJ — Third, 1896-1970;
North Haledon, NJ — Trinity, 1970-1986 when it
merged with North Haledon, NJ — North Haledon
pastors: J. Berdan, 1887-89; S.I. Vander Beek,
1889-92; A. Van Houten, 1892-95; J.A.
Westervelt; 1896-1927; J.J. Hiemenga, 1928-47;
W. Heynen, 1949-53; D.E. Bradford, 1954-61; A.E.
Rozendal, 1961-65; S. Cooper, 1965-73; C.N. Van
Dalfsen, 1975-82; T.J. Lapinski, 1982-96; B. Van
Eyk, 1997-99; R. Walter, Jr. (I), 1999-2001: A.K.
Chun, 2001-

North Haledon, NJ — North Haledon
1955-1986, merged with North Haledon, NJ —
Trinity to form North Haledon, NJ — Covenant
pastors: E. Boer, 1956-63; J.A. Petersen, 1964-
71; P.C. Holtrop, 1971-77; A. Lindemulder, 1978-
84

North Haledon, NJ — Trinity
merged with North Haledon, NJ — North Haledon
to form North Haledon, NJ — Covenant

**North Hampton, NH — New Covenant
(emerging) 1995-**
pastor: B.A. Averill, 1995-

Northern, VA — Grace
see: Burke, VA — Grace

North Hollywood, CA — Valley
see: Arleta, CA — Valley

**North Miami Beach, FL — Comunidad de
Cristo (emerging)**
1996-1999, merged into Hialeah, FL — Comunidad
Cristiana
pastor: M. Villanueva, 1997-99

North Natomas, CA (church plant)
2000-
pastor: R.D. Vander Well, 2000-

North Overisel, MI — North Overisel
see: Overisel, MI — North Overisel

Northridge, CA — Mission of Love
1993-
former name: Northridge, CA — Valley Shinil,
1993-96; absorbed Northridge, CA — Valley Evangelical Mission, 1998
pastors: J.W. Lee, 1993-95; H.J. Park, 1995-

Northridge, CA — Valley Dong San
1992-
former name: Sepulveda, CA — Valley Dong San,
1992-98
pastor: C.D. Yoon, 1989-

Northridge, CA — Valley Evangelical Mission
1994-1998, merged into Northridge, CA — Mission of Love
former name: Northridge, CA — Valley Shinil,
1994-96
pastor: S.D. Hong, 1994-98

Northridge, CA — Valley Shinil
see: Northridge, CA — Valley Evengelical Mission

North Town, IN — North Town
see: Munster, IN — First

North Township, IN — North Township
see: Munster, IN — First

Norwalk, CA — Messiah Korean
see: Cypress, CA — Messiah Korean

Norwalk, CA — Rok Won
see: Anaheim, CA — Neung-Ryuk

Nyverdal, AB — Nyverdal
1905-1911, dissolved
families from the eastern portion organized as Monarch, AB — Monarch; families from the western portion organized as Granum, AB — Granum and a third group organized as Burdett, AB — Burdett

Oakdale, CA — Community
1979-
former names: Oakdale, CA — Oakdale, 1979-80;
Oakdale, CA — First, 1980-82
pastors: J.J. Van Dyken, Jr., 1979-82; L.K.Tanis,
1992-99; T.W. Koeman, 1999-

Oakdale, CA — First
see: Oakdale, CA — Community

Oakdale, CA — Oakdale
see: Oakdale, CA — Community

Oak Forest, IL — Hope
1962-
pastors: H.R. Vellinga, 1961-82; R.L. Palsrok,
1983-87; W.R. Lenters, 1988-99; R. Nelson,
2002-

Oak Harbor, WA — Dewey Sunday School
1957-1964
staff: P.J. De Vries (L), 1957-60; L. Dams (L),
1959-64

Oak Harbor, WA — Oak Harbor
1896-1898, withdrew to United Presbyterian Church; organized again as Oak Harbor, WA — Oak Harbor
pastor: J.W. Wiebenga (M), 1897

Oak Harbor, WA — Oak Harbor
1902-
pastors: J. Gulker (M), 1901-04; A.J. Brink (M),
1905-08; D.H. Muyskens (M), 1908-11; N.
Gelderloos (M), 1912-16; F.J. Drost (M), 1917-22;
J.J. Werkman, 1923-28; J.M. Byleveld, 1929-41;
P. De Jong, 1942-44; J.R. Van Dyke, 1945-54; J.
Hekman, 1955-61; W.L. De Jong, 1962-66; A.J.
Dahm, 1967-68; J.M. Gray, 1969-73; R.L. Van
Zomeren, 1973-77; J.A. Petersen, 1977-84; B.
Leiter, 1984-86; D.W Lagerwey, 1987-96; H.
Veldman, 1997-

Oakland, CA (mission)
1916

Oakland, MI — Oakland
1887-
former name: Doornspijk, MI — Doornspijk, 1887-
89; absorbed members from North Overisel in 1887 and East Overisel in 1888
pastors: G.H. Hoeksema, 1887-1902; R. Diephuis,
1903-08; H. Walkotten, 1908-11; J.H. Geerlings,
1912-16; W. Terpsma, 1916-18; W. Kuipers, 1919-
23; J. Kolkman, 1923-44; G. Yff, 1944-48; H.J.
Kuizema, 1949-63; M.S. Jorritsma, 1963-67; A.J.
Van Schouwen, 1968-79; S.R. Steenstra, 1980-
84; B.F. Tol, 1985-92; S.R. Sytsma, 1994-99;
R.D. De Young, 2000-

Oak Lawn, IL — Calvin
1887-
former names: Englewood, IL — Englewood,
1887-1904; Chicago, IL — First Englewood, 1904-
62

pastors: J.B. Van der Werp, 1889-92; L. Van Dellen, 1894-07; G.J. Haan, 1908-18; P.D. Van Vliet, 1919-23; I. Westra, 1923-29; C. Huissen, 1929-41; W. Kok, 1942-53; A. Brink, 1953-58; S. Vroon, 1959-68; A.C. De Jong, 1968-74; J.A. De Kruyter, 1975-86; J.D. Hellinga, 1987-91; H.J. Weidenaar, 1992-98; P.S. Leo, 1999-

Oak Lawn, IL — First

1915-
former name: Oak Lawn, IL — Oak Lawn, 1915-62
pastors: N. Fokkens, 1915-18; S. Bouma, 1918-21; J. Van Beek, 1923-45; J.L. Schaver, 1945-53; M. Bolt, 1952-57; C.M. Schemper, 1957-62; R. Veldman, 1962-70; S.M. Voortman, 1971-76; J.L. Meppelink, 1977-84; J.W. Dykstra, 1985-91; H.B. Vanden Heuvel, 1991-2000; T.V. Wagenmaker, 2001-

Oak Lawn, IL — Immanuel Chapel

1958-
former name: Oak Lawn, IL — Southwest Chapel
staff: D. Aardsma (L), 1958-72

Oak Lawn, IL — Kedvale Avenue

1903-
former name: Chicago, IL — Second Englewood, 1903-52; absorbed members from Chicago, IL — Third Roseland, 1971 and Evergreen Park, IL — West Evergreen, 1975
pastors: K. Poppen, 1904-08; J.R. Brink, 1911-13; H.J. Kuiper, 1913-19; E.J. Tuuk, 1919-28; E. Tanis, 1928-42; W. Masselink, 1942-52; O. Breen, 1952-70; J. Bylsma, 1971-75; A.C. De Jong, 1976-80; F.D. Steen, 1981-86; J.A. Vander Slik, 1987-90; H. Lamsma, 1991-92; D.J. Van Loo, 1992-

Oak Lawn, IL — Oak Lawn

see: Oak Lawn, IL — First

Oak Lawn, IL — Southwest Chapel

see: Oak Lawn, IL — Immanuel Chapel

Oak Park, IL — Oak Park

1938-1973, discontinued, members merged into Cicero, IL — Warren Park (see: Elmhurst, IL — Faith)
former names: Berwyn, IL — Berwyn, 1938-45; absorbed members of Chicago, IL — Fourth, 1945
pastors: H. Bel, 1940-44; E. Kooistra, 1944-52; R.J. Frens, 1953-58; E.C. Marlink, 1959-66; J. Morren, 1966-70; O. Breen, 1970-73

Oceanside, CA — First Union Presbyterian

see: Oceanside, CA — Oceanside Korean-American

Oceanside, CA — Oceanside Korean-American

1992-1996, discontinued
former name: Oceanside, CA — First Union Presbyterian
pastors: H.J. Park, 1993-95; J.J. Kim, 1995-96

Ocheyedan, IA — Ocheyedan

1913-
pastors: H.J. Haarsma (M), 1913-15; A. Wassink, 1915-17; N. Fokkens, 1918-34; F. Vander Stoep, 1935-40; J.A. Mulder, 1941-46; C. Vander Ark, 1946-50; B.E. Visscher, 1950-56; L.C. Bossenbroek, 1956-64; P. Van Drunen, 1965-70; H. DeGroot, 1970-76; M.L. Van Donselaar, 1976-89; R.D. Baker, 1990-95; B.B. Blankers, 1996-2001; J.C. Knoester, 2003-

Ogden, UT (mission)

1918-
staff: W. Van Westenberg (L), 1918

Ogden, UT — Family in Christ

1959-
organized: 1962
former name: Ogden, UT — Ogden, 1959-89
pastors: N. Vogelzang (M), 1959-61; D.P. Wisse (M), 1961-65; R.L. Slater (M), 1965-68; G.P. Hutt, 1969-74; A.W. Heersink, 1975-

Ogden, UT — Ogden

1913-1915, discontinued
pastors: W. De Groot (M), 1913-14
also see: Ogden, UT — Family in Christ

Ogilvie, MN — Ogilvie

1910-
organized: 1915
pastors: H.J. De Vries, 1918-21; J.C. De Bruyn, 1921-29; P.F. Dahm, 1934-42; P. Ouwinga, 1942-46; H. Bossenbroek, 1946-50; J. Medendorp, 1951-58; J. Kroon, 1958-62; A.J. Roon, 1962-66; R.J. Noorman, 1966-69; K.E. Kelly, 1969-71; L.D. Slings, 1971-75; P.J. Veenstra, 1975-87; K.J. Vryhof, 1988-95; M.B. Fynaardt, 1996-2000

Oklahoma City, OK (service home)

1943-1945
staff: A.H. Bratt, 1943-45

Oklahoma City, OK — Oklahoma

1954-1958, discontinued

pastor: J.E. Jeffers (M), 1954–57; H.J. Sprik (M), 1957–58

Olympia, WA — Evergreen
see: Olympia, WA – Olympia

Olympia, WA — Gethsemane
see: Aberdeen, WA – Gethsemane

Olympia, WA — Olympia
1972–
former name: Olympia, WA – Evergreen, 1986
pastors: B.N. Huizinga, 1970–74; S.J. Workman, 1974–82; P.J. Mans, 1983–95; M.A. Van Haitsma, 1996–

Omaha, NE — Omaha
see: Omaha, NE – Prairie Lane

Omaha, NE — Prairie Lane
1965–
former name: Omaha, NE – Omaha, 1965–67
pastors: J.C. De Young (M), 1961–66; W.L.De Jong, 1966–72; J.A. Monsma, 1972–75; D.J. Sieplinga, 1975–77; R.L. Jipping, 1978–82; L.M. Fryling, 1982–89; A.J. Van Dellen, 1987–89; R.R. De Vries, 1990–

Onalaska, WI — Hope
1975–2000, discontinued
organized: 1977
former name: La Crosse, WI – Hope
pastors: J.D. Osterhouse, 1975–82; A.L. Louwerse, 1979–86; P.C. Kelder, 1987–95; D.E. Range, 1996–2000

Ontario, CA — Ontario
1928–1998, withdrew to United Reformed Churches
pastors: H.J. De Vries (M), 1928–35; L. Bouma, 1943–53; J. Putt, 1953–63; H. Sonnema, 1963–81; C.P. Venema, 1982–88; R. Lankheet, 1989–98

Oostburg, WI — First
1868
former names: Gibbsville, WI – Gibbsville, 1868–75; Oostburg, WI – Oostburg, 1875–1971
pastors: J. De Rooy, 1876–84; P. Kosten, 1884–89; J. Wyngaarden, 1890–93; M. Borduin, 1896–1905; E.J. Tuuk, 1907–11; D. Zwier, 1911–14; J. Smitter, 1916–19; W. De Groot, 1920–26; R.J. Frens, 1926–30; B. Vanden Brink, 1930–31; J.C. Schaap, 1932–46; J.H. Piersma, 1947–49; R. Rienstra, 1950–54; B.A. Van Someren, 1955–62;

J.H. Olthoff, 1962–79; T. Wevers, 1981–87; L.J. Kuiper, 1988–

Oostburg, WI — Oostburg
see: Oostburg, WI – First

Oostfriesland, IA — Oostfriesland
see: Woden, IA – Woden

Oostfriesland, NE — Oostfriesland
1876–1895, discontinued

Oost Overijsel, MI — Oost Overijsel
see: Overisel, MI – East Overisel

Orange City, IA (mission)
1901–1906
staff: P. Schut, 1901–02; W. Stuart, 1902–05; F.W. Stuart, 1905–06

Orange City, IA — Calvary
1921–
former name: Orange City, IA – Second, 1921–71
pastors: W.P. Van Wyk, 1922–25; G.W. Hylkema, 1925–34; M.J. Vander Werp, 1935–40; A. Jabaay, 1941–44; R.O. De Groot, 1945–48; J. Masselink, 1949–58; H.R. Roelofs, 1958–65; J. De Vries, 1966–70; E.J. Blankespoor, 1971–77; J.T. Ebbers, 1978–88; J.M. Gray, 1989–2001

Orange City, IA — First
1871–
former name: Orange City, IA – Orange City, 1871–1921
pastors: J. Stadt, 1877–84; J. Gulker, 1884–90; E. Vanden Berge, 1891–93; E. Breen, 1893–1903; I. Van Dellen, 1903–07; J. Timmerman, 1908–16; R.L. Haan, 1916–23; N.J. Monsma, 1924–29; R. Bronkema, Sr., 1929–52; A. Dusseljee, 1952–57; J.B. Hulst, 1958–65; R.H. Tjapkes, 1966–71; J.D. Hellinga, 1972–77; M.S. Jorritsma, 1977–79; T.C. Vanden Heuvel, 1979–85; R.A. Pontier, 1986–94; T.J. Ouwinga, 1997–

Orange City, IA — Immanuel
1979–
pastors: R.J. Brouwer, 1979–82; C.E. Zylstra, 1983–96; J.L. Sajdak, 1997–

Orange City, IA — Orange City
see: Orange City, IA – First

Orange City, IA — Second
see: Orange City, IA – Calvary

Orange County, CA — Korean American
see: Fountain Valley, CA — Korean American of Orange County

Orangeville, ON — Orangeville
1950-
pastors: H. Hollander, 1957-62; G. Nonnekes, 1964-75; H.G. Gunnink, 1976-81; F. Heslinga, 1982-89; W.T. Koopmans, 1990-95; D.J. Bierman, 1996-2002

Orillia, ON — First
1953-
former name: Orillia, ON — Orillia, 1953-80
pastors: J. Kuntz, 1958-62; E. Gritter, 1963-66; W. Van Dyk, 1967-73; S.A. Van Houten, 1973-77; P. Slofstra, 1977-81; G. Ringnalda, 1982-87; P. Meyer, 1988-95; H.R. Nanninga, 1996-

Orillia, ON — Orillia
see: Orillia, ON — First

Orlando, FL (service home)
1969-1974
staff: R.D. Natelborg, 1969-74

Orlando, FL — Crosswind Community (emerging)
1994-1998, discontinued
pastor: K.A. Mannes, 1994-98

Orlando, FL — Haitian (emerging)
2002-
pastor: R. Clotaire, 2002-

Orlando, FL — Oasis Community
1964-
former name: Orlando, FL — Orlando, 1964-93
pastors: R.W. Bronkema (M), 1959-66; R. Wezeman, 1966-69; J.D. Natelborg (M), 1969-74; C. Van Ens, 1974-82; S.J. Workman, 1984- ; J.G. AUkema, 2000-

Orlando, FL — Oasis Hispanic (emerging)
1995-2000, discontinued
pastor: G. Ortiz, 1995-1999

Orlando, FL — Orlando
see: Orlando, FL — Oasis Community

Orland Park, IL — Orland Park
1919-
former name: Chicago, IL — Roseland Fourth, 1919-69; absorbed members from Chicago, IL — Roseland Second, 1971

pastors: G.J. Holwerda, 1920-24; A.H. Bratt, 1925-28; H. Kuiper, 1928-44; R.H. Haan, 1945-49; J.A. De Kruyter, 1950-54; W.M. Van Dyk, 1955-59; H.C. Van Wyk, Jr., 1961-64; G. De Young, 1964-68; H. De Mots, 1969-76; A.J. Schoonveld, 1977-87; F.W. Van Houten, 1982-86; C.J. De Boer, 1986-1989; G.R. Erffmeyer, 1988-; M.T. Holtvluwer, 2001-

Oshawa, ON — Hebron
see: Whitby, ON — Hebron

Oshawa, ON — Hope Fellowship
1999-
pastor: A. Koppendrayer, 1999-2001

Oshawa, ON — Oshawa
see: Whitby, ON — Hebron

Oshawa, ON — Zion
1963-
pastors: D.N. Habermehl, 1964-77; P.W. De Haan, 1977-83; H. Wildeboer, 1984-98; K.J. House, 1988-94; A. Koppendrayer, 1995-99; J. Veenstra, 1999-

Oskaloosa, IA — Bethel
1950-
pastors: W.K. Reinsma, 1951-56; J.H Olthoff, 1956-62; W.H. De Vries, 1962-67; W. Swets, 1969-73; L.G. Christoffels, 1974-79; G.J. Bosma, 1980-83; P.E. Bakker, 1984-88; H. Hiemstra, 1991-94; J.E. Powell, 1995-2000; M.J. Leese, 2001-

Oskaloosa, IA — City Mission
see: Oskaloosa, IA — Good News Chapel

Oskaloosa, IA — First
1903-
former name: Oskaloosa, IA — Oskaloosa, 1903-50
pastors: M. Botbyl, 1905-08; H.J. De Vries, 1909-13; P. Bloem, 1914-22; C. Spoelhof, 1922-26; P. De Koekkoek, 1926-28; J.D. Pikaart, 1929-45; F.W. Van Houten, 1946-50; C.R. Veenstra, 1951-57; W. Dryfhout, 1959-68; G. Vander Plaats, 1970-78; P. Vander Weide, 1980-87; R.D. Drenten, 1988-94; R.J. Timmer, 1995-

Oskaloosa, IA — Good News Chapel (emerging)
1949-
emerging, 1965

former name: Oskaloosa, IA – City Mission, 1949-64
staff: D. Sytsma (L), 1949-51; J. Bruxvoort (L), 1949-50; A. Hanstra (L), 1951-54; G. Oppenhuizen (E), 1953-54; H.G. Jager (E), 1953-56; C. Hoven (L), 1956-59; L. Schut (E), 1959-65; A.G. Boetsma (E), 1965-

Oskaloosa, IA — Oskaloosa
see: Oskaloosa, IA – First

Oswego, IL — The Peak Ministries (emerging)
1999-
pastor: J. Wilczewski, 1999-

Otley, IA — Otley
1898-1958, discontinued
pastors: D. Van der Ploeg (M), 1898-99; S. Bouma, 1900-03; T.W.R. Van Loo, 1903-06; A. Bliek, 1909-13; A.H. Bratt, 1913-18; C. Maring, 1918-22; F.J. Drost, 1922-28; P. De Koekkoek, 1928-38; F.W. van Houten, 1938-43; J.W. Visser, 1943-47; J.E. Brink, 1948-51; H. Hollander, 1952-57

Otsego, MI — Otsego
1923-1947, discontinued
pastors: J.L. Koerts, 1923-26; J.R. Brink (M), 1926-27; F.M. Huizenga (stated supply), 1936-37

Ottawa, ON — Barrhaven Fellowship
1991-
pastors: B.J. Hummel, 1991-97; D.J. Meijer, 1999-

Ottawa, ON — Calvary
1958-
former name: Navan, ON – Navan, 1958-65; Ottawa, ON – East, 1965-66
pastors: C. Spoelhof, 1958-62; J.C. De Moor, 1962-65; P. Mantel, 1966-72; J. Postuma, 1972-76; G. Ringnalda, 1977-82; G.J. Hogeterp, 1984-95; N. Cornelisse, 1996-2002

Ottawa, ON — Calvin
1953-
former name: Ottawa, ON – Ottawa, 1953-64
pastors: A.H. Smit (M), 1953-55; P.G. Schrotenboer, 1955-60; S. Woudstra, 1961-65; A.W. Schaafsma, 1965-72; J.A. Quartel, 1973-84; B.H. De Jonge, 1977-81; J. Kerssies, 1985-93; K.M. Gehrels, 1994-

Ottawa, ON — Cumberland Ministry
see: Ottawa, ON – East City Community

Ottawa, ON — East City Community (emerging)
1995-
former name: Ottawa, ON – Cumberland Ministry, 1995-96
pastor: W.J. Kuurstra, 1995-

Ottawa, ON — Eglise Chretienne Reformee St. Paul (emerging)
1985-
pastor: Y. Baudequin (E), 1985-

Ottawa, ON — Kanata Community
1984-
pastor: H.G. Gunnink, 1981-

Ottawa, ON — Ottawa
see: Ottawa, ON – Calvin

Overijsel, SD — Overijsel
see: Platte, SD – Platte

Overisel, MI — East Overisel
1881-1888, members merged with Oakland, MI – Oakland
pastor: W. Coelingh, 1881-83

Overisel, MI — North Overisel
1878-1887, members merged with Oakland, MI – Oakland

Overisel, MI — Overisel
1883-
pastors: J. Vander Werp, 1984-87; P. Schut, 1887-92; H. Douwstra, 1892-93; P. Bakker, 1893-95; M. Van Vessem, 1897-1903; F.W. Stuart, 1904-05; J.J. Hiemenga, 1905-07; H.J. Mokma, 1908-12; R.B. Kuiper, 1912-14; A. Keizer, 1916-19; G.J. Van De Riet, 1920-45; H. Verduin, 1946-53; J.C. Medendorp, 1954-58; J.L. Bult, 1958-65; C. Vander Ark, 1966-69; B.W. Mulder, 1969-81; L.J. Kuiper, 1981-88; D.J. Vrieland, 1989-93; J.L. Alferink, 1994-2001; S.J. Mulder, 2002-

Oviedo, FL — The Journey (emerging)
1999-2001, discontinued
pastors: J.G. Aukema, 1997-2001

Owego, NY — Owego Christian Reformed Chapel
1976-1977, discontinued

pastor: R.H. Tjapkes, 1976-77

Owen Sound, ON — First
1948-
former name: Owen Sound, ON — Owen Sound,
1948-72
pastors: R.J. Bos (M), 1948-52; H. Vander Klay,
1952-61; J. Kuntz, 1962-65; J.H. Hofland, 1965-
68; J.G. Groen, 1968-71; J. Kerssies, 1972-77;
D.A. Gritter, 1979-85; J.W. Hielkema, 1986-88;
H.A. Vander Windt, 1989-92; K.P. De Raaf, 1993-
99; G.E. Holthof, 2000-

Owen Sound, ON — Owen Sound
see: Owen Sound, ON — First

Palco, KS (mission)
1909-1913

Palmer, SD — Palmer
see: Bemis, SD — Bemis

Palmerston, ON — Palmerston
1980-
pastors: A. Dreise, 1980-86; M.T. Mobach, 1986-
92; J. Westerhof, 1993-2001; C.J. Schievink,
2002-

Palo Alto, CA — Palo Alto
1957-
organized: 1960
pastors: G.B. Boerfyn (M), 1957-58; F. De Jong
(M), 1958-63; H. Bouma, 1963-68; R.A. Kok,
1969-74; H.D. Clark, Jr., 1974-78; N.J. Gebben,
Sr., 1978-88; H. De Young, 1989-2001; D.J. Hutt,
2002-

Palos Heights, IL — Palos Heights
1955-
pastors: P. Huisman, 1957-62; K.L. Havert, 1963-
69; J. Vander Lugt, 1970-81; J.C. Lont, 1981-88;
C. Hoogendoorn, 1988-95; S. Hamstra, Jr., 1997-;
D.E. Pruim, 2001-

Paramus, NJ — Paramus
1958-1976, discontinued
pastors: T. Medema, 1961-64; L.K. Tanis, 1965-
73; J. Cooper, 1973-77

Paramus, NJ — Paramus
see also: Paramus, NJ — Ridgewood

Paramus, NJ — Ridgewood
1823-1909, joined the Presbyterian Church USA,
1910; a faction had left in 1899

joined CRC from True Protestant Dutch Reformed
Church, 1890
former name: Paramus, NJ — Paramus, 1890-98
pastors: S. Froeligh, 1923-37; J.G. Brinkerhoff,
1928-45; A. Van Houten, 1857-62; I. De Baun,
1968-75; S.J. Vander Beek, 1886-88; A. Van
Houten, 1892-95; J. Van Houten, 1892-1908

Parchment, MI (mission)
1934

Parchment, MI — Parchment
see: Kalamazoo, MI — Parchment

Parkersburg, IA — Parkersburg
1891-
pastors: H.J. Potgeter, 1892-96; H.C. Bode,
1896-97; J. Plesscher, Sr., 1897-1912; H. Ahuis,
1913-21; J. Beld, 1921-28; G. Westenberg, 1928-
35; K. Tebben, 1935-47; S.P. Miersma, 1948-53;
E.H. Oostendorp, 1955-58; J.H. Draisma, 1959-
62; R.J. Holwerda, 1963-67; F.D. Rietema, 1967-
71; H. Lamsma, 1971-76; N.B. Steen, 1976-80; H.
Vanderaa, 1981-87; T.L. Koster, 1987-92; D.A.
Zylstra, 1992-99; F.E. Pott, 2001-

Pasadena, CA (mission)
1914

Passaic, NJ — Acquackanonk
see: Clifton, NJ — Richfield

Passaic, NJ — Hope Avenue
see: Passaic, NJ — Summer Street

Passaic, NJ — New Horizons (emerging)
2001-
pastor: M. Avila, 2001-

Passaic, NJ — North Side
see: Clifton, NJ — Northside

Passaic, NJ — Passaic
see: Passaic, NJ — Summer Street

Passaic, NJ — Prospect Street
see: Clifton, NJ — Richfield

Passaic, NJ — Summer Street
1876-1975, merged into Clifton, NJ — Richfield
former names: Passaic, NJ — Passaic, 1875-
1894; Passaic, NJ — Hope Avenue, 1894-1925
pastors: W. Greve, 1878-83; R. Drukker, 1886-
88; E. Vanden Berge, 1888-91; P. Kosten, 1892-
97; J. Manni, 1897-1901; D. Vander Ploeg, 1902-

09; G. Westenberg, 1909-14; K.W. Fortuin, 1914-22; C. Bouma, 1923-24; J.H. Monsma, 1924-26; D.R. Drukker, 1926; W. Kuipers, 1927-33; H. Bouma, SR., 1934-54; E. Jabay, 1955-58; D.J. Oostenink, Jr., 1959-68; R.J. Lobbezoo, 1971-73

Passaic/Paterson, NJ — Passaic/Paterson
see: Clifton, NJ — Richfield

Paterson, NJ — Bethel
1921-1989, merged with Wyckoff, NJ — Cedar Hill
pastors: H. Bouma, Sr., 1922-28; H. Bel, 1928-32; J.M. Vande Kieft, 1932-43; W. Haverkamp, 1943-49; A.A. Hoekema, 1950-54; C.J. Vos, 1954-61; H. Hoekstra, 1962-70; C.W. Niewenhuis, 1971-78; D.B. Mouw, 1979-90

Paterson, NJ — Eastside Mission
see: Paterson, NJ — Madison Avenue

Paterson, NJ — First
1856-1999, discontinued
joined CRC 1864, was independent
former name: Paterson, NJ — Paterson, 1856-88
pastors: J. De Rooy, 1856-62; A.H. Bechtold, 1864-66; W.H. Van Leeuwen, 1867-72; F.C. Rederus, 1872-74; L. Rietdyk, 1874-82; E. Vander Vries, 1883-86; L. Rietdyk, 1886-88; P. Van Vlaanderen, 1889-1904; H. Tuls, 1905-08; E.J. Krohne, 1909-12; H. Tuls, 1913-14; P.A. Hoekstra, 1915-18; J. Walkotten, 1919-43; A.C. De Jong, 1947-51; F.L. Netz, 1952-57; N.R. Prins, 1958-74; J.P. Vosteen, 1975-83; R. Zomermaand, 1984-90; S.R. Steenstra, 1991-96

Paterson, NJ — Fourth
see: Wyckoff, NJ — Faith Community

Paterson, NJ — Jewish (Hebrew) Mission
1916-1957
staff: H. Bergman (L), 1917-22; J.H. Schultz, 1922-38; J.R. Rosendale, 1938-53; M. Rosendale, 1940-60; A Vellinga (L), 1942-48; W. Tuit (L), 1947-56; P.G. Berkhout (L), 1952-56; D.B. Muir, 1953-57

Paterson, NJ — Madison Avenue
1909-
began as Eastside Mission
organized: 1910
pastors: D.H. Muyskens, 1911-12; K. Poppen, 1913-23; J. Smitter, 1924-27; J. Beebe, 1928-43; D.E. Houseman, 1944-48; E. Joling, 1950-53; L.B. Smedes, 1954-57; D.J. Griffioen, 1958-64; A. Van Zanten, 1965-76; C.L. Kammeraad, 1977-82; D.C.

Sherow, 1983-86; J.A. Algera, 1979-; E.N. Romero, 1997- ; E. Gray, 1999-2001

Paterson, NJ — Northside Community Chapel
1942-
organized: 1973
pastors: G. Lageveen, 1942-45; J. Vande Water (E), 1945-53; S. Pruiksma (L), 1946-47; M. Huizenga (L), 1949-50; M. Heerschap (L), 1950-51; G. Tolsma (L), 1950-58; A. Feenstra (L), 1952-58; M. Van Dyk (L), 1954-60; S.J. Vander Klay (M), 1960-73; S.J. Vander Klay, 1973-96; R. Smith, 1993-94; S. Holmes, 1998-

Paterson, NJ — Passaic County Community College (campus ministry)
2001-
staff: H. Zapata (L), 2001-

Paterson, NJ — Paterson
see: Paterson, NJ — First

Paterson, NJ — Prospect Park
see: Prospect Park, NJ — Prospect Park

Paterson, NJ — Second
1887-1986; joined the CRC as an independent congregation, 1888; merged into Prospect Park, NJ — Unity
former name: Free Reformed, Paterson, NJ, 1887-88
pastors: H.H. Diepering Langereis, 1887-91; R. Drukker, 1891-1902; K. Van Goor, 1902-14; D.H. Muyskens, 1916-17; J.J. Holwerda, 1919-40; N.J. Monsma, 1940-60; J.G. Van Ryn, 1961-66; B.A. Van Someren, 1967-86

Paterson, NJ — Spanish
see: Prospect Park, NJ — The Good Shepherd

Paterson, NJ — Star of Hope (mission)
1906-1921
staff: A. Hess (L), 1906-10; P. Stam, Sr. (L), 1916-21

Paterson, NJ — Third
see: North Haledon, NJ — Covenant

Paterson, NJ — Way of Life Chapel (mission)
1948

Paterson, NJ — William Paterson College (campus ministry)
1972-
staff: K.J. Vander Wall, 1972-

Paw Paw, MI — Paw Paw
1973-
organized: 1990 from Paw Paw, MI — Unity, 1973-1990
pastors: G.A. Geurink (E), 1973-77; F.J. Van Dyk, 1978-82; A.W. Bytwork (E), 1985-90; M.A. Van Haitsma, 1990-96; K.J. Muyskens, 1997-

Paw Paw, MI — Unity
see: Paw Paw, MI — Paw Paw

Peace River, AB — Chapel
see: Tawatinaw, AB — Peace River Chapel

Pearline, MI — Pearline
see: Allendale, MI — First

Pease, MN — Pease
1895-
pastors: J.E. De Groot, 1900-04; H. Fryling, 1905-06; A.W. Meyer, 1907-18; G.J. Haan, 1918-20; J.G. Vande Lune, 1920-26; J.K. Van Baalen, 1926-29; H. Moes, 1929-43; R.S. De Haan, 1943-50; W.H. Ackerman, 1950-54; J.L. Bult, 1955-58; R. Evenhuis, 1960-67; R.L. Slater, 1968-73; R.A. Kok, 1974-79; F.E. Pott, 1980-86; J. Joldersma, 1987-96; G.W. Vander Hoek, 1998-

Peers, AB — Peers
1950-1983, merged into Edson, AB — Edson-Peers
pastors: J.G. Kruis, 1959-62; P.C. Hogeterp, 1966-70; A.J. Miedema, 1970-74; R. De Moor, 1975-78; E. Vander Woude, 1978-83

Pella, IA (mission)
1902-1908
staff: P. Schut, 1902-03; J. Dolfin, 1903-04; M. Botbyl, 1905-08

Pella, IA — Calvary
1955-
pastors: M.R. Doornbos, 1956-60; G.F. Van Oyen, 1960-64; A.E. Pontier, 1964-73; R.J. Holwerda, 1973-84; J.P. Gorter, 1987-93; T.R. Dykstra, 1994-2002; S. Starkenburg, 1999-

Pella, IA — Faith
1968-
pastors: S. Kramer, 1969-77; J.D. Stoel, 1979-89; J.A. Ritsema, 1990-93; K.L. Schepel, 1994-

Pella, IA — First
1866-
former name: Pella, IA — Pella, 1866-97
pastors: H.R. Koopmans, 1867-69; J. Noordewier, 1869-71; W. Coelingh, 1871-74; S. Baron, 1876-81; E. Broene, 1883-86; J.B. Hoekstra, 1887-91; J. Manni, 1892-97; J. Keizer, 1898-1902; J. Timmerman, 1902-04; T. Vander Ark, 1905-10; C. De Leeuw, 1910-19; J. De Haan, Sr., 1919-29; R.J. Danhof, 1929-34; F. De Jong, 1934-38; J. Vander Ploeg, 1939-45; S. Vroon, 1945-52; P.Y. De Jong, 1953-60; J.A. De Kruyter, 1960-64; J.H. Piersma, 1964-69; R.J. Venema, 1970-75; J.M. Julien, 1975-81; J.R. Sittema, 1981-89; J.M. Beach, 1989-97; H.A. Brink, 1999-

Pella, IA — Grace Fellowship
1995-
organized: 1996
pastor: P.C. Kelder, 1995-

Pella, IA — Pella
see: Pella, IA — First

Pella, IA — Second
1897-
pastors: R. Vande Kieft, 1898-1907; E. Vanden Berge, 1908-11; J.I. Fles, 1911-15; G.G. Haan, 1917-21; H. Walkotten, 1921-25; D. Hollebeek, 1925-33; M. Monsma, 1934-43; T.P. Verhulst, 1943-48; H. Vander Kam, 1950-55; L. Van Laar, 1956-61; B.T. Haan, 1961-64; A. Zylstra, 1965-70; H. Petersen, 1972-80; B. Leiter, 1980-84; P.R. Hoekstra, 1985-90; G.D. Mouw, 1990-95; W.D. Zeilstra, 1995-

Pembroke, ON — Pembroke
see: Pembroke, ON — Zion

Pembroke, ON — Zion
1952-
fromer names: Cobden-Pembroke Coubourg, ON — Cobourg, 1953-54; Pembroke, ON — Pembroke, 1954-70
pastors: G. Rienks, 1959-63; J. Faber, 1963-67; H. Katerberg, 1969-73; D.R. Tigchelaar, 1973-78; J.D. Pereboom, 1979-82; K.R. Ritsema, 1983-89; M. Vellekoop, 1990-94; H. VanderSluis, 1994-

Penticton, BC — Penticton
1965-
organized: 1967
pastors: J. Tensen (L), 1965-66; R. Groeneboer (M), 1966-69; J. Versfelt, 1970-74; J. Bolt, 1973-76; J. Ypma, 1976-80; J.A. Ooms, 1981-86; A.G.

Van Giessen, 1986-91; L.J. Swier, 1992-97; J.R. Kemper, 1999-2002

Peoria, IA — Peoria
1894-
pastors: S. Broekstra, 1894-97; G. Westenberg, 1897-1901; P. Jonker, Sr., 1901-07; A.J. Brink, 1908-11; H. Bultema, 1912-16; J.J. Weersing, 1916-18; P. Van Dyk, 1918-21; D.H. Kromminga, 1922-26; M.J. Vander Werp, 1928-32; J. Weidenaar, 1932-36; D.J. Hoitenga, Sr., 1937-43; R.H. Haan, 1943-45; J.A. Mulder, 1946-50; H. Verduin, 1953-59; D.R. Vander Wall. 1959-62; D.J. Van Beek, 1962-66; D.J. Drost, 1968-73; P. Van Drunen, 1973-82; R.L. Bouwkamp, 1983-2000

Pera, NM (mission)
1944-1945
staff: C.A. Hayenga, 1944-45

Perch Lake, MI — Perch Lake
1896-1899, discontinued

Perkins County, SD — Grand Forks
1910-1915, discontinued
former name: Perkins County, SD — Lodge Pole, 1911

Perkins County, SD — Lodge Pole
see: Perkins County, SD — Grand Forks

Peterborough, ON — Cephas
1952-
former name: Peterborough, ON — Peterborough, 1952-71
pastors: H. Moes (M), 1949-57; K. Hart, 1958-67; H. Numan, 1967-71; D.C. Los, 1972-78; H. Mennega, 1979-88; J.R. Poelman, 1989-93; W.T. Koopmans, 1995-

Peterborough, ON — Living Hope
1993-
pastor: K.J. House, 1994-

Peterborough, ON — Peterborough
see: Peterborough, ON — Cephas

Petoskey, MI — Living Stone (emerging)
1997-
pastor: J.D. Fox, 1997-

Philadelphia, PA — Spirit and Truth Fellowship
1988-
organized: 1999

pastors: E. Lugo, 1988-92; M. Ortiz, 1987-; R. Baker, 1987-

Philadelphia, PA — Trinity
see: Broomall, PA — Trinity

Phoenix, AZ — Arizona Chung-Ang
1993-1997, withdrew
former name: Phoenix, AZ — Chung-Ang [Central] Presbyterian
pastor: R. T.H. Yeo, 1993-97

Phoenix, AZ — Celebration Community (emerging)
1993-
organized: 2000
pastors: J.D. Westra, 1993-2002; A. Lindemulder, 2000-

Phoenix, AZ — Chung-Ang Central Presbyterian
see: Phoenix, AZ — Arizona Chung-Ang

Phoenix, AZ — Cook Training School
1947-1952, 1957-1984
staff: C.G. Hayenga, 1947-52, 1954-57; W. Goudberg, 1950-52; J. Van Bruggen, 1957-66; H.A. Van Dam, 1969-77; H. de Jong, 1979-84

Phoenix, AZ — First
see: Phoenix, AZ — Phoenix

Phoenix, AZ — Orangewood
1962-
pastors: A.J. Haan (M), 1962-64; A.P. Ver Burg, 1964-68; L.F. Stockmeier, 1968-77; F.W. Van Houten, 1978-82; R.J. Buining, 1982-88; G.L. Rutgers, 1988-95; S.R. Steenstra, 1996-99; E. Lugo, 2003-

Phoenix, AZ — Phoenix
1946-
former name: Phoenix, AZ — First, 1984-88
pastors: H.A. Dykstra, 1946-50; H.A. Dykstra (M), 1950-51; N. De Vries (M), 1952-61; D.R. Vander Wall, 1962-67; N.B. Haan, 1969-76; H.D. Clark, Jr., 1978-92; B. Nymeyer, 1994-96; J. Rop, Jr., 1998-

Pickering, ON — New Life Community
1989-1999, discontinued
pastors: J. De Vries, 1987-95; J. Veenstra (E), 1997-99

Picton, ON — Picton
1948-1954, merged into Bloomfield, ON –
Bethany
organized: 1949
pastors: A. Garret (M) 1948-50; D. Grasman,
1951-54

Pine Creek, MI — Pine Creek
see: Holland, MI – Pine Creek

Pinellas Park, FL — Pinellas Park
see: St. Petersburg, FL – Pine Grove Community

Pinetown, NC — Sunday School
1957-1961

Pipestone, MN — First
see: Pipestone, MN – Pipestone

Pipestone, MN — Pipestone
1889-1893, discontinued

Pipestone, MN — Pipestone
1938-
former name: Pipestone, MN – First, 1988-96
pastors: J.H. Rubingh, 1938-43; R.A. Rozeboom,
1943-51; E.O. Holkeboer, 1951-57; J.H.
Groenewold, 1957-61; M.E. Gritters, 1961-65; N.
Roorda, 1965-74; W.G. Van Hal, 1974-78; J.T.
Petersen, 1980-85; T. Genzink, 1986-95; D.A.
Bosch, 1996-2002

Pitt Meadows, BC (mission)
1936-1937

Pitt Meadows, BC — Pitt Meadows
see: Maple Ridge, BC – Maple Ridge

Pittston, NJ (mission)
1937-1942

**Placentia, CA — Christ Reformed
(emerging)**
1995-1997, withdrew to United Reformed
Churches
pastors: M. Horton, 1996-97; K. Riddlebarger,
1996-97

Plainfield, IL — Christ Community
1986-
former name: Naperville, IL – Christ Community,
1986-99
pastors: J. Batts, 1986-93; F.A. De Jong, 1994-

Plainfield, MI — Plainfield
1906-1986, merged into Rockford, MI –
Blythefield
pastors: H.J. Mulder, 1908-10; H. Beute, 1912-16;
J.R. Van Dyke, 1921-25; H.S. Koning, 1926-39; T.
Van Eerden, 1939-42; J.B. Ibershoff, 1942-49; R.
Leetsma, 1951-54; P.E. Bakker, 1954-58; D.
Mellema, 1959-62; E.J. Tamminga, 1963-66; M.
Bolt, 1967-70; J.M. Evenhouse, 1971-77; J.P.
Boonstra, 1977-86

Plainwell, MI — Calvary
1963-
organized: 1973
pastors: G.A. Geurink (E), 1963-73; C.D.
Compagner, 1973-79; B.T. Ballast, 1979-83; J.W.
Van Der Heide, 1984-88; J. De Vries, 1988-93;
M.A. Minegar, 1997-

Platte, SD — Platte
1883-
former name: Overijsel, SD – Overijsel, 1883-
1900
pastors: F.W. Stuart, 1901-04; M. Vander Heide,
1904-08; P. Bloem, 1909-14; J.M. Vande Kieft,
1915-18; H.J. Heynen, 1918-20; A.H. Bratt, 1921-
25; J.C. Ehlers, 1926-30; D. Flietstra, 1931-38;
W. Hekman, 1938-41; J. Zwaanstra, 1942-53; H.
Petersen, 1953-64; C. Van Essen, 1965-72; M.G.
Vande Steeg, 1974-76; C.W. Niewenhuis, 1978-84;
F.E. Pott, 1986-91; W.H. Lammers, 1992-98; W.
Gesch, 1999-

Pleasant Valley, SD — Pleasant Valley
see: Eagle Butte, SD – Pleasant Valley

Plover, WI — Marathon County
see: Birnamwood, WI – Birnamwood

Plymouth, NC — Acre Station
1972-1974
staff: E. Hubers, (L), 1972-73

Plymouth, OH — Calvary Chapel
see: Willard, OH – Calvary Chapel

Polkton, MI — Polkton
1857 (April-October), merged with Polkton RCA

Pomona, CA — Bethesda (emerging)
1997-
pastor: A.J. Melendez, 1998-

Pompton Plains, NJ — Pompton Plains
1955-1992, withdrew, affiliated with United Reformed Churches
organized: 1958
pastors: M. Stegink, 1959-61; R.A. Bruxvoort,
1961-65; J.J. Vanden Hoek, 1965-71; D.J. Janke,
1971-75; W. Kosten, 1975-83; R.J. Kuiken, 1983-
91

Ponoka, AB — Sonrise
1985-
pastors: P.J. Boodt, 1986-96; A. Van Muyen,
1997-2002

Portage, MI — Lexington Green Community
1970-2001, discontinued
organized: 1982
former name: Kalamazoo, MI — Lexington Green
Community, 1982-93
pastors: L. Vander Roest (L), 1970-71; M.N.
Buwalda (M), 1974-82; R.L. Van Zomeren, 1983-
87; A.J. Nikkel, 1991-93; N.R. Rylaarsdam, 1994-
2000

Portage, MI — Portage
1966-1995, discontinued
organized: 1977
pastors: G. Malda (E), 1966-73; A.W. Bytwork
(E), 1973-78; R. Klimp, 1980-86; J.H. Looman,
1988-95

Portage, MI — Prairie Edge
1951-
organized: 1958
former name: Kalamazoo, MI — Prairie Edge,
1958-93
pastors: H. Hoogerheide (L), 1950-53; R. Browneye (L), 1953-54; J. Pinkster (L), 1953-54; R.J.
Buining, 1955-58; J.W. Dykstra, 1958-64; N.
Punt, 1964-69; C. Greenfield, 1970-73; J. Stulp,
1973-83; R.C. Heerspink, 1984-89; P.R. Hoekstra,
1990-97; P.D. Kok, 1998-

**Portage La Prairie, MB — Portage La Prai-
rie**
1950-1958, discontinued
pastor: M. Doornbos (M), 1950-55

Port Alberni, BC — First
1951-
former name: Alberni, BC — Alberni, 1951-55
pastors: G.H. Rientjes (M), 1952-55; C. Spoelhof,
1955-56; J.J. Holwerda, 1956-61; D. Pierik,
1964-68; L. Dekens, 1969-74; R. Duifhuis, 1975-

88; A. Vanden Berg, 1989-95; H.J. Roosma,
1995-

Port Arthur, ON — Bethlehem
see: Thunder Bay, ON — Bethlehem

Port Arthur, ON — Port Arthur
see: Thunder Bay, ON — Bethlehem

Port Arthur, TX (mission)
1936-1937

Portland, MI — Portland
1915-1984, absorbed by Ionia, MI — New Life
pastors: J.R. Brink (M), 1923-25W. Alkema,
1925-28; L. Van Haitsma, 1929-43; D.J.
Oostenink, Jr., 1943-45; B.T. Haan, 1946-49; A.
DeVries, 1950-55; R.J. Vande Kieft, 1955-59; W.
Vande Kieft, 1960-62; H.J. Kuizema, 1963-73;
S.R. Van Klompenberg, 1974-77; R.H. Tjapkes (M),
1977-78; J. Vigh, 1978-84

Portland, OR — Calvin
see: Portland, OR — Parklane

Portland, OR — Christ Community
1990-
organized: 1997
pastor: V.L. Michaels, 1989-

Portland, OR — Korean Myung Sung
1993-1994, merged with Hope Presbyterian to
form Beaverton, OR — Zion Christian Reformed
pastor: S.O. Yoo, 1993-94

Portland, OR — Oak Hills
1965-
pastors: H.B. Spaan, 1965-76; P.J. Niewiek,
1975-81; G.P. Hutt, 1982-87; C.J. Leep, 1987-

Portland, OR — Parklane
1959-
former names: Portland, OR — Portland, 1959-
65; Portland, OR — Calvin, 1965-94
pastors: H.B. Spaan, 1959-65; I.J. Apol, 1965-
67; J.E. Jeffers, 1967-73; K.D. Koeman, 1974-80;
B.J. Niemeyer, 1980-88; D.V. Hays, 1989-

Portland, OR — Portland
see: Portland, OR — Parklane

Portland, OR — Zion Korean (emerging)
1998-
former name: Beaverton, OR — Zion Korean,
1998-2000

pastors: C.S. Won, 1995-97; J. Namkoong, 1998-

Port Perry, ON — Hope
1978-
pastors: J. Geuzebroek, 1978-81; C. Geleynse, 1981-85; B. Van Eyk, 1985-91; K.M.B. Van Schelven, 1992-96; N.A. Sennema, 1998-

Port St. Lucie, FL — Sunlight Community
1984-
organized: 1995
former name: Port St. Lucie, FL — The King's Church, 1984-90
pastors: J. Van Hemert, 1984-87; J.A. Vander Slik, 1990-

Port St. Lucie, FL — The King's Church
see: Port St. Lucie, FL — Sunlight Community

Port William, NS — Port William
see: Kentville, NS — Kentville

Poughkeepsie, NY — Chapel
1962-1963

Prairie City, IA — Prairie City
1904-
pastors: J.A. Vissia, 1911-15; G.W. Hylkema, 1915-18; J.M. Vande Kieft, 1919-21; J.M. Byleveld, 1921-27; W.D. Vander Werp, 1927-32; D.H. Walters, 1933-38; N.L. Veltman, 1938-43; H.J. Kuizema, 1943-49; S.J. De Vries, 1950-53; W. Vande Kieft, 1954-60; T. Wevers, 1960-64; T.L. Brouwer, 1965-71; R.J. Timmer, 1971-75; G.L. Essenburg, 1975-83; L.F. Stockmeier, 1983-87; T.D. Wetselaar, 1987-91; S. Starkenburg, 1992-98; A. Eising, 1999-

Prairie View, KS — Prairie View
1915-1925, discontinued
pastor: H.J. Kuiper, 1909-10

Preakness, NJ — Preakness
see: Wayne, NJ — Preakness

Prince George, BC — Prince George
1961-
pastors: G. Van Laar (M), 1953-58; G.H. Polman (M), 1961-67; J. Versfelt (M), 1967-70; A.C. Groen, 1971-78; W.C.Tuininga, 1978-84; W. Westerhuis, 1985-90; A.G. Vander Leek, 1991-95; J.S. Hielema, 1995-99; R.C. Koopmans, 2000-

Princeton, MN — Bethel
1979-

pastors: C. Vander Neut, 1980-86; K.J. Adams, 1987-91; P. Sausser, 1991-96; W. Versluys, II, 1997-2000; C.J. Friend, 2001-

Princeton, NE — Princeton
1897-1905, discontinued

Prinsburg, MN — First
1886-
former name: Prinsburg, MN — Prinsburg, 1886-1984
pastors: J.H. Schultz, 1894-97; W. Heyns, 1898-1900; J.A. Gerritsen, 1901-04; N. Burggraaf, 1904-08; L. Ypma, 1909-17; J.J. De Jonge, 1917-21; H. Blystra, 1921-28; E.R. Van Farowe, 1928-31; M.J. Vander Werp, 1932-35; W. Terpsma, 1935-44; G.J. Rozenboom, 1945-49; S. Viss, Jr., 1950-57; F.L. Netz, 1957-65; W. Van Antwerpen, 1966-71; T. Wevers, 1971-77; G.W. Van Den Berg, 1978-84; C.J. Klompien, 1984-91; J. Admiraal, 1992-98; D.A. Zylstra, 1998-

Prinsburg, MN — Prinsburg
see: Prinsburg, MN — First

Prinsburg, MN — Unity
1984-
pastors: E.D. Roels, 1984-87; H.G. Faber, 1988-91; D. Deppe, 1992-98; S.A. Zwart, 1999-

Prospect Park, NJ — Prospect Park
1902-1986 merged into Prospect Park, NJ — Unity
pastors: H. Van Hoogen, 1903-07; P. Jonker, Sr., 1907-11; J. Keizer, 1911-16; W.P. Heeres, 1917-20; R.R. Veldman, 1920-27; P. Van Dyk, 1927-47; O. Holtrop, 1947-56; G.H. Stoutmeyer, 1958-63; J.R. Kok, 1964-67; E.L. Shuart, 1968-70; A.A. Arkema, 1971-81; B.P. Bosscher, 1981-84

Prospect Park, NJ — The Good Shepherd (El Buen Pastor)
1972-
organized: 1979
former name: Paterson, NJ — Spanish, 1972-79
pastors: F. Reinoso, 1972-78; J. Abreu, 1979-90; E.N. Romero, 1990-92; R. Orellana, 1994-

Prospect Park, NJ — Unity
1986-
merger of Prospect Park, NJ — Prospect Park and Paterson, NJ — Second
pastors: G.D. Negen, 1986-91; P.R. De Vries, 1989-2001; J. Vugteveen, 1994-98; C. Vander Neut, 2002-; B.W. Bolkema, 2002-

Prosper, MI — Prosper
see: Falmouth, MI – Prosper

Pullman, WA — Washington State and University of Idaho (campus ministry)
1981–1990
pastor: A.D. Bosscher, 1981–90

Punta Gorda, FL — Peace Christian Winter Ministry
1982–1984
pastor: E.W. Oosterhouse, 1983–84

Purewater, SD — Purewater
see: Valentine, NE – Lakeview Community

Quebec, QC — Eglise Reformee de la Rive-Sud (mission)
1981–1998, independent
pastors: H. Kallameyn (M), 1981–86; J.G. DeBlois (E), 1990–98

Quebec, QC — Institute Farel
supported by CRCNA 1981–1997
on faculty: M.D. Geleynse, 1981–1986; J.G. Zoellner, 1989–

Queenstown, ON — Living Waters Chapel
1969–1977
staff: G. De Vries (L), 1969–72, 1974–77

Quincy, IL — Quincy
1928–1929, discontinued

Quincy, WA — Quincy
1964–
pastors: H.M. De Rooy (M), 1963–65; J. Roorda (M), 1965–68; R.D. Kramer (M), 1968–71; J.E. Jeffers, 1973–81; N.R. Rylaarsdam, 1981–87; T.J. Kok, 1987–92; R.A. Bruxvoort, 1993–98; O. Perdomo, 1999–

Racine, WI — Beacon Light Chapel (mission)
1952–1972, discontinued
staff: T. Afman (L), 1952–53; G. Veenstra (L), 1953–64; E. Visscher (E), 1965–72

Racine, WI — Racine
1906–
pastors: D. Van der Ploeg, (M), 1909–11; P.W. De Jonge, 1911–15; H.J. Haarsma, 1916–26; W. De Groot, 1926–29; J. Medendorp, 1930–45; C.M. Schoolland, 1946–50; R. Opperwall, 1952–61;

S.M. Voortman, 1961–66; J.A. Hoeksema, 1967–86; T.J. Ouwinga, 1987–97; G.O. Gerdes, 1999–

Raleigh, NC (service home)
1943–1945
staff: J.M. Vande Kieft, 1943–45

Ramona, CA — Ramona (congregational ministry)
1988–1997, withdrew
pastor: B. Brawdy, 1988–97

Ramsey, NJ — Ramsey
1824–1908, withdrew, affiliated with Jersey City Presbytery, Presbyterian Church USA
joined CRC from True Protestant Dutch Reformed Church, 1890
pastors: J. Demarest, 1824–55; J.Y De Baun, 1855–60; J. Berdan, 1861–65; J. Cooper, 1866; I. De Baun, 1867–75; S.J. Vander Beek, 1875–88; J.N. Trompen, 1891–1907

Rancho Cucamonga, CA — Friendship Community
see: Fontana, CA – Friendship Community

Randolph, WI — First
1908–
former name: Randolph, WI – Randolph, 1908–1937
pastors: J. Homan, 1910–15; W. Bajema, 1915–25; J.M. Voortman, 1925–30; J.J. Holwerda, 1931–48; J.H. De Haan, 1948–56; J.W. Van Stempvoort, 1957–63; J. Entingh, 1964–70; P.W. Vis, 1970–77; L.J. Howerzyl, 1978–84; C.D. Freswick, 1984–89; R.R. Mueller, 1989–95; R.M. Brenton, 1998–

Randolph, WI — Living Hope Community (emerging)
1993–
former name: Fox Lake, WI – Living Hope Community, 1993–95
pastor: R. Kok (E), 1997–2000; J.A. Geleynse, 2002–

Randolph, WI — Randolph
see: Randolph, WI – First

Randolph, WI — Second
1938–
pastors: W. Dryfhout, 1939–49; B.T. Haan, 1949–54; H.J. Baas, 1955–58; B.J. Boerkoel, 1959–63; F. Handlogten, 1963–70; J.C. Verbrugge, 1970–74;

J.S. Meyer, 1975-79; S.J. Keyzer, 1980-87; M. Toonstra, Jr., 1988-98; J. Admiraal, 1998-

Rapid City, SD — Hope
1958- , began as a mission station
organized: 1966
former name: Rapid City, SD — Rapid City, 1958-97
pastors: V. Luchies (M), 1960-65; M.P. Van Houten, 1965-74; A. Gelder, 1974-79; G.A. Terpstra, 1979-83; R. De Young, 1983-89; C.R. Bolt, 1990-95; R. Van Osdol, 1997-

Rapid City, SD — Rapid City
see: Rapid City, SD — Hope

Raymond, MN — Raymond
1938-
pastors: D.E. Houseman, 1938-44; W.K. Reinsma, 1945-48; J.H. Rubingh, 1949-55; J.H. Stek, 1955-61; P.W. Vis, 1961-70; M. Reitsma, 1970-74; P. Veltman, 1974-81; M.J. Hofman, 1981-90; S.J. Van Zanen, 1990-97; D.W. Visser, 1998-

Red Deer, AB — First
1951-
former name: Red Deer, AB — Red Deer, 1951-72
pastors: G. Van Laar (M), 1950-53; R. Kooistra, 1955-60; J.W. Van Weelden, 1960-66; P. Kranenburg, 1966-70; N.B. Knoppers, 1971-83; W.L. Vander Beek, 1983-90; S.R. Schalk, 1984-88; D.J. Heinen, 1991-95; W.D. Nieuwenhuis, 1991-2002; J.E. Pot, 1997-

Red Deer, AB — New Life Fellowship
1989-
pastors: S.R. Schalk, 1988-97; G.J. Kamps, 1998-2003

Red Deer, AB — Red Deer
see: Red Deer, AB — First

Redding, CA — Calvary
see: Redding, CA — Calvary Community

Redding, CA — Calvary Community
1982-1994, discontinued
organized: 1991
former name: Redding, CA — Calvary
pastors: K. Dryfhout (E), 1982, D.W. Lagerwey, 1982-87; G.B. Ebbers, 1988-91; H.C. Kooger, 1992-94

Redlands, CA (service home)
1943-1945, 1958-1959

staff: H.A. Dykstra, 1943-45, 1958-59

Redlands, CA — Bethel
1932-1970, discontinued
joined CRC from the Protestant Reformed Church, 1961
pastors: G. Vos, 1932-43; P. De Boer, 1943-48; L. Vermeer, 1948-55; J. Howerzyl, 1956-64; J. Vigh, Jr., 1964-70

Redlands, CA — Fellowship (emerging)
1993-1997, discontinued
pastor: J.E. Almaraz, 1992-97

Redlands, CA — First
1911-1994, merged into Redlands, CA — Redlands
former name: Redlands, CA — Redlands, 1911-49
pastors: J. Bolt, 1911-14; J.A. Vissia, 1915-19; J. Cupido, 1920-27; M.M. Schans, 1927-40; J. Bolt, 1940-45; H. Radius, 1946-72; J.M. Gray, 1973-78; J.L. Alferink, 1979-85; R.D. Bultman, 1985-94; P.W. Townsend, 1988-91

Redlands, CA — Highland Avenue
1949-1994, merged into Redlands, CA — Redlands
former name: Redland, CA — Second, 1949-62
pastors: H. Kuiper, 1951-53; H. Van Dyken, 1954-57; O. De Groot, 1958-66; W. Van Peursum, 1967-70; M.G. Zylstra, 1971-81; W. Verhoef, 1982-90; T.B. Toeset, 1990-94

Redlands, CA — Redlands
see also: Redlands, CA — The River

Redlands, CA — Second
see: Redlands, CA — The River

Redlands, CA — The River
1994-
merger of Redlands, CA — First, and Redlands, CA — Highland Avenue;
and Redlands, CA — Second
former name: Redlands, CA — Redlands, 1994-2002
pastors: T.B. Toeset, 1994-97; R.D. Bultman, 1994-98; T. Spykstra, 1999-; W. Verhoef, 2002-

Red Valley, AZ — Red Valley
1992-
pastors: P.H. Redhouse, 1963-70; B. Garnanez (E), 1982-92

Reeman, MI — Palmer Chapel
1958-1972
staff: H. Boehm (E), 1958-60; J. Chupp (L),

1960–63; A. Looman (L), 1964–65; D. Tanis (L), 1965–67; A. Vander Wall, (L), 1967–70, 1971–72; F. Brummel (E), 1970–71

Reeman, MI — Reeman
1890–
former name: Sheridan, MI — Sheridan, 1890–1903
pastors: J.R. Brink, 1902–05; J.C. Schaap, 1906–11; J.L. Heeres, 1912–22; H. Goodyke, 1922–45; N. De Vries, 1946–50; A. Walcott, 1951–58; H. Bouma, Jr., 1958–64; J.M. Evenhouse, 1964–71; E.H. Oostendorp, 1972–76; D.A. Kamstra, 1977–82; W. Kosten, 1983–92; L.D. Van Dyke, 1993–

Regina, SK — First
see: Regina, SK — Sonlight Community

Regina, SK — Indian Metis Christian Fellowship (emerging)
1978–
emerging, 1999
pastors: H. Kuperus, 1978–92; B. Adema (E), 1996–

Regina, SK — Regina
see: Regina, SK — Sonlight Community

Regina, SK — Sonlight Community
1954–
former names: Regina, SK — Regina, 1954–80; Regina, SK — First, 1980–95
pastors: G.J. Vander Ziel, 1953–60; L. Van Staalduinen, Jr., 1960–63; P.W. De Bruyne, 1963–66; P. Dekker, 1967–71; J. de Vries, Jr., 1972–75; P.Plug, 1976–81; E.W. Visser, 1981–88; J.S. Mantel, 1989–93; W.D. Nieuwenhuis, 1990–91; C. Pool, 1994–99; H.C. Kooger, 2001–

Rehoboth, NM — Rehoboth
1903–
organized: 1906
pastors: L.P. Brink (M), 1900–1910; J.W. Brink (M), 1912–25; W. Groen (M), 1926–27; J.R. Kamps, 1927–51; N. De Vries (M), 1939–43; A. Poel, 1944–57; G. Yff, 1948–57; R.J. Buining, 1958–63; E.G. Cooke, 1963–68; R.L. Veenstra, 1969–79; N. Vanderzee, 1980–85; L.J. Doornbos, 1986–93; D.E. Byker, 1994–99, R.J. Byker, 2001–

Renfrew, ON — Hebron
1951–
former name: Renfrew, ON — Renfrew, 1951–70
pastors: J. Rubingh (M), 1948–56; H. Uittenbosch, 1957–60; A. Beukema, 1961–64; W.

Renkema, 1965–70; A. Velthoen, 1969–74; J. Veltman, 1975–79; W. Suk, 1981–85; B.P. Velthuizen, 1985–92; A. Vander Berg, 1992–2001

Renfrew, ON — Renfrew
see: Renfrew, ON — Hebron

Renville, MN — Emden
1890–
former name: Emden, MN — Emden, 1890–1962
pastors: J. Gulker, 1892–94; H.J. Potgieter, 1896–1900; H.C. Bode, 1901–04; G.L. Hoefker, 1906–08; J. Beld, 1908–11; F. Sch||rmann, 1912–15; J. Gulker, 1917–25; K. Tebben, 1925–29; A.A. Koning, 1929–49; H. Bruinooge, 1949–51; I.W. Meuzelaar, 1951–56; J.H. De Haan, 1956–62; B. Van Antwerpen, 1962–66; H.J. Kwantes, 1966–71; C.J. Toeset, 1972–83; C.D. Hoekstra, 1983–89; J.C. Fisher, 1989–97; J.C. Vanderhooft, 1999–

Repentigny, QC — Repentigny (unorganized)
1986–1988, discontinued
pastor: H. Kallemeyn, 1986–1988

Richfield Springs, NY — Richfield Springs
see: Richfield Springs, NY — Trinity

Richfield Springs, NY — Trinity
1974–
former name: Richfield Springs, NY — Richfield Springs, 1974–85
pastors: D.G. Belanus, 1974–76; T.B. Toeset, 1976–80; F.J. Mac Leod, 1980–86; D.W. Stevenson, 1987–92; F.F. Gunnink, 1994–96; M.S. McDonald, 1999–2000; K. Prol (E), 2001–

Richland, MI — Richland
see: Lucas, MI — Lucas

Richmond, BC — First
1957–
former name: Richmond, BC — Richmond, 1957–84
pastors: W.L. Vander Beek, 1958–63; A.H. Venema, 1963–69; J. Zantingh, 1969–73; P.M. Jonker, 1974–81; G. Corvers, 1981–85; J.A. Ooms, 1986–93; J. Koster, 1994–@%L1 =

Richmond, BC — Immanuel
1984–
pastors: S.M. Jung, 1979–88; J.C. Yang, 1990–92; W. Ho, 1999–

Richmond, BC — Richmond
see: Richmond, BC — First

Richmond Hill, ON — Community
1984-
pastors: W. Geerts, 1984-92; J. Groen, 1991-

Richton Park, IL — Community
1960-1991, discontinued
former name: Richton Park, IL — Richton Park,
1960-68
pastors: M.D. Hugen (M), 1959-62; D.E.
VanderBrug (M), 1962-66; R.M. Heartwell, Sr.,
1967-91

Richton Park, IL — Richton Park
see: Richton Park, IL — Community

Ridgewood, NJ — Love Korean
see: Midland Park, NJ — Love Korean

Ridgewood, NJ — Ridgewood
1942-
pastors: E. Kooistra (M), 1941-44; E. Boeve,
1945-51; S. Van Dyken, 1952-60; R. Opperwall,
1961-73; J. Timmer, 1974-80; N.B. Steen, 1981-
88; H.A. Stob, 1989-96; L.A. Kuyvenhoven, 1998-
2002

Ridott, IL — Ridott
see: German Valley, IL — German Valley

Rilland, CO — Rilland
1893-1894, discontinued

Rimbey, AB — Rimbey
1983-
organized: 1985
pastors: W. Geerts, 1983-84; H. Devries, 1984-
90; H. VanderSluis, 1991-94; H.L. Burghart,
1995-99; W.D. Nieuwenhuis, 2002-

Ripon, CA — Almond Valley
1978-
pastors: J. Van Dyken, Sr., 1978-83; M.W.
Heyboer, 1984-91; W.D. Zeilstra, 1991-95; P.J.
Kok, 1997-

Ripon, CA — First
1918-
former name: Ripon, CA — Ripon, 1918-46
pastors: P.J. Hoekenga, 1919-24; J. De Jong,
1924-39; J.J. Steigenga, 1939-51; J.W. Visser,
1952-55; J. Morren, 1956-60; H.C. Van Deelen,
1960-65; C.W. Flietstra, 1966-75; W.P. Green, Jr.,

1976-81; B.B. Blankers, 1983-96; E. Vander Lugt,
1998-

Ripon, CA — Immanuel
1946-
pastors: E.Tanis, 1946-69; H.J. Wigboldy, 1970-
77; T. Wevers, 1977-81; T.P. Hoekstra, 1985-88;
T.L. Haan, 1988-94; C. Admiraal, 1981- ; C.J.
Friend, 1995-2001

Ripon, CA — Ripon
see: Ripon, CA — First

River Drive Park, ON — Community
1968-1982
staff: J. De Pater, 1968-69; B. Lennips (L), 1970-
74; Mrs. J. Flooryp (L), 1974-76; E. Boehm (E),
1975-76; F. De Vries (L), 1979-83

Riverside, CA — Hope Community
1961-
former name: Riverside, CA — Riverside, 1961-92
pastors: G. Hubers (M), 1960-66; J.A. Rozeboom,
1969-76; L.E. Van Essen, 1977-89; J.J.Berends,
1990-96; D.S. Hoekstra, 1996-98; C. Pool, 1999-

Riverside, CA — Indian
1926-1928, 1961-1970
former name: Riverside, CA — Sherman Institute
staff: C.W. Cell (L), 1926-27; J. Yazzie (E), 1961-
62; M. Baas (L), 1962-63, 1964-65; K. Vander
Ark (L), 1963-64; C. Thomas (L), 1964-65; M.
Baker (L), 1966-70

Riverside, CA — Riverside
see: Riverside, CA — Hope Community

Riverside, CA — Sherman Institute
see: Riverside, CA — Indian

Riverside, CA — Vientiane Laotian
see: Moreno Valley, CA — Laotian Vientiane

Rochester, NY — Rochester
1877-
pastors: H. Tempel, 1881-83; J. Riemersma,
1884-90; J.M. Remein, 1891-1903; A.J. Vanden
Heuvel, 1904-07; L.J. Lamberts, 1909-14; H. Bel,
1914-18; J.J. Hiemenga, 1918-19; P.J. Yff, 1920-
23; A.J. Rus, 1924-30; H.J. Triezenberg, 1930-38;
O. Holtrop, 1939-47; A.E. Rozendal, 1948-52; E.
Ubels, 1953-54; R. Evenhuis, 1955-57; R.J. Frens,
1958-65; J.C. Verbrugge, 1966-70; R.W. DeVries,
1970-79; P.W.Brink, 1980-95; J.R. Van Tholen,
1996-2000; R.L. Palsrok, 2002-

Rochester, NY — Webster
see: Webster, NY — Webster

Rochester Hills, MI — Han-Bit Korean
1991-
former name: Troy, MI – Han-Bit Korean, 1991-96
pastors: Y.J. Oh, 1988-; A.K. Chun, 1997-98

Rockford, IL — CRC (unorganized)
1970-1972, discontinued
staff: R.D. Bouertje (M), 1970-72

Rockford, MI — Blythefield
1989-
reorganization of Grand Rapids, MI – Arcadia-Plainfield
pastors: J. De Vries, 1985-86; A.A. Gorter, 1988-95; R.J. Visker, 1996-2002

Rockford, MI — River Rock (emerging)
2000-
pastor: J.L. Huizenga, 2000-

Rocklin, CA — Granite Springs
1991-
organized: 1999
pastor: K.J. Adams, 1991-; D.J. Bouws, 2002-

Rock Rapids, IA — Rock Rapids
1922-
pastors: J.J. Dyk, 1924-26; B. Zwaagman, 1928-31; R. Heynen, 1933-38; G.J. Vander Ziel, 1938-43; S. Fopma, 1944-51; P.J. Veenstra, 1952-61; P. Huisman, 1962-66; W. Verwolf, 1966-69; D.E. Houseman, 1970-76; J.L. Hoogeveen, 1976-80; T.B. Toeset, 1980-85; D.W. Brouwer, 1985-91; M.D. Deckinga, 1991-98; C.D. Hoekstra, 1998-

Rock Valley, IA — Calvin
1951-
pastors: J.C. Ribbens, 1952-56; M.R. Doornbos, 1956-60; D.T. Van Oyen, 1960-65; J.H. Engbers, 1966-78; E.J. Knott, 1978-83; J. Van Groningen, 1985-91; R.W. Sparks, 1991-

Rock Valley, IA — First
1891-
former name: Rock Valley, IA – Rock Valley, 1891-1951
pastors: A. Vander Velde Vander Bok, 1897-1904; H.J. Heynen, 1904-08; J.J. Holwerda, 1908-14; H. Kuiper, 1915-23; J.H. Geerlings, 1923-28; J. Gritter, 1929-38; H.J. Triezenberg, 1938-44; H. Kuiper, 1944-51; C. Huissen, 1952-60; J.J.Byker,

1960-64; L. Van Drunen, 1965-72; P.E. Bakker, 1973-79; R.D. Bultman, 1979-85; F.F. Gunnink, 1985-87; C.E. Fennema, 1988-

Rock Valley, IA — Rock Valley
see: Rock Valley, IA – First

Rock Valley, IA — Trinity
1970-
pastors: J. Admiraal, 1971-76; D.W. De Groot, 1976-82; R.J. Timmer, 1983-90; J.P. Groenewold, 1991-2001

Rocky Mountain House, AB — Covenant
2000-
pastor: N. Wolmarans, 2001-

Rocky Mountain House, AB — First
1950-
former name: Rocky Mountain House, AB – Rocky Mountain House, 1950-85
pastors: G. Van Laar, 1950-53; A.J. Vanden Pol, 1955-57; J.H. Binnema, 1960-65; P. Sluys, 1965-70; C. Bishop, 1970-76; P.J. Boodt, 1976-82; J. Ypma, 1982-85; J. Nutma, 1986-90; P. Stel, 1991-

Rocky Mountain House, AB — Rocky Mountain House
see: Rocky Mountain House, AB – First

Roseland, IL — Roseland
see: Chicago, IL – Roseland

Roselawn, IN — Community
1974-
former name: Thayer, IN – Roselawn Community, 1974-79
pastors: J. Zandstra (M), 1975-77; J. Van Schepen, 1978-83; D.E. Byker, 1984-89; J.D. Stoel, 1989-96; J.W. Zuidema, 1998-

Roseville, MI — Immanuel
1958-
organized: 1959
former name: Roseville, MI – Roseville, 1959-68
pastors: W. De Waard, 1958-59; M. Vander Poorte (L), 1958-59; J. Hekman, 1961-66; R.O. Grevengoed, 1967-71; T.G. Kaastra, 1970-; J.G. Busscher, 1979-85

Roseville, MI — Roseville
see: Roseville, MI – Immanuel

Rotterdam, KS — Rotterdam
see: Dispatch, KS – Dispatch

**Round Rock, TX — North Austin
Community**
1993–
organized: 1997
former name: Austin, TX – North Austin Community, 1993–99
pastors: M. Brouwer, 1992–97; J.W. Zuidema, 1993–94; G.G. Van Dam (stated supply), 1994–95; Kenneth R. Rip, 1998–

Rowland Heights, CA — Immanuel
see: La Puente, CA – Joy of Jesus

Royal Oak, MI — North Hills
see: Troy, MI – North Hills

Rudyard, MI — Rudyard
1901–
pastors: H.H. Kamps, 1911–15; L. Van Haitsma, 1920–24; R.J. Bos, 1925–29; J. Hanenburg, 1929–41; S. Kramer, 1941–44; D. Mellema, 1945–54; M. Stegink, 1954–58; L.F. Baker, 1959–64; M.B. Fynaardt, 1965–69; P.C. Hogeterp, 1970–73; R.R. Broekema, 1973–78; J.O. De Bruyn, 1978–82; G.L. Essenburg, 1983–97; R.D. Steen, 1999–

Rusk, MI — Rusk
1897–
pastors: H. Huizingh, 1904–08; W. Kole, 1908–14; J. Robbert, 1916–18; J.O. Bouwsma, 1919–21; D. Jonker, 1921–26; J. Medendorp, 1926–30; W. Vande Kieft, 1930–39; N. Beute, 1937–46; J.A. De Kruyter, 1947–50; C.W. Flietstra, 1950–53; A. Zylstra, 1953–58; R.H. Hooker, 1959–63; R.H. Haan, 1964; W.F. Holleman, 1965–70; W.L. Van Rees, 1970–74; G.J. Bosma, 1974–80; G.D. Mouw, 1980–90; J.J. Stastny, 1990–96; C.D. Vander Meyden, 1997–

Sacramento, CA (campus ministry)
1973–1976
staff: L.B. Mensink, 1973–76

Sacramento, CA — Korean (emerging)
1989–
pastor: S.S. Ahn, 1989–

Sacramento, CA — Sacramento
1963–
pastors: S. Vander Jagt (M), 1960–65; E.C. Marlink, 1966–82; L.B. Mensink, 1973–76; R.W. De Vries, 1983–91; J.R. Van Tholen, 1992–96; P.H. Vander Klay, 1997–

Sacramento, CA — The Gathering (emerging)
2000–
pastor: R. D. Vander Well, 2000–

Saginaw, MI — Community
1940–
former name: Saginaw, MI – Saginaw 1940–55
pastors: M. Huizenga, 1940–43; E. Bossenbroek, 1943–48; H.B. Spaan, 1948–53; S. Ten Brink, 1953–56; W. Prince, 1956–60; V.G. Vander Werp, 1960–63; F.J. Walhof, 1963–68; A.J. Hoogewind, 1969–75; D.J. Van Loo, 1976–83; K.L. Schepel, 1983–89; W. Versluys, II, 1990–97; S.J. Sturing, 1999–

Saginaw, MI — Saginaw
see: Saginaw, MI – Community

St. Albert, AB — St. Albert
1980–
pastors: F.J. Koning, 1981–87; D.J. Heinen, 1987–91; B.G. Adema, 1992–97; J.W. Luth, 1998–

**St. Catharines, ON — Brock Christian
Reformed Campus Ministry**
1986–
pastors: B. Walsh, 1986–88; R. Middleton, 1988–90; C.N. Overduin, 1990–96; P. Schuurman (L), 1996–

St. Catharines, ON — Covenant
1976–
pastors: J. Kuntz, 1976–83; J.B. Vos, 1983–94; D.R. Tigchelaar, 1986–89; E. Groot-Nibbelink, 1990–2001

St. Catharines, ON — Jubilee Fellowship
1987–
pastor: P. Slofstra, 1988–

St. Catharines, ON — Maranatha
1949–
former name: St. Catharines, ON – St. Catharines, 1949–64
pastors: A. Persenaire, 1948–53; W. Van Dyk, 1953–59; A.H. Venema, 1958–63; P.G. Schrotenboer, 1960–64; M.D. Geleynse, 1964–71; H.R. De Bolster, 1971–81; J. Kuntz, 1972–76; D.W. De Groot, 1982–84; H. Katterberg, 1985–94; W.H. Vanderwerf, 1996–

St. Catharines, ON — St. Catharines
see: St. Catharines, ON – Maranatha

St. Catharines, ON — Second
see: St. Catharines, ON – Trinity

St. Catharines, ON — Trinity
1964-
former name: St. Catharines, ON – Second, 1964
pastors: J.D. Hellinga, 1964-68; R.J. Sikkema,
1969-81; H. Jonker, 1981-87; C.J. Tuininga,
1988-1991; R.J. de Lange, 1993-2000; H.A. Winter, 2002-

St. Cloud, MN — Community (emerging)
1971-1977, discontinued
pastors: L.R. Smits (M), 1971-74; R.H. Uken (M),
1975-76

**Ste. Croix, QC — Eglise Chretienne
Reformee de Lotbiniere (unorganized)**
1984-1990
pastors: Guy Dube (E), 1984-86; M. Vielleux (E),
1986-90

St. John, IN — Crossroads Community
see: Schererville, IN – Crossroads Community

St. John, IN — Crossroads Ministry
see: Schererville, IN – Crossroads Community

St. Joseph, MI — St. Joseph
1962-
organized: 1965
pastors: D.J. Hoitenga, Jr. (M), 1962-71; A.D.
Compaan, 1971-74; C.K. Van Winkle, 1975-80; M.
Beelen, 1981-91; N.J. Thomasma, 1991-2000;
P.V. DeJonge, 2001-

**Ste. Lamert, QC — Eglise Reformee de la
Rive-Sud (mission)**
1980-1988
pastor: H. Kallemeyn, 1980-88

St. Louis, MO — Trinity
organized: 1969
pastors: H.M. De Rooy (M), 1965-71; S. Mast,
1971-74; W.A. Stroo, 1975-86; D.S. Sarkipato,
1988-97; T.V. Wagenmaker, 1997-2001; P.J. Mans
(I), 2002-2003; G.J. Kamps, 2003-

St. Paul, MN — South Grove
see: Inver Grove Heights, MN – Grace

St. Petersburg, FL — Calvin-Pinellas Park
see: St. Petersburg, FL – Pine Grove Community

St. Petersburg, FL — Korean Evergreen
see: Tampa, FL – Korean Evergreen

**St. Petersburg, FL — Pine Grove
Community**
1960-
former names: St. Petersburg, FL – St. Petersburg, 1960-61; St. Petersburg, FL – Calvin, 1961-
67; St. Petersburg. FL – Calvin /Pinellas Park,
1967-68; Pinellas Park, FL – Pinellas Park, 1969-
91
pastors: M. Beelen, 1958-61 (M); R.O.
Broekhuizen (M), 1963-64; R.O. Broekhuizen,
1964-65; A. Cammenga, Sr., 1969-73; W.
Hofman, 1973-80; J. Van Hemert, 1980-84; P.
Ingeneri, 1984-97; L.J. Howerzyl, 2001-

St. Petersburg, FL — St. Petersburg Chapel
1969-1975, discontinued

**St. Petersburg, FL — St. Petersburg Laotian
(emerging)**
1996-
pastor: R. Silakhom (E), 1996-

St. Thomas, ON — Fellowship
1985-
pastors: C.N. Overduin, 1985-90; T. Baird, 1991-

St. Thomas, ON — First
1952-
former name: St. Thomas, ON – St. Thomas,
1952-72
pastors: W. Hekman, 1953-59; L.W. Van Dellen,
1960-64; A. Beukema, 1964-69; L.T. Schalkwyk,
1970-75; G.D. Mouw, 1976-80; P. Meyer, 1982-
88; J. Heidinga, 1989-2001

St. Thomas, ON — St. Thomas
see: St. Thomas, ON – First

Salem, OR — Salem
see: Salem, OR – Sunnyslope

Salem, OR — Sunnyslope
1964-
former name: Salem, OR – Salem, 1964-71
pastors: B.J. Niemeyer (M), 1961-67; R.D.
Posthuma, 1967-73; T.E. Dykman, 1973-78; J.S.
Mantel, 1978-83; J. Van Schepen, 1983-90; S.R.
Van Eck, 1991-95; A.J. Machiela, 1996-

Salida, CA (mission)
1916

Salmon Arm, BC — Salmon Arm
1979-
pastors: P. Sluys, 1979-84; E. Vander Woude, 1985-90; W.L. Vander Beek, 1990-94; R.A. Vanden Brink, 1994-

Salt Lake City, UT — Cambodian
see: West Valley, UT – Cambodian

Salt Lake City, UT — First
1957-
former name: Salt Lake City, UT – Salt Lake City, 1957-62
pastors: N. Vogelzang (M), 1955-60; E.J. Schipper, 1960-63; C. Van Slooten, 1963-79; J.A. Molenbeek, 1979-82; T.J. De Vries, 1983-89; G.G. Hofland, 1990-2000; T.H. Vander Ziel, 2001-

Salt Lake City, UT — Immanuel
see: Salt Lake City, UT – Mountain Springs Community

Salt Lake City, UT — Indian Christian Center (emerging)
1957-
pastors: J. Yazzie (E), 1957-61; F. Bakker (E), 1961-65; M. Baas (L), 1963-64; C. Thomas (L), 1965-66; G.J. Klumpenhower, 1966-69; J. Lineweaver (E), 1970-71; J. Yazzie (E), 1970-71; N. Jonkman (E), 1972-80; H. Bielema (L), 1983-88; J. Haswood (L), 1992-

Salt Lake City, UT — Mountain Springs Community
1964-
former name: Salt Lake City, UT – Immanuel, 1964-95
pastors: N. Vogelzang (M), 1961-64; J. Zandstra, 1964-66; D.W. Van Gent, 1966-69; P. Borgdorff, 1969-72; A. Van Heyst, 1973-76; A.L. Kuiper, 1976-81; J.J. Vanden Hoek, 1981-83; D.J. Kruis, 1984-90; D.M. Crump, 1988-97

Salt Lake City, UT — Salt Lake City
see: Salt Lake City, UT – First

San Antonio, TX — Lord of Life Community (emerging)
1986-1989, discontinued
pastors: J.A. Byker (M), 1985-89; E.C. Marlink, (M), 1989

San Bernardino, CA — San Bernardino Korean (emerging)
1997-
pastor: P. Won, 1998-

Sanborn, IA — Sanborn
1911-
pastors: F.W. Stuart, 1912-15; D. Hollebeek, 1915-25; J.G. Vande Lune, 1926-30; B. Van Someren, 1930-38; W.L. Van Rees, 1939-44; R.J. Bos, 1944-48; G.J. Postma, 1949-53; C. Vander Ark, 1955-62; P. Vander Weide, 1963-69; F. Handlogten, 1970-73; J.R. Sittema, 1975-81; S.C. Pastine, 1982-92; G.D. Mouw, 1995; M.D. Fopma, 1996-

San Diego, CA — Christ's Community
1989-1994, discontinued
pastors: T.E. Dykman, 1986-92; L.M. Fryling, 1992-94

San Diego, CA — Christian Servicemen's Center (classical ministry)
1943-1945, 1966-1991, discontinued
directors: G.B. Boerfyn, 1943-45; Mr./Mrs. E. Roby (L), 1967-68; E. Roby (L), 1968-69; Mr./Mrs. L Yett (L), 1969-70; S. Draayer, 1972-73; D. Rottenberg (L), 1973-91

San Diego, CA — El Arca Comunidad Cristiana
see: San Diego, CA – Vida Nueva

San Diego, CA — Monte Sion (church plant)
2000-
pastor: J. Ybarra (L), 2000-

San Diego, CA — Otay Mesa Community
1970-1993, merged into San Diego, CA – Trinity Fellowship
organized: 1976
pastors: J. Zandstra (M), 1970-71; P. Veenstra (M), 1970-71; B.A. Averill, 1971-75; B.N. Huizenga, 1975-81; B.H. Zandstra, II, 1981-84; D.J. Wyenberg, 1985-93

San Diego, CA — San Diego
1943-
absorbed members of San Diego, CA – Vida Nueva, 2000
pastors: G.B. Boerfyn (M), 1943-49; P.A. Hoekstra, 1949-54; C. Van Slooten, 1954-63; P.C. Zylstra, 1964-70; G.D. Klouw, 1970-75; P.J. Kok, 1976-82; D.G. Zandstra, 1983-90; B. van Eyk, 1991-97; N.L. Koch, 1997-; P. Acune, 2000-

San Diego, CA — Trinity Fellowship
1993-
merger of Chula Vista, CA – Trinity and San
Diego, CA – Otay Mesa Community
pastors: D.J. Wyenberg, 1993; A. Rumph, 1993-
1994; D.W. Lagerwey, 1996-

San Diego, CA — Vida Nueva
1994-2000, discontinued, members merged with
San Diego, CA – San Diego
former name: San Diego, CA – El Acra
Comunidad, 1994-96
pastor: F. Acune, 1994-2000

San Francisco, CA — Friendship House
(classical ministry)
1962-1982, discontinued
pastors: L.W. Baas (L), 1963-65; M. Baas (L),
1965-66; R.J. Venema, 1966-70; W. Wellington
(L), 1967-68; R.J. Buining (M), 1971-76; D.J.
Klompeen, 1976-82

San Francisco, CA — Golden Gate
1973-
pastors: P. Yang, 1965-90, 1991-2001; M. Vander
Pol, 1986-93; J.J. Liu, 1987-89; D.R. Ridder, Jr.,
1995-99 ; S. Ng, 1997-; B.K.H. Lim, 2000-:
A.K.W. Lee, 2000-

San Francisco, CA — San Francisco
see: Alameda, CA – First

San Francisco, CA — The New City Church
(emerging)
1987-89, discontinued
pastor: H. De Young, 1987-89

San Jacinto, CA — Hemet (emerging)
1973-1976

San Jose, CA — Friendship Agape
(emerging)
1989-
pastors: J.J. Liu, 1989-98; K. Wong, 1998-

San Jose, CA — Hope
see: San Jose, CA – San Jose New Hope

San Jose, CA — Moorepark
see: San Jose, CA – San Jose

San Jose, CA — San Jose
1954-
former name: San Jose, CA – Moorepark, 1958-
73

pastors: G.B. Boerfyn (M), 1953-57; J. Stulp,
1957-67; G.B. Ebbers, 1968-81; T.F. Thole, 1981-
84; R.E. Van Hofwegen, 1985-95; J.J. Berends,
1996-

San Jose, CA — San Jose New Hope
(emerging)
1988-1994; 2000-, withdrew, returned
pastors: P.H. Kim, 1983-89; H.K. Kim, 1984-88;
I.C. Choo, 1988-94; J.S. Kang, 2000-2001; D.Y.
Chong, 2001-

San Jose, CA — Vietnamese Liberty/Thanh
Duong TuDo (emerging)
1992-
pastor: N.T. Kieu, 1991-

San Lorenzo, CA — Living Faith
Fellowship-Filipino
see: Union City, CA – Living Faith Fellowship-
Filipino

San Marcos, CA — Crossroads
1998-
formed by a combination of San Marcos, CA –
Hope and remaining members from Escondido, CA
pastor: M.D. Vermaire, 1999-

San Marcos, CA — Hope
1987-1998, merged into San Marcos, CA – Crossroads, 1998
pastor: D.L. Alderink, 1989-93

Sanostee, NM — Sanostee (emerging)
1968-
pastors: F. Curley, Sr. (E), 1968-86; R. Slim,
1986-

Santa Ana, CA (mission)
1932-1933

Santa Ana, CA — Mong
1996-
pastor: T.W. Moua (E), 1996-

Santa Fe, NM — Government School
(mission)
1921-1928

Santa Monica, CA — Good Land (emerging)
1991-1993, discontinued
pastor: N Yassa, 1991-93

**Santa Monica, CA — The Talking Stick
(emerging)**
2001-
pastor: R.J. Braaksma, 2001-

**Santa Rosa, CA — Hope Community
(emerging)**
1989-
pastors: N.P. Jasperse, 1988-96; A.J. Nikkel,
1996-2000

Sardis, BC — Sardis (ministry)
1991-1994
pastor: K. Byl (E), 1991-94

Sarnia, ON — First
1934-
former names: Blackwell, ON — Blackwell, 1934-
39; Sarnia, ON — Sarnia, 1939-52
pastors: W. Meyer (M), 1929-34; W. Meyer,
1934-39; H. Wierenga (M), 1939-43; H. Wierenga,
1943-50; J. Rook, 1950-52; H.A. Venema, 1952-
55; S. Cooper, 1956-60; C.W. Flietstra, 1961-66;
P. De Jong, 1966-70; H. Getkate, 1970-78; S.
Cooper, 1978-84; R. Fluit, 1986-88; J. Kuipers,
1989-2000; D.J. Weemhoff, 2001-

Sarnia, ON — Redeemer
1970-
former name: Sarnia, ON — Third, 1970-72
pastors: M. Pool, 1971-77; J. Kerssies, 1977-85;
J.D. Suk, 1985-90; K. de Koning, 1990-2001; J.
Westerhof (I), 2001

Sarnia, ON — Rehoboth
see: Sarnia, ON — Second

Sarnia, ON — Sarnia
see: Sarnia, ON — First

Sarnia, ON — Second
1952-
former name: Sarnia, ON — Rehoboth, 1963-68
pastors: J. Rook, 1952-53; A.B., Hofland, 1954-
63; A.J. Vanden Pol, 1961-63; A. De Jager, 1963-
70; H.A. Venema, 1970-72; J.J. Hoytema, 1973-
78; F.F. Bakker, 1979-86; J.W. Jongsma, 1987-97;
R.S. Wigboldus, 1999-

Sarnia, ON — Third
see: Sarnia, ON — Redeemer

Sarnia, ON — Wayside Chapel
1967-1968

Saskatoon, SK — Bethel
1952-
former name: Saskatoon, SK — Saskatoon, 1952-
71
pastors: G.J. Vander Ziel (M), 1953-59; B.
Boelens, 1960-64; J.C. De Moor; 1965-68; H.C.
Salomons, 1969-74; A.J. Miedema, 1974-77; G.J.
Hogeterp, 1978-84; H. Van Niejenhuis, 1985-88;
W. Versteeg, 1988-93; R.T. Vander Vaart, 1993-
98; B Leiter, 1998-

Saskatoon, SK — Saskatoon
see: Saskatoon, SK — Bethel

Saugatuck, MI — Saugatuck
1882-1883, discontinued
formed by members who left the Refromed
Church in America

Saugatuck, MI — Saugatuck
1962
organized: 1994
pastors: C. Disselkoen (E), 1962-69; P. Vander
Kamp (E), 1970-72; E. Visscher (E), 1972-81; R.V.
Luchies, 1981-85; L.J. Wolters, 1986-91; D.L. Van
Der Wiele, 1992-

Sauk Village, IL — Emmanuel
1958-
organized: 1968
former name: Sauk Village, IL — Emmanuel Chapel, 1958-68
pastors: P. Vander Kamp (L), 1958-64; H.J.
Teitsma (M), 1965-68; W.D. Ribbens, 1969-75;
H.J. Schutt, 1975-83; P.D. Sikkema, 1983-91;
V.G. Van Ee, 1988-91; W.J. Moxey, 1992-95; D.
Pewee, 1996-98; T.L. Koster, 2001-

Sauk Village, IL — Emmanuel Chapel
see: Sauk Village, IL — Emmanuel

**Savage, MN — Bridgewood Community
(emerging)**
1998-
organized: 1999
pastor: M.K. Brouwer, 1997-

Savannah, GA — Savannah
1966-1969, discontinued
pastor: K.E. Kelley (M), 1966-69

Sayville, NY — Sayville
see: West Sayville, NY — West Sayville

Schaumburg, IL — Living-Spring Community
see: Glenview, IL – Living-Spring Community

Schererville, IN — Crossroads Community
1994–
organized: 1998
former name: St. John, IN – Crossroads Ministry, 1994–95; St. John, IN – Crossroads Community, 1995–2001
pastors: K.J. Vos, 1993–; K.J. De Lange, 1998–99; J. Vreeman, 2001–

Schraalenburg, NJ — Schraalenburg
1822–1908, withdrew, became South Presbyterian Church of Bergenfield, 1913
joined CRC 1890 from True Protestant Dutch Reformed Church
pastors: S. Foeligh, 1827; C.J. Blauvelt, 1828–53; E.S. Hammond, 1858–60; A. Van Houten, 1861–68; G.A. Haring, 1868–1908

Scottsdale, AZ — Palm Lane
1964–
pastors: J.F. Hollebeek (M), 1963–68; G. De Young, 1968–74; M.W. Heyboer, 1976–79; P.C. Zylstra, 1981–87; G.J. Kamps, 1988–98; P.J. Van Dyken, Jr., 1999–

Scottsdale, AZ — Principe de Paz (classical ministry)
1994–1998, discontinued
pastor: Esteban Lugo, 1994–98

Seattle, WA (mission)
1912

Seattle, WA — Calvary
1957–1985, discontinued
pastors: L.E. Kok, 1957–62; J. Kroon, 1962–67; G.D. Pars, 1968–73; D.W. Vander Veen, 1973–78; J. Klooster, 1979–85

Seattle, WA — Emmaus Road (emerging)
1997–
pastors: A.R. Sytsma, 1997–99; E. Likkel (E), 1997–

Seattle, WA — First
1939–
former name: Seattle, WA – Seattle, 1939–56
pastors: K. Bergsma, 1938–41; A.H. Smit, 1941–43; W. Groen, 1943–51; P. De Jong, 1952–62; A. Cammenga, Sr., 1962–69; J.A. Wesseling, 1970–

76; P.J. Holwerda, 1977–86; S.J. Keyzer, 1987–97; H.J. Weidenaar, 1998–

Seattle, WA — Hope Korean
see: Tacoma, Wa – New Hope

Seattle, WA — Seattle
see: Seattle, WA – First

Seneca, AZ (mission)
1900
branch of Ft. Defiance, AZ

Seoul, South Korea (service home)
1967–
pastor: E. Roels, 1967–69

Sepulveda, CA — Valley Dong San
see: Northridge, CA – Valley Dong San

Sergeant Bluff, IA — Friendship Community (emerging)
2000–
former name: Sioux City, IA – Sioux City, 2000–2001
pastor: V. Schaap (E), 2000–

Shackleton, SK (mission)
1928–1947

Sharon, OH — Sharon
see: Willard, OH – Willard

Sheboygan, WI — Beacon Light Chapel (mission)
1951–1974
staff: R. Huizenga (E), 1953–58; L. Wolters, 1960–62; C. Buist (E), 1963–66; J. Fikkert (E), 1967–72; J. Van Schepen (M), 1973–74

Sheboygan, WI — Calvin
1958–
pastors: D.H. Aardsma, 1958–63; L.F. Stockmeier, 1963–68; H.G. Vanden Einde, 1968–74; B. De Jong, 1974–83; G.L. Rutgers, 1983–88; S.J. Alsum, 1989–98; R.A. Sizemore, 1999–

Sheboygan, WI — First
1889–
former name: Sheboygan, WI – Sheboygan, 1889–1958
pastors: T.L. De Lange, 1896–1900; H. Huizingh, 1901–04; F. Welandt, 1905–10; H. Guikema, 1911–14; J. Manni, 1916–25; W. Terpstra, 1925–35; E.B. Pekelder, 1935–47; G.J. Rozenboom, 1949–53; H.

Exoo, 1954-76; J.R. Pruim, 1976-85; W.M. Gebben, 1985-97; J. Korenstra, 1999-2000; R.D. Zomermaand, 2001-

Sheboygan, WI — Hmong
1987-
pastor: X.X. Yang, 1987-98; K. Vang (E), 1999-

Sheboygan, WI — Sheboygan
see: Sheboygan, WI — First

Sheldon, IA — First
1906-
former name: Sheldon, IA — Sheldon, 1906-68
pastors: F.W. Stuart, 1908-12; J.M. Voortman, 1913-21; J. Mulder, 1921-25; W. Bajema, 1925-47; J. Griffioen, 1948-53; R.S. De Haan, 1954-60; S.T. Cammenga, 1960-65; B. Van Antwerpen, 1966-69; N. Vogelzang, 1970-76; P.Y. De Jong, 1976-80; J.M. Julien, 1981-89; J.A. Wesseling, 1991-94; J.A. Vermeer, 1995-

Sheldon, IA — Immanuel
1972-
pastors: P.J. Holwerda, 1972-77; N.D. Kloosterman, 1978-82; B.J. Haan, Jr., 1983-89; R.R. Bergsma, 1989-98; R.R. Broekema, 1999-2001

Sheldon, IA — Sheldon
see: Sheldon, IA — First

Shepherd, MT — Shepherd
1908-1943, discontinued
pastors: D. Vander Ploeg (M), 1915-18; D. Vander Ploeg, 1918-19; N. Gelderloos, 1921-26; J. Homan, 1927-37; R. Star, 1938-43

Sheridan, MI — Sheridan
see: Reeman, MI — Reeman

Shiprock, NM — Bethel
1935-
organized: 1985
former name: Shiprock, NM — Shiprock, 1985-91
pastors: L.P. Brink (M), 1936; H.J. Rikkers, 1936-41; J.R. Kamps, 1941-42; F. Vander Stoep (M), 1942-68; C. Vogel (L), 1950-52; S. Yazzie (L), 1951-57, 1960-65; C. Dykema (L), 1951-52; R. Kruis (L), 1952-53; H. Fridsma (L), 1953-57; B. Joe (L), 1953-58; N. Van Mersbergen, 1957-60; B. Garenez, 1957-65; M. Harbets (E), 1958-60; A.W. Koolhaas, 1969-89; E. Lugo, 1992-93; J.J. Greydanus, 1996-

Shiprock, NM — Shiprock
see: Shiprock, NM — Bethel

Shubenacadie, NS — Faith
see: Milford, NS — Faith Community

Sibley, IA — Sibley
1912-
pastors: H.J. Haarsma (M), 1913-16; D. Jonker, 1918-21; C. Van Reenen (M), 1922-25; B. Vanden Brink, 1933-43; O. De Groot, 1944-48; W. Prince, 1949-56; T.L. Brouwer, 1956-61; K.R. Slager, 1962-69; H. Hiemstra, 1969-77; C.E. Fennema, 1978-83; D.S. Sarkipato, 1984-88; W.G. Van Hal, 1989-95; M.J. Leese, 1996-2001

Siebert, CO — Elpis
see: Vona, CO — Vona

Silverdale, WA — Anchor of Hope
1984-
organized: 1986
pastor: D.N. Snapper, 1984-

Silver Spring, MD — Silver Spring
1969-
former name: Washington, DC — Silver Spring, 1969-76
pastors: R.R. De Ridder, 1969-73; A.J. Stienstra, 1975-81; R.J. de Groot, 1982-90; P.A. Apol, 1991-98; D.H. Bratt, 1998-

Simcoe, ON — Immanuel
1957-
pastors: J. Vriend, 1960-64; G. Rienks, 1964-69; F.F. Bakker, 1970-74; R. Fluit, 1975-80; L. Slofstra, 1981-89; J. Roke, 1989-92; H.R. Vander Kooij, 1994-

Sioux Center, IA — Bethel
1922-
former name: Sioux Center, IA — Second, 1922-54
pastors: L. Ypma, 1921-34; M. Keuning, 1936-42; O. Breen, 1942-47; J. Breuker, 1947-52; R.J. Venema, 1954-58; C. Vander Plate, 1960-65; L.M. Tamminga, 1965-70; H.B. Vanden Heuvel, 1970-79; D.E. Tinklenberg, 1980-89; R.J. Holwerda, 1989-94; R.D. Drenten, 1994-2001; S.K. Rhoda, 2002-

Sioux Center, IA — Covenant
1974-
former name: Sioux Center, IA — Third, 1974
pastors: F.D. Steen, 1975-81; G.J. Kamps, 1982-

87; H.J. Weidenaar, 1988-92; D.W. De Groot, 1993-99; J.C. Vander Stelt (I), 1999-2000; H. Van Niejenhuis, 2000-

Sioux Center, IA — Faith
1979-
pastors: D.L. Smit, 1980-87; C.D. Hoekstra, 1989-97; B.J. Haan, Jr., 1998-

Sioux Center, IA — First
1890-
former name: Sioux Center, IA — Sioux Center, 1890-1922
pastors: H. Beets, 1895-99; J. Smitter, 1900-04; W.P. Van Wyk, 1904-11; H.M. Vander Ploeg, 1911- 18; C. De Leeuw, 1919-24; M.M. Schans, 1924- 27; J.M. Dykstra, 1929-39; M. Arnoys, 1939-45; B.J. Haan, 1945-63; R.R. De Ridder, 1964-69; P.Y. De Jong, 1970-76; J.H. Piersma, 1977-81; J.D. Hellinga, 1982-87; J.W. Postman, 1987-91; J.L. Witvliet, 1993-

Sioux Center, IA — Lebanon
1903-
pastors: H.J. Haarsma, 1907-11; S. Bouma, 1911- 15; P. Jonker, Jr., 1915-19; J.J. Steigenga, 1920- 24; W. Kok, 1924-27; A.H. Kort, 1927-34; J. Rubingh, 1935-40; W.K. Reinsma, 1941-45; H. Bajema, 1946-49; P. Vander Weide, 1952-56; A.A. Arkema, 1957-61; H.D. Vanderwell, 1962-66; D.E. Tinklenberg, 1967-71; J. Kroon, 1972-80; K. Eiten, 1980-84; T.A. De Does, 1984-90; D.W. Visser, 1991-98; C. Louvau, 2000-

Sioux Center, IA — Second
see: Sioux Center, IA — Bethel

Sioux Center, IA — Sioux Center
see: Sioux Center, IA — First

Sioux Center, IA — Third
see: Sioux Center, IA — Covenant

Sioux City, IA (mission)
1959-
staff: L.F. Meydrech (L), 1958-59

Sioux City, IA — First
see: Sioux City, IA — Sioux City

Sioux City, IA — Laotian Unity (emerging)
2000-
K. Baccam (E), 2000-

Sioux City, IA — Sioux City (emerging)
1930-2000, discontinued, some members formed Sergeant Bluff, IA — Friendship Community
organized: 1930-1999
former name: Sioux City, IA — First, 1980-99
pastors: J.T. Holwerda, 1931-35; G. Yff, 1935- 38; G. Vander Kooi, 1939-43; W. Meyer (M), 1943-49; J. Zandstra (M), 1949-55; J.W. Van Weelden, 1955-60; J.M. Evenhouse, 1961-64; H.P. Baak, 1965-68; D.W. Boonstra, 1969-75; K.H. Bratt, 1975-81; L.L. Meyer, 1981-88; R.D. Ruis, 1988-92; P.J. Mans, 1995-99; V. Schaap (E), 2000

Sioux City, IA — Sioux City Vietnamese
see: Worthington, MN — Vietnamese

Sioux Falls, SD — First
1923-
former name: Sioux Falls, SD — Sioux Falls, 1923-85
pastors: J.C. De Bruyn, 1929-36; J.C. Verbrugge, 1936-40; W. Vander Haak, 1941-44; G.H. Vande Riet, 1944-49; B. Bruxvoort, 1949-53; E.C. Dykstra, 1954-59; P. De Boer, 1960-70; P.J. Kok, 1971-76; H. De Groot, 1976-85; J.F. Schuurman, 1985-89; S. Scripps, 1991-2002; K.D. Koning, 1992-96; C.H. Bruxvoort, 2001-

Sioux Falls, SD — Heartland Community (emerging)
1996-
pastor: J.L. Hoogeveen, 1995-

Sioux Falls, SD — Shalom
1978-
pastors: J.D. Van Regenmorter, 1979-88; R.W. Bronkema, 1988-95; C.J. De Ridder, 1995-

Sioux Falls, SD — Sioux Falls
see: Sioux Falls, SD — First

Smithers, BC — Smithers
1952-
pastors: G. Van Laar (M), 1953-57; L.M. Tamminga, 1957-60; P. De Jong, 1962-66; J.P. Vosteen, 1966-70; J. Tuininga, 1970-77; S.C. Pastine, 1978-82; H.J. Bierman, 1983-88; B. Beukema, 1988-92; J.S. Hielema, 1990-94; J.R. Poelman, 1993-

Smithville, ON — Smithville
1973-
pastors: A.W. Schaafsma, 1972-77; P.

Ravensbergen, 1977–81; J. Nutma, 1981–86; J. De Jong, 1988–96; H. Vander Beek, 1996-2002

South Bend, IN — South Bend
1959-
pastors: L.J. Wolters (M), 1957–60; T.L.Smith, 1960–68; H.J. Teitsma, 1968–71; R.D. Kramer, 1971–81; C. Terpstra, 1982–90; L.J. Vander Zee, 1990-

South Boardman, MI — South Boardman
1908-1925, discontinued

South Gate, CA — Faith
1990-
organized: 1997
pastor: M.I. Jeong, 1990-

South Haven, MI — Kibbie (emerging)
1959-
former name: Kibbie, MI – Kibbie, 1959–79
pastors: C. Grevengoed (L), 1960–61; M. Keuning (L), 1961-68, 1970–72; R. Kruis (L), 1968–70; J. Vanden Heuvel, 1972–82; A.H. Schipper, 1983–87; R.L. Bouma, 1988–92; E. Visscher (E), 1993–98; G. Haadsma, 2000-

South Holland, IL — Bethany
1925-1996, withdrew to United Reformed Churches
former name: South Holland, IL – Second, 1925-32
pastors: E. Kooistra, 1926–30; J.O. Bouwsma, 1931–38; S. Vroon, 1939–42; P.H. Eldersveld, 1943–46; R.H. Hooker, 1948–54; S. Kramer, 1954–60; M.R. Doornbos, 1960–68; J.H. Piersma, 1969–77; C.G. Werkema, Sr., 1978–83; A.T. Spriensma, 1984–92; G.H. Stoutmeyer, 1993-96

South Holland, IL — Cottage Grove
1956-
pastors: R.E. Van Harn, 1957–61; C. Bolt, 1961–66; C.K.Van Winkle, 1966–71; E.D. Roels, 1972–78; J.M. Gray, 1978–82; C.G. Van Halsema, 1984–87; N. Shepherd, 1989–98; F.A. De Jong, 1991–94; J.H. McCune, 1999-

South Holland, IL — First
1865-
former names: Low Prairie, IL – Low Prairie, 1865–66, South Holland, IL – South Holland, 1866-1926
pastors: E.L. Meinders, 1874–86; R.T. Kuiper, 1889–94; J.C. Groeneveld, 1895-1902; M. De Boer, 1903–07; L. Van Dellen, 1908–14; H.

Guikema, 1915–21; P. Van Dyk, 1921–27; K.W. Fortuin, 1928–33; I. Westra, 1934–44; B. Van Someren, 1945-52; M. Ouwinga, 1956–65; J.G. Van Ryn, 1966–74; R.J. Venema, 1975–80; R.D. Ritsema, 1981–90; R.J. Blauw, 1992-

South Holland, IL — Mision Hispaña Paz
see: Hammond, IN – New Community Fellowship

South Holland, IL — New Community Fellowship
see: Hammond, IN – New Community Fellowship

South Holland, IL — Peace
1965-
pastors: A.J. Vander Griend, 1966–74; D.A. Janke, 1975–85; C.P. Van Reken, 1986–91; T.J. Kok, 1992-

South Holland, IL — Second
see: South Holland, IL – Bethany

South Holland, IL — South Holland
see: South Holland, IL – First

South Olive, MI — South Olive
1885-
pastors: J. Vander Werp, 1887–89; J. Manni, 1889-1902; E. Vanden Berge, 1893–96; J. Smitter, 1896-1900; J.L. Van Tielen, 1900–02; G.D. De Jong, 1903–08; H. Guikema, 1908–11; J. Wyngaarden, 1911-15; J. Bruinooge, 1916–23; P.D. Van Vliet, 1923–44; S. Kramer, 1944–49; T. Heyboer, 1949–58; T. Minnema, 1958–62; D.W. Van Gent, 1962–66; E.J. Tamminga, 1966–71; J.W. Maas, 1972–83; J.A. Ritsema, 1984–90; W.H. Oord, 1991–94; W. Brander (I), 1994–95; D.R. Fauble, 1996-

South St. Paul, MN — Faith
see: New Brighton, MN – Faith

South St. Paul, MN — South Grove
see: Inver Grove Heights, MN – Grace

South Windsor, CT — Avery Street
1966-
pastors: J.A. Bonnema, 1963–71; P.J. Mans, 1971–78; B. Van Antwerpen, 1978–89; D.R. Vander Wall, 1990–95; C.W. Bergman, 1995-2001; N.F. Brown (I), 2000-2001; W. Gardner, 2000-

South Windsor, CT — Christ Church of Glastonbury
see: South Windsor, CT – Christ Community

South Windsor, CT — Christ Community (emerging)
2001-
former name: South Windsor, CT — Christ Church of Glastonbury, 2001-2002
pastor: W. Gardener, 2000-

Southlake, TX — Daybreak (emerging)
1991-1995, discontinued
pastor: D.M. Devadatta, 1991-94

Sparta, MI — Gospel Hall (mission)
1932-1944
staff: H. Fryling (L), 1937-39; H. Vander Lugt (L), 1941-44

Sparta, MI — Trinity
1958-
organized: 1974
pastors: G. Nyenhuis (L), 1958-62; B. Vermeer (L), 1961-62, 1972-74; H. Hoekstra (E), 1962-71; H.J. Teitsma, 1974-79; T. Genzink, 1979-86; J.C. Fisher, 1986-89; C.J. den Dulk, 1992-

Spencer, IA — Spencer (emerging)
1982-1986, discontinued
pastors: J. Jonker (E), 1982-83; A.J. Van Schouwen, 1983-1986

Spokane, WA — First
see: Spokane, WA — New Hope

Spokane, WA — Hope
1988-
former name: Spokane, WA — Korean Grace, 1988-96; Spokane, WA — Hope Korean Presbyterian, 1996-97; Spokane, WA — Hope Presbyterian Korean, 1997-98
pastors: S.O. Yoo, 1989-93; H.K. Song, 1993-95; C. Jung, 1995-98; D.S. Shin, 1999-

Spokane, WA — Hope Korean Presbyterian
see: Spokane, WA — Hope

Spokane, WA — Hope Presbyterian Korean
see: Spokane, WA — Hope

Spokane, WA — Korean Grace
see: Spokane, WA — Hope

Spokane, WA — New Hope
1959-
former name: Spokane, WA — Spokane, 1959-75, Spokane, WA — First, 1976-90
pastors: A.J. Veltkamp, 1955-70; H. Leetsma,

1970-83; J.J. Vanden Hoek, 1983-85; A.L. Van Wyhe, 1986-90; P.J. Tinklenberg, 1991-

Spokane, WA — Spokane
see: Spokane, WA — New Hope

Spring, TX — New Life
see: Houston, TX — New Life

Springdale, ON — Springdale
see: Bradford, ON — Springdale

Springfield, IL — Christ's Fellowship
1984-1994, discontinued
organized: 1988
pastors: M.L. De Young, 1984-90; T.L. Koster, 1992-94

Springfield, VA — Northern Virginia
see: Burke, VA — Grace

Spring Lake, MI — Spring Lake
1882-
pastors: P. Ekster, 1883-86; J. Post, 1887-90; W.H. Frieling, 1891-94; M. De Boer, 1895-98; E. Van Korlaar, 1899-1902; J.L. Van Tielen, 1902-06; P. Bloem, 1907-09; J. Post, 1909-14; B. Zwaagman, 1914-17; J.H. Monsma, 1917-20; E. Boeve, 1922-27; C. VanTil, 1927-29; J.P. De Vries, 1929-47; C. De Haan, 1948-53; E.H. Palmer, 1953-57; C.W. Flietstra, 1957-61; M.J. Vander Werp, 1962-67; E.J. Piersma, 1969-74; A. Zylstra, 1974-83; K.W. Vis, 1984-97; S.J. Datema, 1999-

Stamford, ON — Stamford
see: Niagara Falls, ON — Rehoboth

Stanford, MT — Coffee Creek
1914-1921, discontinued
former name: Stanford, MT — Stanford, 1914-18

Stanford, MT — Stanford
see: Stanford, MT — Coffee Creek

Stauffer, AB — Back to God Chapel
1964-1968
pastors: J. Binnema, 1964-65; R. Bouwkamp (L), 1965-66; P. Sluys (M), 1967-68

Star Lake, NM (mission)
1931-1955
staff: A. Vander Wagen (L), 1931-32; J. Bult, 1934-35; J. Vander Meer, 1942-43; H. Buikema

(E), 1945-47; E. Mc Kenzie (L), 1950-52; S. Begay (L), 1950-51

Steamboat Rock, IA — Steamboat Rock
see: Wellsburg, IA — First

Stephenville, TX — Stephenville
1988-
pastors: J. Van Hemert, 1992-93; E. Vander Lugt, 1994-98; G.E. Wamala, 2002-

Stockton, CA — Cambodian (emerging)
1984-
former name: Stockton, CA — Christian Evangelical Chapel, 1984-87
pastor: J. Andries (E), 1984-89; P.P. Nhem (E), 1987-

Stockton, CA — Christian Evangelical Chapel
see: Stockton, CA — Cambodian

Stockton, CA — Stockton
1926-1931, discontinued

Stoney Creek, ON — Fruitland
1950-
former name: Winona, ON — Winona, 1950-52; Fruitland, ON — Fruitland, 1952-94
pastors: E. Kooistra, 1952-56; S. Terpstra, 1956-60; A. Rumph, 1960-63; L. Praamsma, 1963-72; J. De Jong, 1972-78; J. de Vries, Jr., 1979-85; G. Veeneman, 1986-92; H.A. Vander Windt, 1992-99; A.E. Beunk, 2000-

Stony Plain, AB — Hope
1908-
joined the CRC, 1966
pastors: R. Birk, 1908-13; E. Lehrer, 1913-18; C. Graeser, 1919-20; P. Sommerlatte, 1921; C.H. Reppert, 1921-44; A. Roemer, 1944-46; J.F. Krieger, 1947-61; E.O. Holkeboer (M), 1963-65; E.O. Holkeboer, 1965-74; P. Dekker, 1975-80; R.A. Bruxvoort, 1980-93; J.H. Kits, 1993-94; R.J. Graff, 1994-

Stratford, ON — Stratford
1951-
pastors: C. Spoelhof (M), 1954-55, 1956-58; J. Rubingh (M), 1959-61; J.B. Vos, 1962-65; P.L. Van Katwyk, 1965-68; W. Praamsma, 1968-71; P.J. Boodt, 1971-76; B.B. Bakker, 1976-82; J.R. Payton, Jr., 1983-85; M.D. Geleynse, 1986-90; W.D. Dirksen, 1993-2000; W.F. Hoogland, 2000-

Strathroy, ON — East
see: Strathroy, ON — East Strathroy

Strathroy, ON — East Strathroy
1951-
former names: Ilderton-Strathroy, ON — Ilderton-Strathroy, 1950-52; Strathroy, ON — Strathroy, 1952-65; Strathroy, ON — East, 1965-93
pastors: W.D. Buursma, 1952-55; H. De Moor, Sr., 1958-62; H. Vander Plaat, 1963-69; P. Breedveld, 1963-65; P. Sluys, 1970-74; P. Kranenburg, 1974-79; J.D. Tangelder, 1979-89; J. Nutma, 1990-95; E. Pennings, 1995-2001

Strathroy, ON — Strathroy
see: Strathroy, ON — East Strathroy

Strathroy, ON — West
see: Strathroy, ON — Westmount

Strathroy, ON — Westmount
1965-
former name: Strathroy, ON — West, 1965-66
pastors: H. Eshuis, 1966-70; J. Vugteveen, 1970-76; A. Vanden Ende, 1977-85; D.J. Feddes, 1987-90; J.M. Van de Hoef, 1991-99; A. Vander Berg, 2001-

Sullivan, MI — Sullivan
1894-1962, discontinued
pastors: B. Zwaagman, 1911-14; J.O. Bouwsma, 1915-19; H, Blystra, 1919-21; H.S. Koning, 1923-26; J.H. Mokma, 1926-30; N. Beute, 1931-37; M. Ouwinga, 1937-39; P. Honderd, 1939-42; R. Wildschut, 1943-45; J. Rook, 1947-50; R.A. Rozeboom, 1951-56; A.D. Folkema, 1957-58; C.G. Ter Maat, 1959-60

Sully, IA — Sully
1896-
pastors: G.G. Haan, 1896-97; W. De Groot, 1897-98; J. Vander Mey, 1898-1904; W. Stuart, 1905-08; M. Vander Heide, 1908-10; H. Danhof, 1910-14; J. Haveman, 1915-21; R. Bolt, 1922-27; H. Blystra, 1928-32; J. Griffioen, 1932-43; J. Geels, 1943-56; J.A. Wesseling, 1957-61; B.A. Van Someren, 1962-67; P.E. Bakker, 1968-73; F.W. Van Houten, 1974-78; C.J. Klompien, 1979-84; J.A. Brinks, 1985-91; L.J. Howerzyl, 1992-2001; J.M. Gray, 2002-

Sultan, WA — Sultan
1914-1951, merged with Duvall, WA — Duvall to form Monroe, WA — Monroe
pastors: D.H. Muyskens, 1923-26; A. Guikema,

1926-35; P.J. Hoekstra, 1936-44; J. Paauw, 1944-46; J.P. De Vries, 1947-49

Sumas, WA — Sumas
1935-
pastors: G. Stob, 1935-40; H.R. Van Til, 1940-43; P.A. Spoelstra, 1944-49; W. Verwolf, 1949-57; J. Entingh, 1958-64; H. Petersen, 1964-72; W. Vanden Bos, 1973-84; M.R. Ten Pass, 1985-89; T.D. Wetselaar, 1991-94; L.M. Korf, 1995-2000

Summit, IL — Summit
see: Chicago, IL – Archer Avenue

Sun, MI — Sun
see: Grant, MI – Grant

Sunnyside, WA — Iglesia Evangelica (emerging)
1999-
pastor: G.B. Muller (E), 1999-

Sunnyside, WA — Sunnyside
see also: Zillah, WA – Faith Community

Sunnyside, WA — Sunnyside
1932-
began as a branch of Zillah, WA
pastors: H. Baker, 1934-38 (stated supply); K.E. de Waal Malefyt, 1938-44; W. Terpstra, 1944-47; W. Hekman, 1948-53; J. Griffioen, 1953-65; H. Wildeboer, 1965-71; E.P. Meyer, 1971-76; L.G. Zoerhof, 1976-84; H. De Groot, 1985-88; S.A. Drenthe, 1989-99; J.P. Groenewold, 2001-

Sun Valley, CA — Bethel
1932-
began as a branch of Los Angeles, CA
former name: Glendale, CA – Glendale, 1932-55
pastors: C. Van Dyk, 1932-36; J.J. Weersing, 1938-49; J.A. Petersen, 1949-53; H. Kooistra, 1953-60; G.D. Klouw, 1960-66; W.A. Bierling, 1966-84; T.E. Pettinga, 1974-78; T. Boswell, 1984-88; H.T. Karsten, 1989-95; J.W. De Vries, 1992-2000; G.M. Stevens, 2002-

Sun Valley, CA — Church of Love
see: Los Angeles, CA – Church of Love

Sun Valley, CA — Garden Community Ministry (emerging)
1999-2000, discontinued
pastor: G. De Young (E), 1999-2000

Sun Valley, CA — In-Christ Community (emerging)
2001-
pastor: T. Lim, 2001-

Sun Valley, CA — Sol del Valle
1979-
organized: 1996
pastors: L.W. Wagenveld, 1981-93; G. Varela, 1995-

Surrey, BC — Bridge Community
see: Langley, BC – Bridge Community

Surrey, BC — Fleetwood
1961-
former name: Surrey, BC – Surrey, 1961-2002
pastors: M. DeVries, 1962-65; H. Bade, 1965-70; G.H. Pols, 1970-74; J.H. Kits, 1974-78; A.J. Vanden Pol, 1979-90; A. Westerhuis, 1990-; T.W. Bomhof, 2002-

Surrey, BC — Hope Community
1991-
pastors: S.C. Elzinga, 1987-96; R.A. Sizemore, 1989-90; K. Byl (E), 1991-94; M.R. Dadson, 1993-95; J.J. Heuving, 1995-97; S. Vander Woud (E), 1999-

Surrey, BC — Redwood Community (emerging)
1995-1999, discontinued
pastor: M.R. Dadson, 1995-99

Surrey, BC — Surrey
See: Surrey, BC – Fleetwood

Sussex, NJ — Sussex
1950-
pastors: B.H. Spalink, 1952-56; L. Bouma, 1957-65; J. Koopmans, 1966-73; J.G. Kruis, 1973-83; J.G. Keizer, 1984-

Syracuse, NY — Cold Springs
see: Syracuse, NY – Community

Syracuse, NY — Community
1966-
organized: 1980
former name: Syracuse, NY – Cold Springs, 1980-91
pastors: F. Bultman (M), 1966-76; W.C. De Vries (M), 1976-81; R.D. Steen, 1982-96; S.J. Vander Klay, 1996-2000; D. Van Dalen, 2000-

Syracuse, NY — Cornell Campus Ministry
1966-1969
staff: F. Bultman, 1966-69

Taber, AB (mission)
1911-1913

Taber, AB — First
1951-
former names: Taber, AB — Taber, 1951-75;
Vauxhall, AB — Vauxhall merged in, 1995
pastors: A. De Jager, 1952-54; M. Dornbush,
1955-58; H. Bade, 1959-65; G. Bieze, 1967-77;
J. Corvers, 1977-83; S.A. Van Daalen, 1984-89;
H.D. Zantingh, 1989-94; B. Dykstra, 1995-97;
M.J. Vandyk, 1998-

Taber, AB — Taber
see: Taber, AB — First

Tacoma, WA — Community
1962-
organized: 1968
former name: Tacoma, WA — Tacoma, 1968-71
pastors: N. De Vries (M), 1950-52; R. Tadema,
1962-68 (M); D.W. Van Gent, 1969-72; R. Vander
Ley, 1973-; G.A. Terpstra, 1992-97

Tacoma, WA — Korean
see: Tacoma WA — Tacoma

Tacoma, WA — New Hope
1991-
former name: Seattle, WA — Hope Korean, 1991-
2000
pastor: S.K. Sung, 1991-

Tacoma, WA — Tacoma
1990-
former name: Tacoma, WA — Korean, 1990-2001
pastors: P.S. Kim, 1983-; R. Yeo, 1992-93

Tacoma, WA — Tacoma
see also: Tacoma, WA — Community

Tallmadge, MI — Tallmadge
see: Grandville, MI — Hope

Tampa, FL — Korean Evergreen
see: Tampa, FL — Korean Reformed Presbyterian
Church of Tampa

Tampa, FL — Korean Reformed Presbyterian Church of Tampa (emerging)
1993-

former name: Tampa, FL — Korean Evergreen,
1990-2001
pastor: S.J. Bak, 1990-

Tawatinaw, AB — Back to God Chapel
see: Tawatinaw, AB — Peace River Chapel

Tawatinaw, AB — Peace River Chapel
1963-1969
former name: Tawatinaw, AB — Back to God
Chapel, 1963-68
staff: P. Tanis (L), 1963-64; R. Bouwkamp (E),
1964-65; H. Klok (E), 1966-68

Teec Nos Pos, AZ — Four Corners
1935-1936, 1941-
organized: 1982
former names: Carisso, NM — Mission, 1936-
1960; Teec Nos Pos, AZ — Teec Nos Pos, 1961-84
pastors: T.C. Van Kooten (L), 1939; C.B. Vander
Hart (L), 1942-43; H.J. Schripsema, 1943-45; D.
Boyd (E), 1945-50; P.H. Redhouse (L), 1950-51;
A. Bencenti (L), 1951-52; J. Bileen (L), 1952-56;
R. Kruis (L), 1953-57; J. Talley (L), 1956-57; J.
George (L), 1957-60; M. Vugteveen (L), 1958-61;
H. Redhouse (E), 1960-65; C. Brummel (E), 1961-
70; J. Talley (L), 1965-70; P.H. Redhouse, 1970-
90

Teec Nos Pos, AZ — Teec Nos Pos
see: Teec Nos Pos, AZ — Four Corners

Telkwa, BC — Telkwa
1952-
pastors: G. Van Laar (M), 1953-57; L.M.
Tamminga, 1957-60; P. De Jong, 1962-64; C.W.
Tuininga, 1965-67; D. Velthuizen, 1969-73; P.
Plug, 1973-76; G.H. Vande Riet, 1976-78; J.H.
Binnema, 1978-83; C.J. Tuininga, 1983-88; W.E.
Leigh, 1990; T.J. Van Milligen, 1991-95; E.J.
Vander Horst, 1996-2001

Temecula, CA — Discovery Christian Church (emerging)
1990-1996, discontinued
pastors: D.S. Hoekstra, 1991-96

Tempe, AZ — Arizona State (campus ministry)
1975-1993
pastors: M.C. Nieboer, 1975-84; R.W. Foss,
1986-93

Tempe, AZ — Principe de Paz
see: Scottsdale, AZ — Principe de Paz

Temple City, CA — Kwang Myung
see: West Covina, CA – Kwang Myung

Terrace, BC — Terrace
1952-
pastors: G. Van Laar (M), 1953–58; J. Huizenga, 1959–64; V. Luchies, 1965–69; J. Van Dyk, 1969–73; A.A. Helleman, 1974–77; S.A. Van Daalen, 1977–84; P. Sluys, 1984–92; P.L. Hendriks, 1992-

Terra Ceia, NC — Terra Ceia
1936-
pastors: C. Greenfield, 1935–40; J.J. Kenbeek, 1941–48; H. Minnema, 1948–50; C. Holtrop, 1952–56; I.W. Meuzelaar, 1956–61; R.L. Wiebenga, 1961–66; G.E. De Vries, 1967–71; A.L. Kuiper, 1971–76; R.D. Boertje, 1976–78; K. Vander Heide, 1978–82; R.D. Boertje, 1983–88; C.W. Niewenhuis, 1989–93; J.J. Greydanus, 1994–96; D.K. Watson, 1998–2001

Terre Haute, IN — New Hope Community
1960-1989, discontinued
former name: Terre Haute, IN – Terre Haute, 1960–85
pastors: W. Gebben (L), 1960–61; J.A. Houseward, 1961–67 (M); W. Brander, 1968; A.G. Beerens (M), 1968–73; P.W. Brink, 1974–80; C. Aardsma, 1981–86; P. Ipema (stated supply), 1986–87; W.J. Holwerda, 1987–89

Terra Haute, IN — Terra Haute
see: Terra Haute, IN – New Hope Community

Thayer, IN — Roselawn Community
see: Roselawn, IN – Community

Thoreau, NM — San Antone Mission
1929-1977
staff: H. Boyd (L), 1929–32; C. Damon (L), 1931–34; M. Bouma (L), 1932–34, 1935–36; J. Bolt, 1934–35; G. Oppenhuizen (E), 1937–42; G. Vander Meulen (L), 1943–45; J.R. Kamps (L), 1951–52; J. Bol (L), 1952–57, 1961–62; H. Redhouse (L), 1952–56; N. Harlan (L), 1956–57; J. Bol (L), 1957–62; A. Becenti (L), 1962–77; L. Largo (L), 1962–64

Three Rivers, MI — Three Rivers
1961-
organized: 1996
began as a chapel
pastors: P. Kooreman (E), 1961–76; A.J. Dykstra (E), 1981–82; P. Sausser, 1988–91; K.I. Dwyer, 1998-2002

Thunder Bay, ON — Bethlehem
1959-
former names: Port Arthur, ON – Port Arthur, 1959–68; Port Arthur, ON – Bethlehem, 1968–69
pastors: J.D. Pereboom, 1961–64; C.T. Fennema, 1964–68; J.K. Jansen, 1969–75; W.A. Ludwig, 1976–77; R. Fluit, 1980–86; T.J. Niehof, 1987–92; W. Versteeg, 1993-2002

Thunder Bay, ON — Christian Community Centre (emerging)
1998-

Thunder Bay, ON — First
1950-
former name: Fort William, ON – Fort William, 1950–69
pastors: S. Terpstra, 1952–56; L. Mulder, 1957–61; A.G. Van Eek, 1962–66; G. Corvers, 1967–72; G.D. Mouw, 1973–76; J. Nutma, 1977–81; A.C. Leegwater, 1982–87; W.D. Dirksen, 1987–93; W.H. Kooienga, 1994–2001; P.J.A. Moelker, 2000–2001; H. Vander Beek, 2002-

Thunder Bay, ON — Hope
1985-
pastors: G.K. Haagsma, 1986–94; J.C. Dekker, 1994-

Tillsonburg, ON — Tillsonburg
1977-
pastors: C. Pool, 1978–83; W.J. Kuurstra, 1983–88; W. De Jong, 1989–96; H.A. Van Hoff, 1997–2000

Tinley Park, IL — Faith
1979-
pastors: T.E. Hofman, 1981–87; J.M. Ouwinga, 1988- ; D. Jennings, 1996–99

Toadlena, NM — Toadlena (emerging)
1910-
former name: Two Grey Hills, NM – Two Grey Hills, 1910–16; operated as a single church with Farmington, NM, 1927–47
pastors: L.P. Brink (M), 1914–25; J.C. Kobes (M), 1925–63; J.W. Dykstra (M), 1964–65; G.J. Klumpenhower, 1969–81; F. Frank (E), 1971–87; B. Boyd (E), 1987–96; R. Slim, 1994–2000

Todd County, SD — Todd County
see: Valentine, NE – Lakeview

Tohatchi, NM — First Navajo
1898-

organized: 1928-1950, 1983-
former name: Tohatchi, NM — Tohatchi, 1898-2002
pastors: A. Vander Wagen (E), 1898-99; J. De Groot (E), 1898-1900; L.P. Brink (M), 1900-13; L.S. Huizenga (M), 1913-16; M. Bouma (L), 1915-25; G. Oppenhuizen (E), 1925-26; W. Goudberg (M), 1926-44; G.D. Pars, 1946-51; J.R. Kamps, 1951-63; T. Stuit (M), 1964-67; E. Henry, 1968-83; G.J. Klumpenhower, 1986-93, 1994-95; S.A. Jim, 1996-

Tohatchi, NM — Tohatchi
see: Tohatchi, NM — First Navajo

Tohlakai, NM — Bethlehem
1912-
organized: 1982
former name: Tohlakai, NM — Tohlakai, 1982-84
pastors: J.W. Brink (M), 1912-25; W. Mierop (M), 1925-28; J.R. Kamps, 1927-48; B. Sprick, 1928-32; G. Yff, 1948-57; R. Kruis (L), 1957-6, 1962-68; J. George, 1960-62; E. Benally, 1969-70; J. Yazzie (E), 1969-70; C. Grey (E), 1971-74; M.A. Harberts, 1977-90; R.E. Honaker (L), 1993-95; B. Boyd (E), 1996-

Tohlakai, NM — Tohlakai
see: Tohlakai, NM — Bethlehem

Toledo, OH — Community
1963-
pastors: E.S. Holkeboer, 1961-69; J.M. Moes, 1968-71; C.L. Kammeraad, 1972-77; D.K. Kelderman, 1977-83; D.R. Buursma, 1984-85; D. Deppe, 1985-92; P.J. De Vries, 1993-2001; M.A. Scheffers (I), 2002-

Toms River, NJ — Faith Community (congregational ministry)
1982-1991, withdrew
former names: Whiting, NJ — Whiting, 1989-90; Toms River, NJ — Toms River, 1990
pastor: A.C. Gordon, 1984-85

Toms River, NJ — Toms River
see: Toms River, NJ — Faith Community

Toronto, ON (mission)
1926-1927
staff: J.R. Brink (M), 1926-27

Toronto, ON — All Nations Christian Fellowship (emerging)
1990-

absorbed Toronto, ON — The Barnabas Network, 1999
pastors: P.F. Paas, 1988-97; T.J. Berends, 1996-

Toronto, ON — Annette Street
see: Toronto, ON — Rehoboth Fellowship

Toronto, ON — Campus Worship Community
see: Toronto, ON — Fellowship of St. Matthews

Toronto, ON — Chinese
1990-
pastor: T.K. Chan, 1991-

Toronto, ON — Fellowship
1971-1989, merged into Toronto, ON — Rehoboth Fellowship
pastors: R.L. Malarkey, 1973-76; P. Nicolai, 1976-82; H.D. Praamsma, 1983-89

Toronto, ON — Fellowship of St. Matthews
1969-1987, discontinued
former names: Toronto, ON — Campus Worship Community, 1976-79; Toronto, ON — St. Matthews Fellowship, 1979-85
pastor: M. Greidanus, 1969-70; J. Veenstra, 1974-80

Toronto, ON — First
1950-
former name: Toronto, ON — Toronto, 1950-52
pastors: S.G. Brondsema, 1949-53; R.J. Bos (M), 1952-53; J. Rook, 1953-57; L. Praamsma, 1958-62; A. De Jager, 1961-63; R. Kooistra, 1964-73; C.D. Tuyl. 1974-85; J.M. Rottman, 1987-92; R.M. Hofman, 1996-99; C.N. Overduin, 2002-

Toronto, ON — First Korean Presbyterian
1979-1989, withdrew
pastor: Y.C. Kim, 1979-89

Toronto, ON — Friendship Community (emerging)
1993-
pastor: F.J. Witteveen, 1991-

Toronto, ON — Grace, Scarborough
1963-
pastors: J. Geuzebroek, 1964-70; J.B.Vos, 1971-83; S. Wolfert, 1985-93; J.M. Rottman, 1994-

Toronto, ON — Heart Lake (emerging)
1985, discontinued
pastor: D.A. Gritter, 1985

Toronto, ON — Maranatha
see: Woodbridge, ON — Woodbridge-Maranatha

Toronto, ON — Maranatha-Woodbridge
see: Woodbridge, ON — Woodbridge-Maranatha

Toronto, ON — Rehoboth
see: Toronto, ON — Rehoboth Fellowship

Toronto, ON — Rehoboth Fellowship
1953-
former names: Toronto, ON — Annette Street,
1953-62; Toronto, ON — Fellowship, 1962-89; absorbed Toronto, ON — Rehoboth, 1989
pastors: F. Guillaume, 1953-65; M. De Vries,
1965-72; H.D. Praamsma, 1973-79; P. Van
Egmond, 1980-87; J. Tenyenhuis, 1988-

Toronto, ON — St. Matthews Fellowship
see: Toronto, ON — Fellowship of St. Matthews

Toronto, ON — Second
1952-1995, withdrew to United Reformed
Churches
pastors: H.A. Venema, 1955-64; J.J. Byker,
1964-77; P. Kranenburg, 1979-84; G.V. Martin,
1985-92

**Toronto, ON — The Barnabas Network
(emerging)**
1996-1999, merged with Toronto, ON — All Nations Christian Fellowship
pastor: T.J. Berends, 1996-99

**Toronto, ON — The Lighthouse Centre
(emerging)**
1968-
began as a classical ministry
pastors: K.J. Verhulst, 1971-77; J.W. Hielkema,
1978-80

Toronto, ON — Toronto
see: Toronto, ON — First

**Toronto, ON — Toronto Hospital Ministry
(emerging)**
2000-
pastor: N. de Boer (C), 1995-

**Toronto, ON — University of Toronto/
McMaster University (campus ministry)**
1970-
staff: M. Greidanus, 1970-74; J. Veenstra, 1974-
79; D. Pierik, 1979-94; B. Walsh (L), 2001-

Toronto, ON — Willowdale
1963-
pastors: L. Slofstra, 1964-70; L.M. Tamminga,
1970-80; J. Westerhof, 1981-88; H. Van
Niejenhuis, 1989-2000; M. Benckhuysen, 2002-

**Toronto, ON — York University
(campus ministry)**
2001-
pastor: S. Chong, 2001-

Torrance, CA — Torrance Glory
see: Gardena, CA — Elim of South Bay

Tracy, CA — Heartland (emerging)
1998-
pastor: M. Humphreys (E), 1998-

Tracy, IA — Tracy
1902-
former name: Harvey, IA — Harvey, 1903-14
pastors: W. Kole, 1903-08; R. Vande Kieft, 1915-
22; M.J. Wyngaarden, 1923-24; I.D.
Couwenhoven, 1924-31; J.J. Dyk, 1931-34; J.
Vander Meer, 1935-38; H.S. Koning, 1939-43; C.
De Leeuw, 1944-53; E.G. Cooke, 1954-58; L.K.
Tanis, 1958-62; F.L. Christensen, 1962-66; G.T.
Stuit, 1967-74; I.W. Meuzelaar, 1975-84; J.P.
Boonstra, 1986-92; F. Varga, 1993-96

Transcona, MB — Transcona
see: Winnipeg, MB — Transcona

Traverse City, MI — Fellowship
1986-
pastor: J.O. De Bruyn, 1983-

Trenton, ON — Ebenezer
1949-
pastors: C. Witt, 1950-58; R. Kooistra, 1960-64;
R.W. Popma, 1964-78; A.C. Leder, 1973-77; A.A.
Van Geest, 1977-84; J. Koole, 1978-87; J. Groen,
1985-91; E.W. Visser, 1988-96; R.G. Fisher,
1993-; J. Kuipers, 2000-

Troy, MI — Han-Bit Korean
see: Rochester Hills, MI — Han-Bit Korean

Troy, MI — North Hills
1963-
organized: 1966
former name: Royal Oak, MI — North Hills, 1963-
69
pastors: M. Stegink, 1961-64: J.H. Ellens, 1965-
67; J.T. Malestein, 1968-88; G.F. Vander Weit,

1989-2000; L. Van Milligen (E), 1995-1999; T.J. Van Milligen, 1995-1999; R.D. Engel, 2001-

Trumbauersville, PA — Trumbauersville
1915-1917, discontinued

Truro, NS — John Calvin
1954-
former name: Belmont, NS — Belmont, 1954-55; Truro, NS — Truro, 1955-67
pastors: R.J. Bos (M), 1953-57; A. Haalboom (M), 1957-60; J.G. Kunst, 1961-65; D.J. Hart, 1966-70; J. Veenstra, 1970-74; I. Verhage (E), 1974-76; H. Vriend, 1976-81; B.B. Bakker, 1982-88; D.J. Weemhoff, 1988-92; W.O. Steele, 1993-96; H. Boehm (E), 1997-

Truro, NS — Truro
see: Truro, NS — John Calvin

Tucson, AZ — Bethel
1949-
former name: Tucson, AZ — Tucson, 1949-68
pastors: G.B. Boerfyn (M), 1949-53; R.D. Posthuma (M), 1953-62; G.W. Van Den Berg, 1962-65; D.E. Houseman, 1966-70; J. Hekman, 1972-82; T. Medema, 1983-91; F.E. Pott, 1991-2001

Tucson, AZ — Desert View Community
1965-1997, discontinued
organized: 1968
former name: Tucson, AZ — Elim in the Desert, 1968-91
pastors: J. Huizenga (M), 1965-68; C.O. Buus, 1969-77; J. Hofman, Jr., 1977-84; T.B. Toeset, 1985-90; T.R. Hull, 1991-96

Tucson, AZ — Elim in the Desert
see: Tucson, AZ — Desert View Community

Tucson, AZ — Rock the Desert Ministries
see: Tucson, AZ — The Village

Tucson, AZ — The Village (emerging)
1997-
former name: Tucson, AZ — Rock the Desert Ministries, 1997-2001
pastor: R. Hugen (E), 1997-

Tucson, AZ — Tucson
see: Tucson, AZ — Bethel

Tustin, CA — Fellowship Vietnamese
1993-1995, merged with Westminster, CA — Little Saigon
pastor: M.M. Le, 1993-94

Tustin, CA — First Harvest Chapel
2002-

Two Grey Hills, NM — Two Grey Hills
see: Toadlena, NM — Toadlena

Two Wells Station, NM (mission)
1931-1965
staff: J.W. Brink, 1931-32; C. Hayenga, 1932-36; M. Bouma (L), 1936-41; F. Vander Stoep, 1941-42; J.B. Swierenga, 1944-56; M. Chavez (L), 1950-65; J. Lee (L), 1963-65

Tyler, MN — Tyler
1949-1968, discontinued
pastors: A.H. Selles, 1951-55; G.B. Ebbers, 1955-59; A. Walma, 1959-64

Union City, CA — Living Faith Fellowship-Filipino (emerging)
1995-
pastor: F. del Rosario (E), 1995-

Valentine, NE — Lakeview Community
1913-
former names: Todd County, SD — Todd County, 1919-20; Purewater, SD — Purewater, 1920-1964; Lakeview, SD — Lakeview, 1964-1979
pastors: M. Verduin, 1919-21; R.A. Rozeboom, 1922-29; R. Star, 1930-38; G.J. Vander Ziel, 1943-47; H. Bode, 1956-59; F.L. Christensen, 1959-62; K. Vander Heide, 1969-73; H.J. Westra, 1973-78; W.J. Moxey, 1978-82; P. De Jong, 1983-89; A. Eising, 1991-99

Valparaiso, IN — Daybreak Community (emerging)
2001-
pastor: R. Knol, 2001-

Vanastra, ON — Vanastra
see: Vanastra, ON — Vanastra community

Vanastra, ON — Vanastra Community
1974-
organized: 1989
former name: Vanastra, ON — Vanastra, 1974-91
pastors: J.K. Boersema, 1974-78; P. Mantel, 1979-80; J. Visser (E), 1981-89; P.G. Weaver,

1989–92; C.R. Cunningham, 1995–98; S.A. Speelman, 1999–

Vancouver, BC — Bethel
1953–1970, discontinued
pastors: A.H. Oussoren, 1955–58; R. Groeneboer, 1959–66; C. Bishop, 1967–70

Vancouver, BC — Faith and Action Vietnamese (emerging)
1991–
former name: Vancouver, BC – Vietnamese Ministry, 1991–93
pastor: V.P. Le, 1994–

Vancouver, BC — First
1926–
former name: Vancouver, BC – Vancouver, 1926–53
pastors: P.J. Hoekstra (M), 1927–36; K. Bergsma, 1936–38; J. De Jong, 1939–42; G.D. Pars, 1943–46; J. Paauw, 1946–51; C.M. Schoolland, 1953–58; G.H. Rientjes; 1959–63; J.A. Botting, 1963–68; B. Nederlof, 1969–75; H. Numan, 1976–86; F.J. Koning, 1987–93; J. Van Hemert, 1994–99; H. Numan, 1999–

Vancouver, BC — Killarney Sunday School
1961–1964
staff: T.G. Baarsma (L), 1961–64

Vancouver, BC — Mininistry to Seafarers (emerging)
1970–
emerging, 1999
pastors: J. Dresselhuis, 1970–93; S. Wolfert, 1993–

Vancouver, BC — Vancouver
see: Vancouver, BC – First

Vancouver, BC — Vietnamese Ministry
see: Vancouver, BC – Faith and Action Vietnamese

Vancouver, WA — River Rock (emerging)
2001–
pastor: B.E. Van Kley, 2001–

Vancouver, WA — Trinity
1968–1999, discontinued
pastors: K.R. Slager, 1969–74; J.L. Alferink, 1975–79; T.J. Van't Land, 1980–85; H. Lamsma, 1985–91; F.C. Guter, 1992; D.J. Wyenberg, 1993–99

Vanderwagen, NM — Skeets Chapel
1965–1966
staff: J. George (L), 1965–66

Vauxhall, AB — Vauxhall
1952–1995, discontinued; members joined Taber, AB–First
pastors: P.J. Hoekstra (M), 1953–58; H. Bade, 1959–65; G. Bieze, 1967–73; D. Velthuizen, 1973–78; D.R. Smith, 1979–85; J.R. Huizinga, 1986–91

Vergennes, VT — Champlain Valley
1964–
organized: 1966
former name: Ferrisburg, VT – Ferrisburg, 1966–76
pastors: W. Osterrman (L), 1964–68; H. Vander Klay, 1976–71; G. Oosterman, 1971–72; G.D. Cooper, 1973–77; R.L. Bouwkamp, 1977–80; J. Van Dyk, 1980–86; P. Vander Weide, 1987–92; R.A. Heerema, 1992–96; T. Gray, 1998–

Vermillion, SD — Calvary (emerging)
1968–1999, discontinued
pastors: A.P. Ver Burg (M), 1968–72; J. Van Ens, 1973–77; M.A. Davies, 1977–80; E. Visscher (E), 1981–89; M. Winnowski, 1990–93; G. Horner (L), 1994–96

Vermillion, SD — University of South Dakota (campus ministry)
1966–1981
staff: H. De Boer (L), 1966–67; A. VerBurg, 1968–75; J. Van Ens, 1973–76; M.A. Davies, 1977–80

Vernon, BC — Vernon
1954–
former name: Vernon, BC – Vernon-Kelowna, 1955–57
pastors: P. De Koekkoek, 1954–56; H. Moes (M), 1957–60; S. Kistemaker (M), 1961–63; J. Roorda (M), 1963–65; J.D. Tangelder, 1967–70; P. Dekker, 1971–75; G.G. Vink, 1975–80; P. Plug, 1981–87; W. Brouwer, 1987–92; A. Van Muyen, 1993–97; W.J. Kempkes, 1998–

Vernon, BC — Vernon-Kelowna
see: Vernon, BC – Vernon

Vesper, WI — Vesper
see: Wisconsin Rapids, WI – New Hope Community

Vicksburg, MI — Korean
1987-
former name: Kalamazoo, MI – Korean, 1987-96
pastors: J.S. Rhee, 1987-88; J.S.S. Kim, 1989-91; S.J. Kang, 1991-96; K. Kim, 1997-

Victoria, BC — Christ Community
1985-
pastors: H.J. Pott, 1987-91; N.H. Prenger, 1991-97; L.H. Batterink, 2001-

Victoria, BC — First
see: Victoria, BC – Victoria

Victoria, BC — Victoria
1952-
former name: Victoria, BC – Victoria, 1952-85; Victoria, BC – First, 1985-2000
pastors: G.H. Rientjes, 1952-55; C. Spoelhof, 1955-56; R.W. Popma, 1957-64; J.S. Hielema, 1966-70; P.W. De Bruyne, 1971-79; D.R. Tigchelaar, 1978-85; B. Nederlof, 1981-86; H. Jonker, 1987-99; J. Heidinga, 2001-

Victorville, CA — Church of the Way
see: Apple Valley, CA – Church of the Way

Virginia Beach, VA — Christ Community
1985-1995, discontinued
former name: Virginia Beach, VA – Virginia Beach, 1985
pastors: W.D. Ribbens, 1981-86; A.A. Mulder, 1987-95

Virginia Beach, VA — Virginia Beach
see: Virginia Beach, VA – Christ Community

Visalia, CA (campus ministry)
1973-1974
staff: C. Vander Neut, 1973-74

Visalia, CA — First
1965-
former name: Visalia, CA – Visalia, 1965-90
pastors: B.N. Huizenga (M), 1965-70; G.G. Hofland, 1971-79; C. Vander Neut, 1973-74; W.C. Boelkins, 1979-92; P.J. Boender, 1987-93; G.G. Vink, 1993-; L.E. Van Essen, 2002-

Visalia, CA — Trinity
1990-
pastors: C.J. Klompien, 1991-97; A. Dieleman, 1997-

Visalia, CA — Visalia
see: Visalia, CA – First

Vogel Center, MI — Vogel Center
1872-
former name: Clam Union, MI – Clam Union, 1872-82
pastors: J. Schepers, 1882-1902; J. Walkotten, 1903-05; T.W. Van Loo, 1906-18; J. Homan, 1919-25; J.J. Dyk, 1926-29; H. Guikema, 1929-39; B.E. Visscher, 1940-48; W. Tolsma, 1948-53; H.D. Bultje, 1953-58; A.H. Jongsma, 1958-62; A.A. Mulder, 1963-65; A. Hannink, 1965-70; G. Compaan, 1971-76; A.J. Bultman, 1977-80; B. Den Ouden, 1980-84; J.D. Lion, 1984-90; D.J. Timmermans, 1992-

Volga, SD — Volga
1903-
pastors: G.W. Hylkema, 1907-09; J.B. Vanden Hoek, 1914-18; J.J. Werkman, 1918-23; T. De Boer, 1924-28; P. Bloem, 1930-38; T.C. Van Kooten, 1939-43; M. Doornbush, 1943-50; R. Wezeman, 1951-54; J.H. Bergsma, 1955-60; N.B. Haan, 1960-64; H. Bajema, 1964-69; H. Vanderaa, 1969-81; M.G. Zylstra, 1981-88; H.J. Westra, 1989-98; J.P. Douma, 1999-

Vona, CO — Vona
1910-1946, discontinued
former name: Elpis, CO – Elpis, 1910-25
pastor: M.H. Faber, 1934-36

Vriesland, MI — Vriesland
1857-1893, discontinued
pastors: W.H. Frieling, 1866-71; L. Rietdyk, 1872-74; G.K. Hemkes, 1877-83; G.D. De Jong, 1886-88; T.M. Vanden Bosch, 1888-89

Walker, MI — Walker
see: Grand Rapids, MI – Walker

Wallaceburg, ON — Wallaceburg
1951-
pastors: K. Hart, 1953-58; J.G. Groen, 1959-64; P.J.Boodt, 1964-66; C.D.Tuyl, 1966-69; A. Kuyvenhoven, 1970-71; S. Vander Meer, 1971-75; R. Praamsma, 1976-82; J.R. Poelman, 1983-89; C.A. Persenaire, 1989-93; R.T. Vander Vaart, 1998-

Walnut Creek, CA — Faith Christian Fellowship
1961-

former name: Walnut Creek, CA – Walnut Creek, 1961–99
pastors: J.F. Hollebeek (M), 1958–63; H. Visscher, 1964–73; N.L. Veltman, 1973–77; H.A. Brink, 1978–82; D.L. Aldrink, 1983–89; C.J. DeRidder, 1990–95; G.L. Dykstra, 1996–

Walnut Creek, CA — Walnut Creek
see: Walnut Creek, CA – Faith Christian Fellowship

Wanamassa, NJ — Wanamassa
1953–1973, discontinued
emerging, 1971–73
pastors: F.J. MacLeod, 1956–59; J.O. Handley, 1960–64; G.H. Rientjes (M), 1966–70; J. Zandstra (M), 1969–70; R.D. Steen (M), 1971–73

Wappingers Falls, NY — Immanuel
1963–
organized: 1968
former name: Wappingers Falls, NY – Wappingers Falls, 1966–71
pastors: B.W. Mulder (M), 1963–66; F.J. MacLeod, 1968–75; L.B. Mensink, 1976–82; B.A. Averill, 1982–90; R.J. Kuiken, 1992–94; J. Vande Lune, 1996–

Wappingers Falls, NY — Wappingers Falls
see: Wappingers Falls, NY – Immanuel

Warrensville Heights, OH — Warrensville Heights
see: Cleveland, OH – East Side

Washington, DC — Silver Spring
see: Silver Spring, MD – Silver Spring

Washington, DC — Washington, DC
1943–
pastors: J.M. Ghysels, 1944–51; W.P. De Boer, 1951–56; R.M. Hartwell, Sr., 1957–67; G. Stob, 1967–74; T.C. Limburg, 1970–72; D.W. Boonstra, 1975–84; T.C. Limburg, 1984–95; J. Reiffer, 1996–98; N.B. Steen, 1999–

Washington, PA — Washington
1965–1993, withdrew
organized: 1971
pastors: R.O. Broekhuizen (M), 1965–73; A.L. Van Whye, 1973–78; D.C. Bouma, 1979–84

Waterdown, ON — Bethel
1969–

former name: Burlington, ON – Aldershot, 1969–78; Burlington, ON – Bethel, 1978–79
pastors: H.D. Praamsma, 1970–73; J.G. Groen, 1974–80; J. Postuma, 1981–89; A. Kuyvenhoven, 1989–92; E.J. Schuringa, 1993–2002

Waterloo, IA — Waterloo
see: Cedar Falls, IA – Cedar Falls

Waterloo, ON — Huron Campus Ministry (campus ministry)
1973–
pastor: R. Kooistra, 1973–82; G.E. Morbey, 1982–

Waterloo, ON — Waterloo
1978–
pastors: R.D. Vanden Berg, 1982–88; D.R. Tigchelaar, 1989–92; H. Lunshof, 1993–95; M. Winnowski, 1997–

Waupun, WI — Alto
see: Alto, WI – Alto

Waupun, WI — Bethel
1961–
pastors: T.C. Vanden Heuvel, 1961–64; A. Walcott, 1965–76; J.R. Jackson, 1976–79; J. Cooper, 1980–87; A. Dieleman, 1988–97; J.J. Brower, 1999–

Waupun, WI — First
1921–
former name: Waupun, WI – Waupun, 1921–61
pastors: H. Moes, 1923–29; C.R. Veenstra, 1930–40; C. Groot, 1940–48; H. Petroelje, 1949–53; J.J. Byker, 1954–60; C.W. Niewenhuis, 1961–65; C.G. Werkema, Sr., 1966–71; J.H. Groenewold, 1971–75; N.B.Haan, 1976–83; G.W. Van Den Berg, 1984–90; D.W. Brouwer, 1991–98; K.D. Van De Griend, 2001–

Waupun, WI — Waupun
see: Waupun, WI – First

Wayland, MI — Wayland
1951–
organized: 1957; began as a Sunday school ministry
pastors: A. Vander Zwaag (L), 1951–52; G. Wiers (L), 1951–54; A. Vander Veer (L), 1955–56; D.P. Wisse, 1957–61; E.F. Visser, 1962–68; G.F. Vander Weit, 1968–71; H.J. Sprik, 1972–86; L.J. Sikkema, 1987–92; R.J. Dieleman, 1992–95; J.H. McCune, 1996–99; R.L. Bouwkamp, 2000–

Wayne, NJ — Preakness
1933-1998, withdrew to United Reformed Churches
former name: Preakness, NJ — Preakness, 1933-Wayne, NJ — Wayne, 1965-71
pastors: J. van Bruggen, 1933-38; P.Y. De Jong, 1940-42; J. Daane, 1943-45; G. Stob, 1946-47(stated supply); B.H. Spalink, 1948-52; B. Bruxvoort, 1953-59; F.J. MacLeod, 1959-65; W.C. Boelkins, 1966-74; P.C. Zylstra, 1976-81; T.D. Draayer, 1982-88; L.G. Christoffels, 1990-98

Wayne, NJ — Wayne
see: Wayne, NJ — Preakness

Webster, NY — Webster
1965-
organized: 1968
former name: Rochester, NY — Webster, 1968-92
pastors: E. Walhout (M), 1965-71; C. Planmtinga, Jr., 1971-75; J.L. Vanderlaan, 1976-84; M.L. Tidd, 1984-91; V.G. Van Ee, 1991-

Welland, ON — Grace
1962-
former name: Welland, ON — Welland Junction, 1962-83
pastors: A. Vanden Ende, 1963-69; P.D. Stadt, 1969-75; J. Postuma, 1976-81; S. Vander Meer, 1982-91; P.A. Heerema, 1992-

Welland, ON — Welland Junction
see: Welland, ON — Grace

Wellandport, ON — Riverside
1951-
former name: Wellandport, ON — Wellandport, 1951-66
pastors: A. Persenaire, 1951-55; J. Geuzebroek, 1955-59; P. Van Egmond, 1960-65; L.T. Schalkwyk, 1966-70; J.D. Tangelder, 1970-77; A.W. Schaafsma, 1972; H. Katerberg, 1977-85; J. Veltman, 1986-89; J.S. Gangar, 1990-92; G.J. Klumpenhower (I), 1993-94; D.W. Cowart, 1995-2000

Wellandport, ON — Wellandport
see: Wellandport, ON — Riverside

Wellsburg, IA — First
1867-
former names: Steamboat Rock, IA — Steamboat Rock, 1867-89; Wellsburg, IA — Wellsburg, 1889-1920
pastors: E.L. Meinders, 1867-74; B. Mollema,

1874-79; H. Bode, 1881-93; H. Walkotten, 1893-95; J. Timmerman, 1896-1902; W.R. Smidt, 1902-05; H. Walkotten, 1907-08; G.L. Hoefker, 1908-17; H.C. Bode, 1917-37; L.F. Voskuil, 1937-46; J. Vande Kieft, 1946-51; A. Hannink, 1952-55; B.E. Visscher, 1956-65; A. Hollander, 1966-76; L.J. Kuiper, 1976-81; J.P. Gorter, 1981-86; T.J.Vos, 1987-

Wellsburg, IA — Second
1919-1997, withdrew to Presbyterian Church of America
pastors: C. Holtrop, 1921-26; E. Boeve, 1927-33; J.C. De Korne, 1934-38; R.H. Haan, 1939-43; J.H., Rubingh, 1943-49; J.H. Olthoff, 1950-56; C.J. Toeset, 1957-64; J.H. Elenbaas, 1966-83; O.W. Duistermars, 1984-87; H. Kooger, 1988-92

Wellsburg, IA — Wellsburg
see: Wellsburg, IA — First

West Branch, MI — West Branch
see: McBain, MI — Calvin

West Covina, CA — Kwang Myung
1995-2000, discontinued
former name: Temple City, CA — Kwang Myung, 1996-98
pastor: P. Lee, 1996-2000

Western Springs, IL — Western Springs
1938-
pastors: C. Vander Ark, 1939-42; T.C. Van Kooten, 1943-47; J.Betten, 1947-51; A.H. De Kruyter, 1951-65; W.R. Witte, 1965-76; T. Medema, 1977-83; D.R. Fauble, 1983-90; L.J. Sikkema, 1992-2002

West Harlem, MI — West Harlem
see: Holland, MI — Pine Creek

West Hollywood, CA — The Salt and Light Church (emerging)
2001-
pastor: J.J. Kim, 2000-

West Jasper Place, AB (mission)
1948-1953
staff: J. Kruis (L), 1952-53

West Kendall, FL — Iglesia Renacer (emerging)
2002-
pastor: H. Garcia, 2002-

West Lafayette, IN — Purdue University (campus ministry)
1966-1995
staff: J.C. Ribbens, 1966-68; D. Bos, 1968-75; T. Van't Land, 1975-77; W.R. Lenters, 1981-88; A.D. Bosscher, 1990-95

Westlock, AB — Westlock
1950-1987, withdrew
pastors: S.G. Brondsema (M), 1952-55; G.H. Polman, 1955-57; W.G. Dubois, 1962-66; W. Dryfhout, 1968-72I J. Visser, 1972-79; D. Van der Wekken, 1979-83

Westminster, CA — Garden of Grace
1987-
merger of: Garden Grove, CA — Elim, 1987-1992 and Garden Grove, CA — Orange Dongsan, 1987-1995; Los Alamitos, CA — Calvin merged in, 2001
former name: Garden Grove, CA — Orange Dongsan, 2000-01
pastors: B.Y. Jang, 1989-99; I. Chang, 1989-2001; T.S. Won, 1999-; C.S. Change, 2001-

Westminster, CA — Korean CRC of Orange County (emerging)
1987-
former name: Buena Park, CA — Korean CRC of Orange County, 1987-99
pastors: P.Y. Shin, 1987-; S.P. Lee, 1991-93; S.J. Kim, 1991-96; M.H. Chan, 2002- ; M.C. Kim, 2003-

Westminster, CA — Little Saigon (emerging)
1994-
former name: Westminster, CA — Saigon, 1994-96; Tustin, CA — Fellowship Vietnamese, merged 1995
pastors: N.X. Bao, 1986-93; M.M. Le, 1994-

Westminster, CA — Orange Han Min
see: La Palma, CA — Orange Han Min

Westminster, CA — Saigon
see: Westminster, CA — Little Saigon

Westmoreland, NH — Westmoreland
1989-1995, withdrew to Independent Christian Reformed Church
pastor: K. Sanders, 1991-95

West Olive, MI — West Olive
1942-
organized: 1979

pastors: A. Vander Veer (E), 1942-44; B. De Boer, (E), 1944-50; J. Keuning (E), 1950-53; E. Vanden Brink (E), 1953-55; M. Keuning, (E), 1956-57; B. De Boer (E), 1958-63; P. Vander Kamp (E), 1963-69; W. Masselink, Jr., (M), 1969-73; R.D. Bultman (M), 1974-79; L.P. Troast, 1980-85; R.R. Sprik, 1985-91; J.E. Versluys, 1993-96; M. Stephenson, 1996-

West Olive, MI — West Olive
see also: Holland, MI — Pine Creek

West Sayville, NY — West Sayville
1876-1997, withdrew from the denomination
former name: Sayville, NY — Sayville, 1876-1906
pastors: J. De Vries, 1890-95; E. Vanden Berge, 1899-1903; H.J. Haarsma, 1904-07; P.Kosten, 1907-12; M. Botbyl, 1912-18; L. Trap, 1919-21; J.L. Van Tielen, 1921-30; J. Cupido, 1931-46; D.J. Hoitenga, Sr., 1946-49; H. Bossenbroek, 1950-54; A.E. Pontier, 1955-60; H. Vander Klay, 1961-67; E.G. Cooke, 1968-73; L.J. Vander Zee, 1973-78; V. Luchies, 1978-85; T.R. Dykstra, 1987-94; J.J. Stastny, 1996-97

West Valley, UT — Cambodian
1992-
former name: Salt Lake City, UT — Cambodian, 1992-99
pastors: C. Phim(E), 1984-; M. Tak (E), 1985-91

Wheaton, IL — Vietnamese New Hope
see: Winfield, IL — Vietnamese New Hope

Wheaton, IL — Wheaton
1950-
pastors: J.E. Luchies, 1952-57; H. Guikema, 1957-62; G. Stob, 1962-67; G.D. Vanderhill, 1968-88; J.F. Schuurman, 1989-

Wheeling, IL — Korean
1969-
organized: 1971
former name: Chicago, IL — Korean, 1969-99
pastors: M.J. Lee, 1967-92; D.H. Jou, 1993-95; H.J. Kim, 1996-2000

Whitby, ON — Hebron
1954-
former names: Oshawa, ON — Oshawa, 1954-63; Oshawa, ON — Hebron, 1964-69
pastors: M. Vrieze, 1955-58; J. Van Harmelen, 1958-69; C.D. Tuyl, 1969-74; F.F. Bakker, 1974-79; L. Mulder, 1980-82; R.G. Fisher, 1983-91; B.B. Bakker, 1992-

Whitby, ON — Real Life (emerging)
2001-
pastor: J. Wildeboer (L), 2001-

White Cloud, MI (mission)
1944
staff: D. Mellema, 1944

White Cloud, MI — Woodville
see: Woodville, MI – Community

Whitesboro, NY — Whitesboro
1912-1920, discontinued

Whiting, NJ — Whiting
see: Toms River, NJ – Faith Community

Whitinsville, MA — Fairlawn
1958-
pastors: H.J. Teitsma, 1959-65; D.T. Van Oyen, 1965-72; N.R. Rylaarsdam, 1972-76; B. van Eyk, 1976-82; J.M. Gray, 1982-89; J.G. Aupperlee, 1990-2003

Whitinsville, MA — Operation Reachout
1975-1980
staff: R. Sikma (E), 1975-80

Whitinsville, MA — Pleasant Street
1896-
former name: Whitinsville, MA – Whitinsville, 1896-1958
pastors: F.J. Drost, 1896-1902; J. Jansen, 1904-06; F. Fortuin, 1907-21; L. Trap, 1921-26; R. Bolt, 1927-39; L. Van Laar, 1939-45; N.L. Veltman, 1947-53; R.R. De Ridder, 1953-56; W.F. Vander Hoven, 1957-62; J.T. Holwerda, 1963-69; J.P. Vosteen, 1970-75; J. Admiraal, 1976-80; J.H. Piersma, 1981-84; J. J. Wiegers, 1984-92; W.G. Vis, 1993-

Whitinsville, MA — Whitinsville
see: Whitinsville, MA – Pleasant Street

Wichert, IL — Wichert
1894-1903, joined Reformed Church in America

Willard, OH — Calvary Chapel
1955-1979
former names: Celeryville, OH – Calvary Chapel, 1955-63; Plymouth, OH – Calvary Chapel, 1965-70
staff: P. Laning (L), 1959-62; J. Davies (L), 1963-67; D. Jabaay (L), 1969-70; M. Gremmer (L), 1970-74

Willard, OH — Willard
1896-
former names: Sharon, OH – Sharon, 1896-1906; Chicago Junction, OH – Chicago Junction, 1906-07; Chicago, OH – Chicago, 1907-18
pastors: J.H. Geerlings, 1910-12; W.M. Trap, 1913-16; C. Cooper, 1915-21; J. Breuker, 1921-25; S. Struyk, 1925-34; G. Van Laar, 1934-43; J.C. Scholten, 1943-48; J.C. Ehlers, 1948-53; M. Beelen, 1954-58; G.B. Ebbers, 1959-68; C. De Haan, 1968-74; J.H. Scholten, 1975-80; B.F. Tol, 1980-85; W.C. Hensen, 1985-93; L.T. Riemersma, 1994-

Williamsburg, ON — Williamsburg
1952-
pastors: C.W. Tuininga, 1955-58; H. Vander Plaat, 1959-63; J.D. Pereboom, 1964-69; J. de Pater, 1970-75; L.T. Schalkwyk, 1975-80; W. De Jong, 1982-89; J.D. Tangelder, 1989-93; G.J. Rowaan, 1994-

Williams Lake, BC — Cariboo Community (emerging)
2000-
pastor: P. Lomavatu, 2000-

Willmar, MN — Willmar
1950-
pastors: S.A. Werkema (M), 1950-52; K.R. Slager, 1953-57; R.J. Bos, 1959-62; N.L. Meyer, 1962-66; P. Ouwinga, 1966-75; A.L. Louwerse, 1975-79; M. Toonstra, Jr., 1979-88; K.D. Van De Griend, 1989-96; A.J. Van Dellen, 1996-

Wilmette, IL — Eden's Korean (emerging)
1992-
pastor: K.H. Hong, 1991-

Wilmington, CA (mission, branch of Los Angeles, CA)
1931-1931

Window Rock, AZ — Window Rock
1965-
organized: 1980
pastors: S. Redhouse (M), 1965-75; C. Grey (E), 1978-86; G.T. Stuit, 1988-93; G.J. Klumpenhower, 1995-

Windsor, ON (mission)
see: Essex, ON – Essex

Windsor, ON — Ambassador Community
1966-

organized: 1979
pastors: D. Kwantes (M), 1966-68; H. De Bruyn, 1969-73; P.C. Hogeterp, 1973-88; K.R. Ritsema, 1989-96; D. Edgar (interim), 1996-99, D. Edgar, 1999-

Windsor, ON — Windsor
see: Essex, ON — Essex

Winfield, IL — Vietnamese New Hope (emerging)
1991-
classical ministry, 1991-93
former name: Wheaton, IL — Vietnamese New Hope, 1997-98
pastor: H.P. Nguyen, 1993-

Winfield, IL — Winfield
1964-1997, discontinued
pastors: H.L. De Weerd, 1964-65; J. Vugteveen, 1966-70; J.L. Alferink, 1971-75; N.R. Rylaarsdam, 1976-81; H. De Vries, 1983-90; L.R. Smits, 1991-97

Winnie, TX — Winnie
1910-1916, discontinued

Winnipeg, MB — College Avenue
1908-1993, merged into Winnipeg, MB — Covenant
former name: Winnipeg, MB — Winnipeg, 1907-67
pastors: H.J. Haarsma (M), 1911-13; I. Westra, 1917-19; T. De Boer, 1920-24; J. Vanden Hoek (M), 1925-29; H. Wierenga, 1930-38; A. Disselkoen, 1939-53; J.H. Rubingh, 1955-61; H. Van Dyken, 1962-67; C.W. Tuininga, 1967-75; J. Van Dyk, 1977-80; C.Bishop, 1980-93

Winnipeg, MB — Covenant
1993-
merger of: Winnipeg, MB — College Avenue and Winnipeg, MB — Kildonan
pastors: C. Bishop, 1993-96; G.J. Bomhof, 1993-98; W.C. Tuininga, 1999-

Winnipeg, MB — Good News Fellowship Ministries
1986-
organized: 1989
pastors: T.J. Berends, 1987-96; R. Visser (E), 1996-

Winnipeg, MB — Hope Centre (emerging)
1974-

emerging, 1977
pastors: Mrs. R. Calverley (L), 1974-77; D.N. Habermehl, 1977-85; A. Schweitzer, 1986-

Winnipeg, MB — Indian Family Centre (emerging)
1974-
classical ministry, 1974-98
pastor: H. De Bruyn, 1974-2000

Winnipeg, MB — Kildonan
1961-1993, merged into Winnipeg, MB — Covenant
pastors: J.D. Hellinga, 1961-64; J.W. Postman, 1964-68; A.G. Van Eek, 1970-78; A.C. Groen, 1978-85; G.J. Bomhof, 1987-93

Winnipeg, MB — Red River Christian Fellowship (emerging)
1994-
former name: Winnipeg, MB — Step by Step Ministries, 1994-97
pastors: P. Tuininga, 1991-95; J.J. Van Drongelen, 1996-

Winnipeg, MB — Step by Step Ministries
see: Winnipeg, MB — Red River Christian Fellowship

Winnipeg, MB — Transcona
1953-
former name: Transcona, MB — Transcona, 1953-61
pastors: A. Disselkoen, 1953-57; E.O., Holkeboer, 1957-63; W.L. Vander Beek, 1963-66; S. Viss, Jr., 1967-72; R.G. Fisher, 1973-76; H.A. Van Hoff, 1976-80; J. Hanegraaff, 1980-88; R.D. Gorter, 1988-92; G.V Martin, 1992-98; D. Swinney, 2000-2001

Winnipeg, MB — West Winnipeg Community
1994-1996, discontinued
pastor: J.A. Broekema, 1992-96

Winnipeg, MB — Winnipeg
see: Winnipeg, MB — College Avenue

Winona, ON — Winona
see: Stony Creek, ON — Fruitland

Winter Haven, FL — Cypress Gardens
see: Cypress Gardens, FL — Cypress Gardens

Winter Haven, FL — Hammondale Campground (mission)
1979-1980
pastor: J. Van Ens, 1979-80

Wisconsin Rapids, WI — Hmong (emerging)
1991-2000, discontinued
pastors: V. Khang (E), 1991-94; K. Vang (E), 1994-2000

Wisconsin Rapids, WI — New Hope Community
1898-
former names: Vesper, WI — Vesper, 1898-1973; Wisconsin Rapids, WI — Wisconsin Rapids, 1973-2000
pastors: T.L. De Lange, 1900-06; A. Guikema, 1909-11; E. Van Korlaar, 1912-16; D. Weidenaar, 1917-20; J. Vanden Hoek, 1920-25; H. Ahuis, 1925-32; H. Vander Klay, 1932-40; G. Andre, 1942-48; W. Meyer, 1949-53; C.G. Ter Maat, 1954-59; G.J. Vander Ziel, 1960-64; R.H. Uken, 1968-75; L.W. Van Dellen, 1975-81; W.G. Brouwers, Jr., 1981-92; A. Veenstra, 1993-2000; T.M. Grotenhuis, 2000-

Wisconsin Rapids, WI — Wisconsin Rapids
Wisconsin Rapids, WI — New Hope Community

Woden, IA — Woden
1896-
former name: Oostfriesland, IA — Oostfriesland, 1896-1945
pastors: H.C. Bode, 1897-1901; W. Bode, 1902-06; H.C. Bode, 1906-08; G. Kramer, 1908-13; D.J. Meyer, 1913-34; H.J. Kuizema (stated supply), 1934-35; H.J. Kuizema, 1935-43; C. De Haan, 1944-48; E. Bossenbroek, 1948-52; J.J.Vanden Hoek, 1952-57; J.W. Maas, 1957-63; P. Honderd, 1963-68; H.P. Baak, 1968-75; B.J. Van Ee, 1976-80; T.B. Swierenga, 1980-83; R.R. Graves, 1984-88; G.E. De Vries, 1988-96; K.L. Jordan, 1998-

Woodbridge, IL — Horizon Community
see: Elmhurst, IL — Horizon Community

Woodbridge, ON — Woodbridge-Maranatha
1967-
former name: Toronto, ON — Maranatha-Woodbridge, 1967-78, Toronto, ON — Maranatha, 1979-93
pastors: H. Van Dyken, 1967-73; J. Klooster, 1975-79; J.W. Van Stempvoort, 1980-93; H.P. Bruinsma, 1993-

Woodstock, ON — Covenant
1977-
pastors: D.C. Los, 1978-83; R.W. Ouwehand, 1984-94; G.J. Hogeterp, 1995-2001

Woodstock, ON — First
see: Woodstock, ON — Maranatha

Woodstock, ON — Maranatha
1949-
former name: Woodstock, ON — Woodstock, 1949-78; Woodstock, ON — First, 1978-93
pastors: C. Spoelhof (M), 1949-51; J. Hoogland, 1951-58; W. Feenstra, 1959-64; J. Zantingh, 1965-69; A.P. Geisterfer, 1969-74; H. Lunshof, 1971-76; J. Van Harmelen, 1973-76; H. Eshuis, 1977-83; P.W. De Haan, 1983-91; R.J. Van der Borgh, 1992-98

Woodstock, ON — Woodstock
see: Woodstock, ON — Maranatha

Woodville, MI — Community
1935-
organized: 1994
former names: Woodville, MI — Woodville Chapel, 1935-81; White Cloud, MI — Woodville, 1981-86; Woodville, MI — Woodville, 1987-94
pastors: D. Mellema, 1937-44; J. Poel (E), 1949-54; C. Disselkoen (E), 1954-62; F. Brummel (E), 1963-92; R.W. Jansons, 1993-95; M.G. Hewitt, 1995-99; M.S. McDonald, 2000-2002

Woodville, MI — Woodville
see: Woodville, MI — Community

Woodville, MI — Woodville Chapel
see: Woodville, MI — Community

Wortendyke, NJ — First
1889-1892, discontinued, members joined, Midland Park, NJ
former name: Wortendyke, NJ — Wortendyke, 1889-91

Wortendyke, NJ — Second
1892-1893, discontinued

Wortendyke, NJ — Wortendyke
see: Wortendyke, NJ — First

Worthington, MN — Lao (emerging)
2001-
pastor: S. Dedthanou (E), 1999-

Worthington, MN — Vietnamese (emerging)
1994-2001, discontinued
former name: Sioux City, IA – Sioux City
Vietnamese, 1994-98
pastor: V.H. Tran, 1994-99

Worthington, MN — Worthington
1913-
pastors: J. Gulker (M), 1914-15; D.H. Muyskens,
1915-16; L. Ypma, 1918-21; A. Wassink, 1922-29;
J. Weidenaar, 1929-32; H. Zwaanstra, 1932-40; J.
Rubingh, 1940-46; K. Tebben, 1947-50; H.
Minnema, 1950-59; J.H. Rubingh, 1961-66; G.
Compaan, 1966-71; L.G. Zoerhof, 1971-76; R.L.
Fynewever, 1977-83; N.B. Haan, 1983-91; R.D.
Gorter, 1992-97; L.G. Christoffels, 1998-

Wright, IA — Wright
see: Kanawha, IA – Wright

Wyckoff, NJ — Calvin
1946-1990, merged into Wyckoff, NJ – Cedar Hill
pastors: B.E. Visscher, 1948-50; T. Van Eerden,
1951-55; J.P. Smith, 1956-68; K.L. Havert, 1969-
72; R.W. Klingenberg, 1974-77; B.B. Blankers,
1977-83; D.R Zimmerman, 1983-89

Wyckoff, NJ — Cedar Hill
1990-
former name: Wyckoff, NJ – Calvin, 1990-98,
absorbed Paterson, NJ – Bethel, 1990 and Midland Park, NJ – Irving Park, 1998
pastors: D.B. Mouw, 1990-95; D.D. Poolman,
1993-; J.C. Fisher, 1997-; R.D. Steen, 1998-99

Wyckoff, NJ — Faith Community
1896-
former name: Paterson, NJ – Fourth, 1896-1978
pastors: P. Kosten, 1898-1904; G. Westenberg,
1904-09; J. Robbert, 1911-12; R. Bolt, 1912-15; H.
Baker, 1915-19; J. Timmerman, 1920-33; P.G.
Holwerda, 1933-39; H.J. Evenhouse, 1939-44;
J.P. Smith, 1944-50; H. Sonnema, 1950-57; C.
Terpstra, 1958-65; W.H. Kooienga, 1967-80; H.J.
Vugteveen, 1981-95; W. Van Dyk, 1993-

Wyoming, MI — Beverly
1953-1995, withdrew to United Reformed
Churches
former names: Grand Rapids, MI – Beverly
Protestant Reformed, 1953-61; Grand Rapids, MI
– Beverly, 1961-69
pastors: R. Wezeman, 1954-61; E.J. Knott, 1961-
71; J.W. Uitvlugt, 1971-81; H.D. Schuringa, 1982-
85; A. Besteman, 1986-92

Wyoming, MI — Calvary
1959-
pastors: J.W. Uitvlugt, 1959-63; J.L. Meppelink,
1963-70; W. Van Antwerpen, 1971-81; R.
Huisman, 1991-95; D.A. Kamstra, 1982-; P.
Sausser, 1996-

Wyoming, MI — Community
1944-
organized: 1984
former name: Grand Rapids, MI – Community,
1971-94
pastors: J. Vredevoogd (E), 1944-46; D.
Lotterman (L), 1946-48; P. Schotenboer (L),
1948-49; A.H. Selles, 1949-59; H. Brinks (E),
1950-54; A.Mulder (E), 1955-61; W. Timmer (E),
1961-69; H.J. Schutt, 1970-75; P.E. Brink, 1976-
85; D.A. Struyk, 1986-

Wyoming, MI — Emanuel Hispanic
1967-
organized: 1981
former names: Grand Rapids, MI – Spanish,
1981; Wyoming, MI – Spanish, 1981-96; Wyoming, MI – Hispana Emanuel, 1997-2000
pastors: C.M. Cortina, 1967-73; D. Romero,
1973-95; C.G. Tapanes, 1994-

Wyoming, MI — Faith Community
1919-
former names: Grand Rapids, MI – Wyoming
Park, 1919-69; Wyoming, MI – Wyoming Park,
1969-93
pastors: E.B. Pekelder, 1921-25; J.P. Battema,
1926-29; A. Van Dyken, 1930-39; J.F.
Schuurmann, 1940-44; J. Hoogland, 1945-51;
W.F. Vander Hoven, 1952-57; F.W. Van Houten,
1957-62; T. Wevers, 1964-71; L.C. Bossenbroek,
1971-84; R.A.Heerema, 1985-89; K.L. Havert,
1990-98; R.C. Heerspink, 1999-

Wyoming, MI — Godwin Heights
1927-
former name: Grand Rapids, MI – Godwin
Heights, 1927-92
pastors: H.J. Rikkers, 1929-33; J.L. Bult, 1933-
44; W. Vander Haak, 1944-49; R.S. De Haan,
1950-54; E.B. Pekelder, 1956-62; V.C Licatesi,
1963-70; H.J. Kwantes, 1971-87; H. Veldman,
1990-97; M.G. Hewitt, 1999-

Wyoming, MI — Grace Korean
1999-
organized: 2000
pastor: M.B. Kim, 1998-

Wyoming, MI — Hahn-In
1981-
organized: 1985
former name: Grand Rapids, MI – Korean, 1985-
93
pastors: Y.S. Kang, 1981-83; B.N. Choi, 1984-86;
Y.K. Chung, 1988-95; M.B. Kim, 1995-98; B.E.
Park, 1999-

Wyoming, MI — Hispana Emanuel
see: Wyoming, MI – Emanuel Hispanic

Wyoming, MI — Ideal Park
see: Grand Rapids, MI – Ideal Park

Wyoming, MI — Immanuel
1948-
former name: Grand Rapids, MI – Immanuel,
1948-93
pastors: H.A. Venema, 1948-52; W. Kok, 1953-
58; C. Vanden Heuvel, 1958-64; G.W. Sheeres,
1966-72; M. Goote, 1972-77; A.H. Jongsma,
1978-81; J.C. Hutt, 1982-85; E.R. Tigchelaar,
1986-95; R.L. Knol, 1997-2001

Wyoming, MI — Lee Street
1926-
pastors: J.J. Steigenga, 1927-39; P.G. Holwerda,
1939-50; W. Van Peursem, 1951-58; C. Greenfield, 1959-70; L. Kerkstra, 1971-78; H.C. Van
Wyk, Jr., 1979-89; J.M. Boer, 1989-95; D.R.
Zimmerman, 1995-98; K.A. Rottman, 1999-

Wyoming, MI — Rogers Heights
1955-
organized: 1958
absorbed Grand Rapids, MI – Franklin Street,
1966 and Wyoming, MI – Thirty-Sixth Street,
1996
former name: Grand Rapids, MI – Rogers
Heights, 1955-69
pastors: F P. Doot (L), 1955-58; R. De Boer,
1959-65; J.M. Julien, 1966-68; H.A. Venema,
1968-70; A.H. Jongsma, 1971-78; R.A. Kok,
1979-86; D.L.Smit, 1987-95; D.J. Steenhoek,
1997-

Wyoming, MI — Spanish
see: Wyoming, MI – Emanuel Hispanic

Wyoming, MI — Thirty-Sixth Street
1953-1996, merged with Wyoming, MI – Rogers
Heights
pastors: S.A. Werkema, 1954-60; E.J. Masselink,
1962-66; A.J. Bultman, 1966-70; K.W. Vis, 1971-

79; J.C. Ribbens, 1980-85; P.H.Vruwink, 1982-89;
R.L. Bierenga, 1989-95

Wyoming, MI — West Forty-Fourth Street
1953-
organized: 1976; began as a chapel
pastors: G. Oppenhuizen (L), 1954-58; K. Navis
(E), 1958-75; J. Morren, 1978-84; R.D.
Goudzwaard, 1984-95; H. Vlaardingerbroek, 1997-

Wyoming, MI — Wyoming Park
see: Wyoming, MI – Faith Community

Wyoming, ON — Wyoming
1952-
pastors: H. Numan, Sr., 1952-56; J.A. Quartel,
1956-61; A. Vanden Berg, 1962-66; J. Wieringa,
1966-71; J. Nutma, 1971-77; W. Renkema, 1979-
86; J. Van Dyk, 1986-91; K.F. Benjamins, 1992-
99; P.J.A. Moelker, 2001-

Yakima, WA — Summitview
1967-
organized: 1969
former name: Yakima, WA – Yakima, 1967-71
pastors: B.J. Niemeyer (M), 1967-74; A.J. De
Vries, 1974-77; F.D. Rietema, 1977-81; D.R.
Vander Wall (M), 1981-90; E.P. Heerema, 1991-
95; D.L. Recker, 1995-

Yakima, WA — Yakima
see: Yakima, WA – Summitview

York, ON — Maranatha
1957-
former name: York, ON – York, 1957-71
pastors: G.J. Hoytema, 1959-66; N. Vander
Kwaak, 1966-71; M. De Vries, 1972-76; P. Stel,
1977-82; J. de Pater, 1983-88; J. Postuma,
1989-2001

York, ON — York
see: York, ON – Maranatha

**Ypsilanti, MI — Eastern Michigan Christian
Forum (campus ministry)**
1999-
pastor: M. Benckhuysen, 1999-2002

Ypsilanti, MI — Ypsilanti
1943-1945, discontinued

Zant, MB — Zant
1917-1920, discontinued

Zeeland, MI (mission)
1942
staff: C. Stremler, 1942

Zeeland, MI — Bethel
1950-
pastors: G.P. Holwerda, 1950-54; G. Haan, 1954-59; R.R. Graves, 1960-65; M. Ouwinga, 1965-71; G.W. Sheeres, 1972-79; H.B. Vanden Heuvel, 1979-91; G. Veenstra, 1992-99; J. Vander Plate, 2000-

Zeeland, MI — First
1862-
former name: Zeeland, MI — Zeeland, 1862-1888; includes minutes of Zeeland, MI — First Old School Presbyterian
pastors: K. Van den Bosch, 1862-64; J. Stadt, 1870-72; W. Coelingh, 1874-77; G.H. Hoeksema, 1877-79; L. Rietdyk, 1882-86; J. Keizer, 1888-90; J. Groen, 1891-1900; G.J. Haan, 1901-06; W.D. Vander Werp, 1906-11; D.R. Drukker, 1911-14; M. Van Vessem, 1915-26; W. Kok, 1927-40; D.D. Bonnema, 1941-51; A.E. Rozendal, 1952-61; H.G. . Arnold, 1962-70; C. Bolt, 1971-77; M.R. Doornbos, 1977-80; E.L. Shuart, 1980-92; W. Walter, Jr., 1993-99; N.R. Rylaarsdam, 2001-; P.E. Baker, 2001-

Zeeland, MI — Gateway Community
1993-
pastor: D.A. Gritter, 1994-2001; J.G. Aukema, 2002-

Zeeland, MI — Haven
1963-
pastors: V.G. Vander Werp, 1963; J.E. De Vries, 1964-69; A. Hannink, 1970-78; K.E. Van Wyk, 1979-96; H. Lengkeek, 1997-

Zeeland, MI — North Street
1882-
former name Zeeland, MI — Second, 1882-1930
pastors: J.I. Fles, 1882-89; J. Riemersma, 1890-91; K. Kreulen, 1892-98; J.B. Jonkman, 1899-1906; J. Smitter, 1908-15; J.H. Geerlings, 1916-19; H.E Oostendorp, 1919-38; J.M. Dykstra, 1939-49; J. Guichelaar, 1950-56; L.J. Hofman, 1959-65; C.W. Niewenhuis, 1965-71; A. Besteman, 1972-86; J. Admiraal, 1987-92; B.F. Tol, 1992-

Zeeland, MI — Second
see: Zeeland, MI — North Street

Zeeland, MI — Third
1914-
pastors: L. Trap, 1914-17; D.R.Drukker, 1918-26; W. Hendriksen, 1927-31; A. Jabaay, 1931-41; J.H. Bruinooge, 1941-60; A.W. Hoogstrate, 1961-67; E.W. Los, 1968-74; J.A. Wesseling, 1976-86; J. Cooper, 1987-98; M.A. Nelesen, 1996-

Zeeland, MI — Zeeland
see: Zeeland, MI — First

Zenith, ND — Zenith
1912-1921, discontinued

Zillah, WA — Faith Community
1901-
former names: Sunnyside, WA — Sunnyside, 1901-06; Zillah, WA — Zillah, 1906-95
pastors: V. Vriesman, 1911-16; J. De Jong, 1918-24; J.W. Brink, 1925-30; N. De Vries, 1930-44; D. Flietstra, 1944-50; R.D. Posthuma, 1950-53; C.A Persenaire, 1953-56; P. De Koekkoek, 1956-58; G. Van Laar, 1958-62; G.G. Hofland, 1962-67; J. Riemersma, 1968-72; R.L. Fynewever, 1972-77; J.G. Keizer, 1977-84; W.G. Van Hal, 1984-89; J. Hofman, Jr., 1990-96; R.J. Van Antwerpen, 1997-

Zillah, WA — Zillah
see: Zillah, WA — Faith Community

Zuni, NM — Zuni
1897-
organized: 1987
pastors: H. Fryling (M), 1897-1926; C.G.Hayenga (M), 1925-31; J.W. Brink, 1931-36; G. Yff (M), 1938-44; C. Kuipers, 1950-54; B. Haven (M), 1954-61; R.D. Posthuma (M), 1965-67; D.J. Klompeen, 1970-73; R.D. Posthuma (M), 1973-85; M.J. Meekhof, 1989-

Zutphen, MI — Zutphen
1880-
former name: Jamestown, MI — Jamestown, 1880-1902
pastors: G. Broene, 1884-89; A.J. Vanden Heuvel, 1890-92; P. Schut, 1892-1900; W. Veenstra, 1901-02; W. Borgman, 1903-07; H. Vander Werp, 1908-13; H. Tuls, 1914-23; K. Bergsma, 1923-28; W. Van Peursem, 1928-32; S.Vroon, 1932-39; S.A. Werkema, 1940-47; J.W. Visser, 1947-52; J. Breuker, 1952-59; P.I Vermaire, 1959-63; R.H. Hooker, 1963-64; O. De Groot, 1966-79; R.J. Blauw, 1980-86; S.J. De Vries, 1986-95; R.J. Noorman, 1997-

Ministers

Aardsma, Calvin
b. 03/31/1955, Chicago, IL
training: Calvin Theological Seminary, MDiv, 1980
ordained: 1981
charges: New Hope Community, Terre Haute, IN, 1981–86; Knollbrook, Corvallis, OR, 1986–97; Park Lane, Evergreen Park, IL, 1997–

Aardsma, Dirk Herman
b. 07/16/1931, Chicago, IL
training: Calvin Theological Seminary, BD, 1955
ordained: 1955
charges: Hope, Muskegon, MI, 1955–58; Calvin, Sheboygan, WI, 1958–63; Home missionary, Calvary, Minneapolis, MN, 1963–68; Missionary, Ridgeview Hills, Denver, CO, 1968–72; Missionary, general assignment for Rocky Mountains area, 1972–81
d. 09/15/1981, Denver, CO

Aasman, John Thomas
b. 12/25/1972, Medicine Hat, AB
training: Reformed Bible College, BRE, 1994; Calvin Theological Seminary, MDiv, 1998
ordained: 1998
charges: Roosevelt Park Community, Grand Rapids, MI, 1998–

Abbas, Cornelius
b. 12/31/1909, Wellsburg, IA
training: Calvin Theological Seminary, BD, 1938
ordained: 1938
charges: Mountain Lake, MN, 1938–44; Cincinnati, OH, 1944–49; German Valley, IL, 1949–76
retired: 1976
d. 03/29/1997, Freeport, IL

Abma, Michael Frederick
b. 04/22/1962, Strathroy, ON

training: University of Toronto, MA, 1985; Calvin Theological Seminary, MDiv, 1989
ordained: 1989
charges: Rehoboth, Bowmanville, ON, 1989–98; Woodlawn, Grand Rapids, MI, 1998–

Abreu, Josué
b. 09/11/1930, Cuba
ordained: 1965
charges: Evangelical Convention of Cuba, 1955–66; General Mennonite Conference, USA, 1971–79; CRC: Good Shepherd, Paterson, NJ, 1979–90; Leave, 1990–91; Good Samaritan, Miami, FL, 1991–94
retired: 1994

Ackerman, Daniel R.
b. 05/27/1960, Bellingham, WA
training: Calvin Theological Seminary, MDiv, 1991
ordained: 1991
charges: Youth director, Alpine Ave., Grand Rapids, MI, 1987–89; Minister of youth and education, Caledonia, MI, 1989–90; Georgetown, Hudsonville, MI, 1991–95; Maranatha, Holland, MI, 1995–99; Church Leadership Specialist, Home Missions of the Christian Reformed Church, Grand Rapids, MI, 1999–

Ackerman, Walter H.
b. 12/22/1918, German Valley, IL
training: Calvin Theological Seminary, BD, 1943
ordained: 1943
charges: Coopersville, MI, 1943–47; Austinville, IA, 1947–50; Pease, MN, 1950–54; Auburn Park, Chicago, IL, 1954–59; Third, Lynden, WA, 1959–64; First, Bellflower, CA, 1964–73; First, Everett, WA, 1973–78; Enumclaw, WA, 1978–82
d. 12/17/1982, Enumclaw, WA

Acuña, Felipe
b. 11/17/1956, Tijuana, Baja California, Mexico

training: Berean Bible College, Latin American Seminar of La Puente, CA
ordained: 1985
charges: CRC: El Arca Communidad Cristiana/ Vida Nueva, San Diego, CA, 1994–2000; resigned from denomination

Adams, Kevin Jay
b. 09/21/1960, Kalamazoo, MI
training: Calvin Theological Seminary, MDiv, 1987
ordained: 1987
charges: Bethel, Princeton, MN, 1987–91; Granite Springs, Rocklin, CA, 1991–

Adema, Bruce Gerald
b. 09/17/1962, Brampton, ON
training: Calvin Theological Seminary, MDiv, 1992
ordained: 1992
charges: St. Albert, AB, 1992–97; Missionary, Philippines, 1997–

Admiraal, Case
b. 07/12/1948, Maassluis, Zuid Holland, Netherlands
training: Calvin Theological Seminary, BD, 1973
ordained: 1974
charges: Bethel, Fulton, IL, 1974–81; Immanuel, Ripon, CA, 1981–

Admiraal, Henry
b. 04/09/1946, Maassluis, Zuid Holland, Netherlands
training: Calvin Theological Seminary, BD, 1971
ordained: 1973
charges: Minister for youth and evangelism, Seymour, Grand Rapids, MI, 1971–75; Seymour, Grand Rapids, MI, 1975–92; Westend, Grand Rapids, MI, 1992–

Admiraal, James A.
b. 04/09/1946, Maassluis, Zuid Holland, Netherlands
training: Calvin Theological Seminary, BD, 1971
ordained: 1971
charges: Trinity, Rock Valley, IA, 1971–76; Pleasant St., Whitinsville, MA, 1976–80; Second, Kalamazoo, MI, 1980–87; North St., Zeeland, MI, 1987–92; First, Prinsburg, MN, 1992–98; Second, Randolph, WI, 1998–

Afman, Carl Jay
b. 01/15/1943, Chicago, IL
training: Calvin Theological Seminary, BD, 1970
ordained: 1970
charges: Hancock, MN, 1970–75; Missionary to

Taiwan, 1975–86; Hammond, IN, 1986–96; Missionary, Philippines, 1996–2002; Interim, Momence, IL, 2002

Ahn, Samuel S.
b. 03/01/1947, Suwon, South Korea
training: Seoul Theological Seminary, MDiv, 1978
ordained: 1989
charges: Korean Presbyterian Church of Rancho Cordova; CRC: Korean, Sacramento, CA, 1989–

Ahuis, Henry
b. 01/10/1865, Georgsdorf, Bentheim, Germany
training: Calvin Theological Seminary, diploma, 1899
ordained: 1899
charges: Hull, ND, 1899–01; Bunde, MN, 1901–04; Ackley, IA, 1904–13; Parkersburg, IA, 1913–21; Ridott, IL, 1921–25; Vesper, WI, 1925–32
retired: 1932
d. 07/24/1946, Fremont, MI

Albaugh, Thomas George
b. 12/16/1950, Dayton, OH
training: Westminster Theological Seminary-CA, MDiv, 1995
ordained: 1995
charges: OPC: New Life, Wasilla, AK, 1995–98; CRC: Nobleford, AB, 1999–

Aldrink, Douglas Lee
b. 05/01/1951, Grand Rapids, MI
training: Westminster Theological Seminary-PA, MDiv, 1976; Calvin Theological Seminary, Special Program for Ministerial Candidacy, 1978
ordained: 1978
charges: Parchment, Kalamazoo, MI, 1978–83; Walnut Creek, CA, 1983–89; Hope, San Marcos, CA, 1989–93; Bradenton, FL, 1993–

Alexander, Rodney Eugene
b. 10/02/1949, Newark, NJ
training: Covenant Theological Seminary, MDiv, 1979
ordained: 1980
charges: Calvary Gospel Church, Newark, NJ, 1980; OPC: Park Hill, Denver, CO, 1980–81; Faculty, Covenant Theological Seminary, St. Louis, MO, 1984–87; Beverly, Los Angeles, CA, 1987–88; CRC: First, Grand Rapids, MI, 1982–84; Independent: Chaplain, Oregon State Penitentiary, Salem, OR, 1988–

Alferink, Jerry Lynn
b. 05/04/1945, Holland, MI

training: Calvin Theological Seminary, BD, 1971; MDiv, 1975
ordained: 1971
charges: Winfield, IL, 1971–75; Trinity, Vancouver, WA, 1975–79; First, Redlands, CA, 1979–85; Chaplain, Pine Rest Christian Hospital, Cutlerville, MI, 1985–87; Hillcrest, Denver, CO, 1987–94; Overisel, MI, 1994–2001

Algera, John Albert
b. 11/28/1952, Ridgewood, NJ
training: Calvin Theological Seminary, MDiv, 1978
ordained: 1979
charges: Madison Ave., Paterson, NJ, 1979–

Alkema, William
b. 07/30/1893, Tjerkwerd, Friesland, Netherlands
training: Calvin Theological Seminary, diploma, 1925
ordained: 1925
charges: Portland, MI, 1925–28; East Martin, MI, 1928–48; Alto, WI, 1948–57
retired: 1957
d. 10/24/1977, Grand Rapids, MI

Almaraz, Joseph E.
b. 12/07/1941
ordained: 1975
charges: High Desert Christian Center, Barstow, CA, 1973–76; Blythefield AFB Chapel, 1978–81; United States Navy, Chapel Programs, 1981–84; Oasis Christian Center, 1986–89; Veterans Administration Chaplaincy, 1990–97, and church planting, Dominion Fellowship, Redlands, CA, 1992–97; Eligible for call, 1997–

Alsum, Steven John
b. 12/21/1955, Denver, CO
training: Calvin Theological Seminary, MDiv, 1985
ordained: 1985
charges: Morrison, IL, 1985–89; Calvin, Sheboygan, WI, 1989–98; Cragmor, Colorado Springs, CO, 1998–

Alvarez, Isay Benitez
b. 11/04/1959
ordained: 1994
charges: Belen, Bellflower, CA, 1994–2002

Amsing, Bert Alexander
b. 10/21/1959, Clinton, ON
training: Reformed Bible College, BRE, 1984; Calvin Theological Seminary, MDiv, 1988
ordained: 1989

charges: Covenant, Calgary, AB, 1989–92; Leave, 1992–93; Non-ministerial vocation, 1993

Anderson, Bruce Marshall
b. 12/26/1954, Elkhart, IN
training: Calvin Theological Seminary, MDiv, 1982
ordained: 1982
charges: Grangeville, ID, 1982–87; Command Chaplain, United States Navy, 1987–

Anderson, Victor
b. 05/27/1955, New York, NY
training: Chicago Bible College, BTh, 1977; Calvin Theological Seminary, MDiv, 1987
ordained: 1978
charges: Associate pastor, Canaan Baptist Church, Chicago, IL, 1974–82; Faculty, Calvin College, Grand Rapids, MI, 1986–88; CRC: Grace, Grand Rapids, MI, 1987–90; Non-ministerial vocation, Yale University, 1990

Anderson, Zachary Guy
b. 12/15/1960, Sault Ste. Marie, MI
training: Calvin Theological Seminary, MDiv, 1990
ordained: 1990
charges: Director of education, North St., Zeeland, MI, 1986–88; Ideal Park, Grand Rapids, MI, 1990–93; Pine Creek, Holland, MI, 1993–98; Goshen, NY, 1998–2002; RCA: Seventh, Grand Rapids, MI, 2002

André, Garret
b. 10/09/1895, Paterson, NJ
training: Calvin Theological Seminary, diploma, 1923
ordained: 1923
charges: Bemis, SD, 1923–42; Vesper, WI, 1942–48; Home missionary at Picton, ON, 1948–50, at Port Credit, ON, 1950–53, at Montreal, QC, 1953–56; Home missionary in Ontario at Barrie, ON, 1956–60; Home missionary for Maritime Provinces, at Halifax, NS, 1960
retired: 1960
d. 02/25/1970, Grand Rapids, MI

Antonides, Mary Sue Hulst
see: Hulst, Mary Sue

Apol, Isaac John
b. 10/30/1926, Cutlerville, MI
training: Calvin Theological Seminary, ThB, 1951
ordained: 1951
charges: Hamilton, MI, 1951–54; Archer Ave., Chicago, IL, 1954–58; Anaheim, CA, 1958–65; Calvin, Portland, OR, 1965–67; Sherman St., Grand

Rapids, MI, 1967-71; Irving Park, Midland Park, NJ, 1971-76; First, Highland, IN, 1976-83; Richfield, Clifton, NJ, 1983-87
retired: 1987

Apol, Philip Arthur
b. 06/22/1958, Chicago, IL
training: Calvin Theological Seminary, MDiv, 1988
ordained: 1989
charges: Religion editor, Wm. B. Eerdmans Publishing Co., Grand Rapids, MI, 1989-91; Silver Spring, MD, 1991-97; Leave, 1997-98; Geneva Fellowship, Kingston, ON, 1998-

Apoll, Philip Anthony
b. 05/21/1970, Edmonton, AB
training: Calvin Theological Seminary, MDiv, 1998
ordained: 1998
charges: Covenant, Barrie, ON, 1998-

Aragon, Ricardo
b. 02/08/1950, San Marcos, Carazo, Nicaragua
training: Rio Grande Biblical Seminary, BA, 1975
ordained: 1978
charges: International Baptist Church: El Calvaria, Managua, Nicaragua, 1977-85; Radio ministry, Nicaragua, 1986-89; CRC: Camarillo Hispanic, Camarillo, CA, 1993-

Aranguiz, Carlos
ordained: 1993
charges: Anglican Church of Chile, 1996-97; CRC: Hartford Hispanic, Hartford, CT, 1997-

Arbogast, Robert Allan
b. 08/03/1960, Manistique, MI
training: Calvin Theological Seminary, MDiv, 1987
ordained: 1987
charges: Exeter, ON, 1987-90; Comstock, Kalamazoo, MI, 1990-98; Eligible for call, 1998-99; Olentangy, Columbus, OH, 1999-

Arevalo, Edwin R.
b. 03/20/1952, El Salvador
training: declared eligible on the basis of exceptional gifts, 1999
ordained: 2000
charges: Jersey City Mission, Jersey City, NJ, 1989-2001
d. 11/06/2001, Jersey City, NJ

Arkema, Alan August
b. 09/15/1929, Sully, IA
training: Calvin Theological Seminary, BD, 1954
ordained: 1954

charges: Bemis, SD, 1954-57; Lebanon, IA, 1957-61; Missionary to Australia, 1961-66; East Islip, NY, 1966-71; Prospect Park, NJ, 1971-81; Calvary Community, Dayton, OH, 1981-86; Bozeman, MT, 1986-91; Seymour, Grand Rapids, MI, 1991-94
retired: 1995

Armstrong, David R.
b. 12/04/1937, Burlington, IA
training: Reformed Presbyterian Theological Seminary, diploma, 1963; University of Pittsburgh, MEd, 1964; Trinity Evangelical Divinity School, MCE, 1971; Fuller Theological Seminary, DMin, 1982
ordained: 1965
charges: Reformed Presbyterian Church: First, Beaver Falls, PA, 1965-70; Leave, 1970-71; Denominational director of education, Pittsburgh, PA, 1971-73; First, Chicago, IL, 1973-75; Independent: Christ's Community, Woodbridge, IL, 1975-80; Good Shepherd Community, Woodbridge, IL, 1980-86; CRC: Elmhurst, IL, 1987-

Arnold, Harry George
b. 12/27/1925, Paterson, NJ
training: Calvin Theological Seminary, BD, 1953; ThM, 1970; Trinity Evangelical Divinity School, DM, 1981
ordained: 1953
charges: Minneapolis, MN, 1953-57; East Palmyra, NY, 1957-62; First, Zeeland, MI, 1962-70; First, Lansing, IL, 1970-83; Grace, Kalamazoo, MI, 1983-91
retired: 1991

Arnoys, Marinus
b. 01/08/1900, Heinkenszand, Zeeland, Netherlands
training: Calvin Theological Seminary, BD, 1927
ordained: 1927
charges: Dutton, MI, 1927-30; East Leonard, Grand Rapids, MI, 1930-39; First, Sioux Center, IA, 1939-45; First Roseland, Chicago, IL, 1945-54; Trinity, Jenison, MI, 1954-65
retired: 1965
d. 03/04/1977, Grand Rapids, MI

Arrick, Stephen Marcey
b. 09/05/1955, Charleston, WV
training: Reformed Theological Seminary, MDiv, 1980; Calvin Theological Seminary, Special Program for Ministerial Candidacy, 1985
ordained: 1985
charges: CRC: Calvary, Lowell, MI, 1985-88; Cor-

nerstone, Hudsonville, MI, 1988-93; United Reformed Churches: Cornerstone, Hudsonville, MI, 1993-98; PCA: Delaware, MD, 1998

Aukema, John Gerald
b. 05/02/1970, Shelburne, ON
training: Calvin Theological Seminary, MDiv, 1997
ordained: 1997
charges: New church ministry, Orlando, FL, 1997-2002; Gateway Community, Zeeland, MI, 2002-

Aupperlee, John George
b. 04/12/1947, Paterson, NJ
training: Calvin Theological Seminary, MDiv, 1972
ordained: 1973
charges: Assistant minister, Midland Park, NJ, 1973-77; Indian Harbour Beach, FL, 1977-85; Northern Heights, Kalamazoo, MI, 1985-90; Fairlawn, Whitinsville, MA, 1990-2003; Christian Reformed Word Relief Committee, Grand Rapids, MI, 2003-

Averill, Brent Allen
b. 09/24/1942, Farmington, ME
training: Gordon-Conwell Theological Seminary, MDiv, 1968
ordained: 1969
charges: Congregational Church: Medway Village, Medway, MA, 1968-71; CRC: Missionary, Otay Mesa, CA, 1971-75; Minister of education and evangelism, Brookside, Grand Rapids, MI, 1975-77; Irving Park, Midland Park, NJ, 1977-82; Immanuel, Wappingers Falls, NY, 1982-90; On loan: New Covenant Congregational Church, North Hampton, NH, 1990-95; New Covenant, North Hampton, NH, 1995-

Avila, Marco Antonio
b. 07/21/1966, Comoyaguo, Honduras
training: Reformed Bible College, BRE, 1996; Calvin Theological Seminary, MDiv, 2000
ordained: 2001
charges: New Horizon, Passaic, NJ, 2001-

Avila, Mariano
b. 06/04/1952, Mexico City, Mexico
training: Juan Calvino Seminario Teologico, BATh, 1975; Calvin Theological Seminary, ThM, 1980; Temple University, MA, 1991; Westminister Theological Seminary, PhD, 1996
ordained: 1983
charges: Prebyterian Church of Mexico: Faculty, Seminario Teologico Presbiteriano de Mexico, 1981-86; Coordinator of urban ministries, 1986-

87; Leave, 1987-91; CITE-CRC, Mexico, 1991-94; Puerta de Salvacion, Chilalistac, Mexico, 1993-97; Leave, 1997-98; PCA: El Redentor, Miami, FL, 1999-2000; Faculty Calvin Theological Seminary, 2000- (CRC, 2002-)

Aviles, Pedro
b. 03/03/1955, Chicago, IL
training: declared eligible on the basis of exceptional gifts, 1985
ordained: 1985
charges: Grace and Peace Fellowship, Chicago, IL, 1985-

Baak, David Paul
b. 12/19/1943, Charlottetown, PE
training: Calvin Theological Seminary, BD, 1970; MDiv, 1975
ordained: 1970
charges: CRC: First, Flint, MI, 1970-72; Leave, 1972-74; Director, Citizen's Probationary Authority, Genesee Co., MI, 1974-75; RCA: Pre-Trial Services Program, Genesee, Co., MI, 1975-80; Pre-Trial Services Program, Salt Lake City, UT, 1980-83; Director, Grand Rapids Area Center for Ecumenism, Grand Rapids, MI, 1983-

Baak, Henry Peter
b. 10/14/1916, Grand Rapids, MI
training: Westminster Theological Seminary-PA, ThB, 1942
ordained: 1942
charges: PC: Marshfield, PE, 1943-44; Cobden, ON, 1944-48; UPC: Carlisle, IA, 1948-51; Boyden, IA, 1951-57; Bible teacher, Northern Christian High School, McBain, MI, 1957-59; CRC: Dispatch, KS, 1959-65; Sioux City, IA, 1965-68; Woden, IA, 1968-75; Hills, MN, 1975-81
retired: 1981
d. 09/04/2001, Kentwood, MI

Baar, Larry Duane
b. 10/24/1949, Downey, CA
training: Calvin Theological Seminary, MDiv, 1986
ordained: 1987
charges: Prairie View, Luctor, KS, 1987-94; New Era, MI, 1994-

Baarda, Steven George
b. 07/04/1967, Cochrane, ON
training: Calvin Theological Seminary, MDiv, 1998
ordained: 1998
charges: Calvary, Chatham, ON, 1998-

Baarman, Marvin Chris
b. 01/19/1919, Zeeland, MI
training: Calvin Theological Seminary, ThB, 1951
ordained: 1951
charges: Lodi, NJ, 1951–56; Home missionary, Ft. Lauderdale, FL, 1956–60; Executive Secretary, Board of Home Missions, Grand Rapids, MI, 1960–73; leave, 1973–74; Miami, FL, 1974–75
retired: 1975
d. 02/21/1991, Grand Rapids, MI

Baas, Harvey J.
b. 04/12/1929, Falmouth, MI
training: Calvin Theological Seminary, BD, 1955; MDiv, 1976
ordained: 1955
charges: Second, Randolph, WI, 1955–58; Bradenton, FL, 1958–63; Evergreen Park, IL, 1963–69; Bethany, Holland, MI, 1969–77; Pioneer, Cedar Springs, MI, 1977–94
retired: 1994

Bade, Herman
b. 05/14/1922, Sneek, Friesland, Netherlands
training: Theologische Universiteit, Kampen, diploma, 1953
ordained: 1953
charges: GKN: Valthermond, 1953–59; Landsmeer, 1971–80; Koudekerk aan den Rijn, 1980–87; CRC: Taber and Vauxhall, AB, 1959–65; Surrey, BC, 1965–70
retired: 1987

Baird, Thomas Stephen
b. 09/16/1957, Oak Park, IL
training: Reformed Theological Seminary, MDiv, 1985; Calvin Theological Seminary, Special Program for Ministerial Candidacy, 1986
ordained: 1986
charges: Kincardine, ON, 1986–91; Calvary, Chatham, ON, 1991–

Bajema, Clifford Earl
b. 06/01/1941, Bellingham, WA
training: Calvin Theological Seminary, BD, 1966; ThM, 1985
ordained: 1966
charges: Cragmor, Colorado Springs, CO, 1966–69; Campus minister, University of Colorado, Boulder, CO, 1969–73; Akron, OH, 1973–77; Ferrysburg, MI, 1977–83; 14th Street, Holland, MI, 1983–88; Campus minister, Geneva Chapel, Madison, WI, 1988–

Bajema, Henry
b. 06/17/1919, Grand Rapids, MI
training: Calvin Theological Seminary, BD, 1944; Princeton Theological Seminary, ThB, 1946
ordained: 1946
charges: Lebanon, IA, 1946–49; Parkview Heights, Cincinnati, OH, 1949–54; Immanuel, Hudsonville, MI, 1954–59; First, Lacombe, AB, 1959–64; Volga, SD, 1964–69; Hanford, CA, 1969–80; Holland Center, SD, 1980–84
retired: 1984

Bajema, William
b. 04/22/1881, Terzool, Friesland, Netherlands
training: Calvin Theological Seminary, diploma, 1912
ordained: 1912
charges: Randolph, WI, 1915–25; Sheldon, IA, 1925–47
retired: 1947
d. 04/21/1952, Orange City, IA

Bak, Sung Jin
b. 12/06/1956, Seoul, South Korea
training: Philadelphia Bible College, MDiv, 1989
ordained: 1984
charges: Chaplain, Sam Sung Middle/High School, 1984–86; St. Petersburg Presbyterian Church, 1988–90; Korean Reformed Presbyterian Church, Tampa, FL, 1990; CRC: Evergreen, Tampa, FL, 1990–

Baker, Andrew
b. 01/15/1906, Munster, IN vicinity
training: Calvin Theological Seminary, BD, 1934
ordained: 1939
charges: Stated supply, Sunnyside, WA, 1934–38; Birnamwood, WI, 1939–43; Flint, MI, 1943–45; East Palmyra, NY, 1945–50; Middleburg, IA, 1950–59
retired: 1959
d. 04/24/1970, Grand Rapids, MI

Baker, Henry
b. 09/27/1887, Grand Rapids, MI
training: Calvin Theological Seminary, diploma, 1910
ordained: 1910
charges: Jamestown, MI, 1910–15; Fourth, Paterson, NJ, 1915–19; Second Roseland, Chicago, IL, 1919–26; Franklin Street, Grand Rapids, MI, 1926–37; Home missionary-at-large, 1937–53; Auburn Park, Chicago, IL, 1946–53; Harderwyk, Holland, MI, 1953–57
retired: 1957

d. 02/25/1985, Grand Rapids, MI

Baker, Kenneth Alan
b. 02/14/1952, Paterson, NJ
training: Calvin Theological Seminary, MDiv, 1978
ordained: 1978
charges: Ebenezer, Leduc, AB, 1978-82; Immanuel, Hamilton, ON, 1982-89; Coquitlam, BC, 1989-92; Third, Kalamazoo, MI, 1992-

Baker, Louis Frederick
b. 12/21/1924, Portland, MI
training: Calvin Theological Seminary, BD, 1953
ordained: 1954
charges: Bejou, MN, 1954-59; Rudyard, MI, 1959-64; Holland Center, SD, 1964-68; Kenosha, WI, 1968-79; Chaplain, Evanston General Hospital, Evanston, IL, 1979-85; Hull, ND, 1985-90
retired: 1990

Baker, Ralph David
b. 01/20/1924, Ripon, CA
training: Calvin Theological Seminary, ThB, 1952
ordained: 1952
charges: Accepted call to South India, 1952-53, temporarily at: West Park, Cleveland, OH, 1952; Goshen, IN, 1953; Missionary to Nigeria, 1953-54; Principal, Benue Bible Institute, Nigeria, 1954-73, teacher, Benue Bible Institute, Nigeria, 1973-76; Principal, Benue Bible Institute, Nigeria, 1976-78; Commentary writer, The Church of Christ in the Sudan, among the TIV, Nigeria, 1978-89
retired: 1989

Baker, Randolph
b. 02/04/1943, Norwood, MA
training: declared eligible on the basis of exceptional gifts, 1978
ordained: 1978
charges: Independent: Spirit and Truth Fellowship, Chicago, IL, 1977-83; CRC: Spirit and Truth Fellowship, Chicago, IL, 1983-87; Spirit and Truth Fellowship, Philadelphia, PA, 1987-

Baker, Ronald Dennis
b. 05/24/1937, Volga, SD
training: Calvin Theological Seminary, BD, 1971
ordained: 1971
charges: Eastern Hills, Kalamazoo, MI, 1971-81; Bravo, Fennville, MI, 1981-90; Ocheyedan, IA, 1990-95; Covenant, Lansing, MI, 1995-99; Holland Deacons Conference, Holland, MI, 1999-

Baker, Ronald Gene
b. 11/17/1952, Cleveland, OH

training: Calvin Theological Seminary, MDiv, 1982
ordained: 1982
charges: Bradenton, FL, 1982-97; Westview, Grand Rapids, MI, 1997-

Bakker, Batavus Bernardus
b. 02/01/1949, Bedum, Groningen, Netherlands
training: Westminster Theological Seminary-PA, MDiv, 1975; Calvin Theological Seminary, Special Program for Ministerial Candidacy, 1976
ordained: 1976
charges: Stratford, ON, 1976-82; John Calvin, Truro, NS, 1982-88; Essex, ON, 1988-92; Hebron, Whitby, ON, 1992-

Bakker, Frederich (Freek) Fritz
b. 06/03/1929, Enschede, Overijsel, Netherlands
training: Calvin Theological Seminary, BD, 1970
ordained: 1970
charges: Immanuel, Simcoe, ON, 1970-74; Hebron, Whitby, ON, 1974-79; Second, Sarnia, ON, 1979-86; Missionary, Nigeria, 1986-90
d. 07/10/1990, London, ON

Bakker, Kenneth Ray
b. 04/05/1941, Grand Rapids, MI
training: Calvin Theological Seminary, BD, 1967
ordained: 1967
charges: Missionary, Mason City, IA, 1967-70; Resigned from denomination, 1970, pastor in West Palm Beach, FL, 1999

Bakker, Paul Ed
b. 04/15/1960, Hamilton, ON
training: Calvin Theological Seminary, MDiv, 1993
ordained: 1993
charges: West Park, Cleveland, OH, 1993-2001; First, Zeeland, MI 2001-

Bakker, Paul Edward
b. 03/06/1929, Dike, IA
training: Calvin Theological Seminary, BD, 1954
ordained: 1954
charges: Plainfield, MI, 1954-58; New Holland, SD, 1958-63; Faith, Grand Rapids, MI, 1963-68; Sully, IA, 1968-73; First, Rock Valley, IA, 1973-79; Second, Byron Center, MI, 1979-84; Bethel, Oskaloosa, IA, 1984-88; Luverne, MN, 1988-94
retired: 1994

Bakker, Pier
b. 05/20/1854, Rinsumageest, Friesland, Netherlands
training: Calvin Theological Seminary, diploma, 1893

ordained: 1893
charges: Overisel, MI 1893-95
d. 08/06/1895, Overisel, MI

Ballast, Bruce Terry
b. 01/05/1953, Grand Rapids, MI vicinity
training: Calvin Theological Seminary, MDiv, 1978
ordained: 1979
charges: Calvary, Plainwell, MI, 1979-83; Calvary, Chino, CA, 1983-

Balt, John S.
b. 02/14/1869, St. Annaparochie, Friesland, Netherlands
training: with Herman Bel
ordained: 1918
charges: East Palmyra, NY, 1918-28; Hamilton, ON, 1928-39
retired: 1939
d. 06/07/1954, Grand Rapids, MI

Bandstra, Andrew John
b. 12/06/1926, Taintor, IA
training: Calvin Theological Seminary, BD, 1953; Vrije Universiteit, Amsterdam, ThD, 1964
ordained: 1955
charges: Lincoln Center, IA, 1955-57; Faculty Calvin College, Grand Rapids, MI, 1957-63; Faculty, Calvin Theological Seminary, Grand Rapids, MI, 1963-92
retired: 1992

Bang, Chul Sup
ordained: 2001
charges: Presbyterian Church of Korea; CRC: Wheeling, IL, 2001-

Bang, Soon Min
b. 10/17/1956, Seoul, South Korea
training: Fuller Theological Seminary, MDiv, 1994
ordained: 1999
charges: Bethany Korean Community, Burbank, CA, 1999-

Bao, Nguyen Xuan
see: Nguyen, Bao Xuan

Baron, Sietse Hanse
b. 11/10/1813, Makkinga, Friesland, Netherlands
training: with Wolter Alberts Kok at Ruinerwold, then Frederik Alberts Kok at Birdaard, and then Tamme Foppe deHaan at Groningen, completed in 1844
ordained: 1844
charges: GKN: lay preacher, Compagnie, 1842-

43, and at Wanswerd/Birdaard, 1843-44; Koudum-Hindelopen, 1844-46; Ferwerd, 1846-51; Bergum, 1851-69; CRC: Niekerk, 1869-76; Pella, 1876-81
retired: 1882
d. 05/02/1889, Zeeland, MI

Basson, Andre F.
b. 04/23/1952, Johannesburg, Gauteng, South Africa
training: University of Preoria, BD, 1976, Theology Diploma, 1977; University of Provence, Doctorate, 1995
ordained: 2000
charges: South African Dutch Reformed Church: Chaplain, South African Navy, 1978-79; Andrew Murray Church, 1979-99; CRC: Rehoboth, Niagara Falls, ON, 2000-

Battema, John Peter
b. 11/17/1888, Muskegon, MI
training: Calvin Theological Seminary, 1917
ordained: 1917
charges: CRC: Maple Ave., Holland, MI, 1917-20; Third, Kalamazoo, MI, 1920-26; Wyoming Park, MI, 1926-29; Undenominational: Wyoming Park, MI, 1929-31; Three Rivers, MI, 1931-33; Non-ministerial vocation, 1937, Kalamazoo, MI; Editor, Jail Evangelist, Los Angeles, CA, 1947
d. 10/09/1963, Bexley, OH

Batterink, Leonard Henry
b. 05/02/1956, Sarnia, ON
training: Calvin Theological Seminary, MDiv, 1983
ordained: 1983
charges: Essex, ON, 1983-87; Shalom, Brantford, ON, 1987-94; First, Dunan, BC, 1994-2001; Christ Community, Victoria, BC, 2001-

Batts, Jerome (Jerry) William
b. 05/19/1935, Detroit, MI
training: Calvin Theological Seminary, BD, 1962; ThM, 1977
ordained: 1962
charges: CRC: Home missionary, Jackson, MI, 1963-67; Missionary, Bellevue, WA, 1967-71; Second, Lynden, WA, 1971-72; Denominational Board of Publications, 1972-74; Christ Community, Naperville, IL, 1986-93; Leave, 1993-94; RCA: Fourth, Grand Rapids, MI, 1974-77; Independent: Christ Church, Oak Brook, IL, 1977-83; Christ Community, Naperville, IL, 1983-86
retired: 1994; resigned from denomination, 1997

Bauman, Bobbyjon
b. 07/15/1968, Dodgeville, WI
training: Reformed Theological Seminary, MDiv, 1995
ordained: 1995
charges: Associate Reformed Presbyterian Church: New Albany, MS, 1995-99; CRC: Crossroads, Madison, WI, 1999-

Bay, Myung Whan
b. 05/06/1956, South Korea
training: Pusan Ko-Shin Theological Graduate School, MDiv, 1986
ordained: 1989
charges: Korean Presbyterian Church in America, 1989-90; CRC: Rok Won, Norwalk, CA, 1991-92; left the denomination

Bazuin, Lugene A.
b. 07/30/1926, Lucas, MI
training: Calvin Theological Seminary, ThB, 1950
ordained: 1950
charges: Kanawha, IA, 1950-54; Fulton, IL, 1954-58; Second, Denver, CO, 1958-63; First, Munster, IN, 1963-91
retired: 1991

Beach, James Mark
b. 09/30/1957, Albuquerque, NM
training: Calvin Theological Seminary, MDiv, 1984, ThM, 1994
ordained: 1985
charges: First, Hospers, IA, 1985-89; First, Pella, IA, 1989-97; Faculty, Mid-America Reformed Seminary, Dyer, IN, 1997-

Bechtold, Arend Hendrick
b. 04/19/1822, Amsterdam, Noord Holland, Netherlands
training: licensed by North Suffolk Congregational Association, MA
ordained: 1862
charges: RCA: Missionary to New England Dutch and German immigrants, 1862-64; CRC: First, Paterson, NJ, 1864-66; RCA: Lennox Street Chapel, Boston, MA, 1866-70; Holland Church, New York, NY, 1870-84
d. 11/15/1884, New York, NY

Becksvoort, Benjamin Jay
b. 10/27/1947, Holland, MI
training: Calvin Theological Seminary, BD, 1972
ordained: 1972
charges: Chaplain, University of Minnesota, Minneapolis, MN, 1972-78; Akron, OH, 1978-85;

Brookside, Grand Rapids, MI, 1985-97; Home Missions, Regional Director of Great Lakes Region, Grand Rapids, MI, 1997-

Beebe, John
b. 02/29/1892, West Sayville, NY
training: Calvin Theological Seminary, diploma, 1925
ordained: 1925
charges: Home missionary Classes Hudson and Hackensack, 1925-28; Madison Ave., Paterson, NJ, 1928-43; Niekerk, Holland, MI, 1943-57
retired: 1957
d. 01/24/1969, Zeeland, MI

Beelen, David Henry
b. 09/05/1954, Grand Rapids, MI
training: Calvin Theological Seminary, MDiv, 1982
ordained: 1982
charges: Madison Square, Grand Rapids, MI, 1982-

Beelen, Marvin
b. 03/26/1929, Holland, MI
training: Calvin Theological Seminary, BD, 1954
ordained: 1954
charges: Willard, OH, 1954-58; Home missionary to St. Petersburg, FL, 1958-61; First, Grand Rapids, MI, 1961-70; Bethany, Muskegon, MI, 1970-80; Leave, 1980-81; St. Joseph, MI, 1981-91
retired: 1991

Beerens, Arnold Gene
b. 03/18/1943, Marion, MI
training: Calvin Theological Seminary, BD, 1968; ThM, 1981
ordained: 1968
charges: CRC: Missionary, Terre Haute, IN, 1968-73; Leave, 1973-76; Christ's Community, Grand Rapids, MI, 1976-87; Eligible for call, 1987-88; Chaplain, Director Follow-up Ministry, Exodus Ministries, Grand Rapids, MI, 1988-95; Resigned from CRC ministry, Grand Rapids areas prison ministry, 1995

Beets, Henry
b. 01/05/1869, Koedyk, Noord Holland, Netherlands
training: Calvin Theological Seminary, diploma, 1895
ordained: 1895
charges: Sioux Center, IA, 1896-99; LaGrave Ave., Grand Rapids, MI, 1899-1915; Burton Heights, Grand Rapids, MI, 1915-20; Director of

Missions, Christian Reformed Church, Grand Rapids, MI, 1920-39
retired: 1939
d. 10/29/1947, Grand Rapids, MI

Begay, Anthony
b. 04/09/1938, Gallup, NM
training: Calvin Theological Seminary, BD, 1974
ordained: 1974
charges: Missionary, Church Rock, NM, 1974-78; Chaplain, United States Army, 1978-82; Campus minister, Inter Varsity Christian Fellowship, New Mexico University, Albuquerque, NM, 1982-85; SW Campus Christian Fellowship, New Mexico University, Albuquerque, NM, 1985-2001
retired: 2001

Bekker, Gary John
b. 04/20/1951, Atlantic City, NJ
training: Calvin Theological Seminary, BD, 1977; MDiv, 1981; Michigan State University, PhD, 1991
ordained: 1977
charges: Missionary to the Philippines, 1977-78; Faculty, Christian Reformed Seminary and Bible College, Bacolod City, Philippines, 1978-84; Leave, 1984-86; Director of research, Ockenga Institute/Faculty, Gordon-Conwell Theological Seminary, South Hamilton, MA, 1986-93; Faculty, Hope, Boston-Framingham, MA, 1993-95; Faculty, Calvin Theological Seminary, Grand Rapids, MI, 1995-2001; Exectuive director, Christian Reformed World Missions, Grand Rapids, MI, 2001-

Bel, Herman
b. 03/23/1886, Uithuizen, Groningen, Netherlands
training: Calvin Theological Seminary, diploma, 1914; Lewis Institute; McCormick Theological Seminary
ordained: 1914
charges: Rochester, NY, 1914-18; Detroit, MI, 1918-21; First, Muskegon, MI, 1921-23; Fourth, Chicago, IL, 1923-28; Bethel, Paterson, NJ, 1928-32; LaGrave Ave., Grand Rapids, MI, 1932-40; Berwyn, IL, 1940-44; Bible teacher at Chicago (IL) Christian High School, 1940-51; Dorr, MI, 1951-57
retired: 1957
d. 05/19/1971, Grand Rapids, MI

Belanus, Donald George
b. 03/30/1948, Paterson, NJ
training: Calvin Theological Seminary, BD, 1973; MDiv, 1975; ThM, 1986; Walden University, PhD, 1997
ordained: 1974

charges: CRC: Trinity, Richfield Springs, NY, 1974-76; Oakwood, Belding, MI, 1976-79; Chaplain, United States Navy, 1979-2001; resigned from denomination, 2001

Beld, John (Jan) Hendrik
b. 01/04/1876, Vorwald, Bentheim, Germany
training: Calvin Theological Seminary, diploma, 1907
ordained: 1907
charges: Lamont, MI, 1907-08; Emden, MN, 1908-11; Harrison, SD, 1911-15; Middleburg, IA, 1915-19; Chicago Jewish Mission, 1919-21; Parkersburg, IA, 1921-28; Comstock, MI, 1928-32
d. 03/06/1932, Kalamazoo, MI

Benckhuysen, Amanda J. Wiersma
b. 12/20/1969, Hamilton, ON
training: Calvin Theological Seminary, MDiv, 1997
ordained: 1998
charges: Campus minister, Ann Arbor, MI, 1998-2001; Educational leave, 2001-

Benckhuysen, Martin Anthony
b. 01/28/1969, Sorel, ON
training: Calvin Theological Seminary, MDiv, 1997
ordained: 1999
charges: Campus minister, Eastern Michigan University, 1999-2002; Willowdale, ON, 2002-

Benjamins, Kenneth Frank
b. 03/21/1964, Hamilton, ON
training: Calvin Theological Seminary, MDiv, 1992
ordained: 1992
charges: Wyoming, ON, 1992-99; Ebenezer, Jarvis, ON 1999-

Bennink, Mark David
b. 05/22/1971, Kalamazoo, MI
training: Calvin Theological Seminary, MDiv, 1997
ordained: 1997
charges: Newton, IA, 1997-2002; First, Fremont, MI, 2002-

Benton, Rayfield Jr.
b. 03/21/1959, Kansas City, MO
training: Navigator Ministries; Moody Bible Institute, Reformed Bible College
ordained: 1992
charges: Chicagoland Bible Fellowship Church, Chicago, IL, 1985-94; CRC: Oakdale Park, Grand Rapids, MI, 1995-97; New church development, Cleveland, OH, 1998-2000; Resigned from denomination, 2000

Berends, John Jacob
b. 01/25/1945, Paterson, NJ
training: Calvin Theological Seminary, BD, 1970;
MDiv, 1992
ordained: 1970
charges: Bethel, Fulton, IL, 1970-74; Missionary,
Scottsdale, El Paso, TX, 1974-79; Lakeside Community, Alto, MI, 1979-81; Family in Christ Community, Denver, CO, 1981-90; Hope Community,
Riverside, CA, 1990-96; San Jose, CA, 1996-

Berends, Timothy John
b. 01/29/1958, Grand Rapids, MI
training: Calvin Theological Seminary, MDiv, 1986
ordained: 1986
charges: Sunshine, Grand Rapids, MI, 1986-87;
Good News Fellowship, Winnipeg, MB, 1987-96;
The Barnabas Network, Toronto, ON, 1996-99; All
Nations Christian Fellowship, Toronto, ON, 1996-

Bergman, Carl Wayne
b. 10/26/1952, Holland, MI
training: Calvin Theological Seminary, MCE, 1978;
MDiv, 1986
ordained: 1986
charges: Minister of education and evangelism,
Elmhurst, IL, 1978-80; Oakdale Park, Grand
Rapids, MI, 1980-85; Ivanrest, Grandville, MI,
1985-86; Bakersfield, CA, 1986-89; Hanley,
Grandville, MI, 1989-95; Avery St., South Windsor,
CT, 1995-

Bergsma, Derke Peter
b. 08/29/1927, Racine, WI
training: Calvin Theological Seminary, BD, 1954;
Chicago Theological Seminary, ThD, 1968
ordained: 1954
charges: Colton, SD, 1954-58; Warren Park,
Cicero, IL, 1958-62; post graduate study, Free
University, 1962-64; East Muskegon, MI, 1965-67;
Faculty, Trinity Christian College, Palos Heights,
IL, 1968-81; Faculty, Westminster Theological
Seminary, Escondido, CA, 1981-92; Faculty, Trin-
ity Christian College, Palos Heights, IL, 1968-81;
Faculty, Westminster Theological Seminary,
Escondido, CA, 1981-92
retired: 1992; affiliated with United Reformed
Church, 2002

Bergsma, Herbert Leonard
b. 08/31/1936, Racine, WI
training: Calvin Theological Seminary, MDiv, 1961
ordained: 1962
charges: CRC: Bible teacher, South Christian High
School, Cutlerville, MI, 1962-63; Covenant, Grand
Rapids, MI, 1963-66; Chaplain, United States
Navy, 1966-91; Covenant, Cutlerville, MI, 1991-
94; Leave, 1994-95; United Methodist Church:
Newaygo, MI, 1996

Bergsma, John Henry
b. 08/25/1930, Racine, WI
training: Calvin Theological Seminary, BD, 1955
ordained: 1955
charges: Volga, SD, 1955-60; East Saugatuck,
MI, 1960-66; Alpine Ave., Grand Rapids, MI,
1966-90
d. 01/27/1990, Grand Rapids, MI

Bergsma, Karst
b. 01/05/1887, Arum, Friesland, Netherlands
training: Calvin Theological Seminary, diploma,
1914
ordained: 1914
charges: Corsica, SD, 1914-16; Creston, Grand
Rapids, MI, 1916-23; Zutphen, MI, 1923-28; First,
Denver, CO, 1928-36; Vancouver, BC, 1936-38;
Missionary at Seattle and Mt. Vernon, WA, 1938-
41
retired: 1941
d. 01/23/1950, Cutlerville, MI

Bergsma, Louis Calvin
b. 01/10/1926, Winnipeg, MB
training: Calvin Theological Seminary, BD, 1959
ordained: 1960
charges: CRC: Ackley, IA, 1960-64; Ivanrest,
Grandville, MI, 1964-72; Leave, 1972-73; Independent: Maranatha Fellowship, Grandville, MI,
1973-75
d. 08/06/1975, Grandville, MI

Bergsma, Paul J.
b. 08/15/1943, Grand Rapids, MI
training: Calvin Theological Seminary, BD, 1969;
ThM, 1970
ordained: 1969
charges: Missionary to Mexico, 1969-77; Missionary to Honduras, 1977-83; Missionary, Costa
Rica, 1983-

Bergsma, Randall Ray
b. 01/10/1962, Grand Rapids, MI
training: Calvin Theological Seminary, MDiv, 1989
ordained: 1989
charges: Immanuel, Sheldon, IA, 1989-99; First,
Highland, IN, 1999-

Berkenbosch, Roy M. A.
b. 12/24/1951, Ede, Gelderland, Netherlands

149

training: Calvin Theological Seminary, MDiv, 1990
ordained: 1990
charges: Pastor of youth and education, Third, Edmonton, AB, 1985-88; Field director CRWRC, Bangladesh, 1990-92; Eastern Ave., Grand Rapids, MI, 1992-95; Campus minister/Dean of students, King's University College, Edmonton, AB, 1995-

Berkhof, Louis
b. 10/13/1873, Emmen, Drenthe, Netherlands
training: Calvin Theological Seminary, diploma, 1900; Princeton Theological Seminary, BD, 1904
ordained: 1900
charges: Allendale, MI, 1900-02; Leave, 1902-04; Oakdale Park, Grand Rapids, MI, 1904-06; Faculty, Calvin Theological Seminary, Grand Rapids, MI, 1906-44
retired: 1944
d. 05/18/1957, Grand Rapids, MI

Berry, James Russell
b. 02/07/1956, Sarnia, ON
training: Calvin Theological Seminary, MDiv, 1989
ordained: 1990
charges: First Ladner, Delta, BC, 1990-98; Home missions church planting, Vancouver, BC, 1998-99; West Coast Community, Delta, BC, 1999-

Bersach, Manny
b. /1958, Cuba
training: Reformed Theological Seminary, Jackson, MS, MDiv, 1987
ordained: 1987
charges: PCA: Iglesia Pedras Vivas, Miami, FL, -2000; CRC: Iglesia Piedras Vivas, Miami, FL, 2000-

Besteman, Arthur Jr.
b. 05/23/1933, Grand Rapids, MI
training: Calvin Theological Seminary, BD, 1958
ordained: 1959
charges: CRC: Leota, MN, 1959-64; Messiah, Hudsonville, MI, 1964-72; North St., Zeeland, MI, 1972-86; Beverly, Wyoming, MI, 1986-92; Alliance of Reformed Churches: Beverly, Wyoming, MI, 1992-96; United Reformed Churches: Beverly, Wyoming, MI, 1999
retired: 1999

Besteman, Gerrit
b. 09/04/1955, Puttershoek, Zuid Holland, Netherlands
training: Westminster Theological Seminary-CA, MDiv, 1995
ordained: 1999

charges: Independent: Wellspring Christian Fellowship, 1995-98; CRC: Mountain Lake, MN, 1998-2001; Bethel, Edgerton, MN, 2001-

Betten, Joseph
b. 12/06/1895, Haulerwijk, Friesland, Netherlands
training: Calvin Theological Seminary, ThB, 1928
ordained: 1928
charges: Doon, IA, 1928-36; Highland, MI, 1936-47; Western Springs, IL, 1947-51; Missionary pastor to Southwest BC, 1951-54; Bloomfield, ON, 1954-61
retired: 1961
d. 03/08/1977, Grand Rapids, MI

Beukema, Alvin
b. 03/01/1936, Assen, Drenthe, Netherlands
training: Calvin Theological Seminary, BD, 1961; MDiv, 1987
ordained: 1961
charges: Renfrew, ON, 1961-64; St. Thomas, ON, 1964-69; Clinton, ON, 1969-75; Bethel, London, ON, 1975-81; First, Abbotsford, BC, 1981-95; First, Medicine Hat, AB, 1995-2000
retired: 2000

Beukema, Barry Jay
b. 06/09/1957, Grand Rapids, MI
training: Westminster Theological Seminary-PA, MAR/MDiv, 1983; Special Program for Ministerial Candidacy, Calvin Theological Seminary, 1984
ordained: 1984
charges: CRC: Burdett, AB, 1984-88; Smithers, BC, 1988-92; Alliance of Reformed Churches: Bethel Reformed, Smithers, BC, 1992-95; United Reformed Churches: Bethel Reformed, Smithers, BC, 1995

Beuker, Henricus
b. 06/04/1834, Volzel, Bentheim, Germany
training: Theologische Universiteit, Kampen, diploma, 1862
ordained: 1862
charges: GKN: Zwolle, 1862-64, Rotterdam, 1864-67; Giessendam, 1867-69; Harlingen, 1869-73; Amsterdam, 1873-61; Leiden, 1884-93; Altreformierte Kirche: Emlichheim, Germany, 1861-84; CRC: Allen Ave., Muskegon, MI, 1893-94; Faculty, Calvin Theological Seminary, Grand Rapids, MI, 1894-1900
d. 05/18/1900, Grand Rapids, MI

Beunk, Andrew Edward
b. 04/30/1966, Oakville, ON
training: Calvin Theological Seminary, MDiv, 2000

ordained: 2000
charges: Fruitland, Stoney Creek, ON, 2000–

Beute, Hiram K.
b. 03/24/1878, Grand Rapids, MI
training: Calvin Theological Seminary, diploma, 1912
ordained: 1912
charges: Plainfield, Grand Rapids, MI, 1912–16; Harderwyk, Holland, MI, 1916–19; Ellsworth MI, 1919–24; Grant, MI, 1924–39
retired: 1939
d. 02/11/1965, Grand Rapids, MI

Beute, Nicholas
b. 09/21/1902, Jenison, MI
training: Calvin Theological Seminary, BD, 1931
ordained: 1931
charges: Sullivan, MI, 1931–37; Rusk, MI, 1937–46; Inwood, IA, 1946–52; North Blendon, MI, 1952–60; Bethel, Lacombe, AB 1960–68
retired: 1968
d. 01/21/1975, Jenison, MI

Beversluis, Nicholas Henry
b. 06/10/1915, Paterson, NJ
training: Calvin Theological Seminary, ThB, 1943; Westminster Theological Seminary, ThM; Columbia University, AM; Columbia University, EdD, 1966
ordained: 1944
charges: Chaplain, 1944–47; Bible teacher, Grand Rapids (MI) Christian High School, 1947–48; Bible teacher, Eastern Academy (principal, 1953–59), Paterson, NJ, 1948–59; Bible teacher, at Calvin, 1959–60; principal, Eastern Christian Junior High School, Paterson, NJ, 1960–61; Bible teacher, Eastern Christian Junior High School, Paterson, NJ, 1962–63; Faculty, Calvin College, Grand Rapids, MI, 1966–68; Non-ministerial vocation: Faculty, Calvin College, Grand Rapids, MI, 1968–80
retired: 1980
d. 01/22/1998, Grand Rapids, MI

Bierenga, Robert L.
b. 08/21/1952, Kalamazoo, MI
training: Calvin Theological Seminary, MDiv, 1985
ordained: 1985
charges: Bemis, SD, 1985–89; Thirty-Sixth St., Wyoming, MI, 1989–95; Eligible for call, 1995–96; Allen Ave., Muskegon, MI, 1996–

Bierling, William Arend
b. 02/26/1938, Denver, CO
training: Calvin Theological Seminary, BD, 1962

ordained: 1962
charges: Cragmor, Colorado Springs, CO, 1962–66; Bethel, Sun Valley, CA, 1966–84; Leave, 1984–85; Chaplain, CARE Ministries for the Developmentally Disabled, Sun Valley, CA, 1985–2000
retired: 2000

Bierma, Lyle Dean
b. 12/07/1950, Grand Rapids, MI
training: Calvin Theological Seminary, BD, 1976; Duke University, PhD, 1980
ordained: 2000
charges: Faculty, Reformed Bible College, Grand Rapids, MI, 1980–99; Faculty, Calvin Theological Seminary, Grand Rapids, MI, 1999–

Bierma, Merle Henry
b. 11/16/1943, Grand Rapids, MI
training: Calvin Theological Seminary, BD, 1972
ordained: 1972
charges: Alamosa, CO, 1972–79; Escalon, CA, 1979–85; Cragmor, Colorado Springs, CO, 1985–96; Paseo Community, Camarillo, CA, 1996–

Bierman, Darrell John
b. 04/03/1969, Grand Rapids, MI
training: Calvin Theological Seminary, MDiv, 1996
ordained: 1996
charges: Orangeville, ON, 1996–2001; River City, Cambridge, ON, 2001–

Bierman, Harry John
b. 02/26/1942, Aalten, Gelderland, Netherlands
training: Calvin Theological Seminary, BD, 1972
ordained: 1972
charges: Ingersoll, ON, 1972–77; Barrie, ON, 1977–83; Smithers, BC, 1983–88; Maranatha, Lethbridge, AB, 1988–94; Community, Kitchener, ON, 1994–

Bieze, Gerrit Albert
b. 04/09/1936, Chicago, IL
training: Calvin Theological Seminary, BD, 1962
ordained: 1962
charges: Alliston, ON, 1962–67; Taber and Vauxhall, AB, 1967–73; Taber, AB, 1973–77; Athens, ON, 1977–92
retired: 1992

Binnema, Jacob Hendrix Sr.
b. 01/01/1921, Munnekezijl, Groningen, Netherlands
training: Vrije Universiteit, Amsterdam, diploma, 1947
ordained: 1947

charges: GKN: Siegerswoude, 1947-50; Chaplain, Dutch Army in Indonesia, 1950-52; Oude Pekela, 1952-57; Lemmer, 1957-60; CRC: Rocky Mountain House, AB, 1960-65; Maranatha, Galt, ON, 1965-69; New Glasgow, NS, 1969-73; Cochrane, ON, 1973-78; Telkwa, BC, 1978-83; Nobleford, AB, 1983-87
retired: 1987

Binnema, Jacob Hendrix Jr.
b. 12/13/1949, Emmen, Drenthe, Netherlands
training: Calvin Theological Seminary, MDiv, 1986
ordained: 1986
charges: Dresden, ON, 1986-91; Maranatha, Bowmanville, ON, 1991-94; Eligible for call, 1994-2000; released from ministry 2000

Bischof, Michael George
b. 02/11/1963, Santa Monica, CA
training: Master's Seminary, MDiv, 1988
ordained: 1988
charges: Baptist: -2000; CRC: Foothill Ranch, CA, 2000-

Bishop, Clarence (Klaas)
b. 01/08/1933, Avereest, Overijsel, Netherlands
training: Calvin Theological Seminary, BD, 1963
ordained: 1963
charges: Brooten, MN, 1963-67; Bethel, Vancouver, BC, 1967-70; Rocky Mountain House, AB, 1970-76; Exeter, ON, 1976-80; College Ave., Winnipeg, MB, 1980-93; Covenant, Winnipeg, MB, 1993-96
retired: 1996

Bisschop, Clarence
see: Bishop, Clarence

Black, Ronald
training: declared eligible on the basis of exceptional gifts, 1987
ordained: 1987
charges: Church of God in Christ: Normandy Community Church, 1987-89; Peace Church, 1989-95; New Ground Harvest, Los Angeles, CA, 1995-2000; CRC: New Ground Harvest, Los Angles, 2000-

Blacketer, Raymond Andrew
b. 03/15/1965, Laguna Beach, CA
training: Calvin Theological Seminary, MDiv, 1991; ThM, 1992; PhD, 1998
ordained: 1998
charges: Hillside, Cutlerville, MI, 1998-2000; Neerlandia, AB, 2000-

Blackmon, Timothy Daniel
b. 05/07/1970, Den Haag, Zuid Holland, Netherlands
training: Calvin Theological Seminary, MDiv, 1995
ordained: 1995
charges: Oasis Community, Moreno Valley, CA, 1995-98; River Rock, Folsom, CA, 1998-

Blankers, Barry B.
b. 04/28/1936, Bellingham, WA
training: Calvin Theological Seminary, BD, 1961
ordained: 1961
charges: Cedar, IA, 1961-65; Missionary to the Philippine Islands, 1965-77; Calvin, Wyckoff, NJ, 1977-83; First, Ripon, CA, 1983-96; Ocheyedan, IA, 1996-2001
retired: 2001

Blankespoor, Edward James
b. 01/03/1941, Inwood, IA
training: Calvin Theological Seminary, BD, 1966; ThM, 1982
ordained: 1967
charges: Hollandale, MN, 1967-71; Calvary, Orange City, IA, 1971-77; Trinity, Jenison, MI, 1977-84; Park, Holland, MI, 1984-95; Beckwith Hills, Grand Rapids, MI, 1995-

Blankespoor, John
b. 09/30/1914, Rock Valley, IA
training: Calvin Theological Seminary, BD, 1939
ordained: 1939
charges: PRC: Orange City, IA, 1939-44; Doon, IA, 1943-49; Second, Grand Rapids, MI, 1949-58; Holland, MI, 1958-61; CRC: Bible and Reformed Doctrine teacher, Holland Christian High School, Holland, MI, 1961-62; First, Hudsonville, MI, 1962-75; Pine Creek, Holland, MI, 1975-79;
retired: 1979

Blauw, Richard James
b. 07/17/1942, Chicago, IL
training: Calvin Theological Seminary, MDiv, 1975
ordained: 1975
charges: Bethlehem, Freeman, SD, 1975-80; Zutphen, MI, 1980-86; First, Chino, CA, 1986-92; First, South Holland, IL, 1992-

Bliek, Abraham
b. 04/08/1877, Oud-Beijerland, Zuid Holland, Netherlands
training: Calvin Theological Seminary, diploma, 1909
ordained: 1909
charges: Otley, IA, 1909-13; Edgerton, MN, 1913-

21; Allendale, MI, 1921–24; Fulton, IL, 1924–40; Chandler, MN, 1940–46
retired: 1946
d. 01/28/1957, Edgerton, MN

Block, Bert Jr.
b. 04/30/1937, Grand Rapids, MI
training: Fuller Theological Seminary, MDiv, 1975; Calvin Theological Seminary, Special Program for Ministerial Candidacy, 1976
ordained: 1977
charges: Missionary, Mexico, 1977; Non-ministerial vocation, 1977–2002

Bloem, Peter
b. 09/27/1877, Dorkwerd, Groningen, Netherlands
training: Calvin Theological Seminary, diploma, 1904
ordained: 1904
charges: Alto, WI, 1904–07; Spring Lake, MI, 1907–09; Platte, SD, 1909–14; Oskaloosa, IA, 1914–22; Luctor, KS, 1922–30; Volga, SD, 1930–38
retired: 1938
d. 04/16/1942, Grand Rapids, MI

Blom, Jerry Lee
b. 04/24/1948, Kansas City, MO
training: Calvin Theological Seminary, MDiv, 1999
ordained: 1999
charges: Creston, Grand Rapids, MI, 1999–

Blystra, Harry
b. 04/29/1891, Anjum, Friesland, Netherlands
training: Calvin Theological Seminary, diploma, 1919
ordained: 1919
charges: Sullivan MI, 1919–21; Prinsburg, MN, 1921–28; Sully, IA, 1928–32; Graafschap, MI, 1932–47; Secretary, Home Missions, 1947–60
retired: 1960
d. 05/02/1974, Holland, MI

Bode, Cornelius
b. 08/12/1843, Emden, Oostfriesland, Germany
training: Calvin Theological Seminary, diploma, 1879
ordained: 1879
charges: Niekerk, Holland, MI, 1879–87; Harrison, SD, 1887–91; Ackley, IA, 1891–1903; Kanawha, IA, 1903–17
d. 05/16/1917, Kanawha, IA

Bode, Cornelius Hugo
b. 05/04/1903, Renville, MN

training: Princeton Theological Seminary, ThB and ThM, 1928; Calvin Theological Seminary, Special Program for Ministerial Candidacy, 1929
ordained: 1929
charges: CRC: Home missionary Classis Ostfriesland at Mountain Lake, MN, 1929–33; RCA: Bethel, Aplington, IA, 1933–40; Forreston, IL, 1940–47; Dean, Cook Christian Training School, Phoenix, AZ, 1947–57
d. 11/29/1957, Phoenix, AZ

Bode, Harold
b. 07/18/1929, McBain, MI
training: Calvin Theological Seminary, BD, 1954; MDiv, 1975
ordained: 1956
charges: Purewater, SD, 1956–59; Kanawha, IA, 1959–62; Chaplain, United States Air Force, 1962–74; Director, Denominational Chaplain Committee, Grand Rapids, MI, 1974–94
retired: 1994

Bode, Henry (Hendrik)
b. 02/14/1845, Fruchtenburg, Oostfrieland, Germany
training: Calvin Theological Seminary, diploma, 1881
ordained: 1881
charges: Steamboat Rock, IA, 1881–93; Home missionary at Leighton, IA, 1893–95; Leighton, IA, 1895–1900
d. 01/19/1900, Chicago, IL

Bode, Henry C.
b. 10/26/1871, Freeport, IL
training: Dubuque Presbyterian Seminary, diploma, 1896
ordained: 1896
charges: Parkersburg, IA, 1896–97; Oostfriesland, IA, 1897–1901; Emden, 1901–04; Missionary, Kanawha, IA, 1904–06; Oostfriesland, IA, 1906–08; Ridott, IL, 1908–17; First, Wellsburg IA, 1917–37
retired: 1937
d. 06/27/1951, Kalamazoo, MI

Bode, William (Willem) C.
b. 09/07/1876, Muskegon, MI
training: Calvin Theological Seminary, diploma, 1902; University of Chicago, AM, 1912; Temple University, STD, 1913
ordained: 1902
charges: Woden, IA, 1902–06; Burton Heights, Grand Rapids, MI, 1906–10; Home missionary Classis Oostfriesland at Lincoln Center, IA, 1912–

16; President, Grundy College, Grundy Center, IA, 1916–30; Bunde, MN, 1930–41
d. 10/22/1941, Bunde, MN

Boekhoven, Henry John
b. 11/16/1924, Hardenberg, Overijsel, Netherlands
training: Vrije Universiteit, Amsterdam, diploma, 1949; Western Theological Seminary, BD, 1954; Faith Theological Seminary, ThD, 1980
ordained: 1955
charges: RCA: First, Edmonton, AB, 1954–57; Bethel, Abbotsford, BC, 1957–61; First, St. Catharines, ON, 1961–69; New Life, Grand Rapids, MI, 1969–76; CRC: First, Kalamazoo, MI, 1976–80; Aylmer, ON, 1980–90
retired: 1990

Boelens, Boelo
b. 10/22/1917, Groningen, Groningen, Netherlands
training: Vrije Universiteit, Amsterdam, diploma, 1947
ordained: 1947
charges: GKN: Beilen, 1945–59; Breda, 1950–54; Reformed Church of New Zealand: Christchurch, 1954–60; CRC: Saskatoon, SK, 1960–64; Home missionary, Hessel Park, Champaign, IL, 1964–69; GKN: Castricum, 1969–82
retired: 1982
d. 08/20/1984, Amsterdam, Netherlands

Boelkins, Winston C.
b. 09/14/1930, Muskegon, MI
training: Calvin Theological Seminary, BD, 1955; ThM, 1964
ordained: 1955
charges: Riverside, Grand Rapids, MI, 1955–60; First, Edmonton, AB, 1960–66; Preakness, Wayne, NJ, 1966–74; Park Lane, Evergreen Park, IL, 1974–79; First, Visalia, CA, 1979–92
retired: 1992

Boender, Philip Joel
b. 07/20/1959, Oskaloosa, IA
training: Calvin Theological Seminary, MDiv, 1987
ordained: 1987
charges: First, Visalia, CA, 1987–93; Community, Fort Wayne, IN, 1993–2000; Fellowship, Grandville, MI, 2000–

Boer, Edward G.
b. 04/03/1920, De Motte, IN
training: Calvin Theological Seminary, ThB, 1945
ordained: 1945
charges: Parchment, MI, 1945–49; Lamont, MI, 1949–52; Milwaukee, WI, 1952–56; North Haledon,

NJ, 1956–63; Missionary-pastor, Green Ridge, Muskegon, MI, 1963–68; Brigham City, UT, 1968–85
retired: 1985

Boer, Gerrit Egberts
b. 03/01/1832, Roderwolde, Drenthe, Netherlands
training: Theologische Universiteit, Kampen, diploma, 1865
ordained: 1865
charges: GKN: Sappemeer, 1865–69; Niezijl, 1869–73; CRC: First, Grand Rapids, MI, 1873–76; Faculty, Calvin Theological Seminary, 1876–1902
retired: 1902
d. 03/26/1904, Grand Rapids, MI

Boer, Harry Hendrick
b. 12/31/1940, Holland, MI
training: Calvin Theological Seminary, BD, 1968; MDiv, 1976
ordained: 1968
charges: Grangeville, ID, 1968–73; Charlottetown, PE, 1973–78; Beacon Light, Gary, IN, 1978–91; Chaplain, Howard Community Hospital, Kokomo, IN, 1991–92; Chaplain, Queen's Medical Center, Honolulu, HI, 1992; Chaplain, minister of visitation, Central Union '94, Honolulu, HI, 1992–98; Hospitality House, Honolulu, HI, 1992–98; Chaplain, Aurora Christian Health Service, Aurora, IL, 1998–2001; Chaplain, Rest Haven West/Saratoga Grove, Downers Grove, IL, 2001–

Boer, Harry Reinier
b. 04/04/1913, Hillegom, Noord Holland, Netherlands
training: Calvin Theological Seminary, ThB, 1941; Union Theological Seminary, ThM, 1950–51; Vrije Universiteit, Amsterdam, ThD, 1955
ordained: 1942
charges: Chaplain, United States Navy, 1942–46; Missionary to Africa-Nigeria, 1947–50; Faculty, Calvin Theological Seminary, Grand Rapids, MI, 1951–52; Missionary to Nigeria, 1955–78
retired: 1978
d. 04/21/1999, Grand Rapids, MI

Boer, James Marshall
b. 03/11/1962, Grand Rapids, MI
training: Calvin Theological Seminary, MDiv, 1989
ordained: 1989
charges: Pastor of evangelism, Burton Heights, Grand Rapids, MI, 1987–89; Lee Street, Wyoming, MI, 1989–95; Fellowship, Grandville, MI, 1995–

Boer, Jan (John) Harm

b. 02/18/1938, Lutjegast, Groningen, Netherlands
training: Calvin Theological Seminary, BD, 1965
ordained: 1965
charges: Missionary, Wukari, Nigeria, 1966-69;
Pastor/Evangelist, Baissa, Nigeria, 1974-76; Director, Northern Area, Institute of Church and Society, Jos, Nigeria, 1977-89; Consultant, Institute of Church and Society, Jos, Nigeria, 1989-94; Education Department of Christian Reformed Church of Nigeria, Jos, Nigeria, 1994-96; Non-ministerial vocation, 1996

Boer, Warren J.

b. 06/24/1938, Holland, MI
training: Calvin Theological Seminary, BD, 1963;
Princeton Theological Seminary, MA, 1969; Fuller
Theological Seminary, DMin, 1974
ordained: 1963
charges: Franklin Lakes, NJ, 1963-68; Leave,
1968-69: Calvin, Grand Rapids, MI, 1969-73;
leave to Fuller Theological Seminary, 1973-74;
Boer Marriage and Family Counseling Services,
Grand Rapids, MI, 1975-81; Director, Broene
Counseling Center, Calvin College, Grand Rapids,
MI, 1981-2000
retired: 2000

Boerfyn, Gerrit Bastian

b. 02/06/1911, Peoria, IA
training: Calvin Theological Seminary, ThM, 1940
ordained: 1940
charges: Flint, MI, 1940-43; Home missionary
and service pastor at San Diego, CA, 1943-49;
Home missionary at Tucson, AZ, 1949-53; Home
missionary at San Jose, CA, 1953-57; Home missionary at Palo-Alto/Redwood City, CA, 1957-58;
Missionary pastor at Beacon Light Church, Gary,
IN, 1958-64; Home missionary, Fort Collins, CO,
1964-69; Missionary on general assignment,
1969-72; Regional Home Missionary for West
Coast, 1972-76
retired: 1976
d. 07/20/2000, Ripon, CA

Boerkoel, Benjamin John Sr.

b. 12/12/1931, Grand Rapids, MI
training: Calvin Theological Seminary, BD, 1956
ordained: 1956
charges: First, Lacombe, AB, 1956-59; Second,
Randolph, WI, 1959-63; Non-ministerial vocation,
1963; President, Westminster Institute of Theology, Grand Rapids, MI, 1967

Boersma, Jan Karel

b. 11/01/1948, Grand Rapids, MI
training: Calvin Theological Seminary, MDiv, 1974;
New York Theological Seminary, DMin, 1988
ordained: 1974
charges: CRC: Clinton, ON, 1974-78; leave, 1978-
79; Manhattan, New York, NY, 1979-83; Extension
coordinator at Sing Sing Correctional Facility, New
York Theological Seminary, New York, NY, 1983-
84; RCA: Stated supply, Beacon, NY, 1985-89; Interim, Cherry Hill, River Edge, NJ, 1991-92; Congregational: First Congregational, Riverhead, NY,
1993; Old Steeple Community UCC, 1994-98; Union Congregational, Richmond Hill, NY, 1998-

Boersma, Jeffrey A.

b. 06/26/1964, Grand Rapids, MI
training: Calvin Theological Seminary, MDiv, 1990
ordained: 1990
charges: Calvin, Muskegon, MI, 1990-

Boersma, Robert Lee

b. 04/25/1957, Chicago, IL
training: Calvin Theological Seminary, MDiv, 1992
ordained: 1992
charges: Parchment, Kalamazoo, MI, 1992-

Boertje, Paul Arthur

b. 11/22/1919, Pella, IA
training: Calvin Theological Seminary, BD, 1944;
Westminster Theological Seminary, ThM, 1945
ordained: 1945
charges: Chaplain United States Navy, 1945-46;
Leave, 1946-57; Decatur, MI, 1947-50; Alamosa,
CO, 1950-54; Assoc. Pastor, Hull, IA and Bible
teacher Western Christian High School, Hull, IA,
1954-62; Bible teacher, Valley Christian High
School, Bellflower, CA, 1962-81
retired: 1981
d. 04/02/1999, Bellflower, CA

Boertje, Robert Donald

b. 11/22/1944, Grand Rapids, MI
training: Calvin Theological Seminary, BD, 1970
ordained: 1970
charges: Missionary, Rockford, IL, 1970-72;
Bunde, MN, 1972-76; Terra Ceia, NC, 1976-78;
Leave, 1978-80; Franklin Lakes, NJ, 1980-83;
Terra Ceia, NC, 1983-88; Gibson, Holland, MI,
1988-98; Fredericton, NB, 1998-

Boeskool, Roy Jr.

b. 08/13/1929, Grand Rapids, MI
training: Calvin Theological Seminary, BD, 1954
ordained: 1954

charges: Highland, MI, 1954-58; Cascade, Grand Rapids, MI, 1958-64; Home missionary, El Paso, TX, 1964-67; Immanuel, Muskegon, MI, 1967-71
d. 01/04/1971, Lake Wales, FL vicinity

Boeve, Edward
b. 01/29/1891, Overisel Township, Allegan County, MI
training: Calvin Theological Seminary, diploma, 1922
ordained: 1922
charges: Spring Lake, MI, 1922-27; Second, Wellsburg, IA, 1927-33; Kelloggsville, MI, 1933-45; Ridgewood, NJ, 1945-51; Ellsworth, MI, 1951-54; Cadillac, MI, 1954-58
retired: 1958
d. 03/02/1968, Grand Rapids, MI

Bolkema, Brain Wayne
b. 10/21/1975, Sheldon, IA
training: Calvin Theological Seminary, MDiv, 2002
ordained: 2002
charges: Unity, Prospect Park, NJ, 2002-

Bolt, Calvin
b. 12/09/1933, Holland, MI
training: Calvin Theological Seminary, BD, 1958
ordained: 1958
charges: Cadillac, MI, 1958-61; Cottage Grove, South Holland, IL, 1961-66; Oakdale Park, Grand Rapids, MI, 1966-71; First, Zeeland, MI, 1971-77; Faith, Holland, MI, 1977-82; Twelfth Ave., Jenison, MI, 1982-97
retired: 1997
d. 09/17/1997, Jenison, MI

Bolt, Carl Raymond
b. 11/27/1953, Grand Rapids, MI
training: Calvin Theological Seminary, MDiv, 1988
ordained: 1990
charges: Rapid City, SD, 1990-95; Goshen, IN, 1995-2002

Bolt, Jacob
b. 05/29/1875, Grand Rapids, MI
training: Calvin Theological Seminary, diploma, 1899
ordained: 1899
charges: Leonia, NJ, 1899-1901; Second, Jamestown, MI, 1901-04; West Park, Cleveland, OH, 1904-08; Prospect Park, Holland, MI, 1908-10; Missionary, Kuner, CO, 1910-11, Redlands, CA, 1911-14; Missionary, Crownpoint, NM, 1914-40; Redlands, CA, 1940-45
retired: 1945

d. 11/04/1967, Grand Rapids, MI

Bolt, John
b. 10/07/1947, Grootegast, Groningen, Netherlands
training: Calvin Theological Seminary, BD, 1973; ThM, 1977; University of St. Michael's College, PhD, 1982
ordained: 1973
charges: Kelowna and Penticton, BC, 1973-76; Leave, 1976-80; Faculty, Calvin College, 1980-82; Faculty, Redeemer Reformed Christian College, Hamilton, ON, 1982-88; Faculty, Calvin Theological Seminary, Grand Rapids, MI, 1988-

Bolt, Martin
b. 12/03/1902, Prinsburg, MN
training: Calvin Theological Seminary, ThB, 1930
ordained: 1930
charges: Niekerk, MI, 1930-37; New Era, MI, 1937-42; Allendale, MI, 1942-47; Drenthe, MI, 1947-52; Oak Lawn, IL, 1952-57; Harderwyk, MI, 1957-63; Highland, MI, 1963-67; Plainfield, Grand Rapids, MI, 1967-70
retired: 1970
d. 07/20/1978, Holland, MI

Bolt, Ralph (Roelof)
b. 04/09/1873, Groningen, Groningen, Netherlands
training: Calvin Theological Seminary, diploma, 1903
ordained: 1903
charges: Luctor, KS, 1903-06; Lucas, MI, 1906-12; Fourth, Paterson, NJ, 1912-15; Graafschap, MI, 1915-22; Sully, IA, 1922-27; Whitinsville, MA, 1927-39
retired: 1939
d. 04/07/1951, Grand Rapids, MI

Bolt, Robert Dale
b. 02/13/1958, Zeeland, MI
training: Calvin Theological Seminary, MDiv, 1985
ordained: 1986
charges: Missionary, Guinea, West Africa, 1986-96; Burton Heights, Grand Rapids, MI, 1996-

Bomhof, Gerrit Johannes
b. 06/27/1949, Nunspeet, Gelderland, Netherlands
training: Calvin Theological Seminary, BD, 1976
ordained: 1976
charges: Mt. Brydges, ON, 1976-80; Maranatha, Lethbridge, ON, 1980-87; Kildonan, Winnipeg, MB, 1987-93; Covenant, Winnipeg, MB, 1993-98; Drayton, ON, 1998-

Bomhof, Thomas W.

b. 06/27/1962, Victoria, BC
training: Calvin Theological Seminary, MDiv, 1988
ordained: 1989
charges: Burdett, AB, 1989-93; Mundy Park Christian Fellowship, Coquitlam, BC, 1993-2002; Fleetwood, Surrey, BC, 2002-

Bonnema, David Douwe

b. 07/30/1893, Rock Valley, IA
training: Calvin Theological Seminary, diploma, 1924
ordained: 1924
charges: First, Denver, CO, 1924-27; First, Grand Rapids, MI, 1927-41; First, Zeeland, MI, 1941-51; Hospers, IA, 1951-56
d. 03/26/1956, Hospers, IA

Bonnema, James A.

b. 06/26/1934, Denver, CO
training: Calvin Theological Seminary, BD, 1959; Vrije Universiteit, Amsterdam, 1960
ordained: 1960
charges: Conrad, MT, 1960-62; Avery St., South Windsor, CT, 1963-71; Non-ministerial vocation, Grand Rapids, MI, 1971

Boodt, Peter John

b. 10/19/1929, Brandwijk, Zuid Holland, Netherlands
training: Calvin Theological Seminary, ThB, 1964
ordained: 1964
charges: Wallaceburg, ON, 1964-66; Leave, 1966-68; Stratford, ON, 1971-76; Rocky Mountain House, AB, 1976-82; Bethel, Brockville, ON, 1982-86; Sonrise, Ponoka, AB, 1986-96
retired: 1996

Boogerd, Dennis John

b. 09/16/1947, Sioux Center, IA
training: Calvin Theological Seminary, BD, 1972; ThM, 1973
ordained: 1973
charges: Forest Grove, MI, 1973-78; Leighton, IA, 1978-85; Chandler, MN, 1985-89; Leave, 1989-92; New Holland, SD, 1992-96; Forest Grove, MI, 1996-2000; Non-ministerial vocation, Grand Rapids, MI, 2000

Boomsma, Clarence

b. 03/09/1917, Hammond, IN
training: Calvin Theological Seminary, ThB, 1943; Union Theological Seminary; New College, Edinburgh, Scotland
ordained: 1943

charges: Imlay City, MI, 1943-48; Calvin, Grand Rapids, MI, 1948-83
retired: 1983

Boonstra, Dennis Warren

b. 11/04/1940, Hammond, IN
training: Calvin Theological Seminary, BD, 1965
ordained: 1966
charges: Hills, MN, 1966-69; First, Sioux City, IA, 1969-75; Washington, DC, 1975-84; Fellowship, Grandville, MI, 1984-87; Non-ministerial vocation, Grand Rapids, MI, 1987, later minister in Baptist Church

Boonstra, Harry

b. 12/23/1935, Aldehoven, Groningen, Netherlands
training: University of Chicago, MA, 1967; Loyola University, PhD, 1973; Western Theological Seminary, MRE, 1986, MDiv, 1988; Calvin Theological Seminary, Special Program for Ministerial Candidacy, 1988
ordained: 1992
charges: Theological librarian, Calvin College, Grand Rapids, MI, 1992-99
retired: 1999

Boonstra, Jacob Paul

b. 01/14/1927, Grand Rapids, MI
training: Calvin Theological Seminary, BD, 1950; ThB, 1953
ordained: 1953
charges: Cascade, MI, 1953-57; Twelfth St., Grand Rapids, MI, 1957-63; First, Cicero, IL, 1963-68; Hillcrest, Denver, CO, 1968-77; Plainfield, Rockford, MI, 1977-86; Tracy, IA, 1986-92
retired: 1992

Boonstra, John

b. 11/26/1930, Donkerbroek, Friesland, Netherlands
training: Calvin Theological Seminary, BD, 1962; MDiv, 1988
ordained: 1962
charges: Brandon, MB, 1962-65; Duncan, BC, 1965-71; Ottewell, Edmonton, AB, 1971-80; Maple Ridge, BC, 1980-91; Kelowna, BC, 1991-98
retired: 1998

Boonstra, Juan Samuel

b. 03/10/1926, Tres Arroyos, Argentina
training: Calvin Theological Seminary, BD, 1954
ordained: 1954
charges: Iglesia Reformada de Argentina, 1954-62; Home missionary in Spanish-speaking work,

1962–65; Back to God Hour, Spanish-speaking broadcasting, Palos Heights, IL, 1965–92
retired: 1992
d. 03/23/1995, Hebron, IN

Boonstra, Kenneth Dale
b. 01/27/1955, Grand Rapids, MI
training: Calvin Theological Seminary, MDiv, 1984
ordained: 1985
charges: German Valley, IL, 1985–88; London Campus Ministry, London, ON, 1988–95; First, Langley, BC, 1995–

Boot, Joel Raymond
b. 03/30/1947, Ann Arbor, MI
training: Calvin Theological Seminary, BD, 1972
ordained: 1972
charges: Le Mars, IA, 1972–76; Dearborn, MI, 1976–84; Calvin, Grand Rapids, MI, 1984–92; Ridgewood, Jenison, MI, 1992–

Bootsma, Michael William
b. 10/22/1967, Hamilton, ON
training: Calvin Theological Seminary, MDiv, 1993
ordained: 1993
charges: Youth pastor, Cadillac, MI, 1992–93; Blenheim, ON, 1993–2002; Community, Frankford, ON, 2002–

Borduin, Menno
b. 10/16/1867, Joure, Friesland, Netherlands
training: Calvin Theological Seminary, diploma, 1896
ordained: 1896
charges: Oostburg, WI, 1896–1905; Hull, ND, 1905–07; Home missionary at Yakima, WA, 1909, at Huntley, MT, 1910–11, at Conrad, MT, 1912–15; Galesburg IA, 1915–25; Home missionary at Conrad, MT, 1925–34
retired: 1934
d. 12/01/1946, Grand Rapids, MI

Borgdorff, Peter
b. 11/14/1939, Rotterdam, Zuid Holland, Netherlands
training: Calvin Theological Seminary, BD, 1969; MDiv, 1975
ordained: 1969
charges: Immanuel, Salt Lake City, UT, 1969–72; Regional home missionary for Canada, 1972–75; Field Secretary, Board of Home Missions, 1975–83; Bethany, Holland, MI, 1983–90; Executive director, World Ministries, Christian Reformed Church in North America, Grand Rapids, MI, 1990–92; Executive Director of Ministries, Chris-

tian Reformed Church in North America, Grand Rapids, MI, 1992–

Borgman, William
b. 04/27/1866, Wester Nieland, Groningen, Netherlands
training: Calvin Theological Seminary, diploma, 1901
ordained: 1901
charges: Fulton, IL, 1901–03; Zutphen, MI, 1903–07; Munster, IN, 1907–11; Second Roseland, Chicago, IL, 1911–19; Lucas, MI, 1919–25; Alto, WI, 1925–32
retired: 1932
d. 03/02/1954, Grand Rapids, MI

Borrego, Ramon C.
b. 02/02/1930, Cuba
training: Cuban Seminary
ordained: 1964
charges: Iglesia Evangelica Reformada of Cuba, 1962–67; Spanish worker, Hoboken, NJ, 1967–73; Missionary to Argentina, 1973–78; Good Samaritan, Miami, FL, 1978–89; Church planting, Good News, Miami, FL, 1989–95
retired: 1995

Bos, Daniel Gilbert
b. 10/01/1940, Holland, MI
training: Calvin Theological Seminary, BD, 1965; University of Chicago Divinity School, 1968
ordained: 1968
charges: Campus minister, Purdue University, Lafayette, IN, 1968–76; Fellowship, Grandville, MI, 1976–83; First, Grand Rapids, MI, 1983–84; Nonministerial vocation, Grand Rapids, MI, 1984

Bos, Evert
b. Fall/1845, Wildervank, Groningen, Netherlands
training: Theologische Universiteit, Kampen, diploma, 1876
ordained: 1876
charges: PCUSA: Milwaukee, WI, 1877–78; Cedar Grove, WI; RCA, 1878–82: First, Holland, MI, 1882–85; CRC: 9th Street, Holland, MI, 1885–92; Luctor, KS, 1892–96; Dispatch, KS, 1896–1902; Lynden, WA, 1902–06; Dispatch, KS, 1906–09
d. 01/03/1909, Rotterdam, KS

Bos, Ralph J.
b. 06/05/1896, Assen, Drenthe, Netherlands
training: Calvin Theological Seminary, diploma, 1925
ordained: 1925
charges: Rudyard, MI, 1925–29; Prosper, MI,

1929-44; Sanborn, IA, 1944-48; Home missionary at Owen Sound, ON, 1948-52, at Toronto, 1952-53, at Truro, NS, 1953-57, at Halifax, NS, 1957-59; Willmar, MN, 1959-62
retired: 1962
d. 04/04/1984, Grand Rapids, MI

Bosch, David Alan
b. 09/12/1957, Zeeland, MI
training: Calvin Theological Seminary, MDiv, 1992
ordained: 1993
charges: CRC: Northern Heights, Kalamazoo, MI, 1993-96; Pipestone, MN, 1996-2002; URC: Covenant, Loveland, CO, 2002

Bosch, Gerrit
b. 03/21/1873, Netherlands
training: Western Theological Seminary, diploma, 1908
ordained: 1908
charges: RCA: Lafayette, IN, 1908-09; Newton, IL, 1909-11; Fourth, Grand Rapids, MI, 1911-15; Steen, MN, 1915-20; Carmel, Rock Valley, IA, 1925-31; Colton, SD, 1931-33; Lester, IA, 1933-42; CRC: Leota, MN, 1920-23
retired: 1942
d. 12/24/1963, Lakewood, CA

Bosma, Carl John
b. 06/12/1944, Oostermeer, Friesland, Netherlands
training: Calvin Theological Seminary, BD, 1973; Vrije Universiteit, Amsterdam, Drs, 1975
ordained: 1973
charges: Missionary to Brazil, 1973-76; language study, 1976-77; Missionary-pastor, Camboriu, S.C., Brazil, 1977-82; Leave, 1982-83; Missionary-pastor, Camboriu, SC, Brazil, 1983-90; Faculty, Calvin Theological Seminary, Grand Rapids, MI, 1990-

Bosma, G. John
b. 08/08/1946, Chicago, IL
training: Westminster Theological Seminary-PA; Calvin Theological Seminary, BD, 1974
ordained: 1974
charges: Rusk, MI, 1974-80; Bethel, Oskaloosa, IA, 1980-83; Leave, 1983-85
retired: 1985
d. 08/15/1987, Des Moines, IA

Bosma, Menno J.
b. 05/21/1874, Grand Rapids, MI
training: Calvin Theological Seminary, diploma, 1900
ordained: 1900

charges: Broadway Ave., Grand Rapids, 1900-07; Third, Kalamazoo, MI , 1907-10
retired: 1910
d. 06/14/1912, Denver, CO

Bosscher, Arthur Douglas
b. 01/29/1948, Rehoboth, NM
training: Calvin Theological Seminary, MDiv, 1974
ordained: 1975
charges: Campus minister, Corvallis, OR, 1973-74; Campus minister, Western Washington State College, Bellingham, WA, 1975-81; Campus pastor, Washington State University and University of Idaho, 1982-90; Campus pastor, Purdue University, West Lafayette, IN, and Assistant pastor, Lafayette, IN, 1990-95; Eligible for call, 1995-2002; released from ministry, 2002

Bosscher, Brian Paul
b. 01/01/1955, Grand Rapids, MI
training: Calvin Theological Seminary, MDiv, 1981
ordained: 1981
charges: Prospect Park, NJ, 1981-84; Ada, MI, 1984-89; Director, Youth Unlimited, Grand Rapids, MI, 1989-2000; Sunshine Community, Grand Rapids, MI, 2000-

Bossenbroek, Edward
b. 10/08/1914, Waupun, WI
training: Calvin Theological Seminary, ThB, 1943
ordained: 1943
charges: Saginaw, MI, 1943-48; Woden, IA, 1948-52; Grant, MI, 1952-56; Faculty, Illiana Christian High School, 1956-80
retired: 1980

Bossenbroek, Harold
b. 03/19/1912, Waupun, WI
training: Calvin Theological Seminary, ThB, 1946
ordained: 1946
charges: Ogilvie, MN, 1946-50; West Sayville, NY, 1950-54; Assoc. pastor, Second, Pella, IA and Bible teacher at Pella (IA) Christian High School, 1954-65; Bible teacher, Grand Rapids (MI) Christian High School, 1965-68; First, Cutlerville, MI, 1968-72; Leighton, IA, 1972-78
retired: 1978
d. 11/30/2000, Grand Rapids, MI

Bossenbroek, Leonard Christian
b. 04/09/1920, Waupun, WI
training: Calvin Theological Seminary, ThB, 1952
ordained: 1952
charges: Harrison, SD, 1952-56; Ocheyedan, IA,

1956–64; Moline, MI, 1964–71; Wyoming Park, Wyoming, MI, 1971–84
retired: 1984

Bossenbroek, Timothy Scott
b. 11/20/1967, Columbus, OH
training: Calvin Theological Seminary, MDiv, 2001
ordained: 2001
charges: Hessel Park, Champaign, IL, 2001–

Boswell, Theodore Johnson
b. 08/19/1953, Louisville, KY
training: Calvin Theological Seminary, MDiv, 1983
ordained: 1984
charges: Bethel, Sun Valley, CA, 1984–88; Leave, 1988–90; Missionary, Japan, 1990–

Botbyl, Meindert
b. 11/15/1868, Paterson, NJ
training: Calvin Theological Seminary, diploma, 1902
ordained: 1902
charges: Hull, ND, 1902–05, Home missionary, Pella, IA, 1905–08, Home missionary, East Palmyra, NY, 1908–12, West Sayville, NY, 1912–18; West Side, Cleveland, 1918–28; Home missionary at Monsey, NY, 1928–40
d. 05/13/1940, Paterson, NJ

Botting, John Abraham
b. 04/26/1915, Grand Rapids, MI
training: Westminster Theological Seminary, BD, 1942
ordained: 1942
charges: Presbyterian Church of Canada: Valley Field, QC, 1942–44; Kemptville, ON, 1944–48; Glencoe, ON, 1948–52; CRC: New Era, MI, 1952–57; Faith, Holland, MI, 1957–63; First, Vancouver, BC, 1963–68; New Holland, SD, 1968–75: Bethel, DeMotte, IN, 1975–80; Noordeloos, MI, 1980–83
retired: 1983

Botts, Harold Eugene
b. 06/28/1923, Grand Rapids, MI
training: Calvin Theological Seminary, ThB, 1952
ordained: 1952
charges: Missionary in Muskegon area, 1952–54; Grace, Muskegon, MI, 1954–56; Home missionary at Inkster, MI, 1956–64; at Dearborn, 1964–66; at Community, Detroit, MI, 1966–72; Missionary, Pullman, Chicago, IL, 1972–80; Sherman St., Grand Rapids, MI, 1980–87
retired: 1987
d. 06/28/1990, Grand Rapids, MI

Bouma, Clarence
b. 11/30/1891, Harlingen, Friesland, Netherlands
training: Calvin Theological Seminary, diploma, 1917; Princeton Theological Seminary, BD, 1918; Princeton University, AM, 1919; Harvard Divinity School, ThD, 1921; Vrije Universiteit, Amsterdam, 1923
ordained: 1923
charges: Hope Ave., Passaic, NJ, 1923–24; Faculty, Calvin Theological Seminary, 1924–52
retired: 1952
d. 08/12/1962, Cutlerville, MI

Bouma, Dick Clarence
b. 09/09/1927, Grand Rapids, MI
training: Calvin Theological Seminary, MDiv, 1954
ordained: 1955
charges: Reformed Church in Australia: Blacktown, New South Wales, 1955–60; Moe, Victoria, 1960–61; CRC: Home missionary, La Glace, Grande Prairie and Blueberry Mountain, AB, 1961–65; Missionary pastor, Gallatin Gateway, MT, 1965–68; Missionary, Philippines, 1968–75; Mountain View, Lynden, WA, 1975–79; Washington, PA, 1979–84; Missionary, Philippines, 1984–93
retired: 1993

Bouma, Gerard
b. 03/24/1922, Zwolle, Overijsel, Netherlands
training: Theologische Universiteit, Kampen, diploma, 1950
ordained: 1951
charges: GKN: Cappelle a/d. IJsel, 1951–52; CRC: Essex, ON, 1952–58; London, ON, 1958–72; East Paris, Grand Rapids, MI, 1972–85
retired: 1985

Bouma, Henry
b. 12/27/1925, Hull, IA
training: Calvin Theological Seminary, BD, 1958
ordained: 1959
charges: Granum, AB, 1959–63; Palo Alto, CA, 1963–68; Missionary, Pasco, Kennewick and Richland, WA, 1968–80; Hammond, IN, 1980–85; Leave, 1985–86; Chaplain, Menard Correctional Institution, Menard, IL, 1986–90; Chaplain, Dixon Correctional Facility, Dixon, IL, 1990–96
retired: 1997

Bouma, Hessel Sr.
b. 10/06/1884, Harlingen, Friesland, Netherlands
training: McCormick Seminary, BD, 1915; Princeton Seminary, 1919
ordained: 1915
charges: Presbyterian Church: First, Fairgrove,

MI, 1915-18; RCA: First, Paterson, NJ, 1919-22;
CRC: Bethel, Paterson, NJ, 1922-28; Fourteenth
St., Holland, MI, 1928-34; Summer St., Passaic,
NJ, 1934-54
retired: 1954
d. 02/27/1971, Wyckoff, NJ

Bouma, Hessel Jr.
b. 12/26/1918, Paterson, NJ
training: Calvin Theological Seminary, BD, 1958
ordained: 1958
charges: Reeman, MI, 1958-64; Comstock,
Kalamazoo, MI, 1964-79
retired: 1984

Bouma, Louis
b. 10/25/1899, Hull, IA
training: Calvin Theological Seminary, ThB, 1938
ordained: 1938
charges: Artesia, CA, 1938-43; Ontario, CA,
1943-53; Inwood, IA, 1953-57; Sussex, NJ, 1957-
65; Dispatch, KS, 1965-69
retired: 1969
d. 07/13/1994, Sioux Center, IA

Bouma, Mary-Lee
b. 09/06/1962, Lethbridge, AB
training: Calvin Theological Seminary, MDiv, 1994
ordained: 1997
charges: CRC: InterVarsity Christian Fellowship,
1984-88; Pullman, Chicago, IL, 1989-90; Missions
and Outreach, Sunshine, Grand Rapids, MI, 1990-
91; Church Planting, Gospel Fellowship, Oakdale
Park, Grand Rapids, MI, 1991-93; Trinity, Mount
Pleasant, MI, 1994- ; Lutheran: Amazing Grace,
Grand Rapids, MI, 1993-94

Bouma, Roger Lee
b. 02/05/1960, Grand Rapids, MI
training: Calvin Theological Seminary, MDiv, 1987
ordained: 1988
charges: Kibbie, South Haven, MI, 1988-92;
Chaplain, United States Navy, 1992-

Bouma, Rolf T.
b. 09/12/1956, Grand Rapids, MI
training: Calvin Theological Seminary, MDiv,
1986, ThM, 1996
ordained: 1987
charges: Eastern Ave., Grand Rapids, MI, 1987-
96; Hope, Framingham, MA, 1996-2002; Pastor of
academic ministries, Chapel, Ann Arbor, MI,
2002-

Bouma, Sjouke
b. 04/17/1868, Menaldum, Friesland, Netherlands
training: Lane Seminary, Cincinnati, OH, diploma,
1900
ordained: 1900
charges: Presbyterian Church; Raymond, SD,
1900; CRC: Otley, IA, 1900-03; Friesland, SD,
1903-05; Lodi, NJ, 1905-09; Galesburg, IA,
1909-11; Lebanon IA, 1911-15; Bemis, SD, 1915-
18; Oak Lawn, IL, 1918-21; Atwood, MI, 1921-27
retired: 1927
d. 04/28/1944, Cutlerville, MI

Bout, Harry J.
b. 02/03/1942, Netherlands
training: Westminster Theological Seminary-PA,
MDiv, 1977; Calvin Theological Seminary, Special
Program for Ministerial Candidacy, 1978
ordained: 1978
charges: CRC: Cambridge, ON, 1978-81;
Maranatha, Bowmanville, ON, 1981-82; Orthodox
Christian Reformed Church of Canada, 1982

Bouwers, John Henry
b. 05/23/1963, Brockville, ON
training: Calvin Theological Seminary, MDiv, 2000
ordained: 2000
charges: Maranatha, St. Catharines, ON, 1991-
92; Fellowship, Ancaster, ON, 2000-

Bouwkamp, Ronald Lee
b. 07/11/1943, East Paris, MI
training: Calvin Theological Seminary, MDiv, 1977
ordained: 1977
charges: Champlain Valley, Vergennes, VT, 1977-
80; Trinity, Mt. Pleasant, MI, 1980-83; Peoria, IA,
1983-2000; Wayland, MI, 2000-

Bouwman, Roger Allan
b. 01/25/1951, Rock Rapids, IA
training: Calvin Theological Seminary, BD, 1977
ordained: 1977
charges: Calvin, Le Mars, IA, 1977-81;
Brookfield, WI, 1981-87; First, Fulton, IL, 1987-
92; First, Hull, IA, 1992-96; Eligible for call,
1996-98; Chelwood, Albuquerque, NM, 1998-

Bouws, Douglas John
b. 01/29/1973, Alameda, CA
training: Calvin Theological Seminary, MDiv, 2002
ordained: 2002
charges: Granite Springs, Rocklin, CA, 2002-

Bouwsma, John O.
b. 11/18/1891, Muskegon, MI

training: Calvin Theological Seminary, diploma, 1914; Princeton Seminary, BD, 1915
ordained: 1915
charges: Sullivan, MI, 1915–19; Rusk, MI, 1919–21; Jenison, MI, 1921–27; Graafschap, MI, 1927–31; South Holland, IL, 1931–38; First, Kalamazoo, MI, 1938–46; Hope, Grandville, MI, 1946–52; Comstock, Kalamazoo, MI, 1952–58
retired: 1958
d. 08/06/1976, Kalamazoo, MI

Boyd, George
b. 05/19/1958, Plainfield, NJ
training: Columbia Theological University, MDiv, 1997
ordained: 1997
charges: Vision One, Decatur, GA, 1997–98; Vision One, Atlanta, GA, 1998–

Bradford, Dallas Eugene
b. 11/15/1915, Philadelphia, PA
training: Westminster Theological Seminary-PA, ThB, 1941
ordained: 1941
charges: Independent: Faith Presbyterian, Fawn Grove, PA, 1941–44; OPC: Calvary, Philadelphia, PA, 1944–51; CRC: Flint, MI, 1951–54; Third, Paterson, NJ, 1954–61; Associate pastor, Third, Paterson and Executive Secretary of Westminster Theological Seminary, 1961–63; Ebenezer, Berwyn, IL, 1963–69; Franklin Lakes, NJ, 1969–74; Maple Ave., Holland, MI, 1974–80
retired: 1980

Brander, William
b. 07/31/1938, Winsum, Groningen, Netherlands
training: Calvin Theological Seminary, BD, 1967
ordained: 1968
charges: CRC: Chaplain, United States Army, 1968–84; Leave, 1985; Chaplain, Marriage and Family Center, Grand Rapids, MI, 1985–89; Pastoral counselor, Christian Counseling Center, Grand Rapids, MI, 1989–90; Chaplain, Department of Correction, State of Michigan, Grand Rapids, MI, 1990–94; Interim pastor, South Olive, MI, 1994–95; Leave, 1995–96
retired: 1996; affiliated with United Reformed Churches, 2000

Brands, Michael T.
b. 11/02/1962, Pipestone, MN
training: Fuller Theological Seminary, MDiv, 1988; Calvin Theological Seminary, Special Program for Ministerial Candidacy, 1992
ordained: 1992

charges: CRC: Minister of music and evangelism, Arcadia, CA, 1985–86; Crenshaw, Los Angeles, CA, 1992–95; Youth with a Mission, Ukraine, 1995–96; Pune, India, 1996–98; Leave, 1998–2000; resigned from denomination, 2000

Bratt, Albert H.
b. 08/11/1887, South Olive, MI
training: Calvin Theological Seminary, diploma, 1913
ordained: 1913
charges: Otley IA, 1913–18; Chaplain to soldiers, 1918–19; Eddyville, IA, 1919–21; Platte, SD, 1921–25; Fourth Roseland, Chicago, IL, 1925–28; Manhattan, MT, 1928–41; Edmonton, AB, 1941–43; Service pastor in Oklahoma City, OK, 1943–45; Hollandale, MN, 1945–49; Doon, IA, 1949–52; Service pastor, Midland Park, NJ, 1952–54
retired: 1954
d. 01/17/1962, Grand Rapids, MI

Bratt, Daniel Lee
b. 07/01/1948, Lansing, MI
training: Calvin Theological Seminary, MDiv, 1983
ordained: 1983
charges: CRC: Franklin Lakes, NJ, 1983–96; Independent: Bible Fellowship Church, Franklin Lakes, NJ, 1996

Bratt, Douglas H.
b. 12/30/1957, Camp Zama, Japan
training: Calvin Theological Seminary, MDiv, 1987
ordained: 1987
charges: Lincoln Center, IA, 1987–92; Fruitport, MI, 1992–98; Silver Spring, MD, 1998–

Bratt, John Harold
b. 08/23/1909, Holland, MI
training: Calvin Theological Seminary, ThB, 1937; Harvard Divinity School, STM, 1939; Union Theological Seminary, ThD, 1942
ordained: 1942
charges: Bible teacher, Grand Rapids (MI) Christian High School, 1939–42; Dorr, MI, 1942–46; Faculty, Calvin College, Grand Rapids, MI, 1946–76
retired: 1976
d. 12/22/2000, Grand Rapids, MI

Bratt, Karl H.
b. 04/21/1949, Holland, MI
training: Calvin Theological Seminary, MDiv, 1975
ordained: 1975
charges: First, Sioux City, IA, 1975–81; Alamo

Ave., Kalamazoo, MI, 1981-87; Ebenezer, Leota, MN, 1987-91; East Palmyra, NY, 1991-

Breedveld, Peter
b. 02/19/1931, Rotterdam, Zuid Holland, Netherlands
training: Westminster Theological Seminary-PA, BD, 1961; Calvin Theological Seminary, Special Program for Ministerial Candidacy, 1963
ordained: 1963
charges: Strathroy, ON, 1963-65; Bethany, Bloomfield, ON, 1965-70; Holland Marsh, ON, 1970-73; First, Kitchener, ON, 1973-82; Ottewell, Edmonton, AB, 1982-92; On loan GKN: Grootegast, 1992-96
retired: 1996

Breems, Alan Dwight
b. 12/26/1957, Chicago, IL
training: Calvin Theological Seminary, MDiv, 1985
ordained: 1985
charges: Second, Grand Haven, MI, 1985-89; Residency, Chino, CA, 1989-90; Oasis Community, Moreno Valley, CA, 1990-

Breen, Evert
b. 01/05/1863, Cocksdorp, Noord Holland, Netherlands
training: Calvin Theological Seminary, diploma, 1889
ordained: 1889
charges: CRC Home missionary, 1889-91; Firth, NE, 1891-93; First, Orange City, IA, 1893-1903; First, Chicago, IL, 1903-09; Grandville Ave., Grand Rapids, MI, 1909-14; First, Lynden, WA, 1914-21
d. 01/15/1921, Lynden, WA

Breen, Oliver
b. 11/07/1906, Chicago, IL
training: Calvin Theological Seminary, ThB, 1938
ordained: 1938
charges: Goshen, NY, 1938-42; Second, Sioux Center, IA, 1942-47; Bethany, Holland, MI, 1947-52; Kedvale Ave., Oak Lawn, IL, 1952-70; West Suburban, Cicero, IL, 1970-73; Elmhurst, IL — Faith, 1975-77
retired: 1975
d. 11/29/1991, Bradenton, FL

Breen, Quirinus
b. 03/03/1896, Orange City, IA
training: Calvin Theological Seminary, diploma, 1920; University of Chicago, PhD, 1931
ordained: 1921

charges: Twelfth St., Grand Rapids, MI, 1921-24; Non-ministerial vocation, Higher education, 1924
d. 03/25/1975, Eugene, OR

Breisch, Frank (Francis) David Jr.
b. 09/04/1927, Slatington, PA
training: Westminster Theological Seminary-PA, BD, 1951; ThM, 1953; Calvin Theological Seminary, Special Program for Ministerial Candidacy, 1952; Fuller Theological Seminary, DMin, 1984
ordained: 1952
charges: OPC: Harrisville and New Brachtron, PA, 1952-55; Bible teacher, Kalamazoo (MI) Christian High School, 1955-59; Bethel, Wheaton, IL, 1959-69; CRC: Missionary, Corvallis, OR, 1969-74; First, Calgary, AB, 1974-81; on loan to: St. Paul's Presbyterian Church, Banff, AB, 1981-86; Presbyterian Church of Canada: St. Paul's, Banff, AB, 1987

Bremer, Calvin Lee
b. 07/02/1947, Zeeland, MI
training: Calvin Theological Seminary, BD, 1972
ordained: 1972
charges: Arcadia, Grand Rapids, MI, 1972-78; Bethel, Lansing, IL, 1978-96; Director of Ministry, Back to God Hour, Palos Heights, IL, 1996-

Bremer, Paul Lowell
b. 07/18/1942, Hamilton, MI
training: Calvin Theological Seminary, MDiv, 1967; Princeton Theological Seminary, PhD, 1974
ordained: 1976
charges: Faculty, Reformed Bible College, Grand Rapids, MI, 1975-

Brenton, Robert Maurice III
b. 05/02/1954, Great Lakes, IL
training: Reformed Theological Seminary, MDiv, 1984; Calvin Theological Seminary, ThM, 1988
ordained: 1989
charges: CRC: Kanawha, IA, 1989-93; On loan: Reformed Church of New Zealand, Brookly, Wellington, New Zealand, 1993-94; Reformed Church of New Zealand, 1994-98; First, Randolph, WI, 1998-

Breuker, John
b. 11/07/1897, Graafschap, MI
training: Calvin Theological Seminary, diploma, 1921
ordained: 1921
charges: Willard, OH, 1921-25; Lamont, MI, 1925-28; Immanuel, Muskegon, MI, 1928-47; Second, Sioux Center, IA, 1947-52; Zutphen, MI, 1952-59; Hope, Muskegon, MI, 1959-63

retired: 1963
d. 07/09/1987, Grand Rapids, MI

Brink, Abel J.
b. 10/02/1865, Haren, Groningen, Netherlands
training: Calvin Theological Seminary, diploma, 1899
ordained: 1899
charges: Home missionary, Lynden, WA 1899-1900; First, Lynden, WA, 1900-01; Bemis, SD, 1901-03; Home missionary, Palmer, SD, 1903-05; Home missionary, Oak Harbor, WA, 1905-08; Peoria, IA, 1908-11; Home missionary, Kuner, CO, 1911-13
retired: 1913
d. 06/15/1930, Grand Rapids, MI

Brink, Arnold
b. 11/27/1912, Kuner, CO
training: Calvin Theological Seminary, ThB, 1938
ordained: 1938
charges: Bluffton Chapel, Branch of Bethany, Muskegon, MI, 1938-43; Bethany, Muskegon, MI, 1943-47; Education Secretary, Calvin College, Grand Rapids, MI, 1947-53; First Englewood, Chicago, IL, 1953-58; Burton Heights, Grand Rapids, MI, 1958-78
retired: 1978
d. 02/28/1990, Grand Rapids, MI

Brink, Daniel Jay
b. 06/19/1952, Grand Rapids, MI
training: Calvin Theological Seminary, MDiv, 1977; ThM, 1978
ordained: 1979
charges: Park Lane, Evergreen Park, IL, 1978-86; Rosewood, Bellflower, CA, 1986-

Brink, Harvey Arnold
b. 01/06/1945, Muskegon, MI
training: Calvin Theological Seminary, BD, 1969; MDiv, 1984
ordained: 1969
charges: Battle Creek, MI, 1969-78; Walnut Creek, CA, 1978-82; Faith, Holland, MI, 1982-86; Bellevue, WA, 1986-99; First, Pella, IA, 1999-

Brink, John Evart
b. 11/27/1902, East Saugatuck, MI
training: Calvin Theological Seminary, BD, 1934
ordained: 1938
charges: CRC: Hanley Street Mission, Grand Rapids, MI, 1935-37; Carnes, IA, 1938-42; Hull, ND, 1942-46; Luverne, MN, 1946-48; Otley, IA,

1948-51; Chandler, MN, 1951-55; Emo, ON, 1955-57
retired: 1963; affiliated with RCA, 1980

Brink, John Herbert
b. 06/10/1906, Cleveland, OH
training: Princeton Theological Seminary, ThB, 1935; Princeton University, MA, 1936; Calvin Theological Seminary, Special Program for Ministerial Candidacy 1954
ordained: 1934
charges: PCUSA: Cleves, OH, 1936-41; Faculty, Pikesville College, Pikesville, KY, 1941-44; Maple Heights, OH, 1944-54; CRC: Providence, Holland, MI, 1954-68; East Lansing, MI, 1968-72
retired: 1972
d. 12/08/1992, Grand Rapids, MI

Brink, John R.
b. 11/23/1872, Onnen, Groningen, Netherlands
training: Calvin Theological Seminary, diploma, 1902
ordained: 1902
charges: Reeman, MI, 1902-05; Home missionary Grand Rapids, MI, 1905-07; East Side, Cleveland, OH, 1907-11; Second, Englewood, IL, 1911-13; Missionary for Classes Grand Rapids East and Grand Rapids West, 1913-28; Missionary for Classis Illinois: at Gallup, NM, 1928-30; at Chicago, 1931-37; Home missionary for denomination, 1937-43; Conrad, MT, 1943-46
retired: 1946
d. 07/22/1960, Grand Rapids, MI

Brink, John (Jan) W.
b. 12/14/1865, De Leek, Groningen, Netherlands
training: Calvin Theological Seminary, diploma, 1895
ordained: 1895
charges: Home missionary, 1895-96; Allendale, MI, 1896-1900; Grandville Ave., Grand Rapids, MI, 1900-04; Fourth, Muskegon, MI, 1904-09; Broadway Ave., Grand Rapids, MI, 1909-12; Missionary, Rehoboth, NM, 1912-25; Zillah, WA, 1925-30; Missionary, Two Wells, NM, 1930-31, Zuni, NM, 1931-38
retired: 1938
d. 04/08/1948, Albuquerque, NM

Brink, Leonard Peter
b. 09/10/1876, East Saugatuck, MI
training: Calvin Theological Seminary, diploma, 1900
ordained: 1900
charges: Missionary at Rehoboth, NM, 1900-09,

at Tohatchi, NM, 1910-13, at Hanford CA, 1913-
15, at Crozier, NM 1915-23, at Toadlena, NM,
1923-25, at Farmington, NM, 1925-36
d. 03/24/1936, Pomeroy, WA

Brink, Paul William
b. 11/28/1942, Goshen, IN
training: Calvin Theological Seminary, BD, 1967
ordained: 1968
charges: Minster of education, Grace, Grand
Rapids, MI, 1968-70; Grace, Grand Rapids, MI,
1970-74; Terre Haute, IN, 1974-80; Rochester, NY,
1980-95; Ann Arbor, MI, 1995-

Brink, Peter Edward
b. 06/07/1949, Fremont, MI
training: Calvin Theological Seminary, MDiv, 1976
ordained: 1976
charges: Community, Grand Rapids, MI, 1976-85;
Oak Grove Fellowship, Grand Haven, MI, 1985-91;
First, Grand Haven, MI, 1992-93; Non-ministerial
vocation, 1993
d. 05/29/1999, Grand Haven, MI

Brink, William Paul
b. 09/21/1916, Chicago, IL
training: Calvin Theological Seminary, ThB, 1941
ordained: 1941
charges: Goshen, IN, 1941-44; Archer Ave., Chicago, IL, 1944-48; Creston, Grand Rapids, MI,
1948-52; Bethany, Holland, MI, 1952-64; Second,
Fremont, MI, 1964-70; Denominational stated
clerk, Grand Rapids, MI, 1970-83
retired: 1983
d. 09/28/1999, Grand Rapids, MI

Brinks, Joseph A.
b. 05/31/1949, Grand Rapids, MI
training: Calvin Theological Seminary, BD, 1974;
ThM, 1975
ordained: 1975
charges: Noordeloos, MI, 1975-79; Jamestown,
MI, 1979-85; Sully, IA, 1985-91; Grace,
Kalamazoo, MI, 1991-

Brinks, Raymond Gerald
b. 12/19/1933, McBain, MI
training: Calvin Theological Seminary, BD, 1958;
ThM, 1985
ordained: 1958
charges: Missionary to South America-Argentina,
1958-78; Youth director, National Church, Argentina, 1978-80; Missionary-evangelist, Santo
Domingo, Dominican Republic, 1980-96
retired: 1997

Brix, Shawn Ronald
b. 07/08/1962, St. Catharines, ON
training: Calvin Theological Seminary, MDiv, 1995
ordained: 1995
charges: Bethel, Acton, ON, 1995-2002;
Burlington, ON, 2002-

Broekema, James Albert Richard
b. 09/04/1963, Brampton, ON
training: Calvin Theological Seminary, MDiv, 1992
ordained: 1992
charges: West Winnipeg Community, Winnipeg,
MB, 1992-95; Leave, 1995-96; Burlington, ON,
1996-2000

Broekema, Robert Ray
b. 12/20/1945, Kalamazoo, MI
training: Calvin Theological Seminary, BD, 1973
ordained: 1973
charges: Rudyard, MI, 1973-78; Lynnwood, WA,
1978-89; Covenant, Lansing, MI, 1989-94;
Alameda, CA, 1994-99; Immanuel, Sheldon, IA,
1999-2001; Leave, 2001-

Broekhuizen, Rensselaer O.
b. 08/20/1933, Midland Park, NJ
training: Westminster Theological Seminary-PA,
BD, 1963; Calvin Theological Seminary, BD, 1962;
ThM, 1979
ordained: 1963
charges: CRC: Home missionary, St. Petersburg,
FL, 1963-64; St. Petersburg, FL, 1964-65; Home
missionary, Washington, PA, 1965-72; Fourteenth
St., Holland, MI, 1973-82; Leave, 1982-83; Missionary to Liberia, 1983-91; Providence, Holland,
MI, 1991-93; Independent: Holland, MI, 1993

Broekstra, Sietse
b. 09/04/1851, Burum, Friesland, Netherlands
training: Calvin Theological Seminary, diploma,
1894
ordained: 1894
charges: Peoria, IA, 1894-97
d. 03/04/1897, Peoria, IA

Broene, Egbert
b. 01/27/1840, Uelsen, Bentheim, Germany
training: Calvin Theological Seminary, diploma,
1883
ordained: 1883
charges: First, Pella, IA, 1883-86; Drenthe, MI,
1886-95; First, Kalamazoo, MI, 1895-00;
Kelloggsville, Grand Rapids, MI, 1900-07
retired: 1907
d. 02/05/1911, Grand Rapids, MI

Broene, Geert
b. 09/16/1838, Hocklingkamp, Bentheim, Germany
training: Calvin Theological Seminary, diploma, 1877
ordained: 1877
charges: Noordeloos, MI, 1877-79; First Roseland, Chicago, IL, 1879-84; Zutphen, MI, 1884-89; West Leonard, Grand Rapids, MI, 1889-1904
retired: 1904
d. 04/12/1919, Grand Rapids, MI

Brondsema, Samuel Greve
b. 03/14/1890, Middelstum, Groningen, Netherlands
training: Calvin Theological Seminary, diploma, 1917
ordained: 1917
charges: Home missionary, Classis Sioux Center, at Colton, SD, 1917-19; Colton, SD, 1919-22; Baldwin, WI, 1922-26; Muskegon Heights, MI, 1926-40; Lacombe, AB, 1940-43; Everson, WA, 1943-46; Compton, CA, 1946-48; Home missionary at Toronto; ON, Brampton, ON; Barrie, ON, 1948-56
retired: 1956
d. 03/14/1976, Grand Rapids, MI

Bronkema, Ralph Sr.
b. 06/10/1893, Grand Rapids, MI
training: Calvin Theological Seminary, diploma, 1924; Free University, Amsterdam, ThD, 1929
ordained: 1929
charges: Bible teacher Grand Rapids (MI) Christian High School, 1920-25; First, Orange City, IA, 1929-52; Stated supply at Dresden, ON, 1956-58
retired: 1952
d. 05/04/1973, Sioux City, IA

Bronkema, Ralph Waldon
b. 06/15/1930, Grand Rapids, MI
training: Calvin Theological Seminary, BD, 1954; MDiv, 1979
ordained: 1954
charges: Missionary for greater Muskegon, MI, 1954-59; Home missionary, Orlando, FL, 1959-66; Chaplain, United States Air Force, 1966-86; Pastor for Special Ministries, Indian Harbour Beach, FL, 1986-88; Shalom, Sioux Falls, SD, 1988-95
retired: 1995

Brooks, Roy
b. 09/14/1934

training: International Theological Seminary, MDiv, 1990
ordained: 1991
charges: Assembly of God: Faith, Nicaragua, 1990-91; CRC: Eternal Covenant, Monrovia, CA, 1991-95; Resigned from denomination, 1995

Brouwer, Daniel Wayne
b. 02/28/1956, Grand Rapids, MI
training: Calvin Theological Seminary, MDiv, 1983
ordained: 1985
charges: Rock Rapids, IA, 1985-91; First, Waupun, WI, 1991-98; East Paris, Kentwood, MI, 1998-

Brouwer, Mark Kendall
b. 07/08/1964, Willmar, MN
training: Calvin Theological Seminary, MDiv, 1991
ordained: 1991
charges: Sunrise Community, Austin, TX, 1991-92; North Austin Community, Austin, TX, 1992-97; Bridgewood, Savage, MN, 1997-

Brouwer, Peter W.
b. 06/09/1929, Chicago, IL
training: Calvin Theological Seminary, BD, 1953
ordained: 1953
charges: Momence, IL, 1953-59; Chino, CA, 1959-67; First, Edgerton, MN, 1967-94
retired: 1994

Brouwer, Pieter
b. 02/06/1930, Wouterswoude, Friesland, Netherlands
training: Calvin Theological Seminary, BD, 1967
ordained: 1967
charges: Bethel, Acton, ON, 1967-72; Ebenezer, Jarvis, ON, 1972-79; First, New Westminster, BC, 1979-95
retired: 1995

Brouwer, Randall Jay
b. 06/04/1953, Downey, CA
training: Calvin Theological Seminary, MDiv, 1979
ordained: 1979
charges: Immanuel, Orange City, IA, 1979-82; Faith, Nashville, TN, 1982-91; Faith, New Brighton, MN, 1991-94; Calvary, Holland, MI, 1994-

Brouwer, Theodore Lloyd
b. 05/30/1932, Chicago, IL
training: Calvin Theological Seminary, BD, 1956
ordained: 1956
charges: Sibley, IA, 1956-61; Missionary to

Dayton, OH, 1961–65; Prairie City, IA, 1965–71; Borculo, MI, 1971–86; Delavan, WI, 1986–95
retired: 1995

Brouwer, Wayne Allen
b. 08/09/1954, Willmar, MN
training: Calvin Theological Seminary, MDiv, 1980, ThM, 1984
ordained: 1980
charges: Iron Springs, AB, 1980–85; Faculty, Reformed Theological College of Nigeria, 1985–86; First, London, ON, 1986–94; Harderwyk, Holland, MI, 1994–

Brouwer, Wout (Walt)
b. 03/22/1956, Veenendaal, Utrecht, Netherlands
training: Calvin Theological Seminary, MDiv, 1987
ordained: 1987
charges: Vernon, BC, 1987–92; Christ Community, Nanaimo, BC, 1992–

Brouwers, Gary William
b. 06/01/1967, Grand Rapids, MI
training: Calvin Theological Seminary, MDiv, 2002
ordained: 2002
charges: Hollandale, MN, 2002–

Brouwers, William G. Jr.
b. 05/15/1934, Grand Rapids, MI
training: Calvin Theological Seminary, MDiv, 1975
ordained: 1975
charges: New Holland, SD, 1975–81; Wisconsin Rapids, WI, 1981–92; Leave, 1992–94; Wright, Kanawha, IA, 1994–98
retired: 1998

Brower, Jeffrey Jon
b. 06/29/1970, Grand Rapids, MI
training: Calvin Theological Seminary, MDiv, 1996
ordained: 1996
charges: First, Munster, IN, 1996–99; Bethel, Waupun, WI, 1999–

Brown, Norman Franklin
b. 01/24/1947, Providence, RI
training: Calvin Theological Seminary, MDiv, 1980
ordained: 1980
charges: Pine Creek, Holland, MI, 1980–83; Chaplain, United States Navy, 1983–2001; Interim, Avery Street, South Windsor, ON, 2000–2001

Brown, Timothy John
b. 05/01/1951, Boston, MA
training: Reformed Theological Seminary, MDiv,

1976; Calvin Theological Seminary, Special Program for Ministerial Candidacy, 1978
ordained: 1978
charges: Lucas, MI, 1978–85; Dearborn, MI, 1985–95; First, Edgerton, MN, 1995–

Bruinooge, Henry
b. 11/22/1922, Sheboygan, WI
training: Calvin Theological Seminary, ThB, 1946
ordained: 1947
charges: Missionary to China, 1947–49; Emden, Renville, MN, 1949–51; Missionary to Japan, 1951–80; Minister for listener contact, Back to God Hour, Palos Heights, IL, 1980–91
retired: 1991
d. 08/08/1994, Grand Rapids, MI

Bruinooge, Jacob Harry
b. 08/23/1894, Sheboygan, WI
training: Calvin Theological Seminary, diploma, 1922; Princeton University, AM, 1923; Princeton Seminary, ThM, 1924; Southern Baptist Seminary, ThD, 1926
ordained: 1926
charges: East Muskegon, Muskegon, MI, 1926–41; Third, Zeeland, MI, 1941–60
retired: 1960
d. 04/01/1965, Grand Rapids, MI

Bruinooge, James B.
b. 11/16/1877, Nieuwdorp, Zeeland, Netherlands
training: Calvin Theological Seminary, diploma, 1906
ordained: 1906
charges: Hudsonville, MI, 1906–11; First, Grand Haven, MI, 1911–16; South Olive, MI, 1916–23; Moline, MI, 1923–43
retired: 1943
d. 01/22/1954, Zeeland, MI

Bruins, Rozanne Meyer
b. 06/24/1950, Willmar, MN
training: Calvin Theological Seminary, MDiv, 1998
ordained: 1999
charges: Chaplain, Pine Rest Christian Hospital, Cutlerville, MI, 1999–

Bruinsma, Hendrik Pieter
b. 11/16/1956, Longview, AB
training: Westminster Theological Seminary-PA, MDiv, 1981; Calvin Theological Seminary, Special Program for Ministerial Candidacy, 1982
ordained: 1982
charges: Holland Marsh, ON, 1982–88; Grace,

Chatham, ON, 1988–93; Maranatha, Woodbridge, ON, 1993–

Brummel, Robert Lee
b. 01/29/1936, Grand Rapids, MI
training: Calvin Theological Seminary, BD, 1963
ordained: 1966
charges: Chaplain, United States Navy, 1966–79; Chaplain, Jackson Memorial Hospital, Miami, FL, 1979–83; Director of Pastoral Care, Ohio State University, Columbus, OH, 1983–

Bruxvoort, Brandt
b. 03/28/1900, Sully, IA
training: Calvin Theological Seminary, ThB, 1930
ordained: 1930
charges: Missionary to San Cayetano, Tres Arroyos, and Los Pinos, Argentina and Carambehy, Brazil, 1930–35; Evangelism, Grand Rapids, MI, 1936–42; Superintendent, Beacon Light Mission, Kelloggsville, MI, 1942; Lay missionary, Denver, CO, 1943–49; Sioux Falls, SD, 1949–53; Preakness, NJ, 1953–59; Home missionary, Cochrane and New Liskeard, ON, 1959–63; Home missionary, Good Samaritan, Miami, FL, 1963–66
retired: 1966
d. 10/18/1987, Fort Collins, CO

Bruxvoort, Carl Henry
b. 05/17/1951, Orange City, IA
training: Calvin Theological Seminary, MDiv, 1978
ordained: 1979
charges: Dispatch, KS, 1979–84; McBain, MI, 1984–93; First, Muskegon, MI, 1993–2001; First, Sioux Falls, SD, 2001–

Bruxvoort, Ralph Adrian
b. 04/11/1933, Tres Arroyos, Argentina
training: Calvin Theological Seminary, BD, 1958
ordained: 1958
charges: Alamosa, CO, 1958–61; Pompton Plains, NJ, 1961–65; Ada, MI, 1965–73; First, Manhattan, MT, 1973–80; Hope, Stony Plain, AB, 1980–93; Quincy, WA, 1993–98
retired: 1998

Buining, Rodger James
b. 01/08/1931, Muskegon, MI
training: Calvin Theological Seminary, BD, 1955; MDiv, 1976
ordained: 1955
charges: Prairie Edge Chapel and Assoc. Pastor, Grace, Kalamazoo, MI, 1955–58; Rehoboth, NM, 1958–63; Caledonia, MI, 1963–67; Bozeman, MT, 1967–71; Missionary, Friendship House, San Fran-

cisco, CA, 1971–76; Faith, New Brighton, MN, 1976–82; Orangewood, Phoenix, AZ, 1982–88; Bethel, Grand Rapids, MI, 1988–93
retired: 1993

Buis, Daniel George
b. 01/04/1961, Holland, MI
training: Fuller Theological Seminary, MDiv, 1988, Calvin Theological Seminary, Special Program for Ministerial Candidacy, 1992
ordained: 1992
charges: Lombard, IL, 1992–97; New Hope, Atlanta, GA, 1997–

Bult, John Lucas
b. 06/12/1900, Albany, NY
training: Calvin Theological Seminary, BD, 1932
ordained: 1933
charges: Godwin Heights, Grand Rapids, MI, 1933–44; Moline, MI, 1944–49; Munster, IN, 1949–55; Pease, MN, 1955–58; Overisel, MI, 1958–65
retired: 1965
d. 06/20/1981, Zeeland, MI

Bultema, Harry (Harke)
b. 07/16/1884, Uithuizen, Groningen, Netherlands
training: Calvin Theological Seminary, diploma, 1912
ordained: 1912
charges: CRC: Peoria, IA, 1912–16; First, Muskegon, MI, 1916–20; Berean Reformed: Muskegon, MI, 1920–52
d. 09/21/1952, Rochester, MN

Bulthuis, William Keith
b. 01/17/1946, Artesia, CA
training: Calvin Theological Seminary, BD, 1970
ordained: 1971
charges: InterVarsity Chr. Fellowship, Bellingham, WA, 1971–74; Missionary to the Philippines, 1974–77; Campus minister, University of Wisconsin, Madison, WI, 1977–84; Bethany, Gallup, NM, 1984–

Bultje, Harvey D.
b. 12/28/1923, Kalamazoo, MI
training: Calvin Theological Seminary, BD, 1953
ordained: 1953
charges: Vogel Center, MI, 1953–58; Missionary to Columbus, OH, 1958–60; Minister of evangelism, Kalamazoo, MI, 1960–63; Hanley, Grandville, MI, 1963–69; Grace, Muskegon, MI, 1969–86
retired: 1986
d. 05/23/1986, Grand Rapids, MI

Bultman, Allen Jay
b. 10/30/1929, Fremont, MI
training: Calvin Theological Seminary, BD, 1959
ordained: 1959
charges: Irving Park, NJ, 1959-62; Southern
Heights, Kalamazoo, MI, 1962-66; 36th St., Grand
Rapids, MI, 1966-70; Hanley, Grandville, MI, 1970-
77; Vogel Center, MI, 1977-80; Bauer, MI, 1980-
84; Hope, Grandville, MI, 1984-92
retired: 1992

Bultman, Fred Jr.
b. 04/29/1924, Fremont, MI
training: Calvin Theological Seminary, BD, 1953
ordained: 1953
charges: Jamestown, MI, 1953-57; Home missionary at West Sayville, NY, 1957-59; at East
Islip, NY, 1959-61; at Midland Park, NJ, 1961-62;
at East Islip, NY, 1962-66; Missionary, Syracuse,
NY, 1966-76; Lake Odessa, MI, 1976-81; First,
Fulton, IL, 1981-86
retired: 1986

Bultman, Fred Mark
b. 11/11/1951, Grand Rapids, MI
training: Calvin Theological Seminary, MDiv, 1997
ordained: 1997
charges: Boston Square, Grand Rapids, MI, 1997-
2002; Trinity, Edmonton, AB, 2002

Bultman, James A.
b. 01/20/1924, Oak Harbor, WA
training: Calvin Theological Seminary, BD, 1953
ordained: 1956
charges: Bethel, Allison, IA, 1956-60; Iowa Falls,
IA, 1960-66; Trinity, Denver, CO, 1966-69;
Decatur, MI, 1969-76; Colton, SD, 1976-82;
Leave, 1982-86
retired: 1986

Bultman, Roger Dale
b. 04/14/1948, Wausau, WI
training: Calvin Theological Seminary, BD, 1974
ordained: 1974
charges: Missionary, West Olive, MI, 1974-79;
First, Rock Valley, IA, 1979-85; First, Redlands,
CA, 1985-94; Redlands, CA, 1994-98; Lakeside
Community, Alto, MI, 1998-

Bultman, Stanley J.
b. 02/17/1939, Fremont, MI
training: Calvin Theological Seminary, BD, 1965
ordained: 1966
charges: Missionary, Mount Pleasant, MI, 1966-
69; Atwood, MI, 1969-74; Northern Heights,
Kalamazoo, MI, 1974-84; Leave, 1984-86; Executive director, Hospital Chaplaincy Services, Inc.,
Grand Rapids, MI, 1986-

Burggraaf, Nicholas J.
b. 04/11/1869, Oosterbierum, Friesland, Netherlands
training: Calvin Theological Seminary, diploma,
1902
ordained: 1902
charges: CRC: Middleburg, IA, 1902-04;
Prinsburg, MN, 1904-08; Doon IA, 1908-12;
Bishop MI, 1912-16; Muskegon Heights, 1916-23;
RCA: First, Lodi, NJ, 1923-28
d. 08/11/1928, Grand Rapids, MI

Burghart, H. Lloyd
b. 06/01/1936, Stamford, CT
training: declared eligible on the basis of exceptional gifts, 1995
ordained: 1995
charges: Rimbey, AB, 1995-99; Harbor Chaplain,
Montreal, QC, 1999-

Burgos, Elias
b. 06/15/1960, Santiago, Chile
training: Evangelical Institute of Chile, BA
ordained: 1998
charges: National Presbyterian Church of Chile:
The Way and Life, Santiago, Chile, 1984-89; Vox
Dei National, Santiago, Chile, 1990-95; CRC:
Iglesia El Redentor, Hialeah, FL, 1996-97; Sun Valley Community, Denver, CO, 1997-

Burton, Jerome
training: declared eligible on the basis of exceptional gifts, 2002
ordained: 2002
charges: Coit Community, Grand Rapids, MI,
1994-

Busink, Evert Sander Hendrick
b. 02/26/1951, Zwanenburg, Noord Holland, Netherlands
training: Calvin Theological Seminary, MDiv, 1976
ordained: 1976
charges: Coquitlam, BC, 1976-88; First, Brandon,
MB, 1988-

Busscher, James Carl
b. 02/15/1957, Holland, MI
training: Calvin Theological Seminary, MDiv, 1985
ordained: 1985
charges: Montello Park, Holland, MI, 1985-94;

Trinity, Jenison, MI, 1994-98; Georgetown, Hudsonville, MI, 1998-2001; Leave, 2001

Busscher, James Gregg
b. 01/23/1953, Grand Rapids, MI
training: Calvin Theological Seminary, MDiv, 1979
ordained: 1979
charges: Immanuel, Roseville, MI, 1979-85; Grace, Inver Grove Heights, MN, 1985-

Buursma, Dirk Richard
b. 10/31/1953, Strathroy, ON
training: Calvin Theological Seminary, MDiv, 1983
ordained: 1984
charges: Community, Toledo, OH, 1984-85; Theological editor, Zondervan Bible Publishers, Grand Rapids, MI, 1986-

Buursma, William D.
b. 08/16/1925, Hogebeintum, Friesland, Netherlands
training: Calvin Theological Seminary, ThB, 1952
ordained: 1952
charges: Strathroy, ON, 1952-55; Munster, IN, 1955-63; Bethel, Grand Rapids, MI, 1963-73; Third, Kalamazoo, MI, 1973-91
retired: 1991

Buus, C. Oliver
b. 06/30/1912, Holland, IA
training: Calvin Theological Seminary, ThB, 1943
ordained: 1943
charges: Austinville, IA, 1943-46; Bible teacher at Bellflower (CA) Christian High School, 1946-49; Walker, MI, 1949-54; Second, Highland, IN, 1954-60; First, Edgerton, MN, 1960-66; West Evergreen, Evergreen Park, IL, 1966-69; Elim in the Desert, Tucson, AZ, 1969-77
retired: 1977; resigned from denomination, 1997
d. 07/07/2001, Tucson, AZ

Buwalda, Jerry Dale
b. 12/12/1943, Sioux Center, IA
training: Calvin Theological Seminary, BD, 1969
ordained: 1969
charges: Holland Center, SD, 1969-73; Grangeville, ID, 1973-77; Ridott, German Valley, IL, 1977-82; New Holland, SD, 1982-92; Ebenezer, Leota, MN, 1992-98; Corsica, SD, 1998-

Buwalda, Merlin Neal
b. 07/03/1944, Waupun, WI
training: Calvin Theological Seminary, BD, 1969
ordained: 1969

charges: Bethel, De Motte, IN, 1969-74; Lexington Green, Kalamazoo, MI, 1974-82; Caledonia, MI, 1982-92; Lake City, MI, 1992-

Byker, Donald Eugene
b. 09/11/1952, Grand Rapids, MI
training: Calvin Theological Seminary, MDiv, 1984
ordained: 1984
charges: Community, Roselawn, IN, 1984-89; Chaplain, Wedgwood Acres Christian Youth Home, Inc., Grand Rapids, MI, 1989-94; Rehoboth, NM, 1994-99; Faculty, Calvin Theological Seminary, Grand Rapids, MI, 1999-

Byker, John Arvid
b. 12/14/1946, Orange City, IA
training: Calvin Theological Seminary, MDiv, 1974
ordained: 1985
charges: Lord of Life Community, San Antonio, TX, 1985-89; Faith Community Fellowship, Mount Vernon, WA, 1989-2000; Atlantic Community, Jacksonville, FL, 2000-2002

Byker, John Jay
b. 07/22/1924, Rock Valley, IA
training: Calvin Theological Seminary, BD, 1954
ordained: 1954
charges: CRC: Waupun, WI, 1954-60; First, Rock Valley, IA, 1960-64; Second, Toronto, ON, 1964-77; Leave, 1977-80; Independent: Orthodox Christian Reformed Church, Allendale, MI, 1980-91
retired: 1991

Byker, Robert Jeremy
b. 01/21/1972, Grand Rapids, MI
training: Calvin Theological Seminary, MDiv, 1998
ordained: 1998
charges: Second, Grand Haven, MI, 1998-2001; Rehoboth, NM, 2001-

Byleveld, John (Jan) M.
b. 06/23/1879, Westeremden, Groningen, Netherlands
training: Calvin Theological Seminary, diploma, 1906
ordained: 1906
charges: Edgerton, MN, 1906-09; Highland IN, 1909-13; New Holland, SD, 1913-21; Prairie City, IA, 1921-27; Dispatch, KS, 1927-29; Oak Harbor, WA, 1929-41
retired: 1941
d. 08/19/1969, Grand Rapids, MI

Bylsma, John
b. 06/28/1925, Hollum, Friesland, Netherlands

training: Calvin Theological Seminary, BD, 1955
ordained: 1955
charges: East Paris, Grand Rapids, MI, 1955-60; Fourth Roseland, Chicago, IL, 1960-65; Third Roseland, Chicago, IL, 1965-71; Kedvale Ave., Oak Lawn, IL, 1971-75; Calvary, Minneapolis, MN, 1980-87; Brookfield, WI, 1987-96
retired: 1996

Byma, Bernard
b. 01/28/1925, Ureterp, Friesland, Netherlands
training: Calvin Theological Seminary, BD, 1953
ordained: 1953
charges: Bellwood, IL, 1953-60; First, Lynden, WA, 1960-70; Second, Denver, CO, 1970-75; First, Hudsonville, MI, 1975-88
retired: 1988

Byma, Peter Robert
b. 12/10/1964, Sussex, NJ
training: Calvin Theological Seminary, MACE, 1991
ordained: 1998
charges: Pioneer, Cedar Springs, MI, 1986-89; Grand Rapids North Diaconal Consultant, 1988-89; Ministry coordinator, Heritage, Byron Center, MI, 1990-97; Cadillac, MI, 1998-

Byun, Young Ik
b. 05/24/1945, Korea
ordained: 1975
charges: Hap Dong Presbyterian Church: Korea, 1975-76; Seoul Presbyterian Church, Los Angeles, CA, 1976-77; Bethel Presbyterian Church, Los Angeles, CA, 1977-84; CRC: West Bethel, Los Angeles, CA, 1984-93; released from denomination to work in China as an unaffiliated missionary, 1993

Callender, Eugene St. Clair
b. 01/21/1926, Boston, MA
training: Westminster Theological Seminary-PA, BD, 1950
ordained: 1952
charges: CRC: Lay work, Paterson, NJ, 1950-51; Home missionary, New York, NY (and evangelism, Hawthorne, NJ, 1952-54), 1952-59; PCUSA: Church of the Master, New York, NY, 1959

Camarigg, Alan Lee
b. 01/09/1957, Sheldon, IA
training: Mid-America Reformed Seminary, MDiv, 1989; Calvin Theological Seminary, Special Program for Ministerial Candidacy, 1991
ordained: 1991

charges: CRC: Hills, MN, 1991-97; Orthodox Christian Reformed Church: Lynden, WA, 1997

Cammenga, Andrew A. Sr.
b. 09/12/1908, Grand Rapids, MI
training: Protestant Reformed Theological Seminary, diploma, 1929
ordained: 1929
charges: PRC: Rock Valley, IA, 1929-33; Los Angeles, CA, 1933-35; Rock Valley, IA, 1935-38; Hull, IA, 1938-50; Home missionary, Canada, 1950-54; Fourth, Grand Rapids, MI, 1954-61; CRC: Faith, Grand Rapids, MI, 1961-62; First, Seattle, WA, 1962-69; Calvin, Pinellas Park, FL, 1969-73
retired: 1973
d. 07/01/1991, Grand Rapids, MI

Cammenga, Andrew A. Jr.
b. 06/11/1936, Rock Valley, IA
training: Calvin Theological Seminary, BD, 1970
ordained: 1970
charges: CRC: Brookfield, Milwaukee, WI, 1970-76; Second, Lynden, WA, 1976-85; Escondido, CA, 1985-97; United Reformed Churches: Escondido, CA, 1997-2000
retired: 2000

Cammenga, Sebastian T. Sr.
b. 04/04/1920, Grand Rapids, MI
training: Protestant Reformed Theological Seminary, diploma, 1943
ordained: 1943
charges: PRC: Orange City, IA, 1943-45; Second, Grand Rapids, MI, 1945-48; Rock Valley, IA, 1948-60; CRC: Sheldon, IA, 1960-65; Drenthe, MI, 1965-71; Hope, Grandville, MI, 1971-83
retired: 1983
d. 09/09/1991, Grand Rapids, MI

Carney, Glandion
b. 06/07/1949
ordained: 1996
charges: Church planting, Centre Pointe, Kentwood, MI, 1996-97; Leave, 1997-

Casanova, Humberto Luis
b. 08/20/1952, Lima, Peru
training: Juan Calvino Seminary, Chile, diploma, 1975; Calvin Theological Seminary, MTS, 1983
ordained: 1978
charges: Presbyterian Church of Chile: Juan Calvino Seminary, Quillota, Chile, 1975 Peter Church, 1975-80; Instituto Evangelico de Chile, 1983-93; Los Angeles National Presbyterian

Church, 1988–91; Holy Trinity National Presbyterian Church, 1992–93; Faculty, Comunidad Teologica, 1994; CRC: Director, TELL, 1995–96; Editor, World Literature Ministries, Grand Rapids, MI, 1996–

Cha, Paul
b. 02/19/1968, Seoul, South Korea
training: Fuller Theological Seminary, MDiv, 2000; Calvin Theological Seminary, Ethnic Minority Program for Ministerial Candidacy, 2002
ordained: 2002
charges: Los Angeles Home Korean, Los Angeles, CA, 2002–

Chan, Matthew (Chang) H.
b. 08/22/1965, Seoul, South Korea
training: Fuller Theological Seminary, MDiv, 2001; Calvin Theological Seminary, Ethnic Minority Program for Ministerial Candidacy, 2002
ordained: 2002
charges: Korean CRC of Orange County, Westminster, CA, 2002–

Chan, Timothy K.
b. 05/04/1951, Swaton, China
training: Hong Kong Baptist Theological Seminary, ThB, 1976; Calvin Theological Seminary, Special Program for Ministerial Candidacy, 1991
ordained: 1991
charges: Chinese, Toronto, ON, 1990–

Chang, Ike
b. 07/28/1930, Jeon Nam Chag Heung-Shi, Korea
training: Presbyterian General Assembly Theological Seminary, MDiv, 1955
ordained: 1955
charges: Korea: Mok Po Hee Sung Church, 1955–57; Ham Pyeung Gung San Church, 1957–59; Ham Pyeung Chung Anf Church, 1959–65; Gwang Ju Seo Bu Church, 1965–68; Chaplain, Seung Il Middle School, 1968–69; Mok Po Sae Han Church, 1969–72; Seoul C.C.C., 1972–77; Sung Ji Church, 1979–80; US: Westminster Presbyterian Church, 1980–85; Nok Won Church, 1985–89; CRC: Elim Dongsan, Garden Grove, CA, 1989–2001
retired: 2001

Chang, Jae-Young (Peter)
b. /1944, Korea
ordained: 1976
charges: Hap Dong Presbyterian Church, Korea: Missionary, West Germany, 1977–83; CRC: Korean, Los Angeles, CA, 1983–85; on loan to

Dongsan Presbyterian, Burbank, CA, 1985–86; Changhoondai Church: Suwan, Korea, 1986

Chei, Han Ku (Alan)
b. 12/03/1945, Korea
training: Tokyo Union Theological Seminary, MDiv, 1974; McCormick Theological Seminary, DMin, 1982; Trinity Theological Seminary, PhD, 1985
ordained: 1992
charges: Korea; Rockford Presbyterian, Rockford, IL, 1976–80; faculty, Divinity School, Pierson University, 1981–91; CRC: Rivershore Korean, Artesia, CA, 1982–84; President, Jilin Theological Seminary, Chang Choon, China, 1994–96; Eligible for call, 1996

Chen, Jason Yong-San
b. 09/27/1938, Amoy, China
training: Calvin Theological Seminary, BD, 1967; MDiv, 1980
ordained: 1970
charges: InterVarsity staff, Iowa City, IA, 1968–71; Campus minister, University of Iowa, Iowa City, IA, 1971–78; Campus minister, University of Iowa, Iowa City, IA, 1978–98; Chinese Church, Iowa City, IA, 1992– ; Director, Campus ministry, University of Iowa, Iowa City, IA, 1998–

Chen, Livingstone
b. 04/01/1934, Amoy, China
training: New York Theological Seminary, MDiv, 1960
ordained: 1964
charges: United Evangelical Church: Naga, Philippines, 1962–67; Trinity, Bacolod City, Philippines, 1967–78; American Baptist: First Chinese Baptist, Fresno, CA, 1978–81; CRC: Indo-Chinese ministry, Zion, Abbotsford, BC, 1981–88; RCA: Fujian Evangelist, Richmond, BC, 1988

Cho, Chung Choo
b. 02/18/1938, Jeonraham-Do Ham Pyeung-Gun, Korea
training: Presbyterian General Assembly Theological Seminary, MDiv, 1970
ordained: 1971
charges: Dae Seoung Church, 1966–71; Oh San Church, 1971–74; Seong San Church, 1975–82; Sae Seoul Church, 1983–85; Texas A & M Korean, College Station, TX, 1985–87; CRC: So Mang Presbyterian, Las Vegas, NV, 1990–

Cho, John Dong-Sung
b. 10/29/1938, North Korea

training: Pacific Christian College
ordained: 1985
charges: Korean Church of South Florida, Ft. Lauderdale, FL, 1980-82; Korean United Methodist Church, Ft. Lauderdale, FL, 1982-84; CRC: Korean, Boca Raton, FL, 1987-93; Chaplain, Korean Community Concerns, Inc., Boca Raton, FL, 1987-

Cho, Joseph
b. 01/15/1920
ordained: 1946
charges: Choong Chun Presbyterian Church, Seoul Korea, 1945-50; North Osaka Presbyterian Church, Osaka, Japan, 1950-57; Tokyo Mikawashima Presbyterian Church, Tokyo, Japan, 1957-76; Tustin Korean, Tustin, CA, 1975-86; CRC: Hebron, Fife, WA, 1986-95
retired: 1995; withdrew from denomination, 1999

Cho, Kenneth K.
b. 05/16/1941, Seoul, South Korea
training: Reformed Presbyterian Seminary, MDiv, 1980; Westminster Theological Seminary-CA, MDiv, 1987
ordained: 1981
charges: Korean, Los Angeles, CA, 1982; Hacienda Immanuel, La Puente, CA, 1982-2001
retired: 2001

Choe, Ken T.
b. 03/07/1965
training: Fuller Theological Seminary, MDiv, 1994
ordained: 1996
charges: Korean Presbyterian Church of America: West Hills, Los Angeles, CA, 1993-97; Los Angeles Home, Los Angeles, CA, 1997-2000; CRC: Los Angeles Home, Los Angeles, CA, 2000-

Choi, Byung Nam
b. 01/02/1943, South Korea
training: Presbyterian General Assembly Theological Seminary, BD, 1975; Reformed Episcopal Theological Seminary, MDiv, 1984
ordained: 1975
charges: Dong Do Presbyterian, Seoul, Korea, 1975-81; North Pennsylvania Presbyterian, Lansdale, PA, 1981-84; CRC: Korean, Grand Rapids, MI, 1984-86; Korean Presbyterian Church: Wang-Sip-Ree, Seoul, Korea, 1986

Choi, Jin
ordained: 1979
charges: Korean Presbyterian Church, 1979-2000; CRC: Church of One Heart, Los Angeles, CA, 2000-

Choi, John (Jong Tae)
b. 11/26/1957, Seoul, South Korea
training: Chong-Shin Theological Seminary, MDiv, 1985
ordained: 1984
charges: Orange Korean, Fullerton, CA, 1985-86; Korean, Long Beach, CA, 1986-89; Intercultural Ministries Director, Christian Reformed Home Missions, Bellflower, CA, 1989-98; New Life, Bellflower, CA, 1998-

Choi, Sung Chang
b. 02/14/1954, Choongcheongnam-Do Gong Ju-Shi, Korea
training: Presbyterian General Assembly Theological Seminary, MDiv, 1981
ordained: 1999
charges: Chaplain, Korean military, 1981-86; Shim Hyeun Church, 1986-89; Han Min Church, 1989-96; Calvin Korean, Los Alamitos, CA,, 1996-99; CRC: Calvin Korean, Los Alamitos, CA, 1999-2001; Garden of Grace, Westminster, CA, 2001-

Chong, David Daesung Yoon
b. 08/18/1972, Seoul, South Korea
training: Talbot School of Theology, MDiv, 1998; Calvin Theological Seminary, Ethnic Minority Program for Ministerial Candidacy, 2000
ordained: 2000
charges: Orange Korean, Fullerton, CA, 2000-2001; San Jose New Hope, San Jose, CA, 2001-

Choo, In Cheong
b. 12/09/1939
ordained: 1967
charges: High school chaplain, 1967-69; Navy chaplain, 1969-72; Pohang Presbyterian Church, 1972-86; Inchon Presbyterian Church, 1986-88; CRC: Hope, San Jose, CA, 1988-94; released to chaplaincy service, 1994

Choy, Eugene Jinho
training: declared eligible on the basis of exceptional gifts, 1982
ordained: 1982
charges: CRC: Korean, Los Angeles, CA, 1982-85; Leave, 1985-89; Resigned from denomination, 1989

Christensen, Francis Lyle
b. 12/11/1928, Grand Rapids, MI
training: Calvin Theological Seminary, BD, 1959
ordained: 1959
charges: Purewater, SD, 1959-62; Tracy, IA,

1962-66; Fruitport, MI, 1966-71; Leave, 1971-75; Non-ministerial vocation, Grandville, MI, 1975

Christoffels, LeRoy Gene

b. 03/21/1944, Luverne, MN
training: Westminster Theological Seminary-PA, BD, 1969; Calvin Theological Seminary, Special Program for Ministerial Candidacy, 1970
ordained: 1970
charges: Hartley, IA, 1970-74; Bethel, Oskaloosa, IA, 1974-79; Trinity, Artesia, CA, 1979-90; Preakness, Wayne, NJ, 1990-98; Worthington, MN, 1998-

Chun, Andrew Kyung-Jin

b. 07/12/1970, Seoul, South Korea
training: Calvin Theological Seminary, MDiv, 1997
ordained: 1997
charges: Han-Bit Korean, Rochester Hills, MN, 1997-98; eligible for call, 1998-99; Anaheim, CA, 1999-2001; Covenant, North Haledon, NJ, 2001-

Chun, Jae-Rin

ordained: 1956
charges: Korean Presbyterian Church: Korea; Phoenix, AZ; CRC: Korean, Phoenix, AZ, 1984-89; Resigned from denomination

Chung, Do Ryang

b. 07/16/1936
ordained: 1987
charges: Yong Hyun Presbyterian Church: Inchon, Korea, 1968-82; Korean Church of Orange County, CA, 1982-87; CRC: So Mang Korean, Garden Grove, CA, 1987-94; On Loan: Central Bible Church, Seoul, Korea, 1994-98; resigned from CRC, serving church in Korea, 1998

Chung, Moses

b. 08/09/1969, Inchon, South Korea
training: Calvin Theological Seminary, MDiv, 1999
ordained: 1999
charges: First, Bellflower, CA, 1999-

Chung, Sung Ho

b. 09/11/1937, Chingja, Korea
training: New York Korean Seminary, MDiv, 1991; ThM, 1993
ordained: 1994
charges: Korean Presbyterian Galilee, Albuquerque, NM, 1996-97; Love Korean, Midland Park, NJ, 1997-

Chung, Woo-Song

b. 04/18/1959, Seoul, South Korea

training: Presbyterian General Assembly Theological Seminary, MDiv, 1989
ordained: 1992
charges: Peace Church, 1983-85; Central Bible Church, 1986; Han Kwang Church, 1987-90; Washington Pyeokang Church, 1990-91; CRC: Dae Il Korean, Anaheim, CA, 1992-96/So Mang Korean, Anaheim, CA, 1995-96; Associate pastor for parish ministry, on loan: Oriental Mission Church, Los Angeles, CA, 1996-

Chung, Youn-Kyoo

b. 06/22/1948, Seoul, South Korea
training: Calvin Theological Seminary, MDiv, 1987
ordained: 1988
charges: CRC: Hahn-In, Wyoming, MI, 1988-95; Korean-American Presbyterian Church, 1995

Clark, Harold Dexter Jr.

b. 07/02/1927, Oklahoma City, OK
training: Calvin Theological Seminary, BD, 1966; MDiv, 1977
ordained: 1966
charges: Parkview Heights, Cincinnati, OH, 1966-72; Escalon, CA, 1972-74; Palo Alto, CA, 1974-78; Phoenix, AZ, 1978-92
retired: 1992; affiliated with United Reformed Churches, 1997

Claus, Charles Henry

b. 01/02/1956, Terrace, BC
training: Calvin Theological Seminary, MDiv, 1986
ordained: 1986
charges: CRC: Peace Community, Calgary, AB, 1986-88; eligible for call, 1988-89; Hope Community, Campbell River, BC, 1989-95; Independent: Vineyard Church, Campbell River, BC

Clotaire, Raymond

training: Reformed Theological Seminary, Orlando
charges: Haitian Baptist: -2002; CRC: Elohim, Orlando, FL, 2002-

Coelingh, Willem

b. 01/24/1826, Coevorden, Drenthe, Netherlands
training: with Wolter Alberts Kok
ordained: 1847
charges: GKN: Enter, 1852-54; Bolsward, 1854-55; Twelloo, 1855-60; Genemuiden, 1860-65; Schoonebeek, 1865-71; CRC: First, Pella, IA, 1871-74; First, Zeeland, MI, 1874-77; Ridott, IL, 1877-81; East Overisel, MI, 1881-83
retired: 1883
d. 01/25/1895, Pella, IA

Cok, Ronald Henry
b. 06/04/1947, Bozeman, MT
training: Calvin Theological Seminary, BD, 1972
ordained: 1974
charges: Pleasant Valley, Longmont, CO, 1974-81;
Chelwood, Albuquerque, NM, 1981-92; Leave,
1992-95; Chaplain, Veterans Administration Medical Center, Albuquerque, NM, 1995-

Colyn, Darren Glen
b. 05/15/1973, Port Alberni, BC
training: Calvin Theological Seminary, MDiv, 2001
ordained: 2002
charges: First, Duncan, BC, 2002-

Compaan, Arlo Don
b. 06/11/1943, Hull, ND
training: Calvin Theological Seminary, BD, 1968;
Claremont School of Theology, ThD, 1971
ordained: 1971
charges: St. Joseph, MI, 1971-74; Faculty, Trinity
College, 1974-79; Executive Director, Center for
Life Skills, Chicago, IL, 1979-89; Pastoral counselor, Toletine Personal Resource Center, Olympia
Fields, IL, 1989-

Compaan, Gilmer
b. 08/23/1924, Hull, ND
training: Calvin Theological Seminary, BD, 1966
ordained: 1966
charges: Worthington, MN, 1966-71; Vogel Center, MI, 1971-76; East Martin, MI, 1976-83;
Hollandale, MN, 1983-89
retired: 1989

Compagner, Calvin Dale
b. 03/09/1946, Zeeland, MI
training: Calvin Theological Seminary, BD, 1973
ordained: 1973
charges: Calvary, Plainwell, MI, 1973-79; Providence, Cutlerville, MI, 1979-84; Second, Denver,
CO, 1984-88; Friendship, Byron Center, MI, 1988-

Contant, Isaac
b. 01/05/1843, Cadzand, Zeeland, Netherlands
training: Theologische Universiteit, Kampen, diploma, 1874
ordained: 1874
charges: GKN: Brielle, 1874-79; Oud-Loosdrecht,
1879-81; Alkmaar, 1881-93; Kapelle-Biezelinga,
1893-96; CRC: Lodi, NJ, 1896-99; Independent:
Free Christian Reformed, Lodi, NJ, 1899-1923
retired: 1923
d. 01/29/1929, Lodi, NJ

Contant, Martin John
b. 01/26/1950, Goes, Zeeland, Netherlands
training: Calvin Theological Seminary, MDiv, 1976
ordained: 1976
charges: Intern, Brantford, ON, 1975-76;
Ancaster, ON, 1976-80; First, Langley, BC, 1980-
94; Regional director, Christian Reformed Home
Missions, North Pacific Regions, Surrey, BC,
1994-

Cooke, Edward Goddard Jr.
b. 11/28/1929, Detroit, MI
training: Calvin Theological Seminary, BD, 1954
ordained: 1954
charges: Tracy, IA, 1954-58; Maranatha, Holland,
MI, 1958-63; Home missionary, Rehoboth, NM,
1963-68; West Sayville, NY, 1968-73; First, De
Motte, IN, 1973-80; Rosewood, Bellflower, CA,
1980-85; Westwood, Kalamazoo, MI, 1985-89;
medical leave, 1989-90
d. 05/18/1990, Kalamazoo, MI

Cooper, Clarence
b. 10/24/1885, Chicago, IL
training: Calvin Theological Seminary, diploma,
1914; Princeton, BD, 1916
ordained: 1916
charges: Willard, OH, 1915-21
d. 06/18/1921, Chicago, IL

Cooper, Dale Jay
b. 11/28/1941, Holland, MI
training: Calvin Theological Seminary, BD, 1968;
Vrije Universiteit, Amsterdam, ThD, 1970
ordained: 1972
charges: Bible teacher, Calvin Chr. High School,
Grandville, MI, 1972-76; Faculty (chaplain since
1979), Calvin College, 1976-

Cooper, George
ordained: 2000
charges: Fox Valley, Crystal Lake, IL, 2000-

Cooper, George Dennis
b. 09/30/1945, Chicago, IL
training: Calvin Theological Seminary, MDiv, 1971
ordained: 1973
charges: Ferrisburg, VT, 1973-77; Missionary to
Guam, 1977-80; Chaplain, United States Navy,
1980-

Cooper, James
b. 09/03/1947, Evergreen Park, IL
training: Westminster Theological Seminary-PA,

MDiv, 1972; Calvin Theological Seminary, Special Program for Ministerial Candidacy, 1973
ordained: 1973
charges: Hope, Hull, IA, 1973-80; Bethel, Waupun, WI, 1980-87; Third, Zeeland, MI, 1987-98; Ada, MI, 1998-

Cooper, John
b. 08/10/1924, Clifton, NJ
training: Westminster Theological Seminary-PA, BD, 1956
ordained: 1956
charges: German Reformed Church: Ashley, ND, 1956-59; CRC: Forest, ON, 1959-62; Grace, Muskegon, MI, 1962-68; East Palmyra, NY, 1968-70; Leave, 1970-73; Paramus, NJ, 1973-77; Bethel, Acton, ON, 1978-83
retired: 1987

Cooper, John Wesley
b. 07/08/1947, Passaic, NJ
training: University of Toronto, MA, 1973; PhD, 1978; Calvin Theological Seminary, MTS, 1983
ordained: 1985
charges: Faculty, Calvin Theological Seminary, Grand Rapids, MI, 1985-

Cooper, Samuel
b. 10/05/1957, Clifton, NJ
training: Calvin Theological Seminary, MDiv, 1993
ordained: 1994
charges: Community of Meadowvale, Mississauga, ON, 1994-

Cooper, Sidney
b. 03/08/1930, Clifton, NJ
training: Westminster Theological Seminary-PA, BD, 1954; Vrije Universiteit, Amsterdam, Drs, 1956
ordained: 1956
charges: First, Sarnia, ON, 1956-60; Missionary to New Zealand, 1960-66; Trinity, North Haledon, NJ, 1966-73; Trinity, Artesia, CA, 1973-78; First, Sarnia, ON, 1978-84; on loan to Palmerston, New Zealand Reformed Church, 1984-87; Alliston, ON, 1987-93
retired: 1993

Corey, Thomas Michael
b. 02/19/1947, Baltimore, MD
training: Westminster Theological Seminary-PA, MDiv 1973
ordained: 1976
charges: OPC: Church of the City, Philadelphia, PA, 1976-78; Southwest Philadelphia Reformed Fellowship, Philadelphia, PA, 1978-81; PCA:

Church of the Redeemer, Philadelphia, PA, 1981-91; Hope, Ballston Spa, NY, 1994- ; CRC: Glad Tidings, Edmonton, AB, 1991-94

Cornelisse, Charles Ray
b. 08/09/1952, Grand Rapids, MI
training: Calvin Theological Seminary, MDiv, 1984
ordained: 1984
charges: Westside Fellowship, Kingston, ON, 1984-89; Seymour, Grand Rapids, MI, 1989-91; Chaplain, United States Air Force, 1991-

Cornelisse, Nicolaas
b. 03/30/1941, Oostkappelle, Zeeland, Netherlands
training: Covenant Theological Seminary, MDiv, 1963; Vrije Universiteit, Amsterdam, diploma, 1970
ordained: 1972
charges: GKN: Dordrecht, Zwijndrecht, 1972-79; Eck en Wiel, 1979-82; director, L'Arbi, Swift Current, SK, 1982-85; CRC: Ebenezer, Jarvis, ON, 1985-89; Maranatha, Edmonton, AB, 1989-96; Calvary, Ottawa, ON, 1996-2002; Bethel, Brockville, ON, 2002-

Cortina, Carlos M.
b. 04/16/1927, Camagüe, Cuba
training: Calvin Theological Seminary, BD, 1966
ordained: 1966
charges: Missionary for Cuban Evangelism, 1966-72; Spanish, Wyoming, MI, 1972-73
d. 04/10/1973, Grand Rapids, MI

Corvers, Gysbertus (Guy)
b. 11/08/1932, Zwijndrecht, Zuid Holland, Netherlands
training: Calvin Theological Seminary, BD, 1964
ordained: 1964
charges: Luverne, MN, 1964-67; Thunder Bay, ON, 1967-72; Maranatha, Bowmanville, ON, 1972-81; Richmond, BC, 1981-85
retired: 1985
d. 04/15/1990, New Castle, ON

Corvers, Jacobus
b. 03/10/1937, Zwijndrecht, Zuid Holland, Netherlands
training: Calvin Theological Seminary, BD, 1972
ordained: 1973
charges: Bethel, Acton, ON, 1973-77; Taber, AB, 1977-83; Agassiz, BC, 1983-91; Brooks, AB, 1991-2000
retired: 2002

Couperus, Sidney
b. 01/16/1959, Belleville, ON
training: Calvin Theological Seminary, MDiv, 1986
ordained: 1986
charges: First, Guelph, ON, 1986-88; New Life, Guelph, ON, 1988-94; Trinity, Abbotsford, BC, 1994-

Couwenhoven, Isaac D.
b. 08/09/1893, South Holland, IL
training: Calvin Theological Seminary, diploma, 1923; Princeton Seminary, ThM, 1924
ordained: 1924
charges: Tracy, IA, 1924-31; McBain, MI, 1931-59
retired: 1959
d. 02/21/1984, Lansing, IL

Cowart, Donald Wayne
b. 05/30/1958, Modesto, CA
training: Theologische Universiteit, Kampen, Drs, 1991; Calvin Theological Seminary, Special Program for Ministerial Candidacy, 1994
ordained: 1995
charges: Riverside, Wellandport, ON, 1995-2000; New Holland, SD, 2000-

Crawford, Robert M.
b. 12/08/1946, Chicago, IL
training: declared eligible on the basis of exceptional gifts, 1977
ordained: 1978
charges: Independent: Spirit and Truth Fellowship, Chicago, IL, 1977-83; CRC: Spirit and Truth Fellowship, Chicago, IL, 1983-87; Eligible for call, 1987-2001

Crump, David M.
b. 02/26/1956, Los Angeles, CA
training: Regent College, MDiv, 1985; University of Aberdeen, PhD, 1988; declared eligible on the basis of exceptional gifts, 1990
ordained: 1990
charges: Mountain Springs Community/Immanuel, Salt Lake City, UT, 1988-97; Faculty, Calvin College, Grand Rapids, MI, 1997-

Crushshon, Dennis Alexander Sr.
b. 03/24/1951, Chicago, IL
training: Calvin Theological Seminary, MDiv, 1981
ordained: 1981
charges: Back to God Church, Chicago, IL, 1981-

Culbertson, Edwin Neil
b. 05/11/1954, Klamath Falls, OR
training: Calvin Theological Seminary, MDiv, 1983

ordained: 1983
charges: Missionary, Guam, 1983-96; Faith Presbyterian Reformed Church, Guam, 1983-

Cumberland, Gregory Lynn
b. 02/12/1959, Georgetown, OH
training: Calvin Theological Seminary, MMin, 1992
ordained: 1993
charges: CRC: Madison Square, Grand Rapids, MI, 1993-95; Independent, 1995

Cunningham, Craig Richard
b. 07/09/1965, Pittsburgh, PA.
training: Calvin Theological Seminary, MDiv, 1995
ordained: 1995
charges: Vanastra Community, Vanastra, ON, 1995-98; Hanley, Grandville, MI, 1998-2000; Non-ministerial vocation, 2000

Cupido, Jacob
b. 11/03/1888, Orange City, IA
training: Calvin Theological Seminary, diploma, 1916
ordained: 1916
charges: Hancock, MN, 1916-20; Redlands, CA, 1920-27; Harrison, SD, 1927-31; West Sayville, NY, 1931-46; Hawarden, IA, 1946-53
retired: 1953
d. 04/05/1954, Orange City, IA

Daane, James
b. 05/31/1914, Grand Haven, MI
training: Calvin Theological Seminary, ThB, 1940; Princeton Seminary, ThM, 1945; Vrije Universiteit, Amsterdam, ThD, 1953
ordained: 1943
charges: Preakness, NJ, 1943-45; Lafayette, IN, 1945-49; Los Angeles, CA, 1949-61; Editor at Christianity Today, 1961-66; Faculty, Fuller Theological Seminary, 1966-79
retired: 1979
d. 04/13/1983, Grand Rapids, MI

Dadson, Michael Robert
b. 10/25/1959, Surrey, BC
training: Calvin Theological Seminary, MDiv, 1993
ordained: 1993
charges: Church residency, Surrey, BC, 1993-95; Redwood Community, Surrey, BC, 1995-1999; Counseling, Trinity Western University, Langley, BC, 2001-

Dahm, Arlo Jay
b. 04/16/1934, Ogilvie, MN

training: Calvin Theological Seminary, BD, 1958
ordained: 1958
charges: Chaplain, United States Navy, 1958–67; Oak Harbor, WA, 1967–68; Non-ministerial vocation, 1969

Dahm, Peter Francis
b. 11/30/1903, Nieuw Beijerland, Zuid Holland, Netherlands
training: Calvin Theological Seminary, BD, 1934
ordained: 1934
charges: Ogilvie, MN, 1934–42; Bunde, MN, 1942–54; Stated supply at Leamington, ON, 1957–58; Leamington, ON, 1958–63; Immanuel, Cornwall, ON, 1963–66; Bigelow, MN, 1966–69
retired: 1954
d. 09/30/1976, Ogilvie, MN

Dahnke, Gordon Lee
b. 12/04/1936, Battle Creek, MI
training: Calvin Theological Seminary, BD, 1963
ordained: 1963
charges: East Side, Cleveland, OH, 1963–71; Fuller Ave., Grand Rapids, MI, 1971–74; Leave, 1974–81; Non-ministerial vocation, 1981

Daley, Andre
b. 01/04/1962, Kingston, Jamaica, West Indies
training: Princeton Theological Seminary, MDiv, 1988
ordained: 1988
charges: RCA: North Branch Reformed Somerville, NJ, 1988–91; Second Reformed Church, Irvington, NJ, 1991–98; CRC: CentrePointe Community, Kentwood, MI, 1998–2002; Leave, 2002

Daley, G. David
b. 10/03/1955, St. Johns, NB
ordained: 1988
charges: Reformed Presbyterian Church: Covenant, Newcastle, NB, 1988–91; Faculty, Beacon Christian High School, St. Catharines, ON, 1991–92; CRC: Kanawha, IA, 1994–2002; West Park, Cleveland, OH, 2002–

Danhof, Benjamin John
b. 12/14/1896, Chicago, IL
training: Calvin Theological Seminary, diploma, 1924; ThB, 1933
ordained: 1925
charges: Protestant Reformed Church; Hull, IA, 1925–27; CRC: First, Grand Haven, MI, 1927–30; Drenthe, MI, 1930–37; leave, 1937–43; PCUSA: Home missionary, Texas, 1943–45; Associate Re-

formed Presbyterian: Grande Prairie, TX, 1945–50; leave, 1950–52; Bethel, Oak Hill, AL, 1952–53; Grande Prairie, TX, 1953–60
d. 06/06/1960, Dallas, TX

Danhof, Henry
b. 05/01/1879, Uithuizermeeden, Groningen, Netherlands
training: Calvin Theological Seminary, diploma, 1910
ordained: 1910
charges: CRC: Sully, IA, 1910–14; Dennis Ave., Grand Rapids, MI, 1914–18; First, Kalamazoo, MI, 1918–24; Independent: Protesting First Christian Reformed, Kalamazoo, MI, 1924–45
retired: 1945
d. 07/26/1952, Kalamazoo, MI

Danhof, Ralph J.
b. 07/28/1900, Chicago, IL
training: Calvin Theological Seminary, diploma, 1925; Vrije Universitiet, ThD, 1929
ordained: 1929
charges: First, Pella, IA, 1929–34; Fourteenth St., Holland, MI, 1934–45; Neland, Ave. and part-time denominational stated clerk, Grand Rapids, MI, 1945–56; Denominational stated clerk, Grand Rapids, MI, 1956–71
retired: 1970
d. 10/13/1971, Grand Rapids, MI

Datema, Steven James
b. 09/19/1967, Grand Rapids, MI
training: Calvin Theological Seminary, MDiv, 1999
ordained: 1999
charges: Spring Lake, MI, 1999–

Davelaar, Wendell Dean
b. 05/14/1958, Sioux Center, IA
training: Calvin Theological Seminary, MDiv, 2000
ordained: 2000
charges: First, Fulton, IL, 2000–

Davies, Mark Arthur
b. 03/15/1944, Sheboygan, WI
training: Westminster Theological Seminary-PA, BD, 1970; MDiv, 1977; Princeton Theological Seminary, PhD, 1971; Calvin Theological Seminary, Special Program for Ministerial Candidacy, 1972
ordained: 1972
charges: Hollandale, MN, 1972–77; Calvary Ministries, Vermillion, SD, 1977–80; East Islip, NY, 1980–84; Hamilton, MI, 1984–91; Lake Worth, FL, 1991–2000; Bethel, Newmarket, ON, 2000–

De Baun, Isaac. J.
b. 09/21/1835, Monsey, NY
training: with J.D. Demarest, J.Y. De Baun,
A. Van Houten
ordained: 1861
charges: True Protestant Dutch Reformed: Montville, NJ, 1861-65; Paramus, NJ, 1868-77; Leave,
1878-90; CRC: Leave, 1890-95
d. 01/14/1895

De Baun, John Yeury
b. 08/22/1827, Monsey, NY vicinity
training: with J.D. Demarest, A. Van Houten, G.T.
Demarest
ordained: 1855
charges: True Protestant Dutch Reformed:
Monsey, NJ and Rumsey, NY, 1855-60;
Hackensack and Leonia, NJ, 1860-75;
Hackensack, NJ, 1875-87; CRC: LaGrave Avenue,
Grand Rapids, MI, 1887-92; Leonia, NJ, 1892-95
d. 02/07/1895, Leonia, NJ

De Beer, Dirk
b. 03/17/1877, Holland, MI
training: Calvin Theological Seminary, diploma,
1908
ordained: 1908
charges: Jenison, MI, 1908-13; Prospect St.,
Passaic, NJ, 1913-46
retired: 1946
d. 01/19/1960, Grand Rapids, MI

De Beer, Johan Boelens
b. 04/19/1819, Haren, Groningen, Netherlands
training: declared eligible on the basis of exceptional gifts, 1859
ordained: 1859
charges: GKN: Haren, 1859-60; Alt Reformierde
Kirche: Emden, 1860-66; CRC: Central Ave., Holland, MI, 1867; RCA: Foreston, IL, 1867-70; Grand
Haven, MI, 1870-72; Cleveland, OH, 1872-74;
Parkersburg, IA, 1874-80; GKN: Uithuizermeeden,
1880-87
retired: 1887
d. 12/22/1891, Emden, Germany

De Berdt, August J.
b. 02/19/1934, Brugge, Belgium
training: University of Innsbruck, Austria, 1964
ordained: 1965
charges: CRC: Home missionary, Good Samaritan,
Miami, FL, 1965-67; United Church of Christ,
1972

De Berdt, Michiel M.
b. 10/20/1930, Assehoek, Belgium
training: Calvin Theological Seminary, BD, 1962
ordained: 1962
charges: Missionary to Japan, 1962-95
retired: 1995

De Boer, Cornelius Jay
b. 08/10/1958, Chicago, IL
training: Calvin Theological Seminary, MDiv,
1985, ThM, 1993
ordained: 1988
charges: Orland Park, IL, 1986-1999; Training,
Advocate Health Care, Oak Lawn, IL, 1999-2001;
Chaplain, Advocate Christ Medical Center, Oak
Lawn, IL, 2001-

De Boer, Floyd Robert
b. 01/10/1930, Maywood, NJ
training: Calvin Theological Seminary, BD, 1954
ordained: 1954
charges: Beaverdam, MI, 1954-59; Rogers
Heights, Grand Rapids, MI, 1959-65; Newton, NJ,
1965-71; Milwood, Kalamazoo, MI, 1971-83;
Ackley, IA, 1983-92
retired: 1992

De Boer, Joel A.
b. 06/25/1958, Denver, CO
training: Calvin Theological Seminary, MDiv, 1989
ordained: 1989
charges: CRC: Mountain View, Lynden, WA, 1989-
94; Church planting, Salt Lake City, UT, 1994-95;
Horizon Hills, Denver, CO, 1995-96; Interim,
Ridgeview Hills, Denver, CO, 1995; Baymeadows
Community, Jacksonville, FL, 1996-98; Eligible for
call, 1998-99; Bridge Community, Langley, BC,
1999-2001; resigned from denomination

De Boer, John
b. 09/03/1943, Utrecht, Utrecht, Netherlands
training: Calvin Theological Seminary, BD, 1969
ordained: 1972
charges: Campus minister, Muskegon Community
College, Muskegon, MI, 1972-79; Campus minister, Grand Valley State University, Allendale, MI,
1979-

De Boer, Menno
b. 06/06/1856, Grijpskerk, Groningen, Netherlands
training: Calvin Theological Seminary, diploma,
1895
ordained: 1895
charges: Spring Lake, MI, 1895-98; Prosper, MI,

1898-1900; Alto, WI, 1900-03; First, South Holland, IL, 1903-07; New Holland, SD, 1907-12; Doon, IA, 1912-17; Highland, IN, 1917-20; Holland, MN, 1920-21
d. 02/04/1921, Holland, MN

De Boer, Peter
b. 03/10/1908, Grand Rapids, MI
training: Protestant Reformed Theological Seminary, diploma, 1932
ordained: 1932
charges: PRC: South Holland, IL, 1932-38; Holland, MI, 1938-43; Redlands, CA, 1943-48; Edgerton, MN, 1948-60; CRC: Sioux Falls, SD, 1960-70; Dorr, MI, 1970-73
retired: 1973
d. 05/21/1979, Edgerton, MN

De Boer, Tice
b. 06/20/1878, Hindeloopen, Friesland, Netherlands
training: Calvin Theological Seminary, diploma, 1918
ordained: 1918
charges: Beaverdam, MI, 1918-20; Winnipeg, MB, 1920-24; Volga, SD, 1924-28; Chatham, ON, 1928-37
retired: 1937
d. 04/14/1943, Grand Rapids, MI

De Boer, Willis Peter
b. 04/18/1923, East Grand Rapids, MI
training: Calvin Theological Seminary, ThB, 1951; Vrije Universiteit, Amsterdam, ThD, 1962
ordained: 1951
charges: Washington, DC, 1951-56; Bradenton, FL, 1956-58; Faculty, Calvin College, Grand Rapids, MI, 1962-88
retired: 1988

De Bolster, Henry R.
b. 11/02/1926, Rotterdam, Zuid Holland, Netherlands
training: Calvin Theological Seminary, BD, 1962; MDiv, 1972
ordained: 1962
charges: Immanuel, Brampton, ON, 1962-65; Second, Brampton, IN, 1965-66; Emmanuel, Calgary, AB, 1966-71; Maranatha, St. Catharines, ON, 1971-81; President, Redeemer College, Ancaster, ON, 1981-94
retired: 1994

De Bree, Cornelius
b. 10/13/1935, Broek op Langedijk, Noord Holland, Netherlands
training: Calvin Theological Seminary, ThB, 1965
ordained: 1965
charges: Brooks, AB, 1965-68; Agassiz, BC, 1968-69; Non-ministerial vocation, Calgary, AB, 1969

De Bruyn, Hendrick
b. 01/18/1935, Lemmer, Friesland, Netherlands
training: Calvin Theological Seminary, BD, 1965; MDiv, 1975
ordained: 1965
charges: Home missionary, Fredericton, NB, 1965-69; Ambassador, Windsor, ON, 1969-73; Missionary, Community, Detroit, MI, 1973-74; Director, Indian Family Centre, Winnipeg, MB, 1974-2000
retired: 2000

De Bruyn, Jacob Cornelius
b. 03/01/1875, Hoornaar, Zuid Holland, Netherlands
training: Calvin Theological Seminary, diploma, 1911
ordained: 1911
charges: Grant, MI, 1911-14; Hull, ND, 1914-21; Ogilvie, NM, 1921-29; Sioux Falls, SD, 1929-36; Home missionary at Sioux Falls, SD, 1936-38
retired: 1938
d. 12/15/1946, Grand Rapids, MI

De Bruyn, Jelle Anskes
b. 07/07/1846, Nijehaske, Friesland, Netherlands
training: Theologische Universiteit, Kampen, diploma, 1872
ordained: 1872
charges: GKN: Kollum, 1872-75; Meeden, 1875-77; Hazerswoude, 1877-80; Niezijl, 1880-83; Niezijl, 1885-94; Emmen, 1894-1900; Oud-Vossemeer, 1900-15; CRC: Central Ave., Holland, MI 1883-85; RCA: Paterson, NJ, 1885
retired: 1915
d. 03/03/1927, Kollum, Friesland, Netherlands

De Bruyn, Jon Otto
b. 02/21/1949, Sioux Falls, SD
training: Calvin Theological Seminary, MDiv, 1978
ordained: 1978
charges: Rudyard, MI, 1978-82; Fellowship, Traverse City, MI, 1983-

De Bruyne, Peter W.

b. 10/08/1932, Vrouwenparochie, Friesland, Netherlands
training: Calvin Theological Seminary, BD, 1962
ordained: 1963
charges: Regina, SK, 1963-66; Ottewell, Edmonton, AB, 1966-71; Victoria, BC, 1971-79; Second, Brampton, ON, 1979-87; Mountainview and Shalom Manor, Grimsby, ON, 1987-92; Chaplain, Shalom Manor, Grimsby, ON, 1992-96
retired: 1996

Deckinga, Mark Dennis

b. 03/22/1958, Chicago, IL
training: Calvin Theological Seminary, MDiv, 1991
ordained: 1992
charges: Evangelist, Christian Indian Center, Denver, CO, 1985-89; Rock Rapids, IA, 1991-98; Chaplain, Mishawaka, IN, 1998-99; Chaplain, St. Joseph Hospital, Kokomo, IN, 1999-

Deckinga, Peter Wayne

b. 01/03/1951, Chicago, IL
training: Calvin Theological Seminary, MDiv, 1977
ordained: 1977
charges: Grace, Inver Grove Heights, MN, 1977-85; Christ's Fellowship, Austin, TX, 1985-89; Leave, 1989-98; Non-ministerial vocation, 1998

De Does, Thomas Alan

b. 07/03/1956, Kalamazoo, MI
training: Reformed Theological Seminary, MDiv, 1982; Calvin Theological Seminary, Special Program for Ministerial Candidacy, 1984
ordained: 1984
charges: Lebanon, IA, 1984-90; Lucas, MI, 1990-

De Groot, Daniel W.

b. 02/14/1947, Jamestown, MI
training: Calvin Theological Seminary, BD, 1976
ordained: 1976
charges: Trinity, Rock Valley, IA, 1976-82; Maranatha, St. Catharines, ON, 1982-84; Leave, 1984-86; Bethel, Edgerton, MN, 1986-93; Covenant, Sioux Center, IA, 1993-99; Justice for All, Rock Valley, IA, 1999-

De Groot, Harold

b. 10/20/1928, Orange City, IA
training: Calvin Theological Seminary, ThB, 1952
ordained: 1952
charges: Hull, ND, 1952-55; Missionary to Nigeria, 1955-70; Ocheyedan, IA, 1970-76; Sioux Falls, SD, 1976-85; Sunnyside, WA, 1985-88; Bethel, De Motte, IN, 1988-92

retired: 1992

De Groot, Jan (John) E.

b. 08/19/1871, Province of Groningen, Netherlands
training: Calvin Theological Seminary, diploma, 1900
ordained: 1900
charges: Pease, MN, 1900-04, New Holland, SD, 1904-07
d. 01/22/1907, Grand Rapids, MI

De Groot, Otto

b. 10/07/1914, Volga, SD
training: Calvin Theological Seminary, BD, 1944
ordained: 1944
charges: Sibley, IA, 1944-48; East Side, Cleveland, OH, 1948-52; First, Muskegon, MI, 1952-54; Leota, MN, 1954-58; Second, Redlands, CA, 1958-66; Zutphen, MI, 1966-79
retired: 1979
d. 01/15/2000, Grand Rapids, MI

De Groot, Renze Otto

b. 04/10/1908, Volga, SD
training: Calvin Theological Seminary, ThB, 1933; Northern Baptist Theological Seminary, ThD, 1935
ordained: 1936
charges: Momence, IL, 1935-41; Fourth, Chicago, IL, 1941-45; Second, Orange City, IA, 1945-48; Denominational minister, Classis Chicago North, Bellwood, IL, 1948-49; Denominational minister, Elmhurst, Park Lane and Wheaton, IL, 1949-53; Creston, Grand Rapids, MI, 1953-59; First, Kalamazoo, MI, 1959-69; Coopersville, MI, 1969-75
retired: 1975
d. 04/10/1991, Grand Rapids, MI

de Groot, Ronald John

b. 06/23/1950, Winnipeg, MB
training: Calvin Theological Seminary, MDiv, 1978
ordained: 1978
charges: CRC: Calvin, McBain, MI, 1978-82; Silver Spring, MD, 1982-90; Leave, 1990-96; PSUSA, 1996

De Groot, William (Willem)

b. /1872, Niezijl, Groningen, Netherlands
training: Calvin Theological Seminary, diploma, 1897; Princeton Seminary, ThM, 1918; University of Chicago, 1918-19
ordained: 1897
charges: Home missionary, 1897-98; Hospers, IA, 1898-1901; Borculo, MI, 1901-03; Graafschap, MI, 1903-09; Sixteenth St., Holland, MI, 1909-13;

Home missionary at Ogden, UT, 1913-14, Leota, MN, 1914-16; Home missionary at Chicago, IL, 1918-19; Grundy Center, IA, 1919-20; Oostburg, WI, 1920-26; Racine, WI, 1926-29; Non-ministerial vocation: Various CRC denominational assignments
d. 11/23/1955, Grand Rapids, MI

De Haan, Clarence
b. 04/22/1916, De Motte, IN
training: Calvin Theological Seminary, ThB, 1944
ordained: 1944
charges: Woden, IA, 1944-48; Spring Lake, MI, 1948-53; Oak Glen, Lansing, IL, 1953-58; Borculo, MI, 1958-68; Willard, OH, 1968-74
retired: 1974
d. 08/03/1990, East Grand Rapids, MI

De Haan, Gerrit A.
b. 01/07/1862, Enumatil, Groningen, Netherlands
training: Calvin Theological Seminary, diploma, 1891
ordained: 1891
charges: Oakdale Park, Grand Rapids, MI, 1891-95
d. 08/20/1895, Grand Rapids, MI

De Haan, John Sr.
b. 03/03/1865, Den Haag, Zuid Holland, Netherlands
training: Presbyterian Church
ordained: 1890
charges: PCUSA.: Gull Lake, MI, 1890-92; Raisin, MI, 1893-94; Grindstone City-Huron-Port Austin, MI, 1894-96; Moody Bible Instit., 1896-98; American Reformed Church: Summit, IL, 1898-1903; RCA: Sixth, Grand Rapids, MI, 1903-10; Third, Kalamazoo, MI, 1910-17; CRC: East Paris, MI, 1917-19; First, Pella, IA, 1919-29; Lamont, MI, 1929-38
retired: 1938
d. 08/15/1940, Grand Rapids, MI

De Haan, John Jr.
b. 07/15/1891, Holloway, MI
training: Calvin Theological Seminary, diploma, 1921
ordained: 1921
charges: Lamont, MI, 1921-25; Ninth St., Holland, MI, 1925-29; Broadway Ave., Grand Rapids, MI, 1929-45
retired: 1945
d. 10/28/1945, Grand Rapids, MI

De Haan, John H.
b. 07/17/1901, Harrison, SD
training: Calvin Theological Seminary, BD, 1927; Princeton Seminary, ThM, 1928
ordained: 1929
charges: Bauer, MI, 1928-46; Ridott, IL, 1946-48; First, Randolph, WI, 1948-56; Emden, MN, 1956-62
retired: 1962
d. 11/24/1988, Waupun, WI

De Haan, Peter William
b. 02/14/1947, Vinkeveen, Utrecht, Netherlands
training: Calvin Theological Seminary, BD, 1972
ordained: 1972
charges: First, Hospers, IA, 1972-77; Zion, Oshawa, ON, 1977-83; Maranatha, Woodstock, ON, 1983-91; Maple Ave., Holland, MI, 1991-1999; Maple Ave. Ministries, Holland, MI, 1999-

De Haan, Reuben Samuel
b. 11/04/1900, Chicago, IL
training: Calvin Theological Seminary, BD, 1929
ordained: 1929
charges: Dispatch, KS, 1929-37; Austinville, IA, 1937-43; Pease, MN, 1943-50; Godwin Heights, Grand Rapids, MI, 1950-54; Sheldon, IA, 1954-60; Walker, Grand Rapids, MI, 1960-66
retired: 1966
d. 07/22/1978, Grand Rapids, MI

De Jager, Anthony
b. 06/25/1922, Kampen, Overijsel, Netherlands
training: Theologische Universiteit, Kampen, diploma, 1951; Calvin Theological Seminary, BD, 1952
ordained: 1952
charges: Taber, AB, 1952-54; Jasper Place, Edmonton, AB, 1954-57; Brockville, ON, 1957-61; First, Toronto, ON, 1961-63; Second, Sarnia, ON, 1963-70; Trinity, Artesia, CA, 1970-73; Rehoboth, Bowmanville, ON, 1973-87
retired: 1987

De Jong, Alexander C.
b. 06/29/1922, Grand Rapids, MI
training: Calvin Theological Seminary, ThB, 1946; Westminster Theological Seminary-PA, ThM, 1946; Vrije Universiteit, Amsterdam, ThD, 1954
ordained: 1947
charges: First, Paterson, NJ, 1947-51; Boston Square, Grand Rapids, MI, 1951-52; Leave, 1952-54; Highland Hills, Grand Rapids, MI, 1954-60; Second, Highland, IN, 1960-64; Second, Denver, CO, 1964-66; President, Trinity College, Palos

Heights, IL, 1966–68; Calvin, Oak Lawn, IL, 1968–74; Faculty, Trinity Christian College, Palos Heights, IL, 1974–76; Kedvale, Oak Lawn, IL, 1976–80
retired: 1980

De Jong, Andrew (Anne)
b. 04/09/1947, Sneek, Friesland, Netherlands
training: Calvin Theological Seminary, MCE, 1977; declared eligible on the basis of unique gifts, 1997
ordained: 1997
charges: Director of Youth Evangelism, Grand Rapids, MI, 1971–79; Director of Christian education, Palos Heights, IL, 1979–80; Campus pastor, University of Colorado, Boulder, CO, 1980–85; Campus ministry, Madison, WI, 1985–87; Covenant Life, Grand Haven, MI, 1989–

De Jong, Bert
b. 04/01/1945, Den Haag, Zuid Holland, Netherlands
training: Calvin Theological Seminary, BD, 1970; MDiv, 1983
ordained: 1970
charges: Beacon Light, Gary, IN, 1970–74; Calvin, Sheboygan, WI, 1974–83; Elmhurst, IL, 1983–

De Jong, Frank
b. 07/15/1900, Hull, IA vicinity
training: Calvin Theological Seminary, ThB, 1930
ordained: 1930
charges: Luctor, KS, 1930–34; First, Pella, IA, 1934–38; Missionary Classis California at Monrovia, CA, 1938–39; at Arcadia, CA, 1939–43; at Bellflower, CA, 1943–44; Second, Bellflower, CA, 1944–49 and at Long Beach, CA, 1946–49; Home missionary at Lakewood, CA, 1949–56; Home missionary including part-time chaplain in Veterans Administration Hospital, Anaheim, CA, 1956–57; at Bellflower, CA, 1957–58; at Palo Alto, 1958–63; at Fresno, CA, 1962–66
retired: 1966
d. 02/06/1993, Ripon, CA

De Jong, Frederick A.
b. 07/03/1963, Winnipeg, MB
training: Calvin Theological Seminary, MDiv, 1991
ordained: 1991
charges: Cottage Grove, South Holland, IL, 1991–94; Christ Community, Plainfield, IL, 1994–

De Jong, Gabriel Dooitze
b. 03/02/1864, Minnertsga, Friesland, Netherlands

training: Calvin Theological Seminary, diploma, 1886
ordained: 1886
charges: Vriesland, MI, 1886–88; Second, Grand Haven, MI, 1888–1903 South Olive, MI, 1903–08, Faculty, Calvin Theological Seminary, 1908–14; Leighton, IA, 1914–20; Highland IN, 1920–25
retired: 1925
d. 05/01/1928, Grand Rapids, MI

De Jong, Gene (Eugene) Allen
b. 09/06/1957, Orange City, IA
training: Calvin Theological Seminary, MDiv, 1989
ordained: 1989
charges: Sunrise, Holland, MI, 1989–93; Victory Point, Holland, MI, 1993–94; Keystone Community, Grand Rapids, MI, 1994–

De Jong, George John
b. 03/24/1956, Brockville, ON
training: Calvin Theological Seminary, MDiv, 1986
ordained: 1986
charges: Georgetown, Hudsonville, MI, 1986–90; Holland Heights, Holland, MI, 1990–

de Jong, Harold
b. 07/12/1948, Winnipeg, MB
training: Calvin Theological Seminary, BD, 1968
ordained: 1971
charges: Missionary to Nigeria, 1971–76; Leave, 1976–79; Cook Christian Training School, Phoenix, AZ, 1979–83; Missionary to Nigeria, 1983–87; CRWM, Regional director, Nigeria and West Africa, 1987–91; Missionary, Zambia/Faculty, Justo Mwale Theological College, Lusaka, Zambia, 1991–95; Dispatch, KS, 1995–

De Jong, Harold Tinus
b. 04/19/1935, Bolsward, Friesland, Netherlands
training: Calvin Theological Seminary, ThB, 1964
ordained: 1965
charges: Conrad, MT, 1965–68; Hillside Community, Cutlerville, MI, 1968–75; Church of the Savior, Corvallis, OR, 1975–76; Leave, 1976–78; Chaplain, St. Peter Hospital, Olympia, WA, 1978–92; Chaplain, Exeter House Retirement Center, Seattle, WA, 1992–94; Eligible for call, 1994–96; Pastoral Care Chaplain, Sumas, WA, 1996–2000
retired: 2000

De Jong, James Allan
b. 07/10/1941, Paterson, NJ
training: Calvin Theological Seminary, BD, 1966; Vrije Universiteit, Amsterdam, ThD, 1970
ordained: 1970

charges: Faculty, Trinity Christian College, 1970–74; Faculty, Dordt College, 1974–83; President, Calvin Theological Seminary, 1983–2003
retired: 2003

De Jong, John
b. 01/04/1931, Echten, Friesland, Netherlands
training: Calvin Theological Seminary, BD, 1961
ordained: 1961
charges: Iron Springs, AB, 1961–65; New Holland, SD, 1965–68; Essex, ON, 1968–72; Fruitland, ON, 1972–78; Georgetown, ON, 1978–88; Smithville, ON, 1988–96
retired: 1996

De Jong, John
b. 03/04/1885, Allendale, MI
training: Calvin Theological Seminary, diploma, 1918
ordained: 1918
charges: Zillah WA, 1918–24; Ripon, CA, 1924–39; Vancouver, BC, 1939–42; Manhattan, MT, 1942–48; Missionary, Alberta, 1948–49; Iron Springs, AB, 1949–55; Brandon, MB, 1955–56
retired: 1956
d. 05/05/1964, Ripon, CA

De Jong, John Doedes
b. 08/30/1902, Hallum, Friesland, Netherlands
training: Protestant Reformed Theological Seminary, diploma, 1929
ordained: 1929
charges: PRC: Doon, IA, 1929–32; Hudsonville, MI, 1932–41; Creston, Grand Rapids, MI, 1941–50; Hull, IA, 1950–61; CRC: Hull, IA, 1961; Second, Lynden, WA, 1961–68
retired: 1968
d. 08/20/1975, Hudsonville, MI

De Jong, Peter
b. 07/10/1915, Grand Rapids, MI
training: Calvin Theological Seminary, ThB, 1939
ordained: 1939
charges: Hamshire, TX, 1939–42; Oak Harbor, WA, 1942–44; Chaplain, United States Navy, 1944–46; Language study, University of California, 1946–47; Missionary to China, 1947–49; East Saugatuck, MI, 1949–52; Seattle, WA, 1952–62; Smithers and Telkwa, BC, 1962–64; Smithers, BC, 1964–66; First, Sarnia, ON, 1966–70; Dutton, MI, 1970–80
retired: 1980; affiliated with Independent Reformed Church, Dutton, MI, 1984
d. 07/11/1999, Dutton, MI

De Jong, Peter
b. 08/21/1943, Koudum, Friesland, Netherlands
training: Calvin Theological Seminary, BD, 1971
ordained: 1971
charges: Missionary, Church Rock, NM, 1971–73; Dispatch, KS, 1973–79; Conrad, MT, 1979–83; Lakeview Community, Valentine, NE, 1983–89; German Valley, IL, 1989–2000; Harrison, SD, 2000–

De Jong, Peter Ymen
b. 10/28/1915, Grand Rapids, MI
training: Calvin Theological Seminary, 1939; Hartford Theological Foundation, STM, 1940; PhD, 1942
ordained: 1940
charges: Preakness, NJ, 1940–42; Alpine Ave., Grand Rapids, MI, 1942–48; Oakdale Park, Grand Rapids, MI, 1948–52; Missionary to South India, 1952–53; First, Pella, IA, 1953–60; First, Hamilton, ON, 1960–63; Alger Park, Grand Rapids, MI, 1963–64; Faculty, Calvin Theological Seminary, 1964–70; First, Sioux Center, IA, 1970–76; First, Sheldon, IA, 1976–80
retired: 1980; affiliated with United Reformed Churches, 1982

De Jong, Wieger
b. 06/25/1937, Loosduinen, Zuid Holland, Netherlands
training: Calvin Theological Seminary, BD, 1969
ordained: 1969
charges: Grace, Cobourg, ON, 1969–72; Bethel, Dunnville, ON, 1972–76; Essex, ON, 1976–82; Williamsburg, ON, 1982–89; Tillsonburg, ON, 1989–96; Clinton, ON, 1996–2001
retired: 2001

De Jong, Wilbur Leon
b. 09/21/1929, Oskaloosa, IA
training: Calvin Theological Seminary, BD, 1957; MDiv, 1975
ordained: 1957
charges: Houston, BC, 1957–62; Oak Harbor, WA, 1962–66; Prairie Lane, Omaha, NE, 1966–72; Sherman Street, Grand Rapids, MI, 1972–79; Ann Arbor, MI, 1979–95
retired: 1995

De Jong, Ymen Peter
b. 11/12/1876, Oosterbierum, Friesland, Netherlands
training: Calvin Theological Seminary, diploma, 1905; Vrije Universiteit, Amsterdam, DD, 1913
ordained: 1905

charges: East Paris, MI, 1905-07; Oakdale Park, Grand Rapids, MI, 1907-11; Coldbrook Ave., Grand Rapids, MI, 1914-17; Grandville Ave., Grand Rapids, MI, 1917-45
retired: 1945
d. 06/13/1958, Grand Rapids, MI

De Jonge, Albert Willem
b. 09/22/1868, Appingedam, Groningen, Netherlands
training: Western Theological Seminary, diploma, 1898
ordained: 1898
charges: RCA: Fourth Holland, MI, 1898-1903; Third, Grand Rapids, MI, 1903-05; Hull, IA, 1905-14; Seventh, Grand Rapids, MI, 1914-18; First, Steen, MN, 1921-23; First, Paterson, NJ, 1923-43; CRC: Franklin Street, Grand Rapids, MI, 1918-21
retired: 1943
d. 11/10/1952, Hawthorne, NJ

De Jonge, Bernard (Berend)
b. 04/14/1870, Netherlands
training: Western Theological Seminary, diploma, 1900
ordained: 1900
charges: RCA: Gelderland, Holland, MI, 1900-02; Northwestern, Chicago, IL, 1902-04; Central, Sioux Center, IA, 1904-12; Bethel (Leota), Rock Valley, IA, 1912-14; First, Rock Valley, IA, 1914-17; Bethel, Edgerton, MN, 1922-25; Third, Muskegon, MI, 1925-37; Chandler, MN, 1937-47; CRC: Doon, IA, 1917-22
retired: 1947
d. 02/10/1965, Muskegon, MI

De Jonge, Bernard Henry
b. 05/18/1949, Hardenberg, Overijsel, Netherlands
training: Calvin Theological Seminary, MDiv, 1977
ordained: 1977
charges: Minister of education and evangelism, Calvin, Ottawa, ON, 1977-81; Exeter, ON, 1981-86; Ancaster, ON, 1986-99; Leave, 1999; Fellowship, Ancaster, ON, 1999-2000; Community, Kitchener, ON, 2000-

De Jonge, John J.
b. 01/20/1876, Kapelle, Zeeland, Netherlands
training: Calvin Theological Seminary, diploma, 1908
ordained: 1908
charges: Ellsworth, MI, 1908-11; Alto, WI, 1911-13; Moline, MI, 1913-17; Prinsburg, MN, 1917-21; Hanford, CA, 1921-29; Home Missionary Classis

California at Los Angeles, CA, 1929-33; at Buena Park, CA, 1933-39; at South Gate, CA, 1939; at Milwaukee, WI, 1939-42
retired: 1942
d. 07/15/1946, Los Angeles, CA

De Jonge, Peter W.
b. 07/18/1881, Zeeland, MI vicinity
training: Calvin Theological Seminary, diploma, 1911
ordained: 1911
charges: Racine, WI, 1911-15; Jamestown, MI, 1915-18; Kenosha, WI, 1918-26
retired: 1926
d. 05/13/1940, Grand Rapids, MI

De Jonge, Philip Verne
b. 09/12/1938, Paterson, NJ
training: Calvin Theological Seminary, MDiv, 1976; ThM, 1979
ordained: 1976
charges: Minister of education and missions, Harderwyk, Holland, MI, 1976-79; Missionary to Jordan, 1979-82; Missionary, Owari Ashai, Japan, 1982-88; Friendship Chapel, Jenison, MI, 1988-94; Valley Community, Napa, CA, 1994-2001; St. Joseph, MI, 2001-

Dekens, Louis
b. 06/25/1924, Loppersum, Groningen, Netherlands
training: Calvin Theological Seminary, BD, 1969
ordained: 1969
charges: First, Port Alberni, BC, 1969-74; Granum, AB, 1974-78
d. 06/17/1978, Granum, AB

Dekker, Abram
b. 10/23/1887, Chicago, IL
training: Calvin Theological Seminary, diploma, 1912
ordained: 1912
charges: Cincinnati, OH, 1912-16; West Park, Cleveland, OH, 1916-18
d. 07/13/1918, Chicago, IL

Dekker, Erika Lenore
b. 08/14/1973, Grand Rapids, MI
training: Calvin Theological Seminary, MDiv, 2000
ordained: 2000
charges: Chaplain, Bronson Hospital, Kalamazoo, MI, 2000-01; Chaplain, Spectrum Health, Grand Rapids, MI, 2001-

Dekker, Harold

b. 06/26/1918, Chicago, IL
training: Calvin Theological Seminary, ThB, 1942
ordained: 1942
charges: Service pastor, 1942; Chaplain, United
States Navy, 1943–46; Faculty, Calvin College,
Grand Rapids, MI, 1946–47; Englewood, NJ, 1947–
50; Minister of Radio Evangelism, 1950–54; Faculty, Calvin College, Grand Rapids, MI, 1954–56;
Faculty, Calvin Theological Seminary, Grand
Rapids, MI, 1955–87
retired: 1987

Dekker, Henry

b. 12/08/1881, Chicago, IL
training: Calvin Theological Seminary, diploma,
1906
ordained: 1906
charges: Friesland, SD, 1906–09; Ebenezer, SD,
1909–13; Hoboken, NJ, 1913–16; Cincinnati, OH,
1916–21; Ada, MI, 1921–42
retired: 1942
d. 07/24/1961, Cutlerville, MI

Dekker, James Cornelius

b. 02/14/1948, Chicago, IL
training: Calvin Theological Seminary, MDiv, 1977
ordained: 1977
charges: Missionary to Brazil, 1977–79; Missionary to Guatemala, 1979–84; Missionary to Venezuela, 1984–86; Covenant, Edmonton, AB, 1986–
94; Hope, Thunder Bay, ON, 1994–

Dekker, Peter

b. 01/20/1915, Sheboygan, WI
training: Calvin Theological Seminary, ThB, 1945
ordained: 1945
charges: Ackley, IA, 1945–47; Missionary to Africa-Nigeria, 1947–61; Grace, Bellflower, CA,
1961–67; Regina, SK, 1967–71; Vernon, BC, 1971–
75; Hope, Stony Plain, AB, 1975–80
retired: 1980
d. 10/23/1994, Edmonton, AB

De Koekkoek, John Mark

b. 07/18/1953, Seattle, WA
training: Calvin Theological Seminary, MDiv, 1986
ordained: 1987
charges: CRC: Assistant to the pastor, East Leonard, Grand Rapids, MI, 1986–87; Conrad, MT,
1987–91; Agassiz, BC, 1991–92; Independent Reformed Church: Agassiz, BC, 1992–96; Faith Reformed, North Seattle, WA, 1996

De Koekkoek, Paul

b. 06/07/1890, Hillegom, Zuid Holland, Netherlands
training: Calvin Theological Seminary, diploma,
1923
ordained: 1923
charges: Comstock, MI, 1923–26; Oskaloosa, IA,
1926–28; Otley, IA, 1928–38; Hills, MN, 1938–45;
First, Edmonton, AB, 1945–49; Missionary in
southern British Columbia, 1949–56; Zillah, WA,
1956–58
retired: 1958
d. 11/13/1982, Seattle, WA

de Koning, Kornelis (Neil)

b. 11/11/1953, Amsterdam, Noord Holland, Netherlands
training: Calvin Theological Seminary, MDiv, 1981
ordained: 1982
charges: Youth pastor, Emmanuel and Maranatha,
Calgary, AB, 1982–84; Emmanuel, Calgary, AB,
1984–90; Redeemer, Sarnia, ON, 1990–2001;
Woodynook, Lacombe, AB, 2001–

De Korne, John Cornelius

b. 10/16/1888, Grand Rapids, MI
training: Calvin Theological Seminary, diploma,
1917; Princeton, ThM, 1918
ordained: 1917
charges: Englewood, NJ, 1917–18; United States
Army, YMCA, 1918; with Lee Huizenga to report
on Mid African and China mission fields, 1919–20;
Missionary to China (on furlough, 1926), 1920–34;
Second, Wellsburg, IA, 1934–38; Director of Missions, Grand Rapids, MI, 1939–51
d. 12/09/1951, Long Beach, CA

De Kruyter, Arthur H.

b. 03/11/1926, Grand Rapids, MI
training: Calvin Theological Seminary, ThB, 1950
ordained: 1951
charges: CRC: Western Springs, IL, 1951–65; Independent: Christ Church, Oak Brook, IL, 1965

De Kruyter, John Adrian

b. 08/06/1921, Muskegon, MI
training: Calvin Theological Seminary, ThB, 1946;
Columbia Theological Seminary, ThM, 1947;
ordained: 1947
charges: Rusk, MI, 1947–50; Fourth Roseland,
Chicago, IL, 1950–54; Maple Ave., Holland, MI,
1954–60; First, Pella, IA, 1960–64; Seymour,
Grand Rapids, MI, 1964–75; Calvin, Oak Lawn, IL,
1975–86
retired: 1986

De Lange, Karl J.
b. 09/01/1965, Grand Rapids, MI
training: Reformed Theological Seminary, MDiv, 1994; Calvin Theological Seminary, Special Program for Ministerial Candidacy, 1998
ordained: 1998
charges: CRC: Crossroads Community, St. John, IN, 1997-99; Chicago Christian Counseling Center, Chicago, IL, 1999-2001; RCA

De Lange, Ray Phillip
b. 11/01/1974, Grand Rapids, MI
training: Calvin Theological Seminary, Mdiv, 2002
ordained: 2002
charges: Christ's Community, Chandler, AZ, 2002-

de Lange, Richard J.
b. 07/26/1963, Thunder Bay, ON
training: Calvin Theological Seminary, MDiv, 1993
ordained: 1993
charges: Pastoral assistant, Rogers Heights, Wyoming, MI, 1990-91; Trinity, St. Catharines, ON, 1993-2000; Aylmer, ON, 2000-

De Lange, Robert Allen
b. 04/12/1946, Harvey, IL
training: Calvin Theological Seminary, BD, 1972
ordained: 1973
charges: CRC: Missionary, Charlotte, MI, 1974-77; Imlay City, MI, 1977-82; Hope, Framingham, MA, 1982-88; Leave, 1988-89; Resigned from denomination, 1989

De Lange, Theodore Leenert
b. 03/24/1861, Netherlands
training: Calvin Theological Seminary, diploma, 1892
ordained: 1896
charges: CRC: Pulpit supply as a candidate in New Era, MI and West Olive, MI, 1892-96; Sheboygan, WI, 1896-1900; Vesper, WI, 1900-06; West Olive, MI, 1906-09; RCA: Pulpit supply in Classis Holland to six churches, 1910-15; Friesland, MN and Sandstone, MN, 1915-19; Valley Springs, SD, 1919-25
retired: 1925
d. 11/09/1940, Denver, CO

De Leeuw, Cornelius
b. 01/08/1876, Nieuwdorp, Zeeland, Netherlands
training: Calvin Theological Seminary, diploma, 1904; Princeton Seminary, ThM, 1905
ordained: 1905
charges: Douglas Park, Chicago, IL, 1905-10;

First, Pella, IA, 1910-19; Sioux Center, IA, 1919-24; Lansing, IL, 1924-44; Tracy, IA, 1944-53
retired: 1953
d. 06/09/1963, Palos Heights, IL

De Moor, Henry Jr.
b. 01/01/1947, Schiedam, Zuid Holland, Netherlands
training: Calvin Theological Seminary, BD, 1971; Johannes Calvijn Academie, Kampen, ThD, 1986
ordained: 1971
charges: CRC: Duncan, BC, 1971-74; First, Edmonton, AB, 1974-80; Faculty, Calvin Theological Seminary, Grand Rapids, MI, 1986-; GKN: Doornspyk, 1980-86

De Moor, Henry (Hendrinus) Sr.
b. 12/31/1912, Den Haag, Zuid Holland, Netherlands
training: Vrije Universiteit, Amsterdam, diploma, 1936
ordained: 1936
charges: GKN: Nes, 1936-42; Boskoop, 1942-46; Schiedam, 1946-48; Chaplain, Dutch Army, Indonesia, 1948-50; Enschede, 1950-58; CRC: Strathroy, ON, 1958-62; Clarkson, ON, 1962-70; Medicine Hat, AB, 1970-75; First, Abbotsford, BC, 1975-78
retired: 1978
d. 02/01/1999, Woerden, Netherlands

De Moor, Johannes Cornelius
b. 09/24/1937, Nes, Friesland, Netherlands
training: Calvin Theological Seminary, BD, 1962
ordained: 1962
charges: CRC: Navan, ON, 1962-65; Saskatoon, SK, 1965-68; GKN: Rotterdam-Hillegersberg, 1968-72; Rotterdam-Hillegersberg/Schiebroek, 1972-77; Faculty, Theologische Universiteit Kampen, 1977-78; Kampen, 1979-81; Waddinxveen, 1981-

De Moor, Robert
b. 12/23/1950, Enschede, Overijsel, Netherlands
training: Calvin Theological Seminary, BD, 1975
ordained: 1975
charges: Peers and Edson, AB, 1975-78; Third, Edmonton, AB, 1978-84; First, Langley, BC, 1984-95; Editor in Chief, Education, Worship and Evangelism Dept., Christian Reformed Publications, Grand Rapids, MI, 1995-

De Mots, Henry
b. 01/15/1911, Leota, MN
training: Calvin Theological Seminary, ThB, 1938

ordained: 1938
charges: Delavan, WI, 1938–43; De Motte, IN, 1943–47; First, Bellflower, CA, 1947–54; Mayfair, Grand Rapids, MI, 1954–69; Orland Park, IL, 1969–76
retired: 1976

De Mott, Cornelius D.
b. 05/24/1853, United States
training: with John Calvin Voorhis
ordained: 1891
charges: Monsey, NY, 1891–92; Englewood, NJ, 1892–96; Broadway Ave., Grand Rapids, MI, 1896–99; provided pulpit supply in Classis Hackensack, 1899; Resigned from denomination, 1899
d. 11/24/1928, Englewood, NJ

Den Bleyker, Merle
b. 06/30/1947, Holland, MI
training: Calvin Theological Seminary, BD, 1972; ThM, 1983
ordained: 1972
charges: Missionary to Puerto Rico, 1972–82; Calvin, Le Mars, IA, 1982–87; International programs director, Asia and Latin America, World Missions, Grand Rapids, MI, 1987–97; Executive director, World Missions, Grand Rapids, MI, 1997–2001; Ebenezer, Berwyn, IL, 2001–

den Dulk, C. James
b. 09/27/1965, Grand Rapids, MI
training: Westminster Theological Seminary-CA, MDiv, 1990; Calvin Theological Seminary, Special Program for Ministerial Candidacy, 1992
ordained: 1992
charges: Trinity, Sparta, MI, 1992–

den Dulk, Donald Edward
b. 08/07/1938, Manteca, CA
training: Calvin Theological Seminary, MDiv, 1965; San Francisco Theological Seminary, DMin, 1981
ordained: 1965
charges: CRC: Lake City, MI, 1965–71; Lakewood, Long Beach, CA, 1971–75; Chaplain, United States Navy, 1975–83; RCA: Chaplain, United States Navy, 1983–2000, Faculty, United States International University, 1983

Den Haan, David Edward
b. 09/19/1967, Grand Rapids, MI
training: Calvin Theological Seminary, MDiv, 1994
ordained: 1994

charges: Bethel, Edgerton, MN, 1994–99; Fairway, Jenison, MI, 1999–

Den Haan, Edward Adrianus Maarten
b. 04/30/1938, Den Haag, Zuid Holland, Netherlands
training: Calvin Theological Seminary, BD, 1968; MDiv, 1974
ordained: 1968
charges: Charlottetown, PE, 1968–73; Maranatha, Calgary, AB, 1973–77; Campus minister, University of Guelph, Guelph, ON, 1977–

Den Herder, Bert
b. 12/18/1933, Sioux City, IA
training: Calvin Theological Seminary, BD, 1955
ordained: 1955
charges: Bethel, Lacombe, AB, 1955–60; Burnaby, BC, 1960–63; Chilliwack and Agassiz, AB, 1964–67; Luverne, MN, 1967–80; Kanawha, IA, 1980–89
retired: 1989

Den Ouden, Bernard
b. 03/08/1919, Sioux Center, IA
training: Calvin Theological Seminary, ThB, 1951
ordained: 1951
charges: Modesto, CA, 1951–67; Graafschap, MI, 1967–80; Vogel Center, MI, 1980–84
retired: 1984
d. 03/26/1995, Grandville, MI

de Pater, John (Jan)
b. 10/15/1923, Scherpenzeel, Gelderland, Netherlands
training: Calvin Theological Seminary, BD, 1966
ordained: 1966
charges: Holland Marsh, ON, 1966–70; Williamsburg, ON, 1970–75; Escalon, CA, 1975–78; Duncan, BC, 1978–83; Maranatha, York, ON, 1983–88
retired: 1988; affliated with Free Reformed Church of Vineland, ON, 1996–2000

Deppe, Dean Brian
b. 05/16/1951, Grand Rapids, MI
training: Calvin Theological Seminary, MDiv, 1977; ThM, 1978; Vrije Universiteit, ThD, 1989
ordained: 1978
charges: Christ's Community, Grand Rapids, MI, 1978–82; Leave, 1982–84; Oakdale Park, Grand Rapids, MI, 1984–85; Faculty, Calvin College, Grand Rapids, MI, 1985; Community, Toledo, OH, 1985–92; Unity, Prinsburg, MN, 1992–98; Faculty,

Calvin Theological Seminary, Grand Rapids, MI, 1998–

De Raaf, Kevin Paul
b. 03/18/1967, Brampton, ON
training: Calvin Theological Seminary, MDiv, 1993
ordained: 1993
charges: First, Owen Sound, ON, 1993–99; Faith, Burlington, ON, 1999–

De Ridder, Charles Jon
b. 08/12/1950, Holland, MI
training: Calvin Theological Seminary, MDiv, 1976
ordained: 1976
charges: Alamo Ave., Kalamazoo, MI, 1976–80; Second, Fremont, MI, 1980–90; Walnut Creek, CA, 1990–95; Shalom, Sioux Falls, SD, 1995–

De Ridder, Richard Ralph
b. 05/09/1921, Holland, MI
training: Calvin Theological Seminary, ThB, 1946; Hartford Seminary, MA, 1956; Vrije Universiteit, Amsterdam, ThD
ordained: 1946
charges: Dispatch, KS, 1946–49; Coldbrook, Grand Rapids, MI, 1949–53; Whitinsville, MA, 1953–56; Missionary to Ceylon, 1956–60; First, Muskegon, MI, 1960–64; First, Sioux Center, IA, 1964–69; Silver Spring, MD, 1969–73; Faculty, Calvin Theological Seminary, Grand Rapids, MI, 1973–86
retired: 1986

Derksen, John C.
b. 03/09/1918, Arnhem, Gelderland, Netherlands
training: Vrije Universiteit, Amsterdam, diploma, 1945
ordained: 1945
charges: GKN: Ten Post, 1945–48; 's Graveland, 1948–53; Middlestum-Steens, 1952– 57; CRC: First, Guelph, ON, 1957–76; First, Kemptville, ON, 1976–83
retired: 1983

De Rooy, Henry Morgan
b. 07/07/1929, Everett, WA
training: Calvin Theological Seminary, BD, 1956; MDiv, 1974
ordained: 1956
charges: Harrison, SD, 1956–59; Missionary pastor at Green Ridge Chapel, North Muskegon, MI, 1959–63; Home missionary, Quincy, WA, 1963–65; Home missionary, Trinity, St. Louis, MO, 1965–71; Regional minister of evangelism at Hawthorne, NJ, 1971–74; Associate minister of evangelism, Board

of Home Missions, 1974–81; Regional director, North Pacific, Board of Home Missions, 1981–94
retired: 1994

De Rooy, Jacobus
b. 07/23/1812, Hellevoetsluis, Zuid Holland, Netherlands
training: service leader in an independent congregation
ordained: 1853
charges: Independent: Paterson, NJ, 1853; Baptist: Cincinnati, OH, 1853–55; Independent: itinerated to Lodi, NJ; Boston, MA; Hackensack, NJ-Paterson, NJ, 1857–62 (this congregation joined the CRC in 1864); itinerant preacher, later at Woerden, Zuid Holland, Netherlands, 1862–65; Presbyterian USA: Oostburg, WI, 1865–75; CRC: Oostburg, WI, 1875–84
d. 01/14/1884, Oostburg, WI

De Ruiter, Richard John
b. 08/28/1957, Welland, ON
training: Calvin Theological Seminary, MDiv, 1987
ordained: 1987
charges: Missionary, Dominican Republic, 1987–94; Church planting, Sugarland, TX, 1994–96; Alger Community, Alger, WA, 1996–

De Ruiter, Walter
b. 08/01/1957, Den Hoorn, Noord Holland, Netherlands
training: Reformed Bible College, BRE, 1985; declared eligible on the basis of exceptional gifts, 1996
ordained: 1996
charges: Williamsburg, ON, 1986–90; Evangelist, Hanover, ON, 1990–95; Collingwood, ON, 1996–2000
retired: 2000

de Ruyter, Herbert George
b. 08/23/1953, Smithers, BC
training: Calvin Theological Seminary, MACS, 1990; declared eligible on the basis of exceptional gifts, 1996
ordained: 1996
charges: Director of education and evangelism, Arcadia, Grand Rapids, MI, 1978–85; Minister of youth and adult education, First, Denver, CO, 1985–86; Minister of youth and education, Calvin, Ottawa, ON, 1986–90; Youth, Second, Abbotsford, BC, 1990–94; First, Chilliwack, BC, 1994–2002; West End, Edmonton, AB, 2002–

Deters, David Jay
b. 01/15/1952, Grand Rapids, MI
training: Calvin Theological Seminary, MDiv, 1978
ordained: 1979
charges: West Leonard, Grand Rapids, MI, 1979–83; Home missionary, Eastern Hills, Aurora, CO, 1983–88; Lighthouse Community, Holland, MI, 1988–93; VictoryPoint, Holland, MI, 1993–94; Alger Park, Grand Rapids, MI, 1994–

Devadatta, Daniel Madhukar
b. 07/03/1963, Vellore, India
training: Reformed Bible College, BRE, 1985; Calvin Theological Seminary, MDiv, 1991
ordained: 1991
charges: CRC: Resident pastor, Arlington, TX, 1991; Church planting, Daybreak, Grapevine, TX, 1991–94; Faculty, Calvin Theological Seminary, Grand Rapids, MI, 1994–2000; First, New Westminster, BC, 2000–2002; Christian Fellowship: Chicago, IL, 2002

De Velder, Gary Lee
b. 09/13/1942, Corsica, SD
training: Calvin Theological Seminary, BD, 1969
ordained: 1969
charges: Religious education at Gallup, NM, 1970–71, at Rehoboth, NM, 1971–74; Church Education Foundation, Scottsdale, AZ, 1974–81; Non-ministerial vocation, 1981

De Vos, Christopher James
b. 08/30/1957, Grand Rapids, MI
training: Reformed Bible College, BRE, 1985; Calvin Theological Seminary, MDiv, 1991
ordained: 1985
charges: Campus pastor, University of Colorado, Boulder, CO, 1985–90; New Hope, Atlanta, GA, 1990–97; First, Kingston, ON, 1997–

De Vries, Albert J.
b. 04/06/1947, Grand Rapids, MI
training: Calvin Theological Seminary, MDiv, 1974
ordained: 1974
charges: Summitview, Yakima, WA, 1974–77; Ackley, IA, 1977–82; Emmanuel, New Glasgow, NS, 1982–87; Nobleford, AB, 1987–90; Decatur, MI, 1990–94; First, Fulton, IL, 1994–97; Faith, Kalamazoo, MI, 1997–2002

De Vries, Andrew
b. 04/21/1890, Dokkum, Friesland, Netherlands
training: Calvin Theological Seminary, diploma, 1920
ordained: 1920

charges: Niekerk, MI, 1920–25; Leighton, IA, 1925–29; Borculo, MI, 1929–45; Colton, SD, 1945–50; Portland, MI, 1950–55
retired: 1955
d. 08/30/1957, Zeeland, MI

De Vries, Ecko
b. 09/14/1940, Groningen, Groningen, Netherlands
training: Calvin Theological Seminary, BD, 1967; MDiv, 1979
ordained: 1967
charges: First, Minneapolis, MN, 1967–74; First, Muskegon, MI, 1974–87; Alger Park, Grand Rapids, MI, 1987–

De Vries, Gary Allan
b. 11/28/1953, Ann Arbor, MI
training: Calvin Theological Seminary, MDiv, 1985
ordained: 1985
charges: Knollwood, Kalamazoo, MI, 1985–87; Campus pastor, Western Michigan University, Kalamazoo, MI, 1987–89; Hancock, MN, 1989–92; Clinical pastoral education, Rochester, MN, 1992–92; Chaplain, Mercy Medical Center, Cedar Rapids, IA, 1993–98; Chaplain, Sparrow Health Systems, Lansing, MI, 1998–

De Vries, Gerald Edwin
b. 06/23/1934, Princeton, MN
training: Calvin Theological Seminary, BD, 1966; ThM, 1967
ordained: 1967
charges: Terra Ceia, NC, 1967–71; Alto, WI, 1971–79; Faith, Kalamazoo, MI, 1979–88; Woden, IA, 1988–96; Lafayette, IN, 1996–

De Vries, Hendrik
b. 07/16/1943, Gorredijk, Friesland, Netherlands
training: Calvin Theological Seminary, BD, 1970; MDiv, 1984; ThM, 1990
ordained: 1971
charges: Missionary to the Philippines, 1971–83; Winfield, IL, 1983–90; Missionary, Guam/Micronesia, 1990–

Devries, Henry
b. 05/22/1953, Oudebildtzijl, Friesland, Netherlands
training: Calvin Theological Seminary, MDiv, 1984
ordained: 1984
charges: Rimbey, AB, 1984–90; Sahali Fellowship, Kamloops, BC, 1990–

De Vries, Henry J.
b. 01/09/1883, Ackley, IA

training: Calvin Theological Seminary, diploma, 1909
ordained: 1909
charges: Oskaloosa, IA, 1909-13; Baldwin, WI, 1913-18; Ogilvie, MN, 1918-21; Dispatch, KS, 1922-27; Home missionary Classis California at Compton, CA, 1927-28; at Ontario, CA, 1928-35; at Modesto, CA, 1935-37
retired: 1921
d. 04/09/1938, Redlands, CA

De Vries, Jacob
b. 12/10/1957, Trenton, ON
training: Calvin Theological Seminary, MDiv, 1983
ordained: 1983
charges: Alliston, ON, 1983-87; New Life Community, Pickering, ON, 1987-95; Bethel, Listowel, ON, 1995-

De Vries, James Edwin
b. 01/31/1939, Grand Rapids, MI
training: Calvin Theological Seminary, ThB, 1964
ordained: 1964
charges: Haven, Zeeland, MI, 1964-69; Second, Highland, IN, 1969-76; Millbrook, Grand Rapids, MI, 1976-92; Second, Allendale, MI, 1992-

De Vries, Jay
b. 11/27/1930, McBain, MI
training: Calvin Theological Seminary, BD, 1957; MDiv, 1972
ordained: 1957
charges: Holland, IA, 1957-61; Elmhurst, IL, 1961-66; Second, Orange City, IA, 1966-70; Second, Byron Center, MI, 1970-78; Arcadia, Grand Rapids, MI, 1978-85; Arcadia-Plainfield, Grand Rapids, MI, 1985-88; Calvary, Plainwell, MI, 1988-93
retired: 1993

De Vries, Joanne Grace Vander Beek
b. 08/23/1958, Vancouver, BC
training: Calvin Theological Seminary, MDiv, 2001
ordained: 2002
charges: Clarkson, Mississauga, ON, 2001

De Vries, John Jr.
b. 09/20/1944, Zierikzee, Zeeland, Netherlands
training: Calvin Theological Seminary, BD, 1970; Western Theological Seminary, ThM, 1971
ordained: 1971
charges: First, Regina, SK, 1972-75; Penitentiary service, St. Vincent de Paul, Laval, QC, 1975-79; Fruitland, ON, 1979-85; Leave, 1985-86; Chaplain, St. Thomas Psychiatric Hospital, St. Thomas,

ON, 1986-88; Regional coordinator, Pastoral Services, Windsor-Woodstock Region, 1988-2002; Chaplain, Kent Health Alliance, Chatham, ON, 2002-

De Vries, John
b. 05/26/1858, Westerboek, Drenthe, Netherlands
training: Calvin Theological Seminary, diploma, 1889
ordained: 1890
charges: CRC: Sayville, NY, 1890-1895; Independent: West Sayville, NY, 1895-1919
d. 05/18/1919, West Sayville, NY

De Vries, John Fredric
b. 12/03/1936, Galesburg, IL
training: Calvin Theological Seminary, BD, 1961
ordained: 1961
charges: Luverne, MN, 1961-64; Hope, Grandville, MI, 1964-68; Leave, 1968-69; World Home Bible League, 1969-77; Highland Hills, Grand Rapids, MI, 1977-83; President, Bibles for India, Grand Rapids, MI, 1983-87; Director, International Ministries, World Home Bible League, Grand Rapids, MI, 1987-90; Mission 21 India, Grand Rapids, MI, 1990-2002
retired: 2002

De Vries, John Robert
b. 12/27/1965, Valparaiso, IN
training: Calvin Theological Seminary, MDiv, 2000
ordained: 2000
charges: Maranatha, Holland, MI, 2000-

De Vries, John William
b. 03/24/1963, Oak Lawn, IL
training: Calvin Theological Seminary, MDiv, 1991
ordained: 1992
charges: Bethel, Sun Valley, CA, 1992-2000; Leave, 2000-01; Providence St. Joseph/Holy Cross Med. Ctr., Burbank, CA, 2001-

De Vries, Joseph (Jelle) Pieters
b. 10/06/1884, Gaast, Friesland, Netherlands
training: Calvin Theological Seminary, diploma, 1917
ordained: 1917
charges: New Era, MI, 1917-21; West Leonard, Grand Rapids, MI, 1921-26; Harderwyk, MI, 1927-29; Spring Lake, MI, 1929-47; Sultan, WA, 1947-49
retired: 1926-27
d. 09/30/1949, Wyckoff, NJ

De Vries, Michael

b. 06/27/1935, Leeuwarden, Friesland, Netherlands
training: Calvin Theological Seminary, BD, 1961; Westminster Theological Seminary-PA, ThM, 1962; Vrije Universiteit, Drs, 1970
ordained: 1962
charges: Surrey, BC, 1962-65; Rehoboth, Toronto, ON, 1965-72; Maranatha, York, ON, 1972-76; Arcadia, CA, 1976-80; Harderwyk, Holland, MI, 1980-93; Pillar, Holland, MI, 1993-2000
retired: 2000

de Vries, Nathan

b. 07/06/1970, Orange City, IA
training: Calvin Theological Seminary, MDiv, 2000
ordained: 2000
charges: Hawarden, IA, 2000-

De Vries, Nicholas

b. 12/21/1892, Baflo, Groningen, Netherlands
training: Calvin Theological Seminary, diploma, 1926; Princeton Theological Seminary, ThB, 1928
ordained: 1926
charges: Missionary to China, 1926-28 (Union Language School, 1926-27); Missionary for Classis California, Alameda, CA, 1928-37; Missionary, Farmington, NM, 1937-39; at Rehoboth, NM, 1939-43; Chaplain, United States Army, 1943-46; Reeman, MI, 1946-50; Home missionary at Tacoma, WA, 1950-52; First, Phoenix, AZ, 1952-61
retired: 1961
d. 09/18/1983, Ripon, CA

De Vries, Nick (Nicholas)

b. 05/28/1898, Prairie City, IA
training: Calvin Theological Seminary, BD, 1930
ordained: 1931
charges: Zillah, WA, 1930-44; Crookston, MN, 1944-48; Non ministerial vocation, 1948
d. 12/14/1957, Grand Rapids, MI

De Vries, Paul Robert

b. 11/22/1963, Grand Rapids, MI
training: Calvin Theological Seminary, MDiv, 1989
ordained: 1989
charges: Unity, Prospect Park, NJ, 1989-2001; Brookside, Grand Rapids, MI, 2001-

De Vries, Peter John

b. 08/07/1954, Petrolia, ON
training: Calvin Theological Seminary, MDiv, 1981
ordained: 1981
charges: Bethany, Bloomfield, ON, 1981-89;

Everson, WA, 1989-91; Leave, 1991-93; Community, Toledo, OH, 1993-2001; Community, Fort Wayne, IN, 2001-

De Vries, Richard Ralph

b. 05/05/1957, Artesia, CA
training: Calvin Theological Seminary, MDiv, 1983
ordained: 1984
charges: Dispatch, KS, 1984-90; Prairie Lane, Omaha, NE, 1990-

De Vries, Robert Charles

b. 03/08/1942, Grand Rapids, MI
training: Calvin Theological Seminary, BD, 1967; ThM, 1973; McCormick Theological Seminary, DMin, 1983; Michigan State University, PhD, 1987
ordained: 1968
charges: Boca Raton, FL, 1968-70; Missionary, Fellowship, Big Rapids, MI, 1970-77; Faculty, Calvin Theological Seminary, Grand Rapids, MI, 1977-

De Vries, Robert Wallace

b. 07/25/1935, Princeton, MN
training: Calvin Theological Seminary, BD, 1972
ordained: 1972
charges: Missionary to the Philippines, 1972-79; New Life, Louisville, KY, 1979-82; Eligible for call, 1982-83; Sacramento, CA, 1983-91; Interim pastor, Jackson, MI, 1991-92; Jackson, MI, 1992-2000
retired: 2000

De Vries, Robert Wopke

b. 08/02/1928, Groningen, Groningen, Netherlands
training: Westminster Theological Seminary-PA, BD, 1956; Calvin Theological Seminary, Special Program for Ministerial Candidacy, 1956
ordained: 1956
charges: Home missionary at Franklin Lakes, NJ, 1956-60; Franklin Lakes, NJ, 1960-63; Framingham, MA, 1963-70; Rochester, NY, 1970-79; Northside, Clifton, NJ, 1979-93
retired: 1993; affiliated with United Reformed Churches, 1997

De Vries, Simon John

b. 12/20/1921, Denver, CO
training: Calvin Theological Seminary, ThB, 1949; Union Theological Seminary, STM, 1950; ThD, 1958
ordained: 1950
charges: Prairie City, IA, 1950-53; Northside, Passaic, NJ, 1953-56; Instructor, Drew University,

Madison, NJ, 1957-58; Fourteenth St., Holland, MI, 1958-61; RCA: Faculty, Hope College, Holland, MI, 1961-62; PCUSA (in 1965): Methodist Theological School in Ohio, 1962-92
retired: 1992

De Vries, Stanley James
b. 10/08/1942, Peoria, IA
training: Calvin Theological Seminary, BD, 1971
ordained: 1972
charges: Missionary, Alger, Bellingham, WA, 1971-75; Flagstaff, AZ, 1975-79; Peace, Menno, SD, 1979-86; Zutphen, MI, 1986-95; Chaplain, Lutheran General Hospital, Park Ridge, IL, 1995-96; Chaplain, Hospice of Northeastern Illinois, Barrington, IL, 1996-

De Vries, Steven Jon
b. 07/21/1960, Grand Rapids, MI
training: Calvin Theological Seminary, MDiv, 1987
ordained: 1988
charges: Missionary, Dominican Republic, 1988-2002; Plymouth Heights, Grand Rapids, MI, 2002-

De Vries, Thomas John
b. 08/29/1951, Grand Rapids, MI
training: Calvin Theological Seminary, MDiv, 1977
ordained: 1979
charges: Youth, Hillcrest, Hudsonville, MI, 1978-79; Missionary to New Guinea, 1979-83; First, Salt Lake City, UT, 1983-89; Bible teacher, South Christian High School, Cutlerville, MI, 1989-92; Missionary, Philippines, 1992-2002; Middleville, MI, 2002-

De Vries, Willard H.
b. 04/05/1933, Randolph, WI
training: Calvin Theological Seminary, BD, 1958
ordained: 1958
charges: Brooten, MN, 1958-62; Bethel, Oskaloosa, IA, 1962-67; First, Hull, IA, 1967-72; Moline, MI, 1972-90; Holland Center, Lodgepole, SD, 1990-98
retired: 1998

De Vries, William Cornelius
b. 05/22/1946, Harvey, IL
training: Calvin Theological Seminary, BD, 1973; MDiv, 1975
ordained: 1973
charges: Ann Arbor, MI, 1973-76; Missionary, Syracuse, NY, 1976-81; Christ's Community, El Paso, TX, 1981-87; First, Detroit, MI, 1987-

De Vries, William Thomas
b. 05/01/1930, Grand Rapids, MI
training: Calvin Theological Seminary, BD, 1954
ordained: 1954
charges: Leighton, IA, 1954-57; Missionary to South America-Argentina, 1957-78; Missionary to Puerto Rico, 1978-79; Seminary Faculty, and church planter, San Juan, Puerto Rico, 1979-85; Latin America secretary, World Missions, Grand Rapids, MI, 1985-87; Director, Latin America Regional Office, Board for World Missions, Grand Rapids, MI, 1987-92; Director, Eastern Europe and Russia, World Missions, Grand Rapids, MI, 1992-95
retired: 1995

de Vuyst, Gerald David
b. 03/11/1971, Grand Rapids, MI
training: Calvin Theological Seminary, MDiv, 1998
ordained: 1998
charges: Missionary, Ukraine, 1998-

De Waal, Sidney C.J.
b. 09/22/1935, Waalwijk, Noord Brabant, Netherlands
training: Drake University, MEd, 1960; Calvin Theological Seminary, BD, 1963; Chicago Theological Seminary, RelD, 1971
ordained: 1963
charges: Ft. Lauderdale, FL, 1963-67; Missionary to Mexico, 1967-70; Leave, Chicago Institute of Pastoral Care, 1970-71; Faculty, Trinity Christian College, 1971-74; Dean, The King's College, University of Alberta, 1974-76; Third, Edmonton, AB, 1976-78; President, King's College, Edmonton, AB, 1978-83; Third, Edmonton, AB, 1983-88; Faculty, Gordon-Conwell Theological Seminary, South Hamilton, MA, 1988-93; President, Institute of Holy Land Studies, Jerusalem, Israel, 1993-2001
retired: 2001

de Waal Malefyt, Karel Everhard Frederick Johannes
b. 01/26/1900, Georgetown, South Africa
training: Calvin Theological Seminary, BD, 1930
ordained: 1930
charges: Edmonton, AB, 1930-38; Sunnyside, WA, 1938-44; First, Artesia, CA, 1944-65
retired: 1965
d. 02/16/1980, Artesia, CA

De Weerd, Harold Lee
b. 03/06/1931, Orange City, IA
training: Calvin Theological Seminary, BD, 1957
ordained: 1957

charges: Goshen, IN, 1957–64; Winfield, IL, 1964–65; Non-ministerial vocation

de Winter, John
b. 05/31/1954, Newmarket, ON
training: Calvin Theological Seminary, MDiv, 1980
ordained: 1981
charges: Covenant, Barrie, ON, 1981–84; Non-ministerial vocation, 1984

De Wolf, Hubert
b. 07/12/1912, Pella, IA
training: Protestant Reformed Theological Seminary, diploma, 1936
ordained: 1936
charges: PRC: Grandville, MI, 1936–40; Manhattan, MT, 1940–44; First, Grand Rapids, MI, 1944–61; CRC: First, Byron Center, MI, 1961–77
retired: 1977
d. 03/03/1980, Wyoming, MI

De Young, Gerrit
b. 04/19/1929, Whitinsville, MA
training: Calvin Theological Seminary, BD, 1960
ordained: 1960
charges: CRC: Olentangy, Columbus, OH, 1960–64; Fourth Roseland, Chicago, IL, 1964–68; Palm Lane, Scottsdale, AZ, 1968–74; PCA: Trinity, Scottsdale, AZ, 1974–91; Calvin, Phoenix, AZ, 1993–94
retired: 1995

De Young, Hendrik
b. 07/02/1936, Den Haag, Zuid Holland, Netherlands
training: Calvin Theological Seminary, BD, 1969
ordained: 1969
charges: Trinity, Denver, CO, 1969–74; staff of IVCF at UCLA, 1974–79; Calvary, Loveland, CO, 1979–87; The New City Church, San Francisco, CA, 1987–89; Palo Alto, CA, 1989–2001
retired: 2001

De Young, James C.
b. 01/13/1931, Archer, IA
training: Westminster Theological Seminary, BD, 1956; ThM; Vrije Universiteit, Amsterdam, ThD
ordained: 1961
charges: Home missionary at Omaha, NE, 1961–66; Faculty, Reformed Theological Seminary, Jackson, MS, 1966–88; Faculty, Asian Theological Seminary, Manila, Philippines, 1988–96
retired: 1996

De Young, Maurice Lee
b. 03/23/1949, McBain, MI
training: Calvin Theological Seminary, MDiv, 1974
ordained: 1974
charges: Minister of education and evangelism, First, Denver, CO, 1974–76; Rolling Acres, Mason City, IA, 1976–84; Christ's Fellowship, Springfield, IL, 1984–90; Kelloggsville, Kentwood, MI, 1990–

De Young, Roger
b. 10/23/1948, Hammond, IN
training: Calvin Theological Seminary, MDiv, 1976
ordained: 1977
charges: Alger Park, Grand Rapids, MI, 1977–81; Chaplain, Hillcrest School, Jos, Nigeria, 1981–85; Hope, Houston, TX, 1985–

De Young, Ronald
b. 10/23/1948, Hammond, IN
training: Calvin Theological Seminary, MDiv, 1979
ordained: 1979
charges: Baldwin St., Jenison, MI, 1979–83; Rapid City, SD, 1983–89; East Saugatuck, MI, 1989–97; Chaplain, Western Michigan University, Kalamazoo, MI, 1997–

De Young, Ronald Duane
b. 10/28/1946, McBain, MI
training: Calvin Theological Seminary, BD, 1971; MDiv, 1978
ordained: 1971
charges: Bethlehem, Freeman, SD, 1971–76 Goshen, IN, 1976–82; Anaheim, CA, 1982–93; Hamilton, MI, 1993–99; Oakland, MI, 2000–

De Young, Ronald William
b. 06/21/1942, Grand Rapids, MI
training: Fuller Theological Seminary, BD, 1970; Calvin Theological Seminary, Special Program for Ministerial Candidacy, 1971
ordained: 1971
charges: Missionary to Japan, 1971–74; Chaplain resident, Pine Rest Christian Hospital, Cutlerville, MI, 1974–76; Iowa Falls, IA, 1976–81; Park Lane, Evergreen Park, IL, 1981–86; Leave, 1986–88; Chaplain, Christian Hospital and Medical Center, Oak Lawn, IL, 1988–89; Pastoral counselor, Wholistic Health Center, Hinsdale, IL, 1989–91; Chaplain, Hospice Care, Chicagoland, Homewood, IL, 1991–92; Chaplain, Alden Nursing Centers, Naperville, IL, 1992–93; Chaplain, Hospice of Illinois, Masonic Medical Center, Chicago, IL, 1993–96; Chaplain, Hospice of Integrated Health Services, Schaumburg, IL, 1996–2001; Chaplain, Ad-

vocate Christ Medical Center, Oak Lawn, IL,
2001–

De Young, Wayne Dale
b. 03/02/1941, Ellsworth, MI
training: Calvin Theological Seminary, BD, 1966
ordained: 1966
charges: Missionary, Fairbanks, AK, 1966–68;
Leave, 1968–69; Bible teacher, Westminster Christian School, Miami, FL, 1969–72; Non-ministerial vocation: High school teacher, 1972

De Young, Wayne Roger
b. 05/01/1950, Kalamazoo, MI
training: Calvin Theological Seminary, BD, 1976
ordained: 1977
charges: Missionary, Santo Domingo, Dominican Republic, 1977–86; Missionary, Haiti, 1986–93;
Faith in Christ Fellowship, Marquette, MI, 1993–

Dieleman, Adrian
b. 01/12/1953, Woodstock, ON
training: Calvin Theological Seminary, MDiv, 1979
ordained: 1979
charges: Blyth, ON, 1979–83; Bethany, Fenwick, ON, 1983–88; Bethel, Waupun, WI, 1988–97; Trinity, Visalia, CA, 1997–

Dieleman, Randall Joe
b. 09/16/1955, Grand Rapids, MI
training: Calvin Theological Seminary, MDiv, 1992
ordained: 1992
charges: Intern, Vernon, BC, 1977–78; Wayland, MI, 1992–95; Faculty, Miami (FL) Christian High School, 1995–97; Faculty, Westminster Christian High School, Miami, FL, 1997–

Diemer, Fred
b. 06/18/1928, Grand Rapids, MI
training: Calvin Theological Seminary, BD, 1958;
MDiv, 1981
ordained: 1958
charges: Knollwood, Kalamazoo, MI, 1958–65; Arcadia, CA, 1965–68; Good Samaritan, Miami, FL, 1968–79; Faculty, Reformed Bible College, Grand Rapids, MI, 1979–81; Eligible for call, 1981–83;
Missionary to Central America, 1983–93
retired: 1993

Dieperink Langereis, Hendrik Haagen
b. 11/30/1830, Medemblik, North Holland, Netherlands
training: Theologische Universiteit, Kampen, then with J.H. Donner and B. de Beij
ordained: 1880

charges: Lederboerian: Exhorter, Benthuizen, 1874–80; Stad a/h Haaringvliet, 1880–87; Den Bommel, 1883–85; Independent: Free Reformed, Paterson, NJ, 1887–88; CRC: Second, Paterson, NJ, 1888–91; Beaverdam, MI, 1890–93; Burdick Street, Kalamazoo, MI, 1893–1903
d. 07/01/1903, Kalamazoo, MI

Diephuis, Roelof
b. 08/12/1871, Putten, Gelderland, Netherlands
training: Calvin Theological Seminary, diploma, 1900
ordained: 1900
charges: Lodi, NJ, 1900–03; Oakland, MI, 1903–08; Harderwyk, MI, 1908–11; Second, Kalamazoo, MI, 1911–19; Alto, WI, 1919–25; Goshen, IN, 1925–36
retired: 1936
d. 08/15/1945, Grand Rapids, MI

Dik, Jack Bryan
b. 06/09/1954, Grand Rapids, MI
training: Calvin Theological Seminary, MCE, 1978;
MDiv, 1994
ordained: 1994
charges: Third, Kalamazoo, MI, 1983–96; Park, Holland, MI, 1996–

Dirksen, Willem Dirk
b. 06/21/1935, Leeuwarden, Friesland, Netherlands
training: Calvin Theological Seminary, BD, 1969
ordained: 1969
charges: Missionary to Brazil, 1969–80; Chula Vista, CA, 1980–87; First, Thunder Bay, ON, 1987–93; Stratford, ON 1993–2000
retired: 2000

Disselkoen, Arie
b. 08/15/1892, Chicago, IL
training: Calvin Theological Seminary, BD, 1930
ordained: 1930
charges: Chandler, MN, 1930–39; Winnipeg, MB, 1939–53; Home missionary at Stonewell, Winnipeg, MB, 1953–54; at Selkirk, Transcona and Winnipeg, MB and Kenora, ON, 1954–57; at East Kildonan, MB, 1957–58
retired: 1958
d. 05/10/1984, Denver, CO

Doezema, Frank
b. 07/16/1871, Niezijl, Groningen, Netherlands
training: Calvin Theological Seminary, diploma, 1899
ordained: 1899

charges: Midland Park, NJ, 1899–1905; West Leonard, Grand Rapids, MI, 1905–14; First Roseland, Chicago, IL, 1914–44
retired: 1944
d. 11/21/1967, Palos Heights, IL

Doezema, Lambert
b. 12/08/1912, Grand Rapids, MI
training: Vrije Universiteit, Amsterdam, diploma, 1940
ordained: 1940
charges: PRC: Bellflower, CA, 1940–56; Creston, Grand Rapids, MI, 1956–61; CRC: Drayton, ON, 1961–66; Parchment, Kalamazoo, MI, 1966–77
retired: 1977

Dokter, Gerrit Bernard
b. 07/27/1929, Hull, IA
training: Calvin Theological Seminary, BD, 1953; MDiv, 1977
ordained: 1953
charges: Hills, MN, 1953–56; Chaplain, United States Air Force, 1956–60; Ferrysburg, MI, 1960–64; Missionary to South America-Argentina, 1964–72; Missionary to Honduras, 1972–79; Latin America area secretary, Board of Foreign Missions, 1979–85; Allen Ave., Muskegon, MI, 1985–94
retired: 1994

Dolfin, John (Jan)
b. 09/17/1880, Lafayette, IN
training: Calvin Theological Seminary, diploma, 1903
ordained: 1903
charges: Home missionary at Pella IA, 1903–04; Englewood, NJ, 1904–09; Bethany, Muskegon, MI, 1909–43
d. 06/12/1943, Muskegon, MI

Doorn, Thomas Paul
b. 11/20/1947, Kalamazoo, MI
training: Calvin Theological Seminary, MDiv, 1981
ordained: 1981
charges: Community, Los Angeles, CA, 1981–

Doornbos, Keith Milton
b. 01/01/1956, Grand Rapids, MI
training: Calvin Theological Seminary, MDiv, 1983
ordained: 1983
charges: Calvary, Holland, MI, 1983–93; Providence, Holland, MI, 1993–

Doornbos, Larry John
b. 02/11/1958, Sioux Center, IA
training: Calvin Theological Seminary, MDiv, 1985

ordained: 1986
charges: Rehoboth, NM, 1986–93; EverGreen Ministries, Hudsonville, MI, 1993–

Doornbos, Marvin Robert
b. 05/01/1930, Jenison, MI
training: Calvin Theological Seminary, BD, 1956
ordained: 1956
charges: Calvary, Pella, IA, 1956–60; Bethany, South Holland, IL, 1960–68; Highland Hills, Grand Rapids, MI, 1968–77; First, Zeeland, MI, 1977–80
d. 03/16/1980, Zeeland, MI

Doornbos, Milton Roger
b. 05/01/1930, Grand Rapids, MI
training: Calvin Theological Seminary, BD, 1956; ThM, 1967
ordained: 1956
charges: Calvin, Rock Valley, IA, 1956–60; Immanuel, Hudsonville, MI, 1960–69; Mayfair, Grand Rapids, MI, 1969–74; Coordinator of congregational evangelism, Board of Home Missions, 1974–78; Ridgewood, Jenison, MI, 1978–89; Home missionary regional director, Western Michigan, 1989–96
retired: 1996

Dornbush, Menzo
b. 05/19/1903, Grandville, MI
training: Calvin Theological Seminary, BD, 1929
ordained: 1929
charges: Atwood, MI, 1929–43; Volga, SD, 1943–50; Home missionary, Brandon, MB, 1950–55; Taber, AB, 1955–58; Brandon, MB, 1958–62; Home missionary, Charlottetown, PE, 1962–68 and New Glasgow, NS, 1968
retired: 1968
d. 10/23/1999, Grand Rapids, MI

Douma, John Phillip
b. 03/15/1969, Sarnia, ON
training: Calvin Theological Seminary, MDiv, 1998
ordained: 1999
charges: Volga, SD, 1999–

Douma, Timothy Harold
b. 11/08/1949, Chicago, IL
training: Calvin Theological Seminary, MDiv, 1979
ordained: 1979
charges: Gibson, Holland, MI, 1979–87; Loop Christian Ministries, Chicago, IL, 1987–

Douwstra, Harm (Henry)
b. 05/16/1851, Groningen, Groningen, Netherlands

training: Calvin Theological Seminary, diploma, 1880
ordained: 1881
charges: CRC: East Saugatuck, MI, 1881-91; First, Chicago, 1890-1892; Overisel, MI, 1892-93; RCA: Third, Pella, IA, 1894-1901; Third, Kalamazoo, MI, 1901-03; Free Grace, Middleburg, IA, 1903-20
retired: 1920
d. 02/07/1930, Pella, IA

Downs, Harry Lee

b. 09/09/1934, Chili, NY
training: Calvin Theological Seminary, ThB, 1965; ThM, 1972
ordained: 1965
charges: CRC: Hartley, IA, 1965-67; Missionary, West Broadway, Paterson, NJ, 1967-70; Dresden, ON, 1972-78; released from denomination, 1978; pastor in Lancaster, PA, 1999

Doyle, David Michael

b. 06/29/1935, Grand Rapids, MI
training: Calvin Theological Seminary, BD, 1966; MDiv, 1984
ordained: 1966
charges: Missionary, Crownpoint, NM, 1966-69; Pioneer, Cedar Springs, MI, 1969-74; Missionary to Mexico, 1974-78; Trinity, Chula Vista, CA, 1978-80; Non-ministerial vocation, 1980-95; Pinegate Community, Cutlerville, MI, 1995-98; Leave, 1998-2000
retired: 2000

Draayer, Donald Glenn

b. 03/05/1950, Orange City, IA
training: Calvin Theological Seminary, BD, 1975; MDiv, 1983
ordained: 1976
charges: Newton, IA, 1976-80; First, Bellflower, CA, 1980-89; Campus minister, Dordt College, Sioux Center, IA, 1989-

Draayer, Sidney

b. 01/04/1931, Grand Rapids, MI
training: Calvin Theological Seminary, BD, 1958; MDiv, 1978
ordained: 1958
charges: Trinity, Philadelphia, PA, 1958-62; Maple Heights, Cleveland, OH, 1962-67; Ann Arbor, MI, 1967-72; Director, Christian Servicemen's Center, San Diego, CA, 1972-73; Knollwood, Kalamazoo, MI, 1973-78; Executive director, Christian Counseling Center, Grand Rapids, MI, 1978-

90; Executive director, Paraklesis Ministries, Grand Rapids, MI, 1990-99
retired: 1999

Draayer, Thomas Dale

b. 06/10/1954, Grand Rapids, MI
training: Calvin Theological Seminary, MDiv, 1982
ordained: 1982
charges: Preakness, Wayne, NJ, 1982-88; Third, Denver, CO, 1988-

Draisma, John Henry

b. 05/29/1934, Oak Lawn, IL
training: Calvin Theological Seminary, BD, 1959
ordained: 1959
charges: Parkersburg, IA, 1959-62; First, Des Plaines, IL, 1962-68; Holland Heights, Holland, MI, 1968-75
d. 04/05/1975, Oak Lawn, IL

Dreise, Albert

b. 03/02/1939, Groningen, Groningen, Netherlands
training: Calvin Theological Seminary, BD, 1968
ordained: 1968
charges: Immanuel, Cornwall, ON, 1968-72; Newmarket, ON, 1972-75; Emmanuel, New Glasgow, NS, 1975-80; Palmerston, ON, 1980-86; Calvary, Flamborough, ON, 1986-88; Executive director/chaplain, Salem Christian Mental Health Association, Cornwall, ON, 1989-

Drenten, Robert Dale

b. 11/17/1961, Zeeland, MI
training: Calvin Theological Seminary, MDiv, 1988
ordained: 1988
charges: First, Oskaloosa, IA, 1988-94; Bethel, Sioux Center, IA, 1994-2001; Prosper, Falmouth, MI, 2001-

Drenth, Stanley Allan

b. 06/25/1951, Charlevoix, MI
training: Calvin Theological Seminary, MDiv, 1978; ThM, 1990
ordained: 1978
charges: Nobleford, AB, 1978-82; Missionary, Sierra Leone, 1982-88; Eligible for call, 1988-89; Sunnyside, WA, 1989-99; Searchlight Ministries, Jamestown, MI, 1999-

Dresselhuis, John (Jan) Eddo Frans

b. 09/19/1927, Oldeboorn, Friesland, Netherlands
training: Vrije Universiteit, Amsterdam, DB, 1954
ordained: 1954
charges: GKN: Lobith, 1954-59; CRC: Maranatha,

Belleville, ON, 1959–62; Ottewell, Edmonton AB, 1962–66; Brandon, MB, 1966–70; Seaman's Chaplain, British Columbia Classes, 1970–93
retired: 1993

Drost, Donald Joseph
b. 07/26/1908, Holland, MI
training: Calvin Theological Seminary, BD, 1933
ordained: 1936
charges: Evangelist, Classis Holland, 1933–35; Grundy Center and Holland, IA, 1935–36; Coster, IA, 1936–40; East Side, Cleveland, OH, 1940–48; Allendale, MI, 1948–52; Allen Ave., Muskegon, MI, 1952–60; Brookside, Grand Rapids, MI, 1960–68; Peoria, IA, 1968–73
retired: 1973
d. 10/19/1991, Grand Rapids, MI

Drost, Frederik J.
b. 01/11/1863, Joure, Friesland, Netherlands
training: with E. Otten, L. Wagenaar, and D.J.B. Wijers
ordained: 1890
charges: GKN: Wartena, 1886–95; CRC: Whitinsville, MA. 1896–1902; Eastmanville, MI, 1902–05; Byron Center, MI, 1905–10; Leighton, IA, 1910–14; Home missionary, Los Angeles, CA, 1914–17; Home missionary, Oak Harbor, WA, 1917–22; Otley, IA, 1922–28
d. 02/22/1928, Cedar Rapids, IA

Drukker, Douwe R.
b. 05/17/1868, Stroobos, Friesland, Netherlands
training: Calvin Theological Seminary, diploma, 1895
ordained: 1898
charges: Overisel, MI, 1895; Midland Park, NJ, 1896–98; Drenthe, MI, 1898–1902; Fourteenth St., Holland, MI, 1902–11; First, Zeeland, MI, 1911–14; Third, Kalamazoo, MI, 1914–18; Third, Zeeland, MI, 1918–26; Summer St., Passaic, NJ, 1926
d. 12/27/1926, Morristown, NJ

Drukker, Roelof
b. 10/14/1842, Wanswerd, Friesland, Netherlands
training: Calvin Theological Seminary, diploma, 1883
ordained: 1883
charges: Lamont, MI, 1883–86; Passaic, NJ, 1886–88; Kelloggsville, MI, 1889–91; Second, Paterson, NJ, 1891–1902
retired: 1902
d. 09/06/1912, Paterson, NJ

Dryfhout, William
b. 12/04/1912, Chicago, IL
training: Calvin Theological Seminary, BD, 1937; Theologische Universiteit, Kampen, 1938; Princeton Theological Seminary, ThM, 1939
ordained: 1939
charges: Second, Randolph, WI, 1939–49; Hanford, CA, 1949–59; First, Oskaloosa, IA, 1959–68; Barrhead-Westlock, AB, 1968–72; Doon, IA, 1972–77
retired: 1978
d. 04/04/2001, Randolph, WI

Dubois, Walter G.
b. 01/12/1912, Hilversum, Noord Holland, Netherlands
training: Calvin Theological Seminary, ThB, 1944
ordained: 1944
charges: Arlene, MI, 1944–48; Madison Square, Grand Rapids, MI, 1948–62; Barrhead-Westlock, AB, 1962–66; Mountain Lake, MN, 1966–73
retired: 1973
d. 02/12/1996, Grand Rapids, MI

Duifhuis, Richard
b. 10/10/1937, Barneveld, Gelderland, Netherlands
training: Calvin Theological Seminary, BD, 1966
ordained: 1966
charges: Emo, ON, 1966–75; First, Port Alberni, BC, 1975–88; Leave, 1988–93
retired: 1993; withdrew from denomination 1999

Duiker, Roelof
b. 01/18/1825, De Wijk, Drenthe, Netherlands
training: with Wolter Alberts Kok
ordained: 1850
charges: GKN: Lippenhuizen, 1850–51; Oudega, 1851–56; Surhuisterveen, 1856; Niezijl, 1856–67; CRC: First, Grand Rapids, MI, 1867–72; Second, Grand Haven, MI, 1881–87; RCA: Danforth, IL, 1872–74; Milwaukee, WI, 1874–77; Grand Haven, MI, 1878–81; Grandville, MI, 1887–90; Third, Kalamazoo, MI, 1890–92; Eighth, Grand Rapids, MI, 1892–96
retired: 1896
d. 08/09/1917, Grand Rapids, MI

Duistermars, Orwin Wayne
b. 12/12/1922, LeMars, IA
training: Calvin Theological Seminary, BD, 1961
ordained: 1961
charges: Trinity, Fremont, MI, 1961–64; Bethany, Bellflower, CA, 1964–70; Beckwith Hills, Grand Rapids, MI, 1970–74; Third, Lynden, WA, 1974–79;

Battle Creek, MI, 1979–84; Second, Wellsburg, IA, 1984–87
retired: 1988

Dusseljee, Aldrich
b. 10/04/1893, Delfzijl, Groningen, Netherlands
training: Calvin Theological Seminary, diploma, 1924; ThB, 1933
ordained: 1924
charges: East Martin, MI, 1924–28; Jenison, MI, 1928–40; Missionary at Compton, CA, 1940–41; at Upland, CA, 1941–43; Chaplain, 1943–46; Sixteenth St., Holland, MI, 1946–48; Milwood, Kalamazoo, MI, 1948–52; First, Orange City, IA, 1952–57; Dorr, MI, 1957–59
retired: 1959
d. 03/25/1966, Holland, MN

Dwyer, Kevin Lawrence
b. 08/24/1956, Hinsdale, IL
training: University of Cincinnati, MEd, 1986; Calvin Theological Seminary, MDiv, 1994
ordained: 1994
charges: Milwood, Kalamazoo, MI, 1994–98; Three Rivers, MI, 1998–2002

Dyk, John J.
b. 03/16/1886, Thesinge, Friesland, Netherlands
training: Calvin Theological Seminary, diploma, 1919
ordained: 1919
charges: Inwood, IA, 1919–24; Rock Rapids, IA, 1924–26; Vogel Center, MI, 1926–29; Tracy, IA, 1931–34
retired: 1929
d. 09/13/1958, Grand Rapids, MI

Dyk, Wilbur Dean
b. 11/23/1949, Bozeman, MT
training: Calvin Theological Seminary, MDiv, 1977
ordained: 1979
charges: Youth and singles pastor, First, Calgary, AB, 1979–84; Pacific Community, Honolulu, HI, 1984–90; Director, Pastoral Care, Behavioral Health, Bethesda Campus, Denver, CO, 1990–98; Director, Pastoral Care and Education, The Medical Center of Aurora, Aurora, CO, 1998; Director, Pastoral Care, Swedish Medical Center, Englewood, CO, 2000–

Dykema, Earl Donald
b. 08/29/1928, Shiprock, NM
training: Calvin Theological Seminary, BD, 1954
ordained: 1954
charges: Wright/Kanawha, IA, 1954–58; Missionary, Crownpoint, NM, 1958–64; Beacon Light, Gary, IN, 1964–70; Missionary, Cedar Rapids, IA, 1970–77; Regional director, West Central US, Home Missions, Bedford, TX, 1977–93
retired: 1993

Dykema, Henry
b. 08/06/1938, Westeremden, Groningen, Netherlands
training: Calvin Theological Seminary, BD, 1965
ordained: 1965
charges: Missionary to Guam, 1965–77; Decatur, MI, 1977–81; Maple Ave., Holland, MI, 1981–90; Bravo, Fennville, MI, 1990–96; Hollandale, MN, 1996–2001
retired: 2001

Dykema, Jeffrey Allan
b. 10/29/1950, Grand Rapids, MI
training: Westminster Theological Seminary-PA, MDiv, 1976; Calvin Theological Seminary, Special Program for Ministerial Candidacy, 1978
ordained: 1978
charges: Fruitport, MI, 1978–89; Sunshine Community, El Paso, TX, 1989–

Dykhouse, Herman
b. 12/25/1894, Kalamazoo, MI
training: Calvin Theological Seminary, diploma, 1923; Princeton, ThM, 1924
ordained: 1924
charges: Eastmanville, MI, 1924–29; Jamestown, MI, 1929–47; Lansing, MI, 1947–56
retired: 1956
d. 08/28/1966, Kalamazoo, MI

Dykhuis, John William
b. 09/23/1957, Holland, MI
training: Calvin Theological Seminary, MDiv, 1990
ordained: 1991
charges: Fellowship, Albuquerque, NM, 1991–

Dykman, Thomas Earl
b. 01/01/1945, Fremont, MI
training: Calvin Theological Seminary, BD, 1971; MDiv, 1983
ordained: 1971
charges: Bible teacher, Illiana Christian High School, 1971–73; Sunnyslope, Salem, OR, 1973–78; Hillcrest, Denver, CO, 1978–86; Christ's Community, San Diego, CA, 1986–92; Leave, 1992–93; Sunrise, Austin, TX, 1993–

Dykstra, Allan Henry
b. 06/11/1924, McGrath, MN

training: Western Theological Seminary, BD, 1952; Calvin Theological Seminary, ThM, 1964
ordained: 1952
charges: RCA: Union, Paterson, NJ, 1952-57; First, DeMotte, IN, 1957-60; Third, Grand Rapids, MI, 1960-66; CRC: Bible teacher, Southwest Minnesota Christian High, 1966-70; Hope, Hull, IA, 1970-73
retired: 1973
d. 01/09/1993, Sioux Falls, SD

Dykstra, Bernard
b. 09/02/1942, Oostrerend, Friesland, Netherlands
training: Reformed Theological Seminary, MDiv, 1979; Calvin Theological Seminary, Special Program for Ministerial Candidacy, 1986
ordained: 1986
charges: Peace, Menno, SD, 1986-95; First, Taber, AB, 1995-98; Holland Center, Lodgepole, SD, 1998-

Dykstra, Daniel Scott
b. 05/04/1965, Holland, MI
training: Calvin Theological Seminary, MDiv, 1991
ordained: 1992
charges: Unity, Allegan, MI, 1992-97; Leave, 1997-

Dykstra, David John
b. 09/05/1955, Grand Rapids, MI
training: Calvin Theological Seminary, MDiv, 1992
ordained: 1993
charges: Lincoln Center, Grundy Center, IA, 1993-2001; Faith Community, Beaver Dam, WI, 2001-

Dykstra, Edwin J.
b. 07/23/1940, Grand Rapids, MI
training: Calvin Theological Seminary, BD, 1969
ordained: 1972
charges: CRC: Parkview Heights, Cincinnati, OH, 1972-75; Chaplain, State Hospital, Allentown, PA, 1975-78; Chaplain, Larue D. Carter Hospital, Indianapolis, IN, 1978-82; United Presbyterian Church: Ministry, Indianapolis, IN, 1982-91; Trinity, Rushville, IN, 1992; Ministry, Michigan City, IN, 1993; First, Alliance, OH, 1994

Dykstra, Ellsworth C.
b. 12/12/1909, Andover, SD
training: Western Theological Seminary, diploma, 1944
ordained: 1944
charges: RCA: Barnard, Charlevoix, MI, 1944-48; Central, Oskaloosa, IA, 1948-49; Free Grace, Middleburg, IA, 1949-54; CRC: Sioux Falls, SD,

1954-59; Kenosha, WI, 1959-62; Battle Creek, MI, 1962-69; Borculo, MI, 1969-70
retired: 1970
d. 02/01/1994, Grand Rapids, MI

Dykstra, Gerard Lee
b. 02/23/1950, Holland, MI
training: Calvin Theological Seminary, MDiv, 1990
ordained: 1990
charges: Pastor of congregational care, Ada, MI, 1988-90; Cascade Fellowship, Grand Rapids, MI, 1990-96; Walnut Creek, CA, 1996-

Dykstra, Harry Andrew
b. 06/06/1894, Ferwerd, Friesland, Netherlands
training: Calvin Theological Seminary, diploma, 1920; post graduate study at Calvin Theological and Hartford Seminaries, 1926-27; Kennedy School of Missions, MA, 1928
ordained: 1920
charges: Medical missionary, China, 1920-26; Medical missionary, China, 1927-41; Camp Pastor in California, 1941-46; Phoenix, AZ, 1946-50; Home missionary at Phoenix, AZ, 1950-51; Service pastor in California, 1951-59;
retired: 1959
d. 01/08/1987, Visalia, CA

Dykstra, Jacob
b. 06/09/1931, Chicago, IL
training: Calvin Theological Seminary, BD, 1968
ordained: 1968
charges: Chilliwack, BC, 1968-72; Creston, Grand Rapids, MI, 1972-82; First, Lynden, WA, 1982-87
d. 04/11/1987, Lynden, WA

Dykstra, Jerry
b. 05/05/1932, Andijk, Noord Holland, Netherlands
training: Westminster Theological Seminary-PA, MDiv, 1964
ordained: 1964
charges: Halifax, NS, 1964-71; Clinical pastoral education, Victoria General Hospital, Halifax, NS, 1971-78; Coordinator of pastoral care, Halifax Infirmary, Halifax, NS, 1978-80; Non-ministerial vocation, 1980

Dykstra, John M.
b. 02/22/1895, Onderdendam, Groningen, Netherlands
training: Calvin Theological Seminary, diploma, 1924; Princeton Seminary, ThM, 1925
ordained: 1925
charges: Bejou and Crookston, MN, 1925-29;

First, Sioux Center, IA, 1929–38; North St., Zeeland, MI, 1938–49; Battle Creek, MI, 1949–52; Jarvis, ON, 1952–59; Momence, IL, 1959–64
retired: 1964
d. 03/12/1981, Zeeland, MI

Dykstra, John S.
b. 09/23/1895, Holland, MI
training: Calvin Theological Seminary, diploma, 1921
ordained: 1921
charges: Eddyville, IA, 1921–26; Leave, 1926–34; Non-ministerial vocation, 1934
d. 10/09/1979, Grand Rapids, MI

Dykstra, John William
b. 05/17/1932, Berwyn, IL
training: Calvin Theological Seminary, BD, 1958
ordained: 1958
charges: Prairie Edge, Kalamazoo, MI, 1958–64; Home missionary, Toadlena, NM, 1964–65; Home missionary, Kettering, Dayton, OH, 1965–68; Newton, IA, 1968–72; Twelfth St., Grand Rapids, MI, 1972–85; First, Oak Lawn, IL, 1985–91
retired: 1991
d. 01/20/1991, Pontiac, IL

Dykstra, Louis John
b. 05/29/1924, Paterson, NJ
training: Calvin Theological Seminary, ThB, 1949
ordained: 1949
charges: Pine Creek, Holland, MI, 1949–53; Ebenezer, Berwyn, IL, 1953–57; Alger Park, Grand Rapids, MI, 1957–62; Irving Park, Midland Park, NJ, 1962–67; Chino, CA, 1967–75; Modesto, CA, 1975–81; Graafschap, MI, 1981–88
retired: 1988

Dykstra, Simon A.
b. 07/07/1891, Ferwerd, Friesland, Netherlands
training: Calvin Theological Seminary, diploma, 1919
ordained: 1919
charges: Baldwin, WI, 1919–22; Home Missionary, Classis Muskegon, 1922–24; Missionary to China, 1924–27; Missionary to Chatham, ON, 1928–29; Missionary to China, 1929–43 (furlough, 1937–39); Duvall, WA, 1943–45; Hamilton, ON, 1945–50; Decatur, MI, 1950–57
retired: 1957
d. 10/27/1959, Lake Worth, FL

Dykstra, Thomas Ray
b. 04/11/1955, Kalamazoo, MI
training: Calvin Theological Seminary, MDiv, 1981

ordained: 1981
charges: Iowa Falls, IA, 1981–87; West Sayville, NY, 1987–94; Calvary, Pella, IA, 1994–2002; Lake Worth, FL, 2002–

Dykstra, William
b. 04/25/1939, Birdaard, Friesland, Netherlands
training: Calvin Theological Seminary, BD, 1968; ThM, 1969
ordained: 1969
charges: Haney, BC, 1969–74; Campus minister, Queen's University, Kingston, ON, 1974–82; First, Chatham, ON, 1982–90; Bethel, Newmarket, ON, 1990–98; Chaplain, Beaver Creek Correctional Institution, Gravenhurst, ON, 1998–

Dykstra, William J.
b. 12/14/1935, Grand Rapids, MI
training: Calvin Theological Seminary, BD, 1962
ordained: 1962
charges: Alto, WI, 1962–65; McBain, MI, 1965–68; Jackson, MI, 1968–78; Chaplain, Southern Michigan State Prison, Jackson, MI, 1978–90
retired: 1990

Ebbers, George Bernard
b. 06/12/1929, Edmonton, AB
training: Calvin Theological Seminary, BD, 1955
ordained: 1955
charges: Tyler, MN, 1955–59; Willard, OH, 1959–68; San Jose, CA, 1968–80; Leave, 1980–86; Eligible for call, 1986–88; Calvary Community, Redding, CA, 1988–91
retired: 1991

Ebbers, John Tony
b. 11/07/1930, Edmonton, AB
training: Calvin Theological Seminary, BD, 1956
ordained: 1956
charges: Grace, Muskegon, MI, 1956–61; Corsica, SD, 1961–69; Lombard, IL, 1969–78; Calvary, Orange City, IA, 1978–88; Leave, 1988–91; Eligible for call, 1991–92; Conrad, MT, 1992–96
retired: 1996

Ebbers, Richard Jay
b. 01/20/1964, Sheboygan, WI
training: Calvin Theological Seminary, MDiv, 1995
ordained: 1995
charges: Escalon, CA, 1995–99; The Journey, Longmont, CO, 1999–

Edgar, Darrell
b. 10/18/1959, Moncton, NB
training: University of Winnipeg, MDiv, 1991

ordained: 1993
charges: Church of the Nazarene: Hamilton, ON, 1991–94; Windsor, ON, 1994–96; CRC: Interim, Ambassador, Windsor, ON, 1996–99; Ambassador, Windsor, ON, 1999–

Ehlers, John Willem Christian
b. 02/25/1899, Amsterdam, Noord Holland, Netherlands
training: Calvin Theological Seminary, diploma, 1925; McCormick Seminary, ThM, 1926
ordained: 1926
charges: Platte, SD, 1926–30; Edgerton, MN, 1930–48; Willard, OH, 1948–53; Mt. Hamilton, Hamilton, ON, 1953–64
retired: 1964
d. 12/18/1978, Willard, OH

Einfeld, Douglas John
b. 06/14/1952, Cadillac, MI
training: Calvin Theological Seminary, MDiv, 1979
ordained: 1982
charges: Fox Valley, Crystal Lake, IL, 1982–92; Immanuel Community, Columbia, MO, 1992–95; Leave, 1995–96; Hospice Chaplain, Health Care, Inc., Columbia, MO, 1996–2001; Hospice chaplain, Boone Hospital Hospice, MO, 1999– ; Chaplain, University Hospital, Columbia, MO, 2001–

Einfeld, Frank
b. 09/23/1920, Winnipeg, MB
training: Calvin Theological Seminary, BD, 1946
ordained: 1947
charges: Purewater, NE, 1947–50; Calvin, McBain, MI, 1950–65; Wright, Kanawha, IA, 1965–77; Grangeville, ID, 1977–82
retired: 1982; afilliated with United Reformed Church, 2001

Einink, Bernard Henry
b. 09/18/1865, Clymer, NY
training: Calvin Theological Seminary, diploma, 1893
ordained: 1893
charges: Jenison, MI, 1893–95; Lafayette, IN, 1895–1902; First Roseland, Chicago, IL, 1902–09; First, Muskegon, MI, 1909–15; Central Ave., Holland, MI, 1915–25; Ellsworth, MI, 1925–34
retired: 1934
d. 03/21/1949, Cutlerville, MI

Eising, Adrian
b. 11/26/1960, Tillsonburg, ON
training: Calvin Theological Seminary, MDiv, 1986
ordained: 1986

charges: Missionary, Haiti, 1986–89; Eligible for call, 1989–91; Lakeview Community, Valentine, NE, 1991–99; Prairie City, IA, 1999–

Eising, Henry
b. 03/19/1955, Simcoe, ON
training: Reformed Bible College, BRE, 1981; Calvin Theological Seminary, MDiv, 1985
ordained: 1987
charges: Emmanuel, New Glasgow, NS, 1987–90; Leave, 1990–92; Assistant chaplain, Holland Home, Grand Rapids, MI, 1992–

Eiten, Kenneth Howard
b. 07/14/1954, Grundy Center, IA
training: Calvin Theological Seminary, MDiv, 1980
ordained: 1980
charges: CRC: Lebanon, IA, 1980–84; Alamosa, CO, 1984–92; Lynwood, IL, 1992; United Reformed Church: Lynwood, IL, 1992

Ekster, Peter
b. 11/30/1855, Baflo, Groningen, Netherlands
training: Calvin Theological Seminary, diploma, 1883
ordained: 1883
charges: Spring Lake, MI, 1883–86; Alpine Ave., Grand Rapids, MI, 1886–1905; Midland Park, NJ, 1905–08; First, Grand Rapids, MI, 1908–18
d. 07/11/1918, Grand Rapids, MI

Eldersveld, Peter Herman
b. 01/18/1911, Kalamazoo, MI
training: Calvin Theological Seminary, ThB, 1936
ordained: 1938
charges: Holland, IA, 1938–43; Bethany, South Holland, IL, 1943–46; Denominational radio minister, 1946–65
retired: 1965
d. 10/14/1965, Chicago, IL

Eldersveld, Samuel P.
b. 01/11/1874, Noordhorn, Groningen, Netherlands
training: Calvin Theological Seminary, diploma, 1906
ordained: 1906
charges: Beaverdam, MI, 1906–09; First, Kalamazoo, MI, 1909–18; West Leonard, Grand Rapids, MI, 1918–20; Corsica, SD, 1920–24; First, Muskegon, MI, 1924–41; Momence, IL, 1941–42
d. 06/16/1942, Kankakee, IL

Elenbaas, John Hanover
b. 02/09/1925, Lynden, WA
training: Calvin Theological Seminary, BD, 1952

ordained: 1952
charges: Holland Center, SD, 1952-55; Mountain Lake, MN, 1955-60; Doon, IA, 1960-66; Second, Wellsburg, IA, 1966-83; Conrad, MT, 1983-87
retired: 1987

Elgersma, Nathaniel
b. 07/15/1963, Langley, BC
training: Calvin Theological Seminary, MDiv, 1991
ordained: 1992
charges: Kincardine, ON, 1992-98; Lombard, IL, 1998-

Elgersma, Winson Melvin
b. 09/04/1943, Barrhead, AB
training: Calvin Theological Seminary, BD, 1970
ordained: 1970
charges: CRC: Ackley, IA, 1970-73; Leave, 1973-75; Resigned from denomination, 1975, pastor Sylvan Lakes, AB

Ellens, Dale Duane
b. 03/17/1953, Cadillac, MI
training: Calvin Theological Seminary, MDiv, 1979
ordained: 1979
charges: Forest Grove, MI, 1979-83; Chaplain, United States Army, 1983-95; Bethesda Christian Counseling, Midwest, Inc., Rock Valley, IA, 1995-

Ellens, Jay Harold
b. 07/16/1932, McBain, MI
training: Calvin Theological Seminary, MDiv, 1956
ordained: 1956
charges: CRC: Chaplain, USA, 1956-61; Newton, NJ, 1961-65; Home missionary, Royal Oak, MI, 1965-68; Missionary, University Hills, Farmington, MI, 1968-79; PCUSA: Farmington Hills, MI, 1979

Elliott, Timothy
b. 03/11/1947, Kansas City, MO
training: Covenant Theological Seminary, MDiv, 1994
ordained: 1997
charges: PCA: Warsaw, IN; Columbus, OH; CRC: Stated supply, New Hope, Monsey, NY, 2000-

Elzinga, Steven Craig
b. 11/10/1955, Byron Center, MI
training: Calvin Theological Seminary, MDiv, 1981
ordained: 1982
charges: Highland, MI, 1982-87; Hope Community, Surrey, BC, 1987-96; Life Net 21, Lockport, IL, 1996-2000; Director, USA Ministries of the Bible League, Lockport, IL, 2000-

Engbers, John Henry
b. 03/15/1927, Otley, IA
training: Calvin Theological Seminary, BD, 1966
ordained: 1966
charges: Calvin, Rock Valley, IA, 1966-78; Cutlerville East, Cutlerville, MI, 1978-90; Chandler, MN, 1990-94
retired: 1994

Engelhard, David Herman
b. 08/23/1941, Grand Rapids, MI
training: Calvin Theological Seminary, BD, 1966; Brandeis University, MA, 1967; PhD, 1970
ordained: 1971
charges: Faculty, Calvin Theological Seminary, 1971-94; General Secretary, Christian Reformed Church in North America, Grand Rapids, MI, 1994-

Engle, Randall Dean
b. 05/05/1965, Pella, IA
training: Calvin Theological Seminary, MDiv, 1992
ordained: 1992
charges: Calvary, Minneapolis, MN, 1992-2001; North Hills, Troy, MI, 2001-

Entingh, Henry Gerard
b. 07/31/1936, Cadillac, MI
training: Calvin Theological Seminary, BD, 1960
ordained: 1960
charges: Noordeloos, MI, 1960-64; Ebenezer, Leota, MN, 1964-72; Caledonia, MI, 1972-82; Twelfth Street, Grand Rapids, MI, 1987-94; eligible for call, 1994-98
retired: 1998

Entingh, John
b. 01/01/1911, Grand Rapids, MI
training: Calvin Theological Seminary, ThB, 1936
ordained: 1940
charges: Dearborn, MI and Windsor, ON, 1936-43; Milwood, Kalamazoo, MI, 1943-48; East Martin, MI, 1948-53; Westwood, Kalamazoo, MI, 1953-58; Sumas, WA, 1958-64; First, Randolph, WI, 1964-70; Holland, IA, 1970-76
retired: 1976
d. 02/12/1998, Grand Rapids, MI

Eppinga, Jacob Dirk
b. 06/07/1917, Detroit, MI
training: Westminster Theological Seminary-PA, MDiv, 1943; Calvin Theological Seminary, Special Program for Ministerial Candidacy, 1944
ordained: 1945
charges: Dearborn, MI, 1944-51; Highland Hills,

Grand Rapids, MI, 1951–54; LaGrave Ave., Grand Rapids, MI, 1954–87
retired: 1987

Erffmeyer, Gerald Ray
b. 07/06/1947, Grand Rapids, MI
training: Calvin Theological Seminary, BD, 1972; MDiv, 1984
ordained: 1972
charges: Newton, IA, 1972–76; Second, Denver, CO, 1976–82; Alger Park, Grand Rapids, MI, 1982–88; Orland Park, IL, 1988–

Erffmeyer, Henry Nicholas
b. 02/27/1916, Dolton, IL
training: Calvin Theological Seminary, ThB, 1948
ordained: 1948
charges: Immanuel, Hudsonville, MI, 1948–53; First, Denver, CO, 1953–57; First, Cicero, IL, 1957–63; Millbrook, Grand Rapids, MI, 1963–68; Twelfth Ave., Jenison, MI, 1968–81
retired: 1981

Eshuis, Hendrik
b. 08/03/1934, Wierden, Overijsel, Netherlands
training: Calvin Theological Seminary, BD, 1962
ordained: 1962
charges: Athens, ON, 1962–66; Westmount, Strathroy, ON, 1966–70; First, Barrie, ON, 1970–77; Maranatha, Woodstock, ON, 1977–83; First, Guelph, ON, 1983–88; Bethany, Fenwick, ON, 1988–97
retired: 1997

Essenburg, Benjamin
b. 11/13/1890, Holland, MI
training: Calvin Theological Seminary, diploma, 1921
ordained: 1921
charges: Franklin St., Grand Rapids, MI, 1921–25; Drenthe, MI, 1925–29; First, Chicago, IL, 1929–45; First, Jenison, MI, 1945–61
retired: 1961
d. 09/19/1976, Berwyn, IL

Essenburg, Gerald Lee
b. 04/27/1941, Zeeland, MI
training: Calvin Theological Seminary, BD, 1970
ordained: 1970
charges: Harrison, SD, 1970–75; Prairie City, IA, 1975–83; Rudyard, MI, 1983–97; Hancock, MN, 1997–2001
retired: 2001

Estrada, Matthew Rudy
b. 04/29/1958, Biloxi, MS
training: Calvin Theological Seminary, MDiv, 1990
ordained: 1992
charges: Missionary, Honduras, 1992–99; non-ministerial vocation, 1999

Evans, Aalt Dirk
b. 02/06/1940, Barneveld, Gelderland, Netherlands
training: Calvin Theological Seminary, BD, 1967; MDiv, 1975
ordained: 1967
charges: Englewood, NJ, 1967–70; leave for education at St. Luke's Hospital, 1970–73; Clinical chaplain, Outer Drive Hospital, Lincoln Park, MI, 1973–78; Director of pastoral care, Harper-Grace Hospital, Detroit, MI, 1978–88; Teacher, Specialized Pastoral Education, Toronto Western Hospital, Toronto, ON, 1988–96; Teaching chaplain, St. Michael's Hospital, Toronto, ON, 1996–98; Interim, Immanuel, Brampton, ON, 1998; Immanuel, Brampton, ON, 1999–2001; Second, Brampton, ON, 2001–

Evenhouse, Henry John
b. 11/28/1910, Chicago, IL
training: Calvin Theological Seminary, BD, 1935
ordained: 1938
charges: Fourth, Paterson, NJ, 1939–44; Burton Heights, Grand Rapids, MI, 1944–51; First, Denver, CO, 1951; Director of Indian and Foreign Missions, Grand Rapids, MI, 1952–64; Director of Foreign Missions, Grand Rapids, MI, 1964–76
retired: 1976
d. 03/02/1995, Grand Rapids, MI

Evenhouse, James Melvyn
b. 06/21/1934, Chicago, IL
training: Calvin Theological Seminary, BD, 1960
ordained: 1961
charges: Sioux City, IA, 1961–64; Reeman, MI, 1964–71; Plainfield, MI, 1971–77; Springdale, ON, 1977–82; Bozeman, MT, 1982–84; Leave, 1984–85; Atwood, MI, 1985–99
retired: 1999

Evenhuis, Eric Franz
b. 07/29/1946, Holland, MI
training: Calvin Theological Seminary, BD, 1972; Fuller Theological Seminary, DMin, 1974
ordained: 1973
charges: RCA: Christ's Community, Spring Lake, MI, 1973–78; CRC: Voorman's Psychiatric Medical Clinic, Upland, CA, 1978–82; Acting supervisor,

ACPE, Horizon Hospital, Pomona, CA, 1982-89; Chaplain, Charter Oak Hospital and Magnolia Counseling Center, Covina, CA, 1989; Chaplain, Charter Oak Hospital, Covina, CA, 1989-93; Fellowship, Traverse City, MI, 1993-95; Samaritan Counseling Center, Upland, CA, 1995-

Evenhuis, Robert
b. 01/25/1912, Holland, MI
training: Calvin Theological Seminary, BD, 1948
ordained: 1948
charges: Baldwin, WI, 1948-51; Borculo, MI, 1951-55; Rochester, NY, 1955-57; health leave, 1957-60; Pease, MN, 1960-67; Rehoboth, Bellflower, CA, 1969-72
retired: 1967
d. 05/12/1982, between Redlands and Redwood City, CA

Exter, Peter
see: Ekster, Peter

Exoo, Henry
b. 03/07/1911, Cleveland, OH
training: Calvin Theological Seminary, ThB, 1942
ordained: 1942
charges: Battle Creek, MI, 1942-48; First, Fremont, MI, 1948-54; First, Sheboygan, WI, 1954-76
retired: 1976
d. 05/10/1982, Sheboygan, WI

Faber, Harley Gene
b. 09/06/1956, Sioux Center, IA
training: Calvin Theological Seminary, MDiv, 1983
ordained: 1984
charges: CRC: Trinity, Fremont, MI, 1984-88; Unity, Prinsburg, MN, 1988-91; Church planting, Cornerstone Community Church, Bakersfield, CA, 1991-98; Christ Community, Chandler, AZ, 1998-2001; Independent ministry, Casa Grande, AZ, 2001

Faber, Jacob
b. 10/24/1936, Den Kerk, Friesland, Netherlands
training: Vrije Universiteit, Amsterdam, diploma, 1962; Calvin Theological Seminary, Special Program for Ministerial Candidacy, 1963
ordained: 1963
charges: CRC: Pembroke, ON, 1963-67; leave, 1967-68; GKN: assistant pastor, Nigtevecht, 1968-70; Rijswijk, 1970-75; Kampen-Chaplain to students, 1970-98
retired: 1998

Faber, Morris Henry
b. 08/16/1908, Grand Rapids, MI
training: Calvin Theological Seminary, ThB, 1933
ordained: 1934
charges: Vona, CO, 1934-36; Morrison, IL, 1936-44; East Paris, MI, 1944-52; Bible teacher, Grand Rapids (MI) Christian High School, 1952-73
retired: 1973
d. 12/14/2002, Grand Rapids, MI

Fauble, Douglas Raymond
b. 04/14/1950, Cadillac, MI
training: Calvin Theological Seminary, MDiv, 1979
ordained: 1979
charges: Minister of youth and evangelism, Bethel, Lansing, IL, 1976-78; Park, Holland, MI, 1979-83; Western Springs, IL, 1983-90; Ada, MI, 1990-96; South Olive, MI, 1996-

Feddes, David Jon
b. 08/20/1961, Bozeman, MT
training: Calvin Theological Seminary, MDiv, 1987
ordained: 1987
charges: Youth and singles minister, Zion, Oshawa, ON, 1986-87; Westmount, Strathroy, ON, 1987-90; Back to God Hour, Palos Heights, IL, 1990-

Feenstra, Ronald Jay
b. 06/21/1955, Grand Rapids, MI
training: Calvin Theological Seminary, MDiv, 1980; Yale University, PhD, 1984
ordained: 1993
charges: Faculty, Marquette University, 1984-92; Faculty, Calvin Theological Seminary, Grand Rapids, MI, 1992-

Feenstra, Wiebe
b. 01/08/1917, Netherlands
ordained: 1942
charges: GKN: Pingjum, 1942-45; Hyum and Finkum, 1945-47; Dokkum, 1947-55; Rinsumageest, 1964-68; Leek, 1968-75; Urk, 1975-76; Marum, 1976-82; CRC: Haney, BC, 1955-59; Woodstock, ON, 1959-64
retired: 1982

Fennema, Charles Tjepke
b. 08/03/1929, Ermelo, Gelderland, Netherlands
training: Calvin Theological Seminary, ThB, 1964
ordained: 1964
charges: Port Arthur, ON, 1964-68; Second, Brampton, ON, 1968-79; Bethel, Edmonton, AB, 1979-89; Rehoboth, Bowmanville, ON, 1989-94
retired: 1994

Fennema, Clarence Eric
b. 11/08/1948, Chicago, IL
training: Calvin Theological Seminary, MDiv, 1974
ordained: 1975
charges: Beacon Light, Gary, IN, 1975-78; Sibley, IA, 1978-83; Napa Valley, Napa, CA, 1983-88; First, Rock Valley, IA, 1988-

Fisher, John Charles
b. 07/02/1955, Ridgewood, NJ
training: Calvin Theological Seminary, MDiv, 1986
ordained: 1986
charges: Trinity, Sparta, MI, 1986-89; Emden, Renville, MN, 1989-97; Cedar Hill, Wyckoff, NJ, 1997-

Fisher, Ronald Gene
b. 02/05/1938, Everett, WA
training: Calvin Theological Seminary, BD, 1969; MDiv, 1975
ordained: 1969
charges: Brooks, AB, 1969-73; Winnipeg, Transcona, MB, 1973-76; Calvary, Chatham, ON, 1976-83; Hebron, Whitby, ON, 1983-91; Clinical pastoral education, Toronto General Hospital/Western Hospital, Toronto, ON, 1991-92; Interim pastor, Community of Meadowvale, Mississauga, ON, 1992-93; Minister of care and service, Ebenezer, Trenton, ON, 1993-

Fles, Johan Izak
b. 06/02/1842, Aalten, Gelderland, Netherlands
training: Theologische Universiteit, Kampen, diploma, 1874
ordained: 1874
charges: PCUS: Cedar Grove Presbyterian, WI, 1874-80; Pella, IA, 1880-82; CRC: North Street, Zeeland, 1882-90; First, Muskegon, MI, 1890-1908; Leave, 1908-11; Second, Pella, IA, 1911-15
retired: 1915
d. 03/29/1921, Kalamazoo, MI

Flietstra, Clarence William
b. 01/30/1922, Moline, MI
training: Calvin Theological Seminary, ThB, 1950
ordained: 1950
charges: Rusk, MI, 1950-53; De Motte, IN, 1953-57; Spring Lake, MI, 1957-61; First, Sarnia, ON, 1961-66; First, Ripon, CA, 1966-75; Hancock, MN, 1975-84
retired: 1984
d. 10/28/1991, Des Moines, IA

Flietstra, Dirk
b. 04/06/1884, Harlingen, Friesland, Netherlands

training: Calvin Theological Seminary, diploma, 1918
ordained: 1918
charges: Moline, MI, 1918-23; Allen Ave., Muskegon, MI, 1923-31; Platte, SD, 1931-38; Leighton, IA, 1938-44; Zillah, WA, 1944-50
retired: 1950
d. 10/28/1966, Artesia, CA

Flikkema, Melvin John
b. 10/07/1946, Bozeman, MT
training: Calvin Theological Seminary, BD, 1971; MDiv, 1975
ordained: 1972
charges: Mountain View, Lynden, WA, 1972-75; Long Beach, CA, 1975-82; Leave, 1983; Chaplain, Long Beach Community Hospital, Long Beach, CA, 1983-88; Assistant executive director, Chaplain's Committee, Grand Rapids, MI, 1988-93; Faculty, Reformed Bible College, Grand Rapids, MI, 1993-

Flores, Juan
b. 02/12/1951, Chicago, IL
training: declared eligible on the basis of exceptional gifts, 1990
ordained: 1990
charges: Youth director, Spirit and Truth Fellowship, Chicago, IL, 1985-88; Christ's Vineyard, Diaconal Ministry, Chicago, IL, 1988-

Fluit, Christopher Alan
b. 07/19/1974, Grand Rapids, MI
training: Calvin Theological Seminary, MDiv, 2002
ordained: 2002
charges: Brooks, AB, 2002-

Fluit, Ralph
b. 09/12/1946, DeWijk, Drenthe, Netherlands
training: Calvin Theological Seminary, MDiv, 1975
ordained: 1975
charges: CRC: Immanuel, Simcoe, ON, 1975-80; Bethlehem, Thunder Bay, ON, 1980-86; First, Sarnia, ON, 1986-88; Presbyterian Church of Canada: Dutton, ON, 1988

Fokkens, Nicholas
b. 10/29/1885, Fulton, IL
training: Calvin Theological Seminary, diploma, 1915
ordained: 1915
charges: Oak Lawn, IL, 1915-18; Ocheyedan, IA, 1918-34
retired: 1934
d. 12/02/1934, Ocheyedan, IA

Folkema, Andrew D.
b. 11/11/1888, Netherlands
training: Calvin Theological Seminary, diploma, 1919
ordained: 1919
charges: Estelline, SD, 1919-26; Ackley, IA, 1926-35; Hawarden, IA, 1935-45; Ebenezer, Berwyn, IL, 1945-52; Drayton, ON, 1952-57; Sullivan, MI, 1957-58
retired: 1958
d. 07/01/1959, Grand Rapids, MI

Fondse, Charles Herbert
b. 04/16/1951, Ripon, CA
training: Calvin Theological Seminary, MDiv, 1993
ordained: 1996
charges: Calvary Rehabilitation, Denver, CO, 1996-99; Eligible for call, 1999-

Fondse, John
b. 12/02/1922, Hanford, CA
training: Calvin Theological Seminary, BD, 1958
ordained: 1958
charges: Trinity, Denver, CO, 1958-62; First, Manhattan, MT, 1962-67; Mount Vernon, WA, 1967-73; First, Hull, IA, 1973-79; Calvin, Holland, MI, 1979-87
retired: 1987

Fopma, Marlon Dale
b. 10/14/1967, Newton, IA
training: Calvin Theological Seminary, MDiv, 1996
ordained: 1996
charges: Sanborn, IA, 1996-

Fopma, Samuel
b. 01/05/1887, Spannum, Friesland, Netherlands
training: Calvin Theological Seminary, diploma, 1917; Princeton Seminary, ThM, 1918
ordained: 1918
charges: Lamont, MI, 1918-20; Arlene, MI, 1920-26; Noordeloos, MI, 1926-44; Rock Rapids, IA, 1944-51
retired: 1951
d. 11/18/1972, Cincinnati, OH

Fortuin, Foppe
b. 09/10/1853, Heeg, Friesland, Netherlands
training: Utrecht, diploma, 1878
ordained: 1878
charges: Hervormde Kerk Netherlands: Bruinisse, 1878-81; Heeg, 1881-84; Barendrecht, 1884-86; GKN: Barendrecht, 1886- 91; Hilversum, 1891-98; CRC: Second, Kalamazoo, MI, 1898-1901; Hull IA,

1903-07; Whitinsville, MA, 1907-21; RCA: Free Grace, Middleburg, IA, 1901-03
retired: 1921
d. 01/07/1928, Whitinsville, MA

Fortuin, Karel Wilhelm
b. /1883, Heeg, Friesland, Netherlands
training: Calvin Theological Seminary, diploma, 1911
ordained: 1911
charges: Harderwyk, MI, 1911-14; Hope Ave., Passaic NJ, 1914-22; Borculo, MI, 1922-28; South Holland, IL, 1928-33; Alto, WI, 1933-37; Non-ministerial vocation, 1937
d. 12/10/1960, Kalamazoo, MI

Foss, Richard Wayne
b. 10/28/1956, Cincinnati, OH
training: Calvin Theological Seminary, MDiv, 1982
ordained: 1986
charges: Campus pastor, Arizona State University, Tempe, AZ, 1986-93; Leave, Education, PhD Counseling Program, 1993-

Fox, Joseph Dwight
b. 09/15/1954, Tecumseh, MI
training: Calvin Theological Seminary, MDiv, 1982
ordained: 1982
charges: Church planting, Philippines, 1982-85; Bible teacher, Kalamazoo (MI) Christian High School, 1985-97; Living Stone Church, Petoskey, MI, 1997-2002; Staff, Harbor Light Christian School, Harbor Springs, MI, 2002-

Francois, Ambroise D.
training: declared eligible on the basis of exceptional gifts, 1985
ordained: 1985
charges: Maranatha, Lake Worth, FL, 1985-88; Eligible for call, 1988-2000

Fraser, John Cameron
b. 08/31/1954, Bulawayo, Zimbabwe
training: Westminster Theological Seminary-PA, MDiv, 1978; ThM, 1986
ordained: 1985
charges: Grace Reformed Presbyterian Church, Sechelt, BC, 1985-94; Editor, Coast to Coast, 1992-94; CRC: Burdett, AB, 1995-

Frens, Gerald Wayne
b. 03/27/1943, Fremont, MI
training: Calvin Theological Seminary, BD, 1968
ordained: 1968
charges: Assistant pastor, Chino, CA, 1968-72;

Newton, NJ, 1972-80; Madison, WI, 1980-84;
Leave, 1984-85; Chaplain, NW Community Hospital Continuing Care Facility, Arlington Heights, IL, 1985-91; Chaplain, VITAS (Innovative Hospice Care), Lombard, IL, 1991-

Frens, Richard J.
b. 01/19/1898, Fremont, MI
training: Calvin Theological Seminary, diploma, 1925; Princeton Seminary, ThM, 1926
ordained: 1926
charges: Oostburg, WI, 1926-30; Hanford, CA, 1930-40; Seymour, Grand Rapids, MI, 1940-53; Oak Park, IL, 1953-58; Rochester, NY, 1958-65
retired: 1965
d. 04/13/1976, Grand Rapids, MI

Freswick, Casey Duane
b. 12/07/1954, Bozeman, MT
training: Calvin Theological Seminary, MDiv, 1984
ordained: 1984
charges: CRC: First, Randolph, WI, 1984-89; Newton, NJ, 1989-97; United Reformed Churches: Covenant, Newton, NJ, 1997

Frieling, Willem Hendrik
b. 09/09/1820, Noorbarge, Drenthe, Netherlands
training: with Wolter Alberts Kok
ordained: 1847
charges: GKN: Dalfsen, 1847-50; Deventer, 1850-53; Bedum, 1853-63; Sappemeer, 1863-65; Burum, 1865-66; CRC: Vriesland, MI, 1866-71; Ridott, IL, 1871-74; Graafschap, MI, 1874-78; Muskegon, MI, 1878-81; Cincinnati, OH, 1881-82; Alpine Ave., Grand Rapids, MI, 1882-86; Lamont, MI, 1886-91; Spring Lake, MI, 1891-94
retired: 1894
d. 11/29/1905, Grand Rapids, MI

Friend, Calvin Jay
b. 06/26/1964, Colorado Springs, CO
training: Calvin Theological Seminary, MDiv, 1995
ordained: 1995
charges: Immanuel, Ripon, CA, 1995-2001; Bethel, Princeton, MN, 2001-

Friend, Jan
b. 10/26/1932, Andijk, Noord Holland, Netherlands
training: Calvin Theological Seminary, BD, 1962
ordained: 1962
charges: Chaplain, United States Army, 1962-78; Chaplain, Bethesda Pastoral Counseling Center, Denver, CO, 1978-88; Director, Marriage and Family Counseling, Lutheran Social Services, Tacoma, WA, 1988-94

retired: 1994

Frieswick, Steven Dale
b. 12/14/1952, Worchester, MA
training: Worcester State College, ME, 1987; Reformed Theological Seminary, MDiv, 1991; Calvin Theological Seminary, Special Program for Ministerial Candidacy, 1993
ordained: 1993
charges: Everson, WA, 1993-2001; African Inland Mission, 2001-

Fryling, Herman (Harko)
b. 10/02/1869, Munnekezijl, Friesland, Netherlands
training: Calvin Theological Seminary, diploma, 1896
ordained: 1896
charges: Missionary, Fort Defiance, AZ, 1896-1905; Pease, MN, 1905-06; Missionary, Classis Muskegon at Zuni, NM, 1906-26, at Black Rock, NM, 1926-29
retired: 1929
d. 08/15/1947, Grand Rapids, MI

Fryling, Larry Michael
b. 02/06/1954, Anniston, AL
training: Calvin Theological Seminary, MDiv, 1982
ordained: 1982
charges: Youth, education and evangelism minister, Sunshine, Grand Rapids, MI, 1977-80; Prairie Lane, Omaha, NE, 1982-89; Alger Park, Grand Rapids, MI, 1989-92; Christ's Community, San Diego, CA, 1992-94; Eligible for call, 1994-95; Christ's Community, Hayward, CA, 1995-

Fynaardt, Marion Bernard
b. 02/03/1935, Leighton, IA
training: Calvin Theological Seminary, BD, 1965
ordained: 1965
charges: Rudyard, MI, 1965-69; Calvary, Lowell, MI, 1969-75; Ireton, IA, 1975-86; Kimberly Village, Davenport, IA, 1986-96; Ogilvie, MN, 1996-2000
retired: 2000

Fynewever, Ronald Lee
b. 01/15/1946, Holland, MI
training: Calvin Theological Seminary, BD, 1972; MDiv, 1985; ThM, 2000
ordained: 1972
charges: Zillah, WA, 1972-77; Worthington, MN, 1977-83; Imlay City, MI, 1983-88; Kelloggsville, Kentwood, MI, 1988-

Gamble, Richard Craig
b. 01/12/1955, Pittsburgh, PA
training: Pittsburgh Theological Seminary, MA, 1978; University of Basel, ThD, 1983
ordained: 1985
charges: OPC: Faculty, Westminster Theological Seminary, Philadelphia, PA, 1983–87; CRC: Faculty, Calvin College and Director of Meeter Center, Grand Rapids, MI, 1987–97; ARPC: Faculty, Reformed Theological Seminary-FL, 1997

Gangar, Joghinda Singh
b. 10/30/1954, Punjab, India
training: Westminster Theological Seminary-PA, MAR, 1983, MDiv, 1984; Calvin Theological Seminary, Special Program for Ministerial Candidacy, 1986
ordained: 1986
charges: CRC: Maranatha, Calgary, AB, 1986–90; Riverside, Wellandport, ON, 1990–92; United Reformed Churches: Wellandport, ON, 1992–98; Trinity, Walnut Creek, CA, 1998

Gangar, Kuldip Singh
b. 11/17/1950, Janchi, India
training: Western Theological Seminary-PA, MDiv, 1979,ThM, 1983; Princeton Theological Seminary, ThM, 1982; Rutgers University, MLS, 1988; Calvin Theological Seminary, Special Program for Ministerial Candidacy, 1989
ordained: 1989
charges: CRC: Kelowna, BC, 1989–90; Eligible for call, 1990–91; Non-ministerial vocation, Kelowna, BC, 1991

Garcia, Hector
b. 03/08/1969, Ciego de Avila, Cuba
training: Reformed Bible College, BRE, 1995; Calvin Theological Seminary, MDiv, 2002
ordained: 2002
charges: Iglesia Renacer, West Kendall, FL, 2002–

Gardner, William Elliott IV
b. 04/07/1961, Meriden, CT
training: Gordon-Conwell Theological Seminary, MDiv, 1998; Calvin Theological Seminary, Special Program for Ministerial Candidacy, 2000
ordained: 2000
charges: Christ Church of Glastonbury, Glastonbury, CT, 2000–

Gebben, Nelson J. Sr.
b. 05/24/1931, Borculo, MI
training: Calvin Theological Seminary, BD, 1969

ordained: 1969
charges: Kettering, Dayton, OH, 1969–73; South Grove, St. Paul, MN, 1973–77; Appleton, WI, 1977–78; Palo Alto, CA, 1978–88; Hope, Framingham, MA, 1988–93
retired: 1993

Gebben, Wendell M.
b. 09/15/1935, Shelbyville, MI
training: Calvin Theological Seminary, BD, 1962; MDiv, 1981
ordained: 1962
charges: Home missionary, Rolling Acres, Mason City, IA, 1962–67; Muskegon Heights, MI, 1967–74; Boston Square, Grand Rapids, MI, 1974–85; First, Sheboygan, WI, 1985–97; Classical interim pastor, Central California, 1997–2001
retired: 2001

Geelhoed, Robert Keith
b. 10/24/1954, Grand Rapids, MI
training: Calvin Theological Seminary, MDiv, 1981; ThM, 1983
ordained: 1983
charges: Lincoln Center, IA, 1983–87; Leave, 1987–90; Director, Counseling Center, Christ Church, Oak Brook, IL, 1990–

Geels, John
b. 11/13/1904, Orange City, IA
training: Calvin Theological Seminary, ThB, 1929
ordained: 1929
charges: Beaverdam, MI, 1929–43; Sully, IA, 1943–56; Bozeman, MT, 1956–66; Alto, WI, 1966–69
retired: 1969
d. 01/24/1979, Pella, IA

Geerlings, John H.
b. 06/23/1880, Niekerk, MI
training: Calvin Theological Seminary, diploma, 1910
ordained: 1910
charges: Willard, OH, 1910–12; Oakland, MI, 1912–16; North St., Zeeland, MI, 1916–19; East Saugatuck, MI, 1919–23; Rock Valley, IA, 1923–28; New Holland, SD, 1928–36; Hospers, IA, 1936–46
retired: 1946
d. 12/02/1953, Holland, MI

Geerts, Wiebe (Bill)
b. 07/25/1945, Wolvega, Friesland, Netherlands
training: Calvin Theological Seminary, BD, 1977; MDiv, 1988
ordained: 1977

charges: Agassiz, BC, 1977-83; Rimbey, AB, 1983-84; Community, Richmond Hill, ON, 1984-92; Specialized Pastoral Education, Chilliwack, BC, 1992-93; eligible for call, 1993-2002; released from ministry in denomination, 2002

Gehrels, Kenneth Martin
b. 09/27/1959, Toronto, ON
training: Calvin Theological Seminary, MDiv, 1987
ordained: 1987
charges: Collingwood, ON, 1987-94; Calvin, Ottawa, ON, 1994-

Geisterfer, Aren Peter
b. 11/21/1930, Malang, East Java, Indonesia
training: Calvin Theological Seminary, BD, 1965
ordained: 1965
charges: Ladner, BC, 1965-69; First, Woodstock, ON, 1969-74; Campus pastor, McMaster University, Hamilton, ON, 1980-98
retired: 1998

Gelder, Alvern
b. 06/09/1945, Zeeland, MI
training: Calvin Theological Seminary, BD, 1969; MDiv, 1981
ordained: 1969
charges: Terra Haute, IN, 1960-61; Missionary, Crownpoint, NM, 1969-74; Rapid City, SD, 1974-79; Lane Ave., Kansas City, MO, 1979-85; Oakwood, Belding, MI, 1985-94; Valley, Binghamton, NY, 1994-

Gelderloos, Nicholas
b. 12/21/1878, Spedium, Groningen, Netherlands
training: Calvin Theological Seminary, diploma, 1910
ordained: 1910
charges: Bishop, MI, 1910-12; Oak Harbor, WA, 1912-16; Home missionary Classis Pacific at Nobleford, AB, 1916-21; Shepherd, MT, 1921-26; Niekerk, MI, 1926-29
d. 06/19/1929, Holland, MI

Geleynse, Albert Carel
b. 02/11/1954, Winsum, Friesland, Netherlands
training: Calvin Theological Seminary, MDiv, 1981
ordained: 1981
charges: Hope, Port Perry, ON, 1981-85; Charlottetown, PE, 1985-93; Calvary, Flamborough, ON, 1993-2001; Leave, 2001-2002; CRWM, Port-Au-Prince, Haiti, 2002-

Geleynse, John Andrew
b. 10/13/1961, Medicine Hat, AB

training: Calvin Theological Seminary, MDiv, 2002
ordained: 2002
charges: Living Hope Community, Randolph, WI, 2002-

Geleynse, Martin D.
b. 03/31/1925, Barneveld, Gelderland, Netherlands
training: Vrije Universiteit, Amsterdam, diploma, 1950; Calvin Theological Seminary, ThM, 1973
ordained: 1950
charges: GKN: Winsum, 1950-56; Roermond, 1956-60; CRC: Medicine Hat, AB, 1960-64; Maranatha, St. Catharines, ON, 1964-71; leave for study, 1971-72; Faculty, Calvin Theological Seminary, 1972-74; Montreal, QC, 1974-81; Coordinator, Alliance Reformi Evangilique, Quebec, QC, 1981-86; Stratford, ON, 1986-90
retired: 1990

Gelwicks, Roger Lewis
b. 08/23/1944, Great Neck, NY
training: Reformed Bible College, BRE, 1980; Calvin Theological Seminary, MDiv, 1984
ordained: 1984
charges: Blyth, ON, 1984-87; Community, Fort Wayne, IN, 1987-92; Alto, WI, 1992-96; Hammond, IN, 1996-

Genzink, Terry L.
b. 06/17/1948, Zeeland, MI
training: Calvin Theological Seminary, MDiv, 1974
ordained: 1974
charges: Brooten, MN, 1974-79; Trinity, Sparta, MI, 1979-86; First, Pipestone, MN, 1986-95; Messiah, Hudsonville, MI, 1995-

Gerdes, Glenn Owen
b. 06/01/1963, Sioux Falls, SD
training: Bethel Theological Seminary, 1989; Calvin Theological Seminary, Special Program for Ministerial Candidacy, 1999
ordained: 1999
charges: Racine, WI, 1999-

Gerdes, Henry N.
b. 08/06/1870, Ludwigsdorf, Oostfriesland, Germany
training: German Presbyterian Seminary, Dubuque, IA, diploma, 1901
ordained: 1901
charges: Presbyterian Church: Lansing, IA; Sutter, IL; Lennox, SD, 1906-14; Kamrar, IA, 1914-28; Little Rock, IA, 1929-30; CRC: Lincoln Center, IA, 1928-29, 1930-31

d. 04/24/1931, Lincoln Center, IA

Gerrits, Sander John
b. 09/03/1958, Kentville, NS
training: Calvin Theological Seminary, MDiv, 1989
ordained: 1989
charges: Community of Matilda Township, Dixon's Corner, ON, 1989-98; Kelowna, BC, 1998-

Gerritsen, John Arend
b. 06/12/1869, Assen, Drenthe, Netherlands
training: Calvin Theological Seminary, diploma, 1901
ordained: 1901
charges: Prinsburg, MN, 1901-04; Leighton, IA, 1904-09; Allendale, MI, 1909-12; Kenosha, WI, 1912-18; Conrad, MT, 1918-21; Holland, MN, 1921-26
retired: 1926
d. 03/08/1939, Holland, MI

Gesch, Wilfred
b. 12/12/1945, Sheboygan, WI
training: declared eligible on the basis of exceptional gifts, 1999
ordained: 1999
charges: Platte, SD, 1999-

Geschiere, Charles Leonard
b. 12/29/1957, Windsor, ON
training: Calvin Theological Seminary, MDiv, 1987
ordained: 1987
charges: Archer Ave., Chicago, IL, 1987-93; Grace, Burke, VA, 1993-2002; Riverside, Grand Rapids, MI, 2002-

Getkate, Henry (Hendrik)
b. 06/03/1937, Enter, Overijsel, Netherlands
training: Calvin Theological Seminary, BD, 1970
ordained: 1970
charges: First, Sarnia, ON, 1970-78; Maranatha, Belleville, ON, 1978-84; research, Salem Psychiatric Institute, 1984-85; Cobourg, ON, 1985-87; Leave, 1987-88; Resigned from denomination, 1988

Geurkink, Vernon Frederick
b. 07/28/1936, St. Cloud, MN
training: Calvin Theological Seminary, BD, 1961; MDiv, 1977; American Institute, Jerusalem; Vrije Universiteit, Amsterdam
ordained: 1964
charges: Ellsworth, MI, 1964-68; Missionary, Madison Square, Grand Rapids, MI, 1968-74; Calvin Theological Seminary, 1974-77; Eastern Ave.,

Grand Rapids, MI, 1977-82; Grace, Burke, VA, 1982-91; Chaplain, Christian Health Care Center, Wyckoff, NJ, 1992-2001
retired: 2001

Geuzebroek, Jacob
b. 05/15/1917, Haarlem, Noord Holland, Netherlands
training: Theologische Universiteit, Kampen, diploma, 1941
ordained: 1944
charges: GKN: Appelscha, 1944-49; Amsterdam hospitals, 1949-55; CRC: Riverside, Wellandport, ON, 1955-59; Barrie, ON, 1959-64; Grace Scarborough, Toronto, ON, 1964-70; First, Kingston, ON, 1970-74; Rehoboth, Niagara Falls, ON, 1974-78; Hope, Port Perry, ON, 1978-81
retired: 1981
d. 10/01/1995, Whitby, ON

Gho, InSoon J.
b. 02/22/1964, Sun Cheon, South Korea
training: Calvin Theological Seminary, MA, 1998
ordained: 1998
charges: Chaplain, United States Army, 1998-

Gho, Jeong S.
b. 06/05/1955, Sun Cheon, South Korea
training: Calvin Theological Seminary, MDiv, 1988
ordained: 1988
charges: Calvary Presbyterian Church, 1982-86; CRC: Our Shepherd Korean Church, Arlington Heights, IL, 1988-95; Missionary, Japan, 1995-

Ghysels, James Marnius
b. 09/21/1885, Grand Rapids, MI
training: Calvin Theological Seminary, diploma, 1908; Princeton, BD, 1909
ordained: 1909
charges: Prospect Street, Passaic, NJ, 1909-13; Second, Grand Haven, MI, 1913-19; Ninth St., Holland, MI, 1919-25; Twelfth St., Grand Rapids, MI, 1925-28; Lafayette, IN, 1928-44; Washington, DC, 1944-51
retired: 1951
d. 09/24/1966, Grand Rapids, MI

Godfrey, William Robert
b. 10/04/1945, Oakland, CA
training: Gordon Conwell, MDiv, 1970; Stanford University, PhD, 1974; Calvin Theological Seminary, MDiv, 1979
ordained: 1979
charges: CRC: Faculty, Westminster Theological Seminary-Escondido, CA, 1979-97; United Re-

formed Churches: Faculty, Westminster Theological Seminary, Escondido, CA, 1997

Goheen, Michael Winston

b. 09/23/1955, Rapid City, SD
training: Westminster Theological Seminary, MA, 1983; Univeriteit of Utrecht, PhD, 2000
ordained: 1984
charges: PCC: First Presbyterian, Unionville, ON, 1984-91; Faculty, Dordt College, 1991-94; Faculty, Redeemer College, 1991-2000; CRC: Faculty, Redeemer College, 2000- ; First, Hamilton, ON, 1999-

Gomez, Enrique

ordained: 2001
charges: Comunidad Cristiana: Vida Nueva, Holland, MI, 2001-

Goodyke, Herman

b. 03/09/1884, Sexbierum, Friesland, Netherlands
training: Calvin Theological Seminary, diploma, 1918
ordained: 1918
charges: McBain, MI, 1918-22; Reeman, MI, 1922-45; Atwood, MI, 1945-53
retired: 1953
d. 07/18/1959, Fremont, MI

Goote, Marinus

b. 07/14/1912, Grand Rapids, MI
training: Calvin Theological Seminary, ThB, 1939
ordained: 1939
charges: Aetna, MI, 1939-43; Chaplain, United States Army, 1943-46; Allen Ave., Muskegon, MI, 1946-51; Second, Lynden, WA, 1951-54; Evergreen Park, IL, 1954-62; Boston Square, Grand Rapids, MI, 1962-72; Immanuel, Grand Rapids, MI, 1972-77
retired: 1977
d. 02/27/1999, Grand Rapids, MI

Goris, George

b. 02/22/1895, Lafayette, IN
training: Calvin Theological Seminary, diploma, 1918; Princeton Seminary, BD, 1919; Columbia University, MA, 1928; Union Seminary, ThD, 1931
ordained: 1919
charges: Eastmanville, MI, 1919-21; Second, Grand Haven, MI, 1921-27; Englewood, NJ, 1927-30; Fuller Ave., Grand Rapids, MI, 1930-41; Sherman St., Grand Rapids, MI, 1941-45; LaGrave Ave., Grand Rapids, MI, 1945-53; Hope, Grandville, MI, 1953-63
d. 04/08/1963, Grandville, MI

Gorter, Andrew Albert

b. 04/20/1961, New Westminister, BC
training: Calvin Theological Seminary, MDiv, 1988
ordained: 1988
charges: Blythefield, Rockford, MI, 1988-95; Harderwyk, Holland, MI, 1995-

Gorter, John Peter

b. 09/25/1954, Sioux Center, IA
training: Reformed Theological Seminary, MDiv, 1979; Calvin Theological Seminary, Special Program for Ministerial Candidacy, 1980
ordained: 1981
charges: First, Wellsburg, IA, 1981-86; Calvary, Pella, IA, 1987-93; Second, Byron Center, MI, 1993-

Gorter, Rodney Dean

b. 05/06/1960, Luverne, MN
training: Westminster Theological Seminary-CA, MDiv, 1987; Calvin Theological Seminary, Special Program for Ministerial Candidacy, 1988
ordained: 1988
charges: Transcona, Winnipeg, MB, 1988-92; Worthington, MN, 1992-97; Christ for Russia, Ukraine, Russia, 1997-

Goudberg, William

b. 10/17/1887, Groningen, Groningen, Netherlands
training: Calvin Theological Seminary, diploma, 1921
ordained: 1922
charges: Cincinnati, OH, 1921-26; Missionary at Tohatchi, NM, 1926-44; Bible translation into Navajo, 1944-48; Missionary to Navajo at Phoenix, AZ, 1948-54
d. 06/08/1954, Phoenix, AZ

Goudzwaard, Ronald Dale

b. 02/24/1948, Grand Rapids, MI
training: Calvin Theological Seminary, MDiv, 1976
ordained: 1976
charges: Boca Raton, FL, 1976-80; Kimberly Village, Davenport, IA, 1980-84; West Forty-Fourth St., Wyoming, MI, 1984-95; First, Artesia, CA, 1995-

Gracia, Gianni

b. 07/26/1961
training: declared eligible on the basis of exceptional gifts, 1995
ordained: 1984
charges: Good News, Miami, FL, 1995-99; Hialeah Comunidad Cristiana, Hialeah, FL, 2001-

Graff, Russell John

b. 06/24/1952, Pender, NE
training: University of Nebraska, MA, 1979; Westminster Theological Seminary-PA, MAR, 1981; Calvin Theological Seminary, MDiv, 1986
ordained: 1987
charges: Frankfort, ON, 1987-94; Hope, Stony Plain, AB, 1994-

Grasman, David

b. 03/01/1896, Piaam, Friesland, Netherlands
training: Calvin Theological Seminary, ThB, 1933
ordained: 1934
charges: Imlay City, MI, 1934-42; Hamilton, ON, 1942-44; Hoboken, NJ, 1944-48; Newton, IA, 1948-51; Picton, ON, 1951-54; Chaplain, Christian Seamen's Home, Hoboken, NJ, 1954-62
retired: 1962
d. 05/22/1975, Hawthorne, NJ

Graves, Raymond Richard

b. 03/24/1924, Dike, IA
training: Calvin Theological Seminary, ThB, 1952; MDiv, 1976
ordained: 1952
charges: Cedar, IA, 1952-56; Iowa Falls, IA, 1956-60; Bethel, Zeeland, MI, 1960-65; Bunde, MN, 1965-72; Calvin, Holland, MI, 1972-78; Cadillac, MI, 1978-84; Woden, IA, 1984-88
retired: 1988

Gray, Eric

b. 08/21/1953, Chicago, IL
training: declared eligible on the basis of exceptional gifts, 1998
ordained: 1998
charges: Maple Ave., Holland, MI, 1998-99; Crossroads Community Ministries, Paterson, NJ, 1999-2001; Youth, North Street, Zeeland, MI 2001-

Gray, Jack Mitchell

b. 04/06/1943, Lansing, MI
training: Calvin Theological Seminary, BD, 1969; MDiv, 1976
ordained: 1969
charges: Oak Harbor, WA, 1969-73; First, Redlands, CA, 1973-78; Cottage Grove, South Holland, IL, 1978-82; Fairlawn, Whitinsville, MA, 1982-89; Calvary, Orange City, IA, 1989-2001; Third, Lynden, WA, 2001-2002; Sully, IA, 2002

Gray, Ted F.

b. 06/14/1950, East Lansing, MI
training: Reformed Episcopal Theological Seminary/Philadelphia Theological Seminary, diploma, 1984
ordained: 1986
charges: OPC: Stated supply, Trinity, Medford, OR, 1985-86; Trinity, Medford, OR, 1986-90; Faith, Ocala, FL, 1990-98; CRC: Champlain Valley, Vergennes, VT, 1998-

Green, William Painter Jr.

b. 05/01/1931, Wheaton, IL
training: Westminster Theological Seminary-PA, BD, 1957; New Brunswick Theological Seminary, 1958
ordained: 1958
charges: RCA: Fairfield, NJ, 1957-65; PCA: Assistant pastor, Bethany, Ft. Lauderdale, FL, 1965-68; CRC: Bemis, SD, 1968-72; Bethel, Edgerton, MN, 1972-76; First, Ripon, CA, 1976-81
retired: 1981; Affiliated with United Reformed Churches, 2001

Green, William Painter III

b. 06/29/1958, Wheaton, IL
training: Westminster Theological Seminary, CA., MDiv, 1984; Calvin Theological Seminary, ThM, 1984
ordained: 1984
charges: CRC: Missionary, Costa Rica, 1984-97; URC: General Sec. World Fellowship of Reformed Churches, 1997

Greenfield, Charles

b. 01/11/1908, Paterson, NJ
training: Calvin Theological Seminary, ThB, 1935
ordained: 1936
charges: Stated supply, Terra Ceia, NC, 1935; Terra Ceia, NC, 1936-40; Ackley, IA, 1940-44; Leighton, IA, 1944-48; Oak Glen, Lansing, IL, 1948-52; Second, Kalamazoo, MI, 1952-59; Lee St., Grand Rapids, MI, 1959-70; Prairie Edge, Kalamazoo, MI, 1970-73
retired: 1973
d. 11/02/1991, Grand Rapids, MI

Greenway, Leonard

b. 02/28/1907, Seattle, WA
training: Calvin Theological Seminary, ThB, 1932; Western Theological Seminary, ThM; Burton Theological Seminary, ThD
ordained: 1932
charges: RCA: Second, Grand Haven, MI, 1932-39; Eighth, Grand Rapids, MI, 1939-43; CRC: School pastor and Bible teacher, Grand Rapids (MI) Christian High School, 1943-52; Burton Heights, MI, 1952-57; Bethel, Grand Rapids, MI,

1957-63; Third, Kalamazoo, MI, 1963-66; Ninth St., Holland, MI, 1966-69; Riverside, Grand Rapids, MI, 1969-77
retired: 1977
d. 09/16/1985, Grand Rapids, MI

Greenway, Roger Scott
b. 02/12/1964, Mexico City, Mexico
training: Calvin Theological Seminary, MDiv, 1991
ordained: 1991
charges: Irving Park, Midland Park, NJ, 1991-95; Caledonia, MI, 1995-

Greenway, Roger Selles
b. 01/08/1934, Holland, MI
training: Calvin Theological Seminary, BD, 1958; ThM, 1963; Southwestern Baptist Theological Seminary, ThD, 1972
ordained: 1958
charges: Missionary to Ceylon, 1958-63; Missionary to Mexico, 1963-70; Leave, 1970-72; Secretary for Latin America, Board of Foreign Missions, 1972-78; Burton Heights, Grand Rapids, MI, 1978-82; Faculty, Westminster Theological Seminary, Philadelphia, PA, 1982-86; Executive director, World Ministries, Grand Rapids, MI, 1986-89; Faculty, Calvin Theological Seminary, Grand Rapids, MI, 1989-2001
retired: 2001

Greidanus, Morris Norman
b. 10/01/1936, Amsterdam, Noord Holland, Netherlands
training: Calvin Theological Seminary, BD, 1963
ordained: 1964
charges: Medicine Hat, AB, 1964-68; Campus minister, Toronto and Hamilton, ON, 1968-74; Immanuel, Brampton, ON, 1974-80; First, London, ON, 1980-85; First, Grand Rapids, MI, 1985-2002
retired: 2002

Greidanus, Sidney
b. 04/13/1935, Amsterdam, Noord Holland, Netherlands
training: Calvin Theological Seminary, BD, 1964; Vrije Universiteit, Amsterdam, ThD, 1970
ordained: 1970
charges: Clarkston, ON, 1970-75; Delta, BC, 1975-78; Faculty, Calvin College, 1978-79; Faculty, The King's College, Edmonton, AB, 1979-90; Faculty, Calvin Theological Seminary, Grand Rapids, MI, 1990-

Greve, Willem
b. 01/16/1836, Bentheim, Bentheim, Germany

training: with D.J. Vander Werp, 1869
ordained: 1869
charges: Cincinnati, OH, 1869-74; First, Chicago, IL, 1875-78; Passaic, NJ, 1878-83; Cincinnati, OH, 1883-86; First, Chicago, IL, 1886-90; Borculo, MI, 1890-93; Grandville Ave., Grand Rapids, MI, 1893-96; Hull, IA, 1897-1903
retired: 1896
d. 03/06/1906, Englewood, IL

Grevengoed, Richard O.
b. 04/15/1941, Chicago, IL
training: Calvin Theological Seminary, BD, 1967; MDiv, 1972
ordained: 1967
charges: Immanuel, Roseville, MI, 1967-71; Lawndale, Chicago, IL, 1971-81; Minister-Director, Helping Hand Mission, Chicago, IL, 1981-83; Executive Director, New Leaf Resources, Lansing, IL, 1983-

Greydanus, Johannes Jelte
b. 05/19/1958, Bant, Flevoland, Netherlands
training: Calvin Theological Seminary, MDiv, 1990
ordained: 1994
charges: Terra Ceia, NC, 1994-96; Bethel, Shiprock, NM, 1996-

Greydanus, Robert John
b. 01/22/1942, Paterson, NJ
training: Calvin Theological Seminary, BD, 1967
ordained: 1968
charges: CRC: Ellsworth, MI, 1968-72; RCA: Faith, Lodi, NJ, 1972-79; without charge, 1979

Griffioen, Donald Jay
b. 04/10/1932, Grand Rapids, MI
training: Calvin Theological Seminary, BD, 1957; MDiv, 1973
ordained: 1958
charges: Madison Ave., Paterson, NJ, 1959-64; Home missionary for Classes Hackensack and Hudson at Hawthorne, NJ, 1964-71; Missionary at large, Grand Rapids Board of Evangelism, Grand Rapids, MI, 1970-86; Director, Grand Rapids Area Ministries, 1986-92; Eligible for call, 1992-93; Archer Ave., Chicago, IL, 1993-97
retired: 1997

Griffioen, John
b. 11/28/1900, Utrecht, Utrecht, Netherlands
training: Calvin Theological Seminary, BD, 1932
ordained: 1932
charges: Sully, IA, 1932-43; Oakdale Park, Grand

Rapids, MI, 1943-48; Sheldon, IA, 1948-53;
Sunnyside, WA, 1953-65
retired: 1965
d. 07/09/1967, Rochester, MN

Grift, Richard Evert
b. 04/27/1963, Chatham, ON
training: Calvin Theological Seminary, MDiv, 1996
ordained: 1996
charges: Hope, Brantford, ON, 1996-

Gritter, Bruce Edward
b. 06/21/1965, Orillia, ON
training: Calvin Theological Seminary, MDiv, 1994
ordained: 1994
charges: New Life, Abbotsford, BC, 1994-2001;
Bethel, Edmonton, AB, 2001-

Gritter, Dan Alan
b. 04/07/1952, Grand Rapids, MI
training: Calvin Theological Seminary, MDiv, 1978
ordained: 1979
charges: First, Owen Sound, ON, 1979-85; Living
Hope, Brampton, ON, 1985-94; Gateway Community, Zeeland, MI, 1994-2001; First, Cutlerville, MI,
2001-

Gritter, Evert
b. 07/09/1934, Nijverdal, Overijsel, Netherlands
training: Calvin Theological Seminary, BD, 1962;
MDiv, 1986; Vrije Universiteit, Amsterdam, diploma, 1962
ordained: 1963
charges: Orillia, ON, 1963-66; Maranatha,
Belleville, ON, 1966-72; Campus minister,
McMaster University, Hamilton, ON, 1972-80;
Bethel, Lacombe, AB, 1980-88; Grace, Cobourg,
ON, 1988-97; Edson-Peers, Edson, AB, 1997-2000
retired: 2000

Gritter, George
b. 11/07/1911, Froombosch, Groningen, Netherlands
training: Calvin Theological Seminary, BD, 1935;
ThM, 1954
ordained: 1936
charges: North Blendon, MI, 1936-40; Ninth St.,
Holland, MI, 1940-47; Grace, Kalamazoo, MI,
1947-50; Fuller Ave., Grand Rapids, MI, 1950-62;
Maple Ave., Holland, MI, 1962-65; Alger Park,
Grand Rapids, MI, 1965-73; Ivanrest, Grandville,
MI, 1973-76
retired: 1976
d. 03/20/1991, Grand Rapids, MI

Gritter, John
b. 10/27/1894, Daarlerveen, Overijsel, Netherlands
training: Calvin Theological Seminary, diploma,
1924
ordained: 1924
charges: Prosper, MI, 1924-29; Rock Valley, IA,
1929-38; Franklin St., Grand Rapids, MI, 1938-
48; Missionary to Canada at Aylmer, ON, 1948-
49; at London, ON, 1949-54; London, ON, 1954-
58; Jamestown, MI, 1958-64
retired: 1964
d. 12/18/1970, Grand Rapids, MI

Gritter, Michelle Ruby Anne
b. 04/02/1968, Belleville, ON
training: Calvin Theological Seminary, MDiv, 1997
ordained: 1999
charges: Chaplain, Abbotsford (BC) Christian High
School, 1999-

Gritter, Wayne Sanford
b. 08/19/1934, Grand Rapids, MI
training: Calvin Theological Seminary, BD, 1959;
MDiv, 1974
ordained: 1960
charges: CRC: Austinville, IA, 1960-64; Cherry
Hill, Inkster, MI, 1964-68; LaGrave Ave., Grand
Rapids, MI, 1968-71; Halifax, NS, 1971-76;
Devington, Indianapolis, IN, 1976-81; United Methodist Church, 1981

Gritters, Martin E.
b. 04/02/1906, Boyden, IA
training: Protestant Reformed Theological Seminary, diploma, 1932
ordained: 1932
charges: PRC: Holland, MI, 1932-38; Sioux Center, IA, 1938-45; Oak lawn, IL, 1945-48; Pella, IA,
1948-59; Bellflower, CA, 1959-61; CRC:
Pipestone, MN, 1961-65; Inwood, IA, 1965-71
retired: 1971
d. 12/23/1991, Pella, IA

Groelsema, Thomas Kevin
b. 08/12/1965, Grand Rapids, MI
training: Westminster Theological Seminary-CA,
MDiv, 1991; Calvin Theological Seminary, Special
Program for Ministerial Candidacy, 1992
ordained: 1992
charges: Bunde, MN, 1992-98; First, Byron Center, MI, 1998-

Groen, Allan Cornelius
b. 04/29/1940, Heeg, Friesland, Netherlands

training: Calvin Theological Seminary, BD, 1968; MDiv, 1984; University of Winnipeg, STM, 1984
ordained: 1968
charges: Dresden, ON, 1968-71; Prince George, BC, 1971-78; Kildonan, Winnipeg, MB, 1978-85; Trinity, Edmonton, AB, 1985-94; Immanuel, Cornwall, ON, 1994-2000; Interim, First, London, ON, 2000-2001; Interim, Covenant, St.Catharines, ON, 2001-2002; Interim, First, Montreal, QC, 2002-

Groen, Johannes
b. 02/17/1865, Vriesland, MI
training: Calvin Theological Seminary, diploma, 1891
ordained: 1891
charges: First, Zeeland, MI, 1891-1900; Eastern Ave., Grand Rapids, MI, 1900-19; Los Angeles, CA, 1920-24
retired: 1919
d. 03/19/1924, Los Angeles, CA

Groen, John
b. 01/08/1952, Hamilton, ON
training: Calvin Theological Seminary, MDiv, 1985
ordained: 1985
charges: Ebenezer, Trenton, ON, 1985-91; Community, Richmond Hill, ON, 1991-

Groen, John Gerrit
b. 01/12/1930, Broek op Langedijk, Noord Holland, Netherlands
training: Calvin Theological Seminary, BD, 1956; Vrije Universiteit, Amsterdam, ThD, 1959
ordained: 1959
charges: Wallaceburg, ON, 1959-64; Kentville, NS, 1964-68; Owen Sound, ON, 1968-71; Missionary to Mexico, 1971-74; Bethel, Burlington, ON, 1974-80; Burnaby, BC, 1980-90; Westside Fellowship, Kingston, ON, 1990-95
retired: 1995

Groen, Watson
b. 09/23/1893, Zeeland, MI
training: University of Michigan, AM; Calvin Theological Seminary, diploma, 1917; Princeton Seminary, BD, 1918
ordained: 1918
charges: First, Grand Haven, MI, 1918-24; Creston, Grand Rapids, MI, 1924-26; Missionary, Rehoboth, NM, 1926-27; Los Angeles, CA, 1927-34; Second, Lynden, WA, 1934-43; Seattle, WA, 1943-51
d. 02/12/1951, Seattle, WA

Groenboom, Roger Bruce
b. 03/19/1965, Hinsdale, IL
training: Calvin Theological Seminary, MDiv, 1994
ordained: 1994
charges: Westview, Grand Rapids, MI, 1994-

Groeneboer, Ralph (Rolf)
b. 02/13/1915, Assen, Drenthe, Netherlands
training: Theologische Universiteit, Kampen, diploma, 1944
ordained: 1944
charges: GKN: Barchem, 1944-46; Wirdum, 1946-49; Weesp, 1949-53; Chaplain, Royal Dutch Army, 1953-54; CRC: Acton, ON, 1955-59; Bethel, Vancouver, BC, 1959-66; Missionary, Penticton, BC, 1966-69
retired: 1969
d. 02/06/1980, Abbotsford, BC

Groenendyk, Marion Cornelius
b. 02/07/1925, Leighton, IA
training: Calvin Theological Seminary, BD, 1966
ordained: 1966
charges: Bristolwood, Grand Rapids, MI, 1966-84; Eastmanville, MI, 1984-90
retired: 1990; affiliated with United Reformed Church, 2000

Groeneveld, John C.
b. 01/25/1850, Ten Boer, Groningen, Netherlands
training: McCormick Theological Seminary, diploma, 1881
ordained: 1881
charges: RCA: Fynaart (East Saugatuck), MI, 1881-82; CRC: Ackley, IA, 1882-84; Alto, WI, 1884-94; New Holland, SD, 1894-95; South Holland, IL, 1895-1903; Non-ministerial vocation, 1903

Groenewold, Jelmer Peter
b. 07/07/1952, Hanford, CA
training: Calvin Theological Seminary, MDiv, 1978
ordained: 1978
charges: Hospers, IA, 1978-84; Ebenezer, Leduc, AB, 1984-91; Trinity, Rock Valley, IA, 1991-2001; Sunnyside, WA, 2001-

Groenewold, John Henry
b. 03/18/1916, Chicago, IL
training: Calvin Theological Seminary, BD, 1957
ordained: 1957
charges: Pipestone, MN, 1957-61; First, Detroit, MI, 1961-67; First, Fulton, IL, 1967-71; First, Waupun, WI, 1971-75
d. 07/28/1975, Waupun, WI

Groot, Clarence

b. 05/30/1902, Orange City, IA
training: Calvin Theological Seminary, BD, 1928
ordained: 1928
charges: Brooten, MN, 1928-35; Middleburg, IA, 1935-40; Waupun, WI, 1940-48; Imlay City, MI, 1948-51
d. 09/04/1951, Imlay City, MI

Groot-Nibbelink, Eric (Hendrick) Jack

b. 07/10/1960, Picton, ON
training: Calvin Theological Seminary, MDiv, 1990
ordained: 1990
charges: Covenant, St. Catharines, ON, 1990-2001; Bethel, London, ON, 2001-

Grotenhuis, Todd Martin

b. 03/02/1970, DeKalb, IL
training: Calvin Theological Seminary, MDiv, 1998
ordained: 1998
charges: Kimberley Village, Davenport, IA, 1998-2000; New Hope Community, Wisconsin Rapids, WI, 2000-

Gruessing, Johannes (John) H.

b. 03/30/1881, Deternerlebe, Ostfriesland, Germany
training: Calvin Theological Seminary, diploma, 1916
ordained: 1916
charges: Lincoln Center, IA, 1916-19
d. 01/05/1919, Lincoln Center, IA

Guichelaar, John

b. 01/10/1907, Prairie View, KS
training: Calvin Theological Seminary, ThB, 1930; Princeton Theological Seminary, ThM, 1931
ordained: 1931
charges: Birnamwood, WI, 1931-35; Brooten, MN, 1935-41; Corsica, SD, 1941-45; First, Denver, CO, 1945-50; North St., Zeeland, MI, 1950-56; Oakdale Park, Grand Rapids, MI, 1956-64; Cascade, MI, 1964-72
retired: 1972
d. 11/11/1989, Grand Rapids, MI

Guikema, Arend

b. 02/24/1867, Groningen, Groningen, Netherlands
training: Calvin Theological Seminary, diploma, 1909
ordained: 1909
charges: Vesper, WI, 1909-11; Home missionary Classis Pacific at Everett, WA, 1911-16; Harrison, SD, 1916-26; Sultan, WA, 1926-35
retired: 1936

d. 11/25/1951, Everett, WA

Guikema, Henry

b. 02/04/1928, Grand Rapids, MI
training: Calvin Theological Seminary, ThM, 1952
ordained: 1952
charges: Missionary, Kalamazoo, MI, 1952-55; Knollwood, Kalamazoo, MI, 1955-57; Wheaton, IL, 1957-62; Chaplain, United States Air Force, 1962-80; Chaplains Committee, Grand Rapids, MI, 1980-83; Chaplain, United States Air Force, 1983-85; Seymour, Grand Rapids, MI, 1985-89
retired: 1990
d. 08/12/1995, Grand Rapids, MI

Guikema, Henry

b. 01/27/1875, Groningen, Groningen, Netherlands
training: Calvin Theological Seminary, diploma, 1908
ordained: 1908
charges: South Olive, MI, 1908-11; Sheboygan, WI, 1911-14; South Holland, IL, 1915-21; Byron Center, MI, 1921-29; Vogel Center, MI, 1929-39
retired: 1939
d. 03/20/1950, Grandville, MI

Guillaume, Francois

b. 07/26/1905, Amsterdam, Noord Holland, Netherlands
training: Vrije Universiteit, Amsterdam, diploma, 1928
ordained: 1928
charges: GKN: Oosterend, 1928-32; Klundert, 1932-39; Sneek, 1939-47; Amsterdam West, 1947-53; CRC: Rehoboth, Toronto, ON, 1953-65; Third, Edmonton, AB, 1965-69
retired: 1969
d. 10/17/1972, Brantford, ON

Gulker, Johann

b. 01/08/1855, Brandlecht, Bentheim, Germany
training: Veldhausen Seminary; Calvin Theological Seminary, diploma, 1884
ordained: 1884
charges: Orange City, IA, 1884-90; Home missionary, Hastings, NE, 1890-92; Emden, MN, 1892-94; Hull, IA, 1894-97; George, IA, 1897-1901; Home missionary at Parkersburg, IA, 1902-03; Oak Harbor, WA, 1904; Leota, MN, 1904-14; Home missionary at Worthington, MN, 1914-15; Carnes, IA, 1915-17; Emden, MN, 1917-25
retired: 1925
d. 01/22/1942, Leota, MN

Gunnink, Fred F.
b. 07/01/1932, Leeuwarden, Friesland, Netherlands
training: Calvin Theological Seminary, BD, 1975
ordained: 1975
charges: Coopersville, MI, 1975–82; Ebenezer, Berwyn, IL, 1982–85; First, Rock Valley, IA, 1985–87; Leave, 1987–90; First, Hospers, IA, 1990–93; Eligible for call, 1993–94; Trinity, Richfield Springs, NY, 1994–96
retired: 1996, affiliated with United Reformed Churches, 1997

Gunnink, Henry Gaylon
b. 06/03/1946, Luverne, MN
training: Calvin Theological Seminary, BD, 1972
ordained: 1976
charges: Orangeville, ON, 1976–81; Kanata Community, Ottawa, ON, 1981–

Gunnink, Jerrien Junior
b. 11/04/1928, Edgerton, MN
training: Calvin Theological Seminary, BD, 1953; MDiv, 1973
ordained: 1953
charges: Holland, MN, 1953–56; Millbrook, Grand Rapids, MI, 1956–62; First, Grand Haven, MI, 1962–69; Providence, Holland, MI, 1969–76; First, Denver, CO, 1976–87; First, Manhattan, MT, 1987–94
retired: 1994

Guter, Frank C.
b. 12/26/1962, Rochester, NY
training: Calvin Theological Seminary, MDiv, 1991
ordained: 1992
charges: CRC: Coordinator of evangelism, Alpine Ave., Grand Rapids, MI, 1987–88; Trinity, Vancouver, WA, 1992; Eligible for call, 1992–94; On loan: American Protestant Church, Den Haag, Netherlands, 1994–95; Eligible for call, 1995–96; First, Montreal, QC, 1996–2002; Church planting in England

Haagsma, Gerrit Klaas
b. 09/07/1943, Leeuwarden, Friesland, Netherlands
training: Calvin Theological Seminary, BD, 1972
ordained: 1973
charges: Executive Director, Laymen's League for Evangelism, Lynden, WA, 1973–77; Ft. Wingate, NM, 1977–86; Hope, Thunder Bay, ON, 1986–94; Bethel, London, ON, 1994–2000; Kibbie, South Haven, MI, 2000–

Haalboom, Aris
b. 04/23/1907, Wageningen, Gelderland, Netherlands
training: Calvin Theological Seminary, BD, 1957
ordained: 1957
charges: Home missionary, Maritime Provinces at Truro, NS, 1957–60; Jarvis, ON, 1960–62
d. 05/04/1962, Zeeland, MI

Haan, Albert J.
b. 10/12/1929, Grand Rapids, MI
training: Calvin Theological Seminary, BD, 1954
ordained: 1954
charges: CRC: Home missionary at Philadelphia, PA, 1954–58; Home missionary at Colorado Springs, CO, 1958–62; Home missionary, Orangewood, Phoenix, AZ, 1962–64; Home missionary, Cedar Rapids, IA, 1964–65; Chelwood Community, Albuquerque, NM, 1965–68; Inter-Varsity Christian Fellowship, New York, NY, 1968–69; Richfield, Clifton, NJ, 1969–73; Center of Hope, Denver, CO, 1973–81; Independent: Center of Hope, Denver, CO, 1981

Haan, Bernard John Sr.
b. 04/24/1917, Sully, IA
training: Calvin Theological Seminary, ThB, 1942
ordained: 1942
charges: Ridott, IL, 1942–45; First, Sioux Center, IA, 1945–63; President, Dordt College, 1963–82
retired: 1982
d. 12/08/1994, Sioux Center, IA

Haan, Bernard John Jr.
b. 05/14/1956, Sioux Center, IA
training: Calvin Theological Seminary, MDiv, 1983
ordained: 1983
charges: Immanuel, Sheldon, IA, 1983–89; First, De Motte, IN, 1989–98; Faith, Sioux Center, IA, 1998–

Haan, Bernard Top
b. 11/14/1921, Grand Rapids, MI
training: Calvin Theological Seminary, BD, 1946
ordained: 1946
charges: Portland, MI, 1946–49; Second, Randolph, WI, 1949–54; Everett, WA, 1954–61; Second, Pella, IA, 1961–64
retired: 1964

Haan, Enno Leonard
b. 08/25/1910, Denver, CO
training: Calvin Theological Seminary, ThB, 1936
ordained: 1937
charges: Goshen, IN, 1937–40; Muskegon

Heights, MI, 1940–44; Coldbrook Ave., Grand Rapids, MI, 1944–49; Warren Park, Cicero, IL, 1949–56; Second, Lynden, WA, 1956–60; Oak Glen, Lansing, IL, 1960–71; North Blendon, MI, 1971–75
retired: 1975
d. 11/10/1982, Grandville, MI

Haan, Enno Ralph
b. 05/20/1845, Delfzijl, Groningen, Netherlands
training: Theologische Universiteit, Kampen and Theologische Universiteit Leiden, diploma, 1873
ordained: 1873
charges: Christelijke Gereformeerde Kerk: missionary to Batavia, Java, 1873–83; Leave due to illness, 1883; Elburg, 1884–85; Genderen, 1885–90; RCA: Wortendyk (Midland Park), NJ, 1890–91; CRC: Midland Park, NJ, 1891–96; Grandville, Ave., Grand Rapids, MI, 1896–98
d. 09/06/1898, Grand Rapids, MI

Haan, Gerrit Johannes
b. 11/18/1875, Batavia, Java, Dutch East Indies
training: Calvin Theological Seminary, diploma, 1901
ordained: 1902
charges: First, Zeeland, MI, 1901–06; First, Grand Rapids, MI, 1906–08; First Englewood, Chicago, IL, 1908–18; Pease, MN, 1918–1920; Second, Kalamazoo, MI, 1920–38; Brooten, MN, 1941–45
retired: 1938
d. 04/22/1954, Kalamazoo, MI

Haan, Gilbert
b. 09/30/1928, Midland Park, NJ
training: Calvin Theological Seminary, BD, 1953
ordained: 1954
charges: Bethel, Zeeland, MI, 1954–59; Archer Ave., Chicago, IL, 1959–64; Montello Park, Holland, MI, 1964–74; Non-ministerial vocation, social work, 1974
d. 04/08/1982, Grand Rapids, MI

Haan, Gilbert G.
b. 10/07/1862, Vriesland, MI
training: Calvin Theological Seminary, diploma, 1893
ordained: 1893
charges: CRC: Borculo, MI, 1893–96; Home missionary Classis Iowa, Sully, IA, 1896–98; Second, Muskegon, MI, 1898–1900; Home missionary in Classes Muskegon and Illinois (at Atwood and Ellsworth, MI), 1901–03; Home missionary, Atwood, MI, 1903–11; Second, Pella, IA, 1917–20; RCA: Bethel, Pella, IA, 1921–23

retired: 1911–1917, 1923
d. 05/23/1925, Atwood, MI

Haan, Norman Bruce
b. 03/10/1930, Grand Rapids, MI
training: Calvin Theological Seminary, BD, 1960; MDiv, 1984
ordained: 1960
charges: Volga, SD, 1960–64; First, Flint, MI, 1964–69; First, Phoenix, AZ, 1969–76; First, Waupun, WI, 1976–83; Worthington, MN, 1983–91; Bakersfield, CA, 1991–95
retired: 1995

Haan, Ralph (Roelf) L.
b. 07/30/1874, Batavia, Java, Dutch East Indies
training: Calvin Theological Seminary, diploma, 1898
ordained: 1898
charges: Kelloggsville, MI, 1898–1900; Second, Muskegon, MI, 1900–04; Central Ave., Holland, MI, 1904–14; Grandville Ave., Grand Rapids, MI, 1914–16; Orange City, IA, 1916–23; Midland Park, NJ, 1923–30; Hull, IA, 1930–43
retired: 1943
d. 12/08/1949, Grand Rapids, MI

Haan, Raymond H.
b. 12/20/1903, Zeeland, MI
training: Calvin Theological Seminary, BD, 1931
ordained: 1931
charges: Aetna, MI, 1931–39; Second, Wellsburg, IA, 1939–43; Peoria, IA, 1943–45; Fourth Roseland, Chicago, IL, 1945–49; Third, Lynden, WA, 1949–53; Franklin St., Grand Rapids, MI, 1953–59; Bunde, MN, 1959–64; Rusk, MI, 1964
retired: 1964
d. 07/24/1989, Grandville, MI

Haan, Thomas Lee
b. 02/18/1958, Grand Rapids, MI
training: Calvin Theological Seminary, MDiv, 1984
ordained: 1984
charges: Madison, WI, 1984–88; Immanuel, Ripon, CA, 1988–94; Second, Lynden, WA, 1994–2000; Eligible for call, 2000–2002; New Beginnings Counseling Center, Bellingham, WA, 2002–

Haarsma, Henry J.
b. 03/21/1875, Minnertsga, Friesland, Netherlands
training: Dubuque Seminary, 1901; Calvin Theological Seminary, diploma, 1904
ordained: 1904
charges: West Sayville, NY, 1904–07; Lebanon,

IA, 1907–11; Home missionary Classis Orange City (Winnipeg, MB, 1911–13; Sibley IA, 1913; Ocheyedan, IA 1913–16); Racine, WI, 1916–26
retired: 1926
d. 06/06/1927, Racine, WI

Habermehl, Dirk Nicolaas
b. 05/17/1928, Nieuwveen, Zuid Holland, Netherlands
training: Vrije Universiteit, Amsterdam, diploma, 1953
ordained: 1953
charges: GKN: Wormer, 1953–59; CRC: Newmarket, ON, 1959–64; Zion, Oshawa, ON, 1964–77; Hope Center, Winnipeg, MB, 1977–85; Regional coordinator of pastoral service, Province of Ontario, 1985–93
retired: 1993; affiliated with United Church of Canada, 2001

Hager, Terry Allyn
b. 05/09/1942, Grand Rapids, MI
training: Western Theological Seminary, BD, 1968; Calvin Theological Seminary, BD, 1969, ThM, 1974
ordained: 1969
charges: CRC: Grand Rapids Youth Ministry, 1969–73; Leave, 1973–78; Chaplain, Community Counseling and Personal Growth Ministry, Grand Rapids, MI, 1978–90; Methodist Church: Psychological counseling, 1990

Hahn, Paul (Chul) Soo
b. 05/08/1933, Korea
training: Korean Theological Seminary, MDiv
ordained: 1966
charges: Korea: Chaplain, Kyesung Girls Senior High School, 1965–75; Shin Yongsan Presbyterian, Seoul, 1975–80; Western Korean Church, Burbank, CA, 1980–85; CRC: Cerritos Central, Artesia, CA, 1985–92
retired: 1992

Hamstra, Albert Arthur
b. 07/25/1949, Rensselaer, IN
training: Calvin Theological Seminary, MDiv, 1979
ordained: 1979
charges: Missionary to Sri Lanka, 1980–81; Missionary, Dhaka, Bangladesh, 1981–91; Director, Chinese ministries, Hong Kong, China, 1991–97; Program director for Asia, World Missions, Grand Rapids, MI, 1997–

Hamstra, Richard John
b. 01/28/1955, Rensselaer, IN

training: Calvin Theological Seminary, MDiv, 1983
ordained: 1983
charges: Neland Ave., Grand Rapids, MI, 1983–86; Leave, 1986–87; Olentangy, Columbus, OH, 1987–98; First, Grand Haven, MI, 1998–

Hamstra, Sam Jr.
b. 04/17/1954, Oak Park, IL
training: McCormick Theological Seminary, MDiv, 1980; Wheaton Graduate School, MA, 1984; Marquette University, PhD, 1990
ordained: 1980
charges: RCA: Community, Delavan, WI, 1979–84; Peace, Mt. Prospect, IL, 1984–89; Thorn Creek, South Holland, IL, 1989–93; Chaplain, Trinity Christian College, Palos Heights, IL, 1994–97; CRC: Palos Heights, IL, 1997–

Han, Paul
b. 12/30/1918, Mukden, China
training: Faith Theological Seminary, STM, 1946; New York University, Graduate School of Theology, PhD
ordained: 1960
charges: Poli Presbyterian Church: China, 1944–60; CRC: Hyde Park, Chicago, IL, 1960–83
retired: 1983

Handley, James O'Banion Jr.
b. 08/10/1925, Pacific Grove, CA
training: Calvin Theological Seminary, BD, 1955
ordained: 1955
charges: Missionary for Classis Holland, 1955–59; New Richmond, MI, 1959–60; Wanamassa, NJ, 1960–64; PCA: 1964–82

Handlogten, Fred
b. 03/19/1908, Lamont, MI
training: Calvin Theological Seminary, ThB, 1940
ordained: 1940
charges: Bethel, Allison, IA, 1940–43; Dutton, MI, 1943–52; Montello Park, Holland, MI, 1952–63; Second, Randolph, WI, 1963–70; Sanborn, IA, 1970–73
retired: 1973; affiliated with United Reformed Churches, 1997

Hanegraaff, Johannis
b. 01/05/1923, Leiden, Zuid Holland, Netherlands
training: Calvin Theological Seminary, BD, 1969
ordained: 1970
charges: CRC: Noordeloos, MI, 1970–75; Transcona, Winnipeg, MB, 1980–88; Missionary, Nigeria, 1988; GKN: Puttershoek, Maasdam, 1975–80

retired: 1988
d. 09/03/1997, Woodstock, ON

Hanenburg, John
b. 03/02/1897, Oosterbierum, Friesland, Netherlands
training: Calvin Theological Seminary, BD, 1929
ordained: 1929
charges: Rudyard, MI, 1929–41; Harrison, SD, 1941–44; Hull, IA, 1944–50; Immigrant pastor in central Alberta, 1950–59; Holland Marsh, ON, 1959–66
retired: 1966
d. 05/23/1990, Grand Rapids, MI

Hannink, Alfred
b. 02/02/1922, Harrison, SD
training: Calvin Theological Seminary, ThB, 1952
ordained: 1952
charges: First, Wellsburg, IA, 1952–55; Bethel, Lynden, WA, 1955–58; Ireton, IA, 1959–65; Vogel Center, MI, 1965–70; Haven, Zeeland, MI, 1970–78; Lincoln Center, IA, 1978–83; Brooten, MN, 1983–85
retired: 1985
d. 01/06/1995, Grand Rapids, MI

Hansen, Paul A.
b. 12/19/1952, Chicago, IL
training: Western Theological Seminary, MDiv, 1982; Fuller Theological Seminary, MTh, 1984; Western Michigan University, MA, 1986
ordained: 1982
charges: RCA: Lincoln Ave., Pomona, CA, 1982–85; Doster, Plainwell, MI, 1985–89; CRC: Hayward, CA, 1991–94; Evergreen Park, IL, 1994–98; First, Lynden, WA, 1998–

Harberts, Marinus (Mike) A.
b. 06/06/1930, Grand Rapids, MI
training: Reformed Bible College, 1958; declared eligible on the basis of exceptional gifts, 1983
ordained: 1983
charges: Shiprock, NM, 1958–60; Naschitti, NM, 1960–77; Bethlehem, Tohlakai, NM, 1977–90; Crownpoint, NM, 1990–93
retired: 1993

Haring, Garret A.
b. 11/11/1829, Pearl River, NY
training: with John Y. De Baun, 1861–65
ordained: 1869
charges: True Protestant Dutch Reformed: Stated supply, Schraalenburgh, NJ, 1869–90; CRC:

Schraalenburgh, NJ, 1890–93; Bergenfield, NJ, 1894–05
retired: 1905
d. 06/24/1906, Bergenfield, NJ

Harms, Frederik August Victor
b. 07/04/1960, Utrecht, Utrecht, Netherlands
training: Reformed Bible College, BRE, 1986; Westminster Theological Seminary-CA, MDiv, 1989; Theologische Universiteit Apeldoorn, Drs, 1992; Calvin Theological Seminary, Special Program for Ministerial Candidacy, 1994
ordained: 1994
charges: CRC: Bethlehem, Freeman, SD, 1994–98; United Reformed Churches: Champlain Valley, Ferrisburg, VT, 1998

Harnden, Harrison F.
b. 03/20/1934, Wilton, ME
training: Garrett Theological Seminary, MDiv, 1971
ordained: 1970
charges: United Methodist Church: Arden, Berrien Springs, MI, 1970–73; PCA: Westminster, Milton, FL, 1973–74; RCA: Nooksack Valley, Nooksack, WA, 1974–77; CRC: Houston, BC, 1977–81; Ft. Lauderdale, FL, 1981–85; Bible teacher, Ft. Lauderdale Christian School, Ft. Lauderdale, FL, 1985–88; Cedar Falls, IA, 1988–92; High River, AB, 1992–96
retired: 1996

Harris, Robert Brian
b. 04/15/1957, Grand Rapids, MI
training: Calvin Theological Seminary, MDiv, 1992
ordained: 1992
charges: Director of youth and evangelism, Cottonwood Heights, Jenison, MI, 1990–91; Community, Fountain Valley, CA, 1992–98; Leadership Development, Philippines, 1998–

Harrison, David Keith
b. 04/06/1944, Hustler, WI
training: Bethel Theological Seminary, MDiv, 1999; Calvin Theological Seminary, Special Program for Ministerial Candidacy, 2001
ordained: 2001
charges: Cedar Falls, IA, 2001–

Harrison, Emmett Arden
b. 10/31/1951, Meridian, MS
training: Colloquium doctum, 1987
ordained: 1987
charges: Roseland Christian Ministries, Chicago, IL, 1987–90; East Side, Cleveland, OH, 1990–

Hart, Dirk Jan

b. 12/21/1938, Oostwold, Gelderland, Netherlands
training: Westminster Theological Seminary-PA, BD, 1966
ordained: 1966
charges: John Calvin, Truro, NS, 1966–70; Montreal, QC, 1970–74; First, London, ON, 1974–80; Minister of Evangelism, Board of Home Missions, Grand Rapids, MI, 1980–2001
retired: 2001

Hart, Klaas

b. 12/17/1906, Zaandam, Noord Holland, Netherlands
training: Free University, Amsterdam, diploma, 1935
ordained: 1935
charges: GKN: Oostwold, 1935–41; Velp, 1941–46; Utrecht, 1946–53; CRC: Wallaceburg, ON, 1953–58; Peterborough, ON, 1958–67; Ingersoll, ON, 1967–72
retired: 1972
d. 01/20/1977, Toronto, ON

Hartwell, Richard Maxwell Sr.

b. 01/24/1926, Grand Rapids, MI
training: Westminster Theological Seminary-PA, ThB, 1956; Calvin Theological Seminary, Special Program for Ministerial Candidacy, 1957
ordained: 1957
charges: Washington, DC, 1957–67; Community, Richton Park, IL, 1967–91
retired: 1991

Hartwell, Richard Maxwell Jr.

b. 11/10/1951, Philadelphia, PA
training: Calvin Theological Seminary, MDiv, 1977
ordained: 1977
charges: Framingham, MA, 1977–81; Chaplain, United States Air Force, 1981–

Hasper, Jacob

b. 12/04/1920, Chicago, IL
training: Calvin Theological Seminary, ThB, 1947
ordained: 1947
charges: New Era, MI, 1947–50; Trinity, Jenison, MI, 1950–53; Seymour, Grand Rapids, MI, 1953–62; Midland Park, NJ, 1962–70; Bethany, Bellflower, CA, 1970–76; Pillar, Holland, MI, 1976–86
retired: 1986

Haveman, Jan

b. 05/22/1877, Nieuwe Smilde, Drenthe, Netherlands
training: Calvin Theological Seminary, diploma, 1909
ordained: 1909
charges: Prosper, MI, 1910–15; Sully, IA, 1915–21; New Holland, SD, 1921–27; Inwood, IA, 1927–28
d. 04/30/1928, Sioux Falls, SD

Haven, Bernard

b. 07/24/1926, Midland Park, NJ
training: Calvin Theological Seminary, BD, 1954
ordained: 1954
charges: Missionary, Zuni, NM, 1954–61
d. 12/27/1961, Albuquerque, NM

Haven, Robert John

b. 02/19/1951, Rehoboth, NM
training: John Knox College, MDiv, 1978
ordained: 1979
charges: Presbyterian Church of Canada: Church planter, Seymour Community, North Vancouver, BC, 1978–80; Faculty, London District Christian Secondary School, London, ON, 1980–90; CRC: Good News, London, ON, 1990–

Haverkamp, William

b. 02/12/1908, Zuidbroek, Groningen, Netherlands
training: Calvin Theological Seminary, ThB, 1933
ordained: 1933
charges: De Motte, IN, 1933–37; Second Roseland, IL, 1937–43; Bethel, Paterson, NJ, 1943–49; Central Ave., Holland, MI, 1949–55; Eastern Ave., Grand Rapids, MI, 1955–60; Second, Kalamazoo, MI, 1960–66; East Leonard, Grand Rapids, MI, 1966–73
retired: 1973
d. 08/22/1983, Grand Rapids, MI

Havert, Kenneth Leon

b. 01/25/1933, Newark, NY
training: Calvin Theological Seminary, ThM, 1958
ordained: 1958
charges: Newton, IA, 1958–63; Palos, Heights, IL, 1963–69; Calvin, Wyckoff, NJ, 1969–72; Messiah, Hudsonville, MI, 1972–83; Bethel, Lynden, WA, 1983–90; Faith Community, Wyoming, MI, 1990–98
retired: 1998

Hayenga, Calvin Godfrey

b. 04/19/1887, Stacyville, IA
training: Presbyterian Seminary, Dubuque, IA, diploma, 1914; McCormick Seminary, 1917; McCormick Seminary and Moody Bible College, 1918
ordained: 1912

charges: Presbyterian: Morrison, IA, 1914–16; Faculty, Grundy College, Grundy Center, IA, 1917–18; CRC: Home missionary Classis Ostfriesland, Holland, IA, 1918–20; at Austinville IA, 1920–22; at Mountain Lake, MN, 1922–25; Missionary at Zuni, NM, 1925–31; at Two Wells, NM, 1931–35; at Gallup and Ft. Wingate, NM, 1935–46; Navajo camps, Phoenix, AZ, 1946–57; retired: 1957; continued camp work and teaching at board request, 1957–58
retired: 1958
d. 05/20/1960, Phoenix, AZ

Hays, David Vance
b. 04/05/1951, Astoria, OR
training: Westminster Theological Seminary-CA, MAR, 1982; Calvin Theological Seminary, MDiv, 1988
ordained: 1989
charges: Director, young adults, young couples, singles ministries, Heritage, Byron Center, MI, 1986–87; Parklane/Calvin, Portland, OR, 1989–

Heard, Matthew
b. 06/09/1958, Mobile, AL
training: Wheaton College, MA; Reformed Theological Seminary, MDiv
ordained: 1986
charges: High Road, Lockport, IL, 1981–84; Moody Church, Chicago, IL, 1984–87; Park Community Church, Chicago, IL, 1987–90; CRC: Sunshine, Grand Rapids, MI, 1993–98; Vantage Point Forum, Grand Rapids, MI, 1998–2002; Interdenominational: Woodmen Valley Chapel, Colorado Springs, CO, 2002

Heerema, Edward
b. 11/05/1912, Orange City, IA
training: Westminster Theological Seminary-PA, ThB, 1937; ThM, 1939
ordained: 1939
charges: OPC: Hospital pastor, Christian Sanitorium, Wyckoff, NJ, 1939–49; Public Relations Secretary, National Union of Christian Schools, 1949–53; CRC: Plymouth Heights, Grand Rapids, MI, 1953–64; Bradenton, FL, 1964–77
retired: 1977; affiliated with United Reformed Churches, 1993

Heerema, Evan Paul
b. 08/18/1951, Paterson, NJ
training: Calvin Theological Seminary, MCE, 1979; MDiv, 1990
ordained: 1991
charges: Minister of evangelism, Midland Park,

NJ, 1979–84; Director of youth, education and evangelism, South Grandville, Grandville, MI, 1986–90; Summitview, Yakima, WA, 1991–95; Covenant, Cutlerville, MI, 1995–2001; Faculty, Reformed Bible College, Grand Rapids, MI, 2001–

Heerema, Jacob Peter
b. 04/16/1937, Paterson, NJ
training: Calvin Theological Seminary, BD, 1968
ordained: 1968
charges: Ft. Lauderdale, FL, 1968–71; Director of Servicemen's Home, Seoul, Korea, 1971–74; minister of education and visitation, Calvin, Grand Rapids, MI, 1974–80; Faculty, RBC, Grand Rapids, MI, 1980–82; Covenant, Lansing, MI, 1982–88; Chaplain, Pine Rest Christian Hospital, Cutlerville, MI, 1988–91; Bethany, Holland, MI, 1991–94; Director, Chaplaincy Ministries Division, Grand Rapids, MI, 1994–2002
retired: 2002

Heerema, Pieter Allert
b. 03/17/1956, Calgary, AB
training: Calvin Theological Seminary, MDiv, 1992
ordained: 1992
charges: Grace, Welland, ON, 1992–

Heerema, Robert Allen
b. 05/03/1945, Paterson, NJ
training: Westminster Theological Seminary-PA, MAR, 1983, MDiv, 1984; Calvin Theological Seminary, Special Program for Ministerial Candidacy, 1985
ordained: 1985
charges: CRC: Wyoming Park, Wyoming, MI, 1985–89; Pine Creek, Holland, MI, 1989–92; Champaign Valley, Vergennes, VT, 1992–96; United Reformed Churches: Zion Reformed, Sheffield, ON, 1996

Heeres, Jacob L.
b. 09/01/1876, Muskegon, MI
training: Calvin Theological Seminary, diploma, 1912
ordained: 1912
charges: Reeman, MI, 1912–22; Graafschap, MI, 1922–27; Dennis Ave., Grand Rapids, MI, 1927–32
d. 09/01/1932, Grand Rapids, MI

Heeres, Walter P.
b. 07/17/1877, Muskegon, MI
training: Calvin Theological Seminary, diploma, 1912
ordained: 1912

charges: New Era, MI, 1912–17; Prospect Park, Paterson, NJ, 1917–20
retired: 1920
d. 12/16/1920, Muskegon, MI

Heersink, Adolph William
b. 05/10/1941, Alamosa, CO
training: Calvin Theological Seminary, BD, 1968; MDiv, 1979
ordained: 1968
charges: Missionary, Flagstaff, AZ, 1968–75; Family in Christ, Ogden, UT, 1975–

Heersink, Gerrit Jan
b. 10/24/1926, Aalten, Gelderland, Netherlands
training: Vrije Universiteit, Amsterdam, diploma, 1957
ordained: 1957
charges: GKN: Hasselt, 1957–61; CRC: Cobourg, ON, 1961–64; Clinton, ON, 1964–67; Blenheim, ON, 1967–77; First, Lacombe, AB, 1977–84; Barrhead, ON, 1984–91
retired: 1991

Heerspink, Robert Clair
b. 10/17/1953, Holland, MI
training: Calvin Theological Seminary, MDiv,1978; ThM, 1979
ordained: 1979
charges: Eastmanville, MI, 1979–84; Prairie Edge, Kalamazoo, MI, 1984–89; Cottonwood Heights, Jenison, MI, 1989–99; Faith Community, Wyoming, MI, 1999–

Hegeman, Cornelius (Neal)
b. 10/11/1951, Sioux Center, IA
training: Calvin Theological Seminary, MDiv, 1980; Westminster Theological Seminary-PA, DMin, 1985
ordained: 1980
charges: CRC: Missionary to Dominican Republic, 1980–93; Alliance of Reformed Churches: London, ON, 1993–95; Ligonier Ministries of Canada, 1995–96; United Reformed Churches: Cornerstone, London, ON, 1996–98; Logoi Ministries, Miami, FL, 1998

Heidinga, John
b. 02/14/1952, Leeuwarden, Friesland, Netherlands
training: Calvin Theological Seminary, MDiv, 1978
ordained: 1978
charges: Granum, AB, 1978–82; Lindsay, ON, 1982–89; First, St. Thomas, ON, 1989–2001; Victoria, BC, 2001–

Heilman, David Lee
b. 12/28/1957, Grand Rapids, MI
training: Calvin Theological Seminary, MDiv, 1987
ordained: 1987
charges: Director of education and evangelism, Beckwith Hills, Grand Rapids, MI, 1985–86; Trinity, Jenison, MI, 1987–93; Inwood, IA, 1993–2002; Calvary, Orange City, IA, 2002–

Heinen, Dirk (Dick) Jan
b. 02/05/1950, Aalten, Gelderland, Netherlands
training: Calvin Theological Seminary, MDiv, 1987
ordained: 1987
charges: St. Albert, AB, 1987–91; First, Red Deer, AB, 1991–95; Christian Labour Association, Edmonton, AB, 1995–98; Non-ministerial vocation, 1998

Heinse, William
see: Heyns, William

Hekman, Donald Eugene
b. 04/09/1946, Modesto, CA
training: Calvin Theological Seminary, BD, 1971
ordained: 1972
charges: Minister of evangelism, Chula Vista, CA, 1972–74; Wycliffe Bible Translators, 1974–

Hekman, Jacob
b. 11/13/1920, Ripon, CA
training: Calvin Theological Seminary, ThB, 1951
ordained: 1951
charges: Noordeloos, MI, 1951–55; Oak Harbor, WA, 1955–61; Roseville, MI, 1961–66; Missionary, Hayward, CA, 1966–72; Bethel, Tucson, AZ, 1972–82; Decatur, MI, 1982–86
retired: 1986

Hekman, Walter
b. 03/20/1907, Grand Rapids, MI
training: Calvin Theological Seminary, ThB, 1938
ordained: 1938
charges: Platte, SD, 1938–41; Doon, IA, 1941–48; Sunnyside, WA, 1948–53; St. Thomas, ON, 1953–59; Beaverdam, MI, 1959–72
retired: 1972
d. 10/05/1976, Redlands, CA

Helder, Albert
b. 06/29/1942, Grand Rapids, MI
training: Calvin Theological Seminary, BD, 1968
ordained: 1968
charges: Chaplain, Pine Rest Christian Hospital, Cutlerville, MI, 1968–69; Appalachian internship, Harlem, KY 1969–70; Missionary, Trinity, Iowa

City, IA, 1970–78; Immanuel, Fort Collins, CO, 1978–89; Pacific Community, Honolulu, HI, 1991–96; First, New Westminster, BC, 1996–2002; Interim minister, Classis Central California, 2002–

Helleman, Adrian (Art) Arnold
b. 08/05/1944, Den Haag, Zuid Holland, Netherlands
training: Calvin Theological Seminary, BD, 1969; MDiv, 1977; ThM, 1988
ordained: 1974
charges: Terrace, BC, 1974–77; Missionary, Quezon City, Philippines, 1977–87; Leave, 1987–95; Faculty, Moscow State University, Moscow, Russia, 1995–2002; Faculty, University of Jos, Jos, Nigeria, 2002–

Hellinga, John D.
b. 11/10/1935, Anjum, Friesland, Netherlands
training: Calvin Theological Seminary, BD, 1961
ordained: 1961
charges: Kildonan, Winnipeg, MB, 1961–64; Trinity, St. Catharines, 1964–68; Grandville Ave., Grand Rapids, MI, 1968–72; First, Orange City, IA, 1972–77; Guelph, ON, 1977–82; First, Sioux Center, IA, 1982–87; Calvin, Oak Lawn, IL, 1987–91; Second, Grand Haven, MI, 1991–94; Aylmer, ON, 1994–2000
retired: 2000

Hemkes, Gerrit Klaas
b. 05/06/1838, Hallum, Friesland, Netherlands
training: with J.R. Kreulen, then Theologische Universiteit Kampen, diploma, 1865
ordained: 1865
charges: GKN: De Leek, 1865–73; Stadsmusselkanaal, 1873–74; Bunde, Oostfriesland, 1874–77; CRC: Vriesland, MI, 1877–83; Docent, Theological School, 1883–1908
retired: 1908
d. 12/04/1920, Grand Rapids, MI

Hempel, Ronald Wayne
b. 03/21/1944, Bellingham, WA
training: Calvin Theological Seminary, BD, 1969
ordained: 1970
charges: Missionary to Japan, 1970–78; Leave, 1978–80; Chaplain, Veteran's Home, Retsil, WA, 1980–90; released from ministry, 1990

Hemple, Bruce Calvin
b. 11/10/1929, Alameda, CA
training: Calvin Theological Seminary, BD, 1959
ordained: 1959
charges: Chaplain, United States Army, 1959–69;

Institute of Religion, Houston, TX, 1969–77; Director of Lynden's Laymen's League and Lynden's Hope and Wiser Lake Chapel, Lynden, WA, 1977–91
retired: 1991
d. 12/05/1997, Lynden, WA

Hendriks, Pieter Leenert
b. 02/19/1941, Beverwijk, Noord Holland, Netherlands
training: Calvin Theological Seminary, MDiv, 1984
ordained: 1984
charges: Grande Prairie/LaGlace/Faith Fellowship, Fairview, AB, 1984; Grande Prairie/Faith Fellowship, Fairview, AB, 1984–92; Terrace, BC, 1992–

Hendriksen, William
b. 11/18/1900, Tiel, Gelderland, Netherlands
training: Calvin Theological Seminary, BD, 1927; ThM, 1948; Princeton Seminary, ThD, 1942
ordained: 1927
charges: Third, Zeeland, MI, 1927–31; Allen Ave., Muskegon, MI, 1931–35; Oakdale Park, Grand Rapids, MI, 1935–42; Faculty, Calvin Theological Seminary 1943–52; First, Byron Center, MI, 1952–61; Creston, Grand Rapids, MI, 1961–65
retired: 1965
d. 01/12/1982, Grand Rapids, MI

Henry, Edward
b. 10/09/1918, Naschitti, NM
training: Reformed Bible College, 1949; declared eligible on the basis of exceptional gifts, 1968
ordained: 1968
charges: Lay evangelist, Naschitti, NM, 1949–55; Lay evangelist, Sanostee, NM, 1956–64; Lay evangelist, Shiprock, NM, 1964–68; Naschitti Mission; Tohatchi, NM, 1968–87
d. 12/19/1987, Tohatchi, NM

Hensen, William Cornelius
b. 02/08/1957, Brantford, ON
training: Calvin Theological Seminary, MDiv, 1985
ordained: 1985
charges: Willard, OH, 1985–93; Moline, MI, 1993–2003; Millbrook, Grand Rapids, MI, 2003–

Hertel, Richard Arnold
b. 08/21/1938, Flint, MI
training: Calvin Theological Seminary, BD, 1965; ThM, 1970
ordained: 1964
charges: Madison, WI, 1964–69; Brookside, Grand Rapids, MI, 1969–77; Ridgeview Hills, Den-

ver, CO, 1977-83; Faculty, Reformed Bible College, Grand Rapids, MI, 1983-2002
retired: 2002

Heslinga, Frederick (Folkert)
b. 07/06/1946, Arum, Friesland, Netherlands
training: Calvin Theological Seminary, BD, 1972
ordained: 1972
charges: Athens, ON, 1972-77; Kelowna, BC, 1977-82; Orangeville, ON, 1982-89; First, Hamilton, ON, 1989-98; Ottewell, Edmonton, AB, 1998-2002; Essex, ON, 2002-

Heuss, Carl A.
b. 10/28/1952
training: declared eligible on the basis of exceptional gifts, 1994
ordained: 1994
charges: CRC: Evangelism/Outreach, Bethel, Dallas, TX, 1990-94; Bethel, Dallas, TX, 1994-95; Des Moines, IA, 1995-98; Independent Reformed Church: Pella, IA, 1998

Heuving, James Jacob
b. 08/28/1964, Ottawa, ON
training: Calvin Theological Seminary, MDiv, 1994
ordained: 1995
charges: CRC: Hope Community, Surrey, BC, 1995-97; Bridge Community, Langley, BC, 1997-2001; released to another denomination, 2001

Hewitt, Mark Gordon
b. 09/22/1961, Morristown, NJ
training: Calvin Theological Seminary, MDiv, 1990
ordained: 1992
charges: Third Lynden, WA, 1992-95; Woodville Community, Woodville, MI, 1995-99; Godwin Heights, Wyoming, MI, 1999-

Heyboer, Gerry Gene
b. 07/11/1944, Middletown, NY
training: Calvin Theological Seminary, BD, 1970
ordained: 1970
charges: Corsica, SD, 1970-74; Lucas, MI, 1974-77; Delavan, WI, 1977-81; Bethel, De Motte, IN, 1981-88; First, Allendale, MI, 1988-

Heyboer, Marvin Wesley
b. 08/05/1942, Hudsonville, MI
training: Calvin Theological Seminary, BD, 1969
ordained: 1969
charges: Second, Abbotsford, BC, 1969-73; Trinity, Jenison, MI, 1973-76; Palm Lane, Scottsdale, AZ, 1976-79; First, Hull, IA, 1979-84; Almond Val-

ley, Ripon, CA, 1984-91; Trinity, Jenison, MI, 1991-2002; Leave, 2003-

Heyboer, Titus
b. 09/02/1912, Zutphen, MI
training: Calvin Theological Seminary, ThB, 1938
ordained: 1938
charges: Alto, WI, 1938-43; Goshen, NY, 1943-49; South Olive, MI, 1949-58; Abbotsford, BC, 1958-69; Chandler, MN, 1969-77
retired: 1977
d. 06/03/1978, Jenison, MI

Heynen, Hendrick John
b. 02/07/1868, Laren, Gelderland, Netherlands vicinity
training: Calvin Theological Seminary, diploma, 1904
ordained: 1904
charges: Rock Valley, IA, 1904-08; Hull, IA, 1908-11; Home missionary Classis Sioux Center at Sanborn, IA, 1911-14; Inwood, IA, 1914-16; Beaverdam, MI, 1916-18; Platte, SD, 1918-20; Carnes, IA, 1920-23; Middleburg, IA, 1923-26; Beaverdam, MI, 1926-29
retired: 1929
d. 09/14/1933, Orange City, IA

Heynen, Ralph
b. 12/19/1907, Rock Valley, IA
training: Calvin Theological Seminary, BD, 1933
ordained: 1933
charges: Rock Rapids, IA, 1933-38; Niekerk, Holland, MI, 1938-43; Chaplain, Pine Rest Christian Hospital, Cutlerville, MI, 1944-72
retired: 1972
d. 05/10/1993, Wyoming, MI

Heynen, William
b. 08/22/1917, Beaverdam, MI
training: Calvin Theological Seminary, ThB, 1943
ordained: 1943
charges: CRC: Arcadia, CA, 1943-49; Third, Paterson, NJ, 1949-53; Missionary pastor, Trinity, Anchorage, AK, 1953-71; Oakdale Park, Grand Rapids, MI, 1971-73; RCA: Passaic, NJ, 1978-84
retired: 1984

Heyns, Herman
b. 11/16/1889, Allendale, MI
training: Calvin Theological Seminary, diploma, 1914; further study: Princeton Seminary, 1914-15
ordained: 1915
charges: Missionary, Blanco Canyon, NM, 1915-

19; Noordeloos, MI, 1919-20; East Paris, MI, 1920-21
d. 05/08/1921, East Paris, MI

Heyns (Heinse), William (Willem) Wijnand
b. 03/19/1856, Haarlemmermeer polder, Noord Holland, Netherlands
training: Calvin Theological Seminary, diploma, 1885
ordained: 1885
charges: Allendale, MI, 1885-91; Harrison, SD, 1891-98; Prinsburg, MN, 1898-1900; Fourteenth St., Chicago, IL, 1900-02; Faculty, Calvin Theological Seminary, 1902-26
retired: 1926
d. 11/09/1933, Grand Rapids, MI

Hielema, Jacob (Jack) Sytse
b. 11/11/1931, Groningen, Groningen, Netherlands
training: Calvin Theological Seminary, BD, 1963
ordained: 1963
charges: Forest, ON, 1963-66; Victoria, BC, 1966-70; Maranatha, Calgary, AB, 1978-86; Director of studies, Middle East Ministries, Calgary, AB, 1986-90; Smithers, BC, 1990-94; eligible for call, 1994-95; Prince George, BC, 1995-99; GKN, 1970-76; Director of Christian Television, NCRV, 1976-78
retired: 1999

Hielkema, John Wiliam
b. 08/21/1931, Balkbrug, Overijsel, Netherlands
training: Calvin Theological Seminary, BD, 1975
ordained: 1975
charges: Alliston, ON, 1975-78; Inner City Ministry-Lighthouse, Toronto, ON, 1978-80; Kincardine, ON, 1980-86; First, Owen Sound, ON, 1986-88
d. 10/26/1988, Owen Sound, ON

Hiemenga, John (Jan) J.
b. 01/22/1877, Arum, Friesland, Netherlands
training: Calvin Theological Seminary, diploma, 1905; Columbia University, AB, 1915, AM, 1916; Rochester Theological School, BD, 1919
ordained: 1905
charges: Overisel, MI, 1905-07; Coldbrook Ave., Grand Rapids, MI, 1907-13; Northside, Passaic, NJ, 1913-18; Rochester, NY, 1918-19; President, Calvin College, Grand Rapids, MI, 1919-25; Lafayette, IN, 1925-28; Third, Paterson, NJ, 1928-47
retired: 1947
d. 12/23/1974, Worthington, OH

Hiemstra, Harold
b. 01/31/1936, Hancock, MN

training: Calvin Theological Seminary, BD, 1969; MDiv, 1980
ordained: 1969
charges: Sibley, IA, 1969-77; Bethany, Bellflower, CA, 1977-91; Bethel, Oskaloosa, IA, 1991-94; First, Modesto, CA, 1994-2001
retired: 2001

Hills, Edward Freer
b. 05/16/1912, Oak Park, IL
training: Western Theological Seminary, 1938; Columbia Theological Seminary, 1942; Harvard University, 1946; Calvin Theological Seminary, 1954
ordained: 1939
charges: Faculty, Dana College, Blair, NE, 1947-48; Faculty, Heidelberg College, Tiffin, OH, 1948-49; PCUSA: Ocean Springs, MS, 1949-53; CRC: Des Monies, IA, 1954-62; Non-ministerial vocation, teaching, 1962
d. 12/1981, Des Moines, IA

Hoefker, Gerhard Ludwig
b. 06/22/1864, Wybelsum, Oostfriesland, Germany
training: Dubuque Seminary, diploma, 1894
ordained: 1894
charges: Ridott, IL, 1894-1906; Emden, MN, 1906-08; First, Wellsburg, IA, 1908-17; Kanawha, IA, 1917-25
d. 04/01/1925, Kanawha, IA

Hoek, Gerald Lee
b. 09/29/1955, Pipestone, MN
training: Calvin Theological Seminary, MDiv, 1983
ordained: 1983
charges: Peace, Cedar Rapids, IA, 1983-92; Faith, Nashville, TN, 1992-

Hoekema, Anthony Andrew
b. 07/26/1913, Drachten, Friesland, Netherlands
training: University of Michigan, AM, 1937; Calvin Theological Seminary, ThB, 1942; Princeton Seminary, ThD, 1953
ordained: 1944
charges: Faculty, Calvin College, Grand Rapids, MI, 1939-41; Twelfth St., Grand Rapids, MI, 1944-50; Bethel, Paterson, NJ, 1950-54; Alger Park, Grand Rapids, MI, 1954-56; Faculty, Calvin College, Grand Rapids, MI, 1956-58; Faculty, Calvin Theological Seminary, Grand Rapids, MI, 1958-78
retired: 1978
d. 10/17/1988, Frederick, MD

Hoekema, Jon Eric

b. 11/12/1972, Grand Rapids, MI
training: Calvin Theological Seminary, MDiv, 1999
ordained: 2000
charges: Calvary, Chino, CA, 2000–

Hoekenga, Peter J.

b. 09/03/1876, Toornwerd, Groningen, Netherlands
training: Calvin Theological Seminary, diploma, 1905
ordained: 1905
charges: Middleburg, IA, 1905–07; Lynden, WA, 1907–14; City missionary, Chicago, IL, 1914–16; Walker, MI, 1916–18; Home missionary to soldiers at Los Angeles, CA, 1918–19; Ripon, CA, 1919–24; Home missionary for Classis California at San Francisco/Alameda, CA, 1923–27
d. 09/25/1927, Alameda, CA

Hoeksema, Geert Hermanus

b. 01/21/1842, Noordhorn, Groningen, Netherlands
training: Calvin Theological Seminary, diploma, 1877
ordained: 1877
charges: First, Zeeland, MI, 1877–79; Central Ave., Holland, MI, 1879–81; First, Muskegon, MI, 1881–87; Oakland, MI, 1887–1902
d. 09/23/1902, Oakland, MI

Hoeksema, Gerrit

b. 12/20/1886, Westerwijtwerd, Groningen, Netherlands
training: Calvin Theological Seminary, diploma, 1911; Princeton, BD, 1912
ordained: 1912
charges: Ellsworth, MI, 1912–13; Bethel, Grand Rapids, MI, 1913–26; Third Roseland, Chicago, IL, 1926–58
retired: 1958
d. 06/02/1969, Chicago, IL

Hoeksema, Herman

b. 03/13/1886, Hoogezand, Groningen, Netherlands
training: Calvin Theological Seminary, diploma, 1915
ordained: 1915
charges: CRC: Fourteenth St., Holland, MI, 1915–20; Eastern Ave., Grand Rapids, MI, 1920–24; PRC: First, Protestant Reformed Church, Grand Rapids, MI, 1924–65
d. 09/02/1965, Cutlerville, MI

Hoeksema, John Arnold

b. 02/19/1921, Muskegon, MI
training: Calvin Theological Seminary, ThB, 1950; MDiv, 1985
ordained: 1950
charges: Momence, IL, 1950–53; Bethel, Edgerton, MN, 1953–58; Mt. Vernon, WA, 1958–67; Racine, WI, 1967–86
retired: 1986

Hoekstra, Clifford Dale

b. 05/04/1956, Sioux Center, IA
training: Calvin Theological Seminary, MDiv, 1983
ordained: 1983
charges: Emden, Renville, MN, 1983–89; Faith, Sioux Center, IA, 1989–97; Leave, 1997–98; Rock Rapids, IA, 1998–

Hoekstra, Daniel Scott

b. 02/12/1963, Chicago, IL
training: Calvin Theological Seminary, MDiv, 1989
ordained: 1989
charges: Church planting, San Diego, CA, 1989–90; Church planting, Temecula, CA, 1991–96; Hope Community, Riverside, CA, 1996–98; Eligible for call, 1998–

Hoekstra, Herman

b. 06/11/1919, South Holland, IL
training: Calvin Theological Seminary, BD, 1953
ordained: 1953
charges: Albuquerque, NM, 1953–57; Ebenezer, Berwyn, IL, 1957–62; Bethel; Paterson, NJ, 1962–70; Baldwin St., Jenison, MI, 1970–84
retired: 1984

Hoekstra, Johannes B.

b. 09/15/1855, Oude Leije, Friesland, Netherlands
training: Calvin Theological Seminary, diploma, 1887
ordained: 1887
charges: First, Pella, IA, 1887–91; Second, Muskegon, MI, 1891–96; East Saugatuck, MI, 1896–1903; Dennis Ave., Grand Rapids, MI, 1903–09; Midland Park, NJ, 1909–26
retired: 1926
d. 10/18/1949, Grand Rapids, MI

Hoekstra, Paul Robert

b. 05/06/1944, Grand Rapids, MI
training: Calvin Theological Seminary, MDiv, 1982
ordained: 1982
charges: Doon, IA, 1982–85; Second, Pella, IA, 1985–90; Prairie Edge, Kalamazoo, MI, 1990–97; North Blendon, Hudsonville, MI, 1997–

Hoekstra, Peter A.

b. 03/04/1886, Ee, Friesland, Netherlands
training: Calvin Theological Seminary, diploma, 1910
ordained: 1910
charges: Moline, MI, 1910-11; Fourteenth St., Holland, MI, 1911-15; First, Paterson, NJ, 1915-18; Alpine Ave., Grand Rapids, MI, 1919-27; Second, Cicero, IL, 1927-40; Hanford, CA, 1940-49; San Diego, CA, 1949-54
retired: 1954
d. 08/15/1965, Artesia, CA

Hoekstra, Peter John

b. 04/07/1895, Waupun, WI
training: Calvin Theological Seminary, 1927
ordained: 1927
charges: Missionary, Vancouver, BC, 1927-36; Sultan/Duvall, WA, 1936-44; Nobleford, AB, 1944-49; Home missionary in Alberta, 1949-62; at Lethbridge, 1950-53; at Calgary, AB, 1952-55; at High River, 1952-62; at Vauxhall, 1953-58; at Maranatha, Calgary, 1956-60; at Bellevue, 1960-62
retired: 1962
d. 09/22/1973, Calgary, AB

Hoekstra, Timothy Paul

b. 03/04/1959, Chicago, IL
training: Calvin Theological Seminary, MDiv, 1985
ordained: 1985
charges: Immanuel, Ripon, CA, 1985-88; Central Coast, Arroyo Grande, CA, 1988-90; Suburban Community Life, Darien, IL, 1990-; Chaplain, Trinity Christian College, Palos Heights, IL, 2000-

Hoekwater, John L.

b. 01/08/1957, Grand Rapids, MI
training: Calvin Theological Seminary, MDiv, 1994
ordained: 1994
charges: West Leonard, Grand Rapids, MI, 1994-1999; Leave, 1999-2001; Church planting, Chicago, IL, 2001-

Hoezee, Scott Edward

b. 03/12/1964, Holland, MI
training: Calvin Theological Seminary, MDiv, 1990
ordained: 1990
charges: Second, Fremont, MI, 1990-93; Calvin, Grand Rapids, MI, 1993-

Hofland, Abraham B.C.

b. 02/28/1911, Netherlands
training: Theologische Universiteit, Kampen, diploma, 1938

ordained: 1938
charges: GKN: Oostkapelle, 1938-44; West-Ysselmonde, 1944-45; Chaplain, Indonesia, 1945-49; Emmen, 1949-51; Haarlem-Noord, 1951-53; 's Gravenhage-Moerwijk, 1963-68; 's Gravenhage-Escampt, 1968-76; CRC: Second, Sarnia, ON, 1954-63
retired: 1976
d. 04/13/1995, Hillegom, Zuid Holland, Netherlands

Hofland, Gary Gene

b. 04/07/1938, Sanborn, IA
training: Calvin Theological Seminary, BD, 1962; MDiv, 1983
ordained: 1962
charges: Zillah, WA, 1962-67; Delavan, WI, 1967-71; First, Visalia, CA, 1971-79; Fairfield, CA, 1979-89; Eligible for call, 1989-90; First, Salt Lake City, UT, 1990-2000
retired: 2000

Hofland, John J.H.

b. 04/05/1940, Oostkappelle, Zeeland, Netherlands
training: Calvin Theological Seminary, ThB, 1965
ordained: 1965
charges: CRC: Owen Sound, ON, 1965-68; GKN: Rijsoord, 1968-73; 's Gravenhage-Oost, 1973-78; Classis 's Gravenhage, 1978-87; Hillegom, 1987-

Hofland, Mark Allen

b. 11/29/1970, Delavan, WI
training: Calvin Theological Seminary, MDiv, 2000
ordained: 2001
charges: Big Springs, Montague, CA, 2001-

Hofman, John Jr.

b. 03/18/1929, Grand Rapids, MI
training: Protestant Reformed Theological Seminary, diploma, 1955
ordained: 1955
charges: PRC: Lynden, WA, 1955-60, Missionary to Guam, 1960-62; CRC: East Leonard, Grand Rapids, MI, 1962-65; Home missionary, Fort Wingate, NM, 1965-68; Bethel, Lynden, WA, 1968-73; Ridgeview Hills, Denver, CO, 1973-77; Elim in the Desert, Tucson, AZ, 1977-84; Highland Hills, Grand Rapids, MI, 1984-90; Zillah, WA, 1990-96
retired: 1996

Hofman, John Marvin

b. 09/23/1924, Barrow, AB
training: Calvin Theological Seminary, BD, 1952

ordained: 1952
charges: Grangeville, ID, 1952-57; Lansing, MI, 1957-67; Ideal Park, Grand Rapids, MI, 1967-90
retired: 1990

Hofman, Leonard John
b. 01/31/1928, Cutlerville, MI
training: Calvin Theological Seminary, ThB, 1951; MDiv, 1981
ordained: 1951
charges: Wright, IA, 1951-54; Kenosha, WI, 1954-59; North St., Zeeland, MI, 1959-65; Ridgewood, Jenison, MI, 1965-77; Bethany, Holland, MI, 1977-82; Denominational stated clerk, Christian Reformed Church in North America, Grand Rapids, MI, 1982-90; General secretary, Christian Reformed Church in North America, Grand Rapids, MI, 1990-94
retired: 1994

Hofman, Marvin John
b. 06/02/1952, Grand Rapids, MI
training: Calvin Theological Seminary, MDiv, 1981
ordained: 1981
charges: Raymond, MN, 1981-90; Graafschap, MI, 1990-2000; Fourteenth Street, Holland, MI, 2000-

Hofman, Ruth Marlene
b. 06/21/1954, Grangeville, ID
training: Calvin Theological Seminary, MDiv, 1992
ordained: 1996
charges: Director of education, River Terrace, East Lansing, MI, 1985-89; First, Toronto, ON, 1993-99; Grace, Grand Rapids, MI, 1999-2002

Hofman, Tymen Edward
b. 08/24/1922, Nobleford, AB
training: Calvin Theological Seminary, BD, 1951; MDiv, 1977
ordained: 1951
charges: Bozeman, MT, 1951-55; Calgary, AB, 1955-62; Los Angeles, CA, 1962-68; Allen Ave., Muskegon, MI, 1968-72; Neland Ave., Grand Rapids, MI, 1972-81; Faith, Tinley Park, IL, 1981-87
retired: 1987

Hofman, Walter
b. 02/04/1915, Grand Rapids, MI
training: Protestant Reformed Theological Seminary, diploma, 1943
ordained: 1943
charges: PRC: Special ministries, Holland, MI, 1943-47; Home missionary, 1947-51; Orange City,

IA, 1951-54; Bellflower, CA, 1954-59; Kalamazoo, MI, 1959-61; CRC: Alamo Ave., Kalamazoo, MI, 1961-65; Hamilton, MI, 1965-73; Calvin, Pinellas Park, FL, 1973-80
retired: 1980
d. 11/14/2001, Kentwood, MI

Hofmeyer, Garret
b. 03/27/1889, Allendale, MI
training: Calvin Theological Seminary, diploma, 1923
ordained: 1923
charges: McBain, MI, 1923-26; Bethel, Grand Rapids, MI, 1926-45
retired: 1945
d. 04/01/1945, Grand Rapids, MI

Hohman, Johannes
see: Homan, Johannes

Hogan, Orlin James
b. 12/26/1936, Maurice, IA
training: Calvin Theological Seminary, BD, 1971
ordained: 1971
charges: CRC: Missionary, Scottsdale, El Paso, TX, 1971-74; Missionary to Mexico, 1974-78; Bozeman, MT, 1978-81; Bellevue, WA, 1981-86; Leave, 1986-89; Chaplain, The Master's House, Modesto, CA, 1989-91; Burnaby, BC, 1991-94; left the denomination, pastor in Bremerton, WA

Hogendoorn, Robert William
b. 07/13/1961, Weston, ON
training: Calvin Theological Seminary, MDiv, 1987
ordained: 1987
charges: Immanuel, Langley, BC, 1987-92; Forest City Community, London, ON, 1992-

Hogeterp, Gerald Jacob
b. 03/11/1942, Sneek, Friesland, Netherlands
training: Calvin Theological Seminary, BD, 1969
ordained: 1969
charges: High River, AB, 1969-72; First, Chilliwack, BC, 1972-78; Bethel, Saskatoon, SK, 1978-84; Calvary, Ottawa, ON, 1984-95; Covenant, Woodstock, ON, 1995-2001; Missionary, Nigeria, 2001-02; Covenant, Woodstock, ON, 2002-

Hogeterp, Peter C.
b. 09/24/1942, Oudega, Friesland, Netherlands
training: Calvin Theological Seminary, BD, 1966
ordained: 1966
charges: Bowen Mills, Middleville, MI, 1964-66; Peers, AB, 1966-70; Rudyard, MI, 1970-73; Ambassador, Windsor, ON, 1973-88; First, London,

ON, 1988-2000; Georgetown, Hudsonville, MI, 2000-

Hoitenga, Dewey James Sr.
b. 08/25/1902, Ogilvie, MN
training: Calvin Theological Seminary, ThB, 1928
ordained: 1928
charges: Hancock, MN, 1928-37; Peoria, IA, 1937-43; Chaplain, United States Army, 1943-46; West Sayville, NY, 1946-49; Lafayette, IN, 1949-54; First, Cutlerville, MI, 1954-62; Missionary pastor to St. Joseph, MI, 1962-68; St. Joseph, MI, 1968-71
retired: 1971
d. 05/14/1994, Grand Rapids, MI

Hoksbergen, Alvin Lee
b. 10/22/1928, Pella, IA
training: Calvin Theological Seminary, BD, 1959; Vrije Universiteit, Amsterdam, diploma, 1961
ordained: 1961
charges: Ann Arbor, MI, 1961-66; Minister of student evangelism, Michigan State University, East Lansing, MI, 1966-72; River Terrace, East Lansing, MI, 1972-90; Ferrysburg, MI, 1990-94
retired: 1994

Holkeboer, Earl Simon
b. 10/21/1923, Holland, MI
training: Calvin Theological Seminary, BD, 1957; Union Theological Seminary, 1969
ordained: 1957
charges: Minister of evangelism, First, Denver, CO, 1957-61; Toledo, OH, 1961-68; Community, Fort Wayne, IN, 1969-87
retired: 1987

Holkeboer, Edgar O.
b. 09/09/1923, Holland, MI
training: Calvin Theological Seminary, ThB, 1951
ordained: 1951
charges: Pipestone, MN, 1951-57; Transcona, Winnipeg, MB, 1957-63; Home missionary, Stony Plain and Duffield, AB, 1963-65, Missionary, Stony Plain, AB, 1965-68; Hope, Stony Plain, AB, 1968-74; Bellevue, AB, 1974-76; Non-ministerial vocation, 1977-81
d. 12/23/1981, Blairmore, AB

Holkeboer, Gilbert
b. 08/02/1925, Holland, MI
training: Calvin Theological Seminary, BD, 1958
ordained: 1958
charges: Missionary to Nigeria, 1958-67;

Bellingham, WA, 1967-70; Leave, 1970-71; Non-ministerial vocation, 1971
d. 10/31/1992, Grand Rapids, MI

Hollander, Alfred Harold
b. 04/25/1919, Middleburg, IA
training: Calvin Theological Seminary, ThB, 1952; MDiv, 1978
ordained: 1952
charges: Otley, IA, 1952-57; Alliston and Orangeville, ON, 1957-62; Neerlandia, AB, 1962-66; First, Wellsburg, IA, 1966-76; Harrison, SD, 1976-83
retired: 1983
d. 01/23/1998, Lynden, WA

Hollebeek, Dirk
b. 06/04/1880, Franeker, Friesland, Netherlands
training: Calvin Theological Seminary, diploma, 1910
ordained: 1910
charges: Ireton, IA, 1910-15; Sanborn, IA, 1915-25; Second, Pella, IA, 1925-33; First, Lynden, WA, 1933-45
d. 05/21/1945, Grand Rapids, MI

Hollebeek, John Fred
b. 03/04/1915, Ireton, IA
training: Calvin Theological Seminary, BD, 1943
ordained: 1943
charges: Aetna, MI, 1943-47; Hospers, IA, 1947-51; Third, Bellflower, CA, 1951-58; Missionary, Walnut Creek, CA, 1958-63; Home missionary, Palm Lane, Scottsdale, AZ, 1963-68; Missionary, Crenshaw, Los Angeles, CA, 1968-73; Kettering, Dayton, OH, 1973-80
retired: 1980
d. 12/07/1991, Yucaipa, CA

Holleman, Jerry Allan
b. 03/22/1949, Bellingham, WA
training: Calvin Theological Seminary, MDiv, 1974
ordained: 1975
charges: Minister of education, Baldwin St., Jenison, MI, 1975-79; New Life, Houston, TX, 1979-93; Home Missions Regional Director, West Central US, Spring, TX, 1993-

Holleman, William F.
b. 10/17/1934, South Holland, IL
training: Calvin Theological Seminary, BD, 1965
ordained: 1965
charges: CRC: Rusk, MI, 1965-70; Goshen, IN, 1971-74; left the denomination, 1974; pastor, South Bend, IN

Holmes, Sheila
ordained: 1998
charges: Director of youth, Northside Community Chapel, Paterson, NJ, 1990-98; Northside Community Chapel, Paterson, NJ, 1998-

Holthof, George Edward
b. 07/31/1955, Chatham, ON
training: Calvin Theological Seminary, MDiv, 2000
ordained: 2000
charges: First, Owen Sound, ON, 2000-

Holtrop, Cindy Kay
b. 08/24/1956, Sheldon, IA
training: Calvin Theological Seminary, MDiv, 1998
ordained: 2001
charges: Assistant in ministry, Avery St., South Windsor, CT, 1985-89; Director of church life and evangelism, Rochester, NY, 1989-93; Calvin Institute for Christian Worship, Grand Rapids, MI, 1999-

Holtrop, Corneal
b. 08/20/1894, Ferrysburg, MI
training: Calvin Theological Seminary, diploma, 1921
ordained: 1921
charges: Second, Wellsburg, IA, 1921-26; Second, Fremont, MI, 1926-43; Chaplain United States Army, 1943-45; Kelloggsville, MI, 1945-52; Terra Ceia, NC, 1952-56; Home missionary Classis Cadillac at Lake City, MI, 1956-60; Bluffton, Muskegon, MI, 1960-64
retired: 1964
d. 06/16/1968, East Muskegon, MI

Holtrop, Elton John
b. 06/06/1896, Ferrysburg, MI
training: Calvin Theological Seminary, diploma, 1923; Princteon Seminary, BD, 1924
ordained: 1924
charges: Home missionary Classis Muskegon, 1924-28 (at Cadillac, MI, 1926-28); West Park, Cleveland, OH, 1928-43; Chaplain United States Naval Reserve, 1943-47; Chaplain, Veterans Administration Hospital, Tomah, WI, 1947-50; Chaplain, Veterans Administration Hospital, Fort Custer, Battle Creek, MI, 1950-66; Chaplain, Calvary Rehabilitation Center, Phoenix, AZ, 1967-68; Director of Chaplaincy, Evangelical Ministers Union, 1968-69
retired: 1966
d. 04/18/1980, El Paso, TX

Holtrop, Oren
b. 04/16/1898, Muskegon, MI vicinity
training: Calvin Theological Seminary, diploma, 1924; Princeton Theological Seminary, ThM, 1926; Southern Baptist Theological Seminary, ThD, 1927
ordained: 1927
charges: East Side, Cleveland, OH, 1927-39; Rochester, NY, 1939-47; Prospect Park, Paterson, NJ, 1947-56; Parchment, Kalamazoo, MI, 1956-65; Cedar, IA, 1965-69
retired: 1969
d. 09/03/2000, Midland Park, NJ

Holtrop, Paul Francis
b. 02/12/1917, Ferrysburg, MI
training: Calvin Theological Seminary, ThB, 1943
ordained: 1943
charges: Holland, IA, 1943-47; De Motte, IN, 1947-52; Home missionary in the East, 1952-56; Kanawha, IA, 1956-59; Arcadia, Grand Rapids, MI, 1959-62
d. 06/27/1962, Grand Rapids, MI

Holtrop, Philip Cornelius
b. 03/23/1934, Cleveland, OH
training: Calvin Theological Seminary, ThB, 1956; Vrije Universiteit, Drs, 1963; Harvard University, PhD, 1988
ordained: 1971
charges: North Haledon, NJ, 1971-77; Faculty, Calvin College, Grand Rapids, MI, 1977-99
retired: 1999

Holtvluwer, Marshall Todd
b. 04/19/1972, Grand Rapids, MI
training: Calvin Theological Seminary, MDiv, 2001
ordained: 2001
charges: Orland Park, IL, 2001-

Holwerda, David Earl
b. 08/26/1932, Grand Rapids, MI
training: Calvin Theological Seminary, BD, 1956; Vrije Universiteit, Amsterdam, ThD, 1959
ordained: 1961
charges: Faculty, Trinity Christian College, Palos Heights, IL, 1959-63; Faculty, Calvin College, Grand Rapids, MI, 1963-84; Faculty, Calvin Theological Seminary, Grand Rapids, MI, 1984-98
retired: 1998

Holwerda, George P.
b. 08/04/1922, Grand Rapids, MI
training: Calvin Theological Seminary, BD, 1947
ordained: 1947
charges: Aetna, MI, 1947-50; Bethel, Zeeland,

MI, 1950-54; First, Fremont, MI, 1954-61; Alpine Ave., Grand Rapids, MI, 1961-66; Second, Denver, CO, 1966-69; Cutlerville East, Grand Rapids, MI, 1969-77; Second, Highland, IN, 1977-87
retired: 1987
d. 01/27/2002, Byron Center, MI

Holwerda, Gerhardus J.
b. 11/11/1894, Paterson, NJ
training: Calvin Theological Seminary, diploma, 1919; Princeton Theological Seminary, 1920
ordained: 1920
charges: Fourth Roseland, Chicago, IL, 1920-24; Los Angeles, CA, 1924-26; Non-ministerial vocation: educator, 1926
d. 01/1976, San Pedro, CA

Holwerda, James Alyn
b. 08/28/1955, Fremont, MI
training: Calvin Theological Seminary, MDiv, 1980
ordained: 1981
charges: Indianapolis, IN, 1981-92; Trinity, Iowa City, IA, 1992-97; Chaplain, Jellema House/Pathfinder Resources, Inc., Grand Rapids, MI, 1997-

Holwerda, James J.
b. 03/10/1869, Metslawier, Friesland, Netherlands
training: Calvin Theological Seminary, diploma, 1904
ordained: 1904
charges: Manhattan, MT, 1904-08; Rock Valley, IA, 1908-14; Byron Center, MI, 1914-19; Second, Paterson, NJ, 1919-39
retired: 1939
d. 05/29/1956, Midland Park, NJ

Holwerda, John J.
b. 08/27/1896, Grand Rapids, MI
training: Calvin Theological Seminary, diploma, 1925
ordained: 1925
charges: Highland, MI, 1925-31; Randolph, WI, 1931-48; Newton, NJ, 1948-56; Port Alberni, BC, 1956-61
retired: 1961
d. 05/03/1975, Bellflower, CA

Holwerda, John Thomas
b. 03/07/1904, Grand Rapids, MI
training: Calvin Theological Seminary, ThB, 1931
ordained: 1931
charges: Sioux City, IA, 1931-35; Ellsworth, MI, 1935-41; Midland Park, NJ, 1941-48; Alpine Ave., Grand Rapids, MI, 1948-54; First, Bellflower, CA,

1954-63; Pleasant St., Whitinsville, MA, 1963-69; First, Allendale, MI, 1969-72
retired: 1972
d. 11/05/1980, Grand Rapids, MI

Holwerda, Peter G.
b. 02/14/1899, Grand Rapids, MI
training: Calvin Theological Seminary, ThB, 1930
ordained: 1930
charges: Kelloggsville, MI, 1930-33; Fourth, Paterson, NJ, 1933-39; Lee St., Grand Rapids, MI, 1939-50; Lansing, IL, 1950-58; Milwood, Kalamazoo, MI, 1958-65
retired: 1965
d. 04/27/1972, Grand Rapids, MI

Holwerda, Peter Jay
b. 09/06/1947, Cadillac, MI
training: Calvin Theological Seminary, BD, 1972; MDiv, 1980
ordained: 1972
charges: Immanuel, Sheldon, IA, 1972-77; First, Seattle, WA, 1977-86; Regional director, South Pacific, Board of Home Missions, Bellflower, CA, 1986-

Holwerda, Robert John
b. 06/28/1929, Grand Rapids, MI
training: Calvin Theological Seminary, BD, 1963
ordained: 1963
charges: Parkersburg, IA, 1963-67; Harderwyk, Holland, MI, 1967-73; Calvary, Pella, IA, 1973-84; First, Mount Vernon, WA, 1984-89; Bethel, Sioux Center, IA, 1989-94
retired: 1994

Holwerda, Timothy Lee
b. 04/25/1966, Grand Rapids, MI
training: Calvin Theological Seminary, MDiv, 1993
ordained: 1994
charges: Director of youth and education, Caledonia, MI, 1990-91; Missionary, Philippines, 1994-

Holwerda, Willard John
b. 04/08/1950, Grand Rapids, MI
training: Calvin Theological Seminary, MDiv, 1987
ordained: 1987
charges: New Hope Community, Terre Haute, IN, 1987-89; Eligible for call, 1989-94; Non ministerial vocation, 1994

Homan, Johannes
b. 12/31/1871, Groningen, Groningen, Netherlands
training: Calvin Theological Seminary, diploma, 1904

ordained: 1905
charges: Niekerk, MI, 1905-07; Alto, WI, 1907-10; First, Randolph, WI, 1910-15; Prosper, MI, 1915-19; Vogel Center, MI, 1919-25; Shepherd, MT, 1927-37
retired: 1925-27; 1937
d. 10/10/1948, Cutlerville, MI

Hommes, Edward Roy
b. 02/09/1949, Paterson, NJ
training: Calvin Theological Seminary, MDiv, 1975
ordained: 1975
charges: Alger, WA, 1975-81; Missionary, Tinley Park, IL, 1981-84; Trinity, Denver, CO, 1984-93; Chaplain, Borgess Medical Center, Kalamazoo, MI, 1993-2000; VA Medical Center, Battle Creek, MI, 2000-01; Chaplain, Denver Health Medical Center, Denver, CO, 2001-

Hommes, Raymond E.
b. 11/21/1942, Paterson, NJ
training: Calvin Theological Seminary, BD, 1969; ThM, 1980
ordained: 1969
charges: Chaplain intern, Pine Rest Christian Hospital, 1969-70; Missionary to Japan, 1970-89; Eligible for call, 1989-90; Leave, 1990-92; Minister, Pastoral counseling, Samaritan Counseling Centers, Upland, CA, 1992-97; Chaplain, VITAS (Innovative Hospice Care), Encino, CA, 1997-98; Chaplain, VITAS (Innovative Hospice Care), Covina, CA, 1998-2001; Christian Counseling Center, Redlands, CA/Chaplain, St. Jude Medical Center, Fullerton, CA, 2001-

Honderd, Peter
b. 07/24/1903, Grandville, MI
training: Calvin Theological Seminary, ThB, 1933
ordained: 1939
charges: Gun Lake and Bowen Mills, MI missions, 1935; Orange City, IA, 1936; Stated supply, Estelline, SD, 1937-39; Sullivan, MI, 1939-42; Chaplain, United States Army, 1942-45; Morrison, IL, 1945-52; Home missionary, Le Mars, IA, 1952-56; Aetna, MI, 1956-63; Woden, IA, 1963-68
retired: 1968; affiliated with United Reformed Churches, 1995
d. 03/26/1999, Jenison, MI

Hong, (Joseph) Hyun Sook
b. 08/20/1949
ordained: 1981
charges: SeodaeMoon Church, Seoul, Korea, 1979-82; Faithful Church, Los Angeles, CA, 1985-87; NamBu Church, Los Angeles, CA, 1988-91;

South Bay Elim CRC, Gardena, CA, 1991-97; CRC: South Bay Elim, Gardena, CA, 1997-98; resigned from denomination, 1998

Hong, Kyusik Henry
b. 08/28/1940, Seoul, South Korea
training: Trinity Evangelical Divinity School, MDiv, 1988: Calvin Theological Seminary, Special Program for Ministerial Candidacy, 1990
ordained: 1990
charges: Church planting, North Suburbs, Chicago, IL, 1990-91; Eden Korean, Wilmette, IL, 1991-

Hong, Soon Do
b. 07/27/1937
ordained: 1994
charges: CRC: Valley Evangelical Mission, Northridge, CA, 1994-98; Missionary, South America, 1998-

Hoogendoorn, Calvin Roland
b. 02/06/1961, Brockville, ON
training: Calvin Theological Seminary, MDiv, 1988
ordained: 1988
charges: Palos Heights, IL, 1988-95; Chaplain, Trinity Christian College, Palos Heights, IL, 1995-96; Bethel, Lansing, IL, 1996-

Hoogeveen, James L.
b. 03/04/1950, Willmar, MN
training: Calvin Theological Seminary, MDiv, 1976
ordained: 1976
charges: Rock Rapids, IA, 1976-80; Fellowship, Greeley, CO, 1980-86; East, Muskegon, MI, 1986-91; Discovery, Grand Rapids, MI, 1991-95; Heartland Community, Sioux Falls, SD, 1995-

Hoogewind, Allen Jay
b. 10/20/1942, Grand Rapids, MI
training: Calvin Theological Seminary, BD, 1969; MDiv, 1976
ordained: 1969
charges: Community, Saginaw, MI, 1969-75; Cherry Hill, Inkster, MI, 1975-78; Leave, 1978-79; Chaplain, Jellema House, Grand Rapids, MI, 1979-89; Chaplain, Muskegon (MI) Brooks Correctional Facility, 1989-90; Chaplain, Hope Network, Grand Rapids, MI, 1990-2002; East Leonard, Grand Rapids, MI, 2002-

Hoogland, Jacob
b. 03/09/1900, Sonnega, Friesland, Netherlands
training: Calvin Theological Seminary, ThB, 1930
ordained: 1930

charges: Decatur, MI, 1930-36; Allen Ave., Muskegon, MI, 1936-45; Wyoming Park, Grand Rapids, MI, 1945-51; Woodstock, ON, 1951-58; Langley, BC, 1958-62; Nobleford, AB, 1962-66
retired: 1966
d. 03/30/1985, East Grand Rapids, MI

Hoogland, John J.
b. 04/20/1934, Drenthe, MI
training: Calvin Theological Seminary, BD, 1959
ordained: 1959
charges: Chaplain, United States Army, 1959-84; Chaplain, Director, Personnel and Ecclesiastical Relations, United States Army, 1984-85; President, United States Army Chaplain Board, Ft. Monmouth, NJ, 1985-89; Midland Park, NJ, 1989-2002
retired: 2002

Hoogland, Marvin P.
b. 09/21/1935, Decatur, MI
training: Calvin Theological Seminary, BD, 1962; Vrije Universiteit, Amsterdam, ThD, 1966
ordained: 1967
charges: Kanawha, IA, 1967-69; Hessel Park, Champaign, IL, 1969-74; Leave, 1974-75; Pastoral Counselor, Chicago Christian Counseling Center, Chicago, IL, 1976-2000
retired: 2000

Hoogland, William Frank
b. 10/02/1956, Woodstock, ON
training: Calvin Theological Seminary, MDiv, 2000
ordained: 2000
charges: Stratford, ON, 2000-

Hoogsteen, Ted Tjipke
b. 06/22/1941, Netherlands
training: Calvin Theological Seminary, BD, 1972; ThM, 1978
ordained: 1973
charges: CRC: Blyth, ON, 1973-77; Leave, 1977-83; First, Brantford, ON, 1983-90; Leave, 1990-91; Canadian Reformed Church, 1991

Hoogstra, Jacob Tunis
b. 04/19/1900, Prospect Park, NJ
training: Calvin Theological Seminary, BD, 1928; Princeton Seminary, ThM, 1929; University of Tubingen, Germany, 1930; New York Theological Seminary, ThD, 1934
ordained: 1930
charges: Englewood, NJ, 1930-40; Prospect Park, Holland, MI, 1940-65
retired: 1965

d. 06/14/1979, Holland, MI

Hoogstrate, Arthur William
b. 09/10/1915, Passaic, NJ
training: Calvin Theological Seminary, ThB, 1941; ThM, 1970
ordained: 1941
charges: Alamosa, CO, 1941-44; Lamont, MI, 1944-48; Sixteenth St., Holland, MI, 1948-54; Alpine Ave., Grand Rapids, MI, 1954-61; Third, Zeeland, MI, 1961-67; Bethel, Lansing, IL, 1967-71; Second, Fremont, MI, 1971-80
retired: 1980
d. 10/30/1993, Zeeland, MI

Hooker, Rens H.
b. 04/23/1899, Reeman, MI
training: Calvin Theological Seminary, ThB, 1930
ordained: 1930
charges: Des Plaines, IL, 1930-37; Second, Denver, CO, 1937-48; Bethany, South Holland, IL, 1948-54; Cornwall, ON, 1954-59; Rusk, MI, 1959-63; Zutphen, MI, 1963-64
d. 10/09/1964, Zutphen, MI

Horton, Michael Scott
training: Westminster Theological Seminary-CA, MAR; Oxford University, PhD, 1996
ordained: 1996
charges: CRC: Placentia, CA, 1996-97; United Reformed Churches: Christ Reformed, Placentia, CA, 1997; Faculty, Westminster Theological Seminary-CA, 1998-

House, Karl James
b. 05/18/1962, Grand Rapids, MI
training: Calvin Theological Seminary, MDiv, 1988
ordained: 1988
charges: Youth and singles pastor, Zion, Oshawa, ON, 1987-88; Zion, Oshawa, ON, 1988-94; Living Hope, Peterborough, ON, 1994-

Houseman, Donald Esko
b. 06/25/1911, Pullman, WA
training: Calvin Theological Seminary, ThB, 1939
ordained: 1938
charges: Raymond, MN, 1938-44; Madison Ave., Paterson, NJ, 1944-48; Missionary at Gallup, NM, 1948-60; Park, Holland, MI, 1960-66; Bethel, Tucson, AZ, 1966-70; Rock Rapids, IA, 1970-76
retired: 1976; affiliated with United Reformed Churches, 1997

Houseward, John Adrian
b. 08/19/1923, Clifton, NJ

training: Westminster Theological Seminary-PA, BD, 1952; Special Program for Ministerial Candidacy, Calvin Theological Seminary, 1955
ordained: 1955
charges: Faculty, Eastern Academy, Paterson, NJ, 1952–55; Maple Heights Chapel, Cleveland, OH, 1955–58; Maple Heights, Cleveland, OH, 1958–61; Home missionary, Terre Haute, IN, 1961–67; Park, Holland, MI, 1967–78; On loan: Reformed Church of Toowoomba, Australia, 1978–83; available for call, 1983–84; Austinville, IA, 1984–88
retired: 1988
d. 11/29/2001, Zeeland, MI

Howerzyl, James
b. 10/29/1918, Walker, MI
training: Protestant Reformed Theological Seminary, diploma, 1946
ordained: 1946
charges: PRC: Oskaloosa, IA, 1946–56; Redlands, CA, 1956–61; CRC: Bethel, Redlands, CA, 1961–64; Escondido, CA, 1964–84
retired: 1984; affiliated with United Reformed Churches, 1997

Howerzyl, Lawrence John
b. 12/13/1940, Grand Rapids, MI
training: Calvin Theological Seminary, BD, 1974
ordained: 1975
charges: Collingwood, ON, 1975–78; First, Randolph, WI, 1978–84; First, Lansing, IL, 1984–92; Sully, IA, 1992–2001; Pine Grove Community, St. Petersburg, FL, 2001–

Howerzyl, Timothy
b. 11/04/1973, San Jose, CA
training: Calvin Theological Seminary, MDiv, 1999
ordained: 1999
charges: Evergreen Park, IL, 1999–

Hoytema, George Johan
b. 07/25/1901, Tzum, Friesland, Netherlands
training: Theologische Universiteit, Kampen, diploma, 1931
ordained: 1931
charges: GKN: Twijzelerheide, 1931–35; Smilde, 1935–47; Monster, 1947–52; CRC: Clinton and Exeter, ON, 1952–56; Clinton, ON, 1956–59; Dunnville and York, ON, 1959–64; York, ON, 1964–66
retired: 1966
d. 01/21/1985, London, ON

Hoytema, Jerry John
b. 06/01/1938, Smilde, Drenthe, Netherlands

training: Calvin Theological Seminary, BD, 1965; MDiv, 1979
ordained: 1964
charges: Cobourg, ON, 1964–68; Mountainview, Grimsby, ON, 1968–73; Second, Sarnia, ON, 1973–78; Burlington, ON, 1978–89; First, Guelph, ON, 1989–96; Mountainview, Grimsby, ON, 1996–

Hoytema, Peter Alan
b. 12/16/1964, Hamilton, ON
training: Calvin Theological Seminary, MDiv, 1990
ordained: 1990
charges: Fellowship, Ancaster, ON, 1990–98; Midland Park, NJ, 1998–

Hubers, Gerald P.
b. 04/27/1934, Grand Rapids, MI
training: Calvin Theological Seminary, BD, 1960
ordained: 1960
charges: Home missionary, Riverside, CA, 1960–66; Grace, Eau Gallie, FL, 1966–71; Jacksonville, FL, 1971–72; Non-ministerial vocation, 1972

Hubers, Wister (Wick) D.
b. 09/23/1953, Orange City, IA
training: Reformed Bible College, BRE, 1977; Calvin Theological Seminary, MDiv, 1989
ordained: 1989
charges: Cedar, IA, 1989–96; Calvin, Le Mars, IA, 1996–2002; Chaplain, Christian Home Rehabilitation Center, Waupun, WI, 2002–

Hugen, Melvin Dale
b. 04/28/1931, Pella, IA
training: Calvin Theological Seminary, BD, 1956; Vrije Universiteit, Amsterdam, ThD, 1959; University of Chicago, 1959–61
ordained: 1959
charges: Home missionary, Richton Park, IL, 1959–62; Eastern Ave., Grand Rapids, MI, 1962–67; Missionary and service pastor, Honolulu, HI, 1967–70; Faculty, Calvin Theological Seminary, Grand Rapids, MI, 1970–98
retired: 1998

Huiner, Peter Bruce
b. 08/16/1936, Oak Park, IL
training: Calvin Theological Seminary, BD, 1960
ordained: 1962
charges: CRC: Manhattan, New York, NY, 1959–60; Home missionary, Lawndale, IL, 1962–66; Grace, Grand Rapids, MI, 1966–69; Episcopal Church, 1970

Huisman, Peter

b. 01/09/1916, Chicago, IL
training: Calvin Theological Seminary, ThB, 1944
ordained: 1944
charges: Bethel, Allison, IA, 1944-48;
Eastmanville, MI, 1948-51; Corsica, SD, 1951-57;
Palos Heights, IL, 1957-62; Rock Rapids, IA,
1962-66; Pine Creek, Holland, MI, 1966-74; East
Palmyra, NY, 1974-81
retired: 1981

Huisman, Robert

b. 06/30/1965, Harvey, IL
training: Calvin Theological Seminary, MDiv, 1991
ordained: 1991
charges: Calvary, Wyoming, MI, 1991-95; Immanuel, Hudsonville, MI, 1995-

Huissen, Christian

b. 01/22/1896, Krabbendijke, Zeeland, Netherlands
training: Calvin Theological Seminary, diploma,
1925; ThM
ordained: 1925
charges: Hull, IA, 1925-29; First Englewood, Chicago, IL, 1929-41; Eastern Ave., Grand Rapids,
MI, 1941-52; First, Rock Valley, IA, 1952-60;
Bauer, MI, 1960-64
retired: 1964
d. 04/26/1966, Grand Rapids, MI

Huizenga, Bartel Nicholas

b. 10/31/1922, Highland, IN
training: Calvin Theological Seminary, ThB, 1947,
MDiv, 1980; Fuller Theological Seminary, 1955,
1966; University of New Mexico, MA, 1970
ordained: 1966
charges: Le Mars, IA, 1947-50; Kenosha, WI,
1950-54; Bethany, Bellflower, CA, 1954-58; Home
missionary, Albuquerque, NM, 1958-65; Visalia,
CA, 1965-70; Missionary, Evergreen, Olympia, WA,
1970-74; Southwest regional missionary, 1974-75;
Missionary, Otay Mesa, CA, 1975-81; Missionary,
Porterville, CA, 1981-86; Akron, OH, 1986-90
retired: 1990
d. 08/08/1993, Visalia, CA

Huizenga, David Scott

b. 05/09/1965, Harvey, IL
training: Calvin Theological Seminary, MDiv, 1987
ordained: 1988
charges: Community Life Church, Lockport, IL,
1988-93; Colorado Community, Colorado Springs,
CO, 1993-97; Sunshine, Grand Rapids, MI, 1997-

Huizenga, Fred Martin

b. 09/13/1907, East Paris, MI
training: Calvin Theological Seminary, ThM, 1933
ordained: 1938
charges: Lay: Mission, Woodville, MI, 1935;
Stated supply, Otsego, MI, 1936-37; Grundy Center, IA, 1938; Dispatch, KS, 1938-43; Newton, IA,
1943-44; Associate pastor, First, Pella, IA and Bible teacher at Pella (IA) Christian High School,
1944-54; First, Allendale, MI, 1954-68; Bible
teacher, Pella (IA) Christian High School, 1968-72
retired: 1972
d. 05/30/1988, Grand Rapids, MI

Huizenga, James

b. 10/14/1933, Munster, IN
training: Calvin Theological Seminary, BD, 1959
ordained: 1959
charges: Terrace, BC, 1959-64; Harrison, SD,
1964-68; Edson, AB, 1968-75; First, Brandon,
MB, 1975-81
d. 06/09/1981, Grand Rapids, MI

Huizenga, John

b. 10/14/1933, Munster, IN
training: Calvin Theological Seminary, ThB, 1965
ordained: 1965
charges: Home missionary, Elim, Tucson, AZ,
1965-68
d. 10/16/1968, Tucson, AZ

Huizenga, Jonathan Lee

b. 01/02/1958, Bellflower, CA
training: Calvin Theological Seminary, MDiv, 1986
ordained: 1987
charges: Baymeadows Community, Jacksonville,
FL, 1986-87; Atlantic Community, Jacksonville,
FL, 1987-99; River Rock, Rockford, MI, 1999-

Huizenga, Lee (Lieuwe) Sjoerds

b. 06/28/1881, Lioessens, Friesland, Netherlands
training: Calvin Theological Seminary, diploma,
1909; New York Medical College, MD, 1913; Yale
University, 1929
ordained: 1909
charges: Englewood NJ, 1909-13; Missionary MD,
Tohatchi, NM, 1913-16; Englewood, NJ, 1916-17;
Missionary MD, Tohatchi, NM, 1917-20; Medical
missionary to China, 1920-27; Yale University,
Bacteriology, 1927-29; Medical Missionary to
China, 1929-45
d. 07/16/1945, Shanghai, China

Huizenga, Martin

b. 03/12/1903, New Groningen, MI

training: Calvin Theological Seminary, BD, 1933
ordained: 1935
charges: Stated supply, Martin, SD, 1933–35; Holland Center, SD, 1935–40; Saginaw, MI, 1940–43; Alto, WI, 1943–47; Cadillac, MI, 1947–53
d. 02/20/1953, south of Reed City, MI

Huizenga, Thomas Henry
b. 04/26/1961, Terrace, BC
training: Calvin Theological Seminary, MDiv, 1989
ordained: 1992
charges: Pastoral assistant, Saugatuck, MI, 1990–91; Chaplain, Carson City Correctional Facility, Carson City, MI, 1992–97; Richfield, Clifton, NJ, 1997–99; Eligible for call, 1999–2001; released from ministry in denomination

Huizinga, John Raymond
b. 01/14/1959, Melrose Park, IL
training: Calvin Theological Seminary, MDiv, 1985
ordained: 1986
charges: Vauxhall, AB, 1986–91; Maranatha, Lethbridge, AB, 1991–

Huizingh, Herman
b. 09/13/1846, Leeuwarden, Friesland, Netherlands
training: Calvin Theological Seminary, diploma, 1886
ordained: 1886
charges: Ackley, IA, 1886–90; Fulton, IL, 1890–93; Beaverdam, MI, 1893–01; Sheboygan, WI, 1901–04; Rusk, MI, 1904–08; Hull, ND, 1908–13
retired: 1913
d. 08/31/1915, Leota, MN

Hull, Timothy R.
b. 03/21/1951, Hastings, NE
training: Calvin Theological Seminary, MDiv, 1989
ordained: 1989
charges: Director of youth and evangelism, Cottonwood Heights, Jenison, MI, 1987–89; Bethany, Bellflower, CA, 1989–91; Desert View Community, Tucson, AZ, 1991–96; Peace, Menno, SD, 1996–99; Kenosha, WI, 1999–2002

Huls, Albert
b. 01/26/1929, Avereest, Overijsel, Netherlands
training: Calvin Theological Seminary, BD, 1958; Westminster Theological Seminary-PA, MDiv, 1959
ordained: 1959
charges: Blenheim, ON, 1959–62
d. 01/24/1962, Blenheim, ON

Hulst, Frederikus Bernardus
b. 12/05/1827, Dalfsen, Overijsel, Netherlands
training: with Wolter Alberts Kok, Tamme Foppe de Haan, and R. Poelma, 1855
ordained: 1855
charges: GKN: Stedum, 1855–59; Siddeburen, 1859–61; Veendam, 1861–66; Sauwerd, 1866–68; CRC: Central Ave., Holland, MI, 1868–71; First, Chicago, IL, 1871–73
d. 12/22/1873, Chicago, IL

Hulst, John Bernard
b. 09/03/1929, Grand Rapids, MI
training: Calvin Theological Seminary, BD, 1954; ThM, 1973
ordained: 1954
charges: Ireton, IA, 1954–58; First, Orange City, IA, 1958–65; Twelfth Ave., Jenison, MI, 1965–68; Faculty, Dordt College, Sioux Center, 1968–82; President, Dordt College, Sioux Center, IA, 1982–96
retired: 1996

Hulst, Lammert Jan
b. 02/10/1825, Oud-Leusden, Overijsel, Netherlands
training: with Wolter Alberts Kok and Tamme Foppe de Haan
ordained: 1849
charges: GKN: Birdaard, 1849–55; Ferwerd, 1855–64; Stadskanaal, 1864–74; RCA: Danforth IL, 1874–76; Fourth, Grand Rapids, MI, 1876–82; CRC: Coldbrook, Grand Rapids, MI, 1882–1906; Eastmanville, MI, 1906–10
retired: 1910
d. 08/21/1922, Grand Rapids, MI

Hulst, Mary Sue
b. 09/23/1969, Holland, MI
training: Calvin Theological Seminary, MDiv, 1995
ordained: 1996
charges: Eastern Ave., Grand Rapids, MI, 1995–

Hummel, Bryan John
b. 08/13/1962, Lethbridge, AB
training: Calvin Theological Seminary, MDiv, 1990
ordained: 1991
charges: Barrhaven Fellowship, Ottawa, ON, 1991–97; Eligible for call, 1997–

Hunderman, Douglas J.
b. 02/24/1951, Grand Rapids, MI
training: Reformed Bible College, BRE, 1981; Calvin Theological Seminary, MDiv, 1986
ordained: 1986

charges: Living Hope, Brigham City, UT, 1986–93; Chelwood, Albuquerque, NM, 1993–96; Church Planting, Durango, CO, 1996–

Hutt, Daniel John
b. 09/02/1971, Ogden, UT
training: Calvin Theological Seminary, MDiv, 2001
charges: Palo Alto, CA, 2002–

Hutt, Gary Peter
b. 04/26/1937, Noordwijk aan Zee, Zuid Holland, Netherlands
training: Calvin Theological Seminary, BD, 1969
ordained: 1969
charges: Ogden, UT, 1969–74; Immanuel, Burbank, IL, 1974–82; Oak Hills, Portland, OR, 1982–87; Park Lane, Evergreen Park, IL, 1987–96; Sunrise, McMinnville, OR, 1996–2000; Ebenezer, Leota, MN, 2000–

Hutt, John Cornelius
b. 11/24/1944, Noordwijk aan Zee, Zuid Holland, Netherlands
training: Calvin Theological Seminary, BD, 1970; ThM, 1977
ordained: 1970
charges: Missionary to Argentina, 1970–81; Eligible for call, 1981–82; Immanuel, Grand Rapids, MI, 1982–85; Iglesia Hispana/Comunidad Cristiana, Holland, MI, 1985–2001

Huttinga, Jack Allen
b. 07/08/1948, Bozeman, MT
training: Calvin Theological Seminary, MDiv, 1974
ordained: 1974
charges: Missionary to Argentina, 1974–82; First, Alameda, CA, 1982–92; First, Hanford, CA, 1992–2001; Manhattan, MT, 2002–

Huyser, William A.
b. 08/03/1924, Pella, IA
training: Calvin Theological Seminary, BD, 1953; ThM, 1979
ordained: 1953
charges: Prosper, MI, 1953–57; Missionary, Madison, WI, 1957–64; Westwood, Kalamazoo, MI, 1964–77; Campus pastor, Western Michigan University, Kalamazoo, MI, 1977–81; Campus pastor, Western Michigan University and Knollwood, Kalamazoo, MI, 1981–87; Minister of pastoral care, Bethel, Lansing, IL, 1987–91
retired: 1991

Hwang, Ho Kwan
ordained: 1978

charges: Korean Presbyterian Church: Chun Sung, Seoul, Korea, 1978–82; Director and Editor, Agape Vision, US: Agape Vision, 1982–83; Korean United Church, Berkeley, CA, 1983–84; CRC: East Bay Korean, El Cerrito, CA, 1984–94; Resigned from denomination, 1994

Hylkema, George (Tjerk) W.
b. 03/18/1881, Tzummarum, Friesland, Netherlands
training: Calvin Theological Seminary, diploma, 1907
ordained: 1907
charges: Volga, SD, 1907–09; Dispatch, KS, 1909–15; Prairie City, IA, 1915–18; Third Roseland, Chicago, IL, 1918–25; Second, Orange City, IA, 1925–34; Detroit, MI, 1934–38; Hospital pastor, Pine Rest, Cutlerville, MI, 1938–42
d. 12/17/1942, Cutlerville, MI

Hyun, James (Soo Il)
b. 09/03/1954, Seoul, South Korea
training: Theological Graduate School of Presbyterian General Assembly, MDiv 1985
ordained: 1982
charges: Presb.: Hap Dong, Korea, 1982–85; CRC: Korean, Los Angeles, CA, 1987–89; Tyrannus Korean, Los Angeles, CA, 1989–96; Rok Won, Norwalk, CA, 1996–97; Orange Han Min, Buena Park, CA, 1997–

Ibershoff, John Berand
b. 01/06/1917, Grand Rapids, MI
training: Calvin Theological Seminary, ThB, 1942
ordained: 1942
charges: Plainfield, MI, 1942–49; Arcadia, CA, 1949–57, 1990–98; Non-ministerial vocations, 1957–90
d. 02/01/1998, Los Angeles, CA

Ingeneri, Paul Michael
b. 05/06/1949, Winthrop, MA
training: Calvin Theological Seminary, MDiv, 1984
ordained: 1984
charges: Director of education and evangelism, Seymour, Grand Rapids, MI, 1976–80; Pine Grove Community, St. Petersburg/Pinellas Park, FL, 1984–97; Church planting, Crossroads Community, Flanders, NJ, 1997–

Ipema, Paul Richard
b. 02/23/1967
training: Mid-America Reformed Seminary, MDiv, 1992; Calvin Theological Seminary, Special Program for Ministerial Candidacy, 1994

ordained: 1994
charges: CRC: Oak Glen, Lansing, IL, 1994-96; United Reformed Churches: Oak Glen, Lansing, IL, 1996-2001; Nampa, ID, 2001

Ipema, Peter
b. 09/16/1922, Chicago, IL
training: Calvin Theological Seminary, BD, 1947
ordained: 1948
charges: Missionary to West Africa-Nigeria, 1948-79; Research Fellow, Centennial Mission Scholarship Committee, Grand Rapids, MI, 1979-80; Director, Mid-East Fellowship Center, Oak Park, IL, 1981-85; stated supply, Terre Haute, IN, 1986-87
retired: 1987

Ipema, William (Bud)
b. 03/14/1938, Worth, IL
training: Calvin Theological Seminary, BD, 1969
ordained: 1975
charges: Faculty, North Park Seminary, Oak Lawn, IL, 1975-80; Director of Multi-Racial Leadership Development, Synodical Committee On Race Relations, Oak Park, IL, 1980-86; SCORR, Oak Park, IL, 1986-87; President, Mid America Leadership Foundation, Chicago, IL, 1987-2001; Vice President, Council of Leadership Foundations, Chicago, IL, 2001-

Iserman, Harvey
b. 1854
ordained: 1878
charges: True Protestant Dutch Reformed: Leonia, NJ, 1878-90; CRC: Leonia, NJ, 1890-92; Passaic, NJ, 1892-95; New York, NY, 1895-99; Ridgewood, NJ, 1899; Resigned from the denomination, 1899

Jabaay, Albert
b. 01/29/1897, Munster, IN
training: Calvin Theological Seminary, ThB, 1926
ordained: 1926
charges: Cincinnati, OH, 1926-31; Third, Zeeland, MI, 1931-41; Second, Orange City, IA, 1941-44; Evergreen Park, IL, 1944-52; Second, Byron Center, 1954-64
retired: 1952-54; 1964
d. 05/23/1969, Zeeland, MI

Jabay, Earl
b. 03/30/1925, Lansing, IL
training: Calvin Theological Seminary, ThB, 1952
ordained: 1952
charges: Bluffton, Muskegon, MI, 1952-55; Summer St., Passaic, NJ, 1955-58; Leave, 1958-60;

Chaplain, NJ Neuro-Psychiatric Institute, 1960-62; Non-ministerial vocation, 1962

Jackson, John Raymond
b. 06/06/1949, Plainwell, MI
training: Calvin Theological Seminary, MDiv, 1975; ThM, 1983
ordained: 1976
charges: Bethel, Waupun, WI, 1976-79; Walker, Grand Rapids, MI, 1979-85; Non-ministerial vocation, 1985

Jackson, Melvin O'Connor
b. 12/21/1955, Memphis, TN
training: Memphis University and Life Bible College
ordained: 1983
charges: Baptist Church: 1983-2002; CRC: Believer's Christian Fellowship, Los Angeles, CA, 2002-

Jager, Edward
b. 08/21/1957, Edmonton, AB
training: Calvin Theological Seminary, MDiv, 1988
ordained: 1989
charges: Bethel, Lacombe, AB, 1989-93; Immanuel, Langley, BC, 1993-2001; Emmanuel, Calgary, AB, 2001-

Jang, Boo Young
b. 10/22/1941, Seoul, South Korea
training: Ko Shin Theological Seminary, MDiv; Chong Shin Theological Seminary, MDiv, Luther Rice Theological Seminary, MDiv; International Theological Seminary, ThM; Reformed Theological Seminary, DMin; Faith Theological Seminary, PhD
ordained: 1975
charges: Korean Presbyterian Church: Im-Gae Choon-ang, 1969-71; Choon-chon Ham-bu, 1971-74; Hyandong Presbyterian, 1974-77; Dae-heung Je-il, 1977-83; Young-il Presbyterian, 1983-88; Elim Presbyterian, Westminster, CA, 1988-89; CRC: Elim, Garden Grove, CA, 1989-99; resigned from denomination, 1999

Jang, Young-Gil
b. 09/12/1952, Korea
training: Chong-Shin Theological Seminary, MDiv, 1984
ordained: 1985
charges: Presbyterian Church of Korea: Shin-Chung, Seoul, 1985-89; CRC: Korean, Los Angeles, CA, 1990-93; Sum-Ki-Nun Korean, Orlando, FL, 1993-

Janke, David Alan
b. 09/05/1939, Chicago, IL
training: Calvin Theological Seminary, BD, 1971
ordained: 1971
charges: Pompton Plains, NJ, 1971-75; Peace, South Holland, IL, 1975-85; Acting Director of Development, SCORR, Oak Park, IL, 1985-87; Eligible for call, 1988-90; Non-ministerial vocation, 1990

Janke, Gregory Scott
b. 02/11/1966, Grand Rapids, MI
training: Calvin Theological Seminary, MDiv, 1994
ordained: 1994
charges: First, Crown Point, IN, 1994-2001; Bauer, Hudsonville, MI, 2001-

Jansen, Johannes
b. 02/23/1878, Longerhouw, Friesland, Netherlands
training: Vrije Universiteit, Amsterdam, diploma, 1901; Drs, 1904; Theologische Universiteit Kampen, ThD, 1906
ordained: 1904
charges: CRC: Whitinsville, MA, 1904-06; GKN: Bedum, 1906-11
retired: 1911
d. 09/11/1951, Zeist, Netherlands

Jansen, John Keimpe
b. 02/02/1938, Witmarsum, Friesland, Netherlands
training: Calvin Theological Seminary, BD, 1969
ordained: 1969
charges: Bethlehem, Thunder Bay, ON, 1969-75; Glad Tidings, Edmonton, AB, 1977-84; Leave, 1984-86; Chaplain and Clinical pastoral education Supervisor, Alberta Hospital, Edmonton, AB, 1986-

Jansen, Nicholas
b. 12/27/1887, Spijk, Groningen, Netherlands
training: Calvin Theological Seminary, diploma, 1916
ordained: 1916
charges: Leota, MN, 1916-20; Hawarden, IA, 1920-27; Baldwin, WI, 1927-48; Birnamwood, WI, 1948-57
retired: 1957
d. 12/15/1978, Grand Rapids, MI

Jansma, Theodore John
b. 10/04/1909, Dokkum, Friesland, Netherlands
training: Westminster Theological Seminary-PA, BD, 1939
ordained: 1937
charges: OPC: Baltimore, MD, 1937-41; Philadelphia, PA, 1941-43; Bible teacher, Eastern Academy, Paterson, NJ, 1943-44; RCA: Sixth, Paterson, NJ, 1944-49; Eighth, Grand Rapids, MI, 1949-57; Chaplain-counselor, Christian Sanitorium, Wyckoff, NJ, 1957-62; CRC: Chaplain-counselor, Christian Sanitorium, Wyckoff, NJ, 1962-74
retired: 1974
d. 01/28/1994, Holland, MI

Jansons, Robert W.
b. 03/02/1966, Platte, SD
training: Calvin Theological Seminary, MDiv, 1992
ordained: 1993
charges: Woodville, MI, 1993-95; Monroe, WA, 1995-

Janssen, Jeffrey P.
b. 03/16/1972, Burlington, ON
training: Calvin Theological Seminary, MDiv, 1999
ordained: 1999
charges: Mount Hamilton, Hamilton, ON, 1999-

Janssens, Peter J.
b. 03/21/1965, Thunder Bay, ON
training: Calvin Theological Seminary, MDiv, 1996
ordained: 1996
charges: First, Chilliwack, BC, 1996-98; Lucknow, ON, 1998-

Jasperse, Neil Patrick
b. 06/29/1957, Sheboygan, WI
training: Calvin Theological Seminary, MDiv, 1987
ordained: 1988
charges: Candidate resident pastor, Fairfield, CA, 1987-88; Hope Community, Santa Rosa, CA, 1988-96; Hessel Park, Champaign, IL, 1996-2001; West Leonard, Grand Rapids, MI, 2001-

Jeffers, James Emil
b. 11/17/1916, Missouri
training: Westminster Theological Seminary-PA, BD, 1953; Calvin Theological Seminary, Special Program for Ministerial candidacy, 1954
ordained: 1954
charges: Home missionary, Oklahoma City, OK, 1954-57; Clara City, MN, 1957-61; Grangeville, ID, 1961-67; Calvin, Portland, OR, 1967-73; Quincy, WA, 1973-81
retired: 1981

Jeltema, David John
b. 11/23/1969, Kalamazoo, MI

training: Calvin Theological Seminary, MDiv, 1998
ordained: 1998
charges: Bethany, Bellflower, CA, 1998–

Jen, Isaac I. Chun
b. 05/05/1927, Shanghai, China
training: Westminster Theological Seminary-PA, BD, 1952; Calvin Theological Seminary, ThM, 1954
ordained: 1955
charges: Home missionary, Chinese Gospel Chapel, Chicago, IL, 1955–58; Missionary, Taiwan; 1958–70; disability leave, 1970–73; Associate minister, Back to God Hour, 1973–88
d. 06/09/1988, Chicago, IL

Jeon, Charles Yoochul
b. 12/16/1958, Seoul, South Korea
training: Calvin Theological Seminary, MDiv, 1994
ordained: 1995
charges: Shalom Korean, Atlanta, GA, 1995–

Jeong, Moses (Inyeol)
b. 04/09/1947, Korea
training: Hapdong Presbyterian Theological Seminary, MDiv, 1981
ordained: 1982
charges: Korean Presbyterian Church (1982–90): Chilbo First Presbyterian Church; Pacific Presbyterian Church, Guam; CRC: Faith, South Gate, CA, 1990–

Jho, Kyung Soo
b. 09/16/1956, Korea
training: Chong-Shin Theological Seminary, MDiv, 1984
ordained: 1984
charges: Alaskan Korean, Anchorage, AK, 1994–2002; Lynnwood Korean, Lynnwood, WA, 2002–

Jim, Stanley Alfred
b. 09/01/1955, Farmington, NM
training: Reformed Bible College, BRE, 1992; Calvin Theological Seminary, MMin, 1995
ordained: 1996
charges: Tohatchi, NM, 1996–2000; Regional director, CRC Home Missions, Rehoboth, NM, 2000–

Jipping, Robert Lee
b. 06/12/1937, Holland, MI
training: Calvin Theological Seminary, BD, 1969
ordained: 1969
charges: Missionary to Argentina, 1969–74; Cedar, IA, 1974–78; Prairie Lane, Omaha, NE, 1978–

82; Goshen, IN, 1982–93; Crownpoint, NM, 1993–2002
retired: 2002

Jo, David Hwan
b. 07/05/1941
ordained: 1971
charges: Hapdong Presbyterian Church: Missionary, Japan, 1971–73; Pacific Presbyterian Church, 1973–86; CRC: Messiah Korean, La Mirada, CA, 1986–89; on loan to Pacific Presbyterian Church, Guam, 1989–94; Presbyterian Church of Guam, 1994

Johnson, Michael Scott
b. 04/11/1963, Zeeland, MI
training: Calvin Theological Seminary, MDiv, 1989
ordained: 1989
charges: Residency home missionary, New Life, Houston, TX, 1989–90; Community Life, Missouri City, TX, 1990–2001; Associate pastor, Texas Leadership Development, Peace Community, TX, 2001–

Johnson, William S.
b. Maine
ordained: 2001
charges: CRC Ministry, Central Maine, 2000–

Joldersma, John
b. 06/16/1942, Holland, MI
training: Calvin Theological Seminary, BD, 1969
ordained: 1971
charges: Devington, Indianapolis, IN, 1971–76; Beckwith Hills, Grand Rapids, MI, 1976–87; Pease, MN, 1987–96; Third, Kalamazoo, MI, 1996–98; Ridgewood, Jenison, MI, 1998–

Joling, Edward
b. 10/23/1893, Grand Rapids, MI
training: Calvin Theological Seminary, diploma, 1921
ordained: 1921
charges: Second, Lynden, WA, 1921–26; Austinville, IA, 1926–34; Kenosha, WI, 1934–50; Madison Ave., Paterson, NJ, 1950–53; East Martin, MI, 1953–59
retired: 1959
d. 03/19/1972, Grand Rapids, MI

Jolman, David Lee
b. 12/27/1967, Grand Rapids, MI
training: Calvin Theological Seminary, MDiv, 2001
ordained: 2001
charges: Assistant pastor, Community Congrega-

tional Church, Franklin, IN, 1991–93; Second, Fremont, MI, 1994–99; Hanley, Grandville, MI, 2001–

Jongbloed, Tjeerd
b. 02/01/1869, Leeuwarden, Friesland, Netherlands
training: Theologische Universiteit, Kampen, diploma, 1897
ordained: 1897
charges: GKN: Cubaard, 1897–99; Westerlee, 1899–1908; CRC: Cutlerville, MI 1908–11; Edmonton, AB, 1911–19; Hoboken, NJ, 1919–26
d. 01/04/1926, Hoboken, NJ

Jongsma, Allan Henry
b. 09/07/1933, Whitinsville, MA
training: Calvin Theological Seminary, BD, 1958
ordained: 1958
charges: Vogel Center, MI, 1958–62; First, Jenison, MI, 1962–68; Irving Park, Midland Park, NJ, 1968–71; Rogers Heights, Wyoming, MI, 1971–78; Immanuel, Grand Rapids, MI, 1978–81; First, De Motte, IN, 1981–88; Heritage, Kalamazoo, MI, 1988–96; Bauer, Hudsonville, MI, 1996–99
retired: 1999

Jongsma, Daniel Lee
b. 06/02/1958, Grand Rapids, MI
training: Calvin Theological Seminary, MCE, 1983, MDiv, 1987
ordained: 1988
charges: Associate in youth and evangelism, Cottonwood Heights, Jenison, MI, 1985–88; Faith, Elmhurst, IL, 1988–91; Bethel, Fulton, IL, 1991–97; New church developer, Horizon Community, Lisle, IL, 1997–

Jongsma, John William
b. 09/24/1932, Brandon, MB
training: Calvin Theological Seminary, BD, 1961
ordained: 1961
charges: Burdett, AB, 1961–64; Haney, BC, 1964–69; Assistant minister, Maranatha, Edmonton, AB, 1969–73; Mount Hamilton, Hamilton, ON, 1973–79; Shalom, Brantford, ON, 1979–87; Second, Sarnia, ON, 1987–97
retired: 1997

Jonker, Dirk
b. 07/06/1891, Paris Township, Kent County, MI
training: Calvin Theological Seminary, diploma, 1918
ordained: 1918
charges: Sibley, IA, 1918–21; Rusk, MI, 1921–26;

non-ministerial vocation, 1926, affiliated with Protestant Reformed Church
d. 02/19/1953, Grand Rapids, MI

Jonker, Henry
b. 09/15/1946, Wildervank, Groningen, Netherlands
training: Calvin Theological Seminary, BD, 1973
ordained: 1974
charges: Maranatha, Edmonton, AB, 1974–81; Trinity, St. Catharines, ON, 1981–87; First, Victoria, BC, 1987–99; First Ladner, Delta, BC, 1999–

Jonker, Peter Sr.
b. 09/25/1860, Noord Schurwoude, Noord Holland, Netherlands
training: Calvin Theological Seminary, diploma, 1897
ordained: 1897
charges: Jamestown, MI, 1897–99; Third, Muskegon, MI, 1899–1901; Peoria, IA, 1901–07; Prospect Park, Paterson, NJ, 1907–11; Hull, IA, 1911–18; Chaplain, Pine Rest Christian Hospital, Cutlerville, MI, 1918–20; Archer Ave., Chicago, IL, 1920–30
retired: 1930
d. 10/20/1944, Kalamazoo, MI

Jonker, Peter Jr.
b. 11/05/1887, Cutlerville, MI
training: Calvin Theological Seminary, diploma, 1915
ordained: 1915
charges: Lebanon, IA, 1915–19; Dennis Ave., Grand Rapids, MI, 1919–22; First, Lynden, WA, 1922–29; Sixteenth St., Holland, MI, 1929–45; Leota, MN, 1945–48; Coopersville, MI, 1948–52
d. 09/29/1952, Coopersville, MI

Jonker, Peter M.
b. 11/28/1913, Brouwershaven, Zeeland, Netherlands
training: Vrije Universiteit, Amsterdam; Theologische Hogeschool, Apeldoorn, diploma, 1940; Calvin Theological Seminary, MDiv, 1992
ordained: 1940
charges: CGKN: Almelo, 1940–45; Dutch Army chaplain, 1945–51; Apeldoorn, 1951–55; CRC: Belleville, ON, 1955–58; Immanuel, Brampton, ON, 1958–74; Richmond, BC, 1974–81
retired: 1981
d. 10/05/1997, Brampton, ON

Jonker, Peter Marvin
b. 07/29/1966, Toronto, ON

training: Calvin Theological Seminary, MDiv, 1992
ordained: 1993
charges: Pastoral assistant, East Leonard, Grand Rapids, MI, 1990-91; Woodlawn, Grand Rapids, MI, 1993-

Jonkman, John (Jan) Bartels
b. 07/24/1861, Munnekezijl, Friesland, Netherlands
training: Calvin Theological Seminary, diploma, 1899
ordained: 1899
charges: North St., Zeeland, MI, 1899-1906; Hardewyk, MI, 1906-08; Borculo, MI, 1908-12; Fulton, IL, 1912-19
d. 09/28/1919, Clinton, IA

Jonkman, Melvin Jay
b. 03/08/1958, Grand Rapids, MI
training: Calvin Theological Seminary, MDiv, 1987
ordained: 1987
charges: Kenosha, WI, 1987-97; Second, Highland, IN, 1997-2000; Non-ministerial vocation, 2000

Joosse, Andrew
b. 02/08/1941, Middelburg, Zeeland, Netherlands
training: Western Theological Seminary, MDiv, 1989
ordained: 1990
charges: Reformed Church of Canada: Monarch, AB, 1990-93; CRC: First, Lethbridge, AB, 1994-

Joosse, James
b. 07/23/1925, Middelburg, Zeeland, Netherlands
training: Calvin Theological Seminary, BD, 1960
ordained: 1960
charges: Dresden, ON, 1960-63; Georgetown, ON, 1963-67; Newmarket, ON, 1967-71; Third, Edmonton, AB, 1971-76; Emmanuel, Calgary, AB, 1976-86; Kentville, NS, 1986-91
retired: 1991

Jordan, Kevin Lee
b. 06/19/1972, Grand Rapids, MI
training: Calvin Theological Seminary, MDiv, 1998
ordained: 1998
charges: Woden, IA, 1998-

Jorden, Paul
b. 08/03/1953, Chicago, IL
training: Trinity Evangelical Divinity School, MDiv, 1978; Denver Seminary, DMin, 1999
ordained: 1984

charges: Immanuel, Fort Collins, CO, 1983-97; Family in Christ Community, Denver, CO, 1997-

Jorritsma, Menno S.
b. 04/27/1926, Bergum, Friesland, Netherlands
training: Calvin Theological Seminary, BD, 1963
ordained: 1963
charges: Oakland, MI, 1963-67; Covenant, Cutlerville, MI, 1967-73; Hillcrest, Hudsonville, MI, 1973-77; First, Orange City, IA, 1977-79; First, Everett, WA, 1979-87; Emmanuel, Calgary, AB, 1987-91
retired: 1991

Jou, Do Hong
ordained: 1986
charges: Reformed Church of Germany, Jeil, Dortmund, 1982-92; CRC: Korean, Chicago, IL, 1993-95; Faculty, Korean Theological Seminary, 1995

Joung, Woon Chull
b. 05/04/1942, In Cheon-Shi, Korea
training: Golden Gate Baptist Theological Seminary, MDiv, 1990
ordained: 1985
charges: Baptist: Messiah Baptist Church, 1985-91; Oriental Mission Church, Edmonton, AB, 1991-94; CRC: Edmonton Korean Mission, Edmonton, AB, 1996-99; Oriental Mission Church, Edmonton, AB, 1999-2001; resigned from denomination

Julien, Jerome Marshall
b. 09/11/1937, Chicago, IL
training: Western Theological Seminary, MDiv, 1962
ordained: 1962
charges: RCA: Seventh, Grand Rapids, MI, 1962-63; CRC: Franklin St., Grand Rapids, MI, 1963-66; Rogers Heights, Grand Rapids, MI, 1966-68; Faith, Grand Rapids, MI, 1968-75; First, Pella, IA, 1975-81; First, Sheldon, IA, 1981-89; Calvary, Flamborough, ON, 1989-91; Alliance of Reformed Churches: Independent Christian Reformed, Sheffield, ON, 1991-95; Lynwood, IL, 1995; United Reformed Churches: Lynwood, IL, 1995-2001; Leave, 2001

Jung, Chanjoo
b. 03/15/1956, Seoul, South Korea
training: An Yang University, MDiv, 1992
ordained: 1994
charges: Presbyterian Church USA: Covenant, Olympia, WA, 1994-95; So Mang, Spokane, WA, 1994-98; CRC: Hope Korean Presbyterian, Spo-

kane, WA, 1995-99; So Mang, Edmonton, AB, 1999-2000; on loan to Youngman Presbyterian Church, Dae-gu City, Korea, 2001-

Jung, Stephen Moe
b. 06/26/1925, Hong Kong, China
training: California Graduate School of Theology, 1973; Calvin Theological Seminary, MDiv, 1978
ordained: 1978
charges: Crenshaw, Los Angeles, CA, 1973-79; Zion Chinese, Abbotsford, BC, 1979-83 and Immanuel, Richmond, BC, 1979-88
retired: 1988

Kaastra, Thomas George
b. 03/23/1943, Grand Rapids, MI
training: Calvin Theological Seminary, BD
ordained: 1970
charges: Immanuel, Roseville, MI, 1970-

Kaemingk, Franklin
b. 02/18/1934, Hull, IA
training: Calvin Theological Seminary, BD, 1960; San Francisco Theological Seminary, 1961
ordained: 1961
charges: CRC: Cadillac, MI, 1961-64; Hospital pastor, Bethesda, Denver, CO, 1964-76; PCUSA: Lake City, CO, 1976

Kallemeyn, Harold
b. 12/24/1949, Chicago, IL
training: Faculte Libre De Theologie Evangelique, BTh, 1979; Calvin Theological Seminary, Special Program for Ministerial Candidacy, 1980
ordained: 1980
charges: Home missionary to French-speaking people, QC, 1980-86; Repentigny E Ste. Lambert, Montreal, QC, 1986; Repentigny, Montreal, QC, 1986-88; French Ministry Coordinator, Montreal, QC, 1988-89; Faculty, Libre de Theologie Reformee, Aix-en-Provence, Frances, 1989-

Kammeraad, Carl Lee
b. 03/16/1946, Zeeland, MI
training: Calvin Theological Seminary, BD, 1971; ThM, 1972
ordained: 1972
charges: Community, Toledo, OH, 1972-77; Madison Ave., Paterson, NJ, 1977-82; Neland Ave., Grand Rapids, MI, 1982-2002; Seymour, Grand Rapids, MI, 2002-

Kamper, Dennis Arthur
b. 05/26/1948, Sault Ste. Marie, MI
training: Calvin Theological Seminary, MDiv, 1974

ordained: 1974
charges: Creston, Grand Rapids, MI, 1974-78; Faith Community, Beaver Dam, WI, 1978-87; Fellowship, Greeley, CO, 1987-99; Chaplain, Hospice of Northern Colorado, Greeley, CO, 1999-

Kamps, Gilbert Jay
b. 12/10/1949, Bozeman, MT
training: Calvin Theological Seminary, MDiv, 1977
ordained: 1977
charges: High River, AB, 1977-82; Covenant, Sioux Center, IA, 1982-87; Palm Lane, Scottsdale, AZ, 1988-98; New Life, Red Deer, AB, 1998-2003; Trinity, St. Louis, MO, 2003-

Kamps, Henry H.
b. 03/02/1860, Drenthe, MI
training: Calvin Theological Seminary, diploma, 1897
ordained: 1897
charges: New Holland, SD, 1897-01; no congregation, 1901-11; Rudyard, MI, 1911-15; Wright IA, 1915-17
retired: 1917
d. 03/16/1939, Zeeland, MI

Kamps, Jacob R.
b. 08/18/1898, Drenthe, MI
training: Calvin Theological Seminary, diploma, 1925; Princeton Seminary, ThM, 1926
ordained: 1926
charges: Missionary to China, 1926-27; Rehoboth, NM, 1927-51, Tohatchi, NM, 1951-63
retired: 1963
d. 07/02/1976, Rehoboth, NM

Kamstra, Douglas Alan
b. 06/18/1952, East Grand Rapids, MI
training: Calvin Theological Seminary, MDiv, 1977; ThM, 1978; Fuller Theological Seminary, DMin, 1989
ordained: 1977
charges: Reeman, MI, 1977-82; Calvary, Wyoming, MI, 1982- ; Prayer Mobilizer, CRC Home Missions, 1996-

Kang, Ho-Suk
b. 11/23/1947, Chungcheongbuk-Do Bo Euen, Korea
training: Faith Theological Seminary, MDiv, 1977
ordained: 1977
charges: Pyung Hwa Presbyterian, Seoul, Korea, 1976-80; Presbyterian General Assembly, Theological Seminary, Korea, 1976-80; Korean Peace Church of Los Angeles, Mission Hills, CA, 1981-

97; CRC: Korean Peace of Los Angeles, Mission Hills, CA, 1997–2000
d. 01/05/2000, Los Angeles, CA

Kang, Il Yong
b. 04/14/1954, Korea
training: Westminster Theological Seminary-CA, MDiv, 1989; Fuller Theological Seminary, ThM, 1997
ordained: 1999
charges: Korean American Presbyterian: Saudi Arabia, 1990–92; PCA: New Life Mission, Anaheim, CA, 1993–94; New Life Mission, Cerritos, CA, 1994–98; CRC: Orange Korean, Fullerton, CA, 1999–

Kang, Seung Jai
b. 12/24/1937, Seoul, South Korea
training: Chong-Shin Theological Seminary, MDiv, 1967
ordained: 1969
charges: Hapdong Presbyterian Church: Sae Han, Korea, 1979–71; Sintein Jeil, Korea, 1971–78; Sae Han, Korea, 1978–83; Han Woori, Korea, 1983–86; Orange Dongsan, Garden Grove, CA, 1986–87; CRC: Orange Dongsan, Garden Grove, CA, 1987–89; Faculty, General Assembly Theological Seminary, 1989–91; Korean, Kalamazoo, MI, 1991–96; Leave, 1996–97; Garden Grove Korean, Anaheim, CA, 1997–2000; Hope, San Jose, CA, 2000–2001; Yung Kwang, Las Vegas, NV, 2002–

Kang, Sun Man
b. Korea
charges: Sung Chi Presbyterian, Philadelphia, PA, –2002; CRC: Sung Chi, Flourtown, PA, 2002–

Kang, Young Suk
training: General Assembly Presbyterian Theological Seminary, Korea
ordained: 1970
charges: Korean Presbyterian Church: Dong-Boo, Taeku, Korea, 1970–71; Bujeon, Busan, Korean, 1971–79; Korean Church of Grand Rapids, MI, 1979–81; CRC: Korean, Grand Rapids, MI, 1981–83; Cerritos Central, Artesia, CA, 1985–86; PCUSA: Hebron Presbyterian Church, Hebron, WA, 1986

Karsen, Richard J.
b. 06/25/1895, Chicago, IL
training: Calvin Theological Seminary, diploma, 1924
ordained: 1924

charges: Aetna, MI, 1924–27; Second, Grand Haven, MI, 1927–42; Cincinnati, OH, 1942–43
d. 12/06/1943, Cincinnati, OH

Karsten, Henry T.
b. 12/25/1931, Grand Rapids, MI
training: Calvin Theological Seminary, BD, 1958; MDiv, 1980
ordained: 1958
charges: Monroe, WA, 1958–63; Akron, OH, 1963–73; Missionary, Bay Meadows Jacksonville, FL, 1973–82; Alger, WA, 1982–89; Bethel, Sun Valley, CA, 1989–95
retired: 1995

Katerberg, Henry
b. 08/09/1936, Coevorden, Drenthe, Netherlands
training: Calvin Theological Seminary, BD, 1969
ordained: 1969
charges: Zion, Pembroke, ON, 1969–73; Maranatha, Belleville, ON, 1973–77; Riverside, Wellandport, ON, 1977–85; Maranatha, St. Catharines, ON, 1985–94
retired: 1994

Kats, Daryl Edwin
b. 12/18/1957, Norton, KS
training: Westminster Theological Seminary-CA, MDiv, 1987; Calvin Theological Seminary, Special Program for Ministerial Candidacy, 1989
ordained: 1989
charges: CRC: Austinville, IA, 1989–95; Beaverdam, MI, 1995–1999; United Reformed Church: Cloverdale, Boise, ID, 1999

Kauffman, Timothy Dean
b. 08/15/1958, New Wilmington, PA
training: Calvin Theological Seminary, Special Program for Ministerial Candidacy
ordained: 1991
charges: Rosewood, Bellflower, CA, 1991–95; Montello Park, Holland, MI, 1995–98; Bethel, Fulton, IL, 1998–

Kayayan, Aaron R.
b. 01/24/1928, Athens, Greece
training: Reformed Seminary, Aix-en-Provence, LTh, 1959
ordained: 1964
charges: Eglise Riformie Evangilique Independante: Bordes sur Arize, 1958–59; La Bastide sur l'Hers, 1959–64; Eglise Riformie de France: Vienne-Sud, 1964–66; Paris-Belleville, 1966–76; Back to God Hour Perspectives Riformies, 1975–83; CRC: Minister, French broad-

casting, Back to God Hour, Palos Heights, IL, 1983-95
retired: 1995; resigned from denomination, 1998

Keegstra, Carroll Eugene
b. 02/24/1934, Grand Rapids, MI
training: Calvin Theological Seminary, BD, 1959
ordained: 1963
charges: Kenosha, WI, 1963-67; West Park, Cleveland, OH, 1967-75; Franklin Lakes, NJ, 1975-78; Dildine, Ionia, MI, 1978-82; Charlotte, MI, 1982-89; Michigan Ecumenical Forum, 1989-90; Leave, 1990-92; Chaplain, Riverside Psychiatric Center, Ionia, MI, 1992-94; Chaplain, Huron Valley Center, Ypsilanti, MI, 1994-2002
retired: 2002

Keegstra, Henry
b. 02/14/1871, Groningen, Groningen, Netherlands
training: Calvin Theological Seminary, diploma, 1900
ordained: 1900
charges: Leighton, IA, 1900-03; Allendale, MI, 1903-08; Fremont, MI, 1908-19; Sixteenth St., Holland, MI, 1919-28; Allendale, MI, 1928-41
retired: 1941
d. 02/14/1955, Grand Rapids, MI

Keizer, Andrew (Andries)
b. 11/22/1857, Echten, Friesland, Netherlands
training: Calvin Theological Seminary, diploma, 1886
ordained: 1886
charges: Grand Haven, MI, 1886-88; Second, Muskegon, MI, 1888-91; East Saugatuck, MI, 1891-96; Drenthe, MI, 1896-98; Graafschap, MI, 1898-1902; Ninth St., Holland, MI, 1902-10; Beaverdam, MI, 1910-16; Overisel, MI, 1916-19; Harderwyk, MI, 1919-25
retired: 1925
d. 09/12/1935, Holland, MI

Keizer, Herman Jr.
b. 05/21/1938, Chicago, IL
training: Calvin Theological Seminary, BD, 1968; New York Theological Seminary, MTh, 1977; Columbia Teacher's College, MA, 1978
ordained: 1968
charges: Chaplain, Executive Director Armed Forces Chaplains Board, The Pentagon, Washington, DC, 1968-94; Chaplain, Command Chaplain, European Command, Stuttgart, Germany, 1994-97; Special assistant, Army chief of chaplains, The Pentagon, Washington, DC, 1997-98; Assistant Deputy for Human Relations, Office of the As-

sistant Secretary of the Army, The Pentagon, Washington, DC, 1998-2000; Special advisor to the Ambassador at Large, International Religious Freedom, Washington, DC, 2000-2002; Director, CRC Chaplain Ministries, Grand Rapids, MI 2002-

Keizer, John (Jan)
b. 06/30/1860, Steggerda, Friesland, Netherlands
training: Theologische Universiteit, Kampen, diploma, 1883
ordained: 1883
charges: GKN: Landsmeer, 1883-87; CRC: First, Zeeland, MI, 1888-90; Graafschap, MI, 1890-98; First, Pella, IA, 1898-1902; Second, Kalamazoo, MI, 1902-11; Prospect Park, Paterson, NJ, 1911-16; Comstock, MI, 1916-23
retired: 1923
d. 11/20/1950, Kalamazoo, MI

Keizer, John Gilbert
b. 04/08/1949, Le Mars, IA
training: Calvin Theological Seminary, BD, 1976; ThM, 1977
ordained: 1977
charges: Zillah, WA, 1977-84; Sussex, NJ, 1984-

Kelder, Peter Clarence Jr.
b. 08/28/1952, Chicago, IL
training: Calvin Theological Seminary, MDiv, 1977
ordained: 1978
charges: Missionary, East Islip, NY, 1978-80; Kenosha, WI, 1980-87; Hope, La Crosse, WI, 1987-95; Grace Fellowship, Pella, IA, 1995-

Kelderman, Duane Keith
b. 07/30/1952, Oskaloosa, IA
training: Calvin Theological Seminary, MDiv, 1977
ordained: 1977
charges: Community, Toledo, OH, 1977-83; Ridgeview Hills, Denver, CO, 1983-88; Neland, Ave., Grand Rapids, MI, 1988-2001; Vice president, Calvin Theological Seminary, Grand Rapids, MI, 2001-

Kelley, Kent E.
ordained: 1963
charges: UPCUSA: Savannah, GA 1963-66; CRC: Home missionary, Savannah, GA, 1966-69; Ogilvie, MN, 1969-71; Non-ministerial vocation, Grandville, MI, 1971

Kelley, Stephen John
b. 01/16/1957, Port Said, Egypt
training: Calvin Theological Seminary, MDiv, 1989
ordained: 1989

charges: CRC: Director, Peace Arab-American Ministries, Dearborn, MI, 1989–96; Independent: Peace Arab American Ministries, Dearborn, MI, 1996

Kemper, John R.
b. 05/11/1952, Brampton, ON
training: Calvin Theological Seminary, MDiv, 1999
ordained: 1999
charges: Penticton, BC, 1999–2002

Kempkes, William John
b. 09/24/1962, St. Thomas, ON
training: Calvin Theological Seminary, MDiv, 1998
ordained: 1998
charges: Vernon, BC, 1998–

Kenbeek, John James
b. 11/20/1899, Leiden, Zuid Holland, Netherlands
training: Calvin Theological Seminary, diploma, 1931
ordained: 1931
charges: Cincinnati, OH, 1931–41; Terra Ceia, NC, 1941–48; Highland, MI, 1948–53; Drenthe, MI, 1953–64
retired: 1964
d. 05/12/1998, Holland, MI

Kerkhof, Jacob (Jack)
b. 08/29/1948, Bedum, Groningen, Netherlands
training: Calvin Theological Seminary, MDiv, 1989; ThM, 2000
ordained: 1989
charges: Burlington, ON, 1989–2000; First, Barrie, ON, 2000–

Kerkstra, Louis
b. 02/15/1930, Battle Creek, MI
training: Calvin Theological Seminary, BD, 1962; ThM, 1980
ordained: 1962
charges: Trinity, Denver, CO, 1962–66; Milwood, Kalamazoo, MI, 1966–71; Lee St., Wyoming, MI, 1971–78; Kelloggsville, Grand Rapids, MI, 1978–86; Second, Lynden, WA, 1986–94
retired: 1994

Kerssies, Johnannes
b. 07/13/1937, Diever, Drenthe, Netherlands
training: Calvin Theological Seminary, BD, 1966; MDiv, 1985
ordained: 1968
charges: Bethel, Dunnville, ON, 1968–72; Owen Sound, ON, 1972–77; Redeemer, Sarnia, ON,

1977–85; Calvin, Ottawa, ON, 1985–93; Covenant, Calgary, AB, 1993–2000; Collingwood, ON, 2000–

Kett, Gregory J.
b. 07/23/1970, Grand Rapids, MI
training: Calvin Theological Seminary, MDiv, 1999
ordained: 1999
charges: New England Chapel, Franklin, MA, 1999–2000; Campus ministries, River Terrace, East Lansing, MI, 2000–

Kett, John A.
b. 08/16/1863, Delft, Utrecht, Netherlands
training: Calvin Theological Seminary, diploma, 1908
ordained: 1908
charges: Kelloggsville, MI, 1908–10; Grand Rapids, Dennis Ave., 1910–14
d. 02/22/1914, Grand Rapids, MI

Keuning, Maynard
b. 11/26/1906, New Holland, SD
training: Calvin Theological Seminary, BD, 1933
ordained: 1934
charges: Arlene, MI, 1934–36; Second, Sioux Center, IA, 1936–42; Neerlandia, AB, 1942–46; Everson, WA, 1946–50; Crookston, MN, 1950–62; Estelline, SD, 1962–67; Iowa Falls, IA, 1967–71
retired: 1971
d. 11/23/1983, Grand Rapids, MI

Keyzer, Sam (Simon) John
b. 05/18/1953, Allendale, MI
training: Reformed Theological Seminary, MDiv, 1978; Calvin Theological Seminary, Special Program for Ministerial Candidacy, 1980
ordained: 1980
charges: Second, Randolph, WI, 1980–87; First, Seattle, WA, 1987–97; Northern Lighthouse, Lincoln, NE, 1997–

Kieft, Gordon Jay
b. 01/27/1942, Grand Rapids, MI
training: Calvin Theological Seminary, BD, 1967
ordained: 1967
charges: CRC: Assistant chaplain, Pine Rest Christian Hospital, Cutlerville, MI, 1967–68; Leave, 1968–69; Assistant chaplain, Institute of Religion, Houston, TX, 1969–70; Chaplain/counselor, Bethesda Pastoral Counseling Center, Denver, CO, 1970–87; Chaplain, Samaritan Center for Counseling and Training, Denver, CO, 1987–93; American Baptist Church: 1993

Kiekover, Harvey Alvin
b. 05/16/1932, Hudsonville, MI
training: Calvin Theological Seminary, BD, 1965
ordained: 1965
charges: Missionary to Nigeria: Missionary, 1965–66, Makurdi, 1966–67, Veenstra Seminary, Lupwe, 1967–70, Theological College of Northern Nigeria, 1970–81, Field Secretary, 1980–85; Calvin, Grand Rapids, MI, 1985–94; Director of pastoral services, Holland Home, Grand Rapids, MI, 1994–

Kieu, Nathan (Nam) Tuan
b. 06/17/1959, Loc Bihn, Quangnon, Vietnam
training: International Theological Seminary, MDiv, 1988; Calvin Theological Seminary, Special Program for Ministerial Candidacy, 1991
ordained: 1991
charges: Vietnamese Reformed, Christian, Kentwood, MI, 1988–90; Thanh-Duong TuDo (Vietnamese Liberty), San Jose, CA, 1991–

Kikkert, Timothy Jay
b. 01/09/1949, Hammond, IN
training: Calvin Theological Seminary, Special Program for Ministerial Candidacy
ordained: 1979
charges: CRC: Brooten, MN, 1979–82; Ridott, Germany Valley, IL, 1982–85; Chaplain, United States Army, 1985–98; Presbyterian Church of the USA: Chaplain, United States Army, 1998

Kim, Daniel Dae Yeul
b. 05/19/1957, Seoul, South Korea
training: Calvin Theological Seminary, MCE, 1987, MDiv, 1988
ordained: 1988
charges: Korean Bible Church, Ann Arbor, MI, 1987–88; CRC: On loan to Korean Bible Church, Ann Arbor, MI, 1988–90; Korean Hope, Ann Arbor, MI, 1990–91; Non-ministerial vocation, 1991

Kim, Dwight Dong-Wan
b. 02/08/1948
ordained: 1974
charges: Chaplain, Korean Air Forces, 1975–82; Seung-Dong Presbyterian Church: Seoul, Korea, 1982–86; Evergreen Korean, Los Angeles, CA, 1986–89; CRC: Evergreen Korean, Los Angeles, CA, 1989–94; Resigned from denomination, 1994

Kim, Gilbert (Kiho)
b. 06/14/1958, Seoul, South Korea
training: Calvin Theological Seminary, MDiv, 1998; ThM, 1999
ordained: 2000

charges: Kent First Korean, Kent, WA, 2000; Garden of Grace, Mill Creek, WA, 2000–

Kim, Hang Keel
ordained: 1984
charges: CRC: Hope, San Jose, CA, 1984–88; Resigned from denomination, 1988

Kim, Hyun-Jin
b. 11/04/1960, Seoul, South Korea
training: Chong-Shin Theological Seminary, MDiv, 1988
ordained: 1988
charges: Sooyoung Ro Presbyterian, Korea, 1988–1992; CRC: Korean, Wheeling, IL, 1996–2000

Kim, In Chul
b. 06/20/1947, Kangwando, South Korea
training: Presbyterian General Assembly Theological Seminary, MDiv, 1977
ordained: 1978
charges: Presbyterian Church of Korea: Sunkok, 1972–74; Daehoo, 1974–78; Yeoryou, 1978–81; Sung Kwane, 1981–89; CRC: Chosen People, Los Angeles, CA, 1993–

Kim, Insung
b. 06/15/1945, Seoul, South Korea
training: Reformed Presbyterian Theological Seminary, MDiv, 1986
ordained: 1990
charges: Korean Presbyterian Church: Seattle, WA, 1980–88; Korean Presb., Lynnwood, WA, 1988–89; CRC: Lynnwood Korean, Lynnwood, WA, 1989–99; Joun, Marysville, WA, 2000–

Kim, Jae Sung S.
b. 10/26/1955, Korea
training: Hapdong Theological Seminary, MDiv, 1982; Calvin Theological Seminary, ThM, 1990
ordained: 1987
charges: Korean, Los Angeles, CA, 1986–89; Korean, Kalamazoo, MI, 1989–91; Eligible for call, 1991–

Kim, Jae Youn Y.
b. 06/02/1946
ordained: 1985
charges: CRC: Korean, Los Angeles, CA, 1985–87; Valley Korean, Arleta, CA, 1987–93; Resigned from denomination, 1993

Kim, James Chang Kyum
b. 05/20/1947, Kyungsangbuk-Do Sun San-Gun, South Korea

training: Presbyterian General Assembly Theological Seminary, MDiv, 1980; Calvin Theological Seminary, ThM, 1998
ordained: 1982
charges: Dae Won Presbyterian Church, Korea, 1984-92; CRC: Church of Love, Sun Valley, CA, 1992-

Kim, James Tai Pyung
b. 06/10/1944, Seoul, South Korea
training: Fuller Theological Seminary, MDiv, 1986; Calvin Theological Seminary, Special Program for Ministerial Candidacy, 1987
ordained: 1987
charges: On loan to Hanmi Presb. Church, Los Angeles, CA, 1987-

Kim, John (Whan) Eui
b. 11/19/1933, Chun Nam, Korea
training: Calvin Theological Seminary, BD, 1962
ordained: 1976
charges: Korean Pres. Church: Faculty, Presb. General Assembly (Hap Dong) Seminary, Seoul, Korea, 1966-76; CRC: Missionary to Koreans, Los Angeles, CA, 1976-78; Korean, Los Angeles, CA, 1978-93; Korean Christian Presbyterian Church: Faculty, International Theological Seminary, 1993

Kim, John (Yohn) Taek
b. 09/08/1948, Inchesum, Korea
training: Reformed Presbyterian Theological Seminary, MDiv, 1980
ordained: 1978
charges: Orange Korean, Fullerton, CA, 1972-82; Leave, 1982-84; Missionary, Korean American, Orange County, CA, 1984-88; Leave, 1988-90; Calvin, Los Alamitos, CA, 1990-94; Faculty, Calvin Theological Seminary, 1994-98; President, Daehan Theological College and Seminary, Korea, 1994-

Kim, John Sang-Joung
b. 01/17/1939, Ong-jan Kon, Kyoung, Korea
training: University of Texas, MA, 1970; Reformed Theological Seminary, MDiv, 1772; Calvin Theological Seminary, ThM, 1973
ordained: 1974
charges: PCA: Korean Presbyterian Church, Austin, TX, 1974-84; CRC: Greater Houston Korean, Houston, TX, 1984-86; Eligible for call, 1986; Church planter, among Koreans, Irvine, CA, 1987-89; Korean Community, Irvine, CA, 1989-93; withdrew from denomination, 1993

Kim, John Young Moon
b. 12/28/1944, Jeonnam Hae Nam, Korea
training: Presbyterian General Assembly Theological Seminary, MDiv, 1976
ordained: 1976
charges: Shin Jung Central Presbyterian, Seoul, Korea, 1970-88; Mt. Zion Presbyterian, Los Angeles, CA, 1988-90; Orange County Choong Hyun Presbyterian, Garden Grove, CA, 1992-94; CRC: Korean American Central Presbyterian, Garden Grove, CA, 1994-

Kim, Jonathan J. (Chae)
b. 10/13/1958, South Korea
training: Calvin Theological Seminary, MDiv, 1992
ordained: 1993
charges: Educational pastor, So Mang Korean, Anaheim, CA, 1993-94; Calvin, Los Alamitos, CA, 1994-95; Oceanside Korean-American, Oceanside, CA, 1995-96; Alaskan Korean, Anchorage, AK, 1996; Los Angeles Open Gate, Los Angeles, CA, 1997-2000; The Salt and Light, West Hollywood, CA, 2000-

Kim, Ki Woong
b. 12/10/1958, Korea
training: Chong-Shin Theological Seminary, MDiv, 1990
ordained: 1994
charges: UPC: Saginaw Presbyterian Church, Saginaw, MI, 1994-96; CRC: Korean, Vicksburg, MI, 1997-

Kim, Kook-Sung
b. 07/03/1953, Korea
training: Tae Han Theological Seminary, ThB, 1983, Calvin Theological Seminary, MDiv, 1989
ordained: 1991
charges: Staff pastor, Korean, Boca Raton, FL, 1991-93; New Life Korean, Ft. Lauderdale, FL, 1992-97; Boca Raton Korean, Boca Raton, FL, 1997-99; New Life Korean, Ft. Lauderdale, FL, 1998-

Kim, Man Sung
b. 11/06/1951, Pusan, South Korea
training: Hap Dong Presbyterian Theological Seminary, MDiv, 1988; Fuller Theological Seminary, MA, 1993
ordained: 1991
charges: Korean American Presbyterian Church; CRC: Korean, Ames, IA, 1993-

Kim, Matthew (Chang H.)
b. 08/22/1965, Seoul, South Korea

ordained: 2002
training: Fuller Theological Seminary, MDiv, 2001, Calvin Theological Seminary, Ethnic Minority Program for Ministerial Candidacy, 2002
charges: Korean of Orange County, Westminister, CA, 2002–

Kim, Moon Bae
b. 08/25/1962, Korea
training: Tae Han Theological Seminary, ThB, 1983; Calvin Theological Seminary, MDiv, 1995
ordained: 1995
charges: Hahn-In, Wyoming, MI, 1995–98; Eligible for call, 1998–99; Grace Korean, Wyoming, MI, 1999–

Kim, Munchul
b. 05/30/1961, Seoul, South Korea
training: Calvin Theological Seminary, MDiv, 1996
ordained: 1998
charges: On loan: Michianna Korean Church, Osceola, IN, 1998–99; Living-Spring Community, Glenview, IL, 1999–2002

Kim, Paul Soomyung
b. 03/19/1943
ordained: 1971
charges: Sung Jwa Presbyterian, Andong, Korea, 1971–77; Korean Presbyterian Church: Tacoma, WA, 1977–83; CRC: on loan to (independent) Tacoma Korean Presbyterian Church, Tacoma, WA, 1983–89; Resigned from denomination, 1989

Kim, Peter H.
b. 09/21/1944
ordained: 1980
charges: Incheon Second Presbyterian Church, 1973–74; Incheon Dongboo Presbyterian Church, 1974– 82; Ilshin Presbyterian Church, Los Angeles, CA, 1982–83; CRC: Hope, San Jose, CA, 1983–89; Southern California Hope, Irvine, CA, 1989–92; Neung-Ryuk, Anaheim, CA, 1992–

Kim, Samuel J.
b. 09/13/1961, Grand Rapids, MI
training: Calvin Theological Seminary, MDiv, 1989
ordained: 1990
charges: Minister of youth, Korean, Grand Rapids, MI, 1989–90; Korean Church of Orange County, Buena Park, CA, 1990–96; Eligible for call, 1996–

Kim, Simon (Sang-eun)
b. 05/22/1955, Korea
training: Calvin Theological Seminary, MDiv, 2000
ordained: 2001

charges: Kent First Korean, Kent, WA, 2001–

Kim, Steve J.
b. 05/21/1959, Taegu, Korea
training: Trinity Evangelica Divinity School, MDiv, 1987, ThM, 1991
ordained: 1988
charges: Christian and Missionary Alliance: Chicago Peace Church, Chicago, IL, 1984–88; Elmhurst, IL, 1988–91; Antioch, VA, 1991–92; East-West Church, Guam, 1992–96; Evergreen Church, Guam, 1997–2001; CRC: Lynnwood Korean, Lynnwood, WA, 2001–

Kim, Yong Ki
training: declared eligible on the basis of exceptional gifts, 1984
ordained: 1984
charges: CRC: West Bethel Korean, Los Angeles, CA, 1984–93; Resigned from denomination, 1993

Kim, Yong Tae
b. 03/14/1946, Korea
training: Kingswood Christian College and Theological Seminary, MDiv, 1988
ordained: 1977
charges: Korean Assembly of God, 1977–80; Jung Bu Young Nak Church, 1982–85; Eastern United Korean Church, Hacienda Heights, CA, 1986–90; CRC: Director of evangelism and Christian education, Orange Korean, Fountain Valley, CA, 1978–80; Eastern United Korean Church, Hacienda Heights, CA, 1990–94; Resigned from denomination

Kim, Yong-Chool
ordained: 1972
charges: Korean Presbyterian Church: Seoul, Korea, 1972–76; Independent: Presbyterian, Toronto, ON, 1976–79; CRC: First Korean Presbyterian, Toronto, ON, 1979–89; Resigned from denomination, 1989

Kim, Youchan
b. 04/11/1956, Pusan, Korea
training: Asia Center for Theological Studies and Missions, MDiv, 1986; Calvin Theological Seminary, Special Program for Ministerial Candidacy, 1991
ordained: 1995
charges: Church planting, Boulder, CO, 1995–2000

Kim, Young Moon
see: Kim, John Young Moon

Kim, Young Ook

b. 05/05/1939, Jeonnam Shin An-Gun, Korea
training: Presbyterian General Assembly Theological Seminary, MDiv, 1971
ordained: 1972
charges: Assistant pastor CRC, Los Angeles, CA, 1974-76; Garden Grove Korean, Anaheim, CA, 1976-88; CRC: Garden Grove Korean, Anaheim, CA, 1988-2001

Kistemaker, Simon

b. 10/21/1930, St. Maarten, Noord Holland, Netherlands
training: Calvin Theological Seminary, BD, 1957; Vrije Universiteit, Amsterdam, ThM, 1961
ordained: 1961
charges: Home missionary, Vernon, BC, 1961-63; Faculty, Dordt College, 1963-71; Faculty, Reformed Theological Seminary, Jackson, MS, 1971-96
retired: 1996

Kits, Jakob Hendrik

b. 01/26/1931, Oldekerk, Groningen, Netherlands
training: Calvin Theological Seminary, MDiv, 1969
ordained: 1969
charges: Agassiz, BC, 1969-74; Surrey, BC, 1974-78; Second, Edmonton, AB, 1978-84; First, Duncan, BC, 1984-92; Interim pastor, Hope Stony Plain, AB, 1993-94
retired: 1994; affiliated with United Reformed Churches, 1998

Klaasen, Thomas George

b. 09/04/1951, Grand Rapids, MI
training: Calvin Theological Seminary, MDiv, 1977
ordained: 1977
charges: Missionary to Central America, El Salvador, 1977-80; Missionary to Honduras, 1980-84; Bible teacher, Contra Costa High School, Walnut Creek, CA, 1984-85; Eligible for call, 1985-86; Chaplain, United States Air Force, 1986-97; Northside, Clifton, NJ, 1997-2002; Chaplain, Christian Health Care Center, Wyckoff, NJ, 2001-

Klazinga, James Dennis

b. 12/18/1964, Goderich, ON
training: Calvin Theological Seminary, MDiv, 1991
ordained: 1991
charges: CRC: Brantford, ON, 1991-93; Alliance of Reformed Churches: Telkwa, ON 1993-95; United Reformed Churches: Telkwa, ON, 1995-

Klein, Hendrik Geert

see: Klyn, Hendrik Geert

Klijn, Hendrik Geert

see: Klyn, Hendrik Geert

Klimp, Ronald Allen

b. 04/11/1951, Kalamazoo, MI
training: Calvin Theological Seminary, MDiv, 1977
ordained: 1977
charges: Plymouth Heights, Grand Rapids, MI, 1977-80; Portage, MI, 1980-86; Prosper, Falmouth, MI, 1986-99; Workplace Ministries, Inc., Cadillac, MI, 1999-

Klingenberg, Michael Jeffrey

b. 08/12/1963, Woodstock, ON
training: Wilfrid Laurier University/Waterloo Lutheran University, MTS, 1998; Calvin Theological Seminary, MDiv, 2002
ordained: 2002
charges: Bradenton, FL, 2002-

Klingenberg, Robert William

b. 11/17/1940, Holland, MI
training: Calvin Theological Seminary, BD, 1966
ordained: 1966
charges: CRC: Lamont, MI, 1966-69; Faith, Kalamazoo, MI, 1969-74; Calvin, Wyckoff, NJ, 1974-77; Ann Arbor, MI, 1977-79; Assemblies of God: First, Grand Rapids, 1979

Klok, Ronald Edward

b. 09/13/1962, Taber, AB
training: Calvin Theological Seminary, MDiv, 1995
ordained: 1995
charges: Glad Tidings, Edmonton, AB, 1995-

Klompeen, Donald John

b. 10/26/1938, Bozeman, MT
training: Calvin Theological Seminary, BD, 1966; MDiv, 1977
ordained: 1966
charges: Hope, Hull, IA, 1966-70; Missionary, Zuni, NM, 1970-73; Leave, Pacific School of Religion, Berkeley, CA, 1973-74; Chaplain, Salvation Army Center, Oakland, CA, 1974-76; Friendship House, San Francisco, CA, 1976-82; Chaplain, Harper-Grace Memorial Hospital, Detroit, MI, 1983-89; Chaplain, Rehoboth McKinley Behavioral Health Services, Gallup, NM, 1989-98; Eligible for call, 1998-99; Chaplain, Mill Creek Community, Mill Creek, WA, 1999-2002
retired: 2002

Klompien, Carl J.

b. 07/03/1941, Harvey, IA
training: Calvin Theological Seminary, BD, 1966

ordained: 1970
charges: Archer Ave., Chicago, IL, 1970-73; Bauer, MI, 1973-79; Sully, IA, 1979-84; First, Prinsburg, MN, 1984-91; Trinity, Visalia, CA, 1991-97; First, Hull, IA, 1997-

Klompien, John Carl
b. 06/17/1970, Oak Lawn, IL
training: Calvin Theological Seminary, MDiv, 2001
ordained: 2001
charges: First, Byron Center, MI, 2001-

Klomps, John Gerald
b. 05/09/1934, Aalten, Gelderland, Netherlands
training: Calvin Theological Seminary, BD, 1962
ordained: 1964
charges: Lindsay, ON, 1964-67; Bethel, Brockville, ON, 1967-71; First, Hamilton, ON, 1971-80; Clarkston, Mississauga, ON, 1980-82; Minister at large, Christian Horizons, Mississauga, ON, 1982-85; Executive director, The Bible League of Canada, Mississauga, ON, 1985-97
retired: 1997

Klooster, Fred H.
b. 12/23/1922, Munster, IN
training: Calvin Theological Seminary, ThB, 1947; Westminster Theological Seminary-PA, ThM, 1949; Vrije Universiteit, Amsterdam, ThD, 1951
ordained: 1952
charges: Home missionary at Champaign-Urbana, IL, 1952-53; Faculty, Calvin College, 1953-56; Faculty, Calvin Theological Seminary, Grand Rapids, MI, 1956-88
retired: 1988

Klooster, John
b. 11/27/1936, Winsum, Groningen, Netherlands
training: Calvin Theological Seminary, BD, 1975
ordained: 1975
charges: Maranatha, Woodbridge, Toronto, ON, 1975-79; Calvary, Seattle, WA, 1979-85; Eligible for call, 1985-90
d. 02/1995, Seattle King, WA

Kloosterman, Nelson Deyo
b. 09/27/1950, Grand Rapids, MI
training: Calvin Theological Seminary, MDiv, 1975; Theologische Hogeschool van de Gereformeerde Kerken in Nederland, Kampen, ThD, 1992
ordained: 1975
charges: CRC: Bethel, Marion, SD, 1975-78; Immanuel, Sheldon, IA, 1978-82; Leave, 1982-84; Faculty, Mid America Reformed Seminary, Orange

City, IA, 1984-94; Alliance of Reformed Churches: Faculty, Mid America Reformed Seminary, Orange City, IA, 1994-95; United Reformed Churches: Faculty, Mid America Reformed Seminary, Dyer, IN, 1995-

Klop, Donald Jack
b. 01/14/1947, Kalamazoo, MI
training: Calvin Theological Seminary, BD, 1973
ordained: 1973
charges: Minister of education and evangelism, First, Grand Rapids, MI, 1973-80; Flagstaff, AZ, 1980-85; Calvary, Chino, CA, 1985-

Klouw, Gordon Don
b. 10/23/1929, Grand Haven, MI
training: Calvin Theological Seminary, BD, 1960
ordained: 1960
charges: CRC: Bethel, Sun Valley, CA, 1960-66; Prospect Park, Holland, MI, 1966-70; San Diego, CA, 1970-75; resigned from denomination

Klumpenhouwer, John Martinus
b. 09/03/1936, Netherlands
training: Calvin Theological Seminary, BD, 1968
ordained: 1968
charges: First, Kemptville, ON, 1968-72; Lindsay, ON, 1972-78; Fredericton, NB, 1978-84; Forest, ON, 1984-92; Eligible for call, 1992-95
retired: 1995

Klumpenhower, Gary John
b. 09/10/1937, Zuidwolde, Drenthe, Netherlands
training: declared eligible on the basis of exceptional gifts, 1986
ordained: 1986
charges: Evangelist, Brigham City, UT, 1963-66; Evangelist, Indian Christian Center, Salt Lake City, UT, 1966-69; Evangelist, Toadlena, NM, 1969-81; Evangelist, Tohatchi, NM, 1981-86; Tohatchi, NM, 1986-93; Interim pastor, Riverside, Wellandport, ON, 1993-94; Tohatchi, 1994-95; Window Rock, AZ, 1995-2002
retired: 2002

Klyn, Hendrik Geert
b. 11/19/1793, Utrecht, Utrecht, Netherlands
training: with Hendrik Pieter Scholte
ordained: 1839
charges: GKN: Kockengen, 1839-45; Middelburg, 1845-49; RCA: Graafschap, MI, 1849-50; Grand Haven, MI, 1850; Milwaukee, WI, 1850; Graafschap, MI, 1851-52; Milwaukee and Franklin, WI, 1852-53; Milwaukee, WI, 1853-54; Second, Grand Rapids, MI, 1854-57; Kalamazoo, MI,

1857-60; Muskegon, MI, 1860; Kalamazoo, MI, 1861-62; First, Chicago, IL, 1862-68; CRC: First, Grand Rapids, MI, 1857
retired: 1868
d. 12/01/1883, Keokuk, IA

Knight, Wayne Albert
b. 08/06/1960, Hamilton, ON
training: Calvin Theological Seminary, MDiv, 2000
ordained: 2000
charges: Bozeman, MT, 2000-

Knoester, John Carl
b. 03/23/1973, Grand Rapids, MI
training: Calvin Theological Seminary, MDiv, 2002
charges: Ocheyeden, IA, 2003-

Knol, Robert Lee
b. 02/13/1961, Grand Rapids, MI
training: University of Minnesota, MEd, 1991; Calvin Theological Seminary, MDiv, 1997
ordained: 1997
charges: Immanuel, Wyoming, MI, 1997-2001; Daybreak Community, Valparaiso, IN, 2001-

Knoper, Marquis (Mark) J.
b. 08/21/1950, Zeeland, MI
training: Calvin Theological Seminary, MDiv, 1979
ordained: 1979
charges: Missionary, Iloilo, Philippines, 1979-94; Church developer, Christian Reformed World Missions, Taiwan, 1994-2001

Knoppers, Nicholas B.
b. 03/03/1917, Almelo, Overijsel, Netherlands
training: Vrije Universiteit, Amsterdam; Leiden Universiteit diploma, 1942; McGill University, Montreal
ordained: 1942
charges: GKN: Lollum, 1942-46; Hardenberg, 1946-49; Hilversum, 1949-52; Dutch Air Force Chaplain, 1952-53; CRC: Beverly, Edmonton, AB, 1955-60; Montreal, QC, 1960-68; Home missionary, Scottsdale Community, El Paso, TX, 1968-71; First, Red Deer, AB, 1971-83
retired: 1983

Knott, Edward John
b. 03/05/1922, Grand Rapids, MI
training: Protestant Reformed Theological Seminary, BD, 1947
ordained: 1947
charges: PRC: Home missionary, 1947-50; Kalamazoo, MI, 1950-59; Second, Grand Rapids, MI, 1959-61; CRC: Beverly, Grand Rapids, MI,

1961-71; West Leonard, Grand Rapids, MI, 1971-78; Calvin, Rock Valley, IA, 1978-83; Forest Grove, MI, 1983-88
retired: 1988; affiliated with United Reformed Churches, 1992

Ko, Victor Y.
b. 11/23/1967, Seoul, South Korea
training: Calvin Theological Seminary, MA, 1998
ordained: 1999
charges: Third, Kalamazoo, MI, 1999-

Kobes, Jacob Cornelius
b. 12/04/1895, Muscatine, IA
training: Los Angeles Bible Institute, diploma, 1926
ordained: 1945
charges: Lay missionary, Toadlena, NM, 1925-45; ordained missionary, Toadlena, NM, 1945-63
retired: 1963
d. 01/15/1963, Rehoboth, NM

Kobes, Wayne Allen
b. 04/10/1947, Sioux City, IA
training: Calvin Theological Seminary, BD, 1972; ThM, 1973
ordained: 1973
charges: Faculty, Dordt College, Sioux Center, IA, 1973-

Koch, Neville Lawson
b. 09/26/1944, Columbo, Sri Lanka
training: Dutch Reformed Church Bible Institute and Seminary, diploma, 1969
ordained: 1969
charges: Dutch Reformed Church in Sri Lanka: Regent Street, Colombo, 1969-74; Dehiwela, 1975-80; Wellawatte, 1981-96; Principal, Columbo Theological Seminary, Columbo, 1994-96; CRC: San Diego, CA, 1997-

Koedoot, Gerrit
b. 01/25/1935, Capelle a/d IJssel, Zuid Holland, Netherlands
training: Calvin Theological Seminary, BD, 1960
ordained: 1961
charges: Home missionary, Jewish Mission, Rogers Park, Chicago, IL, 1961-66; Missionary to Japan, Tokyo, 1966-68, Kunitachi, 1968-77; Kobe Reformed Seminary and Literature Evangelism, 1977-81; Missionary, Christian Reformed Seminary and Bible College, Bacolod City, Philippines, 1981-97; Missionary, Japan, 1997-2000
retired: 2000

Koeman, Kenneth Dean

b. 12/03/1942, Holland, MI
training: Calvin Theological Seminary, BD, 1967
ordained: 1968
charges: Chelwood Community, Albuquerque, NM, 1968–74; Calvin, Portland, OR, 1974–80; Sonlight Community, Lynden, WA, 1980–

Koeman, Scott Brian

b. 04/02/1969, Zeeland, MI
training: Reformed Bible College, BRE, 1994; Calvin Theological Seminary, MDiv, 2001
ordained: 2001
charges: Education/Evangelism Evergreen Ministries, Hudsonville, MI, 1997–2000; Evergreen Ministries, Hudsonville, MI, 2000

Koeman, Tony Wayne

b. 11/23/1972, Holland, MI
training: Calvin Theological Seminary, MDiv, 1999
ordained: 1999
charges: Community, Oakdale, CA, 1999–

Koert, John Leonard

b. 10/24/1896, Netherlands
training: Calvin Theological Seminary, diploma, 1923; Princeton, 1925–26; University of Chicago, 1926–28
ordained: 1923
charges: CRC: Missionary for Classis Zeeland, 1923–25; East Palmyra, NY, 1928–34; Baptist: Calvary Baptist, New York, NY, 1934
d. 06/10/1975, Grand Haven, MI

Koetje, Michael Dale

b. 12/13/1973, Grand Rapids, MI
training: Calvin Theological Seminary, MDiv, 2000
ordained: 2000
charges: Hope, Hull, IA, 2000–

Kok, Bernard

b. 11/23/1903, Amsterdam, Noord Holland, Netherlands
training: Protestant Reformed Theological Seminary, diploma, 1929
ordained: 1929
charges: PRC: Hudsonville, MI, 1942–48; Holland, MI, 1948–58; Lansing, IL, 1958–61; CRC: Home missionary, Cochrane, ON, 1961–64; Dutton, MI, 1964–69
retired: 1969
d. 09/22/1997, Grand Rapids, MI

Kok, Gareth S.

b. 08/29/1903, Randolph, WI

training: Calvin Theological Seminary, ThB, 1930
ordained: 1930
charges: Hills, MN, 1930–35; First, Bellflower, CA, 1935–46; Maple Ave., Holland, MI, 1946–54; First, Edgerton, MN, 1954–60; Hanford, CA, 1960–69; Missionary, Hemet, San Jacinto, CA, 1969–71
retired: 1971
d. 04/06/2002, Artesia, CA

Kok, James Robert

b. 08/29/1931, Grand Rapids, MI
training: Westminster Theological Seminary, 1956
ordained: 1956
charges: PRC: Chino, CA, 1956–60; Manhattan, MT, 1960–61; CRC: Bethel, Manhattan, MT, 1961–64; Prospect Park, Paterson, NJ, 1964–67; Eastern Ave., Grand Rapids, MI, 1967–72; Third, Denver, CO., 1972–91; Classical interim pastor, Central California, 1991–97
retired: 1997

Kok, Jim (James) Robert

b. 03/29/1935, Hills, MN
training: Calvin Theological Seminary, BD, 1962; MDiv, 1972
ordained: 1963
charges: Chaplain, Gowanda State Hospital, Gowanda, NY, 1963–64; Home missionary, Trinity, Iowa City, IA, 1964–69; Chaplain, Pine Rest Christian Hospital, 1969–84; Executive pastor, Crystal Cathedral, Garden Grove, CA, 1984–

Kok, Joel Edward

b. 01/14/1959, Seattle, WA
training: Calvin Theological Seminary, MDiv, 1986
ordained: 1991
charges: Unity, Ames, IA, 1991–96; Trinity, Broomall, PA, 1996–

Kok, Louis E.

b. 02/18/1929, Bellingham, WA
training: Calvin Theological Seminary, BD, 1957; MDiv, 1972
ordained: 1957
charges: Calvary, Seattle, WA, 1957–62; Chaplain, United States Air Force, 1962–89; Ministries coordinator, First, Lynden, WA, 1989–91
retired: 1991

Kok, Philip Dean

b. 04/04/1970, Grand Rapids, MI
training: Calvin Theological Seminary, MDiv, 1998
ordained: 1998
charges: Prairie Edge, Portage, MI, 1998–

Kok, Philip Jay

b. 02/16/1941, Grand Rapids, MI
training: Calvin Theological Seminary, BD, 1971
ordained: 1971
charges: Sioux Falls, SD, 1971-76; San Diego, CA, 1976-82; East Leonard, Grand Rapids, MI, 1982-87; First, Lynden, WA, 1987-97; Almond Valley, Ripon, CA, 1997-

Kok, Roger Allen

b. 07/03/1937, Grand Rapids, MI
training: Calvin Theological Seminary, BD, 1969
ordained: 1969
charges: Palo Alto, CA, 1969-74; Pease, MN, 1974-79; Rogers Heights, Wyoming, MI, 1979-86; Holland Heights, Holland, MI, 1986-90; Shawnee Park, Grand Rapids, MI, 1990-2000
retired: 2000

Kok, Thomas John

b. 08/26/1960, Bozeman, MT
training: Calvin Theological Seminary, MDiv, 1987
ordained: 1987
charges: Administrator of youth and evangelism, Messiah, Hudsonville, MI, 1985-87; Quincy, WA, 1987-92; Peace, South Holland, IL, 1992-

Kok, William

b. 09/02/1892, Amsterdam, Noord Holland, Netherlands
training: Calvin Theological Seminary, diploma, 1924; ThB, 1933
ordained: 1924
charges: Lebanon, IA, 1924-27; First, Zeeland, MI, 1927-40; President's assistant, Calvin College, 1940-42; First Englewood, Chicago, IL, 1942-53; Immanuel, Grand Rapids, MI, 1953-58; Bible teacher South Christian High School, Cutlerville, MI, 1958-60
retired: 1958
d. 05/25/1977, Grand Rapids, MI

Kole, William (Willem)

b. 09/12/1861, Beaverdam, MI
training: Calvin Theological Seminary, diploma, 1898
ordained: 1898
charges: New Era, MI, 1898-1900; Leota, MN, 1900-03; Harvey IA, 1903-08; Rusk, MI, 1908-14; Goshen, IN, 1914-23
retired: 1923
d. 02/12/1941, Holland, MI

Kolkman, John

b. 02/28/1884, Pearline (Allendale Township, Ottawa Co.), MI
training: Calvin Theological Seminary, diploma, 1914
ordained: 1914
charges: Caldwell, MI, 1914-20; Grant, MI, 1920-23; Oakland, MI, 1923-44
retired: 1944
d. 03/31/1960, Grand Rapids, MI

Koll, David Ralph

b. 02/27/1955, Grand Rapids, MI
training: Calvin Theological Seminary, MDiv, 1981
ordained: 1981
charges: Good Shepherd, Flushing, MI, 1981-94; Anaheim, CA, 1994-

Kong, David Hook

b. 11/17/1960, Seoul, South Korea
training: Talbot School of Divinity, MDiv, 1995; Fuller Theological Seminary, MTh, 1999
ordained: 1999
charges: Korean Presbyterian Church: Oriental Mission Church, 1994-96; Crossroad Evangelical Church, 1997-98; Korean Central Presbyterian, 1998-2000; CRC: Bethany Korean, Burbank, CA, 2002-

Koning, Anthony Albertus

b. 01/11/1899, Hilversum, Noord Holland, Netherlands
training: Calvin Theological Seminary, diploma, 1925
ordained: 1925
charges: Coster, IA, 1925-29; Emden, MN, 1929-49; Hollandale, MN, 1949-53; Coopersville, MI, 1953-59; Hollandale, MN, 1959-65
retired: 1965
d. 07/16/1984, Prinsburg, MN

Koning, Frederic John

b. 02/25/1955, New Westminister, BC
training: Calvin Theological Seminary, MDiv, 1981
ordained: 1981
charges: St. Albert, AB, 1981-87; First, Vancouver, BC, 1987-93; Mountainview, Grimsby, ON, 1993-95; Leave, 1995-98; Chaplain, Hamilton General Hospital, Hamilton, ON, 1998-2002; Senior Chaplaincy Service, Toronto University Health Service, Toronto, ON, 2002-

Koning, Gerald Alan

b. 12/29/1956, Kalamazoo, MI

training: Reformed Bible College, BRE, 1980; Calvin Theological Seminary, MDiv 1985
ordained: 1985
charges: Missionary to Central America: Costa Rica, 1985-87, El Salvador, 1987-89; Iglesia Cristiana Reformada Hispana, Boston, MA, 1989-91; Comstock Park, MI, 1991-

Koning, Herman S.
b. 02/01/1888, Groningen, Groningen, Netherlands
training: Calvin Theological Seminary, diploma, 1923
ordained: 1923
charges: Sullivan, MI, 1923-26; Plainfield, MI, 1926-39; Tracy, IA, 1939-43; Bigelow, MN, 1943-49; Houston, BC, 1949-51
retired: 1951
d. 04/16/1955, Bellflower, CA

Koning, Kenneth Dale
b. 07/03/1960, Kalamazoo, MI
training: Calvin Theological Seminary, MDiv, 1990
ordained: 1992
charges: First, Sioux Falls, SD, 1992-96; Calvin, McBain, MI, 1996-

Koning, Lee Allen
b. 03/07/1947, Muskegon, MI
training: Calvin Theological Seminary, BD, 1973
ordained: 1973
charges: Plymouth Heights, Grand Rapids, MI, 1973-76; Fuller Ave., Grand Rapids, MI, 1976-86; Leave, 1986-87; Faith, Elmhurst, IL, 1987-

Konynenbelt, Marvin
b. 09/19/1939, Nyverdal, Overijsel, Netherlands
training: Calvin Theological Seminary, ThB, 1965
ordained: 1965
charges: Chaplain, United States Army, 1965-93; Training/Sabbatical for AAPC Accreditation, 1993-96
retired: 1996

Kooger, Herman Charles
b. 06/15/1957, Lindsay, ON
training: Trenton University, MA, 1984; Calvin Theological Seminary, MDiv, 1987
ordained: 1988
charges: Second, Wellsburg, IA, 1988-92; Calvary Community, Redding, CA, 1992-94; Leave, 1994-95; Community, Frankfort, ON, 1995-2000; Leave, 2000-01; Sonlight Community, Regina, SK, 2001-

Kooienga, William Howard
b. 07/15/1936, Kent County, MI
training: Westminster Theological Seminary-PA, BD, 1962; Calvin Theological Seminary, Special Program for Ministerial Candidacy, 1963; Westminster Theological Seminary-CA, DMin, 1987
ordained: 1963
charges: Clara City, MN, 1963-67; Faith Community, Wyckoff, NJ, 1967-80; First, Crown Point, IN, 1980-94; First, Thunder Bay, ON, 1994-2001
retired: 2001

Kooistra, Elbert (Eeltje)
b. 02/14/1891, Tzummarum, Friesland, Netherlands
training: Calvin Theological Seminary, diploma, 1921
ordained: 1921
charges: Austinville, IA, 1921-26; Bethany, South Holland, IL, 1926-30; Midland Park, NJ, 1930-41; Eastern home missionary at Ridgewood, NJ, 1941-44; Oak Park, IL, 1944-52; Fruitland, ON, 1952-56; Newton, NJ, 1956-60
retired: 1960
d. 03/20/1995, Jenison, MI

Kooistra, Hessel
b. 05/05/1901, Lamont, MI
training: Calvin Theological Seminary, ThB, 1938
ordained: 1938
charges: Des Plaines, IL, 1938-43; Beaverdam, MI, 1943-53; Bethel, Sun Valley, CA, 1953-60
retired: 1960
d. 01/17/1991, San Juan Capistrano, CA

Kooistra, Remkes
b. 05/22/1917, Wijk aan Zee, Noord Holland, Netherlands
training: Theologische Universiteit, Kampen, diploma; Vrije Universiteit, Amsterdam
ordained: 1943
charges: GKN: Siegerswoude, 1943-47; Hengelo, 1947-51; The Hague, 1951-55; CRC: Red Deer, AB, 1955-60; Trenton, ON, 1960-64; First, Toronto, ON, 1964-73; Campus minister, Wilfrid Laurier Univ. and Univ. of Waterloo, ON, 1973-82
retired: 1982

Kool, David John
b. 10/13/1956, Battle Creek, MI
training: Calvin Theological Seminary, MDiv, 1987
ordained: 1987
charges: Missionary, Nigeria, 1987-88; Church Relations administration, CRWRC, Grand Rapids, MI, 1988-90; Personnel Coordinator, CRWRC,

Grand Rapids, MI, 1990–92; River Terrace Church, East Lansing, MI, 1992–93; RCA: Christ Memorial, Holland, MI, 1993–98; Crosswinds Ministries, Saugatuck, MI, 1999–

Kool, Ronald Glenn
b. 03/17/1963, Battle Creek, MI
training: Calvin Theological Seminary, MDiv, 1990
ordained: 1990
charges: Hillside Community, Cutlerville, MI, 1990–

Koole, John M.V.
b. 01/18/1935, Allendale, MI
training: Calvin Theological Seminary, BD, 1960
ordained: 1970
charges: Maranatha, Cambridge, ON, 1970–78; Ebenezer, Trenton, ON, 1978–87; Ingersoll, ON, 1987–95
retired: 1995

Koolhaas, Abram William
b. 05/26/1923, Inwood, IA
training: Calvin Theological Seminary, BD, 1959
ordained: 1961
charges: Bejou, MN, 1961–64; Decatur, MI, 1964–69; Missionary, Bethel, Shiprock, NM, 1969–89
retired: 1989
d. 03/08/1995, Shiprock, NM

Koopman, James Irwin
b. 04/16/1960, Grand Rapids, MI
training: Calvin Theological Seminary, MDiv, 1986
ordained: 1987
charges: CRC: Christ's Fellowship, Austin, TX, 1986–87; Sunrise Community, Austin, TX, 1987–97; Chapel of the Hills, Austin, TX, 1997–98; Independent: Chapel of the Hills, Austin, TX, 1998

Koopmans, Hendrik Ruine
b. 07/10/1824, De Wijk, Drenthe, Netherlands
training: with Frederik Alberts Kok, 1850
ordained: 1850
charges: GKN: Noordeloos, 1850–51; Sleeuwijk, 1851–60; Pernis, 1860–64; Gameren, 1864–65; RCA: Low Prairie, IL, 1865–67; High Prairie, IL, 1870–77; Sixth, Paterson, NJ, 1879–84; CRC: First, Pella, IA, 1867–69
d. 06/24/1884, Paterson, NJ

Koopmans, John
b. 01/08/1927, Jutrijp, Friesland, Netherlands
training: Calvin Theological Seminary, BD, 1958; California Graduate School of Theology, ThD, 1976
ordained: 1958

charges: Aylmer, ON, 1958–61; Bethel, Brockville, ON, 1961–66; Sussex, NJ, 1966–73; Rehoboth, Bellflower, CA, 1973–81; Southern California, Harbor and Seafarers Ministry, 1981–92
retired: 1992

Koopmans, Richard Charles
b. 10/18/1954, Smithers, BC
training: Calvin Theological Seminary, MDiv, 2000
ordained: 2000
charges: Prince George, BC, 2000–

Koopmans, S. George
training: Mid-America Reformed Seminary, MDiv
ordained: 2000
charges: Luverne, MN, 2000–

Koopmans, William Thys
b. 01/11/1959, Smithers, BC
training: Calvin Theological Seminary, MDiv, 1984, ThM, 1985; Theologische Universiteit, Kampen, ThD, 1990
ordained: 1990
charges: Orangeville, ON, 1990–95; Cephas, Peterborough, ON, 1995–

Koops, Hugh Allen
b. 02/07/1932, Allegan County, MI
training: Calvin Theological Seminary, BD, 1956; University of Chicago Divinity School, PhD, 1972
ordained: 1956
charges: CRC: Home missionary, Champaign-Urbana, IL, 1956–60; Faculty, Western Theological Seminary, 1963–70; RCA: Faculty, New Brunswick Theological Seminary, 1970–91
retired: 1991

Koops, Ralph
b. 01/19/1937, Beilen, Drenthe, Netherlands
training: Calvin Theological Seminary, BD, 1977
ordained: 1967
charges: Iron Springs, AB, 1967–71; Grace, Chatham, ON, 1971–83; Maranatha, Cambridge, ON, 1983–2002
retired: 2002

Kooreman, Jack
b. 02/17/1956, Ridgewood, NJ
training: Calvin Theological Seminary, MDiv, 2000
ordained: 2001
charges: Church of the Servant, Grand Rapids, MI, 2000–

Koornneef, Robert
b. 07/16/1940, Pynacker, Zuid Holland, Netherlands
training: Calvin Theological Seminary, BD, 1973
ordained: 1973
charges: Missionary, Oakwood, Belding, MI, 1973-76; Bellingham, WA, 1976-89; Leave, 1989; Chaplain, Hospice, Grand Rapids, MI, 1989-97; Calvin, Grand Rapids, MI, 1997-

Kooy, Michael John
b. 09/26/1956, Hammond, IN
training: Calvin Theological Seminary, MDiv, 1984
ordained: 1985
charges: Leighton, IA, 1985-91; First, Mount Vernon, WA, 1991-

Koppendrayer, Arlan Willis
b. 10/15/1958, Princeton, MN
training: Calvin Theological Seminary, MDiv, 1989
ordained: 1989
charges: West Leonard, Grand Rapids, MI, 1989-93; Leave, 1993-95; Zion, Oshawa, ON, 1995-99; Hope Fellowship, Oshawa, ON, 1999-2002

Korenstra, Joel Craig
b. 07/04/1960, Goshen, IN
training: Reformed Bible College, BRE, 1985; Calvin Theological Seminary, MDiv, 1993
ordained: 1998
charges: Interim pastor, Three Rivers, MI, 1997; Faculty, Kalamazoo Christian High School, Kalamazoo, MI, 1998-99; First, Sheboygan, WI, 1999-2000; Non-ministerial vocation, 2000

Korf, Louis Martin
b. 04/03/1951, Monroe, WA
training: Reformed Bible College, BRE, 1975; Reformed Theological Seminary, MSE, 1979; Calvin Theological Seminary, MDiv, 1986
ordained: 1987
charges: Assistant to the pastor, East Leonard, Grand Rapids, MI, 1985-86; Aetna, MI, 1986-95; Sumas, WA, 1995-2000; Clinical pastoral education resident, Legacy Emanuel Hospital, Portland, OR, 2000-2002; Chaplain, St. John Medical Center, Longview, WA, 2002-

Kort, Arthur H.
b. 04/01/1893, Ooster Hoogeburg, Groningen, Netherlands
training: Calvin Theological Seminary, BD, 1927
ordained: 1927
charges: Lebanon, IA, 1927-34; Hoboken, NJ, 1934-44

d. 03/10/1944, Hoboken, NJ

Kortenhoven, Paul
b. 05/22/1942, Chicago, IL
training: Calvin Theological Seminary, BD, 1972
ordained: 1972
charges: Missionary to Nigeria, 1972-75; Bible teacher, Millbrook Christian School, Grand Rapids, MI, 1975-77; Missionary, Community, St. Cloud, MN, 1977-80; Missionary, Sierra Leone, 1980-

Korver, Curtis Dwight
b. 04/25/1967, Red Deer, AB
training: Calvin Theological Seminary, MDiv, 1994
ordained: 1995
charges: Second, Abbotsford, BC, 1995-2001; Covenant, Calgary, AB, 2001-

Kosten, Peter
b. 12/02/1845, Heinkenszand, Zeeland, Netherlands
training: Calvin Theological Seminary, diploma, 1884
ordained: 1884
charges: Oostburg, WI, 1884-89; Third, Muskegon, MI, 1889-92; Passaic, NJ, 1892-97; Alto, WI, 1897-98; Fourth, Paterson, NJ, 1898-1904; Borculo, MI, 1904-07; West Sayville, NY, 1907-12
retired: 1912
d. 11/13/1938, Zeeland, MI

Kosten, William
b. 04/25/1930, Grand Rapids, MI
training: Calvin Theological Seminary, BD, 1955; Westminster Theological Seminary-PA, ThM, 1960
ordained: 1955
charges: Chaplain, United States Navy, 1955-58; Leave, 1958-60; Missionary to Taiwan, 1960-75; Pompton Plains, NJ, 1975-83; Reeman, MI, 1983-92
retired: 1992; affiliated with United Reformed Churches, 1998

Koster, John
see: Koster, Koendert J.

Koster, Koendert (John) J.
b. 02/05/1950, Hoogeveen, Drenthe, Netherlands
training: Reformed Theological College, Geelong, Australia, LTh, 1976; BD, 1982
ordained: 1978
charges: Reformed Church of Australia: Hobart, Tasmania, 1978-80; Blacktown, NSW, 1980-83;

Missionary to Indonesia, 1983–90; Study leave, 1990–94; CRC: First, Richmond, BC, 1994–

Koster, Phillip Jack
b. 02/20/1942, Grand Rapids, MI
training: Calvin Theological Seminary, BD, 1968
ordained: 1968
charges: CRC: Green Ridge, Muskegon, MI, 1968–72; Ebenezer, Leota, MN, 1972–73; Leave, 1973–75; Chaplain-Resident, Indiana University Medical Center, Indianapolis, IN, 1975–78; Chaplain, Pontiac (MI) General Hospital, 1978–91; Chaplain, Poudre Valley Hospital, Fort Collins, CO, 1991–99; Resigned from denomination, 1999

Koster, Samuel (Sipko) J.
b. 04/25/1867, Joure, Friesland, Netherlands
training: Calvin Theological Seminary, diploma, 1892
ordained: 1892
charges: CRC: Kelloggsville, MI, 1892–93; Second, Kalamazoo, MI, 1893–96; RCA: Stated supply, Middleburg, IA, 1897–98; Middleburg, IA, 1898–1900; Hull, IA, 1900–05; DeMotte, IN, 1908–11; Ebenezer, Morrison, IL, 1911–16; Firth, NE, 1918–25; Second, Little Rock, IA, 1925–29; Sibley, IA, 1929–32
retired: 1932
d. 12/28/1942, Loveland, CO

Koster, Timothy Lee
b. 01/16/1961, Grand Rapids, MI
training: Calvin Theological Seminary, MDiv, 1986
ordained: 1987
charges: Parkersburg, IA, 1987–92; Christ's Fellowship, Springfield, IL, 1992–94; Good Shepherd, Flushing, MI, 1994–2001; Emmanuel, Sauk Village, IL, 2001–

Kotman, Loren Jon
b. 08/13/1956, Holland, MI
training: Calvin Theological Seminary, MDiv, 1986
ordained: 1988
charges: Holland, IA, 1988–90; Fresno, CA, 1990–99; Milwood, Kalamazoo, MI, 1999–

Kotzebue, David Lightner
b. 01/03/1950, Alexandria, NC
training: Calvin Theological Seminary, MDiv, 1990
ordained: 1990
charges: Bellingham, WA, 1990–93; Non-ministerial vocation, 1993

Kraker, Roger Hugh
b. 11/10/1948, Grand Haven, MI

training: Calvin Theological Seminary, MDiv, 1980
ordained: 1980
charges: Missionary, Sierra Leone, 1980–85; Missionary, Liberia, 1985–90; Missionary, Sierra Leone, 1990–98; Eligible for call, 1998–99; Chaplain Resident, Pacific Health Ministries, Honolulu, HI, 1999–2002; E.R. Chaplain, Aurora Health Care, St. Luke's Hospital, Milwaukee, WI, 2002–

Kramer, George
b. 02/06/1872, Forreston, IL
training: Dubuque Presbyterian Seminary, diploma, 1899
ordained: 1898
charges: PCUSA: three churches (including Rudd, IA and Kamrar, IA), 1898–1908; CRC: Woden, IA, 1908–12; RCA: Missionary in Classis Pleasant Prairie, 1912–16; Missionary in Classis Germania, 1916–22; Bristow, IA, 1922–28; Special pastor at Sibley, IA, 1928–30; at Ackley, IA, 1931–39; at Aplington, IA, 1940–44; at Sully, IA, 1945–54
retired: 1954
d. 02/12/1955, Austinville, IA

Kramer, Gerald Lee
b. 07/29/1943, Orange City, IA
training: Calvin Theological Seminary, BD, 1967; MDiv, 1975
ordained: 1967
charges: CRC: Brooten, MN, 1967–70; Faith, New Brighton, MN, 1970–74; Harderwyk, Holland, MI, 1974–76; PCUSA: West Allis, WI, 1976

Kramer, Roger Dale
b. 11/01/1943, Sault Ste. Marie, MI
training: Calvin Theological Seminary, BD, 1968; ThM, 1981
ordained: 1968
charges: Missionary, Quincy, WA, 1968–71; South Bend, IN, 1971–81; Arcadia, CA, 1981–95; Calvary, Bloomington, MN, 1995–

Kramer, Siebert
b. 01/15/1912, Grand Rapids, MI
training: Calvin Theological Seminary, ThB, 1941
ordained: 1941
charges: Rudyard, MI, 1941–44; South Olive, MI, 1944–49; First, Edgerton, MN, 1949–54; Bethany, South Holland, IL, 1954–60; East Cutlerville, MI, 1960–69; Faith, Pella, IA, 1969–77
retired: 1977
d. 03/07/2000, Grand Rapids, MI

Kranenburg, Henry Peter
b. 04/30/1960, Athens, ON

training: Calvin Theological Seminary, MDiv, 1987
ordained: 1987
charges: Bethel, Brockville, ON, 1987-2000; Immanuel, Hamilton, ON, 2000-

Kranenburg, Pieter
b. 11/07/1929, Leiden, Zuid Holland, Netherlands
training: Calvin Theological Seminary, BD, 1957
ordained: 1957
charges: Athens, ON, 1957-60; Springdale, ON, 1960-63; Jarvis, ON 1963-66; Red Deer, AB, 1966-70; Ladner, BC, 1970-74; East, Strathroy, ON, 1974-79; Second, Toronto, ON, 1979-84; Grace, Chatham, ON, 1984-86; Chaplain, Queen Elizabeth Hospital, Toronto, ON, 1988-94
retired: 1994

Kremer, John (Jan)
b. 02/02/1832, Enumatil, Groningen, Netherlands
training: Theologische Universiteit, Kampen, diploma, 1865
ordained: 1865
charges: GKN: Schildwolde, 1865-69; Wanswerd, 1869-77; CRC: First, Grand Rapids, MI, 1877-79; RCA: South Holland, IL, 1879-83; First, Zeeland, MI, 1883-92; Detroit, MI, 1892-1902
retired: 1902
d. 07/19/1907, Detroit, MI

Kress, Arnold Slausen
b. 12/17/1937, Albany, NY
training: Westminster Theological Seminary-PA, BD, 1958; Calvin Theological Seminary, Special Program for Ministerial Candidacy, 1978
ordained: 1959
charges: Orthodox Presbyterian Church: Nashua, Edinburg, PA, 1959-66; Missionary, Japan, 1966-75; CRC: Missionary, Japan, 1978-92; Director, Peniel Bible Conference, Lake Luzerne, NY and Interim pastor, Reformed Church, Buskirk, NY, 1992-94; RCA: Hope Reformed, Grand Rapids, MI, 1975-76; Buskirk, NY, 1994

Kreulen, Klaas
b. 05/15/1833, Nieuwleusen, Overijsel, Netherlands
training: with Wolter Alberts Kok; Theologische Universiteit Kampen, diploma, 1861
ordained: 1861
charges: GKN: Putten, 1861-64; Giessendam, 1864-66; Zierikzee, 1866-69; exhorter, Nieuwleusen, 1887-89; Gereformerde Kerk onder het Kruis: Wissekerke, 1869-87; Independent: Burdick Street, Kalamazoo, MI, 1889-92; CRC: Burdick Street, Kalamazoo, MI, 1892-93; North

Street, Zeeland, MI, 1893-98; Noordeloos, MI, 1898-1900
retired: 1900
d. 06/15/1901, Kalamazoo, MI

Kroeze, Gloria D.
b. 08/19/1950, Holland, MI
training: Calvin Theological Seminary, MAEM, 1998
ordained: 2002
charges: Chaplain, Spectrum Health, Grand Rapids, MI, 2002-

Kroeze, Hendrik Willem
b. 10/05/1908, Middelburg, Zeeland, Netherlands
training: Theologische Universiteit, Kampen, diploma, 1934
ordained: 1934
charges: GKN: Curacao, Dutch West Indies, 1934-47; Middelstum, 1947-51; Oenkerk, 1951-53; CRC: Mississauga, ON, 1953-62; Kitchener, ON, 1962-67; Blyth, ON, 1967-73
retired: 1973
d. 10/09/1982, Hamilton, ON

Krohne, Ebo Jan
b. 02/13/1873, Winschoten, Groningen, Netherlands
training: Calvin Theological Seminary, diploma, 1903
ordained: 1903
charges: Fulton, IL, 1903-09; First, Paterson, NJ, 1909-12; Borculo, MI, 1912-21; Hudsonville, MI, 1921-43
d. 01/17/1943, Hudsonville, MI

Kromminga, Carl Gerhard Sr.
b. 02/12/1925, Peoria, IA
training: Calvin Theological Seminary, ThB, 1948; MDiv, 1981; Vrije Universiteit, Amsterdam, ThD, 1964
ordained: 1948
charges: Lodi, NJ, 1948-51; Harderwyk, Holland, MI, 1951-53; studying in Netherlands, 1953-54; Faculty, Calvin Theological Seminary, Grand Rapids, MI, 1954-90
retired: 1990

Kromminga, Carl Gerhard Jr.
b. 01/14/1952, Holland, MI
training: Calvin Theological Seminary, MDiv, 1978
ordained: 1978
charges: Pullman, Chicago, IL, 1978-86; Trinity Oaks Community, Arlington, TX, 1987-93; New City, Long Beach, CA, 1993-

Kromminga, David Henry
b. 09/19/1960, Grand Rapids, MI
training: Calvin Theological Seminary, MDiv, 1987
ordained: 1988
charges: All Nations, Halifax, NS, 1988-2000; Sherman Street, Grand Rapids, MI, 2000-

Kromminga, Diedrich H.
b. 10/20/1879, Oldersum, Ostfriesland, Germany
training: Mission House, Sheboygan, WI; Old Christian Reformed Church, 1899; Calvin Theological Seminary, diploma, 1906; Princeton Seminary, 1907
ordained: 1907
charges: Home missionary at Parkersburg, IA, 1907-08; at Bunde, MN, 1908-11; Lafayette, IN, 1911-14; Ackley, IA, 1914-16; Faculty, Grundy College, Grundy Center, IA, 1916-22; Peoria, IL, 1922-26; Neland Ave., Grand Rapids, MI, 1926-28; Faculty, Calvin Theological Seminary, Grand Rapids, MI, 1928-47
d. 05/19/1947, Grand Rapids, MI

Kromminga, John Henry
b. 08/25/1918, Grundy Center, IA
training: Calvin Theological Seminary, ThB, 1942; Princeton Theological Seminary, ThD, 1948; Cambridge University
ordained: 1943
charges: Newton, NJ, 1943-46; Des Plaines, IL, 1946-49; First, Grand Haven, MI, 1949-52; Faculty, Calvin Theological Seminary, (President, 1956-83)1952-83
retired: 1983
d. 03/03/1994, Grand Rapids, MI

Kroon, John
b. 07/18/1932, Sismore, MN
training: Calvin Theological Seminary, BD, 1958
ordained: 1958
charges: Ogilvie, MN, 1958-62; Calvary, Seattle, WA, 1962-67; Hull, ND, 1967-72; Lebanon, IA, 1972-80; Alto, WI, 1980-91; Holland, IA, 1991-94; Bemis, SD, 1994-97
retired: 1997
d. 08/31/2001, Sioux Falls, SD

Kruis, Daniel John
b. 12/12/1952, Rehoboth, NM
training: Calvin Theological Seminary, MDiv, 1984
ordained: 1984
charges: Immanuel, Salt Lake City, UT, 1984-90; Church planting, West Valley, Salt Lake City, UT, 1990-91; Rehoboth Christian School, Rehoboth, NM, 1991-92; Path of Renewal Recovery Center,

Fort Wingate, NM, 1992-93; Trinity, Anchorage, AK, 1993-98; Eligible for call, 1998-99; Church planting, Gallup, NM, 1999-2000; released from ministry, 2000

Kruis, John Gerrit
b. 04/04/1923, Kent County, MI
training: Calvin Theological Seminary, BD, 1959
ordained: 1959
charges: Peers, AB, 1959-62; Hills, MN, 1962-66; Niekerk, Holland, MI, 1966-73; Sussex, NJ, 1973-83; Leave, 1983-84; Pastoral counselor, Jenison, MI, 1984-88
retired: 1988; affiliated with United Reformed Churches, 1995

Kruis, Stanley Dale
b. 08/29/1955, Bozeman, MT
training: Calvin Theological Seminary, MDiv, 1984
ordained: 1986
charges: Missionary, Philippines, 1986-

Kruithof, John Cornelius
b. 11/19/1898, Almelo, Overijsel, Netherlands
training: Calvin Theological Seminary, BD, 1926
ordained: 1926
charges: McBain, MI, 1926-29
d. 08/29/1929, McBain, MI

Kuiken, Richard Jay
b. 10/24/1955, Paterson, NJ
training: Calvin Theological Seminary, MDiv, 1983
ordained: 1983
charges: CRC: Pompton Plains, NJ, 1983-91; Alliance of Reformed Churches: Reformed Bible Church, Pompton Plains, NJ, 1991-95; United Reformed Churches: Reformed Bible Church, Pompton Plains, NJ, 1995-

Kuiken, Russell John
b. 01/17/1960, Pequannock, NJ
training: Calvin Theological Seminary, MDiv, 1991
ordained: 1992
charges: Immanuel, Wappingers Falls, NY, 1992-94
retired: 1995

Kuiper, Aldon Lee
b. 04/14/1945, Melvin, IA
training: Calvin Theological Seminary, BD, 1971
ordained: 1971
charges: Terra Ceia, NC, 1971-76; Immanuel, Salt Lake City, UT, 1976-81; Cedar Falls, IA, 1981-87; Hope, Hull, IA, 1987-99; Des Moines, IA, 1999-

Kuiper, Daniel Royce

b. 10/08/1953, Grand Rapids, MI
training: Calvin Theological Seminary, MDiv, 1980
ordained: 1981
charges: Missionary to Latin America, Mexico, 1981–83; Leave, 1983–84; Missionary to Mexico, 1984–93; Faculty, Grand Rapids Christian High School, Grand Rapids, MI, 1993–99; Amistad Cristiana, Sioux Center, IA, 1999–2002; Church developer, CRWM, 2002–

Kuiper, Henry J.

b. 12/22/1885, Grand Rapids, MI
training: Calvin Theological Seminary, diploma, 1907
ordained: 1907
charges: Luctor, KS, 1907–10 and Prairie View, KS, 1909–10; Prospect Park, Holland, MI, 1910–13; Second Englewood, Chicago, IL, 1913–19; Broadway Ave., Grand Rapids, MI, 1919–29; Neland Ave., Grand Rapids, MI, 1929–44; *Banner* editor, 1944–56
retired: 1956
d. 12/12/1962, Grand Rapids, MI

Kuiper, Herman

b. 12/18/1889, Garrelsweer, Groningen, Netherlands
training: Calvin Theological Seminary, diploma, 1913; Princeton Seminary, 1915; Vrije Universiteit, Amsterdam, ThD, 1928
ordained: 1915
charges: Rock Valley, IA, 1915–23; Oakdale Park, Grand Rapids, MI, 1923–25; Fourth Roseland, Chicago, IL, 1928–44; Rock Valley, IA, 1944–51; Second, Redlands, CA, 1951–53; Faculty, Calvin Theological Seminary, 1953–58
retired: 1958
d. 01/13/1963, Grand Rapids, MI

Kuiper, Klaas

b. 06/15/1841, Dwingeloo, Drenthe, Netherlands
training: Theologische Universiteit, Kampen, diploma, 1876
ordained: 1876
charges: GKN: Oud Loosdrecht, 1876–79; Ferwerd, 1879–85; Garrelsweer, 1885–91; CRC: First, Grand Haven, MI, 1891–96; Second Roseland, Chicago, IL, 1896–1911; Niekerk, Holland, MI, 1911–19
retired: 1919
d. 03/08/1921, Holland, MN

Kuiper, Leslie Jay

b. 07/20/1947, Primghar, IA

training: Calvin Theological Seminary, BD, 1972
ordained: 1973
charges: Colton, SD, 1973–76; First, Wellsburg, IA, 1976–81; Overisel, MI, 1981–88; First, Oostburg, WI, 1988–

Kuiper, Rienk Bouke

b. 01/31/1886, Garrelsweer, Groningen, Netherlands
training: Calvin Theological Seminary, diploma, 1911; Princeton Theological Seminary, ThB, 1912
ordained: 1912
charges: CRC: Overisel, MI, 1912–14; West Leonard, Grand Rapids, MI, 1914–17; Sherman St., Grand Rapids, MI, 1917–23; LaGrave Ave., Grand Rapids, MI, 1925–29; President, Calvin College, 1930–33; President Calvin Theological Seminary, 1952–56; RCA: Second, Kalamazoo, MI, 1923–25; OPC: Faculty, Westminster Theological Seminary, 1929–30, 1933–52
retired: 1956
d. 04/22/1966, Grand Rapids, MI

Kuiper, Roelof Times

b. 05/02/1826, Diever, Drenthe, Netherlands
training: with Wolter Alberts Kok
ordained: 1850
charges: GKN: Dalfsen, 1950–53; Wildervank 1853–79; CRC: Graafschap, MI, 1879–89; South Holland, IL, 1889–94
d. 12/31/1894, South Holland, IL

Kuipers, Cornelius

b. 11/22/1898, Orange City, IA
training: declared eligible on the basis of exceptional gifts, 1950
ordained: 1950
charges: Lay missionary: Zuni, NM, 1927–50 (Canyonci Navajos part-time, 1932–39); Intermountain ordained: Zuni, NM, 1950–54; Brigham City, UT, 1954–64
retired: 1964
d. 10/28/1989, Glendale, AZ

Kuipers, Jake

b. 04/24/1949, Heerenveen, Friesland, Netherlands
training: Calvin Theological Seminary, MDiv, 1977
ordained: 1977
charges: Bethany, Bloomfield, ON, 1977–81; Immanuel, Brampton, ON, 1981–89; First, Sarnia, ON, 1989–2000; Ebenezer, Trenton, ON, 2000–

Kuipers, William

b. 12/02/1884, Leeuwarden, Friesland, Netherlands
training: Calvin Theological Seminary, diploma, 1914
ordained: 1914
charges: Second, Fremont, MI, 1914-19; Oakland, MI, 1919-23; Dennis Ave., Grand Rapids, MI, 1923-27; Summer St., Passaic, NJ, 1927-33
d. 12/15/1933, Passaic, NJ

Kuizema, Harmon John

b. 10/10/1908, Grand Rapids, MI
training: Calvin Theological Seminary, ThB, 1934
ordained: 1935
charges: Stated supply, Oostfriesland, IA, 1934-35; Woden, IA, 1935-43; Prairie City, IA, 1943-49; Oakland, MI, 1949-63; Portland, MI, 1963-73
retired: 1973
d. 06/15/1998, Grand Rapids, MI

Kunst, John (Jan) Gerrit

b. 08/13/1932, Deventer, Overijsel, Netherlands
training: Calvin Theological Seminary, BD, 1958
ordained: 1958
charges: CRC: Galt, ON, 1958-61; John Calvin, Truro, NS, 1961-65; Langley, BC, 1965-68; GKN: Gouda, 1968-84; Missionary, South Africa, 1984-93
retired: 1993

Kuntz, Jacob

b. 02/13/1926, Assen, Drenthe, Netherlands
training: Vrije Universiteit, Amsterdam, diploma, 1951
ordained: 1951
charges: GKN: Tzum, 1951-54; Schoonebeek, 1954-56; Army chaplain, 1956-58; CRC: Orillia, ON, 1958-62; Owen Sound, ON, 1962-65; First, New Westminster, BC, 1965-72; Maranatha, St. Catharines, ON, 1972-76; Covenant, St. Catharines, ON, 1976-83; First, Kitchener, ON, 1983-91
retired: 1991

Kuperus, Harry

b. 11/03/1939, Netherlands
training: Calvin Theological Seminary, BD, 1973
ordained: 1974
charges: Kentville, NS, 1974-78; Director, Indian and Metis Christian Fellowship, Regina, SK, 1978-92; Special Pastoral Education, Resident Chaplain, Royal Alexandra Hospital, Edmonton, AB, 1992-93; Chaplain, Mewburn Veteran's Center, Edmonton, AB, 1993-

Kuperus, Timothy A.

b. 05/04/1971, Grand Rapids, MI
training: Westminster Theological Seminary-CA, MDiv, 1995; Calvin Theological Seminary, Special Program for Ministerial Candidacy, 1998
ordained: 1998
charges: Evangelism/Youth, Second, Byron Center, MI, 1996-97; Second, Byron Center, MI, 1998-

Kuurstra, William John

b. 05/29/1956, Hamilton, ON
training: Calvin Theological Seminary, MDiv, 1983
ordained: 1983
charges: Tillsonburg, ON, 1983-88; First, Montreal, QC, 1988-95; East City Community, Orleans (Ottawa), ON, 1995-

Kuyvenhoven, Andrew

b. 03/24/1927, Den Haag, Zuid Holland, Netherlands
training: Calvin Theological Seminary, BD, 1957; Princeton Theological Seminary, MDiv, 1958; Theologische Universiteit, Kampen, Drs, 1963
ordained: 1958
charges: Lethbridge, AB, 1958-64; First, Hamilton, ON, 1964-70; Wallaceburg, ON, 1970-72; Director of education, Board of Publications, 1972-76; Clarkson, Mississauga, ON, 1976-79; Editor of *The Banner,* Grand Rapids, MI, 1979-89; Bethel, Waterdown, ON, 1989-92
retired: 1992

Kuyvenhoven, Leonard Andrew

b. 02/05/1965, Hamilton, ON
training: Calvin Theological Seminary, MDiv, 1998
ordained: 1998
charges: Ridgewood, NJ, 1998-2002; Neland Ave., Grand Rapids, MI, 2002-

Kwantes, Dick J.

b. 04/08/1935, Andijk, Noord Holland, Netherlands
training: Calvin Theological Seminary, BD, 1963
ordained: 1963
charges: Home missionary, High River, AB, 1963-66; Windsor, ON, 1966-68; Missionary to Japan, 1968-80; Missionary, Manila, Philippines. 1980-2000
retired: 2000

Kwantes, Harry John

b. 09/19/1930, Andijk, Noord Holland, Netherlands
training: Calvin Theological Seminary, BD, 1959
ordained: 1959
charges: Ingersoll, ON, 1959-66; Emden, Renville,

MN, 1966-71; Godwin Heights, Grand Rapids, MI, 1971-87; Leave, 1987-98
retired: 1999

Laarman, Edward John
b. 02/22/1949, Cadillac, MI
training: Calvin Theological Seminary, BD, 1978; University of Notre Dame, PhD, 1982
ordained: 1986
charges: Minister of education and witnessing, Calvin, Grand Rapids, MI, 1985-86; Calvin, Grand Rapids, MI, 1986-92; Covenant, Appleton, WI, 1992-

La Fleur, William Roger
b. 07/23/1936, Paterson, NJ
training: Calvin Theological Seminary, BD, 1962
ordained: 1962
charges: Missionary to Japan, 1962-69; Leave to University of Chicago, 1969-72; Non-ministerial vocation: higher education, 1972

Lagerwey, Donald William
b. 07/04/1941, Glendale, CA
training: Calvin Theological Seminary, BD, 1972
ordained: 1972
charges: Missionary to Mexico, 1972-78; Boise, ID, 1978-82; Calvary, Redding, CA, 1982-87; Oak Harbor, WA, 1987-96; Trinity Fellowship, San Diego, CA, 1996-

Lagerwey, Peter
b. 10/04/1924, Grand Rapids, MI
training: Calvin Theological Seminary, BD, 1953; ThB, 1954
ordained: 1954
charges: Holland Marsh, ON, 1954-59; Prosper, Falmouth, MI, 1959-63; Home missionary, East Grand Forks, ND, 1963-74; Lane Ave., Kansas City, MO, 1974-77
d. 03/04/1977, Kansas City, MO

La Grand, James Jr.
b. 04/24/1941, East Grand Rapids, MI
training: Calvin Theological Seminary, ThM, 1975
ordained: 1969
charges: Garfield, Chicago, IL, 1969-74; Leave, 1974-75; Centennial Missions Scholarship, 1975-76; All Nations, Halifax, NS, 1977-87; Leave, 1987-88; Eligible for call, 1988-91; teacher, Chicago Metropolitan Center, Chicago, IL, 1991-92; Faculty, Lutheran School of Theology, Chicago, IL, 1993; Beacon Light, Gary, IN, 1993-

Laird, Michael J.
b. 12/12/1973, Lowell, MA
training: Gordon-Conwell Theological Seminary, MDiv, 1999; Calvin Theological Seminary, Special Program for Ministerial Candidacy, 2000
ordained: 2001
charges: Church plant, Danvers, MA, 2001-

Lam, Paul Sau-wah
b. 04/05/1954, Hong Kong, China
training: declared eligible on the basis of exceptional gifts, 1992
ordained: 1992
charges: CRC: Zion Chinese, Abbotsford, BC, 1991-95; Leave, 1995-96; Asian Ministry, Vancouver, BC, 1996-98; Chinese Presbyterian Church, Victoria, BC, 1998-99; Presbyterian Church of Canada: Victoria, BC, 1999

Lamberts, Lambertus J.
b. 01/02/1881, Grand Rapids, MI
training: Calvin Theological Seminary, diploma, 1909
ordained: 1909
charges: Rochester, NY, 1909-14; East Saugatuck, MI, 1914-19; First, Fremont, MI, 1919-43; Delavan, WI, 1943-48
retired: 1948
d. 02/27/1949, Grand Rapids, MI

Lammers, Ronald John
b. 06/23/1944, Fond du Lac, WI
training: Calvin Theological Seminary, BD, 1970
ordained: 1970
charges: Britt, IA, 1970-77; Bigelow, MN, 1977-90; Asian-American, Bigelow, MN, 1990-2001; eligible for call, 2001-

Lammers, Warren Henry
b. 05/13/1949, Ripon, WI
training: Calvin Theological Seminary, MDiv, 1977
ordained: 1977
charges: Ellsworth, MI, 1977-81; Dutton, MI, 1981-88; Blyth, ON, 1989-92; Platte, SD, 1992-98; Second, Kalamazoo, MI, 1998-

Lamsma, Henry
b. 11/11/1943, Amsterdam, Noord Holland, Netherlands
training: Calvin Theological Seminary, BD, 1971; ThM, 1978
ordained: 1971
charges: Parkersburg, IA, 1971-76; Bethel, Edgerton, MN, 1976-85; Trinity, Vancouver, WA, 1985-91; Kedvale Ave., Oak Lawn, IL, 1991-92

d. 12/31/1992, Maywood, IL

Lamsma, John Hielke
b. 02/02/1946, Haarlem, Noord Holland, Netherlands
training: Calvin Theological Seminary, BD, 1972; MDiv, 1977; ThM, 1978
ordained: 1972
charges: First, Kemptville, ON, 1972–76; Graduate studies and Clinical Pastorate Education, Pine Rest Christian Hospital, Cutlerville, MI, 1976–77; Leave, 1977–78; Chaplain, Federal Correctional Institution, Milan, MI, 1978–89; Chaplain, Federal Correctional Institution, Sheridan, OR, 1989–92; Chaplain, Federal Correctional Institution, Florence, CO, 1992–99; Assistant Chaplaincy Administrator, Fed. Bureau Prison, Washington, DC, 1999–

Lanham, Christopher Brian
b. 03/22/1966, Fayetteville, NC
training: Calvin Theological Seminary, MDiv, 2001
ordained: 2001
charges: Cascades Fellowship, Jackson, MI 2001–

Lankheet, Randal Scott
b. 11/09/1958, Holland, MI
training: Calvin Theological Seminary, MDiv, 1984
ordained: 1985
charges: CRC: Jamestown, MI, 1985–89; Ontario, CA, 1989–98; United Reformed Churches: Ontario, CA, 1998

Lanning, Ray Burton
b. 06/16/1951, Wilmington, DE
training: Westminster Theological Seminary-PA, MDiv, 1977; Calvin Theological Seminary, Special Program for Ministerial Candidacy, 1982
ordained: 1977
charges: ARPC: Charlotte, NC, 1977–78; Home missionary, Grand Rapids, MI, 2002– ; PCA: Panama City, FL, 1978–80; Leave, 1980–82; CRC: Bethel, Grand Rapids, MI, 1982–87; Lamont, MI, 1987–93; Independent: Independent Reformed, Cutlerville, MI, 1993–95; United Reformed Churches: Cutlerville, MI, 1995–2001

Lapinsky, Terry Joseph
b. 06/08/1939, Grand Rapids, MI
training: Calvin Theological Seminary, BD, 1972
ordained: 1972
charges: Kelloggsville, MI, 1972–77; Providence, Holland, MI, 1977–84; Trinity, North Haledon, NJ, 1984–86; Covenant, North Haledon, NJ, 1986–96; Jamestown, MI, 1996–2002

d. 10/11/2002, Hudsonville, MI

Lau, George J.
b. 06/03/1927, Gilbert Islands
training: Fuller Theological Seminary, BD, 1958; Calvin Theological Seminary, 1968
ordained: 1963
charges: Home missionary, Crenshaw, Los Angeles, CA, 1963–66; Leave, 1966–69; Non-ministerial vocation, 1969

Lau, Larry Kin-Wal
b. 04/12/1952, Hong Kong, China
training: Tyndale Seminary, MTS, 1983; Calvin Theological Seminary, Special Program for Ministerial Candidacy, 1990
ordained: 1990
charges: Toronto Chinese Christian and Missionary Alliance Church, 1983–85; Chinese Presbyterian, Windsor, ON, 1985–90; Grace Chinese, Scarborough, ON, 1990–92; Bible College, Texas, 1992–94; Leave, 1994–97; Resigned from denomination, 1997

Le, Matthew Mihn
b. 08/03/1956, Danang, Vietnam
training: Reformed Bible College, BRE, 1989; Azusa Pacific Seminary, MDiv, 1992
ordained: 1993
charges: Fellowship, Tustin, CA, 1993–94; Little Saigon, Westminster, CA, 1994–

Le, Vinh Paul
b. 06/20/1959
training: Reformed Bible College
ordained: 1994
charges: CRC: Faith and Action Vietnamese, Vancouver, BC, 1991–2002; Orthodox Presbyterian Church: Westminster, CA, 2002

Leder, Arie C.
b. 04/16/1946, Wassenaar, Zuid Holland, Netherlands
training: Calvin Theological Seminary, BD, 1973; ThM, 1982; Knox College, University of Toronto, ThD, 1992
ordained: 1973
charges: Trenton, ON, 1973–77; Missionary to Puerto Rico, 1977–82; Faculty, Seminary Evangelico Reformado, Rio Piedras, Puerto Rico, 1982–85; Leave, 1985–87; Faculty, Calvin Theological Seminary, Grand Rapids, MI, 1987–

Lee, Abraham Kei Wing
b. 12/10/1956, Hong Kong, China

training: Singapore Bible College, BTh, 1981; American School of Professional Psychology, PhD, 2000
ordained: 1984
charges: Singapore Assemblies of God: Chinese Christian Mission, Singapore and USA, 1984-99; CRC: Golden Gate, San Francisco, CA, 2000-

Lee, Abraham Sung Soo
b. 01/04/1966, Seoul, South Korea
training: International Theological Seminary, MDiv, 1997; Calvin Theological Seminary, ThM, 1999, Ethnic Minority Program for Ministerial Candidacy, 2000
ordained: 2000
charges: Missionary, Chiapas, Mexico, 2000-

Lee, Byoung Il
b. 07/19/1943, Kyonggi-Do Suwon-Shi, Korea
training: Union Theological Seminary, MDiv, 1992; Vision Theological Seminary, DD, 1996, DMin, 1997
ordained: 1994
charges: Urim, Laguna Nigel, CA, 1995-97; CRC: Urim, Laguna Nigel, CA, 1997-98; Orange County Calvary, Garden Grove, CA, 1999-

Lee, Byung Sun
b. 10/12/1941, Seoul, South Korea
training: Presbyterian General Assembly Theological Seminary, MDiv, 1972
ordained: 1983
charges: PCUSA: Gloria Church, 1985-92; Orange Korean United Church, 1993-99; CRC: Shema Presbyterian, Fullerton, CA, 1999-

Lee, Jae Dong
b. 01/04/1957, Taegu-Shi, South Korea
training: Presbyterian General Assembly Theological Seminary, MDiv, 1986; Faith Baptist Theological Seminary, MA, 1990; Trinity Theological Seminary, DA, 1992
ordained: 1987
charges: Dong San Presbyterian Church: Seoul, Korea, 1987-88; CRC: Korean, Ames, IA, 1988-93; East Bay Korean, El Cerrito, CA, 1995-2000
retired: 2000
d. 12/24/2001, Santa Cruz, CA

Lee, Jae Duk
b. 01/07/1963
training: Azusa Pacific University, MDiv, 1999
ordained: 1999
charges: Hannam Presbyterian Church: The Lord's Church of Love, Gardena, CA, 1999-2000;

CRC: The Lord's Church of Love, Gardena, CA, 2000-

Lee, James Joon Koo
b. 08/30/1948, South Korea
training: Faith Theological Seminary, MA, 1982; Seminary of Washington, MDiv, 1987
ordained: 1980
charges: Korean Presbyterian Churches: Holyland Church, Montgomery County, MD, 1981-83; Dae Kwang, Los Angeles, CA, 1983-84; RCA: Dae Kwang, Los Angeles, CA, 1984-91; Shepherd Korean, Hacienda, CA, 1991-99; CRC: Korean, Boca Raton, FL, 1999-

Lee, Jin-Tae John
b. 01/27/1931, Masan, Korea
training: Presbyterian General Assembly Theological Seminary, BD, 1962
ordained: 1977
charges: Orange Korean, Fullerton, CA, 1977-81; Hap Dong Presbyterian Seminary, Seoul, Korea, 1981-82; On loan to Asian Center, Seoul, Korea, 1982-84; Korean, Los Angeles, CA, 1984-89; Loaned to Hanmi Presbyterian, Los Angeles, CA and Faculty, International Theological Seminary, Fullerton, CA, 1986-89; President, Korean Seminary, Seoul, Korea, 1998-

Lee, Jong Un
b. 01/20/1935, Taegu-Shi, Korea
training: Yun Sae United Theological Seminary, diploma, 1975; Faith Theological Seminary, MA, 1987; Southern California Theological Seminary, ThM, 1991
ordained: 1991
charges: Orange Korean, Fullerton, CA, 1986-2000
retired: 2000

Lee, Jong Whan
b. 07/19/1952, Korea
training: Taehan Theological Seminary, ThB, 1981; Linda Vista Bible College, MDiv, 1986
ordained: 1982
charges: Presbyterian Church of Korea: 1982-93; CRC: Valley Shinil, Northridge, CA, 1993-95; Missionary pastor, Montreal, QC, 1995-98; withdrew from denomination

Lee, Jung Jae
b. 05/27/1937, Haman, Korea
training: Calvin Theological Seminary, MDiv, 1987
ordained: 1987
charges: CRC: Home missionary, Torrence, Los

Angeles, CA, 1987–89; Torrance, CA, 1989–93; Resigned from denomination, 1993

Lee, Ken Hachin
b. 05/28/1959, South Korea
training: Fuller Theological Seminary, MDiv, 1998; Calvin Theological Seminary, Special Program for Ministerial Candidacy, 1999
ordained: 1999
charges: Missionary, Japan, 1999–

Lee, Myung Jae
b. 10/08/1921, Korea
training: Faith Theological Seminary, DMin, 1982
ordained: 1951
charges: Milang Masan Church, Korea, 1946–49; Sinmasan Church, Korea, 1949–51; Sammin Presbyterian Church, 1951–53; Won Nam Church, Seoul, Korea, 1953–67; CRC: Korean, Chicago, IL, 1967–92
retired: 1992

Lee, Myung Soo
b. 01/25/1956, Daejun-Shi, Korea
training: Presbyterian General Assembly Theological Seminary, MDiv, 1985
ordained: 1986
charges: Hap-Dong, Bong Shin, 1987; Sung Ae, 1988–92; CRC: Yung Kwang, Las Vegas, NV, 1994–2001; Body of the Lord, Los Angeles, CA, 2001–

Lee, Paul Seung-Rim
b. 06/27/1959, Seoul, South Korea
training: Talbot School of Theology, MDiv, 1989; Calvin Theological Seminary, Special Program for Ministerial Candidacy, 1990
ordained: 1991
charges: Korean Church of Orange County, Buena Park, CA, 1991–93; Non-ministerial vocation, 1993

Lee, Peter
b. 07/11/1959
training: Los Angeles Christian University, MDiv, 1992
ordained: 1993
charges: On loan: Hanmi Presbyterian Church, Temple City, CA, 1993–95; Kwang-Myung, West Covina, CA, 1995–2000
retired: 2001

Lee, William K.
ordained: 1963
charges: Korean Presbyterian Church: Seoul,

1963–83; CRC: Suburban, Des Plaines, IL, 1983–85; released from denomination, 1985

Lee, Wondae
b. 02/20/1942, Kwang Ju Province, South Korea
training: Presbyterian General Assembly Theological Seminary, South Korea, 1974; Faith Theological Seminary, ThM, 1994
ordained: 1979
charges: Hapdong Presbyterian Church: Korean Church, Greenville, SC, 1979–80; PCA: Korean Saints, Philadelphia, PA, 1980–85; Inland Korean, Pomona, CA, 1985–91; Holy Mountain Korean, Aurora, CO, 1992–96; New Life Korean, Denver, CO, 1996–99; CRC: Korean Presbyterian Galilee Church, Denver, CO, 1999–

Lee, Woo Chun
b. 05/08/1947, Seoul, South Korea
training: Presbyterian Theological Seminary, MDiv, 1988; Calvin Theological Seminary, Special Program for Ministerial Candidacy, 1989
ordained: 1995
charges: Director of church education, Korean American of Orange County, Fountain Valley, CA, 1986–88; Hebron, Fife, WA, 1995–

Leegwater, Arie C.
b. 03/04/1930, Heerhugowaard, Noord Holland, Netherlands
training: Westminster Theological Seminary-PA, BD, 1963; Calvin Theological Seminary, MDiv, 1965
ordained: 1965
charges: First, Lacombe, AB, 1965–70; First, Lynden, WA, 1970–82; First, Thunder Bay, ON, 1982–87; First, Chilliwack, BC, 1987–95
d. 10/19/1995, Chilliwack, BC

Leep, Carl J.
b. 03/05/1954, Plainwell, MI
training: Calvin Theological Seminary, MDiv, 1980
ordained: 1980
charges: Everson, WA, 1980–87; Oak Hills, Portland, OR, 1987–

Leese, Marvin J.
b. 07/07/1944, Grand Rapids, MI
training: Reformed Bible College, BRE, 1965
ordained: 1997
charges: Mountain Lake, MN, 1985–93; Sibley, IA, 1996–2001; Bethel, Oskaloosa, IA, 2001–

Leetsma, Herman
b. 12/23/1925, Jenison, MI

training: Calvin Theological Seminary, ThB, 1952
ordained: 1952
charges: Morrison, IL, 1952-57; Immanuel,
Muskegon, MI, 1957-64; Lakewood, CA, 1964-70;
Calvin, Spokane, WA, 1970-83; Leave, 1983-84;
Eligible for call, 1984-86; stated supply,
Enumclaw, WA, 1986-87; Enumclaw, WA, 1987-91
retired: 1991

Leetsma, Reinder
b. 06/06/1927, Grand Rapids, MI
training: Calvin Theological Seminary, ThB, 1951
ordained: 1951
charges: Plainfield, MI, 1951-54; Dutton, MI,
1954-58; West Leonard, Grand Rapids, MI, 1958-
64; Lynwood, IL, 1964-92
retired: 1992; affiliated with United Reformed
Churches, 1992

Leigh, Wayne Earl
b. 11/08/1950, Seattle, WA
training: Westminster Theological Seminary-PA,
MDiv, 1983; Calvin Theological Seminary, Special
Program for Ministerial Candidacy, 1984
ordained: 1984
charges: CRC: Missionary to Japan, 1984-90; Resigned from denomination, 1990

Leiter, Bruce Campbell
b. 09/18/1942, St. Louis, MO
training: Western Michigan University, MA, 1966;
Calvin Theological Seminary, MDiv, 1980
ordained: 1980
charges: Second, Pella, IA, 1980-84; Oak Harbor,
WA, 1984-86; retired 1986-88; Eligible for call,
1988-90; Morrison, IL, 1990-95; Luverne, MN,
1995-98; Bethel, Saskatoon, SK, 1998-

Lengkeek, Henry Jay
b. 09/28/1955, Volga, SD
training: Calvin Theological Seminary, MDiv, 1997
ordained: 1997
charges: First, Visalia, CA, 1991-97; Haven,
Zeeland, MI, 1997-

Lenters, William Ray
b. 09/12/1941, Chicago, IL
training: Calvin Theological Seminary, BD, 1966;
MDiv, 1975
ordained: 1967
charges: CRC: Chaplain, Pine Rest Christian
Hospital, Cutlerville, MI, 1966-68; Maple Heights,
Cleveland, OH, 1968-73; Chaplain-Director, Calvary Rehabilitation Center, Phoenix, AZ, 1973-81;
Campus minister, Purdue University, West Lafay-

ette, IN, 1981-88; Hope, Oak Forest, IL, 1988-99;
Rosecrance Health Network, Rockford, IL, 1999-
2000; resigned from the denomination, 2000

Leo, Phillip Stephen
b. 09/14/1966, Evergreen Park, IL
training: Calvin Theological Seminary, MDiv, 1994
ordained: 1994
charges: Baldwin, WI, 1994-99; Calvin, Oak
Lawn, IL, 1999-

Leugs, John
b. 05/28/1929, Sarnia, ON
training: Calvin Theological Seminary, BD, 1956;
MDiv, 1977
ordained: 1956
charges: Hartley, IA, 1956-59; Bethel, Edgerton,
MN, 1959-67; East Saugatuck, MI, 1967-80;
Comstock, Kalamazoo, MI, 1980-88
d. 11/21/1988, Kalamazoo, MI

Leung, David Wing Yan
b. 10/25/1948, Canton, China
training: Canadian Theological College, MRE,
1981; Acadia University, MDiv, 1983; Calvin Theological Seminary, MMin, 1992
ordained: 1992
charges: CRC: Bethel Chinese, Mississauga, ON,
1989-98; eligible for call, 1996-99; released from
denomination, 1999

Leunk, Thea Nyhoff
b. 10/13/1954, Beloit, KS
training: Louisville Presbyterian Theological Seminary, MDiv, 1999; Calvin Theological Seminary,
Special Program for Ministerial Candidacy, 2000
ordained: 2001
charges: Crosspoint, Cincinnati, OH, 2000-

Lew, Harry W.
b. 10/13/1947, New York, NY
training: Theological Seminary of the Reformed
Episcopal Church, MDiv, 1984; Calvin Theological
Seminary, Special Program for Ministerial Candidacy, 1988
ordained: 1996
charges: Campus minister, Grand Rapids Area
Ministries, Grand Rapids, MI, 1991-92; Campus
minister, Campus Directions, Grand Rapids, MI,
1992-

Lewis, Edson "Bill" Taft Jr.
b. 07/28/1927, Lewis, CO
training: Calvin Theological Seminary, BD, 1956
ordained: 1956

charges: Monsey, NY, 1956-64; Hoboken, NJ, 1964-76; Campus minister, Ohio State University, Columbus, OH, 1976-93
retired: 1993

Leys, William Wayne
b. 01/12/1944, Cheboygan, MI
training: Calvin Theological Seminary, BD, 1969
ordained: 1969
charges: Cragmor, Colorado Springs, CO, 1969-74; Elmhurst, IL, 1974-83; New Hope of Dunwoody, Atlanta, GA, 1983-89; Ridgeview Hills, Denver, CO, 1989-94; Community Life, Lockport, IL, 1994-

Libolt, Clayton Gene
b. 11/29/1946, Bellingham, WA
training: Calvin Theological Seminary, BD, 1971; University of Michigan, MA, PhD
ordained: 1986
charges: Campus minister, River Terrace, East Lansing, MI, 1983-86; River Terrace, East Lansing, MI, 1986-

Licatesi, Vincent Charles
b. 04/19/1918, Chicago, IL
training: Calvin Theological Seminary, BD, 1943
ordained: 1943
charges: CRC: Boston Square, Grand Rapids, MI, 1943-50; Detroit, MI, 1950-54; Park, Holland, MI, 1954-60; Missionary pastor, Ideal Park Chapel, Grand Rapids, MI, 1960-62; Godwin Heights, Grand Rapids, MI, 1963-70; Independent: Christian Reformation Church, Grand Rapids, MI, 1970-76; Gospel Fellowship, Grand Rapids, MI, 1976-90
retired: 1990
d. 09/20/1992, Dutton, MI

Lie, Hendry L.
b. 03/13/1956, Dobo, Indonesia
training: Southeast Asia Theological College, ThB, 1979; Westminster Theological Seminary-PA, MTh, 1986
ordained: 1990
charges: Independent: Chinese Christian Church, Staten Island, NY, 1989-92; CRC: Monterey Park Indonesian, Monterey Park, CA, 1993-97; Missionary, Christian Reformed World Missions, Taiwan, 1997; Eligible for call, 1997-

Lieverdink, Dirk Jan Marinus
b. 05/24/1932, Eibergen, Gelderland, Netherlands
training: Calvin Theological Seminary, BD, 1961; ThM, 1970
ordained: 1961

charges: Home missionary, Fredericton, NB, 1961-65; Lucknow, ON, 1965-68; Chaplain, Pine Rest Christian Hospital, 1968-73; stated supply, Green Ridge, Muskegon, MI, 1973-74; Green Ridge, Muskegon, MI, 1974-77; Aetna, MI, 1978-86
d. 04/01/1986, Grand Rapids, MI

Likkel, Allen Eugene
b. 11/30/1944, Sumas, WA
training: Calvin Theological Seminary, BD, 1970; MDiv, 1976
ordained: 1970
charges: Cedar Falls, IA, 1970-74; East Islip, NY, 1974-80; Christ Community, Nanaimo, BC, 1980-91; Home Missions Ministry, Recruiting and training, Grand Rapids, MI, 1991-96; Emmaus Road, Seattle, WA, 1996-

Likkel, Lynn Ann Vander Geissen
see: Vander Giessen Likkel, Lynn Ann

Lim, Theodore Ben Kock Hong
b. 02/21/1951, Batu Pahat, Malaysia
training: Fuller Theological Seminary, ThM, 1989; Texas Tech University, PhD, 2000
ordained: 1984
charges: Grace Fellowship, Singapore, 1984-86; Evangelical Free: First, Glendale, CA, 1987-89; Free, Petaling Jaya, Malaysia, 1989-95; Baptist: Chinese, Lubbock, TX, 1996-2000; CRC: In-Christ Community Church, Sun Valley, CA, 2001-2002

Limburg, Timothy Cornelius
b. 11/01/1941, Aplington, IA
training: Calvin Theological Seminary, BD, 1969
ordained: 1970
charges: CRC: Campus ministry, Madison, WI, 1958-69; Washington, DC, 1970-72; Campus Minister, First, East Lansing, MI, 1972-77; Missionary to Appalachia, 1977-84; Washington, DC, 1984-95; Leave, 1995-97; PCUSA: Beulah, Cold Harbor, VA, 1997-

Lin, Jimmy Tai-on
b. 05/23/1950, Hong Kong, China
training: Westminster Theological Seminary-PA, MAR, 1982; MDiv, 1983; Princeton Theological Seminary, MTh, 1984
ordained: 1977
charges: Church of Christ in China: Hong Kong, China, 1984-91; CRC: Chinese broadcasting, Back to God Hour, Palos Heights, IL, 1991-

Lindemulder, Alfred
b. 03/26/1945, Netherlands
training: Calvin Theological Seminary, BD, 1972; MDiv, 1975
ordained: 1972
charges: Momence, IL, 1972-78; North Haledon, NJ, 1978-84; Christ's Community, Chandler, AZ, 1984-98; Eligible for call, 1998-2000; Celebration Community, Phoenix, AZ, 2000-

Lion, Jerald Derk
b. 04/27/1950, Groningen, Groningen, Netherlands
training: Calvin Theological Seminary, MDiv, 1980
ordained: 1981
charges: Community, East Grand Forks, MN, 1981-84; Vogel Center, MI, 1984-90; Tri-Cities, Kennewick, WA, 1990-

Lise, Markus Johannes
b. 10/21/1942, Groningen, Groningen, Netherlands
training: Calvin Theological Seminary, BD, 1970
ordained: 1970
charges: Burdett, AB, 1970-75; Holland Marsh, ON, 1975-81; Mount Brydges, ON, 1981-85; Leave, 1985-86; Chaplain, Whitby Mental Health Centre, Whitby, ON, 1986-

Liu, John Jon-Sen
b. 05/26/1962, Taiwan, Republic of China
training: Christian Witness Theological Seminary, MRE, 1986; Golden Gate Baptist Theological Seminary, MDiv, 1988; Calvin Theological Seminary, Special Program for Ministerial Candidacy, 1989
ordained: 1989
charges: Mission pastor, Golden Gate, San Francisco, CA, 1987-89; Friendship Agape, San Jose, CA, 1989-98; Eligible for call, 1998-2001; Bread of Life Chinese Christian Church, Surrey, BC, 2001-

Lobbezoo, Ronald Jacobus
b. 11/24/1945, Netherlands
training: Calvin Theological Seminary, BD, 1971
ordained: 1971
charges: Summer St., Passaic, NJ, 1971-73; Leave, 1973-78; Non-ministerial vocation, Grand Rapids, MI, 1978

Lobdell, Lawrence Arnold Jr.
b. 09/21/1949, Grand Rapids, MI
training: Reformed Bible College, BRE, 1975; Calvin Theological Seminary, MDiv, 1984
ordained: 1984
charges: Missionary to Nigeria, 1984-89; Medical

leave, 1989-90; Faculty, Reformed Theological Seminary, Nigeria, 1990-92; Eligible for call, 1992-93; Harrison, SD, 1993-99; Coopersville, MI, 1999-

Loerop, Richard Wayne
b. 10/02/1954, Chicago, IL
training: Calvin Theological Seminary, MDiv, 1980
ordained: 1981
charges: Newton, NJ, 1981-88; Richfield, Clifton, NJ, 1988-94; Imlay City, MI (loaned to Community, Ludington, MI, 2000-2002), 1994-

Loerts, Robert John
b. 11/29/1967, Sarnia, ON
training: Calvin Theological Seminary, MDiv, 1997
ordained: 1997
charges: Bethany, Fenwick, ON, 1997-

Lomavatu, Paul
training: declared eligible on the basis of exceptional gifts, 2001
ordained: 2002
charges: Caribou Community, Williams Lake, BC, 2001-

Lont, James C.
b. 01/02/1930, Fairlawn, NJ
training: Calvin Theological Seminary, BD, 1954
ordained: 1955
charges: Bunde, MN, 1955-59; Graafschap, MI, 1959-62; Director, Young Calvinist Federation, 1962-80; Leave, 1980-81; Palos Heights, IL, 1981-88; Director of Ministry Development, World-Wide Christian Schools, Grandville, MI, 1988-96; Recording Secretary for Youth and Christian Education, Reformed Ecumenical Council, 1996
retired: 1996

Looman, John Harvey
b. 09/13/1932, Grand Rapids, MI
training: Calvin Theological Seminary, MDiv, 1975
ordained: 1975
charges: Comstock Park, MI, 1975-84; First, Miami, FL, 1984-88; Portage, MI, 1988-95
retired: 1995

Los, Dick Cornelius
b. 08/16/1923, Sassenheim, Zuid Holland, Netherlands
training: Theologische Universiteit, Kampen, diploma, 1950
ordained: 1950
charges: GKN: Stellendam, 1950-56; Ferwerd, 1956-59; CRC: Georgetown, ON, 1959-62;

Grimsby, ON, 1962-67; Jarvis, ON, 1967-72; Cephas, Peterborough, ON, 1972-78; Covenant, Woodstock, ON, 1978-83; First, Kemptville, ON, 1983-88
retired: 1988

Los, Eugene Wayne
b. 10/07/1931, Lakeview, SD
training: Calvin Theological Seminary, BD, 1957
ordained: 1957
charges: Morrison, IL, 1957-61; Fairview, Denver, CO, 1961-68; Third, Zeeland, MI, 1968-74; Second, Grand Haven, MI, 1974-90; Jamestown, MI, 1990-96
retired: 1996

Los, Scott Douglas
b. 03/26/1963, Denver, CO
training: Calvin Theological Seminary, MDiv, 1992
ordained: 1992
charges: Faith, Elmhurst, IL, 1992-95; Friendship, Gaylord, MI, 1995-2000

Louvau, Charles
ordained: 1994
charges: Intern, Oak Hills, 1991-94; Intern, Sauvies Island, 1991; Balsam Bible Chapel, 1994-97; CRC: Interim Hawarden, IA, 1998; Church planter, Gateway Community, Merced, CA, 1998-1999; Lebanon, Sioux Center, IA, 2000-

Louwerse, Anthony Louis
b. 11/21/1939, Lebanon, IA
training: Calvin Theological Seminary, BD, 1966; MDiv, 1983
ordained: 1966
charges: Cedar Falls, IA, 1966-70; Bellingham, WA, 1970-75; Willmar, MN, 1975-79; Hope, La Crosse, WI, 1979-86; Pine Creek, Holland, MI, 1986-89; Classical Ministry coordinator, Classis Holland, Holland, MI, 1989-2002
retired: 2002

Lucas, James Allan
b. 12/12/1953, Grand Rapids, MI
training: Calvin Theological Seminary, MDiv, 1985
ordained: 1985
charges: CRC: Christ's Community, Grand Rapids, MI, 1985-89; Eligible for call, 1989-98; Independent: Ministry for Gays, Grand Rapids, MI, 1998-2001

Lucas, Mark John
b. 10/16/1946, Paterson, NJ
training: Calvin Theological Seminary, BD, 1978

ordained: 1981
charges: Monsey, NY, 1981-85; Bible teacher, Eastern Christian High School, North Haledon, NJ, 1985-

Luchies, John Elmer
b. 05/19/1912, Fremont, MI
training: Calvin Theological Seminary, ThB, 1938; Princeton Seminary, ThM, 1939; ThD, 1942
ordained: 1942
charges: CRC: Lansing, MI, 1942-46; First, Muskegon, MI, 1946-50; Faculty, Wheaton College, Wheaton, IL, 1950-64; Wheaton, IL, 1952-57; Supportive ministries, Providence, Holland, MI, 1980-89; Minister of congregational care, Pillar, Holland, MI, 1989-2001; Congregational: Faculty, Ohio State, Columbus, OH, 1957-58; First, Cairo, OH, 1962-64; Faculty, Defiance College, Cairo, OH, 1964-78; PCUSA: Faculty, Indiana University, Bloomington, IN, 1966-74; First Presbyterian, Paulding, OH, 1967-78; Faculty, Hope College, Holland, MI, 1979-95
d. 09/08/2002, Holland, MI

Luchies, Ronald Vernon
b. 08/26/1953, Grand Rapids, MI
training: Calvin Theological Seminary, MDiv, 1981
ordained: 1981
charges: Saugatuck, MI, 1981-85; Kalamazoo Youth Ministry, Kalamazoo, MI, 1985-91; Lucknow, ON, 1991-97; Lindsay, ON, 1997-

Luchies, Vernon
b. 07/02/1927, Fremont, MI
training: Calvin Theological Seminary, BD, 1958; MDiv, 1974
ordained: 1958
charges: Wright, Kanawha, IA, 1958-60; Missionary pastor, Rapid City, SD, 1960-65; Terrace, BC, 1965-69; Classical missionary, Immanuel Chapel, Kalamazoo, MI, 1969-78; West Sayville, NY, 1978-85; Missionary, Appalachia Reach Out, Inez, KY, 1985-89
retired: 1989

Ludwig, Wiebo Arienes
b. 12/19/1941, Zwaagwesteinde, Friesland, Netherlands
training: Calvin Theological Seminary, MDiv, 1975
ordained: 1976
charges: Bethlehem, Thunder Bay, ON, 1976-77; Goderich, ON, 1978-80; Independent: Church of Our Shepherd King, Goderich, ON, 1980-81; Non-ministerial vocation, Hythe, AB, 1981

Lugo, Esteban

b. 05/04/1954
ordained: 1978
charges: Spirit and Truth Fellowship, Chicago, IL, 1977-87; Spirit and Truth Fellowship, Philadelphia, PA, 1988-92; Bethel, Shiprock, NM, 1992-93; eligible for call, 1993-94; Principe de Paz, Phoenix, AZ, 1994-98; eligible for call, 1998-2003; Orangewood, Phoenix, AZ, 2003-

Luke, Alfred Selvarajan

b. 06/13/1950, Batu Gajah, Perak, West Malaysia
training: Calvin Theological Seminary, MDiv, 1981
ordained: 1981
charges: Des Moines, IA, 1981-87; Boston Square, Grand Rapids, MI, 1987-95; Director, Synod Committee on Race Relations, Grand Rapids, MI, 1995-99; Non-ministerial vocation, 1999

Lunshof, Henry

b. 11/17/1941, Beilen, Drenthe, Netherlands
training: Calvin Theological Seminary, BD, 1967
ordained: 1967
charges: Drayton, ON, 1967-71; First, Woodstock, ON, 1971-76; Community of Meadowvale, Mississauga, ON, 1976-92; Special Pastoral Education, Ontario Correctional Institute, Brampton, ON, 1992-93; Waterloo, ON, 1993-95; New Life, Guelph, ON, 1995-

Luth, John William

b. 10/11/1963, Woodstock, ON
training: Calvin Theological Seminary, MDiv, 1990
ordained: 1990
charges: First, Barrie, ON, 1990-98; St. Albert, AB, 1998-

Luurtsema, Gary Lee

b. 08/01/1966, Zeeland, MI
training: Calvin Theological Seminary, MDiv, 1992
ordained: 1992
charges: Ireton, IA, 1992-98; East Saugatuck, Holland, MI, 1998-

Lyzenga, Gerrit Anthony

b. 10/22/1896, Ee, Friesland, Netherlands
training: Calvin Theological Seminary, diploma, 1922
ordained: 1922
charges: New Era, MI, 1922-27; Leota, MN, 1927-45; Ellsworth, MI, 1945-50; Erie, ON, 1950
d. 12/01/1950, Jarvis, ON

Lyzenga, Robert Allen

b. 06/12/1956, Ann Arbor, MI
training: Calvin Theological Seminary, MDiv, 1994
ordained: 1994
charges: New Life, Houston, TX, 1994-2002; Sunrise, Lafayette, IN, 2002-

Maan, Tony

b. 01/04/1960, Kingston, ON
training: Calvin Theological Seminary, MDiv, 1986
ordained: 1986
charges: Brooks, AB, 1986-91; Bethel, Edmonton, AB, 1991-2001; Leave, 2001-

Maas, John W.

b. 05/31/1926, Harrison, SD
training: Calvin Theological Seminary, MDiv, 1957
ordained: 1957
charges: Woden, IA, 1957-63; First, Everett, WA, 1963-72; South Olive, MI, 1972-83; Bethel, Marion, SD, 1983-91
retired: 1991

Macaskill, Peter M.

b. 07/17/1923, Montreal, QC
training: United Theological College, BD, 1947; Princeton Theological Seminary, ThM, 1948
ordained: 1948
charges: United Church of Canada: Carmanville, NF, 1948-50; St. Anthony, NF, 1950-63; Bedford, QC, 1963-68; Northlea, Laval, QC, 1968-90; CRC: Chaplain, Concordia University, Montreal, QC, 1990-2000
retired: 1989

Machado, Federico J.

b. 09/21/1947, El Viejo, Nicaragua
training: Calvin Theological Seminary, MMin, 1987
ordained: 1987
charges: Assistant to minister, Sol Del Valle, Sun Valley, CA, 1985-86; Iglesia Cristiana Siervo del Seqor, Chula Vista, CA, 1987-1991; Assistant regional director, Hispanic Ministry, San Diego, CA, 1991-92; Non-ministerial vocation, 1992

Machiela, Alvin Jay

b. 09/09/1944, Zeeland, MI
training: Calvin Theological Seminary, BD, 1969
ordained: 1969
charges: Missionary to Taiwan, 1969-75; First, Flint, MI, 1975-81; Tri Cities, Kennewick, WA, 1981-90; Church planting, Good News, Kent, WA, 1990-93; Immanuel, Burbank, IL, 1993-96; Sunnyslope, Salem, OR, 1996-

MacLarkey, Robert Lee
b. 07/09/1942, Pittsburgh, PA
training: Westminster Theological Seminary-PA, MDiv, 1968; Institute for Christian Studies, MPh, 1981; University of Toronto, MA, 1983; PhD, 1987
ordained: 1970
charges: OPC: Westminster, Bartlesville, OK, 1970–73; CRC: Fellowship, Toronto, ON, 1973–76; teacher, Toronto District Christian High School, ON, 1976–83; Non-ministerial vocation: Teacher, Toronto, ON, 1983–86; Faculty, Redeemer College, Ancaster, ON, 1986

MacLeod, Angus Malcolm
b. 09/22/1925, East Orange, NJ
training: Calvin Theological Seminary, BD, 1954; Westminster Theological Seminary-PA, MDiv, 1955
ordained: 1955
charges: Irving Park, NJ, 1955–58; Missionary to South America-Argentina, 1958–66; Park Lane, Evergreen, Park, IL, 1966–74; Ada, MI, 1974–83; Pine Creek, Holland, MI, 1983–85
d. 11/23/1985, Holland, MI

MacLeod, Douglas Malcolm
b. 09/25/1957, Neptune, NJ
training: Calvin Theological Seminary, MDiv, 1984
ordained: 1985
charges: Burton Heights, Grand Rapids, MI, 1985–93; Peace, Cedar Rapids, IA, 1993–

MacLeod, Farquhar John
b. 09/05/1929, New York, NY
training: Westminster Theological Seminary-PA, Calvin Theological Seminary, ThM, 1956
ordained: 1956
charges: Wanamassa, NJ, 1956–59; Preakness, NJ, 1959–65; Bethel, Lynden, WA, 1965–68; Immanuel, Wappingers Falls, NY, 1968–75; Missionary, Atlanta, GA, 1975–80; Trinity, Richfield Springs, NY, 1980–86; Cape Coral, FL, 1986–91
retired: 1991

MacNeil, Kirk Marcellinus
b. 03/07/1954, Glace Bay, NS
training: Calvin Theological Seminary, MDiv, 1989
ordained: 1990
charges: Youth pastor, Hebron, Whitby, ON, 1989–90; Lindsay, ON, 1990–95; Bethel, Lacombe, AB, 1995–

Madany, Bassam Michael
b. 02/03/1928, Seleucia, Antioch, Syria
training: Reformed Presbyterian Theological Seminary, diploma, 1953; Calvin Theological Seminary, BD, 1966
ordained: 1953
charges: Reformed Presbyterian Church: Mission, Latakia, Syria, 1953–55; Winnipeg, MB, 1955–56; Manitoba Auxiliary, British and Foreign Bible Society, 1956–58; CRC: Minister of Arabic Broadcasting, Back to God Hour, Palos Heights, IL, 1958–94
retired: 1994

Maldonado, Rafael Jr.
b. 10/31/1952, Chicago, IL
training: Calvin Theological Seminary, MMin, 1989
ordained: 1985
charges: Hope Christian Fellowship, Chicago, IL, 1985–92; Non-ministerial vocation, 1992

Male, William Benson
b. 08/19/1905, Long Eddy, NY
training: Westminster Theological Seminary-PA, ThB, 1938
ordained: 1933
charges: Bible Testimony Church, Norristown, PA, 1933–38; Second Congregational, Denver, CO, 1938–33; OPC: Park Hill, Denver, CO, 1944–56; Bible teacher, Denver (CO) Christian High School, 1956–59; Missionary, Beirut, Lebanon, 1974–78; Alexandria Community Church, Egypt, 1979–80; Home missions, Alpine, TX, 1980–82; CRC: Associate pastor, Second, Denver, CO and Bible teacher, Denver (CO) Christian High School, 1959–70
retired: 1970
d. 01/17/1982, Denver, CO

Malestein, John Theodore
b. 08/17/1923, Midland Park, NJ
training: Calvin Theological Seminary, ThB, 1951
ordained: 1951
charges: Escalon, CA, 1951–54; Lafayette, IN, 1954–58; First, Lansing, IL, 1958–62; Richfield, Clifton, NJ, 1962–68; North Hills, Troy, MI, 1968–78; leave, 1978–79; North Hills, Troy, MI, 1979–88
retired: 1988

Maliepaard, John
b. 06/15/1928, Hanford, CA
training: Calvin Theological Seminary, BD, 1954
ordained: 1955
charges: CRC: Hoboken, NJ, 1955–61; Riverside, Grand Rapids, MI, 1961–67; Missionary, Guiding Light Mission, Grand Rapids, MI, 1967–68; Resigned from denomination, 1968; Chaplain, United States Army, Fort Grant, AZ, 1968

Mannes, Keith Allan

b. 02/13/1961, Zeeland, MI
training: Calvin Theological Seminary, MDiv, 1989
ordained: 1989
charges: Calvin, Muskegon, MI, 1989-94;
Crosswinds Community, Orlando, FL, 1994-98;
Highland, MI, 1998-

Manni, Jacob

b. 08/29/1859, Zierikzee, Zeeland, Netherlands
training: Calvin Theological Seminary, diploma,
1889
ordained: 1889
charges: South Olive, MI, 1889-92; Pella, IA,
1892-97; Passaic, NJ, 1897-1901; Third,
Muskegon, MI, 1901-03; East Saugatuck, MI,
1903-10; Douglas Park, Chicago, IL, 1910-16;
Sheboygan, WI, 1916-25; Agent for Pine Rest
Christian Hospital, 1925-29
retired: 1929
d. 01/20/1935, Grand Rapids, MI

Mans, Peter J.

b. 01/18/1936, Volga, SD
training: Calvin Theological Seminary, BD, 1967;
MDiv, 1980
ordained: 1967
charges: Chaplain, United States Navy, 1967-70;
Chaplain, Pennsylvania State Hospital in Philadelphia, 1970-71; Avery St., South Windsor, CT,
1971-78; Leave, 1978-79; Chaplain, Mary Free
Bed Hospital, Grand Rapids, MI, 1979-83; Olympia, WA, 1983-95; First, Sioux City, IA, 1995-99;
Interim, Richfield, Clifton, NJ, 1999-2000; Interim,
Second, Lynden, WA, 2000-2001; Interim, Trinity,
St. Louis, MO, 2001-2002
retired: 2002

Mantel, James Simon

b. 12/16/1937, Andijk, Noord Holland, Netherlands
training: Calvin Theological Seminary, BD, 1967
ordained: 1967
charges: Athens, ON, 1967-71; Nobleford, AB,
1971-78; Sunnyslope, Salem, OR, 1978-83;
Kelowna, BC, 1983-89; First, Regina, SK, 1989-
93; Neerlandia, AB, 1993-2000
retired: 2000

Mantel, Peter

b. 05/08/1927, Andijk, Noord Holland, Netherlands
training: Calvin Theological Seminary, BD, 1963
ordained: 1963
charges: Niagara Falls, ON, 1963-66; Calvary, Ottawa, ON, 1966-72; Leave, 1972-73; Chaplain,
Hamilton (ON) Psychiatric Hospital, 1973-74;

chaplain, Millbrook Correctional Centre,
Peterborough, ON, 1974-78; Leave, 1978-79;
Stated supply, Vanastra, ON, 1979-80; Eligible for
call, 1980-82; Chaplain, S.T.A.R.T. Centre, St.
Thomas, ON, 1983-84; Chaplain, Westover Treat-
ment Center, Thamesville, ON, 1987-93
retired: 1993; withdrew from denomination, 1995

Manuhutu, Pieter A.

ordained: 1999
charges: PCA: ; CRC: Indonesian, Arcadia, CA,
1999-

Marcusse, Edward Jay

b. 04/02/1957, Grand Haven, MI
training: Calvin Theological Seminary, MDiv, 1991
ordained: 1991
charges: CRC: Minister of youth, First, Jenison,
MI, 1989-90; Cloverdale, Boise, ID, 1991-97;
United Reformed Churches: Cloverdale, Boise, ID,
1997-98; Bethel, Calgary, AB, 1998-

Marcusse, Marcus Jan

b. 03/15/1860, Kamperland, Zeeland, Netherlands
training: Calvin Theological Seminary, diploma,
1886
ordained: 1886
charges: Home missionary, Kansas, Nebraska,
Iowa, Wisconsin, Illinois, Ohio, Michigan, New York
and Indiana, 1886-89; Lafayette, IN, 1889-94;
Alto, WI, 1894-96; First, Grand Haven, 1896-98;
Lucas, MI, 1898-06; Caldwell, MI, 1906-13
d. 09/19/1913, Lucas, MI vicinity

Maring, Cornelius

b. 02/17/1884, Stedum, Groningen, Netherlands
training: Calvin Theological Seminary, diploma,
1909
ordained: 1909
charges: Corsica, SD, 1909-13; East Palmyra, NY,
1913-18; Otley, IA, 1918-22; West Branch, MI,
1922-43; Momence, IL, 1943-46; Bejou, MN,
1946-49
retired: 1949
d. 04/09/1955, Holland, MI

Marlink, Earl Charles

b. 01/22/1931, Zeeland, MI
training: Calvin Theological Seminary, BD, 1955;
MDiv, 1977
ordained: 1955
charges: Ackley, IA, 1955-59; Oak Park, IL,
1959-66; Sacramento, CA, 1966-82; West Coast
Interim Home Missionary, Sacramento, CA, 1982-

94; Home Missions, Interim ministry specialist, Faith, New Brighton, MN, 1994-95
retired: 1995

Martin, Gregg Vincent
b. 11/18/1952, Anniston, AL
training: Calvin Theological Seminary, MDiv, 1977
ordained: 1977
charges: Bethel, Dunnville, ON, 1977-81; Charlottetown, PE, 1981-85; Second, Toronto, ON, 1985-92; Transcona, Winnipeg, MB, 1992-98; Leadership training, Costa Rica, 1998-

Martinez, José M.
b. 08/10/1943, Cuba
training: Reformed Episcopal Theological Seminary, BD, 1977
ordained: 1977
charges: PCA: Missionary in Central America, 1977-80; Teacher of Theology with LOGOI, 1980-82; Hispanic missionary, Texas, 1986; CRC: Missionary to Dominican Republic, 1982-86

Masselink, Edward Johann
b. 05/01/1901, Meservey, IA
training: Princeton Theological Seminary, BA; University of Chicago, MA; Southern Baptist Theological Seminary, ThD, 1927; Calvin Theological Seminary, 1927
ordained: 1927
charges: RCA: Trinity Reformed, Grand Rapids, MI, 1927-29; CRC: Burton Heights, Grand Rapids, MI, 1929-40; LaGrave Ave., Grand Rapids, MI, 1940-44; First, Cicero, IL, 1944-50; Twelfth St., Grand Rapids, MI, 1950-55; Central Ave., Holland, MI, 1955-62; Thirty-Sixth St., Wyoming, MI, 1962-66
retired: 1966
d. 07/05/1999, Grand Rapids, MI

Masselink, John
b. 09/23/1891, Reeman, MI vicinity
training: Grundy College and Seminary, diploma, 1918; Southwestern Baptist Theological Seminary, ThD, 1938
ordained: 1918
charges: Ridott, IL, 1918-20; Fulton, IL, 1920-24; Second, Muskegon, MI, 1924-27; Third, Kalamazoo, MI, 1927-43; First, Grand Haven, MI, 1943-49; Second, Orange City, IA, 1949-58
retired: 1958
d. 03/21/1964, Grand Rapids, MI

Masselink, William Sr.
b. 02/15/1897, Meservey, IA

training: Grundy College and Seminary, diploma, 1918; Princeton Theological Seminary, ThM, 1919; Chicago Divinity School, 1920; Southern Baptist Theological Seminary, PhD, 1921; Vrije Universiteit, Amsterdam, ThD, 1937
ordained: 1922
charges: Lafayette, IN, 1922-25; 14th St., Holland, MI, 1925-28; Alpine Ave., Grand Rapids, MI, 1928-42; Second Englewood, Chicago, IL, 1942-52; Faculty, Reformed Bible College, Grand Rapids, MI, 1952-63
retired: 1963
d. 10/19/1973, Grand Rapids, MI

Masselink, William Jr.
b. 04/15/1935, Hoogeveen, Drenthe, Netherlands
training: Calvin Theological Seminary, BD, 1964
ordained: 1965
charges: CRC: Noordeloos, MI, 1965-69; Missionary, West Olive, MI, 1969-73; RCA: Special ministry, Parole officer, State of Michigan, 1973-80; demitted, 1980

Mast, Stanley Paul
b. 07/27/1946, Sioux Falls, SD
training: Calvin Theological Seminary, BD, 1971; ThM, 1986
ordained: 1971
charges: Trinity, St. Louis, MO, 1971-74; Cragmor, Colorado Springs, CO, 1974-78; Heritage, Byron Center, MI, 1978-87; Faculty, Calvin Theological Seminary, Grand Rapids, MI, 1987-90; LaGrave Ave., Grand Rapids, MI, 1990-

Matheis, Jack James
b. 08/05/1924, Cleveland, OH
training: Calvin Theological Seminary, BD, 1955
ordained: 1955
charges: Everson, WA, 1955-61; Hope, Hull, IA, 1961-66; First, Edmonton, AB, 1966-69; Bible teacher, Lynden (WA) Christian High School, 1969-79; Bible teacher, Bellevue (WA) Christian High School, 1979-86
retired: 1986

Matias, John M.
b. 01/16/1958, Chicago, IL
training: Calvin Theological Seminary, MMin, 1991
ordained: 1983
charges: Church planting, Grace and Peace, Chicago, IL, 1983-85; Immanuel, Chicago, IL, 1985-88; Sunshine, Grand Rapids, MI, 1990-92; Sunshine Community, El Paso, TX, 1992-94; Church planting, El Paso, TX, 1994-95; Paso del Norte, El

Paso, TX, 1995-97; Staff, Calvin College, Grand Rapids, MI, 1997- ; City Hope, Grand Rapids, MI, 1999-

Mayo, Thomas E. Jr.
b. 11/24/1957, San Juan, Puerto Rico
training: Reformed Theological Seminary-FL, MDiv, 1994
ordained: 1995
charges: Sunshine Community, Grand Rapids, MI, 1995-99; Non-ministerial vocation, 1999

McCune, James Henry
b. 08/19/1954, Chicago, IL
training: Calvin Theological Seminary, MDiv, 1996
ordained: 1996
charges: Wayland, MI, 1996-99; Cottage Grove, South Holland, IL, 1999-

McDonald, Michael Stewart
b. 07/16/1959, Detroit, MI
training: Westminster Theological Seminary-CA, MAR, 1991; Calvin Theological Seminary, MDiv, 1994
ordained: 1995
charges: First, Hospers, IA, 1995-96; Eligible for call, 1996-99; Trinity, Richfield Springs, NY, 1999-2000; Woodville Community, Woodville, MI, 2000-2002

McGuire, George M.
b. 03/17/1945, Roanoke, VA
training: Bob Jones University Seminary, MDiv, 1972
ordained: 1970
charges: Independent Presbyterian Church, Atlanta, GA, 1968-72; PCA: Claredon, AR, 1972-97; KY, 1975-78; FL, 1978-81; FL, 1981-83; AL, 1986-98; CRC: Austinville, IA, 1996-

McPhee, Howard
b. 07/29/1946, Vancouver, BC
training: Westminster Theological Seminary, MDiv, 1972
ordained: 1972
charges: PCA: Bass River, ND, 1972-73; Tabusintac, NB, 1973-77; Grace and Peace, Toronto, ON, 1977-89; First, Unionville, ON 1989-93; CRC: Springdale, ON, 1993-

Medema, Theodore
b. 01/20/1933, Brandon, WI
training: Calvin Theological Seminary, BD, 1958
ordained: 1958
charges: Britt, IA, 1958-61; Paramus, NJ, 1961-

64; Bethel, Manhattan, MT, 1964-71; Delavan, WI, 1971-77; Western Springs, IL, 1977-83; Bethel, Tucson, AZ, 1983-91; Monroe, WA, 1991-95
retired: 1995

Medenblik, Julius Ted
b. 10/11/1960, Kalamazoo, MI
training: Calvin Theological Seminary, MDiv, 1995
ordained: 1995
charges: New Life, New Lenox, IL, 1995-

Medendorp, John Calvin Sr.
b. 10/18/1892, Grand Rapids, MI
training: Calvin Theological Seminary, diploma, 1921
ordained: 1921
charges: Dutton, MI, 1921-26; Rusk, MI, 1926-30; Racine, WI, 1930-45; Bozeman, MT, 1945-51; Ogilvie, MN, 1951-58
retired: 1958
d. 12/05/1976, Grandville, MI

Medendorp, John Calvin Jr.
b. 05/16/1926, Dutton, MI
training: Calvin Theological Seminary, ThB, 1951
ordained: 1951
charges: Des Moines, IA, 1951-54; Overisel, MI, 1954-58; Second, Fremont, MI, 1958-64; South Grandville, Grandville, MI, 1964-72; Princeton, Grand Rapids, MI, 1972-91
retired: 1991

Medendorp, John William
b. 10/08/1958, Fremont, MI
training: Calvin Theological Seminary, MDiv, 1986
ordained: 1991
charges: Director of outreach, Fairway, Jenison, MI, 1990-91; Missionary, Dominican Republic, 1991-2001; Global Vision, Houston, TX, 2001-

Meekhof, Michael Jay
b. 03/04/1954, Grand Rapids, MI
training: Calvin Theological Seminary, MDiv, 1984
ordained: 1984
charges: Comstock Park, MI, 1984-89; Zuni, NM, 1989-

Meeter, Harm Henry
b. 04/29/1886, Chicago, IL
training: Calvin Theological Seminary, diploma, 1912; Princeton Seminary, BD, 1913; University of Chicago; Vrije Universiteit, Amsterdam, ThD, 1916
ordained: 1917
charges: Neland Ave., Grand Rapids, MI, 1917-26;

Faculty, Calvin College, Grand Rapids, MI, 1926–56
retired: 1956
d. 07/09/1963, Grand Rapids, MI

Meeter, John Edward
b. 10/08/1901, Hammond, IN
training: Calvin Theological Seminary, ThB, 1927; Harvard Divinity School, 1928; Princeton Theological Seminary, ThM 1929; Vrije Universiteit, Amsterdam, ThD, 1932
ordained: 1945
charges: Faculty, Princeton Theological Seminary, 1932–33; Candidate pastor, Flint, 1933–34; Faculty, Wilson College, 1934–45; West Side, Cleveland, OH, 1945–51; Englewood, NJ, 1951–66
retired: 1966
d. 01/06/1993, Olympia, WA

Meijer, Daryl John
b. 10/31/1972, Hamilton, ON
training: Calvin Theological Seminary, MDiv, 1999
ordained: 1999
charges: Barrhaven Fellowship, Nepean, ON, 1999–

Meinders, Ede Luurt
b. 06/01/1827, Manslacht, Oostfriesland, Germany
training: Dubuque Presbyterian Seminary, diploma, 1866
ordained: 1868
charges: CRC: First, Wellsburg, IA, 1867–74; First, South Holland, IL, 1874–86; Independent: True Dutch Reformed, South Holland, IL, 1886–1900
retired: 1900
d. 07/06/1904, South Holland, IL

Meinema, Daniel Allen
b. 02/16/1966, Kalamazoo, MI
training: Calvin Theological Seminary, MDiv, 2002
charges: Barrhead, AB, 2003–

Melendez, Albino J.
b. 11/26/1941, Costa Rica
training: Baptist Seminary, Nicaragua, 1997
ordained: 1997
charges: CRC: Adelante program coordinator, Bethesda, Pomona, CA, 1998–

Mellema, Dirk
b. 07/05/1895, Brighton, NY
training: Calvin Theological Seminary, BD, 1931
ordained: 1931
charges: Home missionary for Classis Pella at Hamshire, TX, 1931–37; Home missionary,

Woodville, MI, 1937–45; Rudyard, MI, 1945–54; Kingston, ON, 1954–59; Plainfield, MI, 1959–62
retired: 1962
d. 06/30/1987, Grand Rapids, MI

Mennega, Harry
b. 03/20/1933, Assen, Drenthe, Netherlands
training: Calvin Theological Seminary, BD, 1958; MDiv, 1984
ordained: 1961
charges: Halifax, NS, 1961–64; Dresden, ON, 1964–67; Mount Hamilton, Hamilton, ON, 1967–73; Second, Abbotsford, BC, 1973–79; Cephas, Peterborough, ON, 1979–88; CRWM Research for mission to Jewish people, Israel and Europe, 1988–91; First, Kingston, ON, 1991–95
retired: 1995

Menninga, Arlan Dale
b. 07/04/1936, Otley, IA
training: Calvin Theological Seminary, BD, 1961
ordained: 1961
charges: CRC: Mountain Lake, MN, 1961–64; Missionary pastor, Ames, IA, 1964–68; Chaplain, United States Air Force, 1968–74; Hessel Park, Champaign, IL, 1975–81; RCA: Lincoln Mall Ministries, Matteson, IL, 1981–91; Stated supply, Dolton, IL, 1992–2000; Chaplain, Rest Haven Christian Services, IL, 1994–

Mensink, Larry Bryce
b. 09/02/1946, Grand Rapids, MI
training: Calvin Theological Seminary, BD, 1971; MDiv, 1978
ordained: 1973
charges: Youth minister, Sacramento, CA, 1973–75; Immanuel, Wappingers Falls, NY, 1976–82; Lafayette, IN, 1982–89; Beckwith Hills, Grand Rapids, MI, 1989–95; Seymour, Grand Rapids, MI, 1995–98; Eligible for call, 1998–2000; Baldwin, WI, 2000–

Meppelink, John Lambertus
b. 02/27/1929, Sully, IA
training: Calvin Theological Seminary, BD, 1954; MDiv, 1975
ordained: 1954
charges: Alamosa, CO, 1954–58; Fulton, IL, 1958–63; Calvary, Wyoming, MI, 1963–70; First, Fremont, MI, 1970–77; First, Oak Lawn, IL, 1977–84; Bauer, MI, 1984–86; Director of pastoral services, Holland Home, Grand Rapids, MI, 1986–94
retired: 1994

Merz, Stephen Martin

b. 12/30/1953, Palo Alto, CA
training: Calvin Theological Seminary, MDiv, 1981
ordained: 1981
charges: Allegan, MI, 1981-86; Decatur, MI, 1986-89; Campus minister, Western Michigan University, Kalamazoo, MI, 1989-93; Leave, 1993-96; Non-ministerial vocation, 1996

Meuzelaar, Isaac William

b. 01/23/1923, Dolton, IL
training: Calvin Theological Seminary, ThB, 1948
ordained: 1948
charges: Ackley, IA, 1948-51; Emden, MN, 1951-56; Terra Ceia, NC, 1956-61; Bethel, Allison, IA, 1961-65; Luctor, KS, 1965-75; Tracy, IA, 1975-84; Holland, IA, 1984-88
retired: 1988

Meyer, Anthony James

b. 07/17/1970, Muskegon, MI
training: Calvin Theological Seminary, MDiv, 1996
ordained: 1996
charges: Gateway Community, Merced, CA, 1996-2001; Ivanrest, Grandville, MI, 2001-

Meyer, Arend W.

b. 12/08/1852, Ulrum, Groningen, Netherlands
training: Calvin Theological Seminary, diploma, 1888
ordained: 1888
charges: New Holland, SD, 1889-94; Baldwin, WI, 1894-1905; Cincinnati, OH, 1905-07; Pease, MN, 1907-18
retired: 1918
d. 09/07/1933, Pease, MN

Meyer, Dirk Jansen

b. 05/25/1862, Grimersum, Ostfriesland, Germany
training: Dubuque Presbyterian Seminary, diploma, 1892
ordained: 1892
charges: Presbyterian Church: Emmanuel and Zoar congregations, near German Valley, IL, 1892-1902; Owensville, IA, 1902-1913; CRC: Oostfriesland, IA, 1913-34
retired: 1934
d. 01/11/1943, Dubuque, IA

Meyer, Edward Peter

b. 11/27/1932, Volga, SD
training: Calvin Theological Seminary, BD, 1958; MDiv, 1978
ordained: 1958
charges: Missionary to South America-Argentina,

1958-71; Sunnyside, WA, 1971-76; Holland Heights, Holland, MI, 1976-85; Southern Heights, Kalamazoo, MI, 1985-89; Latin American Director, The Bible League, Lynwood, IL, 1989-96; Bethel, De Motte, IN, 1996-98
retired: 1998

Meyer, Galen Harris

b. 05/06/1941, Kandiyohi, MN
training: Calvin Theological Seminary, BD, 1966
ordained: 1966
charges: Chaplain, United States Navy, 1966-69; Bible teacher, South Christian High School, Cutlerville, MI, 1969-89; Editor, *The Banner,* CRC Publications, Grand Rapids, MI, 1989-92; Bible teacher, South Christian High School, Cutlerville, MI, 1992-

Meyer, Jeffrey Mark

b. 12/17/1961, Grand Rapids, MI
training: Calvin Theological Seminary, MDiv, 1995
ordained: 1995
charges: Oakwood, Belding, MI, 1995-

Meyer, John S.

b. 01/02/1940, Paterson, NJ
training: Calvin Theological Seminary, BD, 1966
ordained: 1966
charges: Holland, IA, 1966-69; Arcadia, CA, 1969-75; Second, Randolph, WI, 1975-79; Cottonwood Heights, Jenison, MI, 1979-88; Calvin, Holland, MI, 1988-2000; McBain, MI, 2000-

Meyer, Larry Dean

b. 04/19/1945, Titonka, IA
training: Calvin Theological Seminary, BD, 1971
ordained: 1971
charges: Holland, MN, 1971-74; Des Moines, IA, 1974-81; Faculty, Shoreline Christian High School, Shoreline, WA, 1981-2000; Pastoral care associate, University Presbyterian Church, Seattle, WA, 2000-

Meyer, Larry Lee

b. 04/20/1949, Volga, SD
training: Calvin Theological Seminary, MDiv, 1979
ordained: 1979
charges: Seminary intern, Little Farms, Coopersville, MI, 1975-78; Minister of education and evangelism, Immanuel, Burbank, IL, 1979-81; First, Sioux City, IA, 1981-88; Faith Community, Beaver Dam, WI, 1988-2000; Smaller church specialist, Christian Reformed Home Missions, Beaver Dam, WI, 2000-

Meyer, Norman Lee

b. 07/26/1937, Grand Rapids, MI
training: Calvin Theological Seminary, BD, 1962;
MDiv, 1978
ordained: 1962
charges: Willmar, MN, 1962–66; Calvin,
Muskegon, MI, 1966–90; Interim ministry specialist, East Coast, Home Missions, 1990–93;
Brookside, Grand Rapids, MI, 1993–2002
retired: 2002

Meyer, Peter

b. 02/21/1932, Noorddijk, Groningen, Netherlands
training: Calvin Theological Seminary, Special
Program for Ministerial Candidacy
ordained: 1975
charges: Medicine Hat, AB, 1975–82; First, St.
Thomas, ON, 1982–88; First, Orillia, ON, 1988–95
retired: 1995

Meyer, Ronald James

b. 04/18/1950, Grand Rapids, MI
training: Calvin Theological Seminary, MDiv,
1976; ThM, 1981
ordained: 1976
charges: Seminary Intern, Modesto, CA, 1974–75;
North Blendon, MI, 1976–81; Goshen, NY, 1981–
88; Second, Highland, IN, 1988–96; Drenthe, MI,
1996–

Meyer, Wendell Lee

b. 01/21/1954, Montevideo, MN
training: Calvin Theological Seminary, MDiv, 1984
ordained: 1984
charges: Third, Denver, CO, 1984–88; Calvary,
Minneapolis, MN, 1988–94; Non-ministerial vocation, 1994

Meyer, William

b. 08/23/1882, Stiens, Friesland, Netherlands
training: Calvin Theological Seminary, diploma,
1911
ordained: 1911
charges: Galesburg IA, 1911–14; Amsterdam, ID,
1914–17; Missionary, Crookston MN, 1917–24;
Carnes, IA, 1924–29; Home missionary, Windsor
and Blackwell, ON, 1929–39; Hamilton, ON, 1939–
41; Cedar, IA, 1941–43; Missionary-pastor, Sioux
City, IA, 1943–49; Vesper, WI, 1949–53
retired: 1953
d. 06/11/1959, Midland Park, NJ

Meyering, Robert Alan

b. 03/04/1946, McBain, MI
training: Calvin Theological Seminary, BD, 1972

ordained: 1976
charges: West Park, Cleveland, OH, 1976–79;
Managing editor Education Dept., CRC Publications, Grand Rapids, MI, 1979–83; Assoc. theological editor, CRC Publications, Grand Rapids, MI,
1983–90; Curriculum editor, CRC Publications,
Grand Rapids, MI, 1990–94; Faculty, Calvin College, Grand Rapids, MI, 1994–98; Non-ministerial
vocation, staff, Calvin College, Grand Rapids, MI,
1998

Michael, Virgil Lee

b. 08/04/1952, Yakima, WA
training: Calvin Theological Seminary, MDiv, 1985
ordained: 1985
charges: East Paris, Grand Rapids, MI, 1985–89;
Christ Community, Portland/Tualatin, OR, 1989–

Miedema, Arnold James

b. 11/07/1944, Bradford, ON
training: Calvin Theological Seminary, BD, 1970
ordained: 1970
charges: Peers, AB, 1970–74; Bethel, Saskatoon,
SK, 1974–77; Non-ministerial vocation, 1977

Miedema, Derek Edward

b. 09/10/1972, Alliston, ON
training: Calvin Theological Seminary, MDiv, 1999
ordained: 1999
charges: Dresden, ON, 1999–

Miedema, Dirk

b. 02/01/1953, Redvers, SK
training: Calvin Theological Seminary, MDiv, 1981
ordained: 1981
charges: Dresden, ON, 1981–85; Bethel, Acton,
ON, 1985–90; Clinton, ON, 1990–96; Ingersoll,
ON, 1996–2002; Maranatha, Woodstock, ON,
2002–

Miedema, Michael Franklin

b. 04/27/1966, Toronto, ON
training: Calvin Theological Seminary, MDiv, 1996
ordained: 1997
charges: Maranatha, Bowmanville, ON, 1997–

Miersma, Sidney Peter

b. 04/01/1893, Detroit, MI
training: Calvin Theological Seminary, BD, 1933
ordained: 1934
charges: East Saugatuck, MI, 1934–48;
Parkersburg, IA, 1948–53; Hollandale, MN, 1953–
58
retired: 1958
d. 06/25/1985, Aplington, IA

Miller, Gordon Stuart

b. 03/07/1948, Jersey City, NJ
training: Westminster Theological Seminary-PA, MAR, 1982
ordained: 1984
charges: OPC: Immanuel, West Collingswood, NJ, 1983-85; Chaplain, United States Army, 1986-87; Cornerstone, Missoula, MT, 1987-89; Interim pastor, Christian Reformed Church, Monsey, NY, 1989-91; CRC: Monsey, NY, 1991-93; New Hope Community, Kincheloe, MI, 1993-98; Independent: Pentecostal church plant, Sault Ste. Marie, 1999

Minegar, Mark A.

b. 03/13/1954, Plainwell, MI
training: Western Theological Seminary, MDiv, 1984
ordained: 1984
charges: RCA: Sixth Reformed, Holland, MI, 1984-88; Church of the Vine, Oviedo, FL, 1990-93; Church of the Redeemer, Royal Oak, MI, 1993-96; CRC: Calvary, Plainwell, MI, 1997-

Minnema, Herman

b. 12/09/1921, Paterson, NJ
training: Calvin Theological Seminary, ThB, 1947
ordained: 1947
charges: Associate pastor, Bethel, Paterson, NJ and Bible teacher, Eastern Academy, 1947-48; Terra Ceia, NC, 1948-50; Worthington, MN, 1950-59; Comstock, MI, 1959-64; Bible teacher, Kalamazoo Christian High School, Kalamazoo, MI, 1964-85; Battle Creek, MI, 1985-91
retired: 1991

Minnema, Theodore

b. 08/14/1925, Paterson, NJ
training: Calvin Theological Seminary, BD, 1953; Vrije Universiteit, Amsterdam, ThD, 1958
ordained: 1958
charges: South Olive, MI, 1958-62; Faculty, Calvin College, Grand Rapids, MI, 1962-74; Faculty, Calvin Theological Seminary, Grand Rapids, MI, 1974-91
retired: 1991

Mitchell, Christopher Paul

b. 12/24/1968, Framingham, MA
training: Gordon-Conwell Theological Seminary, MDiv, 1994; Calvin Theological Seminary, Special Program for Ministerial Candidacy, 1995
ordained: 1997
charges: New England Chapel, Franklin, MA, 1997-

Mobach, Martin Theodore

b. 04/28/1957, Kingston, ON
training: Calvin Theological Seminary, MDiv, 1986
ordained: 1986
charges: Palmerston, ON, 1986-92; Woodynook, Lacombe, AB, 1992-2000; Missionary, the Philippines, 2000-2001; Interim, Ottewell, Edmonton, AB, 2002-

Moelker, Peter John Adrian

b. 07/23/1972, Trenton, ON
training: Calvin Theological Seminary, MDiv, 2000
ordained: 2000
charges: First, Thunder Bay, ON, 2000-2001; Wyoming, ON, 2001-

Moes, Herman

b. 07/31/1890, Chicago, IL
training: Calvin Theological Seminary, diploma, 1919; Princeton, BD, 1920
ordained: 1920
charges: Third, Chicago, IL, 1920-23; Waupun, WI, 1923-29; Pease, MN, 1929-43; Service pastor in Georgia and Florida, 1943-46; Flint, MI, 1946-49; Home missionary at Bowmanville, ON, 1949-52; at Peterborough, ON, 1952-57; at Vernon, BC, 1957-60
retired: 1960
d. 02/14/1981, Grand Rapids, MI

Moes, John Marcus

b. 10/10/1921, Chicago, IL
training: Calvin Theological Seminary, BD, 1962
ordained: 1962
charges: North Blendon, MI, 1962-66; Community, Toledo, OH, 1968-71; Conrad, MT, 1971-78; Green Meadow Community, Helena, MT, 1978-82; Seaman Ministry, Puget Sound, WA, 1982-87
retired: 1966-68, 1987

Mokma, John Henry

b. 08/16/1868, Graafschap, MI
training: Calvin Theological Seminary, diploma, 1908
ordained: 1908
charges: CRC: Overisel, MI, 1908-12; Munster, IN, 1912-13; Twelfth St., Chicago, IL, 1914-19; Second, Fremont, MI, 1919-26; Sullivan, MI, 1926-30; Independent: Muskegon, MI, 1930-41
d. 09/04/1941, Muskegon, MI

Molenbeek, James Alvin

b. 01/14/1949, Grand Rapids, MI
training: Calvin Theological Seminary, MDiv, 1975
ordained: 1975

charges: Luctor, KS, 1975-79; First, Salt Lake City, UT, 1979-82; Pine Grove, Howard City, MI, 1982-92; East, Muskegon, MI, 1992-98; Plymouth Heights, Grand Rapids, MI, 1998-

Mollema, Bernard
b. 10/03/1843, Niezijl, Groningen, Netherlands
training: with D.J. Vander Werp, 1874
ordained: 1874
charges: CRC: Wellsburg, 1874-79; Munster, IN, 1879-82; Lafayette, IN, 1882-93; RCA: Platte, SD, 1893-1906; Forestville, Ringle, WI, 1906-12
retired: 1912
d. 09/10/1919, Grand Rapids, MI

Monsma, Johan H.
b. 12/30/1888, Franeker, Friesland, Netherlands
training: Calvin Theological Seminary, diploma, 1917
ordained: 1917
charges: Spring Lake, MI, 1917-20; Jewish Mission, Paterson, NJ, 1920-21; Englewood, NJ, 1921-24; Summer St., Passaic, NJ, 1924-26; Munster, IN, 1926-48
d. 03/25/1948, Munster, IN

Monsma, John Arnold
b. 11/27/1940, Washington, DC
training: Calvin Theological Seminary, ThB, 1965
ordained: 1967
charges: Aetna, MI, 1967-72; Prairie Lane, Omaha, NE, 1972-75; Leave, 1975-78; Non-ministerial vocation, 1978

Monsma, John Clover
b. 12/14/1890, Netherlands
training: Calvin Theological Seminary, diploma, 1917
ordained: 1917
charges: CRC: Summit IL, 1917-19; PCUSA: Grandville, NY, 1920-22; First, Oostburg, WI, 1922-28; Non-ministerial vocation: Journalist and author, 1928-70
d. 04/24/1970, Grand Rapids, MI

Monsma, Martin
b. 11/23/1893, Berlikum, Friesland, Netherlands
training: Calvin Theological Seminary, diploma, 1924
ordained: 1924
charges: Doon, IA, 1924-28; Detroit, MI, 1928-34; Second, Pella, IA, 1934-43; Grandville Ave., Grand Rapids, MI, 1943-53; Faculty, Calvin Theological Seminary, Grand Rapids, MI, 1953-64
retired: 1964

d. 01/31/1968, Grand Rapids, MI

Monsma, Nicholas John
b. 01/31/1892, Berlikum, Friesland, Netherlands
training: Calvin Theological Seminary, diploma, 1922
ordained: 1922
charges: Hull, ND, 1922-24; First, Orange City, IA, 1924-29; Ninth St., Holland, MI, 1929-40; Second, Paterson, NJ, 1940-60
retired: 1960
d. 12/01/1973, Grand Rapids, MI

Monsma, Timothy Martin
b. 07/21/1933, Detroit, MI
training: Westminster Theological Seminary-PA, BD, 1957; Calvin Theological Seminary, BD, 1959; ThM, 1963; Fuller School of World Missions, PhD, 1976
ordained: 1959
charges: Chandler, MN, 1959-62; Missionary to Nigeria, 1962-74; Leave, Fuller Theological Seminary, 1974-76; Faculty, Reformed Bible College, Grand Rapids, MI, 1976-82; Faculty, Mid-America Reformed Seminary, Orange City, IA, 1982-85; Director, Cities for Christ Worldwide, Escondido, CA, 1985-98
retired: 1998; affiliated with Presbyterian Church in America, 1999

Moore, Coleman Short
b. 05/07/1956, Greenwich, CT
training: Calvin Theological Seminary, MDiv, 1997
ordained: 1997
charges: The River, Durham, NC, 1997-

Morbey, Graham Edward
b. 02/10/1941, Victoria, BC
training: Westminster Theological Seminary-PA, MDiv, 1965; University of Amsterdam, Postgraduate diploma, 1968; Vrije Universiteit, Drs, 1971; Calvin Theological Seminary, Special Program for Ministerial Candidacy, 1981
ordained: 1982
charges: Campus minister, University of Waterloo and Wilfrid Laurier University, Waterloo, ON, 1982-

Moreno, German
b. 01/10/1947, Colombia
training: Colombia Seminary, 1992
ordained: 1992
charges: Comunidad de Fe ICR, Lake Worth, FL, 1992-

Morren, John

b. 07/21/1923, Byron Center, MI
training: Calvin Theological Seminary, BD, 1953; ThM, 1974
ordained: 1953
charges: Conrad, MT, 1953-56; First, Ripon, CA, 1956-60; Missionary to Brisbane, Australia, 1960-65; Post graduate studies at Calvin Theological Seminary, 1965-66; Oak Park, IL, 1966-70; First, Grand Haven, MI, 1970-78; West 44th St., Wyoming, MI, 1978-84; Lake City, MI, 1984-91
retired: 1991

Mossel, George Robert

b. 04/02/1945, Hammond, IN
training: Calvin Theological Seminary, MDiv, 1980
ordained: 1980
charges: Newman Chapel, Ferry, MI, 1980-86; Hillside Community, Cutlerville, MI, 1986-

Mouw, Daniel Bruce

b. 12/28/1952, Holland, MI
training: Calvin Theological Seminary, MDiv, 1979
ordained: 1979
charges: Bethel, Paterson, NJ, 1979-90; Cedar Hill, Wyckoff, NJ, 1990-95; South Grandville, Grandville, MI, 1995-

Mouw, Gordon Dale

b. 10/23/1939, Holland, MI
training: Westminster Theological Seminary-PA, BD, 1964; ThM, 1984
ordained: 1965
charges: OPC: Community, Garfield, NJ, 1964-60; Grace, Trenton, NJ, 1968-70; CRC: Bejou and Crookston, MN, 1970-73; First, Thunder Bay, ON, 1973-76; First, St. Thomas, ON, 1976-80; Rusk, MI, 1980-90; Second, Pella, IA, 1990-95; Sanborn, IA, 1995
d. 08/23/1995, Sanborn, IA

Moxey, William John

b. 01/12/1952, Cleveland, OH
training: Calvin Theological Seminary, MDiv, 1978
ordained: 1978
charges: Lakeview, Valentine, NE, 1978-82; First, Detroit, MI, 1982-86; Leave, 1986-87; Inwood, IA, 1987-92; Emmanuel, Sauk Village, IL, 1992-95; Chaplain, VITAS, Innovative Hospice Care, Lombard, IL, 1995-97; Chaplain, Seasons Hospice, Park Ridge, IL, 1997-

Mpindi, Mbunga (Paul)

b. 12/31/1961, Kinshasa, Zaire
training: Fac. de Theol. Envangel. de Bangui,

ThM, 1990; CalvinTheological Seminary, ThM, 1999
ordained: 1999
charges: Back to God Hour, Grand Rapids, MI, 1999-

Mueller, Ralph Richard

b. 07/05/1948, Cleveland, OH
training: Calvin Theological Seminary, MDiv, 1984
ordained: 1984
charges: Holland Center, Lodgepole, SD, 1984-89; First, Randolph, WI, 1989-95; Ideal Park, Grand Rapids, MI, 1995-2000; Chaplain, Spectrum Health-Blodgett, Grand Rapids, MI, 2001-

Muir, David B.

b. 10/23/1918, Rochester, NY
training: Westminster Theological Seminary-PA, 1946
ordained: 1946
charges: UPC: Gibson and White Oak, IA, 1946-53; CRC: Paterson Hebrew Mission, Paterson, NJ, 1953-58; Imlay City, MI, 1958-77; Anacortes, WA, 1977-83
retired: 1983

Mulder, Alfred Eugene

b. 04/04/1936, Ireton, IA
training: Calvin Theological Seminary, BD, 1960; MDiv, 1975
ordained: 1960
charges: Luctor, KS, 1960-64; Home missionary, Brigham City, UT, 1964-68; Bethany, Gallup, NM, 1968-84; Director of new church development, Christian Reformed Home Missions, Grand Rapids, MI, 1984-

Mulder, Alvin A.

b. 03/01/1932, Hull, IA
training: Protestant Reformed Theological Seminary, diploma, 1958
ordained: 1958
charges: PRC: Kalamazoo, MI, 1958-62; CRC: Vogel Center, MI, 1962-65; West Leonard, Grand Rapids, MI, 1965-70; Warren Park, Cicero, IL, 1970-73; West Suburban, Cicero, Il, 1973-77; Calvary, Chino, CA, 1977-85; Central Coast, Arroyo Grande, CA, 1985-87; Christ Community, Virginia Beach, VA, 1987-95
retired: 1995

Mulder, Bernard W.

b. 07/12/1933, Allendale, MI
training: Calvin Theological Seminary, BD, 1958
ordained: 1958

charges: Inwood, IA, 1958-63; Home missionary, Wappingers Falls, NY, 1963-66; Dorr, MI, 1966-69; Overisel, MI, 1969-81; Lakeside Community, Alto, MI, 1981-97
retired: 1997

Mulder, Dennis Marlin
b. 02/15/1943, Renville, MN
training: Calvin Theological Seminary, BD, 1969; ThM, 1982
ordained: 1969
charges: Missionary to Taiwan, 1969-77; on loan, Asia coordinator, World Home Bible League, South Holland, IL, 1977-85; President, The Bible League, South Holland, IL, 1985-

Mulder, Henry J.
b. 02/16/1880, Zeeland, MI
training: Calvin Theological Seminary, diploma, 1908
ordained: 1908
charges: Plainfield, MI, 1908-10; Second, Muskegon, MI, 1910-17; Lafayette, IN, 1917-21; Burton Heights, Grand Rapids, MI, 1921-29; Home missionary Classis Grand Rapids East and Grand Rapids West, 1929-38
d. 11/17/1938, Grand Rapids, MI

Mulder, Jacob
b. 11/27/1884, Holland, MI vicinity
training: Calvin Theological Seminary, diploma, 1911; Princeton Seminary, ThB, 1912
ordained: 1912
charges: West Side, Cleveland, OH, 1912-15; Luctor, KS, 1915-21; Sheldon, IA, 1921-25; Everett, WA, 1925-28; Monarch, AB, (and Granum, AB, 1929-39) 1928-42; Estelline, SD, 1942-44; Holland, MN, 1944-49; Cedar, IA, 1949-52
retired: 1952
d. 03/18/1965, Holland, MI

Mulder, John A.
b. 03/12/1913, Cleveland, OH
training: Calvin Theological Seminary, ThB, 1941
ordained: 1941
charges: Ocheyedan, IA, 1941-46; Peoria, IA, 1946-50; Moline, MI, 1950-56; Sherman Street, Grand Rapids, MI, 1956-67; Second, Kalamazoo, MI, 1967-79
retired: 1979
d. 01/17/1998, Grand Rapids, MI

Mulder, Lambertus
b. 03/17/1922, Groningen, Groningen, Netherlands

training: Westminster Theological Seminary-PA, MDiv, 1950
ordained: 1950
charges: OPC: stated supply Philadelphia, PA, 1949; Canadian Presbyterian Church: Lansdoune Station, NS, 1950-52; CRC: Neerlandia, AB, 1952-57; Fort William, ON, 1957-61; First, Chatham, ON, 1961-65; Burlington, ON, 1965-70; Lethbridge, AB, 1970-76; Bethel, Brockville, ON, 1976-80; Hebron, Whitby, ON, 1980-82
d. 08/16/1982, Kingston, ON

Mulder, Steven Jon
b. 10/04/1970, Holland, MI
training: Calvin Theological Seminary, MDiv, 1997
ordained: 1997
charges: Britt, IA, 1997-2002; Overisel, MI, 2002-

Muller, William Vlieken
b. 02/29/1902, Amsterdam, Noord Holland, Netherlands
training: Calvin Theological Seminary, ThB, 1933; Hartford School of Missions, 1934
ordained: 1934
charges: Missionary to Brazil, 1934-70
retired: 1970
d. 06/20/1982, Grand Rapids, MI

Murphy, Paul Thomas
b. 11/03/1953, Rome, Italy
training: Westminster Theological Seminary-PA, MDiv, 1989; Calvin Theological Seminary, Special Program for Ministerial Candidacy, 1990
ordained: 1990
charges: CRC: Dutton, MI, 1990-92; Independent Reformed: Dutton, MI, 1992

Murrel, Samuel Clifford
b. 08/03/1958, Palatka, FL
training: Covenant Theological Seminary, MDiv, 1986; Calvin Theological Seminary, Special Program for Ministerial Candidacy, 1991
ordained: 1992
charges: Grace, Indian Harbour Beach, FL, 1991-92; Non-ministerial vocation, 1992

Muyskens, Derk Henry
b. /1885, Orange City, IA
training: Calvin Theological Seminary, diploma, 1908
ordained: 1908
charges: Oak Harbor, WA, 1908-11; Madison Ave., Paterson, NJ, 1911-12; Missionary at Crownpoint, NM, 1912-13, Sioux Center, IA, 1913-16; Second,

Paterson, NJ, 1916–17; Working among soldiers, 1918; Oak Harbor, WA, 1919; Hawarden IA, 1920; Sultan, WA, 1923–26; Second, Lynden, WA, 1926–34; Non-ministerial vocation, 1934
retired: 1920
d. 11/10/1948, Orange City, IA

Muyskens, Kevin James
b. 02/06/1969, Grundy Center, IA
training: Fuller Theological Seminary, MDiv, 1996; Calvin Theological Seminary, Special Program for Ministerial Candidacy, 1997
ordained: 1997
charges: Youth pastor, Long Beach, CA, 1992–96; Paw Paw, MI, 1997–2002; Immanuel, Sheldon, IA, 2002–

Nagel, Barend
b. 06/07/1862, De Leek, Groningen, Netherlands
training: Calvin Theological Seminary, diploma, 1903
ordained: 1903
charges: East Side, Cleveland, OH, 1903–06; Ebenezer, SD, 1906–08; Wright, IA, 1908–14; West Harlem, MI, 1914–20; Chandler, MN, 1920–29
d. 10/10/1929, Chandler, MN

Nam, Seung Woo
ordained: 2001
charges: Garden Grove Korea, Anaheim, CA, 2000–

Nam, Sung Ho
b. 03/12/1946, Korea
training: Presbyterian General Assembly College and Seminary, MDiv, 1980
ordained: 1980
charges: Presbyterian Church of Korea: Choong Hyun Presbyterian, Seoul, Korea, 1980–83; Buh Oyun Presbyterian, 1983; CRC: Torrance Glory, Torrance, CA/South Bay Elim, Gardena, CA, 1990–99

Namkoong, Jin
b. 02/09/1955, Korea
training: Actes Seminary, Seoul, MDiv, 1989
ordained: 1989
charges: Korean Presbyterian: Everlasting Joy, Suwan, Korea, 1989–93; Calvary Korean, Beaverton, OR, 1993–97; CRC: Zion, Beaverton, OR, 1997–

Nanninga, Henry Richard
b. 09/03/1958, Willowdale, ON

training: Calvin Theological Seminary, MCE, 1983, MDiv, 1996
ordained: 1996
charges: Youth director, Trinity, Edmonton, AB, 1983–87; Pastor of youth and evangelism, Clarkson, Mississauga, ON, 1987–96; First, Orillia, ON, 1996–

Narm, Andrew Chin Saeng
ordained: 2002
charges: Korean Presbyterian Church: -2002; CRC: Immanuel, Richmond, BC, 2002–

Nash, John Al
b. 01/20/1947, Chicago, IL
training: Johnson C. Smith Theological Seminary, MDiv, 1984; Calvin Theological Seminary, Special Program for Ministerial Candidacy, 1985
ordained: 1985
charges: Grace, Grand Rapids, MI, 1984–85; Atlanta Antioch Training Center, South DeKalb, GA, 1985– ; Christ's Community, Atlanta, GA, 1986–2001

Natelborg, John Derrick
b. 04/26/1936, Chicago, IL
training: Calvin Theological Seminary, BD, 1969; MDiv, 1972
ordained: 1969
charges: Missionary, Orlando, FL, 1969–74; Campus minister, Wayne State University, Detroit, MI, 1974–2001
retired: 2001

Nauta, Stephen Jay
b. 01/18/1958, Grand Rapids, MI
training: Calvin Theological Seminary, MDiv, 1992
ordained: 1993
charges: Ferrysburg, MI, 1993–

Nederhood, David Joel
b. 11/21/1966, Grand Rapids, MI
training: Calvin Theological Seminary, MDiv, 1997
ordained: 1997
charges: Alameda, CA, 1997–

Nederhood, Joel Homan
b. 12/22/1930, Cutlerville, MI
training: Calvin Theological Seminary, BD, 1957; Vrije Universiteit, Amsterdam, ThD, 1960
ordained: 1960
charges: Radio minister, The Back-to-God Hour, Palos Heights, IL, 1960–86; Director of ministries, The Back-to-God Hour, Palos Heights, IL, 1986–96
retired: 1996

Nederlof, Bastiaan

b. 11/05/1917, Rotterdam, Zuid Holland, Netherlands
training: Theologische Universiteit, Kampen, diploma, 1943
ordained: 1943
charges: CGKN: Eindhoven, 1943-48; Dokkum, 1948-53; CRC: Houston, BC, 1953-56; Third, Edmonton, AB, 1956-64; Rehoboth, Bellflower, CA, 1964-69; First, Vancouver, BC, 1969-75; Immanuel, Hamilton, ON, 1975-81; First, Victoria, BC, 1981-86
retired: 1986

Negen, Clayton

b. 06/14/1951, Willmar, MN
training: Calvin Theological Seminary, MDiv, 1977
ordained: 1977
charges: Chandler, MN, 1977-78
d. 05/21/1978, Chandler, MN

Negen, Donald Jacob

b. 08/12/1927, Renville, MN vicinity
training: Calvin Theological Seminary, BD, 1953
ordained: 1953
charges: Imlay City, MI, 1953-57; Niekerk, MI, 1957-65; Third, Lynden, WA, 1965-72; Third, Bellflower, CA, 1972-80; Lombard, IL, 1980-88; Monroe, WA, 1988-90
d. 01/24/1990, Monroe, WA

Negen, Gordon Dean

b. 03/13/1932, Renville, MN
training: Calvin Theological Seminary, BD, 1957; ThM, 1965
ordained: 1957
charges: Lodi, NJ, 1957-59; Home missionary at Harlem, NY, 1959-60; at Manhattan, NY, 1960-65; Manhattan, NY, 1965-69; Missionary, Sun Valley Chapel, Denver, CO, 1969-74; ECUM of Denver, CO, 1974-76; Eastern Ave., Grand Rapids, MI, 1976-86; Unity, Prospect Park, NJ, 1986-91; Immanuel, Kalamazoo, MI, 1991
retired: 1991; affiliated with New Community Church (Independent), 1995

Negrete, Nick Anthony

b. 02/04/1957, Denver, CO
training: Calvin Theological Seminary, MMin, 1988
ordained: 1988
charges: CRC: Sun Valley Community, Denver, CO, 1988-95; Resigned from the denomination, 1995

Nelesen, Marc Alan

b. 03/17/1969, Sheboygan, WI
training: Calvin Theological Seminary, MDiv, 1996
ordained: 1996
charges: Third, Zeeland, MI, 1996-

Nelson, Roger Allen

b. 08/20/1959, San Diego, CA
training: Western Theological Seminary, MDiv, 1986
ordained: 1986
charges: RCA: Young Life, Chicago, IL, 1986-88; Chaplain, Grand Rapids (MI) Christian High School, 1988-92; Chaplain, Christian High School, Chicago, IL, 1992-99; First, Schenectedy, NY, 1999-2002; CRC: Hope, Oak Forest, IL, 2002-

Nelson, Timothy Reid

b. 03/14/1950, Portland, OR
training: Calvin Theological Seminary, MDiv, 1978
ordained: 1978
charges: Missionary to Nigeria, 1978-83; Nonministerial vocation, Portland OR, 1983

Netz, Frederick Ludwig

b. 09/16/1910, Paterson, NJ
training: Calvin Theological Seminary, BD, 1941
ordained: 1941
charges: North Blendon, MI, 1941-47; Grant, MI, 1947-52; First, Paterson, NJ, 1952-57; Prinsburg, MN, 1957-65; Lucas, MI, 1965-71; Inwood, IA, 1971-73
d. 11/04/1973, Inwood, IA

Newhouse, Harrison Andrew

b. 03/07/1960, Holland, MI
training: Mid-America Reformed Seminary, MDiv, 1995; Calvin Theological Seminary, Special Program for Ministerial Candidacy, 1996
ordained: 1996
charges: Bethany, Bloomfield, ON, 1996-2000; Medicine Hat, AB, 2000-

Newhouse, Sidney

b. 04/13/1922, Redlands, CA
training: Calvin Theological Seminary, BD, 1954
ordained: 1954
charges: Flint, MI, 1954-58; Highland, MI, 1958-62; New Era, MI, 1962-68; Calvary, Minneapolis, MN, 1968-73; First, Allendale, MI, 1973-87
retired: 1987

Ng, Ezra Shui Cheung

ordained: 1981

charges: Independent Presbyterian Churches, 1981-200; CRC: Immanuel, Richmond, BC, 2001-

Ng, Samuel (Chi Ping)
b. 09/05/1950, Hong Kong, China
training: Hong Kong Overseas Bible Seminary, Bay Area Christian Theological Seminary
ordained: 1982
charges: United Brethren in Christ: Ling Ying, Hong Kong, 1975-90; Grace, Hong Kong, 1990-95; CRC: Golden Gate, San Francisco, CA, 1997-

Nguyen, Bao Xuan
b. 10/24/1948, Danang, Vietnam
training: Vietnamese Evangelical Seminary, 1969; Presbyterian Theological Seminary, Seoul, 1971
ordained: 1969
charges: Presbyterian Church of Korea: Leave, 1969-71; Gia-Dihn, 1972; Moderator, 1972-74; Thi-Nghe, 1975-78; Unaffiliated CRC: established congregation in refugee camp, Pulau Bidong, Malaysia, 1978-82, Missionary to Vietnamese, Garden Grove, CA, 1982-84; CRC: Missionary, Orange County Vietnamese, CA, 1984-86; Saigon, Garden Grove, CA, 1986-93; Alliance of Reformed Churches: Saigon Reformed Presbyterian Church, Santa Ana, CA, 1993-97; United Reformed Churches: Saigon Reformed Presbyterian Church, Santa Ana, CA, 1997-

Nguyen, Huu Phu
b. 09/25/1943, Longxuyen, Vietnam
training: Calvin Theological Seminary, MDiv, 1994
ordained: 1993
charges: Vietnamese New Hope, Winfield, IL, 1993-

Nicolai, Peter
b. 11/09/1938, Edmonton, AB
training: Calvin Theological Seminary, BD, 1972
ordained: 1972
charges: Houston, BC, 1972-76; Fellowship, Toronto, ON, 1976-82; Second, Brampton, ON, 1982-91; Emmanuel, Calgary, AB, 1991-96; Grace, Chatham, ON, 1996-2002
d. 04/15/2002, London, ON

Nieboer, Maynard Christian
b. 06/05/1934, Kalamazoo, MI
training: Calvin Theological Seminary, BD, 1969; ThM, 1970
ordained: 1970
charges: CRC: Missionary, Mount Pleasant, MI, 1970-75; Campus minister at Arizona State University, Tempe, AZ, 1975-84; Grand Canyon Coun-

seling Service, Scottsdale, AZ, 1984-85; RCA: Grand Canyon Counseling Service, Scottsdale, AZ, 1985; Chaplain, San Jose Oak Creek Hospital, San Jose, CA

Niehaus, Harm Heynen
b. 04/08/1871, Bunde, Ostfriesland, Germany
training: Missionary Training School, Baal, Switzerland, 1896
ordained: 1899
charges: Reformed Church US: George, IA, 1899-1904; CRC: Bunde, MN, 1904-06; RCA: Lennox, SD, 1907-1908; Inwood, IA, 1913-14; Baker/Sibley/Melvin, IA, 1914-15

Niehof, Thomas Jay
b. 02/28/1952, Grand Rapids, MI
training: Calvin Theological Seminary, MDiv, 1977
ordained: 1977
charges: Britt, IA, 1977-82; Farmington, NM, 1982-87; Bethlehem, Thunder Bay, ON, 1987-92; Leave, 1992-97; Trinity, Ames, IA, 1997-

Niemeyer, Bernard John
b. 07/31/1926, Chicago, IL
training: Calvin Theological Seminary, ThB, 1953
ordained: 1953
charges: Goshen, IN, 1953-56; Lamont, MI, 1956-61; Home missionary, Salem, OR, 1961-67; Missionary, Yakima, WA, 1967-74; First, Los Angeles, CA, 1974-80; Calvin, Portland, OR, 1980-88; Unity, Allegan, MI, 1988-91
retired: 1991

Nieuwsma, G. Duane
b. 10/25/1946, New Sharon, IA
training: Tyndale Seminary, MDiv, 1989; Calvin Theological Seminary, Special Program for Ministerial Candidacy, 1990
ordained: 1991
charges: Battle Creek, MI, 1991-2002; Dorr, MI, 2002-

Niewenhuis, Calvin Wayne
b. 01/07/1928, Willmar, MN
training: Calvin Theological Seminary, BD, 1956
ordained: 1956
charges: Le Mars, IA, 1956-61; Waupun, WI, 1961-65; North St., Zeeland, MI, 1965-71; Bethel, Paterson, NJ, 1971-78; Platte, SD, 1978-84; Noordeloos, MI, 1984-89; Terra Ceia, NC, 1989-93
retired: 1993

Niewenhuis, William D.

b. 12/21/1957, Elkhorn, WI

training: declared eligible on the basis of exceptional gifts, 1997

ordained: 1997

charges: First, Regina, SK, 1990-91; Education/Evangelism/Youth, First, Red Deer, AB, 1991-97; First, Red Deer, AB, 1998-2002; Rimbey, AB, 2002-

Niewiek, Peter John

b. 02/12/1946, Grand Rapids, MI

training: Calvin Theological Seminary, BD, 1971

ordained: 1972

charges: Director of education, Eastern Ave., Grand Rapids, MI, 1972-75; Oak Hills, Portland, OR, 1975-81; Chaplain, Pine Rest Christian Hospital, Cutlerville, MI, 1981-82; Assistant Exec. Secretary, Chaplain Committee and part time chaplain, Pine Rest Christian Hospital, Cutlerville, MI, 1982-85; Assistant Exec. Secretary, Chaplain Committee, Grand Rapids, MI, 1985-87

d. 03/03/1987, Grand Rapids, MI

Nikkel, Alan James

b. 07/01/1959, Grinnell, IA

training: Westminster Theological Seminary-CA, MDiv, 1988; Calvin Theological Seminary, Special Program for Ministerial Candidacy, 1990

ordained: 1991

charges: Lexington Green Community, Portage, MI, 1991-93; Ocean View, Norfolk, VA, 1993-96; Hope Community, Santa Rosa, CA, 1996-2000; Non-ministerial vocation, 2000

Noh, John Jae Hwan

b. 02/05/1936, Ye San-Gun, Korea

training: San Francisco Baptist Theological Seminary, MDiv, 1967; declared eligible on the basis of exceptional gifts, 1994

ordained: 1994

charges: Minister of youth, Orange Korean, Fullerton, CA, 1989-90; Orange Korean, Fullerton, CA, 1994-

Nonnekes, Gerardus

b. 01/02/1927, Netherlands

training: Calvin Theological Seminary, BD, 1958

ordained: 1958

charges: Jasper Place, Edmonton, AB, 1958-64; Orangeville, ON, 1964-75; Emo, ON, 1975-85; Fredericton, NB, 1985-92

retired: 1992

Noordewier, Jacob

b. 12/27/1839, Niezijl, Groningen, Netherlands

training: with Roelof Duiker

ordained: 1869

charges: First, Pella, IA, 1869-71; First, Kalamazoo, MI, 1871-73; Central Ave., Holland, MI, 1873-78; Lafayette, IN, 1878-79; First, Kalamazoo, MI, 1880-85; First, Fremont, MI, 1885-91; Fundraising for theological school and Home Missions, 1891-93; Kelloggsville, MI, 1893-96; Jenison, MI, 1896-1907; Firth, NE, 1907-12

retired: 1912

d. 02/05/1938, Grand Rapids, MI

Noordhof, John Henry

b. 08/12/1964, Strathroy, ON

training: Calvin Theological Seminary, MDiv, 1992

ordained: 1992

charges: Dresden, ON, 1992-97; Iron Springs, AB, 1997-

Noorman, Ronald Jon

b. 09/30/1941, Grand Rapids, MI

training: Calvin Theological Seminary, BD, 1966

ordained: 1966

charges: Ogilvie, MN, 1966-69; New Era, MI, 1969-73; Niekerk, Holland, MI, 1973-77; First, Byron Center, MI, 1977-84; Providence, Cutlerville, MI, 1984-90; Central Ave., Holland, MI, 1990-97; Zutphen, MI, 1997-

Numan, Hendrix Sr.

b. 08/02/1902, Wolvega, Friesland, Netherlands

training: Vrije Universiteit, Amsterdam, diploma, 1934

ordained: 1934

charges: GKN: Hylaard, 1934-46; Hattem, 1946-52; CRC: Wyoming, ON, 1952-56; Niagara Falls, ON, 1956-63; Essex, ON, 1963-67; Collingwood, ON, 1967-71

retired: 1971

d. 12/08/1982, Palmetto, FL

Numan, Henry Jr.

b. 10/03/1941, Hijlaard, Friesland, Netherlands

training: Calvin Theological Seminary, BD, 1967

ordained: 1967

charges: Cephas, Peterborough, ON, 1967-71; Bethel, Brockville, ON, 1971-76; First, Vancouver, BC, 1976-86; Trinity, Abbotsford, BC, 1986-91; Third, Lynden, WA, 1991-99; First, Vancouver, BC, 1999-

Nutma, Jelle

b. 02/22/1928, Oostrum, Friesland, Netherlands

training: Knox College; Calvin Theological Seminary, MDiv, 1977
ordained: 1959
charges: Acton, ON, 1959-63; Calvin, Dundas, ON, 1963-66; Maranatha, Bowmanville, ON, 1966-71; Wyoming, ON, 1971-77; First, Thunder Bay, ON, 1977-81; Smithville, ON, 1981-86; First, Rocky Mountain House, AB, 1986-90; East Strathroy, Strathroy, ON, 1990-95
retired: 1995

Nydam, Kenneth John
b. 09/30/1949, Whitinsville, MA
training: Calvin Theological Seminary, MDiv, 1981
ordained: 1981
charges: Highland Hills, Grand Rapids, MI, 1981-84; Cadillac, MI, 1984-97; New Life, Grand Junction, CO, 1997-

Nydam, Ronald Jack
b. 07/26/1948, Whitinsville, MA
training: Calvin Theological Seminary, MDiv, 1974; Chicago Theological Seminary, DMin, 1981; Iliff School of Theology/University of Denver, PhD, 1994
ordained: 1974
charges: Third, Denver, CO, 1974-84; Chaplain, Pastoral Counseling for Denver, Inc, Denver, CO, 1984-98; Faculty, Calvin Theological Seminary, Grand Rapids, MI, 1998-

Nyenhuis, Clarence J.
b. 08/15/1931, Grand Rapids, MI
training: Calvin Theological Seminary, BD, 1958
ordained: 1958
charges: Missionary to Cuba, 1958-60, Home missionary, Good Samaritan, Miami, FL, 1960-69; Latin American, Anaheim, CA, 1969-90
d. 01/23/1990, Anaheim, CA

Nyenhuis, Gerald M.
b. 03/21/1928, Sheboygan, WI
training: Calvin Theological Seminary, Bd, 1962; MDiv, 1992
ordained: 1962
charges: Missionary to Mexico, 1962-94
retired: 1994

Nymeyer, Bradd Leland
b. 06/21/1963
training: Westminster Theological Seminary-CA, MDiv, 1992; Calvin Theological Seminary, Special Program for Ministerial Candidacy, 1994
ordained: 1994
charges: CRC: Education/Evangelism/Youth, First,

Highland, IN, 1993-94; Phoenix, AZ, 1994-96; Independent Reformed Churches: Phoenix, AZ, 1996-97; United Reformed Churches: Phoenix, AZ, 1997-

Oberg, Richard George Jr.
b. 11/17/1943, Sacramento, CA
training: Reformed Theological Seminary-Orlando, MDiv, 2001; Calvin Theological Seminary, Special Program for Ministerial Candidacy (adjusted), 2002
ordained: 2002
charges: Friendship, Gaylord, MI, 2002-

Offringa, Robert L.
b. 03/24/1958, Bellflower, CA
training: Calvin Theological Seminary, MDiv, 1988
ordained: 1989
charges: Second, Lynden, WA, 1989-92; Gold Ave., Grand Rapids, MI, 1992-99; Leave, 1999-2000; Non-ministerial vocation, 2000

Oh, Charles C.
b. 10/23/1967, Seoul, South Korea
training: Talbot School of Theology, MDiv, 1997; Calvin Theological Seminary, Ethnic Minority Program for Ministerial Candidacy, 1999
ordained: 1999
charges: Orange Korean, Fullerton, CA, 1998-2002

Oh, Christian Yong-Yu
b. 09/08/1954, Junbuk, Korea
training: International Theological Seminary, MDiv, 1986; Calvin Theological Seminary, MDiv, 1988
ordained: 1988
charges: Han-Bit Korean, Rochester Hills, MI, 1988-

Oh, Jin Hwan
b. 09/16/1950, Seoul, South Korea
training: Christian Theological Seminary, MDiv, 1993; Fuller Theological Seminary, MA, 1995, DMin
ordained: 1993
charges: Union Church, 1993-94; The Gracious Ark Church, Los Angeles, CA, 1995-97; CRC: The Gracious Ark, Los Angeles, CA, 1997-2002

Oh, John Seho
b. 08/14/1957, Pyung Tack, Korea
training: Presbyterian General Assembly Theological Seminary, MDiv, 1986; Acts Theological Semi-

nary, ThM, 1991; Azusa Pacific Univerity, MA, 1994; Fuller Theological Seminary, DMin
ordained: 1988
charges: Bong Chun, 1982–91; Anaheim Presbyterian, 1992–97; CRC: Korean American of Orange County, Fountain Valley, CA, 1998–

Oldenburg, Cornelius
b. 08/18/1901, IJmuiden, Noord Holland, Netherlands
training: Calvin Theological Seminary, BD, 1931
ordained: 1931
charges: CRC: Harrison, SD, 1932–40; Chaplain, United States Army, 1940–42; eligible for call 1942–44; Third, Kalamazoo, MI, 1944–50; UPC: Non-ministerial vocation, educator, 1950
d. 11/26/1988, Sacramento, CA

Olthoff, John Harry
b. 08/23/1914, Chicago, IL
training: Calvin Theological Seminary, ThB, 1944
ordained: 1944
charges: Comstock, MI, 1944–50; Second, Wellsburg, IA, 1950–56; Bethel, Oskaloosa, IA, 1956–62; First, Oostburg, WI, 1962–79
retired: 1979

Ooms, John Albert
b. 10/21/1955, Calgary, AB
training: Calvin Theological Seminary, MDiv, 1981
ordained: 1981
charges: Penticton, BC, 1981–86; First, Richmond, BC, 1986–93; Inglewood, Edmonton, AB, 1994–

Ooms, Matthew David
b. 03/22/1973, Harvey, IL
training: Calvin Theological Seminary, MDiv, 2001
ordained: 2001
charges: Lincoln Center, Grundy Center, IA, 2001–

Oord, Wybren Hotze
b. 08/27/1953, Haskerhorne, Friesland, Netherlands
training: Calvin Theological Seminary, MDiv, 1986
ordained: 1986
charges: CRC: Ireton, IA, 1986–91; South Olive, MI, 1991–94; Alliance of Reformed Churches: Faith, Borculo, MI, 1994–97; United Reformed Churches: Faith, Borculo, MI, 1997–

Oostendorp, Derk William
b. 03/22/1938, Princeton, NJ
training: Calvin Theological Seminary, BD, 1962; Theologische School, Kampen, ThD, 1967

ordained: 1968
charges: Grace, Bellflower, CA, 1968–74; Missionary to Mexico, 1974–81; Faculty, Calvin College, Grand Rapids, MI, 1981–83; Eligible for call, 1983–84; Missionary, Dominican Republic, 1984–90; Missionary, Mexico, 1990–97; Program Director, Latin America, World Missions, Grand Rapids, MI, 1997–2002
retired: 2002

Oostendorp, Elco Herman
b. 07/26/1911, Grand Rapids, MI
training: Calvin Theological Seminary, ThB, 1935
ordained: 1935
charges: Birnamwood, WI, 1935–39; Luctor, KS, 1939–46; Corsica, SD, 1946–50; Lacombe, AB, 1950–55; Parkersburg, IA, 1955–58; Second, Allendale, MI, 1958–71; Reeman, MI, 1972–76
retired: 1976

Oostendorp, Herman E.
b. 11/07/1881, Leens, Groningen, Netherlands
training: Calvin Theological Seminary, diploma, 1911
ordained: 1911
charges: Eastmanville, MI, 1911–14; Grant, MI, 1914–19; North St., Zeeland, MI, 1919–38
d. 07/28/1938, Holland, MI

Oostendorp, Lubbertus
b. 11/22/1912, Eastmanville, MI
training: Calvin Theological Seminary, BD, 1937; Princeton Theological Seminary, ThM, 1938; Vrije Universiteit, Amsterdam, ThD, 1964
ordained: 1939
charges: Battle Creek, MI, 1939–42; Dennis Ave., Grand Rapids, MI, 1942–52; Graafschap, MI, 1953–57; Hillcrest, Hudsonville, MI, 1957–64; Faculty, Reformed Bible College, Grand Rapids, MI, 1964–79
retired: 1952
d. 08/05/1992, Grand Rapids, MI

Oostenink, Dick John Jr.
b. 07/09/1918, Hull, IA
training: Calvin Theological Seminary, ThB, 1943
ordained: 1943
charges: Portland, MI, 1943–45; Chaplain, United States Army, 1945–46; Newton, NJ, 1946–47; Chaplain, United States Army, 1947–57; Bible teacher, Western Michigan Christian High School, Muskegon, MI, 1957–58; Summer St., Passaic, NJ, 1959–68; Staff and Faculty, United States Army Chaplain's Center and School, 1968–83
retired: 1983

Oosterhuis, Thomas Jacob
b. 03/11/1943, Bradford, ON
training: Calvin Theological Seminary, BD, 1967
ordained: 1976
charges: Chaplain, University of Alberta, Edmonton, AB, 1976-

Oosterveen, Gerald A.
b. 06/12/1936, Zuidwolde, Drenthe, Netherlands
training: Calvin Theological Seminary, BD, 1966; ThM, 1977
ordained: 1966
charges: CRC: Doon, IA, 1966-71; Ferrisburg, VT, 1971-72; graduate studies, 1972-74; Chaplain, Dixon State School for Mentally Retarded, Dixon, IL, 1974-81; Chaplain, Elim Christian School and Bethsan Services, Palos Heights, IL, 1981-84; PCUSA: Hickory Hills, IL, 1984

Ophoff, George M.
b. 01/25/1891, Grand Rapids, MI
training: Calvin Theological Seminary, diploma, 1921
ordained: 1922
charges: CRC: Hope, Grandville, MI, 1921-25; PRC: Hope, Walker, MI, 1925-29; Byron Center, MI, 1929-45; Faculty, Protestant Reformed Seminary, Grandville, MI, 1924-59
retired: 1959
d. 06/12/1962, Grand Rapids, MI

Opperwal, Raymond
b. 06/06/1925, Northbridge, MA
training: Calvin Theological Seminary, ThB, 1952
ordained: 1952
charges: Racine, WI, 1952-61; Ridgewood, NJ, 1961-73; Olentangy, Columbus, OH, 1973-86; East Coast Interim Home Missionary, Board of Home Missions, 1986-90
retired: 1990

Orellana, Ricardo E.
b. 07/07/1953, Los Andes, Chile
training: Calvin Theological Seminary, MCE, 1992
ordained: 1985
charges: First National Presbyterian, Quillota, Chile, 1983-89; Spanish CRC, Wyoming, MI, 1990-91; Gracia y Paz National Presbyterian, Santiago, Chile, 1992-94; CRC: The Good Shepherd, Prospect Park, NJ, 1994-

Orostizaga, Ramon
ordained: 2002
charges: Presbyterian Church of Chile: -2002; CRC: Jersey City Mission, Jersey City, NJ, 2002-

Ortiz, Guillermo
b. 05/18/1948, Colombia
training: Baptist Seminary of Cali, MDiv, 1986
ordained: 1991
charges: Presbyterian Church of Columbia: Cumberland, 1980-87; Union Rescue Mission, Los Angeles, CA, 1987-91; CRC: Latin American, Anaheim, CA, 1991-95; Oasis Hispanic, Orlando, FL, 1995-1999

Ortiz, Manuel
b. 11/20/1938, New York, NY
training: Wheaton Graduate School, MA, 1975; Westminster Theological Seminary-PA, DMin, 1989
ordained: 1975
charges: Evangelical Free Church: Salem, Chicago, IL, 1975-79; Independent: Spirit and Truth Fellowship, Chicago, IL, 1979-83; CRC: Spirit and Truth Fellowship, Chicago, IL, 1983-86; Christian Reformed Home Mission Urban Missions Consultant, Chicago, IL, 1986-87; Faculty, Westminster Theological Seminary, Philadelphia, PA/Spirit and Truth Fellowship, Philadelphia, PA, 1987-

Osterhouse, James David
b. 04/07/1945, Lansing, MI
training: Calvin Theological Seminary, BD, 1971
ordained: 1971
charges: Grace, Indian Harbour Beach, FL, 1971-75; Hope, La Crosse, WI, 1975-82; Faith, New Brighton, MN, 1982-90; Regional director, North Central USA, Board of Home Missions, 1990-

Oussoren, Arie Hermanus
b. 04/15/1898, Netherlands
training: Vrije Universiteit, Amsterdam, ThD, 1945
ordained: 1930
charges: GKN: Vollenhove, 1930-34; Middelburg, 1934-42; Teacher of Missions at Christian Lyceum at Goes, 1947-51; CRC: Hoboken, NJ and spiritual advisor of Seamen's and Immigrant's Home, 1951-53; Hoboken, NJ, 1953-55; Bethel, Vancouver, BC, 1955-58; United Church of Canada: Stonewall, Manitoba, 1958

Ouwehand, Rudy Willem
b. 09/12/1946, Amsterdam, Noord Holland, Netherlands
training: Calvin Theological Seminary, MDiv, 1979
ordained: 1979
charges: Grace, Cobourg, ON, 1979-84; Covenant, Woodstock, ON, 1984-94; Agassiz, BC, 1994-

Ouwehand, Tony John

b. 09/18/1942, Amsterdam, Noord Holland, Netherlands
training: Calvin Theological Seminary, BD, 1974; ThM, 1976
ordained: 1974
charges: CRC: Springdale, ON, 1974–76; Charlottetown, PE, 1976–80; Resigned from denomination, 1980

Ouwinga, Harvey Arlen

b. 03/19/1932, Marion, MI
training: Calvin Theological Seminary, BD, 1957
ordained: 1957
charges: Birnamwood, WI, 1957–62; Chaplain, United States Army, 1962–69; Cascade, Marysville, WA, 1969–74; East Leonard, Grand Rapids, MI, 1974–81; Bradenton, FL, 1981–92; Mission 21 India, Grand Rapids, MI, 1992–94; Second, Kalamazoo, MI, 1994–97
retired: 1997

Ouwinga, John Michael

b. 07/01/1947, Detroit, MI
training: Calvin Theological Seminary, MDiv, 1974
ordained: 1974
charges: Campus minister, Grand Rapids Community College and Assistant pastor to Youth, LaGrave Ave., Grand Rapids, MI, 1974–78; Niekerk, Holland, MI, 1978–88; Faith, Tinley Park, IL, 1988–

Ouwinga, Menko

b. 05/16/1905, Highland, MI vicinity
training: Calvin Theological Seminary, BD, 1936
ordained: 1937
charges: Sullivan, MI, 1937–39; East Paris, MI, 1939–44; Detroit, MI, 1944–49; Second, Denver, CO, 1949–56; First, South Holland, IL, 1956–65; Bethel, Zeeland, MI, 1965–71
retired: 1971
d. 03/04/1985, Grand Rapids, MI

Ouwinga, Paul

b. 04/08/1910, Highland, MI vicinity
training: Calvin Theological Seminary, ThB, 1942
ordained: 1942
charges: Ogilvie, MN, 1942–46; Ireton, IA, 1946–51; Baldwin, WI, 1951–56; Grant, MI, 1956–66; Willmar, MN, 1966–75
retired: 1975
d. 10/21/1995, Fremont, MI

Ouwinga, Timothy John

b. 03/07/1955, Baldwin, WI
training: Calvin Theological Seminary, MDiv, 1981
ordained: 1981
charges: Inwood, IA, 1981–87; Racine, WI, 1987–97; First, Orange City, IA, 1997–

Overduin, Cornelius Nick

b. 07/13/1956, St. Thomas, ON
training: Calvin Theological Seminary, MDiv, 1984
ordained: 1985
charges: Fellowship, St. Thomas, ON, 1985–90; Chaplain, Brock Christian Reformed Campus Ministry, St. Catharines, ON, 1990–96; Second, Brampton, ON, 1996–2002; First, Toronto, ON, 2002–

Overweg, Timothy

b. 06/24/1958, Holland, MI
training: Bethel Theological Seminary, MDiv, 1987
ordained: 1989
charges: RCA: Peace, Eagan, MN, 1989–93; Westwood Community, Omaha, NE, 1996–97; Urban Ventures Leadership Foundation, Minneapolis, MN, 1997–; CRC: Missionary, Dominican Republic, 1993–96

Paas, Patrick Francis

b. 12/06/1953, Grand Rapids, MI
training: Reformed Bible College, BRE, 1984; Calvin Theological Seminary, MDiv, 1988
ordained: 1988
charges: CRC: All Nations Christian Fellowship, Toronto, ON, 1988–97; eligible for call, 1997–99; released from denomination, 1999

Paauw, Jack Howard

b. 09/01/1932, Tyler, MN
training: Calvin Theological Seminary, BD, 1957
ordained: 1957
charges: Missionary at Hammond City Mission, Hammond, IN, 1957–61; Lakewood, CA, 1961–64; Bellingham, WA, 1964–67; Leave for study, 1967–70; Non-ministerial vocation, 1970

Paauw, Jacob

b. 10/31/1891, Hindeloopen, Friesland, Netherlands
training: Calvin Theological Seminary, diploma, 1920
ordained: 1920
charges: missionary, Hancock MN, 1920–21; Hancock MN, 1921–27; Holland, MN, 1927–44; Sultan, WA, 1944–46; Vancouver, BC, 1946–51; Dispatch, KS, 1951–55; Holland Center, SD, 1955–57
retired: 1957
d. 06/16/1981, Fresno, CA

Padmos, Cornelis
b. 08/18/1928, Netherlands
training: Vrije Universiteit, Amsterdam, diploma,
1955; Union Theological Seminary, 1956
ordained: 1956
charges: GKN: Geesteren, 1956-58; Chaplain,
Royal Dutch Army, 1958-60; Maarsland, 1969-76;
s' Gravenhage-Loosduinen, 1976-82; CRC:
Maranatha, Calgary, AB, 1960-65; Maranatha, Edmonton, AB, 1965-69
retired: 1982
d. 05/04/1988, Leiden, Netherlands

Padro, Peter L.
charges: PCA : -2002; CRC: Richfield, Clifton, NJ,
2002-

Paek, Noah C.
b. 01/02/1954
ordained: 1993
charges: CRC: Calvin, Los Alamitos, CA, 1995-
96; eligible for call, 1996-99; Resigned from denomination, 1999

Palma, Robert James
b. 05/10/1934, Grand Rapids, MI
training: Calvin Theological Seminary, BD, 1959
ordained: 1960
charges: CRC: Home missionary, Iowa City, IA,
1960-64; Leave for study, 1964-66; Faculty, Hope
College, Holland, MI, 1966-73; RCA: Faculty, Hope
College, Holland, MI, 1973-94
retired: 1994

Palmer, Edwin Hartshorn
b. 06/29/1922, Quincy, MA
training: Westminster Theological Seminary-PA,
ThB, 1949; Vrije Universiteit, Amsterdam, ThD,
1953
ordained: 1953
charges: Spring Lake, MI, 1953-57; Ann Arbor,
MI, 1957-60; Faculty, Westminster Theological
Seminary, 1960-64; Grandville Ave., Grand
Rapids, MI, 1964-68; Executive Secretary New International Version (NIV) Bible/General editor, NIV
Study Bible, New York Bible Society, 1968-80
d. 09/16/1980, Wayne, NJ

Palmer, Timothy Pavitt
b. 03/11/1951, Amsterdam, Noord Holland, Netherlands
training: Calvin Theological Seminary, BD, 1976;
MDiv, 1988
ordained: 1988

charges: Faculty, Theological College of Northern
Nigeria, Jos, Nigeria, 1988-

Palsrok, Matthew Arnold
b. 08/13/1958, Muskegon, MI
training: Calvin Theological Seminary, MDiv, 1985
ordained: 1985
charges: Lucas, MI, 1985-89; Riverside, Grand
Rapids, MI, 1989-2000; Cottonwood Heights,
Jension, MI, 2000-

Palsrok, Russell Lee
b. 03/14/1945, Muskegon, MI
training: Calvin Theological Seminary, BD, 1971;
ThM, 1972; San Fransicisco Theological Seminary,
DMin, 1982
ordained: 1972
charges: Youth director, Hospitality House, Honolulu, HI, 1972-75; Campus minister, University of
Wisconsin, Madison, WI, 1975-77; Honolulu, HI,
1977-83; Hope, Oak Forest, IL, 1983-87; Faculty,
Theological College of Northern Nigeria, Nigeria,
1987-89; Plymouth Heights, Grand Rapids, MI,
1989-2001; Rochester, NY, 2002-

Park, Byoung-Eun
b. 09/17/1954, Pusan, Korea
training: Hapdong Seminary, MDiv, 1983; Talbot
School of Theology, MTh, 1995
ordained: 1984
charges: Korean Presbyterian Reformed Church:
Sainglim, 1984-92; Korean American CRC, Orange
County, CA, 1994-96; Himang Korean Presbyterian Church, 1997-99; CRC: Hahn-In, Wyoming,
MI, 1999-

Park, Daniel Young Don
b. 11/11/1954, Seoul, South Korea
training: International Theological Seminary,
MDiv, 1985; Calvin Theological Seminary, Special
Program for Ministerial Candidacy, 1989
ordained: 1989
charges: CRC: Korean, Los Angeles, CA, 1989-
92; Leave, 1992-93; Resigned from denomination,
1993

Park, Eun Woo
b. 01/15/1951
ordained: 1985
charges: Young Kwang Presbyterian Church, Korea, 1984-87; CRC: Canaan, Houston, TX, 1987-
92; Glory Community, Houston, TX, 1992-98

Park, Gui Je
b. 09/15/1950, Seoul, South Korea

training: Christian Theological Seminary, MA, 1986
ordained: 1986
charges: Whang San, Seoul, Korea, 1982-95; Korean Presbyterian, Barrow, AK, 1995-96; CRC: Barrow, AK, 1996-2002; Sumkee Neun Korean, Tacoma, WA, 2002-

Park, Heu Gyu
b. 08/25/1958, Seoul, South Korea
training: Chong-Shin Theological Seminary, MDiv, 1984
ordained: 1984
charges: Presbyterian Church of Korea: Dong-Do Presbyterian, Seoul, Korea, 1984-89; CRC: Korean, Los Angeles, CA, 1989-93; Resigned from denomination, 1993

Park, Hyung-Ju
b. 07/30/1946
ordained: 1986
charges: Bansuk Central Presbyterian Church, Seoul, Korea, 1986-92; First Union Presbyterian, Oceanside, CA, 1993-95; CRC: Valley Shinil/Mission of Love, Northridge, CA, 1995-

Park, James Jungkya
b. 05/14/1933
ordained: 1990
charges: Korean Presbyterian Church of America; CRC: Missionary, Japan, 1990-99
retired: 1999

Park, Jang Ho
b. 03/03/1961, Yecheon, Korea
training: Presbyterian General Assembly Theological Seminary, MDiv, 1991; International Theological Seminary, ThM, 1993; Westminster Theological Seminary-CA, ThD, 1995
ordained: 1991
charges: Carson Korean, 1991-96; The Spirit Filled, 1996-99; CRC: Spirit Filled, Artesia, CA, 1999-

Park, Seonghwan
b. 06/13/1939
ordained: 1978
charges: CRC: Okto Glory, Los Angeles, CA, 1994-2000
retired: 2000; resigned from denomination, 2001

Park, Soong Kun
b. 02/28/1938, Ham Nam Han Heung, Korea
training: Dae Han Theological Seminary, MDiv, 1972; Presbyterian General Assembly Theological

Seminary, MDiv, 1991; International Theological Seminary, ThM, 1993; Westminster Theological Seminary, DMin, 1975
ordained: 1975
charges: Korea: Sung San Church, 1980-83; Gi Hyang Church, 1983-91; CRC: Mt. Pilgrim Chapel, Los Angeles, CA, 1992-2001

Park, Suk Ho
b. 05/26/1947, Kyung-Nam, Korea
training: Korean Theological Seminary, MDiv, 1976; Calvin Theological Seminary, Special Program for Ministerial Candidacy, 1978
ordained: 1978
charges: Koshin Presbyterian Church: Samil Presbytery, 1978-80; Dae Sin Korean, Artesia, CA, 1978-83; CRC: Dae Sin Korean Presbyterian, Artesia, CA, 1983-84; Leave, 1984-90; Resigned from denomination, 1990

Park, Tong Kun
b. 01/16/1950, Seoul, South Korea
training: Fuller Theological Seminary, MDiv, 1995
ordained: 1995
charges: Miracle Land Baptist, Cypress, CA, 1995-97; CRC: Orange Korean, Fullerton, CA, 1997-98; Intercultural Ministries Director, Christian Reformed Home Missions, Bellflower, CA, 1998-

Pars, Garrett D.
b. 03/12/1908, Franeker, Friesland, Netherlands
training: Calvin Theological Seminary, ThB, 1937
ordained: 1939
charges: Grangeville, ID, 1939-43; Vancouver, BC, 1943-46; Tohatchi, NM, 1946-51; Austinville, IA, 1951-56; East Side, Cleveland, OH, 1956-62; Morrison, IL, 1962-68; Calvary, Seattle, WA, 1968-73
retired: 1973

Pasma, John
b. 02/14/1950, Chatham, ON
training: Calvin Theological Seminary, MDiv, 1988
ordained: 1988
charges: Rehoboth, Niagara Falls, ON, 1988-95; Covenant, Edmonton, AB, 1995-

Pastine, Stuart Clinton
b. 01/13/1941, Brooklyn, NY
training: Westminster Theological Seminary-PA, ThM, 1968; Calvin Theological Seminary, Special Program for Ministerial Candidacy, 1970
ordained: 1970
charges: CRC: Lynnwood, WA, 1970-78; Smithers, BC, 1978-82; Sanborn, IA, 1982-92; Lane Ave.,

Kansas City, MO, 1992–97; United Reformed Churches: Covenant Reformed, Kansas City, MO, 1997–2001

Patterson, Virgil C.
b. 03/18/1933, Indianapolis, IN
training: Boston University School of Theology, 1963
ordained: 1963
charges: United Presbyterian Church: Chaplain, Boston Council of Church, 1963–65; Field staff, Chicago Presbytery, 1965–67; Lawndale, IL, 1967–70; Executive Secretary Association Urban Ministries of Chicago Presbytery, 1970–73; CRC: Minister of church education and evangelism, Fuller Ave., Grand Rapids, MI, 1973–74; Madison Square, Grand Rapids, MI, 1974–77; Independent: Harvest Full Gospel Church, Grand Rapids, MI, 1977–80; Michigan Department of Social Services, 1980–82
d. 10/19/1982, Grand Rapids, MI

Payton, James Richard Jr.
b. 10/15/1947, Galesburg, IL
training: Bob Jones University, MA, 1971; Westminster Theological Seminary-PA, MDiv and ThM, 1975; University of Waterloo, PhD, 1982
ordained: 1977
charges: OPC: Blue Bell, PA, 1977–79; Faculty, Westminster Theological Seminary, 1980–81; CRC: Stratford, ON, 1983–85; Non-ministerial vocation: Faculty, Redeemer College, Ancaster, ON, 1985

Pearson, Steven D.
b. 04/29/1953, Shelby, MI
training: Western Theological Seminary, MDiv, 1979
ordained: 1979
charges: RCA: Sixth Reformed, Grand Rapids, MI, 1979–81; Clinical Pastorate Education, Pine Rest Christian Hospital, Cutlerville, MI, 1981–82; United Methodist Church: Twin Lake, MI, 1983–88; Three Oaks, MI, 1988–95; United Church, Ovid, MI, 1995–97; CRC: Church relations and communications, Christian Reformed Home Missions, Grand Rapids, MI, 1999–2001

Pekelder, Bernard Edward
b. 12/17/1922, Grand Rapids, MI
training: Calvin Theological Seminary, BD, 1946; Northwestern University, MA, 1965
ordained: 1947
charges: Jamestown, MI, 1947–51; East Leonard, Grand Rapids, MI, 1951–55; Midland Park, NJ, 1955–62; Chaplain, Calvin College, Grand Rapids, MI, 1962–71; Chaplain and Vice President of Student Affairs, Calvin College, Grand Rapids, MI, 1971–85
retired: 1985

Pekelder, Edward Bernard
b. 02/24/1896, Muskegon, MI
training: Calvin Theological Seminary, diploma, 1921
ordained: 1921
charges: Wyoming Park, Wyoming, MI, 1921–25, Coldbrook Ave., Grand Rapids, MI, 1925–35; Sheboygan, WI, 1935–47; First, Kalamazoo, MI, 1947–53; Lamont, MI, 1953–56; Godwin Heights, Grand Rapids, MI, 1956–62
retired: 1962
d. 05/25/1974, Grand Rapids, MI

Pellecer, Luis Antonio
b. 09/14/1956, Guatemala City, Guatemala
training: Calvin Theological Seminary, MMin, 1990
ordained: 1990
charges: Faith Hope and Love Hispanic Ministry, Grand Rapids, MI, 1988–94; Good Samaritan, Miami, FL, 1994–

Pennings, Brent Alan
b. 07/11/1963, Orange City, IA
training: Calvin Theological Seminary, MDiv, 1989
ordained: 1989
charges: CRC: Forest Grove, MI, 1989–94; Leave, 1994–97; Independent: Kettle Lake Independent Reformed Church, 1997–2002

Pennings, Eric (Arie)
b. 12/01/1957, Galt, ON
training: Calvin Theological Seminary, MDiv, 1986
ordained: 1986
charges: CRC: Missionary, Costa Rica, 1986–94; Leave, 1994–95; East Strathroy, Strathroy, ON, 1995–2002; Resigned from denomination

Perdomo, Oscar C.
training: DMin
ordained: 1971
charges: PCUSA: Bethel, San Antonio, TX, 1971–76; Irving Park, UCC, Chicago, IL, 1976; Columbia Basin, Mattawa, WA, 1976–79; Riverside, Desert Aire, WA, 1980–90; CRC: Quincy, WA, 1999–

Pereboom, Jan Dirk
b. 04/28/1925, Ede, Gelderland, Netherlands
training: Vrije Universiteit, Amsterdam, diploma, 1954; St. Stephens Theological Seimary, MA, 1979

ordained: 1955
charges: GKN: Pesse, 1955–57; Chaplain Royal Dutch Air Force, 1957–61; CRC: Port Arthur, ON, 1961–64; Williamsburg, ON, 1964–69; Trinity, Edmonton, AB, 1969–76; leave, 1977–79; Zion, Pembroke, ON, 1979–82; Rehoboth, Niagara Falls, ON, 1982–88
retired: 1988

Pereboom, Pieter
b. 04/26/1958, Ruinen, Drenthe, Netherlands
training: declared eligible on the basis of exceptional gifts, 2001
ordained: 2001
charges: Youth, First, London, ON, 1992–94; First, London, ON, 2001–

Persenaire, Adam
b. 06/12/1898, Amsterdam, Noord Holland, Netherlands
training: Calvin Theological Seminary, ThB, 1929
ordained: 1929
charges: Eastmanville, MI, 1929–48; Home missionary at St. Catharines, ON, 1948–51; at Brantford, 1951–54; at Hamilton, ON, 1954–56; at Dundas, ON, 1956–61; Galt, ON, 1961–64
retired: 1964
d. 05/25/1977, Grand Rapids, MI

Persenaire, Bruce A.
b. 08/04/1955, Grand Rapids, MI
training: Calvin Theological Seminary, MDiv, 1981
ordained: 1982
charges: Ellsworth, MI, 1982–86; Escalon, CA, 1986–

Persenaire, Cornelius Adrian
b. 09/06/1928, Chicago, IL
training: Calvin Theological Seminary, BD, 1953
ordained: 1953
charges: Zillah, WA, 1953–55; Missionary to Africa-Nigeria, 1955–62; Kanawha, IA, 1962–65; Missionary to Nigeria, 1965–71; Missionary to Honduras, 1971–76; Iglesia Hispana, Holland, MI, 1976–82; Missionary, Philippines, 1982–83; Fellowship, Brighton, ON, 1984–89; Wallaceburg, ON, 1989–93
retired: 1993
d. 11/20/2002, Muskegon, MI

Persenaire-Hogeterp, Henry Edward
b. 01/09/1968, Grand Rapids, MI
training: Calvin Theological Seminary, MDiv, 1998
ordained: 1998
charges: Missionary, Nigeria, 1998–

Peters, Nico Jacob
b. 02/01/1951, Leiden, Zuid Holland, Netherlands
training: Calvin Theological Seminary, MDiv, 1977
ordained: 1978
charges: CRC: Collingwood, ON, 1978–80; Resigned from denomination

Petersen, Henry
b. 06/16/1915, Grand Haven, MI
training: Calvin Theological Seminary, ThB, 1942
ordained: 1942
charges: Granum, AB, 1942–45; Home missionary for Classis Chicago North, 1945–48; Holland, IA, 1948–53; Platte, SD, 1953–64; Sumas, WA, 1964–72; Second, Pella, IA, 1972–80
retired: 1980
d. 10/24/1990, Grand Haven, MI

Petersen, James Thomas
b. 03/05/1950, San Diego, CA
training: Calvin Theological Seminary, ThM, 1976
ordained: 1976
charges: Bunde, MN, 1976–80; First, Pipestone, MN, 1980–85; Trinity, Jenison, MI, 1985–90; Bellingham, WA, 1990–95; Faith, New Brighton, MN, 1995–

Petersen, John Aldrich
b. 05/07/1919, Redlands, CA
training: Calvin Theological Seminary, ThB, 1949
ordained: 1949
charges: Glendale, CA, 1949–53; Mount Vernon, WA, 1953–58; Second, Grand Haven, MI, 1958–64; North Haledon, NJ, 1964–71; Bozeman, MT, 1971–76; Oak Harbor, WA, 1977–84
retired: 1984

Peterson, Ronald L.
b. 02/25/1937, Holland, MI
training: Calvin Theological Seminary, BD, 1961
ordained: 1961
charges: Crown Point, IN, 1961–64; Goshen, IN, 1964–69; Dearborn, MI, 1969–76; Regional home missionary, Eastern District at Hawthorne, NJ, 1976–92; Residency, Marriage and Family Therapy Residency, Hawthorne, NJ, 1992–94; Chaplain, Marriage and Family Therapy Practice, Cranford, NJ, 1994–98; Chaplain, Classical Care Coordinator, Classis of South GR-RCA, Grand Rapids, MI, 1998–2002
retired: 2002

Petroelje, Allen
b. 04/26/1945, Zeeland, MI

training: Calvin Theological Seminary, BD, 1970; MDiv, 1982
ordained: 1970
charges: Crown Point, IN, 1970–74; Cascade, Marysville, WA, 1974–78; Bethel, Manhattan, MT, 1978–85; Covenant, Cutlerville, MI, 1985–96; First, Fremont, MI, 1996–

Petroelje, Harold
b. 01/03/1918, Byron Center, MI
training: Calvin Theological Seminary, ThB, 1941
ordained: 1941
charges: Holland Center, SD, 1941–43; Cedar, IA, 1943–49; Waupun, WI, 1949–53; Alameda, CA, 1953–82
retired: 1982

Pettinga, Thomas Ernest
b. 07/04/1947, Grand Rapids, MI
training: Calvin Theological Seminary, MDiv, 1974
ordained: 1974
charges: Assistant minister, Bethel, Sun Valley, CA, 1974–78; Ridgewood, Jenison, MI, 1978–83; Immanuel, Columbia, MO, 1983–91; Cedar Hill/ Hope Fellowship, Cedar Hill, TX, 1991–

Pewee, Dongo
b. 06/02/1962, Harbel, Liberia
training: Calvin Theological Seminary, MDiv, 1995
ordained: 1996
charges: Emmanuel, Sauk Village, IL, 1996–98; eligible for call, 1998–99; Unity, Allegan, MI, 1999–

Pierik, Dick (Derk)
b. 08/08/1935, Amsterdam, Noord Holland, Netherlands
training: Calvin Theological Seminary, BD, 1964
ordained: 1964
charges: First, Port Alberni, ON, 1964–68; Burnaby, BC, 1968–79; Campus minister, University of Toronto, Toronto, ON, 1979–94; Non-ministerial vocation, 1994

Piers, Dale Loren
b. 12/28/1960, Modesto, CA
training: Westminster Theological Seminary-CA, MDiv, 1988; Calvin Theological Seminary, Special Program for Ministerial Candidacy, 1989
ordained: 1989
charges: CRC: Anaheim, CA, 1989–93; Calvary, Loveland, CO, 1993–97; United Reformed Churches: Calvary, Loveland, CO, 1997

Piersma, Elton James
b. 03/17/1927, Grand Rapids, MI
training: Calvin Theological Seminary, BD, 1961; ThM, 1982
ordained: 1963
charges: Trinity, Philadelphia, PA, 1963–68; Spring Lake, MI, 1969–74; leave, 1974–75; Executive Director, Christian Life Enrichment Ministries, Grand Haven, MI, 1975–81; Counselor, Marriage and Family Center, Muskegon, MI, 1981–89
retired: 1989

Piersma, John Henry
b. 12/25/1916, Grand Rapids, MI
training: Calvin Theological Seminary, ThB, 1947
ordained: 1947
charges: Oostburg, WI, 1947–49; Franklin St., Grand Rapids, MI, 1949–53; Oakdale Park, Grand Rapids, MI, 1953–56; Second, Edmonton, AB, 1956–60; Grandville Ave., Grand Rapids, MI, 1960–64; First, Pella, IA, 1964–69; Bethany, South Holland, IL, 1969–77; First, Sioux Center, IA, 1977–81; Pleasant St., Whitinsville, MA, 1981–84
retired: 1984

Pikaart, John Dingeman
b. 01/09/1884, Forest Grove, MI
training: Calvin Theological Seminary, diploma, 1914
ordained: 1914
charges: Atwood, MI, 1914–21; North Blendon, MI, 1921–29; Oskaloosa, IA, (service pastor, Alexandria, VA, 1943) 1929–45; Brooten, MN, 1945–52
retired: 1952
d. 05/31/1984, Oskaloosa, IA

Pimentel, Alejandro
b. 12/05/1950, Lima, Peru
training: Calvin Theological Seminary, MDiv, 1998
ordained: 1999
charges: World Literature Ministries, Board of Publications, Grand Rapids, MI, 1999–

Plantinga, Cornelius Jr.
b. 02/14/1946, Jamestown, ND
training: Calvin Theological Seminary, BD, 1971; Princeton Theological Seminary, PhD, 1980
ordained: 1971
charges: Webster, NY, 1971–75; Leave, 1975–79; Faculty, Calvin Theological Seminary, Grand Rapids, MI, 1979–1996; Dean of Chapel, Calvin College, Grand Rapids, MI, 1996–2001; President, Calvin Theological Seminary, Grand Rapids, MI, 2002–

Plesscher, Diedrich H.
b. 08/28/1889, Lincoln Center, IA
training: Calvin Theological Seminary, diploma, 1916
ordained: 1916
charges: Home missionary Cl. Ostfriesland at Parkersburg, IA, 1916-19; Ackley, IA, 1919-25; Kanawha, IA, 1925-50
retired: 1950
d. 07/29/1951, Parkersburg, IA

Plesscher, John (Johan) Gerhard Sr.
b. 05/14/1849, Osterwald, Bentheim, Germany
training: Theologische Universiteit, Kampen and Veldhausen, diploma, 1881
ordained: 1881
charges: Altreformierte Kirche: Neermoor, Germany, 1881-85; CRC: Lincoln Center, IA, 1885-97; Parkersburg, IA, 1897-1912; Bunde, MN, 1912-16
retired: 1916
d. 04/11/1935, Parkersburg, IA

Plesscher, John Gerhard Jr.
b. 12/01/1895, Lincoln Center, IA
training: Grundy College and Seminary, diploma, 1920; Princeton University, AM, 1920; Princeton Theological Seminary, ThM, 1923
ordained: 1920
charges: Faculty, Grundy College, 1920-21 and 1923-26; Ridott, IL, 1926-27
d. 04/30/1927, Ridott, IL

Plug, Peter
b. 12/02/1941, Noordwijk, Zuid Holland, Netherlands
training: Calvin Theological Seminary, BD, 1973
ordained: 1973
charges: Telkwa, BC, 1973-76; First, Regina, SK, 1976-81; Vernon, BC, 1981-87
d. 08/17/1987, Sarnia, ON

Poel, Abel
b. 05/12/1908, Grand Haven, MI
training: Calvin Theological Seminary, BD, 1934
ordained: 1935
charges: Missionary, Parchment, MI, 1935-44; Rehoboth, NM, 1944-57; Missionary for Classis Muskegon at Fruitport, MI, 1957-66; Cadillac, MI, 1966-72
retired: 1972
d. 06/28/1996, Grand Rapids, MI

Poelman, James Ralph
b. 09/18/1951, Cochrane, ON
training: Calvin Theological Seminary, BD, 1978

ordained: 1978
charges: Brantford, ON, 1978-83; Wallaceburg, ON, 1983-89; Cephas, Peterborough, ON, 1989-93; Smithers, BC, 1993-

Pohler, Robert A.
b. 03/08/1953, Zeeland, MI
training: Calvin Theological Seminary, MCE, 1978; Special Program for Ministerial Candidacy, 2000; Trinity Divinity School, MDiv, 1999
ordained: 1999
charges: Bethany, Muskegon, MI, 1978-80; Plymouth Heights, Grand Rapids, MI, 1980-86; Faith, Holland, MI, 1986-2002; Trinity, Fremont, MI, 2002-

Polman, Gerrit Hendrik
b. 06/27/1915, Zwolle, Overijsel, Netherlands
training: Theologische Universiteit, Apeldoorn, diploma, 1941
ordained: 1941
charges: CGKN: Gorinchem, 1941-43; Rozenburg, 1943-47; Hilversum (Missionary to Mamas, Indonesia), 1947-50; The Hague-East, 1950-55; CRC: Barrhead-Westlock, AB, 1955-57; Chilliwack, BC, 1957-61; Home missionary, Prince George, BC, 1961-67; Rehoboth, Niagara Falls, ON, 1967-73; leave, 1973-75; Burdett, AB, 1975-79
retired: 1979

Pols, Gordon Henry
b. 11/08/1941, Aalsmeer, Noord Holland, Netherlands
training: Calvin Theological Seminary, BD, 1970
ordained: 1970
charges: Surrey, BC, 1970-74; West End, Edmonton, AB, 1974-93; Clarkston, Mississauga, ON, 1993-2000; Ancaster, ON, 2000-

Pomykala, Kenneth
b. 02/10/1954, Passaic, NJ
training: Calvin Theological Seminary, MDiv, 1981; Claremont Graduate School, MA, 1988, PhD, 1992
ordained: 1982
charges: Houston, BC, 1982-84; Leave, 1984-88; Faculty, Calvin College, Grand Rapids, MI, 1988-

Ponsen, Benjamin James
b. 01/25/1969, Newmarket, ON
training: Calvin Theological Seminary, MDiv, 2002
ordained: 2002
charges: First, Kemptville, ON, 2002-

Pontier, Arthur Eugene

b. 06/27/1918, Passaic, NJ
training: Calvin Theological Seminary, ThB, 1952
ordained: 1952
charges: East Side, Cleveland, OH, 1952-55;
West Sayville, NY, 1955-60; Coopersville, MI,
1960-64; Calvary, Pella, IA, 1964-73; Grandville
Ave., Grand Rapids, MI, 1973-81
retired: 1981

Pontier, Ralph Andrew

b. 02/07/1950, Passaic, NJ
training: Westminster Theological Seminary-PA,
MDiv, 1976; Calvin Theological Seminary, Special
Program for Ministerial Candidacy, 1977
ordained: 1977
charges: CRC: Cape Coral, FL, 1977-86; First, Orange City, IA, 1986-94; Alliance of Reformed
Churches: Redeemer Alliance Reformed, Orange
City, IA, 1994-95; United Reformed Churches: Redeemer, Orange City, IA, 1995-

Pool, Cornelius

b. 03/10/1951, Lemmer, Friesland, Netherlands
training: Calvin Theological Seminary, MDiv, 1978
ordained: 1978
charges: Tillsonburg, ON, 1978-83; Green
Meadow, Helena, MT, 1983-89; Fresno, CA, 1989-
94; Sonlight Community, Regina, SK, 1994-99;
Hope Community, Riverside, CA, 1999-

Pool, Melle

b. 10/06/1939, Groningen, Groningen, Netherlands
training: Calvin Theological Seminary, BD, 1967
ordained: 1967
charges: Houston, BC, 1967-71; Third, Sarnia,
ON, 1971-77; Trinity, Edmonton, AB, 1977-84;
Glad Tidings, Edmonton, AB, 1984-89; Specialized
pastoral education, Edmonton, AB, 1989-90;
Chaplain, Pastoral Institute, Edmonton, AB, 1990-
92; Director, Pastoral Care and Counseling,
Rehoboth Christian Ministries, Stony Plain, AB,
1992-95; First, Langley, BC, 1995-2000; Interim,
Ebenezer, Leduc, ON, 2000-02; Interim, Sonrise,
Ponoka, AB, 2002-

Poolman, David Duane

b. 02/06/1962, Kalamazoo, MI
training: Calvin Theological Seminary, MDiv, 1988
ordained: 1988
charges: Imlay City, MI, 1988-93; Cedar Hill,
Wyckoff, NJ, 1993-

Poortenga, John

b. 04/08/1956, Harvey, IL

training: Calvin Theological Seminary, MDiv, 1984
ordained: 1985
charges: First, Calgary, AB, 1985-88; New Life,
Abbotsford, BC, 1988-

Poot, Arie

b. 03/27/1949, DeLier, Zuid Holland, Netherlands
training: Calvin Theological Seminary, MDiv, 1976
ordained: 1976
charges: CRC: Anacortes, WA, 1974-75; Lincoln
Center, IA, 1976-77; Leave, 1977-78; Stated supply, Mt. Vernon, WA, 1978-79; First, Mt. Vernon,
WA, 1979-84; Chaplain, Bethesda Cascade,
Bellingham, WA, 1984-90; Resigned from denomination, 1990

Popma, Repko Willem

b. 01/01/1913, Tzum, Friesland, Netherlands
training: Vrije Universiteit, Amsterdam, diploma,
1940
ordained: 1940
charges: GKN: Vreeland, 1940-46; Surabaja, Indonesia, 1946-57; CRC: Victoria, BC, 1957-64;
Ebenezer, Trenton, ON, 1964-78
retired: 1978

Poppen, Klaas

b. 03/28/1864, Drenthe, MI
training: Princeton Theological Seminary, BD,
1900
ordained: 1900
charges: Englewood, NJ, 1900-02; Monsey, NY,
1902-04; Second Englewood, Chicago, IL, 1904-
08; Harrison, SD, 1908-10; Home missionary
Classis Pacific, 1910-11; Burton Heights, Grand
Rapids, MI, 1911-13; Madison Ave., Paterson, NJ,
1913-23; Bradley, MI, 1923-25
retired: 1925
d. 07/14/1936, Holland, MI

Post, Benjamin

b. 02/16/1890, Allendale, MI
training: Calvin Theological Seminary, diploma,
1918; Princeton ThB, 1919
ordained: 1919
charges: Wright IA, 1919-20
d. 11/26/1920, Wright, IA

Post, Henry Richard Jr.

b. 02/18/1944, Grand Rapids, MI
training: Calvin Theological Seminary, BD, 1969
ordained: 1970
charges: Campus minister under IVCF at Kent
State, Akron, OH, 1970-72; Campus minister on
loan to Inter Varsity Christian Fellowship at West-

ern Michigan University, 1972-73; Little Farms, Coopersville, MI, 1973-75; Chaplain, Pine Rest Christian Hospital, Cutlerville, MI, 1975-77; Chaplain, W.A. Foote Memorial Hospital, Jackson, MI, 1976-91; Chaplain, Porter Hills Presbyterian Village, Grand Rapids, MI, 1991-2001; On loan, Park UCC, Grand Rapids, MI, 2001-

Post, John

b. 04/15/1850, Wirdum, Groningen, Netherlands
training: Calvin Theological Seminary, diploma, 1881
ordained: 1881
charges: Eastern Ave., Grand Rapids, MI, 1881-87; Spring Lake, MI, 1887-90; First, Kalamazoo, MI, 1890-95; Lamont and Eastmanville, MI, 1895-1900; Niekerk, MI, 1900-04; Jamestown, MI, 1904-09; Spring Lake, MI, 1909-14; Cutlerville, MI, 1914-20; Chaplain, Pine Rest Christian Hospital, 1920-28
d. 01/17/1928, Cutlerville, MI

Postema, Donald Henry

b. 07/03/1934, Evergreen Park, IL
training: Calvin Theological Seminary, BD, 1960
ordained: 1963
charges: Campus Chapel, Ann Arbor, MI, 1963-98
retired: 1998

Postema, Gerald Dale

b. 08/23/1944, Grand Rapids, MI
training: Calvin Theological Seminary, BD, 1969
ordained: 1972
charges: Fruitport, MI, 1972-78; Big Rapids, MI, 1978-85; Calvin, Muskegon, MI, 1985-88; Fellowship, Grandville, MI, 1988-99; Fruitport, MI, 1999-

Posthuma, Roger Dean

b. 04/06/1923, Grand Rapids, MI
training: Calvin Theological Seminary, ThB, 1950
ordained: 1950
charges: Zillah, WA, 1950-53; Tucson, AZ, 1953-62; Home missionary, Gallup, NM, 1962-65; Home missionary, Zuni, NM, 1965-67; Sunnyslope, Salem, OR, 1967-73; Missionary, Zuni, NM, 1973-85; Missionary trainer, Classis Red Mesa, Gallup, NM, 1985-88
retired: 1988

Posthumus, Richard

b. 08/10/1880, Oosterbierum, Friesland, Netherlands
training: Calvin Theological Seminary, diploma, 1914
ordained: 1914

charges: Ellsworth, MI, 1914-17; Bishop, MI, 1917-25; Pine Creek, MI, 1927-36
retired: 1925-27; 1939
d. 08/08/1967, Lynden, WA

Postma, Gerald John

b. 06/30/1921, Grand Rapids, MI
training: Calvin Theological Seminary, ThB, 1945
ordained: 1947
charges: Associate pastor, Munster, IN and Bible teacher, Illiana Christian High School, 1947-49; Sanborn, IA, 1949-53; East, Muskegon, MI, 1953-59; Kelloggsville, Grand Rapids, MI, 1959-63; Maranatha, Holland, MI, 1963-71; Olentangy, Columbus, OH, 1971-73; Chaplain, Whetstone Convalescent Center, Columbus, OH, 1973-74; Chaplain Administrator, Whetstone Convalescent Center, Columbus, OH, 1974-79; Administrator, Resthaven, Holland, MI, 1979-83
retired: 1983

Postman, John Wallace

b. 11/13/1931, Lethbridge, AB
training: Calvin Theological Seminary, BD, 1956
ordained: 1956
charges: Conrad, MT, 1956-59; Haney, BC, 1959-64; Kildonan, Winnipeg, MB, 1964-68; West End, Edmonton, AB, 1968-73; Georgetown, ON, 1973-77; First, Hamilton, ON, 1980-87; First, Sioux Center, IA, 1987-91; First, Chatham, ON, 1991-95; Non-ministerial vocation, 1995

Postuma, John

b. 09/20/1943, Stiens, Friesland, Netherlands
training: Calvin Theological Seminary, BD, 1972
ordained: 1972
charges: Calvary, Ottawa, ON, 1972-76; Welland Junction, Welland, ON, 1976-81; Bethel, Waterdown, ON, 1981-89; Maranatha, York, ON, 1989-2001; World Wide Christian Schools-Canada, Anacaster, ON, 2001-

Pot, James Eric

b. 10/15/1962, Grimsby, ON
training: Calvin Theological Seminary, MDiv, 1992
ordained: 1992
charges: West End, Edmonton, AB, 1992-97; First, Red Deer, AB, 1997-

Potgeter, Hermann Johann

b. 10/11/1856, Veldhausen, Bentheim, Germany
training: with Jan Schoemaker and Johannes Jäger
ordained: 1883
charges: Altreformierte Kirche: Uelsen, Germany,

1883–85; Ihrhove and Neermoor, Germany, 1885–89; CRC: Ridott, German Valley, IL, 1889–1892; Parkersburg, IA, 1892–96; Bunde and Emden-Renville, MN, 1896–1900; PCUSA: Kamrar, IA, 1900–03; Dubuque, IA, 1903–05; RCA: Forreston, IL, 1906–14
retired: 1914
d. 03/14/1931, Oregon, IL

Pott, Frank Edward
b. 07/20/1942, Tres Arroyos, Argentina
training: Calvin Theological Seminary, BD, 1973
ordained: 1973
charges: Iglesia Hispana, Holland, MI, 1973–76; Missionary to Puerto Rico, 1976–80; Pease, MN, 1980–86; Platte, SD, 1986–91; Bethel, Tucson, AZ, 1991–2001; Parkersburg, IA, 2001–

Pott, Henry Jon
b. 04/13/1942, Groningen, Groningen, Netherlands
training: Calvin Theological Seminary, BD, 1968
ordained: 1969
charges: Campus minister for InterVarsity Christian Fellowship, Los Angeles, CA, 1969–74; Campus minister for InterVarsity International, South Central Africa, 1974–84; Northwest regional director, Campus Ministries, InterVarsity, Tacoma, WA, 1984–87; Christ Community, Victoria, BC, 1987–91; eligible for call, 1991–92; InterVarsity Christian Fellowship, 1992

Pott, John
b. 02/19/1908, Amsterdam, Noord Holland, Netherlands
training: Princeton Theological Seminary, ThB, 1942
ordained: 1942
charges: PCUSA: Deerfield, NJ, 1942–43; RCA: First Holland Reformed, Paterson, NJ, 1943–47; Vriesland, MI, 1947–52; Bible teacher, Chicago (IL) Christian High School, 1953–59; CRC: Third Roseland, Chicago, IL, 1959–64; Second, Grand Haven, MI, 1964–74
retired: 1974
d. 03/28/1992, Holland, MI

Pott, Jurrien Jerry
b. 09/01/1910, Grand Rapids, MI
training: Calvin Theological Seminary, ThB, 1934
ordained: 1935
charges: Hazen St. Mission, Grand Rapids, MI, 1935; Austinville, IA, 1935–37; Missionary, Tres Arroyos, Argentina; 1937–50, Buenos Aires, Argentina, 1950–55, Mar del Plata, Argentina, 1955–58; Missionary to Spanish-speaking migrants, USA,

1958–63; Missionary, Juan Calvino Seminary, Mexico, 1963–75
retired: 1975

Pousma, Richard Hettema
b. 08/14/1892, Prospect Park, NJ
training: Calvin Theological Seminary, diploma, 1919; Rush Medical College, MD, 1926
ordained: 1918
charges: Service pastor, United States Army, 1918; Leave, 1918–1926; Missionary to China, 1926–27; Superintendent of Mission Hospital, Rehoboth, NM, 1927–41; Non-ministerial vocation: medical doctor, 1941
d. 01/06/1979, Sun City, CA

Powell, Jesse E.
b. 05/20/1963, San Diego, CA
training: Calvin Theological Seminary, MDiv, 1995
ordained: 1995
charges: Bethel, Oskaloosa, IA, 1995–2000; Trinity, Anchorage, AK, 2000–

Praamsma, Herman Deodaat
b. 12/25/1944, Wildervank, Groningen, Netherlands
training: Calvin Theological Seminary, BD, 1970
ordained: 1970
charges: Aldershot, Burlington, ON, 1970–73; Rehoboth, Toronto, ON, 1973–79; Maranatha, Edmonton, AB, 1979–83; Fellowship, Toronto, ON, 1983–89; Ontario Correctional Institute, Brampton, ON, 1989–90; Immanuel, Brampton, ON, 1990–98; Chaplain, Holland Christian Homes, Brampton, ON, 1998–

Praamsma, Louis
b. 01/01/1910, Den Helder, Noord Holland, Netherlands
training: Vrije Universiteit, Amsterdam, diploma, 1935
ordained: 1935
charges: GKN: Nieuwolda, 1935–44; Stadskanaal, 1944–49; Groningen, 1949–58; CRC: First, Toronto, ON, 1958–62; Faculty, Calvin Theological Seminary, Grand Rapids, MI, 1962–63; Fruitland, ON, 1963–72; Collingwood, ON, 1972–74
retired: 1974
d. 12/02/1984, Brampton, ON

Praamsma, Riemer
b. 06/11/1936, Nieuwolda, Groningen, Netherlands
training: Calvin Theological Seminary, BD, 1962
ordained: 1963
charges: Collingwood, ON, 1963–67; Brantford,

ON, 1967-71; Bethany, Bloomfield, ON, 1971-76; Wallaceburg, ON, 1976-82; Grandville Ave., Grand Rapids, MI, 1982-90; Ebenezer, Jarvis, ON, 1990-97; Fellowship, Brighton, ON, 1997-2001
retired: 2001

Praamsma, William
b. 04/22/1942, Nieuwolda, Groningen, Netherlands
training: Calvin Theological Seminary, BD, 1968
ordained: 1968
charges: CRC: Stratford, ON, 1968-71; GKN: Boerakker, 1971-76; Nieuweroord, 1976-80; Hallum, 1980-93; Rotterdam-Charlois, 1993-

Prenger, Norman Henry
b. 05/23/1956, Ft. William, ON
training: Calvin Theological Seminary, MDiv, 1988
ordained: 1988
charges: High River, AB, 1988-91; Christ Community, Victoria, BC, 1991-97
retired: 1997

Price, Robert J.
b. 12/20/1946
ordained: 1977
charges: Twin Cities Bible Church; CRC: Intercultural director, Leadership Training, Christian Reformed Home Missions, Matteson, IL, 1995-

Primus, John Henry
b. 01/30/1932, Steamboat Rock, IA
training: Calvin Theological Seminary, BD, 1957; Vrije Universiteit, ThD, 1960; University of Iowa, 1972; Cambridge University, 1979
ordained: 1960
charges: West Park, Cleveland, OH, 1960-63; Faculty, Calvin College, Grand Rapids, MI, 1963-97
retired: 1997

Prince, Wesley
b. 03/28/1893, Osceola County, MI
training: Presbyterian Seminary, Austin, TX; San Francisco Seminary, BD, 1920
ordained: 1920
charges: Presbyterian Church USA: Larene, WA, 1920-22; Southern Presbyterian Church: Llano, TX, 1922-32; Beaumont, TX, 1932-44; CRC: Associate pastor, Prosper, MI and Bible teacher at Northern Michigan Christian High School, McBain, MI, 1944-49; Sibley, IA, 1949-56; Community Church, Saginaw, MI, 1956-60
retired: 1960

d. 07/24/1979, Grand Rapids, MI

Prins, Nicholas Robert
b. 04/15/1929, Paterson, NJ
training: Calvin Theological Seminary, BD, 1953
ordained: 1955
charges: Monroe, WA, 1955-58; First, Paterson, NJ, 1958-74; Bethel, Grand Rapids, MI, 1974-79; Non-ministerial vocation, 1979

Pruim, Douglas Edward
b. 01/03/1975, Palos Heights, IL
training: Calvin Theological Seminary, MDiv, 2001
ordained: 2001
charges: Palos Hieghts, IL, 2001-

Pruim, Jay Richard
b. 06/16/1942, Chicago, IL
training: Calvin Theological Seminary, BD, 1967
ordained: 1967
charges: Calvin, Le Mars, IA, 1967-71; Heritage, Byron Center, MI, 1971-76; First, Sheboygan, WI, 1976-85; Baldwin St. Jenison, MI, 1985-2000; Comstock, Kalamazoo, MI, 2000-

Punt, Neal
b. 11/29/1928, Grand Rapids, MI
training: Calvin Theological Seminary, BD, 1954
ordained: 1954
charges: Atwood, MI, 1954-58; Eastmanville, MI, 1958-64; Prairie Edge, Kalamazoo, MI, 1964-69; Evergreen Park, Evergreen Park, IL, 1969-94
retired: 1994

Putt, James
b. 02/15/1898, Grand Rapids, MI
training: Calvin Theological Seminary, diploma, 1925; Princeton Seminary, ThD, 1938; McCormick Seminary; Pike's Peak Seminary
ordained: 1925
charges: Jamestown, MI, 1925-29; Fourth, Chicago, IL, 1929-40; Fulton, IL, 1940-53; Ontario, CA, 1953-63
retired: 1963
d. 03/23/1965, Upland, CA

Pyun, Eui Nam
ordained: 1976
charges: PCUSA: South Presbyterian, 1976-77; Leave, 1977-82; CRC: Orange Korean, Fullerton, CA, 1986-90; Resigned from denomination, 1990

Quartel, Jacob Arie
b. 07/28/1931, Mijnsheerenland, Zuid Holland, Netherlands

training: Calvin Theological Seminary, BD, 1956
ordained: 1956
charges: Wyoming, ON, 1956-61; Immanuel, Hamilton, ON, 1961-68; Bethel, Listowel, ON, 1968-73; Calvin, Ottawa, ON, 1972-83; Faith, Burlington, ON, 1984-92; Trinity, Goderich, ON, 1992-2000
retired: 2000

Radius, Henry Jr.
b. 10/07/1907, Chicago, IL
training: Calvin Theological Seminary, ThB, 1933
ordained: 1935
charges: Flint, MI, 1934-40; Englewood, NJ, 1940-46; First, Redlands, CA, 1946-72
retired: 1972
d. 09/25/2001, Yucaipa, CA

Range, Donald E.
b. 01/25/1956, Harrisburg, PA
training: declared eligible on the basis of exceptional gifts, 1996
ordained: 1996
charges: Hope, Onalaska, WI, 1996-2000; eligible for call, 2000-2002; Released from office, 2002

Ravensbergen, Peter
b. 01/11/1938, Rijnsburg, Zuid Holland, Netherlands
training: Calvin Theological Seminary, BD, 1977
ordained: 1977
charges: CRC: Smithville, ON, 1977-81; GKN: Wijnewoude, 1981-90; Gramsbergen, 1990-

Ravensbergen, Ronald Douglas
b. 12/25/1957, Vancouver, BC
training: Calvin Theological Seminary, MDiv, 1988
ordained: 1989
charges: Missionary, Costa Rica, 1989-94; Leave, 1994-96; Non-ministerial vocation, 1996

Reardon, Jude Joseph
b. 06/15/1953, New York, NY
training: Westminster Theological Seminary-PA, MDiv, 1986
ordained: 1991
charges: OPC: Pulpit supply, West Waldboro Community Church, West Waldboro, ME, 1988-92; Evangelist, Trinity, Lewiston, ME, 1991-92; Covenant, Cedar Falls, IA, 1992-96; CRC: Ackley, IA, 1996-98; Grangeville, ID, 1998-

Recker, Donald Lee
b. 12/24/1943, Hammond, IN
training: Calvin Theological Seminary, BD, 1968

ordained: 1968
charges: Gallatin Gateway, MT, 1968-73; Trinity, Anchorage, AK, 1973-82; Flanders Valley, Flanders, NJ, 1982-95; Summitview, Yakima, WA, 1995-

Recker, Robert Richard
b. 11/28/1923, Highland, IN
training: Calvin Theological Seminary, ThB, 1947; ThM, 1973; Vrije Universiteit, Amsterdam, 1967
ordained: 1947
charges: Momence, IL, 1947-49; Missionary to Nigeria, 1949-65; leave, 1965-67; Board of Foreign Missions, 1967-69; Faculty, Calvin Theological Seminary, Grand Rapids, MI, 1969-88
retired: 1989

Rederus, Francis C.
b. 08/19/1822, Lutjegast, Groningen, Netherlands
training: Theologische Universiteit, Kampen, diploma, 1852
ordained: 1852
charges: GKN: Genemuiden, 1854-56; Stroobos, 1856-59; Beetgum, 1859-69; Apeldoorn 1869-72; CRC: First, Paterson, NJ, 1872-74; RCA: Passaic, NJ, 1874-76; Third, Pella, IA, 1876-86
d. 05/10/1886, Pella, IA

Redhouse, Paul Harold
b. 04/23/1925, Teec Nos Pos, AZ
training: declared eligible on the basis of exceptional gifts; Flagstaff Indian Bible College, DD, 1999
ordained: 1963
charges: Home missionary, Red Rock, AZ, 1963-70; Four-Corners, Teec Nos Pos, AZ, 1970-90
retired: 1990

Redhouse, Scott K.
b. 12/20/1928, Teec Nos Pos, AZ
training: declared eligible on the basis of exceptional gifts, 1962
ordained: 1962
charges: CRC: Home missionary, Valley, Albuquerque, NM, 1962-65; Home missionary, Window Rock, AZ, 1965-75; Independent ministry, 1975-92
retired: 1992
d. 01/11/1998

Redondo, William
b. 12/26/1951, Los Angeles, CA
training: declared eligible on the basis of exceptional gifts, 1995
ordained: 1981

charges: Missionary, Chiapas, Mexico, 1981–82; Christian Reformed World Missions, Queretaro, Mexico, 1983–89; Christian Reformed Home Missions, Church planting, 1989–91; Love Song Community, Fresno, CA, 1991–

Reeves, Samuel B. Jr.
b. 04/29/1963, Monrovia, Liberia
training: Princeton Theological Seminary, MDiv, 1997
ordained: 1990
charges: Baptist church: Providence, Monrovia, Liberia, 1988–93; Galilee, Trenton, NJ, 1994–97; CRC: Outreach ministries, Madison Square, Grand Rapids, MI, 1998–

Reiffer, Jack Jay
b. 02/12/1944, Grand Rapids, MI
training: Calvin Theological Seminary, BD, 1970
ordained: 1975
charges: Garfield, Chicago, IL, 1975–81; Hessel Park, Champaign, IL, 1981–96; Washington, DC, 1996–98; eligible for call, 1998–99; Non-ministerial vocation, 1999–2001; Eligible for call, 2001–

Reilly, Thomas Henderson
b. 04/19/1954, San Antonio, TX
training: Gordon-Conwell Theological Seminary, MA and MDiv, 1979; Calvin Theological Seminary, MDiv, 1984
ordained: 1984
charges: Missionary to Taiwan, 1984–87; released from ministry to serve in China in an unordained capacity, 1988

Reinders, Philip Frank
b. 07/21/1965, Weston, ON
training: Calvin Theological Seminary, MDiv, 1992; Regent College, ThM, 2000
ordained: 1992
charges: Burnaby, BC, 1992–97; First, Calgary, AB, 1997–

Reinoso, Felix M.
b. 02/25/1923, Vueltas, Las Villas, Cuba
training: Los Pinos Nuevos Seminary, diploma, 1950
ordained: 1975
charges: Iglesia Evangelica Refromada, Cuba: Evangelist, Interior Gospel Mission, Matanzas, Cuba, 1954–68; CRC: Evangelist, Paterson, NJ, 1971–74; Spanish, Paterson, NJ, 1975–78
retired: 1978
d. 12/16/1982, Hialeah, FL

Reinsma, William Korver
b. 05/29/1909, Sheldon, IA
training: Calvin Theological Seminary, ThB, 1935
ordained: 1936
charges: Stated supply, Bejou, MN, 1935–36; Bejou, MN, 1936–41; Lebanon, IA, 1941–45; Raymond, MN, 1945–48; Ada, MI, 1948–51; Bethel, Oskaloosa, IA, 1951–56; First, Lynden, WA, 1956–59; Bible teacher, Lynden (WA) Christian High School, 1959–62; Everson, WA, 1962–65
retired: 1965
d. 03/04/1986, Lynden, WA

Reitsma, Carl John
b. 10/31/1927, Grand Rapids, MI
training: Kampen Theological Universiteit, Amsterdam, diploma, 1951; Westminster Theological Seminary-PA, BD, 1955
ordained: 1955
charges: OPC: Immanuel, West Collingwood, NJ, 1955–60; Calvary, Cedar Grove, WI, 1960–66; Sharon, Hialeah, FL, 1970–73; Reformed Church of New Zealand: Wellington, NZ, 1966–70; CRC: Bible teacher, Timothy Christian Schools, Elmhurst, IL, 1981–89; Eligible for call, 1989–90; Calvary, Lowell, MI, 1990–94
retired: 1994

Reitsma, Michael
b. 01/24/1944, Lacombe, AB
training: Calvin Theological Seminary, BD, 1970; MDiv, 1981
ordained: 1970
charges: Raymond, MN, 1970–74; Calvary, Minneapolis, MN, 1974–79; Fresno, CA, 1979–89; First, Calgary, AB, 1989–

Remein, Johannes (Jan) Marinus
b. 01/10/1840, Colijnsplaat, Zeeland, Netherlands
training: Rotterdam Mission House, 1861–64; Theologische Universiteit Kampen, diploma, 1881
ordained: 1881
charges: Netherlands Evangelical Protestant Society: Evangelist, Oude Leye, 1863–73; Evangelist, Heerenveen, 1873–77; GKN: Bergen op Zoom, 1881–85; Oostzaan, 1885–91; CRC: Rochester, NY, 1891–1903
d. 07/04/1903, Rochester, NY

Remeur, James Frederick
b. 03/04/1942, Kalamazoo, MI
training: Calvin Theological Seminary, BD, 1969; MDiv, 1980
ordained: 1972
charges: Navigator Campus Ministry, in AL 1972–

75; in MS, 1976-79; in TN, 1979-88; Navigator Community Ministries, Memphis, TN, 1988-

Renkema, William
b. 11/21/1939, Holwierde, Groningen, Netherlands
training: Calvin Theological Seminary, BD, 1965
ordained: 1965
charges: CRC: Renfrew, ON, 1965-70; Calvin, Dundas, ON, 1970-74; Aylmer, ON, 1974-79; Wyoming, ON, 1979-86; First, Hull, IA, 1986-91; Coopersville, MI, 1991-98; United Reformed Churches: Salem, OR, 1998

Renkema, William John
b. 04/22/1952, Grand Rapids, MI
training: Calvin Theological Seminary, MDiv, 1978
ordained: 1978
charges: Missionary to Honduras, 1978-89; Missionary, Puerto Rico, 1989-94; Calvary, Lowell, MI, 1994-

Reyenga, Henry Jr.
b. 05/14/1961, Elkhorn, WI
training: Calvin Theological Seminary, MDiv, 1987
ordained: 1988
charges: Community Life Church, Lockport, IL, 1988-93; Church planting, Colorado Springs, CO, 1993-94; Church planting, Eugene, OR, 1994-96; LifeNet 21/The Bible League, Lockport, IL, 1996-2001; Family of Faith, Monee, IL, 2001-

Reyneveld, Clarence Arie
b. 11/15/1953, Long Beach, CA
training: Calvin Theological Seminary, MDiv, 1986
ordained: 1987
charges: Momence, IL, 1987-91; Pillar, Holland, MI, 1991-93; Anacortes, WA, 1993-97; eligible for call, 1997-

Rhee, Jung S.
training: Calvin Theological Seminary, MDiv, 1984; ThM, 1989
ordained: 1985
charges: Faculty, International Theological Seminary, Pasadena, CA, 1985-87; CRC: Korean, Kalamazoo, MI, 1987-88; Faculty, Reformed Theological Seminary, Emsung, South Korea, 1988

Rhoda, Stephen K.
b. 01/11/1967, Grand Rapids, MI
training: Calvin Theological Seminary, MDiv, 1996
ordained: 1997
charges: Immanuel, Burbank, IL, 1996-2002; Bethel, Sioux Center, IA, 2002-

Ribbens, John Carl
b. 02/24/1922, Biggekerke, Zeeland, Netherlands
training: Calvin Theological Seminary, 1952
ordained: 1952
charges: Calvin, Rock Valley, IA, 1952-56; Battle Creek, MI, 1956-61; Radio Minister, Christian Reformed Hour, Northwest, IA, 1961-63; Indianapolis, IN, 1963-65; Lafayette, IN, 1965-74; First, Bellflower, CA, 1974-80; Thirty-Sixth St., Wyoming, MI, 1980-85; Classical Home Missions, Florida, 1985-87
retired: 1987

Ribbens, William DeWitt
b. 12/26/1921, Sheboygan, WI
training: Calvin Theological Seminary, ThB, 1949
ordained: 1949
charges: Goshen, IN, 1949-55; Parish evangelism, Rochester, NY, 1955-58, Back to God Chapel, Marion, MI, 1958-63; Missionary, Lake Odessa, MI, 1963-69; Emmanuel, Sauk Village, IL, 1969-75; Grace, Burke, VA, 1975-81; Christ Community, Virginia Beach, VA, 1981-86; stated supply, Zuni, NM, 1986-87
retired: 1987

Rickers, John Calvin
b. 09/03/1926, Grand Rapids, MI
training: Calvin Theological Seminary, BD, 1955
ordained: 1955
charges: Noordeloos, MI, 1955-60; Ocean View, Norfolk, VA, 1960-91
retired: 1991

Ridder, Ben John
b. 01/28/1956, Oak Park, IL
training: Calvin Theological Seminary, MDiv, 1982
ordained: 1982
charges: Lake Odessa, MI, 1982-

Ridder, Donald Ray Jr.
b. 09/17/1963, Oak Lawn, IL
training: Calvin Theological Seminary, MDiv, 1995
ordained: 1995
charges: Golden Gate, San Francisco, CA, 1995-99; Celebration Community, Muskegon, MI, 1999-

Riddlebarger, Kim
b. 08/29/1954
training: Fuller Theological Seminary, PhD, 1997
ordained: 1988
charges: Reformed Episcopal Church: St. Luke's, Anaheim, CA, 1988-90; Executive Vice President, CURE, Anaheim, CA, 1991-93; CRC: Executive Vice President, CURE, Anaheim, CA, 1993-96;

Christ Reformed, Placentia, CA, 1996–97; United Reformed Churches: Alliance of Confessing Evangelicals, 1997

Riemersma, Jan
b. 07/31/1857, Netherlands
training: Calvin Theological Seminary, diploma, 1884
ordained: 1884
charges: Rochester, NY, 1884–90; North St., Zeeland, MI, 1890–91; First, Chicago, IL, 1893–99; Non-ministerial vocation, teacher, Sioux Center, IA, 1899
d. 03/26/1930, Sioux Center, IA

Riemersma, John
b. 01/09/1920, Lucas, MI
training: Calvin Theological Seminary, BD, 1954
ordained: 1954
charges: Bigelow, MN, 1954–61; Britt, IA, 1961–68; Zillah, WA, 1968–72; Hull, ND, 1972–80; Bemis, SD, 1980–85
retired: 1985

Riemersma, Leonard Theodore
b. 02/09/1954, Johannesburg, South Africa
training: Calvin Theological Seminary, MDiv, 1986
ordained: 1986
charges: Ellsworth, MI, 1986–91; Providence, Cutlerville, MI, 1991–94; Willard, OH, 1994–

Rienks, Gabe
b. 05/09/1915, Netherlands
training: Post graduate study at Knox College, Toronto, 1963–64
ordained: 1945
charges: GKN: De Glind, 1945–48; Chaplain in Indonesia, 1948–50; Wormerveer, 1950–59; CRC: Pembroke, ON, 1959–63; Simcoe, ON, 1964–69; Presbyterian Church of Canada, 1969

Rienstra, Andrew Richard
b. 01/14/1935, Paterson, NJ
training: Calvin Theological Seminary, MDiv, 1959; Princeton Theological Seminary, DMin, 1983
ordained: 1959
charges: CRC: Chaplain, United States Army, 1959–62; Miami, FL, 1962–73; Richfield, Clifton, NJ, 1973–83; RCA: First, Pompton Plains, NJ, 1983

Rienstra, Richard Sr.
b. 10/15/1903, Paterson, NJ
training: Calvin Theological Seminary, ThB, 1933
ordained: 1935

charges: East Palmyra, NY, 1935–45; Muskegon Heights, MI, 1945–50; Oostburg, WI, 1950–54; Beckwith Hills, Grand Rapids, MI, 1954–69
retired: 1969
d. 12/25/1996, Jenison, MI

Rienstra, Robert John
b. 08/21/1961, Grand Rapids, MI
training: Calvin Theological Seminary, MDiv, 1988
ordained: 1988
charges: Missionary, Costa Rica, 1988–98; eligible for call, 1998–

Rientjes, Gerrit Henry
b. 12/10/1904, Nijverdal, Overijsel, Netherlands
training: Western Theological Seminary, ThB, 1939
ordained: 1939
charges: RCA: Lodi, NJ, 1939–42; Chaplain, United States Army Air Corps, 1942–46; Leota, MN, 1946–49; Lynden, WA, 1949–51; CRC: Home missionary to Vancouver Island at First, Port Alberni, BC, 1952–55; First, Kalamazoo, MI, 1955–59; First, Vancouver, BC, 1959–63; Graafschap, MI, 1963–66; Missionary to Wanamassa, NJ, 1966–70
retired: 1970
d. 09/19/1976, Oak Harbor, WA

Rietdyk, Leonard (Leenert)
b. 01/05/1842, Hellevoetsluis, Zuid Holland, Netherlands
training: with D.J. Vander Werp, 1870
ordained: 1870
charges: First, Muskegon, MI, 1870–72; Vriesland, MI, 1872–74; First, Paterson, NJ, 1874–82; First, Zeeland, MI, 1882–86; First, Paterson, NJ, 1886–88; First, Muskegon, MI, 1888–89
d. 08/06/1889, Muskegon, MI

Rietema, Fred Doyce
b. 10/04/1941, Clarion, IA
training: Calvin Theological Seminary, BD, 1967
ordained: 1967
charges: Parkersburg, IA, 1967–71; Bellevue, WA, 1971–76; Leave, 1976–77; Summitview, Yakima, WA, 1977–81; Chaplain/counselor, Comprehensive Mental Health Center, Tacoma, WA, 1981–90; Chaplain, Veterans Affairs Medical Center, Seattle, WA, 1990–

Rietema, Kermit
b. 02/28/1926, Kanawha, IA vicinity
training: Calvin Theological Seminary, BD,1953; MDiv, 1982

ordained: 1953
charges: Newton, IA, 1953-58; Arcadia, CA, 1958-64; Third, Denver, CO, 1964-71; Maranatha, Holland, MI, 1972-78; Faith, Elmhurst, IL, 1978-86; First, Hanford, CA, 1986-91
retired: 1991
d. 08/10/1994, Denver, CO

Rietkerk, Eleanor Mae Kredit
b. 02/05/1945, Mitchell, SD
training: Fuller Theological Seminary, MDiv, 1995; Calvin Theological Seminary, Special Program for Ministerial Candidacy, 1997
ordained: 1997
charges: Director of pastoral care, Mill Creek Community, Mill Creek, WA, 1990-91; Mill Creek Community, Mill Creek, WA, 1997-

Rietkerk, Timothy Lee
b. 05/22/1967, Seattle, WA
training: Calvin Theological Seminary, MDiv, 1994
ordained: 1995
charges: Youth, Cadillac, MI, 1991-92; Youth, Hope, Grandville, MI, 1993-94; Elmhurst, IL, 1995-96; Chaplain, United States Army, 1996-

Rikkers, Henry Jr.
b. 05/25/1900, Hull, IA
training: Calvin Theological Seminary, ThB, 1928
ordained: 1929
charges: CRC: Godwin Heights, Grand Rapids, MI, 1929-33; Dennis Ave., Grand Rapids, MI, 1933-36; Missionary at Shiprock, NM, 1936-41; Ellsworth, MI, 1941-45; Minneapolis, MN, 1945-51; PCUSA: Checotah, OK, 1951-53; Benton, AR, 1953-56; Hospers, IA, 1956-62; Oklahoma City, OK, 1962-64; Greenfield, MO, 1964-65; El Montecito, CA, 1965-67
d. 02/22/1967, Santa Barbara, CA

Ringnalda, Gerard
b. 10/23/1928, Den Haag, Zuid Holland, Netherlands
training: Vrije Universiteit, Amsterdam, BD, 1955
ordained: 1955
charges: GKN: Oudehorne, 1955-58; CRC: Lindsay, ON, 1958-63; Maranatha, Belleville, ON, 1963-66; Second, Edmonton, AB, 1966-71; Burlington, ON, 1971-77; Calvary, Ottawa, ON, 1977-82; First, Orillia, ON, 1982-87; Hospital chaplain, Classis Toronto, 1987-95
retired: 1995

Rip, Kenneth Ray
b. 04/16/1953, Oak Harbor, WA

training: Calvin Theological Seminary, MDiv, 1979
ordained: 1979
charges: Mountain View, Lynden, WA, 1979-88; Mill Creek Community, Mill Creek, WA, 1988-97; Leave, 1997-98; North Austin Community, Austin, TX, 1998-

Ritsema, John Albert
b. 12/08/1949, Grand Rapids, MI
training: Calvin Theological Seminary, MDiv, 1976
ordained: 1976
charges: Kanawha, IA, 1976-80; Oakwood, Belding, MI, 1980-84; South Olive, MI, 1984-90; Faith, Pella, IA, 1990-93; Non-ministerial vocation, 1993

Ritsema, Kenneth Ross
b. 05/18/1956, Grand Rapids, MI
training: Calvin Theological Seminary, MDiv, 1982
ordained: 1983
charges: Zion, Pembroke, ON, 1983-89; Ambassador, Windsor, ON, 1989-96; Third, Lynden, WA, 1996-2002; Church planting, Rochester, MN, 2002-

Ritsema, Robert Dale
b. 07/27/1944, Grand Rapids, MI
training: Calvin Theological Seminary, BD, 1969; MDiv, 1994
ordained: 1969
charges: McBain, MI, 1969-72; Second, Allendale, MI, 1972-78; Bradenton, FL, 1978-81; First, South Holland, IL, 1981-90; South Grandville, Grandville, MI, 1990-94; Leave, 1994-96; Northern Heights, Kalamazoo, MI, 1996-

Ritzema, Jake
b. 09/02/1952, Groningen, Groningen, Netherlands
training: declared eligible on the basis of exceptional gifts, 2001
ordained: 2001
charges: German Valley, IL, 2001-

Robbert, Jan
b. 02/17/1857, Emlichheim, Bentheim, Germany
training: Theologische Universiteit, Kampen, diploma, 1885
ordained: 1885
charges: GKN: De Lier, 1885-91; Lutten-aan-de-Dedemsvaart, 1891-93; CRC: First Roseland, Chicago, IL, 1893-1901; First, Kalamazoo, MI, 1901-08; Niekerk, Holland, MI, 1908-11; Fourth, Paterson, NJ, 1911-12; East Paris, Grand Rapids, MI, 1912-14; Rusk, MI, 1916-18

retired: 1914-16; 1918
d. 10/02/1922, Holland, MI

Roberts, John Lawrence
b. 04/17/1917, Ashland, MO
training: Baptist Theological Seminary, Los Angeles, 1943
ordained: 1943
charges: Baptist: Missionary, Mexico, 1944-46; Community Church, Spartanburg, SC, 1946-48; Missionary, Dominican Republic, 1948-65; CRC: Missionary to Mexico, 1966-84
retired: 1984
d. 03/04/1986, Mexico City, Mexico

Roeda, Daniel Jack
b. 09/23/1959, Montevideo, Uruguay
training: Calvin Theological Seminary, Special Program for Ministerial Candidacy
ordained: 1986
charges: Missionary, Dominican Republic, 1986-90; Newton, IA, 1990-95; Delavan, WI, 1995-

Roeda, Jack
b. 03/22/1945, Wirdum, Friesland, Netherlands
training: Calvin Theological Seminary, BD, 1970; ThM, 1971
ordained: 1971
charges: Exeter, ON, 1971-75; Calvary, Holland, MI, 1975-83; Church of the Servant, Grand Rapids, MI, 1983-

Roelofs, Curtis Gerald
b. 12/05/1943, Holland Township, Kandiyohi County, MN
training: Calvin Theological Seminary, BD, 1970
ordained: 1970
charges: Missionary, Anacortes, WA, 1970-74; Cedar Falls, IA, 1974-79; Chaplain, Harper Grace Hospital, Detroit, MI, 1979-81; Chaplain, Providence Hospital, Southfield, MI, 1981-

Roelofs, Harlan Ray
b. 12/14/1929, Prinsburg, MN
training: Calvin Theological Seminary, BD, 1955
ordained: 1955
charges: Luctor, KS, 1955-58; Second, Orange City, IA, 1958-65; Anaheim, CA, 1965-75; Montello Park, Holland, MI, 1975-85; East Martin, MI, 1985-92
retired: 1992
d. 12/02/1997, Grand Rapids, MI

Roels, Edwin Dale
b. 02/02/1934, Zeeland, MI

training: Calvin Theological Seminary, BD, 1958; Vrije Universiteit, Amsterdam, ThD, 1972
ordained: 1972
charges: Cottage Grove, South Holland, IL, 1972-78; On loan: World Home Bible League, African Coordinator, South Holland, IL, 1978-84; Unity, Prinsburg, MN, 1984-87; President, Reformed Bible College, Grand Rapids, MI, 1987-95
retired: 1995

Roest, Gary
b. 02/07/1947, Zoeterwoude, Zuid Holland, Netherlands
training: Calvin Theological Seminary, MDiv, 1978; ThM, 1979
ordained: 1979
charges: Missionary to Hong Kong, 1979-80; Missionary to Taipei, Taiwan, 1980-82; Chinese Church Research Center, Hong Kong, 1982-84; Missionary to Taipei, Taiwan, 1984-99; Gold Avenue, Grand Rapids, MI, 2000-

Roke, John
b. 01/17/1949, Netherlands
training: Calvin Theological Seminary, MDiv, 1988
ordained: 1989
charges: CRC: Immanuel, Simcoe, ON, 1989-92; Athens, ON, 1992-97; URC: Brockville, ON, 1997

Romero, Domingo
b. 08/04/1930, Cuba
ordained: 1976
charges: Calimete, Cuba, 1959-62; Alacranes, Cuba, 1962-70; CRC: Spanish, Wyoming, MI, 1973-95
retired: 1995

Romero, Ezequiel Naphtalie
b. 08/28/1936, Ancash, Peru
training: Reformed Bible College, ARE, 1975; Calvin Theological Seminary, MMin, 1991
ordained: 1994
charges: The Good Shepherd, Prospect Park, NJ, 1990-92; Joy, Peace and Love, Clifton, NJ, 1994-96; Eligible for call, 1996-97; Madison Ave., Paterson, NJ, 1997-

Romeyn, Ruth Janice
b. 02/06/1944, Orange City, IA
training: Calvin Theological Seminary, MDiv, 1999
ordained: 2000
charges: Chaplain, Spectrum Health, Grand Rapids, MI, 1999-

Rook, Jacob
b. 07/14/1909, Netherlands
ordained: 1939
charges: GKN: Mussel, 1939-42; Epe, 1942-45; Chaplain Dutch Army, 1945-47; Nunspeet, 1972-74; CRC: Sullivan, MI, 1947-50; Sarnia, ON, 1950-52; First, Toronto, ON, 1953-57; Rehoboth, Bellflower, CA, 1957-64
retired: 1974
d. 09/16/1987, Netherlands

Roon, Albert J.
b. 07/24/1936, Holland, MI
training: Calvin Theological Seminary, BD, 1962
ordained: 1962
charges: Ogilvie, MN, 1962-66; Chaplain, United States Navy, 1966-92; Bethany, Holland, MI, 1992-96; Bravo Community, Fennville, MI, 1996-2000
retired: 2000
d. 11/29/2002, Atlanta, GA

Roorda, Darren C.
b. 09/11/1968, Oshawa, ON
training: Calvin Theological Seminary, MDiv, 1999
ordained: 1999
charges: Bellevue, WA, 1999-

Roorda, John
b. 10/24/1903, Britsum, Friesland, Netherlands
training: Calvin Theological Seminary, ThB, 1944
ordained: 1944
charges: Lacombe, AB, 1944-49; Holland, MN, 1949-53; Abbotsford, BC, 1953-57; Escondido, CA, 1957-63; Home missionary, Vernon, BC, 1963-65; Home missionary, Quincy, WA, 1965-68
retired: 1968
d. 06/03/1970, Bellingham, WA

Roorda, Nicholas
b. 08/14/1924, Weed, CA
training: Calvin Theological Seminary, BD, 1961; MDiv, 1975
ordained: 1961
charges: Hancock, MN, 1961-65; Pipestone, MN, 1965-74; Mountain Lake, MN, 1974-79; Charlotte, MI, 1979-82
d. 07/19/1982, Lansing, MI

Roosma, Gary Dean
b. 11/10/1960, Bellingham, WA
training: Regent College, MDiv, 1991; Calvin Theological Seminary, Special Program for Ministerial Candidacy, 1993-
ordained: 1994

charges: On loan: Overseas Missionary Fellowship International, Thailand, 1994-96, Malaysia, 1996-2001; Regional director, OMF-International Canada, 2001-

Roosma, Harvey Jay
b. 07/30/1957, Bellingham, WA
training: Calvin Theological Seminary, MDiv, 1995
ordained: 1995
charges: First, Port Alberni, BC, 1995-

Roossien, Louis Jr.
b. 10/03/1944, Grand Rapids, MI
training: Calvin Theological Seminary, BD, 1969
ordained: 1971
charges: Brooten, MN, 1971-74; Sun Valley Community, Denver, CO, 1974-81; Bethany, Muskegon, MI, 1981-

Rooy, Sidney H.
b. 09/16/1926, Oskaloosa, IA
training: Calvin Theological Seminary, BD, 1853; Vrije University, ThD, 1965
ordained: 1954
charges: Minister of evangelism, Midland Park, NJ, serving Paramus, 1954-61; Leave, 1961-65; Missionary, Argentina, 1965-91
retired: 1992

Rop, John Jr.
b. 07/14/1950, Muskegon, MI
training: Calvin Theological Seminary, MDiv, 1995
ordained: 1995
charges: Highland, MI, 1995-98; Phoenix, AZ, 1998-

Rottier, John A.
b. 03/28/1877, Goes, Zeeland, Netherlands
training: Calvin Theological Seminary, diploma, 1908
ordained: 1908
charges: Atwood, MI, 1908-11; Home missionary for Classis Muskegon at Muskegon Heights, MI, 1911-16; North Blendon, MI, 1916-20; Beaverdam, MI, 1920-26; Highland, IN, 1926-31
retired: 1931
d. 08/08/1942, Kalamazoo, MI

Rottman, John M.
b. 09/20/1955, Muskegon, MI
training: Calvin Theological Seminary, MDiv, 1987
ordained: 1987
charges: First, Toronto, ON, 1987-92; Leave, 1992-94; Grace, Scarborough, Toronto, ON, 1994-

Rottman, Kent Allan
b. 03/25/1955, Fremont, MI
training: Calvin Theological Seminary, MDiv, 1999
ordained: 1999
charges: Lee St., Wyoming, MI, 1999-

Rowaan, George John
b. 01/28/1959, Neerlandia, AB
training: Calvin Theological Seminary, MDiv, 1994
ordained: 1994
charges: Williamsburg, ON, 1994-

Royall, Dennis Wayne
b. 07/21/1945, Phoenix, AZ
training: Arizona State University, MM, 1970; Calvin Theological Seminary, Special Program for Ministerial Candidacy, 1983
ordained: 1983
charges: CRC: Ingersoll, ON, 1983-86; Second, Allendale, MI, 1986-91; Cape Coral, FL, 1992-93; United Reformed Church: Cornerstone, London, ON, 1994

Rozeboom, John A.
b. 12/22/1942, Pipestone, MN
training: Calvin Theological Seminary, BD, 1967; ThM, 1974
ordained: 1969
charges: Riverside, CA, 1969-76; Regional Missionary, West Coast, Board of Home Missions, 1976-86; Executive director, Christian Reformed Home Missions, Grand Rapids, MI, 1986-

Rozeboom, Richard A.
b. 05/18/1888, Fulton, IL
training: Calvin Theological Seminary, diploma, 1920; Princeton Seminary, ThB, 1922
ordained: 1922
charges: Purewater, SD, 1922-29; Bejou and Crookston, MN, 1929-35; Crookston, MN, 1934-43; Pipestone, MN, 1943-51; Sullivan, MI, 1951-56
retired: 1956
d. 08/04/1978, New Era, MI

Rozema, Randy John
b. 05/06/1957, Edmonton, AB
training: Calvin Theological Seminary, MDiv, 1989
ordained: 1990
charges: Community, East Grand Forks, and First, Crookston, MN, 1990-93; Chaplain, Methodist Medical Center, Peoria, IL, 1993-94; eligible for call, 1994-2000; non-ministerial vocation, 2000

Rozenboom, Gysbert John
b. 02/19/1916, Pella, IA
training: Calvin Theological Seminary, ThB, 1941; MDiv, 1975
ordained: 1941
charges: Hollandale, MN, 1941-45; Prinsburg, MN, 1945-49; Sheboygan, WI, 1949-53; Westview, Grand Rapids, MI, 1953-62; First, Hull, IA, 1962-67; Grant, MI, 1967-74; Faith, Kalamazoo, MI, 1974-78; Little Farms, Coopersville, MI, 1978-81
retired: 1981

Rozenboom, Norman Duane
b. 05/25/1949, Oskaloosa, IA
training: Calvin Theological Seminary, MDiv, 1989
ordained: 1989
charges: Christ's Community, Chandler, AZ, 1989-92; eligible for call, 1992-93; Holland, MN, 1993-97; eligible for call, 1997-99; released from the ministry, 1999

Rozendal, Anthony Everett
b. 09/13/1913, Leighton, IA
training: Calvin Theological Seminary, ThB, 1942
ordained: 1942
charges: Ada, MI, 1942-48; Rochester, NY, 1948-52; First, Zeeland, MI, 1952-61; Third, Paterson, NJ, 1961-65; First, De Motte, IN, 1965-73; Beaverdam, MI, 1973-78
retired: 1978
d. 07/14/1998, Zeeland, MI

Rozendal, John R.
b. 12/29/1899, Chicago, IL
training: Calvin Theological Seminary, diploma, 1925; Princeton Seminary, ThM, 1926
ordained: 1927
charges: Hawarden, IA, 1927-34; Supervisor, Paterson Hebrew Mission, Paterson, NJ, 1938-51; Missionary pastor, Chicago Jewish Mission, Chicago, IL, 1951-61; Home missionary for Jewish parish evangelism, 1961-64
retired: 1934-38; 1964
d. 05/31/1982, Hudsonville, MI

Rubingh, Eugene Francis
b. 12/19/1931, Hettinger, ND
training: Calvin Theological Seminary, BD, 1955
ordained: 1957
charges: Missionary to West Africa, 1957-68; Leave, 1968-69; Secretary for recruitment, Board of Foreign Missions, 1969-71; African secretary, Board of Foreign Missions, 1971-76; Executive secretary, Board of Foreign Missions, Grand

Rapids, MI, 1976–86; Research fellow, Centennial Scholarship Committee, Grand Rapids, MI, 1986–87; Vice President for translations, International Bible Society, Grand Rapids, MI, 1987–2000
retired: 2000

Rubingh, John
b. 03/18/1895, Graafschap, MI vicinity
training: Calvin Theological Seminary, diploma, 1925; Princeton Theological Seminary, ThM, 1927
ordained: 1927
charges: Home Missionary for Classis Sioux Center: at Holland Center, SD, 1927–28; at Lodgepole, SD, 1929–35; Lebanon, IA, 1935–40; Worthington, MN, 1940–46; Neerlandia, AB, 1946–48; Home missionary in Canada: at Renfrew, ON, 1948–56; at Truro, NS, 1956–58; Home missionary in Middlebury, VT, 1958–59; Home missionary, Stratford, ON, 1959–61
retired: 1961
d. 01/25/1985, Grand Rapids, MI

Rubingh, John Henry
b. 12/11/1909, Ellsworth, MI
training: Westminster Theological Seminary, BD, 1935; Calvin Theological Seminary, Special Program for Ministerial Candidacy, 1936; Union Theological Seminary, ThM
ordained: 1938
charges: Pipestone, MN, 1938–43; Second, Wellsburg, IA, 1943–49; Raymond, MN, 1949–54; Winnipeg, MB, 1954–61; Worthington, MN, 1961–66; Ireton, IA, 1966–75
retired: 1975
d. 03/18/1978, Orange City, IA

Rubingh, Trevor Alan
b. 05/03/1966, Jos, Nigeria
training: Princeton Theological Seminary, MDiv, 1992; Calvin Theological Seminary, Special Program for Ministerial Candidacy, 1994
ordained: 1995
charges: New City Church, Jersey City, NJ, 1995–

Ruis, Robert Dale
b. 02/16/1932, Mille Lacs County, MN
training: Calvin Theological Seminary, BD, 1963; MDiv, 1978
ordained: 1963
charges: Home missionary for Spanish-speaking people, Escondido, CA, 1963–66; Missionary to Mexico, 1966–80; Bethlehem, Freeman, SD, 1980–88; First, Sioux City, IA, 1988–92; Hancock, MN, 1992–97
retired: 1997

Rumph, Arnold (Arend)
b. 08/06/1929, DeWijk, Drenthe, Netherlands
training: Calvin Theological Seminary, BD, 1957, ThM, 1964
ordained: 1957
charges: Cobourg, ON, 1957–60; Fruitland, ON, 1960–63; Leave, 1963–64; Mount Hamilton, Hamilton, ON, 1964–66; Missionary to Argentina, 1966–73; Missionary to Puerto Rico, 1973–77; Missionary to Guatemala, 1977–81; post graduate study, Overseas Ministry Study Center, 1981–82; Juan Calvino Seminary, Mexico City, Mexico, 1982–84; Faculty, International Theological Seminary, Pasadena, CA, 1984–88; Trinity, Chula Vista, CA, 1988–93; Trinity Fellowship, San Diego, CA, 1993–94
retired: 1994

Rus, Aletinus J.
b. 10/26/1883, Haarlemmermeer, Noord Holland, Netherlands
training: Calvin Theological Seminary, diploma, 1910
ordained: 1910
charges: Byron Center, MI, 1910–13; Prospect Park, Holland, MI, 1913–17; City missionary, Chicago, IL, 1917–19; Prosper, MI, 1919–24; Rochester, NY, 1924–30; Byron Center, MI, 1930–51
retired: 1951
d. 04/04/1971, Grand Rapids, MI

Rusticus, Steven R.
b. 08/28/1961, Grand Rapids, MI
training: Western Theological Seminary, MDiv, 1987
ordained: 1987
charges: RCA: Grace, Holland, MI, 1987–91; Community, Lafayette, IN, 1991–93; Open Door, Dorr, MI, 1993–94; CRC: VictoryPoint Ministries, Holland, MI, 1997–

Rutgers, Gerald Lee
b. 10/03/1952, Bellingham, WA
training: Calvin Theological Seminary, MDiv, 1981
ordained: 1981
charges: CRC: Ivanrest, Grandville, MI, 1981–83; Calvin, Sheboygan, WI, 1983–88; Orangewood, Phoenix, AZ, 1988–95; Resigned from denomination, 1995

Rutgers, William Henry
b. 10/26/1898, Firth, NE
training: Calvin Theological Seminary, ThB, 1926; Princeton Seminary, ThM, 1927; Vrije Universiteit, Amsterdam, ThD, 1930

ordained: 1930
charges: President, Grundy College and pastor, Grundy Center, IA and Holland, IA, 1930–33; First, Cicero, IL, 1933–43; Faculty, Calvin Theological Seminary, 1944–52; Kelloggsville, MI, 1952–58; Bethany, Bellflower, CA, 1958–64; Second, Highland, IN, 1964–69
retired: 1969
d. 07/31/1980, Grand Rapids, MI

Ruys, Henry J.
b. 08/05/1885, Prairie View, KS
training: Calvin Theological Seminary, diploma, 1915; Princeton Theological Seminary, 1916
ordained: 1916
charges: Dispatch, KS, 1916–21; Missionary for Classis Pacific, Edmonton, AB, 1921–22; Non-ministerial vocation, teacher, 1922
d. 05/23/1963, Sioux Falls, SD

Rylaarsdam, David Mark
b. 08/15/1966, Pella, IA
training: Calvin Theological Seminary, Mdiv, 1993; University of Notre Dame, MA, 1997; PhD, 2000
ordained: 2002
charges: Faculty, Calvin Theological Seminary, Grand Rapids, MI, 2001–

Rylaarsdam, Merwin Edward
b. 03/28/1953, Bellingham, WA
training: declared eligible on the basis of exceptional gifts, 2001
ordained: 2001
charges: Hull, IA, 1982–90; Youth, First, Sioux City, IA, 1990–93; First, Lynden, WA, 1993–98; Abbotsford, BC, 1998–2001; Alamosa, CO, 2001–

Rylaarsdam, Neal Roger
b. 06/06/1944, Sumas, WA
training: Calvin Theological Seminary, BD, 1972; MDiv, 1975
ordained: 1972
charges: Fairlawn, Whitinsville, MA, 1972–76; Winfield, IL, 1976–81; Quincy, WA, 1981–87; Bauer, MI, 1987–93; Leave, 1993–94; Lexington Green Community, Portage, MI, 1994–2000; Interim, First, Zeeland, MI, 2000–

Ryou, Daniel H.
b. 10/12/1953, Seoul, South Korea
training: Calvin Theological Seminary, MDiv, 1984
ordained: 1986
charges: On loan to Hap Dong Seminary, Seoul,

Korea, 1986–89; On loan, Korean Church, Toledo, OH, 1989–

Ryu, Roger Y.
b. 12/30/1947, Seoul, South Korea
training: Trinity Evangelical Divinity School, MDiv
ordained: 1996
charges: Windsor Community Church, Northbrook, IL, 1996–97; CRC: Korean Presbyterian Galilee, Albuquerque, NM, 1997–2000; Central Baptist, Orlando, FL, 2000–

Sajdak, Jeffrey Lee
b. 02/12/1963, Milwaukee, WI
training: Bethel Theological Seminary, MDiv, 1990; Calvin Theological Seminary, Special Program for Ministerial Candidacy, 1992
ordained: 1992
charges: Fairway, Jenison, MI, 1992–97; Immanuel, Orange City, IA, 1997–

Salomons, Clarence Harry
b. 01/06/1941, Hoogezand, Groningen, Netherlands
training: Calvin Theological Seminary, BD, 1969
ordained: 1969
charges: Bethel, Saskatoon, SK, 1969–74; First, Kingston, ON, 1974–82; Bethel, Newmarket, ON, 1982–90; Second, Abbotsford, BC, 1990–99; Rehoboth, Bowmanville, ON, 1999–

Salomons, Herman
b. 03/10/1935, Shakleton, SK
training: Calvin Theological Seminary, BD, 1964
ordained: 1964
charges: Ackley, IA, 1964–69; Maranatha, Edmonton, AB, 1969–78; First Ladner, Delta, BC, 1978–90; Bethany, Bloomfield, ON, 1990–95; Maranatha, Lethbridge, AB, 1995–99
retired: 2000

Samplonius, Homer Gerben
b. 04/03/1938, Netherlands
training: Calvin Theological Seminary, BD, 1971
ordained: 1971
charges: Iron Springs, AB, 1971–75; Maple Ridge, BC, 1975–80; First, Edmonton, AB, 1980–85; Clinton, ON, 1985–89; Second, Brampton, ON, 1989–95; West End, Edmonton, AB, 1995–

Sanchez, Jose Marcelo
b. 01/16/1932
ordained: 1971
charges: CRC of Cuba: Sto. Suarez and Emanuel, Habana, Cuba, 1971–82; El Redentor, Hialeah, FL,

1982–85; CRC: Iglesia El Redentor, Hialeah, FL,
1985–94
retired: 1995

Sanchez, Juan Pablo
training: declared eligible on the basis of exceptional gifts, 2002
ordained: 2002
charges: Iglesia El Buen Samaritano, Miami, FL,
2002–

Sanders, Kenneth
b. 12/09/1960, Paterson, NJ
training: Calvin Theological Seminary, MDiv, 1985
ordained: 1988
charges: CRC: Westmoreland, NH, 1988–95; Independent: Independent Christian Reformed,
Westmoreland, NH, 1995

Sarkipato, Daniel S.
b. 05/21/1954, Winton, MN
training: Calvin Theological Seminary, MDiv, 1985
ordained: 1984
charges: Sibley, IA, 1984–88; Trinity, St. Louis,
MO, 1988–97; Southern Heights, Kalamazoo, MI,
1997–

Sausser, Paul O.
b. 12/16/1959, Pontiac, MI
training: Calvin Theological Seminary, MDiv, 1988
ordained: 1988
charges: Three Rivers, MI, 1988–91; Bethel,
Princeton, MN, 1991–96; Calvary, Wyoming, MI,
1996–

Sawyer, Frank
b. 08/04/1946, Victoria, BC
training: Theologische Universiteit, Kampen, Drs,
1977; ThD, 1992
ordained: 1977
charges: NGK: Zoetermeer, 1977–80; post graduate studies, 1980–82; CRC: Missionary, Latin
America, 1982–83; Missionary, Puerto Rico, 1983–
85; Missionary, Honduras, 1985–92; Reformed
Theological Seminary, Sarospatak, Hungary,
1992–

Saythavy, Sririsack
b. 09/01/1963, Vientiane, Laos
training: declared eligible on the basis of exceptional gifts, 1997
ordained: 1997
charges: Lao Christian Church, Napho Camp,
Thailand, 1984–91; Laotian Worshiping Community, Hamilton, ON, 1991–2002

Schaafsma, Arthur (Arend) W.
b. 02/15/1912, Wijk aan Zee, Noord Holland, Netherlands
training: Vrije Universiteit, Amsterdam, diploma,
1935
ordained: 1938
charges: GKN: Assistant pastor, Hoorn, 1935–38;
Oldemarkt, 1938–41; Middenmeer, 1941–46; Rotterdam, 1946–51; Amsterdam, 1951–54; CRC:
Bowmanville, ON, 1954–59; Burlington, ON, 1959–
65; Calvin, Ottawa, ON, 1965–72; Riverside,
Wellandport, ON, 1972; Smithville, ON, 1972–77
retired: 1977
d. 11/05/1980, Victoria, BC

Schaal, John Hamburg
b. 04/28/1908, Kalamazoo, MI
training: Calvin Theological Seminary, ThB, 1933
ordained: 1933
charges: Milwood, Kalamazoo, MI, 1933–43
(United States Army Reserve, Louisiana, 1941);
Second, Fremont, MI, 1943–48; Editor, Sunday
School papers, Board of Publication, Grand
Rapids, MI, 1945–71; Faculty, Reformed Bible
College, Grand Rapids, MI, 1948–73
retired: 1973
d. 09/24/2002, Grand Rapids, MI

Schaap, Aldon Ray
b. 06/12/1954, Waterloo, IA
training: Calvin Theological Seminary, MDiv, 1982
ordained: 1982
charges: Fresno, CA, 1982–84; Gateway Community, Merced, CA, 1984–

Schaap, John C.
b. 02/16/1879, Ackley, IA
training: Calvin Theological Seminary, diploma,
1904
ordained: 1904
charges: Bemis, SD, 1904–06; Reeman, MI,
1906–11; Third, Kalamazoo, MI, 1911–13; Allendale, MI, 1913–21; Prospect Park, Holland, MI,
1921–25; Lucas, MI, 1925–32; Oostburg, WI,
1932–46
retired: 1946
d. 01/05/1956, Sheboygan, WI

Schalk, Stanley Richard
b. 10/14/1958, Regina, SK
training: Calvin Theological Seminary, MDiv, 1984
ordained: 1984
charges: CRC: First, Red Deer, AB, 1984–88; New
Life Fellowship, Red Deer, AB, 1988–97; Resigned
from denomination, 1997

Schalkwyk, Leonard Theodore

b. 04/23/1929, Amsterdam, Noord Holland, Netherlands

training: Bibelheim Bible School, Beatenburg, Switzerland, 1949; Moravian Seminary, Bethlehem, PA, 1951; Vrije Universiteit, Amsterdam, diploma, 1954

ordained: 1955

charges: GKN: Krimpen a/d Lek and Krimpen a/d IJssel, 1955–57; Chaplain, Dutch Army, 1957–58; CRC: Duncan, BC, 1958–62; Emmanuel, Calgary, AB, 1962–66; Riverside, Wellandport, ON, 1966–70; St. Thomas, ON, 1970–75; Williamsburg, ON, 1975–80; Collingwood, ON, 1980–82; Springdale, ON, 1982–92; First, Medicine Hat, AB, 1992–93

d. 04/25/1993, Medicine Hat, AB vicinity

Schans, Martin M.

b. 11/15/1880, Smilde, Drenthe, Netherlands

training: Calvin Theological Seminary, diploma, 1911

ordained: 1911

charges: Ada, MI, 1911–15; Lafayette, IN, 1915–17; Kelloggsville, MI, 1917–24; First, Sioux Center, IA, 1924–27; Redlands, CA, 1927–40; Holland Marsh, ON, 1940–45; Calvin, McBain, MI, 1945–48

retired: 1948

d. 11/22/1955, Holland, MI

Schaver, John L.

b. 01/28/1897, Chicago, IL

training: Calvin Theological Seminary, ThB, 1927

ordained: 1927

charges: New Era, MI, 1927–33; Lucas, MI, 1932–45; Oak Lawn, IL, 1945–53

retired: 1953

d. 05/04/1956, Detroit, MI

Scheffers, Mark Allen

b. 05/30/1954, Kalamazoo, MI

training: Calvin Theological Seminary, MDiv, 1979

ordained: 1979

charges: Missionary to Liberia, 1979–82; Field secretary, Bassa Independent Church, Liberia, 1982–91; Immanuel, Kalamazoo, MI, 1991–2000; Interim, Dorr, MI, 2000–2002; Interim, Community, Lambertville, MI, 2002–

Schemper, Chester M.

b. 12/23/1918, Holland, MI

training: Calvin Theological Seminary, ThB, 1952

ordained: 1952

charges: Second, Allendale, MI, 1952–57; Oak Lawn, IL, 1957–62; First, Calgary, AB, 1962–65;

Missionary to Mexico, 1965–69; Latin American coordinator World Home Bible League, South Holland, IL, 1969–89; Director, New Language Publications, The Bible League, South Holland, IL, 1990–

retired: 1990

Schemper, Lugene Loyd

b. 12/21/1950, Artesia, CA

training: Calvin Theological Seminary, BD, 1979; MDiv, 1982; Dominican University, MLS, 1999

ordained: 1982

charges: Minister of youth and education, Harderwyk, Holland, MI, 1982–84; Valley, Binghamton, NY, 1984–93; Ebenezer, Berwyn, IL, 1993–2000; Theological Librarian, Calvin Theological Seminary, Grand Rapids, MI, 2000–

Schenkel, Henry John Jr.

b. 10/28/1973, Hammond, IN

training: Calvin Theological Seminary, MDiv, 2001

ordained: 2001

charges: Monroe Mall Ministries, Grand Rapids, MI, 2001–

Schepel, Kenneth Lee

b. 01/26/1946, Chicago Heights, IL

training: Calvin Theological Seminary, MDiv, 1980

ordained: 1980

charges: Minister of education and youth, Hillcrest, Hudsonville, MI, 1980–83; Community, Saginaw, MI, 1983–89; Cascade, Marysville, WA, 1989–94; Faith, Pella, IA, 1994–

Schepers, Jacob R.

b. 05/05/1819, Hijken, Drenthe, Netherlands

training: with Wolter Alberts Kok, 1840

ordained: 1852

charges: Associate Presbyterian Church: South Holland, MI, 1852–64; Second Lafayette, IN, 1864–69; CRC: Lafayette, IN, 1869–70; East Saugatuck, MI, 1870–75, Cincinnati, OH, 1875–78

d. 03/19/1878, Cincinnati, OH

Schepers, Jan

b. 05/25/1837, Hijken, Drenthe, Netherlands

training: with D.J. Vander Werp, 1868

ordained: 1868

charges: First, Chicago, IL, 1868–71; Lafayette, IN, 1871–76; Ackley, IA, 1876–82; Vogel Center, MI, 1882–1902

d. 08/13/1902, Vogel Center, MI

Schering, Eric Nicolas

b. 02/21/1951, Easton, NY

training: Calvin Theological Seminary, MDiv, 1976
ordained: 1979
charges: Missionary to New Guinea, 1979–85; Eligible for call, 1985–86; Lane Ave., Kansas City, MO, 1986–91; Family in Christ Community, Denver, CO, 1991–94; Leave, 1994–95; Regional Training Manager, Promise Keepers, Indianapolis, IN, 1995–98; Bethel, De Motte, IN, 1998–

Scheurs, Ronald Lee
b. 12/14/1950, Beaver Dam, WI
training: Westminster Theological Seminary-PA, MDiv, 1976; Calvin Theological Seminary, Special Program for Ministerial Candidacy, 1977
ordained: 1977
charges: CRC: Baldwin, WI, 1977–81; Luverne, MN, 1981–87; Second, Kalamazoo, MI, 1987–93; First, Chino, CA, 1993–97; United Reformed Churches: Chino, CA, 1997

Schievink, Christopher John
b. 10/20/1975, Oshawa, ON
training: Calvin Theological Seminary, MDiv, 2002
ordained: 2002
charges: Palmerston, ON, 2001–

Schipper, Allen H.
b. 12/06/1945, Chicago, IL
training: Calvin Theological Seminary, MDiv, 1983
ordained: 1983
charges: Missionary, Kibbie, South Haven, MI, 1983–87; Leave, 1987–88; Director, Pastoral Service, Battle Creek Health Systems, Battle Creek, MI, 1988–

Schipper, Earl Jay
b. 11/01/1935, Holland, MI
training: Calvin Theological Seminary, BD, 1960
ordained: 1960
charges: Salt Lake City, UT, 1960–63; Missionary pastor, Middleville, MI, 1963–65; Middleville, MI, 1965–68; Campus minister, Ohio University, Columbus, OH, 1968–70; Director of Communications, Board of Home Missions, 1970–73; Religion teacher, Grand Rapids (MI) Christian High School, 1973–85; Director, Evergreen Commons Senior Center, Holland, MI, 1985–90; Non-ministerial vocation, 1990

Schipper, Gary Wayne
b. 04/03/1954, Grand Rapids, MI
training: declared eligible on the basis of exceptional gifts, 1982
ordained: 1981
charges: Honduras Christian Reformed Church:

Missionary, Central America, 1977–84; Leave, 1984–86; Missionary, Central America, 1986–89; CRC: Amor Viviente, El Monte, CA, 1989–92; Home missions evangelist training coordinator, Hispanic ministry assistance at Ontario, CA; 1989–98, at Houston, TX, 1999–

Schlissel, Steve M.
b. 03/23/1952, Brooklyn, NY
training: with Paul Szto and Greg Bahnsen (OPC); declared eligible on the basis of exceptional gifts
ordained: 1980
charges: Baptist: Brooklyn Metropolitan, 1980–81; Missionary to Jews, New York, 1981–83; Independent: Messiah's Congregation, Brooklyn, NY, 1983–86; 1992– ; CRC: Messiah's Congregation, Brooklyn, NY, 1986–92

Scholten, Cornelius J.
b. 02/22/1899, Comstock, MI
training: Calvin Theological Seminary, diploma, 1923
ordained: 1923
charges: Colton, SD, 1923–35; Non-ministerial vocation, 1935
d. 05/06/1979, Kalamazoo, MI

Scholten, D.J. (Dirk Jan)
b. 01/27/1906, Netherlands
training: Vrije Universiteit, Amsterdam, diploma, 1938
ordained: 1938
charges: GKN: Stiens, 1938–46; Bierum, 1946–53; CRC: Lethbridge, AB, 1953–58; Brantford, ON, 1958–66; Exeter, ON, 1966–70
retired: 1970
d. 07/24/1992, Brantford, ON

Scholten, James Henry
b. 06/27/1939, Kalamazoo, MI
training: Calvin Theological Seminary, BD, 1971
ordained: 1971
charges: Hills, MN, 1971–75; Willard, OH, 1975–80; First, Grand Haven, MI, 1980–88; Niekerk, Holland, MI, 1988–98; Central Ave., Holland, MI, 1998–

Scholten, John Cornelius
b. 12/13/1910, Grand Rapids, MI
training: Calvin Theological Seminary, ThB, 1943
ordained: 1943
charges: Willard, OH, 1943–48; Immanuel, Muskegon, MI, 1948–57; First, Highland, IN, 1957–75
retired: 1975

d. 09/14/1995, Grand Rapids, MI

Schoolland, Cornelius M.
b. 08/01/1898, Grand Rapids, MI
training: Calvin Theological Seminary, ThB, 1932
ordained: 1932
charges: Highland, MI, 1932-36; Harderwyk, Holland, MI, 1936-40; Second, Cicero, IL, 1940-43; Chaplain USA, 1943-46; Racine, WI, 1946-50; Mt. Vernon, WA, 1950-53; First, Vancouver, BC, 1953-58; Alto, WI, 1958-62; Pioneer, Cedar Springs, MI, 1962-63
retired: 1963
d. 03/10/1985, Grand Rapids, MI

Schoon, Paul Robert
b. 10/01/1942, Hammond, IN
training: Calvin Theological Seminary, BD, 1968
ordained: 1968
charges: Forest, ON, 1968-71; Leave, 1971-72; Jamestown, MI, 1972-73; Resigned from ministry, 1973
d. 09/15/1993, San Francisco, CA

Schoonveld, Arthur John
b. 01/27/1936, Zuidbroek, Groningen, Netherlands
training: Calvin Theological Seminary, MDiv, 1966
ordained: 1966
charges: East Martin, MI, 1966-71; Calvary, Chino, CA, 1971-77; Orland Park, IL, 1977-87; Faith, Holland, MI, 1987-94; Ivanrest, Grandville, MI, 1994-2001
retired: 2001

Schouten, Johannes
b. 02/12/1968, Welland, ON
training: Calvin Theological Seminary, MTS, 1994; MDiv, 1997
ordained: 1997
charges: Bethel Community, Edmonton, AB, 1997-

Schram, Terry Leonard
b. 03/29/1939, Lansing, MI
training: Calvin Theological Seminary, ThB, 1965
ordained: 1975
charges: Wycliffe Bible Translators, 1975-

Schripsema, Herman J.
b. 10/07/1902, McBain, MI
training: Calvin Theological Seminary, BD, 1932
ordained: 1933
charges: Stated supply, Pleasant Valley, Eagle Butte, SD, 1933-37; Pine Creek, MI, 1937-43;

Cariso Mission, Farmington, NM, 1943-45; Home missionary, Farmington, NM, 1945-65
retired: 1965
d. 06/25/1989, Albuquerque, NM

Schrotenboer, Paul Gerard
b. 05/10/1922, East Saugatuck, MI
training: Calvin Theological Seminary, ThB, 1947; Westminster Theological Seminary-PA; Vrije Universiteit, Amsterdam, ThD, 1955
ordained: 1955
charges: Calvin, Ottawa, ON, 1955-60; St. Catharines, ON, 1960-64; General Secretary, Reformed Ecumenical Synod, 1964-88
retired: 1988
d. 07/16/1998, Grand Rapids, MI

Schultz, Herman Henry
b. 05/27/1886, Uelsen, Bentheim, Germany
training: Mission House, Sheboygan, WI, 1914; Grundy College and Seminary, diploma, 1919
ordained: 1933
charges: Superintendent, Hebrew Mission, Paterson, NJ, 1920-37
d. 06/16/1937, Paterson, NJ

Schultz, Jan Harm
b. 09/22/1852, Kleine Ringe, Bentheim, Germany
training: with Jan Schoemaker and Johannes Jäger
ordained: 1885
charges: Altreformierte Kirche: Uelsen, Germany, 1885-92; CRC: Bunde, MN, 1892-94; Prinsburg, MN, 1894-97; Lincoln Center, IA, 1897-1909; Edgerton MN, 1909-12; Middleburg, IA, 1912-14
d. 12/23/1914, Middleburg, IA

Schultze, Henry
b. 07/18/1893, Prairie City, IA
training: Calvin Theological Seminary, diploma, 1917; Princeton Theological Seminary, 1917-18, BD, 1922; Yale School of Religion, BD, 1919; University of Chicago Divinity School, 1919-20
ordained: 1924
charges: Faculty, Grundy College, Grundy Center, IA, 1920-24; Sherman St., Grand Rapids, MI, 1924-26; Faculty, Calvin Theological Seminary, 1926-40 and 1951-56; President, Calvin College, 1940-51
retired: 1956
d. 03/06/1959, Grand Rapids, MI

Schuring, John Ofrein
b. 05/24/1908, Albany, NY
training: Calvin Theological Seminary, ThB, 1935

ordained: 1935
charges: Battle Creek, MI, 1935-39; Detroit, MI, 1939-44; First, Fremont, MI, 1944-48; Missionary, Sri Lanka, 1948-52; Third, Kalamazoo, MI, 1952-54; Missionary, Sri Lanka, 1954-57; Neland Ave., Grand Rapids, MI, 1957-63; Home missionary, Boca Raton, FL, 1963-68; Campus minister, University of Minnesota, Minneapolis, MN, 1968-72; Missionary to Guam, 1972-74
retired: 1974
d. 03/17/2002, Grand Rapids, MI

Schuringa, Erick John
b. 01/06/1967, Port Colborne, ON
training: Calvin Theological Seminary, MDiv, 1993
ordained: 1993
charges: Bethel, Waterdown, ON, 1993-2002; Immanuel, Brampton, ON, 2002-

Schuringa, Gregory David
b. 10/22/1973, DeMotte, IN
training: Calvin Theological Seminary, MDiv, 1998
ordained: 2002
charges: Faith, Elmhurst, IL, 2002-

Schuringa, H. David
b. 10/18/1952, Evergreen Park, IL
training: Westminster Theological Seminary-PA, MDiv, 1981; Calvin Theological Seminary, Special Program for Ministerial Candidacy, 1982, ThM, 1985
ordained: 1982
charges: Beverly, Wyoming, MI, 1982-85; Leave, 1985-87; Faculty, Westminster Theological Seminary, Escondido, CA, 1987-96; Bethany, Holland, MI, 1996-99; President, Crossroad Bible Institute, Grandville, MI, 1999-

Schut, Peter
b. 11/23/1851, Warfstermolen, Friesland, Netherlands
training: Calvin Theological Seminary, diploma, 1881
ordained: 1881
charges: Kelloggsville, MI, 1881-87; Overisel, MI, 1887-92; Zutphen, MI, 1892-1900; Home missionary Classis Iowa, Orange City and Pella, IA, 1900-03
retired: 1903
d. 08/04/1928, Holland, MI

Schutt, Herman John
b. 10/12/1945, Chicago, IL
training: Calvin Theological Seminary, BD, 1970
ordained: 1970

charges: Community, Grand Rapids, MI, 1970-75; Emmanuel, Sauk Village, IL, 1975-83; Long Beach, CA, 1983-94; First, Munster, IN, 1994-

Schuurman, John Frederick
b. 03/29/1946, Denver, CO
training: Calvin Theological Seminary, MDiv, 1985
ordained: 1985
charges: First, Sioux Falls, SD, 1985-89; Wheaton, IL, 1989-

Schüürmann, Frederic
b. 10/08/1865, Itterbeek, Bentheim, Germany
training: with Wiard Bronger and Johannes Jäger, 1901
ordained: 1901
charges: Altreformierte Kirche: Campen, Oostfriesland, Germany, 1901-12; CRC: Emden, MN, 1912-15; Ireton, IA, 1915-18; Bunde, MN, 1918-26; Middleburg, IA, 1926-34
retired: 1934
d. 09/16/1947, Lynden, WA

Schuurmann, John (Jan) F.
b. 01/24/1903, Campen, Germany
training: Calvin Theological Seminary, BD, 1930; Princeton Seminary, 1931
ordained: 1931
charges: Lincoln Center, IA, 1931-40; Wyoming Park, Grand Rapids, MI, 1940-44; Second, Lynden, WA, 1944-51; Fourteenth St., Holland, MI, 1951-56; Moline, MI, 1956-64; Ferrysburg, MI, 1964-69
retired: 1969
d. 08/13/1977, Grand Rapids, MI

Schweitzer, Anthony
b. 02/05/1943, Maasland, Zuid Holland, Netherlands
training: Calvin Theological Seminary, BD, 1970
ordained: 1970
charges: Brandon, MB, 1970-74; First, Duncan, BC, 1974-79; Leave, 1979; First, Chilliwack, BC, 1979-86; Hope Centre, Winnipeg, MB, 1986-

Scripps, Stanley Richard
b. 02/06/1953, Grand Rapids, MI
training: Calvin Theological Seminary, MDiv, 1986
ordained: 1986
charges: East Palmyra, NY, 1986-91; First, Sioux Falls, SD, 1991-2002; Graafschap, MI, 2003-

Selles, Albert Hendrikus
b. 06/19/1895, Kampen, Utrecht, Netherlands

training: Calvin Theological Seminary, diploma, 1925
ordained: 1926
charges: studying at Union Language School, 1925-27; Home missionary, Edmonton, AB, 1927-29; Missionary, China, 1929-37; Home missionary, Modesto, CA, 1937-38; Missionary, China, 1938-43; Des Plaines, IL, 1943-46; Missionary, China, 1946-49; Tyler, MN, 1951-55; Burdett, AB, 1955-60
retired: 1960
d. 08/05/1967, Holland, MI

Selles, Kurt Donald
b. 12/14/1958, Grand Rapids, MI
training: Calvin Theological Seminary, MDiv, 1987
ordained: 1987
charges: Youth director, Trinity, Broomall, PA, 1983-85; Pastor of evangelism, Burton Heights, Grand Rapids, MI, 1985-87; Missionary, Taiwan, 1987-93; Beijing, China, 1993-98; Leave, 1998-99; Field Director, CRWM/Calvin Study, Beijing, China, 1999-

Sennema, Norman Aldert
b. 05/07/1966, Hamilton, ON
training: Calvin Theological Seminary, MDiv, 1993
ordained: 1993
charges: Evangelism/Youth, Bethel, Dunnville, ON, 1991-92; Charlottetown, PE, 1993-98; Hope, Port Perry, ON, 1998-

Serrano, Guillermo A.
b. 12/12/1951
ordained: 1988
charges: National Presbyterian Church of Chile, 1979-83; Leave, 1983-84; Associate pastor, Sun Valley CRC, Sun Valley, CA, 1984-85; Evangelic Institute of Chile, 1985-87; Good Samaritan CRC, Miami, FL, 1987-88; CRC: Good Samaritan, Miami, FL, 1988-91; Back to God Hour, Palos Heights, IL, 1991-

Sevensma, Sipke B.
b. 01/06/1831, Langweer, Friesland, Netherlands
training: Theologische Universiteit, Kampen, diploma, 1861
ordained: 1861
charges: GKN: Sauwert, 1861-63; Arum, 1863-66; Garrelsweer, 1866-84; Zeist, 1884-86; Nijmegen, 1886-87; CRC: Eastern Ave., Grand Rapids, MI, 1887-1900
d. 05/24/1900, Grand Rapids, MI

Sheeres, Gerrit William (Willem)
b. 06/06/1932, Lutjegast, Groningen, Netherlands
training: Calvin Theological Seminary, BD, 1961
ordained: 1963
charges: Prosper, Falmouth, MI, 1963-66; Immanuel, Grand Rapids, MI, 1966-72; Bethel, Zeeland, MI, 1972-79; Third, Lynden, WA, 1979-90; East Paris, Grand Rapids, MI, 1990-97
retired: 1997

Sheeres, Joel Jeffrey
b. 11/06/1963, Cadillac, MI
training: Calvin Theological Seminary, MDiv, 1995
ordained: 1995
charges: Faith, Elmhurst, IL, 1995-2002; Crown Point, IN, 2002-

Shepherd, Norman
b. 08/13/1933, Fall River, MA
training: Westminster Theological Seminary-PA, BD, 1958; ThM, 1959
ordained: 1963
charges: OPC: Faculty, Westminster Theological Seminary, Philadelphia, PA, 1963-81; CRC: First, Minneapolis, MN, 1983-89; Cottage Grove, South Holland, IL, 1989-98
retired: 1998

Sherda, Zachary J.
b. 04/27/1886, Grand Rapids, MI
training: Calvin Theological Seminary, diploma, 1913; McCormick Theological Seminary
ordained: 1913
charges: Highland IN, 1913-16; Evergreen Park, IL, 1916-30; First, Cutlerville, MI, 1930-53
retired: 1953
d. 06/08/1968, Cutlerville, MI

Sherow, Donald Carl
b. 04/15/1949, Gilmer, TX
training: Covenant Theological Seminary, MDiv, 1976; Calvin Theological Seminary, Special Program for Ministerial Candidacy, 1983
ordained: 1976
charges: PCA: Barachah, Augusta, GA, 1976-78; Leave, 1978-82; CRC: Grace, Grand Rapids, MI, 1982-83; Madison Ave., Paterson, NJ, 1983-86; Chesapeake, Virginia Beach, VA, 1986-89; Eligible for call, 1989-98; Resigned from denomination, 1998; Eligible for call, 2000-

Shim, Jay Jai-Sung
b. 11/25/1956, Seoul, South Korea
training: Calvin Theological Seminary, MDiv, 1991
ordained: 1993

charges: On loan: Korean Presbyterian Church, Saginaw, MI, 1993-95; Hahn-In, Wyoming, MI, 1995-

Shin, David S. (Dae Sun)
b. 01/05/1953, Korea
training: Presbyterian College and Seminary, MDiv, 1989; Linda Vista Bible College and Seminary, MDiv, 1993
ordained: 1980
charges: Presbyterian Church of Korea: Missionary, Sao Paulo, Brazil, 1986-91; CRC: Beverly Hills Korean/California Cho Won, Los Angeles, CA, 1993-98; Hope, Spokane, WA, 1999-

Shin, Eugene Yoonil
b. 06/22/1954, Taegu-Shi, Korea
training: Trinity Theological Seminary, MDiv, 1992
ordained: 1994
charges: CRC: Our Shepherd Korean, Arlington Heights, IL, 1995-2000; resigned from denomination

Shin, Peter Yong
b. 06/17/1942, Keo Chang, Korea
training: Ko Shin Theological Seminary, MDiv, 1977
ordained: 1981
charges: Korean, London, ON, 1981-86; CRC: Korean Church of Orange County, Buena Park, CA, 1987-

Shin, Young Su
b. 10/27/1954, Pusan, Korea
training: Calvin Theological Seminary, MDiv, 1995
ordained: 1996
charges: Gethsemane, Olympia, WA, 1996-

Shuart, Esler LaVerne
b. 12/12/1929, Suffern, NY
training: Calvin Theological Seminary, BD, 1957
ordained: 1957
charges: Minneapolis, MN, 1957-62; Allen Ave., Muskegon, MI, 1962-68; Prospect Park, Paterson, NJ, 1968-70; Ebenezer, Berwyn, IL, 1970-80; First, Zeeland, MI, 1980-92
retired: 1992

Sideco, Alberto
b. 06/27/1944, Philippines
training: Asian Theological Seminary, MCL, 1992
ordained: 1998
charges: Filipino, Jersey City, NJ, 1998-

Sieplinga, David John
b. 09/06/1948, Muskegon, MI
training: Calvin Theological Seminary, MDiv, 1975
ordained: 1975
charges: CRC: Prairie Lane, Omaha, NE, 1975-77; Madison Square, Grand Rapids, MI, 1977-82; Garfield, Chicago, IL, 1982-84; Immanuel, Kalamazoo, MI, 1984-89; RCA: Urban ministry, Indianapolis, IN, 1989-99; Maple Avenue Ministries, Holland, MI, 1999-

Sietsema, Stephen John
b. 07/13/1943, Eastmanville, MI
training: Calvin Theological Seminary, BD, 1972; MDiv, 1981
ordained: 1972
charges: Aetna, MI, 1972-78; Immanuel, Cornwall, ON, 1978-88; Eligible for call, 1988-95; Non-ministerial vocation, 1995

Sikkema, Lambert John
b. 05/31/1957, Bellflower, CA
training: Calvin Theological Seminary, MDiv, 1987
ordained: 1987
charges: Wayland, MI, 1987-92; Western Springs, IL, 1992-2002; First, Hanford, CA, 2002-

Sikkema, Paul Duane
b. 07/11/1950, Grand Rapids, MI
training: Calvin Theological Seminary, MDiv, 1975
ordained: 1979
charges: Austinville, IA, 1979-83; Emmanuel, Sauk Village, IL, 1983-91; New Community/ Crosspoint, Cincinnati, OH, 1991- ; Chaplain, St. Elizabeth Medical Center, Covington, KY/Warren Correctional Institution, Cincinnati, OH, 1998-

Sikkema, Raymond John
b. 08/01/1935, Leek, Groningen, Netherlands
training: Calvin Theological Seminary, BD, 1963; MDiv, 1975
ordained: 1963
charges: CRC: Blyth, ON, 1963-66; Northern Heights, Kalamazoo, MI, 1966-69; Trinity, St. Catharines, ON, 1969-81; Mount Hamilton, Hamilton, ON, 1981-92; United Reformed Churches: Hamilton, Ontario, 1992-2000; Interim, Alymer, ON, 2000-2001

Sikkema, Shawn Kim
b. 08/24/1957, Cadillac, MI
training: Calvin Theological Seminary, MDiv, 1984
ordained: 1985
charges: Summit, Kamloops, BC, 1984-89; Eastern Hills, Aurora, CO, 1989-

Silveira, Richard James
b. 07/25/1949, Newport, RI
training: Calvin Theological Seminary, MDiv, 1985
ordained: 1985
charges: Chaplain, United States Navy, (Chaplain, Chapel of Hope, NETC, 1996-99) 1985-99; Director, CREDO, San Diego, CA, 1999-

Siregar, Leonard
training: International Theological Seminary; Reformed Theological Seminary
charges: Hervormde Kerk, Indonesia: CRC: Indonesian Protestant Eklesia, Claremont, CA, 2000-

Sittema, John Richard
b. 10/27/1949, Chicago, IL
training: Calvin Theological Seminary, MDiv, 1975
ordained: 1975
charges: CRC: Sanborn, IA, 1975-81; First, Pella, IA, 1981-89; Bethel, Dallas, TX, 1989-2002; PCA: Christ Covenant, Charlotte, NC, 2002

Sizemore, Robert Allen
b. 07/16/1963, Grand Rapids, MI
training: Calvin Theological Seminary, MDiv, 1989
ordained: 1989
charges: Hope Community, Surrey, BC, 1989-90; Alger, WA, 1990-94; Discovery Community, Indianapolis, IN, 1994-98; Calvin, Sheboygan, WI, 1999-

Slachter, Terry D.
b. 07/17/1963, Grant, MI
training: Calvin Theological Seminary, MDiv, 1989
ordained: 1989
charges: Youth pastor, Friendship Chapel, Jenison, MI, 1985?-87; Youth Director, First, Allendale, MI, 1987-88; East Leonard, Grand Rapids, MI, 1989-93; Hope Community, Indianapolis, IN, 1994-96; Dearborn, MI, 1996-2002; East Leonard, Grand Rapids, MI, 2002-

Slager, Donald James
b. 05/03/1951, Cypress, CA
training: Westminster Theological Seminary-PA, MDiv, 1976; Calvin Theological Seminary, Special Program for Ministerial Candidacy, 1977
ordained: 1978
charges: Missionary, Liberia, 1978-98; Translation, United Bible Society, 1998-

Slager, Kenneth Ray
b. 06/11/1926, Kalamazoo, MI
training: Calvin Theological Seminary, BD, 1953
ordained: 1953

charges: Willmar, MN, 1953-57; Lincoln Center, IA, 1957-62; Sibley, IA, 1962-69; Trinity, Vancouver, WA, 1969-74; Monroe, WA, 1974-88
retired: 1988

Slater, Ronald Lee
b. 08/11/1934, Kalamazoo, MI
training: Calvin Theological Seminary, BD, 1965
ordained: 1965
charges: CRC: Home missionary, Ogden, UT, 1965-68; Pease, MN, 1968-73; Second, Lynden, WA, 1973-76; Independent: Lynden, WA, 1976

Slim, Raymond
b. 03/20/1945, Crownpoint, NM
training: Calvin Theological Seminary, MMin, 1994
ordained: 1994
charges: Bethany, Gallup, NM and Fort Wingate, NM, 1982-84; Crownpoint, NM, 1984-86; Sanostee, NM, 1986-94; Sanostee, Naschitti, Toadlena/Newcomb, NM, 1994-2000; Sanostee, NM, 2000-

Slings, Dale Lee
b. 10/18/1947, Newton, IA
training: Calvin Theological Seminary, MDiv, 1983
ordained: 1983
charges: Bethel, Dallas, TX, 1983-87; Heritage, Byron Center, MI, 1987-99; Westwood, Kalamazoo, MI, 1999-

Slings, Larry Dean
b. 01/14/1945, Marshalltown, IA
training: Calvin Theological Seminary, BD, 1971
ordained: 1971
charges: Ogilvie, MN, 1971-75; Community, East Grand Forks, MN, 1975-79; Maranatha, Holland, MI, 1979-94; Bible teacher, Holland (MI) Christian High School, 1994-97; Specialized interim ministry, Milwood, Kalamazoo, MI, 1997-98; Specialized interim ministry, Grace, Grand Rapids, MI, 1999; Interim, West Leonard, Grand Rapids, MI, 1999-2000; Interim, Forest Grove, MI, 2001-02; Interim, Hillcrest, Hudsonville, MI, 2002-

Slofstra, Bert
b. 09/13/1952, Hijlaard, Friesland, Netherlands
training: Calvin Theological Seminary, MDiv, 1979; ThM, 1980
ordained: 1980
charges: Intern, Victoria, BC, 1977-78; Lucknow, ON, 1980-84; Georgetown, ON, 1984-90; First, Abbotsford, BC, 1990-

Slofstra, Lammert

b. 06/27/1924, Norg, Drenthe, Netherlands Vrije
training: Vrije Universiteit, Amsterdam, 1950
ordained: 1950
charges: GKN: Hijlaard, 1950-53; Hengelo, 1953-
56; Army Chaplain, 1956-60; CRC: Clinton, ON,
1960-64; Willowdale, Toronto, ON, 1964-70; First,
New Westminster, BC, 1970-75; First, Chatham,
ON, 1975-81; Immanuel, Simcoe, ON, 1981-89
retired: 1989

Slofstra, Peter

b. 08/17/1951, Hijlaard, Friesland, Netherlands
training: Calvin Theological Seminary, MDiv, 1977
ordained: 1977
charges: Orillia, ON, 1977-81; Campus chaplain,
Western Ontario University, London, ON, 1981-88;
Jubilee Fellowship, St. Catharines, ON, 1988-

Sluys, Peter

b. 05/17/1927, Andijk, Noord Holland, Netherlands
training: Calvin Theological Seminary, BD, 1962;
MDiv, 1978
ordained: 1962
charges: Bigelow, MN, 1962-65; Rocky Mountain
House, AB, 1965-70; East Strathroy, Strathroy,
ON, 1970-74; Bethel, Lacombe, AB, 1974-79;
Salmon Arm, BC, 1979-84; Terrace, BC, 1984-92
retired: 1992

Smedes, Lewis Benedict

b. 08/20/1921, Muskegon, MI
training: Calvin Theological Seminary, ThB, 1950;
Vrije Universiteit, Amsterdam, ThD, 1954
ordained: 1954
charges: Madison Ave., Paterson, NJ, 1954-57,
Faculty, Calvin College, Grand Rapids, MI, 1957-
70; Faculty, Fuller Theological Seminary, 1970-86
retired: 1986
d. 12/19/2002, Arcadia, CA

Smedes, Wesley

b. 04/20/1919, Muskegon, MI
training: Calvin Theological Seminary, BD, 1946
ordained: 1945
charges: PCUSA: Cheyenne, WY, 1945-56; Kear-
ney, NE, 1946-56; CRC: Radio minister, Northwest
IA, 1956-59; East Muskegon, MI, 1959-64; Denominational minister for evangelism, Board of
Home Missions, 1964-80
retired: 1980
d. 02/03/1983, Grand Rapids, MI

Smidstra, Henry Herman

b. 12/10/1943, Wieringermeer, Noord Holland,
Netherlands
training: Calvin Theological Seminary, MDiv, 1977
ordained: 1977
charges: Missionary to the Philippines, 1977-85;
Leave, 1985-91; Chaplain, Burnaby Correctional
Centre for Women, Burnaby, BC, 1991-

Smidt, Willem Roelof

b. 11/12/1845, Stapelmoor, Ostfriesland, Germany
training: with G.K. Hemkes
ordained: 1877
charges: Altereformierde Kirche: Uelsen,
Bentheim, 1877-82; CRC: Ridott, IL, 1882-84;
Dispatch, KS, 1887-88; Franklin St., Grand
Rapids, MI, 1888-1902; First, Wellsburg, IA, 1902-
05; Bauer, MI, 1906-12; Resigned from denomination, 1912 preached in Disciples, Baptist and Wesleyan churches; PCUSA: Forreston, IL, 1884-85;
Legal, IL, 1885-87
d. 10/10/1931, Grand Rapids, MI

Smit, Albert H.

b. 10/23/1888, Nijeveen, Drenthe, Netherlands
training: Calvin Theological Seminary, diploma,
1923; Princeton Seminary, 1924; Union Theological Seminary, ThM, 1934
ordained: 1924
charges: Union Language School, China, 1924-
25; Missionary to China, 1925-41; Home missionary in Washington army camps, 1941-43; Church
Committee for China Relief, 1943-46; Missionary
to China, 1946-50; Missionary to Ontario, at
Brockville, ON, 1950-52; at Cornwall, ON, 1950-
54; at Ottawa, ON, 1953-55; at Cobourg, ON,
1956-57
retired: 1957
d. 10/15/1962, Grand Rapids, MI

Smit, David Lee

b. 04/08/1947, Orange City, IA
training: Calvin Theological Seminary, MDiv, 1974
ordained: 1974
charges: Inwood, IA, 1974-80; Faith, Sioux Center, IA, 1980-87; Rogers Heights, Wyoming, MI,
1987-95; Fresno, CA, 1995-

Smit, Harvey Albert

b. 01/09/1928, Shanghai, China
training: Westminster Theological Seminary-PA,
ThM, 1952; Vrije Universiteit, PhD, 195
ordained: 1957
charges: Chaplain, United States Army, 1956-59;
Missionary to Japan, 1959-77; Theological editor,

Board of Publications, Grand Rapids, MI, 1977–80; Editor and Chief, Education, Worship and Evangelism Department, Board of Publications, Grand Rapids, MI, 1980–97
retired: 1997
d. 09/17/1998, Grand Rapids, MI

Smit, Wolter
b. 05/29/1934, Hoek van Holland, Zuid Holland, Netherlands
training: Calvin Theological Seminary, BD, 1976
ordained: 1976
charges: CRC: Ft. McMurray, AB, 1976–82; First, Brandon, MB, 1982–87; available for call, 1987–89; Congregational Christian Churches of Canada: Bay Community, Comox, BC, 1989–

Smith, Duane R.
b. 09/23/1949, Milaca, MN
training: Calvin Theological Seminary, MDiv, 1978
ordained: 1979
charges: Vauxhall, AB, 1979–85; Houston, BC, 1985–98; Bemis, SD, 1998–2001; eligible for call, 2001–

Smith, Edgar H.
b. 03/05/1907, London, England
training: Missionary training colony
ordained: 1941
charges: Sudan United Mission, 1941–45; Missionary to Nigeria, 1945–69; Missionary on special assignment, 1969–72
retired: 1972
d. 03/01/1976, Holland, MI

Smith, Gregory Alan
b. 03/08/1962, Biloxi, MS
training: Calvin Theological Seminary, MDiv, 1990
ordained: 1990
charges: Church planting residency, Rosewood, Bellflower, CA, 1990–91; New Harvest, Camarillo, CA, 1991–95; VictoryPoint Ministries, Holland, MI, 1995–2001; Non-ministerial vocation, 2001

Smith, Jacob Peter
b. 10/02/1903, Grand Rapids, MI
training: Calvin Theological Seminary, ThB, 1933
ordained: 1934
charges: Delavan, WI, 1933–38; Evergreen Park, IL, 1938–44; Fourth, Paterson, NJ, 1944–50; Goshen, NY, 1950–53; Second, Fremont, MI, 1953–56; Calvin, Wyckoff, NJ, 1956–68
retired: 1968
d. 07/20/1980, Grand Rapids, MI

Smith, Kathleen Sue Hofman
b. 05/25/1958, Kenosha, WI
training: Calvin Theological Seminary, MDiv, 2001
ordained: 2001
charges: First, Grand Rapids, MI, 2001–2002; Calvin Institute for Christian Worship, Calvin College, Grand Rapids, MI, 2002–

Smith, Reginald
b. 12/01/1962, Chicago, IL
training: Calvin Theological Seminary, MDiv, 1992
ordained: 1993
charges: Northside Community Chapel, Paterson, NJ, 1993–94; Roosevelt Park Community, Grand Rapids, MI, 1994–

Smith, Thomas Lucas
b. 12/27/1927, Holland, MI
training: Calvin Theological Seminary, BD, 1956
ordained: 1956
charges: Holland, MN, 1956–60; South Bend, IN, 1960–68; Des Moines, IA, 1968–71; Non-ministerial vocation, 1971

Smits, Lee Roger
b. 11/06/1946, Grand Rapids, MI
training: Calvin Theological Seminary, BD, 1871; MDiv, 1975
ordained: 1971
charges: Missionary, Community, St. Cloud, MN, 1971–74; First, Crown Point, IN, 1974–79; Prospect Park, Holland, MI, 1979–90; Winfield, IL, 1991–97; Pastoral Care, Loyala University Medical Center, Marywood, IL, 1999–2000; Chaplain, Loyala University Medical Center, Marywood, IL, 2000–

Smits, Theodore
b. 10/08/1869, Alto, WI
training: with William Heyns
ordained: 1899
charges: Luctor, KS, 1899–1901; Ebenezer, Grand View, SD, 1901–03
d. 03/27/1903, Grand View, SD

Smitter, John (Jan)
b. 01/07/1870, Bierum, Groningen, Netherlands
training: Calvin Theological Seminary, diploma, 1895
ordained: 1895
charges: Home missionary, 1895–96; South Olive, MI, 1896–1900; First, Sioux Center, IA, 1900–04; Third, Muskegon, MI, 1904–08; North Street, Zeeland, MI, 1908–15; Oostburg, WI, 1916–19; Lansing, IL, 1919–23; Madison, Ave., Paterson, NJ, 1924–27

d. 05/25/1927, Oostburg, WI

Snapper, David Nelson
b. 02/19/1950, Cherry Point, NC
training: Calvin Theological Seminary, ThM, 1979
ordained: 1980
charges: Mountain Lake, MN, 1980–84; Anchor of Hope, Silverdale, WA, 1984–

So, Ky-Chun
b. 06/10/1958
ordained: 1987
charges: The Spirit Filled, Cerritos, CA, 1995–96; eligible for call, 1996–

Soerens, Thomas Glenn
b. 04/29/1951, Sheboygan, WI
training: Calvin Theological Seminary, MDiv, 1978
ordained: 1978
charges: Cedar, IA, 1978–83; Missionary, Central America, 1983–97; Faculty, Dordt College, Sioux Center, IA, 1997–2000; Missionary, Central America, 2000–

Song, Byoung II
b. 01/21/1962, Korea
training: Chong-Shin Theological Seminary, MDiv, 1991; Talbot Theological Seminary, ThM, 1996
ordained: 1992
charges: Presbyterian General Assembly, in Korea: Urim, Seoul, 1989–93; Orange Korean, Fullerton, CA, 1995–97; CRC: Urim, Mission Viejo, CA, 1997–

Song, Ho C.
b. 01/24/1950, Korea
training: Faith Evangelical Lutheran Seminary
ordained: 1989
charges: First Korean, Kent, WA, 1994–

Song, Ho Kil
b. 11/01/1955, Inchon, South Korea
training: Covenant Theological Seminary, MDiv, 1989; Western Theological Seminary, DMin, 1997
ordained: 1987
charges: Korean Calvary Baptist, Renton, WA, 1987–91; Hanmi Presbyterian Church: American Korean, Kent, WA, 1989–1991; Central Baptist, Seattle, WA, 1991–93; CRC: Korean Grace, Spokane, WA, 1993–95; Eligible for call, 1995–1995; Missionary, Philippines, 2000–

Sonnema, Harold
b. 04/12/1923, North Haledon, NJ
training: Calvin Theological Seminary, BD, 1947

ordained: 1947
charges: North Blendon, MI, 1947–50; Fourth, Paterson, NJ, 1950–57; Lake Worth, FL, 1957–59; Franklin St., Grand Rapids, MI, 1959–63; First, Ontario, CA, 1963–81
retired: 1984
d. 08/29/1984, Palm Springs, CA

Sossedkine, Serguei
b. 01/13/1971, Moscow, Russian Federation/USSR
training: Calvin Theological Seminary, MDiv, 2001
ordained: 2002
charges: Back to God Hour, Palos Heights, IL, 1996–

Spaan, Howard Bernece
b. 01/26/1920, Lynden, WA
training: Westminster Theological Seminary-PA, ThB and ThM, 1948
ordained: 1948
charges: Community, Saginaw, MI, 1948–53; West Side, Cleveland, OH, 1953–59; Calvin, Portland, OR, 1959–65; Oak Hills, Portland, OR, 1965–75; Clinical pastoral education, Providence Medical Center, Portland, OR, 1975–76; Church of the Savior, Corvallis, OR, 1976–85
retired: 1985

Spalink, Benjamin H.
b. 04/07/1890, Muskegon, MI
training: Calvin Theological Seminary, diploma, 1921
ordained: 1921
charges: Eastmanville, MI, 1921–24; Muskegon Heights, MI, 1924–26; East Leonard, Grand Rapids, MI, 1926–30; Evergreen Park, IL, 1930–37; New Holland, SD, 1937–40; Home missionary for Central Iowa at Newton, IA, 1940–48; Preakness, NJ, 1948–52; Sussex, NJ, 1952–56
retired: 1956
d. 12/11/1967, Grand Rapids, MI

Spalink, Lawrence Kent
b. 11/06/1952, Paterson, NJ
training: Westminster Theological Seminary-PA, MDiv, 1978; Calvin Theological Seminary, Special Program for Ministerial Candidacy, 1980
ordained: 1980
charges: Church developer for Christian Reformed World Missions, Japan, 1980–

Sparks, Roger William
b. 03/08/1959, Orlando, FL
training: Mid-America Reformed Seminary, MDiv,

1985; Calvin Theological Seminary, Special Program for Ministerial Candidacy, 1986
ordained: 1986
charges: First, Medicine Hat, AB, 1986–91; Calvin, Rock Valley, IA, 1991–

Spee, George Robert
b. 07/10/1929, Grand Rapids, MI
training: Calvin Theological Seminary, BD, 1956
ordained: 1956
charges: Missionary to Nigeria: Turan, 1957–65, Makurdi, 1965–66, Kunav and Utanga, 1966–83; Leave, 1983–84; Missionary, Bahamas, 1984–90; On loan Gospel Missionary Union, Elutherea, Bahamas, 1990–91
retired: 1992

Speelman, Siemen Andrew
b. 01/07/1958, Charlottetown, PE
training: Calvin Theological Seminary, MDiv, 1989
ordained: 1993
charges: Grande Prairie and La Glace, AB, 1993–95; La Glace, AB, 1993–99; Vanastra Community, Vanastra, ON, 1999–

Spoelhof, Charles
b. 01/20/1897, Fairlawn, NJ
training: Calvin Theological Seminary, diploma, 1921; Princeton Theological Seminary, ThM, 1922
ordained: 1922
charges: Oskaloosa, IA, 1922–26; Lodi, NJ, 1926–48; Home missionary: Brampton, ON, 1948–49; Clinton, ON, 1948; Kitchener, ON, 1948–54; Woodstock, ON, 1949–51; Listowel, ON, 1952–59; Guelph, ON, 1953–55; Stratford, ON, 1954–55, 1956; Drayton, ON, 1954–55, 1956–58; Duncan, BC, 1955–56; Port Alberni, BC, 1955–56; Victoria, BC, 1955–56; Kemptville, ON, 1958–62; Navan, ON, 1958–62; Ottawa, ON, 1958–62
retired: 1962
d. 03/21/1989, Rochester, NY

Spoelstra, Peter Andrew
b. 05/04/1892, Grand Rapids, MI
training: Calvin Theological Seminary, BD, 1932
ordained: 1932
charges: Comstock, MI, 1932–44; Sumas, WA, 1944–49; Manhattan, MT, 1949–58; New Richmond, MI, 1961–62
retired: 1958
d. 10/26/1978, Holland, MI

Sponholz, Howard August
b. 04/08/1930, Grosse Pointe Farms, MI

training: Reformed Episcopal Seminary, BD, 1959; Calvin Theological Seminary, BD, 1967
ordained: 1960
charges: First Reformed Episcopal Church, New York, NY, 1960–67; CRC: Clara City, MN, 1967–72; Bemis, SD, 1972–76; Chaplain, Lutheran Medical Center, Brooklyn, NY, 1976–79; Chaplain, Cabrini Medical Center and St. Vincent's Hospital, New York NY, 1979–95
retired: 1995

Spoor, Christian C.
b. 09/03/1936, Amsterdam, Noord Holland, Netherlands
training: Calvin Theological Seminary, BD, 1963
ordained: 1963
charges: CRC: Calvin, Le Mars, IA, 1963–67; Aylmer, ON, 1967–73; New Westminster, BC, 1973–78; RCA: New Life Community, Ft. Lauderdale, FL, 1979–83; Christ Community, Pompano Beach, FL, 1984–88; Homewood, IL, 1988

Spriensma, Audred Timothy
b. 10/16/1954, Zeeland, MI
training: Calvin Theological Seminary, MDiv, 1980
ordained: 1981
charges: CRC: Atwood, MI, 1981–84; Bethany, South Holland, IL, 1984–92; PRC: Grandville, MI, 1992

Sprik, Hubert John
b. 06/25/1929, Gallup, NM
training: Calvin Theological Seminary, BD, 1954
ordained: 1954
charges: Home missionary to Columbus, OH, 1954–57, (loaned to Fairbanks, AK, 1957); Missionary at Oklahoma City, OK, 1957–58; Parkview Heights, Cincinnati, OH, 1958–65; Crown Point, IN, 1965–69; Missionary, Greeley, CO, 1969–72; Wayland, MI, 1972–86; Christian Encouragement Center, Grand Rapids, MI, 1986–88
retired: 1986

Sprik, Ronald Roger
b. 04/17/1939, Manton, MI
training: Calvin Theological Seminary, BD, 1967
ordained: 1967
charges: Missionary to Puerto Rico, 1967–85; West Olive, MI, 1985–91; Brooten, MN, 1991–99; Ireton, IA, 1999–

Spykman, Gordon John
b. 03/25/1926, Holland, MI
training: Calvin Theological Seminary, MDiv, 1952; Vrije Universiteit, Amsterdam, ThD, 1955

ordained: 1955
charges: Blenheim, ON, 1955–59; Faculty, Calvin College, Grand Rapids, MI, 1959–91
retired: 1991
d. 07/13/1993, Grand Rapids, MI

Spykstra, Timothy Alan
b. 10/29/1965, Denver, CO
training: Westminster Theological Seminary-CA, MDiv, 1991
ordained: 1993
charges: Independent Reformed: Wellspring Christian Fellowship, 1993–99; CRC: The River, Redlands, CA, 1999–

Stadt, Jan Jr.
b. 10/25/1828, Nieuwveen, Utrecht, Netherlands
training: with Roelof Duiker
ordained: 1869
charges: Collendoorn, MI, 1869–70; First, Zeeland, 1870–72; East Side/West Side, Cleveland, OH, 1872–77; First, Orange City, IA, 1877–84; Le Mars, IA, 1884–85; Ridott, IL, 1885–87
retired: 1887
d. 04/17/1900, Harrison, SD

Stadt, Paul Douglas
b. 03/03/1940, Grand Rapids, MI
training: Calvin Theological Seminary, BD, 1969
ordained: 1969
charges: Welland Junction, ON, 1969–75; Iron Springs, AB, 1975–80; On loan to Reformed Church in New Zealand, 1980–83; Eligible for call, 1983–84; First, Barrie, ON, 1984–89; Georgetown, ON, 1989–96; First, Chatham, ON, 1996–

Stam, Jeffry Ray
b. 10/09/1950, Holland, MI
training: Reformed Bible College, BRE, 1976; Trinity Evangelical Divinity School, MS, 1980
ordained: 1995
charges: Campus pastor, Worthington Community College, Worthington, MN, 1976–79; Faculty, Reformed Bible College, Grand Rapids, MI, 1980–83; Christian Reformed World Missions, Missionary to Central America, 1983–91; Christian Reformed World Missions — Director, CITE, 1991–93; Christian Reformed Church Publication/World Literature Ministries, 1993–96; Director, Set Free Ministries, Friendship Chapel, Jenison, MI, 1995–2000; Interim, Pathway Ministries, Byron Center, MI, 2000–2001; Friendship Chapel, Jenison, MI, 2002–

Star, Ring
b. 09/02/1897, Corsica, SD vicinity
training: Calvin Theological Seminary, ThB, 1930
ordained: 1930
charges: Purewater, SD, 1930–38; Shepherd, MT, 1938–43; Bemis, SD, 1943–50; Compton, CA, 1950–51; Granum, AB, 1951–59; Bemis, SD, 1959–66
retired: 1966
d. 05/03/1999, Grandville, MI

Starkenburg, Sheldon
b. 02/28/1956, Volga, SD
training: Calvin Theological Seminary, MDiv, 1982
ordained: 1992
charges: Prairie City, IA, 1992–98; Eligible for call, 1998–99; Calvary, Pella, IA, 1999–

Stastny, James Joseph
b. 08/03/1949, Chicago, IL
training: Talbot Theological Seminary, MDiv, 1979; Calvin Theological Seminary, Special Program for Ministerial Candidacy, 1989
ordained: 1990
charges: CRC: Program director/Assistant pastor, Cloverdale, Boise, ID, 1986–87; Rusk, MI, 1990–96; West Sayville, NY, 1996–97; Independent: West Sayville, NY, 1997

Steele, William O.
b. 08/28/1948, New Stevenston, Motherwell, Scotland
training: University of Edinburgh, MA, 1975; Knox College, MDiv, 1980
ordained: 1980
charges: Presbyterian Church of Canada: St. Andrew's Presbyterian, Cardinal, ON, 1980–82; Presbyterian, St. John, BC, 1982–89; St. Andrew's Presbyterian, Moncton, AB, 1989–93; Interim pastor, John Calvin, Truro, NS, 1993; CRC: John Calvin, Truro, NS, 1993–96; Missionary, Republic of Guinea, West Africa, 1996–

Steen, Franklin D.
b. 10/12/1936, Paterson, NJ
training: Calvin Theological Seminary, ThB, 1961; Westminster Theological Seminary-PA, ThM, 1963
ordained: 1963
charges: Aetna, MI, 1963–67; First, Detroit, MI, 1967–75; Covenant, Sioux Center, IA, 1975–81; Kedvale Ave., Oak Lawn, IL, 1981–86
d. 11/15/1986, Chicago, IL

Steen, Henry James
b. 09/18/1953, Chicago, IL

training: Calvin Theological Seminary, MDiv, 1983
ordained: 1984
charges: CRC: Missionary, Philippines, 1984-95; Leave, 1995-96; Resigned from denomination, 1996

Steen, Norman Bruce
b. 10/25/1949, Burbank, CA
training: Calvin Theological Seminary, BD, 1976; ThM, 1981
ordained: 1976
charges: Parkersburg, IA, 1976-80; Leave, 1980-81; Ridgewood, NJ, 1981-88; Fourteenth Street, Holland, MI, 1988-99; Washington, DC, 1999-

Steen, Peter Lambert
b. 11/18/1902, Paterson, NJ
training: Calvin Theological Seminary, BD, 1926; Princeton Theological Seminary, ThM, 1927
ordained: 1928
charges: Decatur, MI, 1928-30
retired: 1930
d. 02/19/1935, Paterson, NJ

Steen, Robert Duvalopis
b. 06/30/1946, Paterson, NJ
training: Calvin Theological Seminary, BD, 1971; MDiv, 1973
ordained: 1971
charges: Missionary, Wanamassa, NJ, 1971-73; Gallatin Gateway, MT, 1973-77; Immanuel, Columbia, MO, 1977-82; Community, Syracuse, NY, 1982-96; Irving Park, Midland Park, NJ, 1996-99; Rudyard, MI, 1999-

Steenbergen, Henry Frederick
b. 07/31/1956, Palmerston, ON
training: Calvin Theological Seminary, MDiv, 1989
ordained: 1990
charges: Fellowship, Brighton, ON, 1990-96; First, Abbotsford, BC, 1996-

Steenhoek, Donald John
b. 02/01/1945, Oskaloosa, IA
training: Calvin Theological Seminary, MDiv, 1977
ordained: 1977
charges: Milwaukee, Brookfield, WI, 1977-80; Covenant, Appleton, WI, 1980-87; Industrial chaplain, Waste Management Inc., South Palm Beach, FL, 1987-92; Chaplain, Employee Assistance Services, South Palm Beach, FL, 1992-95; Chaplain, Florida Chaplaincy Service, Jupiter, FL, 1995-97; Rogers Heights, Wyoming, MI, 1997-

Steenland, William Cornelius
b. 07/29/1908, Grand Rapids, MI
training: Calvin Theological Seminary, BD, 1933
ordained: 1934
charges: Conrad, MT, 1934-37; Des Plaines, IL, 1937-38; Leave, 1938-41; Hope, Grandville, MI, 1942-45
d. 11/16/1945, Grandville, MI

Steenstra, Charles Stewart
b. 11/01/1930, Grand Rapids, MI
training: Calvin Theological Seminary, BD, 1955; MDiv, 1979
ordained: 1955
charges: Chandler, MN, 1955-59; Dutton, MI, 1959-64; Faith, Holland, MI, 1964-77; Ivanrest, Grandville, MI, 1977-83; Westview, Grand Rapids, MI, 1983-95
retired: 1996

Steenstra, Stephen Roy
b. 09/23/1952, Paterson, NJ
training: Westminster Theological Seminary, MDiv, 1977; Calvin Theological Seminary, Special Program for Ministerial Candidacy, 1978
ordained: 1980
charges: Oakland, MI, 1980-84; Grant, MI, 1984-87; Bible teacher, Rehoboth Christian School, Rehoboth, NM, 1987-91; First, Paterson, NJ, 1991-96; Orangewood, Phoenix, AZ, 1996-99; Non-ministerial vocation, 1999

Steenwyk, John Henry
b. 05/14/1907, Groningen, Groningen, Netherlands
training: Calvin Theological Seminary, BD, 1937
ordained: 1937
charges: Decatur, MI, 1937-46; Dorr, MI, 1946-51; Muskegon Heights, MI, 1951-67; Prosper, Falmouth, MI, 1967-72
retired: 1972
d. 05/02/1995, Grand Haven, MI

Stegink, Martin
b. 06/20/1927, Holland, MI
training: Calvin Theological Seminary, BD, 1954
ordained: 1954
charges: Rudyard, MI, 1954-58; Pompton Plains, NJ, 1959-61; Classical Home missionary for greater Detroit, MI, 1961-64; Lincoln Center, IA, 1964-72; Prosper, Falmouth, MI, 1972-81; Leave, 1981-82; First, Crookston, MN, 1982-89
retired: 1989

Steigenga, John Jay
b. 03/19/1942, Grand Rapids, MI

training: Calvin Theological Seminary, BD, 1967; MDiv, 1986
ordained: 1968
charges: Cherry Hill, Inkster, MI, 1968-74; Nardin Park Community, Detroit, MI, 1974-78; LaGrave Ave., Grand Rapids, MI, 1978-

Steigenga, Joseph Jay
b. 07/15/1894, Borculo, MI vicinity
training: Calvin Theological Seminary, diploma, 1919; Princeton, 1920
ordained: 1920
charges: Lebanon, IA, 1920-24; First, Grand Haven, MI, 1924-27; Lee St., Grand Rapids, MI, 1927-39; First, Ripon, CA, 1939-51; Everson, WA, 1951-52
retired: 1952
d. 11/03/1966, Ripon, CA

Stek, John Henry
b. 03/07/1925, Mahaska County, IA
training: Calvin Theological Seminary, BD, 1952; Westminster Theological Seminary-PA, ThM, 1956; Vrije Universiteit, Drs
ordained: 1955
charges: Raymond, MN, 1955-61; Faculty, Calvin Theological Seminary, Grand Rapids, MI, 1961-91
retired: 1991

Stel, Philip
b. 04/19/1952, Haren, Groningen, Netherlands
training: Calvin Theological Seminary, MDiv, 1977
ordained: 1977
charges: Maranatha, York, ON, 1977-82; Bethel, London, ON, 1982-91; First, Rocky Mountain House, AB, 1991-

Stellingwerff, Peter Calvin
b. 01/10/1958, Prince George, BC
training: Calvin Theological Seminary, MDiv, 1990
ordained: 1991
charges: Kentville, NS, 1991-94; Maranatha, Calgary, AB, 1995-2002; Leave, YWAM, Costa Rica, 2002-2003

Stephenson, Mark
b. 12/25/1958, Holland, MI
training: Calvin Theological Seminary, MDiv, 1988
ordained: 1989
charges: Hillcrest, Hudsonville, MI, 1989-96; West Olive, MI, 1996-

Stevens, Gary Michael
b. 09/23/1956, Pasadena, CA
training: Calvin Theological Seminary, MDiv, 1996

ordained: 1996
charges: Heritage, Kalamazoo, MI, 1996-2002; Bethel, Sun Valley, CA, 2002-

Stevenson, David W.
b. 04/10/1949, New Castle, PA
training: Westminster Theological Seminary-PA, MAR, 1981; MDiv, 1981
ordained: 1984
charges: PCA: First Charleston, AR, 1984-87; CRC: Trinity, Richfield Springs, NY, 1987-92; Leighton, IA, 1992-99; eligible for call, 1999-2001; released from the denomination, 2001

Stienstra, Arthur J.
b. 06/15/1930, Sneek, Friesland, Netherlands
training: Calvin Theological Seminary, BD, 1961
ordained: 1962
charges: Exeter, ON, 1962-65; Home missionary, Faith, New Brighton, MN, 1965-71; Hawarden IA, 1971-75; Silver Spring, MD, 1975-81; University, Ames, IA, 1981-90; Immanuel, Fort Collins, CO, 1990-92
retired: 1992

Stienstra, Richard
b. 06/10/1932, Baard, Friesland, Netherlands
training: Calvin Theological Seminary, BD, 1967
ordained: 1967
charges: Caledonia, MI, 1967-71; Second, Edmonton, AB, 1971-78; Trinity, Abbotsford, AB, 1978-85; Calvin, Dundas, ON, 1985-90; Bethel, Dunnville, ON, 1990-92; URC: Grace Reformed, Dunnville, ON, 1992-99
retired: 1999

Stieva, Leonard Kevin
b. 07/13/1965, Grimsby, ON
training: Calvin Theological Seminary, MDiv, 2001
ordained: 2001
charges: Heritage, Byron Center, MI, 2001-

Stob, George
b. 05/19/1907, Chicago, IL
training: Calvin Theological Seminary, ThB, 1935; Princeton Theological Seminary, ThD, 1955
ordained: 1936
charges: Sumas, WA, 1935-40; Burton Heights, Grand Rapids, MI, 1940-43; Chaplain, United States Army, 1943-46; Stated supply at Preakness, NJ, 1946-47; Faculty, Calvin Theological Seminary, Grand Rapids, MI, 1947-52; Richfield, Clifton, NJ, 1953-62; Wheaton, IL, 1962-67; Washington, DC, 1967-74
retired: 1974

d. 09/17/2002, Millersville, MD

Stob, Harvey Alan
b. 06/10/1944, Grand Rapids, MI
training: Calvin Theological Seminary, BD, 1972
ordained: 1972
charges: Missionary to Argentina, 1972-84;
Parkview Heights, Cincinnati, OH, 1984-89;
Ridgewood, NJ, 1989-96; Ann Arbor, MI, 1996-

Stob, Henry J.
b. 06/24/1908, Chicago, IL
training: Calvin Theological Seminary, BD, 1935;
Hartford Theological Seminary, ThB; Vrije
Universiteit, Amsterdam, PhD, 1939
ordained: 1953
charges: Faculty, Calvin College, Grand Rapids,
MI, 1939-43, 1946-52; United States Navy, 1943-
46; Faculty, Calvin Theological Seminary, 1952-75
retired: 1975
d. 05/27/1996, Grand Rapids, MI

Stob, Ralph
b. 04/01/1894, Chicago, IL
training: Calvin Theological Seminary, diploma,
1920; University of Chicago, AM, 1928; PhD, 1931
ordained: 1954
charges: Faculty, Calvin College, Grand Rapids,
MI, 1917-53 (President 1933-39); Faculty, Calvin
Theological Seminary, Grand Rapids, MI, 1953-64
retired: 1964
d. 04/05/1965, Grand Rapids, MI

Stob, William John
b. 02/22/1933, Chicago, IL
training: Calvin Theological Seminary, BD, 1966
ordained: 1966
charges: CRC: Missionary to Japan, 1966-82;
Neo Pentecostal missionary in Japan, 1982

Stob, William Kenneth
b. 07/29/1930, Chicago, IL
training: Calvin Theological Seminary, BD, 1955;
ThM, 1970; Western Michigan University, EdD,
1977
ordained: 1955
charges: Trinity, Fremont, MI, 1955-60; Ft. Lauderdale, FL, 1960-63; Bethany, Muskegon, MI,
1963-69; Woodlawn, Grand Rapids, MI, 1969-70;
Dean, Calvin College, Grand Rapids, MI, 1970-92;
Back to God Hour, Grand Rapids, MI, 1992-95
retired: 1995

Stockmeier, Leonard F.
b. 05/11/1925, Sheboygan, WI

training: Mission House College, diploma, 1950;
Calvin Theological Seminary, Special Program for
Ministerial candidacy, 1958
ordained: 1950
charges: Evangelical and Reformed Church:
Campbellsport, WI, 1950-55; German Reformed
Church: Hosmer, SD, 1955-58; CRC: Colton, SD,
1958-63; Calvin, Sheboygan, WI, 1963-68;
Orangewood, Phoenix, AZ, 1968-77; Corsica, SD,
1977-83; Prairie City, IA, 1983-87
retired: 1987

Stoel, James David
b. 07/27/1947, Lake Odessa, MI
training: Calvin Theological Seminary, BD, 1972;
ThM, 1973
ordained: 1973
charges: Austinville, IA, 1973-79; Faith, Pella, IA,
1979-89; Community, Roselawn, IN, 1989-96;
Chaplain, Whispering Pines Health Care Center,
Valparaiso, IN, 1996-2000; Chaplain, St. Mary's
Hospital, Chicago, IL, 2000-

Stoutmeyer, Garrett Hite
b. 12/31/1932, Kalamazoo, MI
training: Calvin Theological Seminary, BD, 1958;
MDiv, 1975
ordained: 1958
charges: Prospect Park, Paterson, NJ, 1958-63;
Calvin, Holland, MI, 1963-67; Elmhurst, IL, 1967-
72; Ft. Lauderdale, FL, 1972-75; Faith, Grand
Rapids, MI, 1975-79; Coopersville, MI, 1983-90;
Eligible for call, 1990-93; Bethany, South Holland,
IL, 1993-97
retired: 1997

Stravers, David Eugene
b. 05/10/1949, Oskaloosa, IA
training: Calvin Theological Seminary, MDiv, 1976
ordained: 1976
charges: Missionary to the Philippines, 1976-83;
Leave, 1983-84; Missionary to the Philippines,
1984-86; Eligible for call, 1986; Director, International ministries, The Bible League, South Holland, IL, 1987-

Stravers, Dick M.
b. 11/07/1927, Reasnor, IA
training: Calvin Theological Seminary, BD, 1963
ordained: 1963
charges: West Park, Cleveland, OH, 1963-67;
Southern Heights, Kalamazoo, MI, 1967-71;
Woodlawn, Grand Rapids, MI, 1971-80; West
Park, Cleveland, OH, 1980-92
retired: 1992

Stroo, William Abraham

b. 12/24/1942, Grand Rapids, MI
training: Calvin Theological Seminary, BD, 1969
ordained: 1969
charges: Chaplain, Appalachian Regional Hospital,
Middlesboro, KY, 1969-70; Missionary, Mason
City, IA, 1970-75; Trinity, St. Louis, MO, 1975-86;
Leave, 1986-89; Minister, Pastoral counseling, Sa-
maritan Counseling Center, South Bend, IN, 1989-
93; Tolentine Personal Resource Center, Olympia,
IL and Pastoral Therapy Ministries, South Bend,
IN, 1993-99; Pastoral counselor, LaGrave Avenue,
Grand Rapids, MI, 1999-

Struyk, David Alan

b. 10/10/1961, Paterson, NJ
training: Calvin Theological Seminary, MDiv, 1986
ordained: 1986
charges: Community, Wyoming, MI, 1986-

Struyk, Sebastian

b. 09/19/1885, Paterson, NJ
training: Calvin Theological Seminary, diploma,
1925
ordained: 1926
charges: Willard, OH, 1925-34; Los Angeles, CA,
1934-48
retired: 1948
d. 11/22/1952, Los Angeles, CA

Strydhorst, Albert Andrew

b. 05/16/1964, Barrhead, AB
training: Reformed Bible College, BRE, 1989; Calvin Theological Seminary, MDiv, 1993
ordained: 1993
charges: Missionary, Nigeria, 1993-

Stuart, Frederik W.

b. 03/01/1870, Assen, Drenthe, Netherlands
training: Calvin Theological Seminary, diploma,
1901
ordained: 1901
charges: Platte, SD, 1901-04; Overisel, MI, 1904-
05; Home missionary, Orange City, IA, 1905-08;
Sheldon, IA, 1908-12; Sanborn, IA, 1912-15;
Hanford, CA, 1915-19
d. 08/29/1919, Hanford, CA

Stuart, William

b. 06/20/1875, Assen, Drenthe, Netherlands
training: Princeton Theological Seminary, BD,
1901
ordained: 1902
charges: Home missionary at Orange City, IA,
1902-05; Sully, IA, 1905-08; Third Roseland, Chi-

cago, IL, 1908-15; LaGrave Ave., Grand Rapids,
MI, 1915-25; Bible teacher at Grand Rapids (MI)
Christian High School, 1925-41
d. 12/25/1941, Grand Rapids, MI

Stuit, Gordon Thomas

b. 08/28/1928, Grand Rapids, MI
training: Calvin Theological Seminary, BD, 1957
ordained: 1957
charges: Field pastor, Rehoboth, NM, 1957-63;
Home missionary, Tohatchi, NM, 1963-67; Tracy,
IA, 1967-74; Crownpoint, NM, 1974-88; Window
Rock, AZ, 1988-93
retired: 1993

Stuit, Otto

b. 04/13/1850, Vierhuizen, Groningen, Netherlands
training: Calvin Theological Seminary, diploma,
1886
ordained: 1886
charges: Cincinnati, OH, 1886-88
d. 09/03/1888, Cincinnati, OH

Stulp, Jack (Jacob)

b. 04/25/1933, Chicago, IL
training: Calvin Theological Seminary, BD, 1957;
MDiv, 1981
ordained: 1957
charges: Moorpark, San Jose, CA, 1957-67; Monroe, WA, 1967-73; Prairie Edge, Kalamazoo, MI,
1973-83; Immanuel, Hudsonville, MI, 1983-94;
Harderwyk, Holland, MI, 1994-95; Noordeloos, MI,
1995-98
retired: 1998

Sturing, Stanley Jay

b. 03/17/1957, Oskaloosa, IA
training: Calvin Theological Seminary, MDiv, 1999
ordained: 1999
charges: Community, Saginaw, MI, 1999-

Suarez, Xavier

b. 06/02/1959, Gauyaquil, Ecuador
training: Philadelphia Seminary; Adelante Seminary
ordained: 1999
charges: CRC: Iglesia El Buen Samaritano, Lake
Worth, FL, 1999-

Suh, Gil Sung

b. 12/23/1968, Seoul, South Korea
training: Calvin Theological Seminary, MDiv, 1999
ordained: 2000

charges: Faculty, Veenstra Seminary, Nigeria, 2000–

Suk, John Donald
b. 10/13/1956, St. Catharines, ON
training: Calvin Theological Seminary, MDiv, 1984
ordained: 1985
charges: Redeemer, Sarnia, ON, 1985–90; Ann Arbor, MI, 1990–93; Editor, *The Banner,* Grand Rapids, MI, 1993–

Suk, William
b. 03/06/1932, Sappermeer, Groningen, Netherlands
training: declared eligible on the basis of exceptional gifts, 1980
ordained: 1980
charges: Pastoral assistant, Georgetown, ON, 1977–80; Georgetown, ON, 1980–81; Hebron, Renfrew, ON, 1981–85; Chaplain, Holland Christian Home/ First, Brampton, ON, 1985–86
d. 10/24/1986, Brampton, ON

Sung, David Kihawk
b. 09/19/1966, South Korea
training: Calvin Theological Seminary, MDiv, 1999
ordained: 2000
charges: On loan to Korean Presbyterian Church, Ann Arbor, MI, 2000; The Lighthouse Community, Ann Arbor, MI, 2000–

Sung, Samuel (Youn-Kyong) K.
b. 12/17/1934, Choongnam Yeungi-Gun, Korea
training: Presbyterian General Assembly Theological Seminary, MDiv, 1991; International Theological Seminary, ThM, 1993; Westminster Theological Seminary, MDiv, 1961; Faith Theological Seminary, DMin, 1986; International Theological Seminary, ThD
ordained: 1963
charges: Korean Presbyterian Church: Man-Suk, Kunsan, 1963–66; Kohyeon, 1966–69; West Daejeon, Daejeon, 1969–73; By Kang, Chung Buk, 1973–79; US Korean Presbyterian Church: First Korean, Tacoma, WA, 1979–84; Korean Hope, Seattle, WA, 1984–85; CRC: Missionary to Koreans, Seattle, WA, 1985–91; Hope Korean, Seattle, WA, 1991–

Sutton, Robert James
b. 12/26/1922, Scranton, PA
training: Denison University, BD; Westminster Theological Seminary-PA, ThM
ordained: 1952

charges: CRC: Missionary to Japan, 1952–61; Independent: Bible College, Japan, 1961

Sweetman, Leonard Jr.
b. 05/11/1924, Paterson, NJ
training: Calvin Theological Seminary, ThB, 1951; Vrije Universiteit, Amsterdam, ThD, 1962
ordained: 1951
charges: Conrad, MT, 1951–53; Missionary to South India studying at Kennedy School, Hartford, CT, 1953–55; Missionary to Japan, 1955–58; Leave, 1958–59, Missionary to Japan, 1959–61; Home missionary, Hessel Park, Champaign, IL, 1962–64; Faculty, Calvin College, 1964–89
retired: 1989

Swets, Walter
b. 01/12/1935, Hammond, IN
training: Calvin Theological Seminary, BD, 1959
ordained: 1959
charges: Hartley, IA, 1959–64; Colton, SD, 1964–69; Bethel, Oskaloosa, IA, 1969–73; First, Cutlerville, MI, 1973–97
retired: 1997

Swier, Loren James
b. 03/21/1951, Modesto, CA
training: Calvin Theological Seminary, MDiv, 1988
ordained: 1988
charges: Bethlehem, Freeman, SD, 1988–92; Penticton, BC, 1992–97; Eligible for call, 1997–2002; Sumas, WA, 2002–

Swierenga, John B.
b. 11/26/1906, Alamosa, CO
training: Calvin Theological Seminary, BD, 1936
ordained: 1938
charges: Sunshine Chapel, Belmont, MI, 1934–36; South Fremont Mission, Freemont, MI, 1938; Conrad, MT, 1938–42; Compton, CA, 1942–44; Two Wells, NM 1944–56; Naschitti Mission, NM, 1956–58
d. 06/16/1958, Denver, CO

Swierenga, Raymond Calvin
b. 07/16/1936, Chicago, IL
training: Calvin Theological Seminary, BD, 1960; MDiv, 1987
ordained: 1960
charges: Chaplain, United States Navy, 1960–83; Chaplain, Michigan Dunes Correctional Facility, Saugatuck, MI, 1983–91; Chaplain, Michigan Correctional Facility, Muskegon, MI, 1991–

Swierenga, William
b. 04/15/1916, Alamosa, CO
training: Calvin Theological Seminary, ThB, 1952
ordained: 1952
charges: Comstock Park, Grand Rapids, MI, 1949-60; Chaplain, Michigan Veterans Facility, Grand Rapids, MI, 1960-76
d. 01/28/1976, Grand Rapids, MI

Swieringa, Thomas B.
b. 02/07/1953, Holland, MI
training: Calvin Theological Seminary, MDiv, 1980
ordained: 1980
charges: Woden, IA, 1980-83; Ridgewood, Jenison, MI, 1983-86; Bethel, Manhattan, MT, 1986-90; Family of Christ, Maple Grove, MN, 1990-96; Discovery, Kentwood, MI, 1996-

Swieringa, Vern Dale
b. 08/29/1959, Holland, MI
training: Reformed Bible College, Grand Rapids, MI, BRE, 1995; Calvin Theological Seminary, MDiv, 2000
ordained: 2000
charges: Gibson, Holland, MI, 2000-

Swinney, David John
b. 07/06/1961, Everett, WA
training: declared eligible on the basis of exceptional gifts, 2000
ordained: 2000
charges: Transcona, Winnipeg, MB, 2000-2001; Brooten, MN, 2001-

Sybenga, Adriana Schouten
b. 07/05/1949, Boskoop, Zuid Holland, Netherlands
training: Fuller Theological Seminary, MDiv, 1998; Calvin Theological Seminary, Special Program for Ministerial Candidacy, 2001
ordained: 2002
charges: Hope Community, Riverside, CA, 2002-

Sybenga, Sid
b. 07/31/1949, Hoogeveen, Drenthe, Netherlands
training: Calvin Theological Seminary, MDiv, 1990
ordained: 1990
charges: Calvary, Chatham, ON, 1990-97; Arcadia, CA, 1997-

Sytsma, Andrew Richard
b. 01/28/1971, Tokyo, Japan
training: Calvin Theological Seminary, MDiv, 1997
ordained: 1997

charges: Emmaus Road, Seattle, WA, 1997-99; Bridgeway Community, Haledon, NJ, 1999-

Sytsma, Richard D.
b. 06/20/1920, Paterson, NJ
training: Calvin Theological Seminary, ThB, 1952
ordained: 1952
charges: Missionary to Japan: Tokyo, 1952-55; Kawagoe, 1955-61; Ominya and Tokorozawa, 1961-65,; Tokiwadaira, 1965-70; Koganehara and Kohokudai, 1970-76; Numzau, 1976-84
retired: 1984

Sytsma, Richard Erwin Jr.
b. 07/10/1942, Denver, CO
training: Calvin Theological Seminary, BD, 1967
ordained: 1968
charges: Missionary, Japan, 1968-2000; Faculty, Calvin Theological Seminary, Grand Rapids, MI, 2000-

Sytsma, Steven R.
b. 11/16/1954, Rensselaer, IN
training: Calvin Theological Seminary, MDiv, 1989
ordained: 1989
charges: Director of evangelism and youth, Twelfth St., Grand Rapids, MI, 1987-88; Faith, Kalamazoo, MI, 1989-94; Oakland, MI, 1994-99; First, Hudsonville, MI, 1999-

Sytsma, William Ray
b. 12/27/1969, Valparaiso, IN
training: Calvin Theological Seminary, MDiv, 1998
ordained: 1998
charges: Cutlerville East, Cutlerville, MI, 1998-

Szto, Paul C.H.
b. 10/01/1924, Guangzhou, China
training: Westminster Theological Seminary-PA, BD, 1952; DMin, 1987; Union Theological Seminary, 1952
ordained: 1957
charges: Missionary to Chinese in Queens, NY, 1952-73; Queens, Jamaica, NY, 1973-86
retired: 1986

Tadema, Rits
b. 08/12/1928, Drachten, Friesland, Netherlands
training: Calvin Theological Seminary, ThB, 1952
ordained: 1952
charges: Everson, WA, 1952-55; Missionary to Nigeria, 1955-58; Manhattan, MT, 1958-62; Home missionary, Tacoma, WA, 1962-68; Chaplain, United States Air Force, 1968-70; Missionary, Community, Fountain Valley, CA, 1970-73; Chap-

lain for Christian Perspectives, Carnation, WA,
1973-90
retired: 1990

Tamming, Stephen Dwayne
b. 06/16/1968, Dunnville, ON
training: Calvin Theological Seminary, MDiv, 2001
ordained: 2001
charges: Trinity, Goderich, ON, 2001-

Tamminga, Edward Jay
b. 09/24/1939, Grand Rapids, MI
training: Calvin Theological Seminary, BD, 1963
ordained: 1963
charges: Plainfield, MI, 1963-66; South Olive, MI,
1966-71; Lake Worth, FL, 1971-77; Georgetown,
Hudsonville, MI, 1977-95; Second, Grand Haven,
MI, 1995-

Tamminga, Louis M.
b. 03/18/1930, Welsrijp, Friesland, Netherlands
training: Calvin Theological Seminary, BD, 1957
ordained: 1957
charges: Smithers and Telkwa, BC, 1957-60;
Maranatha, Edmonton, AB, 1960-65; Bethel, Sioux
Center, IA, 1965-70; Willowdale, Toronto, ON,
1970-80; Communications secretary, World Missions, 1980-83; Director, Pastor-Church Relations
Services, Grand Rapids, MI, 1983-95
retired: 1995

Tandayu, Elmer
b. 08/07/1954
ordained: 1985
charges: CRC: Church planting, Grace Filipino,
Bellflower, CA, 1993-

Tangelder, Johannes Dirk
b. 04/16/1936, Amsterdam, Noord Holland, Netherlands
training: Central Baptist Seminary, BTh, 1962;
Vrije Universiteit, DrsTh, 1963; Calvin Theological
Seminary, Special Program for Ministerial Candidacy
ordained: 1967
charges: Vernon, BC, 1967-70; Riverside,
Wellandport, ON, 1970-77; Missionary to the Philippines, 1977-79; East, Strathroy, ON, 1979-89;
Williamsburg, ON, 1989-93
retired: 1993

Tanis, Edward James
b. 02/16/1887, Paterson, NJ
training: Calvin Theological Seminary, diploma,

1910; University of Chicago Divinity School, MA,
1928; Northern Baptist Theological Seminary
ordained: 1911
charges: Kenosha WI, 1911-12; Broadway Ave.,
Grand Rapids, MI, 1912-19; First, Grand Rapids,
MI, 1919-27; Leave, 1927-28; Second Englewood,
Chicago, IL, 1928-42; Bible teacher at Grand
Rapids (MI) Christian High School, 1942; Second,
Grand Haven, MI, 1943-56
retired: 1956
d. 12/06/1958, Grand Haven, MI

Tanis, Evert
b. 08/12/1901, Fremont, MI
training: Calvin Theological Seminary, ThB, 1931
ordained: 1931
charges: Hull, ND, 1931-37; Alameda, CA, 1937-
46; Immanuel, Ripon, CA, 1946-69
retired: 1969
d. 04/22/1988, Ripon, CA

Tanis, Keith Wayne
b. 08/05/1949, Muskegon, MI
training: Calvin Theological Seminary, MDiv, 1975
ordained: 1975
charges: CRC: Trinity, Mt. Pleasant, MI, 1975-79;
New Life, Houston, TX, 1979-83; Ferrysburg, MI,
1983-90; Faculty, Calvin Theological Seminary,
Grand Rapids, MI, 1990-99; RCA: New Life Community, Artesia, CA, 2000-

Tanis, Leverne Kent
b. 04/06/1933, Hull, ND
training: Calvin Theological Seminary, BD, 1958
ordained: 1958
charges: Tracy, IA, 1958-62; Alamosa, CO, 1962-
65; Paramus, NJ, 1965-73; Community, Fountain
Valley, CA, 1973-82; Community, Oakdale, CA,
1982-99
retired: 1999

Tapanes, Carlos G.
b. 11/04/1953, Cuba
training: Reformed Bible College, BRE, 1990; Calvin Theological Seminary, MDiv, 1993
ordained: 1994
charges: Iglesia Hispana, Holland, MI, 1964-68;
Hispana Emanuel, Wyoming, MI, 1994-

Tapia-Ruano, Carlos
b. 08/20/1924, Quonabacoa, Cuba
training: University of Habana; declared eligible
on the basis of unique gifts
ordained: 1969
charges: Lay missionary to Spanish Church, Hol-

land, MI, 1964-69; Missionary to the Iglesia
Hispana, Holland, MI, 1969-71; Methodist Church,
1971; later non-ministerial vocation
d. 05/15/1989, Chicago, IL

Tebben, Kasjen
b. 11/14/1896, Tichelwarf, Ostfriesland, Germany
training: Calvin Theological Seminary, diploma,
1925
ordained: 1925
charges: Emden, MN, 1925-29; Ridott, IL, 1929-
35; Parkersburg, IA, 1935-47; Worthington, MN,
1947-50; Iowa Falls, IA, 1950-56
retired: 1956
d. 11/24/1984, Cedar Falls, IA

Teitsma, Herman J.
b. 03/05/1925, Grand Rapids, MI
training: Calvin Theological Seminary, ThB, 1951
ordained: 1952
charges: Bauer, MI, 1951-54; Ferrysburg, MI,
1954-59; Fairlawn, Whitinsville, MA, 1959-65;
Missionary pastor, Emmanuel, Sauk Village, IL,
1965-68; South Bend, IN, 1968-71; Director of
Rehabilitation, Hope Rescue Mission, South Bend,
IN, 1971-73; Executive Director, Jellema House,
Grand Rapids, MI, 1973-74; Trinity, Sparta, MI,
1974-79; Minister of evangelism, Sunshine, Grand
Rapids, MI, 1979-82; Chaplain of Life Motivational
Ministries, Grand Rapids, MI, 1982-84; Chaplain,
Christian Encouragement Center, Grand Rapids,
MI, 1984-87
retired: 1987
d. 04/04/2002, Grand Rapids, MI

Tempel, Hermanus
b. 08/28/1854, Groningen, Groningen, Netherlands
training: Calvin Theological Seminary, diploma,
1881
ordained: 1881
charges: Rochester, NY, 1881-83; Lansing, IL,
1883-86; New Holland, SD, 1886-88; West Side,
Cleveland, OH, 1888-93; Lucas, MI, 1893-94
d. 04/11/1894, Cleveland, OH

Ten Brink, Samuel
b. 10/19/1925, Muskegon, MI
training: Calvin Theological Seminary, BD, 1953
ordained: 1953
charges: Community, Saginaw, MI, 1953-56;
Bluffton, Muskegon, MI, 1956-59; Harrison, SD,
1959-63; Lodi, NJ, 1963-67; Northside, Clifton,
NJ, 1967-74; Lafayette, IN, 1974-80; First,
Kalamazoo, MI, 1980-86; Hills, MN, 1986-87

retired: 1990

Ten Harmsel, Wayne Alan
b. 07/04/1954, Holland, MI
training: University of Arizona, MA, 1985; Calvin
Theological Seminary, MDiv, 1997
ordained: 1998
charges: Barrhead, AB, 1998-2000; Mountain
View, Lynden, WA, 2000-

Ten Hoor, Foppe Martin
b. 02/19/1855, Haule, Friesland, Netherlands
training: Theologische Universiteit, Kampen, diploma, 1880
ordained: 1880
charges: GKN: Genderen, 1880-84; Opperdoes,
1884-88; Franeker, 1888-96; CRC: Oakdale Park,
Grand Rapids, MI, 1896-1900; Faculty, Calvin
Theological Seminary, Grand Rapids, MI, 1900-24
retired: 1924
d. 03/21/1934, Grand Rapids, MI

Ten Pass, Merlyn Robert
b. 04/15/1944, Beaver Dam, WI
training: Reformed Theological Seminary, MDiv,
1980; Calvin Theological Seminary, Special Program for Ministerial Candidacy, 1982
ordained: 1982
charges: CRC: Medicine Hat, AB, 1982-85;
Sumas, WA, 1985-89; Eligible for call, 1989-92;
ARPC:

Tenyenhuis, Elzo
b. 09/23/1955, Emmen, Drenthe, Netherlands
training: Calvin Theological Seminary, MDiv, 1999
ordained: 1999
charges: Kincardine, ON, 1999-

Tenyenhuis, John
b. 07/03/1950, Franeker, Friesland, Netherlands
training: Calvin Theological Seminary, BD, 1977;
MDiv, 1984
ordained: 1977
charges: Blenheim, ON, 1977-82; First, Montreal,
QC, 1982-88; Rehoboth, Toronto, ON, 1988-89;
Rehoboth Fellowship, Toronto, ON, 1989-

Tenyenhuis, Lammert
b. 04/13/1943, Emmen, Drenthe, Netherlands
training: Calvin Theological Seminary, BD, 1970
ordained: 1979
charges: CRC: Rehoboth, Niagara Falls, ON,
1979-82; Resigned from denomination, 1982
d. 01/29/1998, Canada

Ter Maat, Christian Gerrit
b. 05/27/1898, Orange City, IA
training: Westminster Theological Seminary-PA, ThB, 1937
ordained: 1938
charges: PCA/OPC: Itinerant evangelist, Midwest, 1938-46; CRC: Estelline, SD, 1946-49; Allison, IA, 1949-54; Vesper, WI, 1954-59; Sullivan, MI, 1959-60
retired: 1960
d. 07/17/1992, Sioux Center, IA

Terpsma, William
b. 09/04/1882, Franeker, Friesland, Netherlands
training: Calvin Theological Seminary, diploma, 1916
ordained: 1916
charges: Oakland, MI, 1916-18; Ireton, IA, 1918-25; Sheboygan, WI, 1925-35; Prinsburg, MN, 1935-44; Sunnyside, WA, 1944-47; Assistant pastor, First, Bellflower, CA, 1947-49
d. 06/24/1949, Bellflower, CA

Terpstra, Charles
b. 02/25/1924, Chicago, IL
training: Calvin Theological Seminary, BD, 1953; MDiv, 1992
ordained: 1953
charges: Brooten, MN, 1953-58; Fourth, Paterson, NJ, 1958-65; Second Roseland, Chicago, IL, 1965-70; First, Grand Rapids, MI, 1970-82; South Bend, IN, 1982-90
retired: 1990

Terpstra, Gerard Herman
b. 09/24/1925, Manhattan, MT
training: Calvin Theological Seminary, ThB, 1952
ordained: 1952
charges: Missionary to Africa-Nigeria (medical Leave, 1961-63), 1952-69; Missionary on special assignment, 1969-71; Academic editor, Zondervan Publishing House, Grand Rapids, MI, 1971-90
retired: 1990

Terpstra, Gordon Arthur
b. 02/12/1942, Bellingham, WA
training: Calvin Theological Seminary, MDiv, 1979
ordained: 1979
charges: Rapid City, SD, 1979-83; Cascade, Marysville, WA, 1983-89; Chaplain, United States Army, 1989-92; Community, Tacoma, WA, 1992-97; Hope in Christ, Bellingham, WA, 1997-

Terpstra, John
b. 07/25/1951, Evergreen Park, IL

training: Calvin Theological Seminary, MDiv, 1977
ordained: 1977
charges: Campus minister, River Terrace, East Lansing, MI, 1977-80; Crestview, Boulder, CO, 1980-90; First, Grand Haven, MI, 1990-97; Immanuel, Fort Collins, CO, 1997-

Terpstra, Richard Allen Jr.
b. 12/18/1958, Hammond, IN
training: Mid-America Reformed Seminary, MDiv, 1994; Calvin Theological Seminary, Special Program for Ministerial Candidacy, 1995
ordained: 1996
charges: Lamont, MI, 1996-

Terpstra, Simon
b. 04/13/1921, Anjum, Friesland, Netherlands
training: Calvin Theological Seminary, BD, 1952
ordained: 1952
charges: Fort William, ON, 1952-56; Fruitland, ON, 1956-60; Listowel and Lucknow, ON, 1960-64; Listowel, ON, 1964-67; Alliston, ON, 1967-75
d. 12/05/1983, Alliston, ON

Thielke, Dwayne Frederick
b. 05/31/1939, Grand Rapids, MI
training: Reformed Theological Seminary, MDiv, 1984; Calvin Theological Seminary, Special Program for Ministerial Candidacy, 1985
ordained: 1985
charges: Lucknow, ON, 1985-90; Missionary, Philippines, 1990-

Thole, Terry Franklin
b. 04/05/1945, Perry, OK
training: Anderson (IN) School of Theology, 1971; Fuller Theological Seminary, MDiv, 1974
ordained: 1974
charges: Lincoln Community Church of God, Corvallis, OR, 1974-78; CRC: Gallatin Gateway, MT, 1978-81; San Jose, CA, 1981-84; PCA: Campbell, CA, 1984-85; New Covenant, Bartlesville, OK, 1985-87; New Life, San Diego, CA, 1989-91; RCA: Fourth, Grand Rapids, MI, 1991-93; OPC: Evangelist, Living Hope, Ionia, MI, 1994-98; Winner, SD, 1998-

Thomasma, Norman John
b. 03/24/1952, Grand Rapids, MI
training: Calvin Theological Seminary, MDiv, 1981
ordained: 1981
charges: New Hope Community, Kincheloe, MI, 1981-91; St. Joseph, MI, 1991-2000; CPE, Bronson Hospital, Kalamazoo, MI, 2000-2002; Pastor Church Relations, Grand Rapids, MI, 2002-

Tidd, Mark Laurence
b. 08/13/1954, Bennington, VT
training: Calvin Theological Seminary, MDiv, 1984
ordained: 1984
charges: Webster, Rochester, NY, 1984-91; Crestview, Boulder, CO, 1991-

Tigchelaar, Daniel Robert
b. 03/15/1946, Hamilton, ON
training: Calvin Theological Seminary, BD, 1973
ordained: 1973
charges: Zion, Pembroke, ON, 1973-78; First, Victoria, BC, 1978-85; Trinity, Arlington, TX, 1985-86; Leave, 1986; Covenant, St. Catharines, ON, 1986-89; Waterloo, ON, 1989-92; Leave, 1992-94; Essex, ON, 1994-2001; Leave, 2001-2002
retired: 2002

Tigchelaar, David John
b. 03/15/1946, Hamilton, ON
training: Calvin Theological Seminary, MDiv, 1971; BD, 1972
ordained: 1972
charges: Immanuel, Cornwall, ON, 1972-76; Home missionary, Kamloops, BC, 1976-84; First, Calgary, AB, 1984-89; Drayton, ON, 1989-96; Director, The Bible League-Canada, Drayton, ON, 1996-

Tigchelaar, Edward Robert
b. 03/20/1942, Hamilton, ON
training: Calvin Theological Seminary, MDiv, 1980
ordained: 1980
charges: Ebenezer, Leota, MN, 1980-86; Immanuel, Grand Rapids, MI, 1986-95; Mountain View, Lynden, WA, 1995-2000; First, De Motte, IN, 2000-

Timmer, John (Jan)
b. 11/03/1927, Haarlem, Noord Holland, Netherlands
training: Calvin Theological Seminary, BD, 1957; Hartford Theological Seminary, ThM, 1958; Vrije Universiteit, Amsterdam, ThD, 1970
ordained: 1959
charges: Missionary to Japan, 1959-74; Ridgewood, NJ, 1974-80; Woodlawn, Grand Rapids, MI, 1980-95
retired: 1995

Timmer, Mark Duane
b. 02/16/1961, Zeeland, MI
training: Calvin Theological Seminary, MDiv, 1987
ordained: 1988
charges: Youth director, Ivanrest, Grandville, MI,

1986-87; Sunrise, McMinnville, OR, 1988-94; West Wind Community, Bartlett, IL, 1994-97; Leave, 1997-98; Hillcrest, Denver, CO, 1998-

Timmer, Robert J.
b. 04/10/1945, Grand Rapids, MI
training: Calvin Theological Seminary, BD, 1971
ordained: 1971
charges: Prairie City, IA, 1971-75; Grant, MI, 1975-83; Trinity, Rock Valley, IA, 1983-90; Noordeloos, MI, 1990-95; First, Oskaloosa, IA, 1995-

Timmer, Wesley
b. 09/23/1935, Zeeland, MI
training: Calvin Theological Seminary, BD, 1963
ordained: 1963
charges: Calvary, Holland, MI, 1963-68; Middleville, MI, 1968-72; Cascade, Grand Rapids, MI, 1972-79; Hanley, Grandville, MI, 1979-88; Goshen, NY, 1988-97
retired: 1997

Timmerman, John
b. 04/12/1865, Neermoor, Ostfriesland, Germany
training: Calvin Theological Seminary, diploma, 1895
ordained: 1895
charges: Cincinnati, OH, 1895-96; Wellsburg, IA, 1896-1902; Pella, IA, 1902-04; Faculty, Dubuque Presbyterian Seminary, Dubuque, IA, 1904-05; Grandville Ave., Grand Rapids, MI, 1905-08; Orange City, IA, 1908-16; Faculty, Grundy Center (IA) College, 1916-20; Fourth, Paterson, NJ, 1920-33
retired: 1933
d. 08/26/1946, Grand Rapids, MI

Timmerman, Roger Gilbert
b. 12/06/1939, Beaver Creek, MN
training: Calvin Theological Seminary, BD, 1965
ordained: 1965
charges: Home missionary, Huntington Beach, CA, 1965-67, Missionary, Community, Fountain Valley, CA, 1967-70; West Evergreen, Evergreen Park, IL, 1970-73; Middleville, MI, 1973-2001
retired: 2001

Timmermans, Duane Jay
b. 05/09/1957, Grand Rapids, MI
training: Calvin Theological Seminary, MDiv, 1986
ordained: 1986
charges: Ebenezer, Berwyn, IL, 1986-92; Vogel Center, MI, 1992-

Tinklenberg, Duane Edwin
b. 04/10/1941, Woodstock, ON
training: Calvin Theological Seminary, BD, 1967
ordained: 1967
charges: Lebanon, IA, 1967-71; Everson, WA, 1971-80; Bethel, Sioux Center, IA, 1980-89; First, Hudsonville, MI, 1989-98; First, Hospers, IA, 1998-

Tinklenberg, Perry Jon
b. 12/03/1955, Ft. Huachuca, AZ
training: Calvin Theological Seminary, MDiv, 1982
ordained: 1982
charges: Missionary, Liberia, 1982-91; New Hope, Spokane, WA, 1991-

Tjapkes, Robert H.
b. 05/18/1923, Muskegon, MI
training: Calvin Theological Seminary, BD, 1956
ordained: 1956
charges: Austinville, IA, 1956-60; West Evergreen, Evergreeen Park, IL, 1960-66; First, Orange City, IA, 1966-71; Home missionary, Boca Raton, FL, 1971-76; Oswego, NY, 1976-77; Home missionary, Portland, MI, 1977-78
retired: 1978
d. 08/09/1987, Grand Rapids, MI vicinity

Toeset, Carl John
b. 07/14/1918, Dexter, NM
training: Calvin Theological Seminary, BD, 1944
ordained: 1944
charges: Birnamwood, WI, 1944-48; Grangeville, ID, 1948-52; Doon, IA, 1952-57; Second, Wellsburg, IA, 1957-64; Momence, IL, 1964-72; Emden, Renville, MN, 1972-83
retired: 1983
d. 08/30/1998, Scottsdale, AZ

Toeset, Timothy Brian
b. 09/20/1950, Grangeville, ID
training: Calvin Theological Seminary, MDiv, 1976
ordained: 1976
charges: Trinity, Richfield Springs, NY, 1976-80; Rock Rapids, IA, 1980-85; Elim in the Desert, Tucson, AZ, 1985-90; Highland Ave., Redlands, CA, 1990-94; Redlands, CA, 1994-97; Cascade, Marysville, WA, 1997-

Tol, Bernard Fahner
b. 01/12/1951, Grand Rapids, MI
training: Calvin Theological Seminary, BD, 1976; MDiv, 1982
ordained: 1976
charges: Bemis, SD, 1976-80; Willard, OH, 1980-

85; Oakland, MI, 1985-92; North St., Zeeland, MI, 1992-

Toledo, Pedro
b. 05/12/1957, Caracas, Venezuela
training: Orlando Reformed Theological Seminary, MDiv, 1996
ordained: 1996
charges: PCA: 1996 -2000; CRC: Comunidad Cristiana San Pablo, Dunwoody, GA, 2000-

Tolsma, Walter
b. 06/09/1909, Oosterbierum, Friesland, Netherlands
training: Calvin Theological Seminary, ThB, 1946
ordained: 1946
charges: Hull, ND, 1946-48; Vogel Center, MI, 1948-53; Goshen, NY, 1953-65; First, Muskegon, MI, 1965-74
retired: 1974

Tong, John T.C.
b. 12/05/1936
ordained: 1977
charges: New Zealand Reformed Church; CRC: Chinese, Los Angeles, CA, 1977-2001
retired: 2001

Tong, Peter (Chung Ping)
b. 06/20/1932, Amoy City, China
training: Calvin Theological Seminary, BD, 1964; California Graduate School of Theology, PhD, 1991
ordained: 1964
charges: Chinese radio and translating work, Chicago, IL, 1964-66; Missionary, Taiwan, 1966-98
retired: 1998

Toonstra, Martin Jr.
b. 12/18/1932, Grand Rapids, MI
training: Calvin Theological Seminary, BD, 1961
ordained: 1961
charges: Minister of evangelism, Sherman St., Grand Rapids, MI, 1961-62; Grace, Grand Rapids, MI, 1962-65; Eastmanville, MI, 1965-79; Willmar, MN, 1979-88; Second, Randolph, WI, 1988-98
retired: 1998

Top, John E.
b. 04/14/1932, Marum, Groningen, Netherlands
training: declared eligible on the basis of exceptional gifts, 1984
ordained: 1984
charges: Collingwood, ON, 1984-87; Mount Brydges, ON, 1987-96
retired: 1996

d. 02/15/2000, Brampton, ON

Torres, Ildefonso
b. 01/31/1946, Ponce, Puerto Rico
training: Seminario Cristiano Reformado
ordained: 1984
charges: CRC in Puerto Rico: Ponce, 1984-91; Mayaguez Mission, 1987-89; CRC: Mission Hispanic Paz/New Community Fellowship, South Holland, IL, 1995-

Tousley, John C.
b. 12/19/1958, Royal Oak, MI
training: Western Theological Seminary, MDiv, 1985
ordained: 1985
charges: RCA: North Park, Kalamazoo, MI, 1985-88; Washington, Ackley, IA, 1988-97; CRC: Alto, WI, 1997-99; Eligible for call, 1999-

Touw, Philip Russell
b. 04/04/1946, Paterson, NJ
training: Calvin Theological Seminary, BD, 1975; ThM, 1977
ordained: 1977
charges: CRC: Coordinator of education and evangelism, Shawnee Park, Grand Rapids, MI, 1975-77; Chaplain, United States Army, 1977-92; Headquarters Department, Office of Deputy Chief of Staff, United States Army, 1992-95; Resigned from denomination, 1995

Townsend, Phillip Wayne
b. 03/12/1958, Akron, OH
training: Calvin Theological Seminary, MDiv, 1988
ordained: 1988
charges: CRC: First, Redlands, CA, 1988-91; Grandville Ave., Grand Rapids, MI, 1991-93; Leave, 1993-94; Cedar Falls, IA, 1994-99; RCA: Servants, Federal Way, WA, 1999

Tran, Viet Hoang
b. 11/16/1961, Kien Ging, Viet Nam
training: Calvin Theological Seminary, MDiv, 1993
ordained: 1994
charges: Vietnamese, Worthington, MN, 1994-99

Trap, Leonard
b. 12/27/1885, Montague, MI
training: Calvin Theological Seminary, diploma, 1914
ordained: 1914
charges: Third, Zeeland MI, 1914-17; First Presbyterian, Battle Creek, MI and USA Chaplain at Camp Custer, 1917-18; Chaplain, USA, 1918-19;

West Sayville, NY, 1919-21; Whitinsville, MA, 1921-26; Second Roseland, Chicago, IL, 1926-36; pastor at Pine Rest Christian Hospital, Cutlerville, MI, 1936-37; Stated supply at Chatham, ON, 1937-45; Home missionary, 1945-50
d. 02/23/1950, Grand Rapids, MI

Trap, William Martin
b. 12/23/1887, Muskegon, MI
training: Calvin Theological Seminary, diploma, 1913
ordained: 1913
charges: Willard, OH, 1913-16; Third Roseland, IL, 1916-17; Camp pastor for Classis Illinois, Camp Grant, IL, 1917-18; Twelfth St., Grand Rapids, MI, 1918-20; Non-ministerial vocation: philosopher, 1920 (PhD, 1925, University of Michigan)
d. 06/28/1958, Dearborn, MI

Triezenberg, Henry J.
b. 09/09/1895, Oldenzijl, Groningen, Netherlands
training: Calvin Theological Seminary, diploma, 1925
ordained: 1925
charges: Kelloggsville, MI, 1925-30; Rochester, NY, 1930-38; Rock Valley, IA, 1938-44; Everett, WA, 1944-49; Archer Ave., Chicago, IL, 1949-54; Brantford, ON, 1954-58
d. 01/14/1958, Brantford, ON

Troast, Leonard P.
b. 09/13/1949, Paterson, NJ
training: Calvin Theological Seminary, MDiv, 1975
ordained: 1975
charges: Monsey, NY, 1975-80; West Olive, MI, 1980-85; First, Fremont, MI, 1985-95; Calvin, Muskegon, MI, 1995-98; Interim, Pine Grove, Howard City, MI, 1998-99; Interim, Fellowship, Grandville, MI, 1999-2000; Interim, Hanley, Grandville, MI, 2000-2001; Interim, Bethany, Holland, MI, 2001-

Trompen, Jacob Nicholas
b. 04/23/1863, Vriesland, MI
training: Calvin Theological Seminary, diploma, 1888; Princeton Theological Seminary, 1891
ordained: 1891
charges: CRC: Ramsey, 1891-1907; Home missionary, Passaic, NJ, 1907-08; Home missionary, Denver, CO, 1908-09; Congregational Church: Home Missionary in Denver, CO, 1909
d. 04/02/1954

Tuin, Simon Anthony

b. 08/07/1973, Abbotsford, BC
training: Calvin Theological Seminary, MDiv, 1999
ordained: 1999
charges: Heritage, Kalamazoo, MI, 1999–

Tuininga, Calvin James

b. 02/20/1952, Grand Rapids, MI
training: Calvin Theological Seminary, MDiv, 1979
ordained: 1979
charges: CRC: Burdett, AB, 1979–83; Telkwa, BC, 1983–88; Trinity, St. Catharines, ON, 1988–91; United Reformed Churches: Trinity Orthodox Christian Reformed, St. Catharines, ON, 1991–1999; Pantego, NC, 1999

Tuininga, Cecil William

b. 02/23/1915, Edmonton, AB
training: Calvin Theological Seminary, BD, 1955
ordained: 1955
charges: Williamsburg, ON, 1955–58; Ladner, BC, 1958–64; Telkwa, BC, 1965–67; College Ave., Winnipeg, MB, 1967–76; Grande Prairie-La Glace, AB, 1976–80
retired: 1980; affiliated with United Reformed Churches, Edmonton, AB, 1989

Tuininga, James

b. 12/05/1937, Neerlandia, AB
training: Calvin Theological Seminary, MDiv, 1980
ordained: 1980
charges: CRC: Ebenezer, Jarvis, ON, 1980–84; Calvary, Chatham, ON, 1984–90; First, Barrie, ON, 1990–93; Resigned from denomination, 1993

Tuininga, Jelle

b. 08/24/1934, Neerlandia, AB
training: Calvin Theological Seminary, BD, 1965
ordained: 1966
charges: CRC: Peace, Grand Prairie, La Glace, AB, 1966–70; Smithers, BC, 1970–77; Second, Lethbridge, ON, 1977–91; United Reformed Churches: Trinity Reformed, Lehtbridge, ON, 1991–99
retired: 1999

Tuininga, Peter D.

b. 04/30/1959, St. Thomas, ON
training: Calvin Theological Seminary, MDiv, 1991
ordained: 1991
charges: Step by Step Ministries, Winnipeg, MB, 1991–95; Exeter, ON, 1995–2002; Ebenezer, Leduc, AB, 2002–

Tuininga, William Cecil

b. 09/10/1950, Grand Rapids, MI
training: Calvin Theological Seminary, MDiv, 1978
ordained: 1978
charges: Intern, First, Brantford, ON, 1976–77; Prince George, BC, 1978–84; First, New Westminster, BC, 1984–96; Leave, 1996–97; New West Community, New Westminster, BC, 1997–99; Covenant, Winnipeg, MB, 1999–

Tuinstra, John Kommerinus

b. 11/08/1943, Heerenveen, Friesland, Netherlands
training: Calvin Theological Seminary, BD, 1969; Vrije Universiteit, Amsterdam, diploma, 1975
ordained: 1969
charges: Missionary to Mexico, 1969–72; Leave, 1972–75; First, Minneapolis, MN, 1975–82; Rehoboth, Bellflower, CA, 1982–85; Non-ministerial vocation, Bellflower, CA, 1985

Tuit, Pieter Cornelius

b. 12/31/1950, Scheveningen, Zuid Holland, Netherlands
training: Reformed Bible College, BRE, 1979; Reformed Theological Seminary, MDiv, 1977
ordained: 1997
charges: Christian Reformed Church-Australia: Ulverstone, Tasmania, 1977–84; Blaxland, New South Wales, 1991; Missionary, Philippines, 1991–99; Leave, 1999–2000; Faculty, Calvin Theological Seminary, Grand Rapids, MI, 2000–2002; Protestant Evangelical Church of Timor: Missionary, Timor, 1984–90; CRC: Faculty, Calvin Theological Seminary, Grand Rapids, MI, 2001–

Tuls, Herman

b. 06/16/1879, Schoonebeek, Drenthe, Netherlands
training: Calvin Theological Seminary, diploma, 1905
ordained: 1905
charges: First, Paterson, NJ, 1905–08; Third, Muskegon, MI, 1908–12; First, Paterson, NJ, 1913–14; Zutphen, MI, 1914–23
retired: 1923
d. 11/04/1924, Holland, MI

Tung, John Pu-Chiang

b. 03/07/1958, Ylan, Taiwan
training: Westminster Theological Seminary-PA, MAR, 1983, MDiv, 1984; Calvin Theological Seminary, Special Program for Ministerial Candidacy, 1985
ordained: 1987

charges: On loan to Chinese Evangelical Church, Wilmington, DE, 1986-90; Resigned from denomination, 1990

Turkstra, Andrew Peter
b. 02/05/1959, Grand Rapids, MI
training: Calvin Theological Seminary, MDiv, 1995
ordained: 1996
charges: Mission Hills Community, Mission, BC, 1996-

Turngren, Timothy Charles
b. 02/16/1960, Harvey, IL
training: Calvin Theological Seminary, MDiv, 1987
ordained: 1988
charges: CRC: Hills, MN, 1988-91; Leave, 1991-92; Momence, IL, 1992-97; United Reformed Church: Beecher, IL, 1997-99; Baptist: 1999

Tuttle, Spencer M.
b. 10/18/1960, Grand Rapids, MI
training: Calvin Theological Seminary, MDiv, 2000
ordained: 2001
charges: Covenant, Grand Ledge, MI, 2001-

Tuuk, Edward J.
b. 04/17/1878, Muskegon, MI
training: Calvin Theological Seminary, diploma, 1906; Princeton Theological Seminary, 1907
ordained: 1907
charges: Oostburg, WI, 1907-11; Ninth St., Holland, MI, 1911-19; Second Englewood, Chicago, IL, 1919-28
retired: 1928
d. 06/02/1933, Chicago, IL

Tuyl, Carl Dirk
b. 04/11/1925, Den Haag, Zuid Holland, Netherlands
training: Calvin Theological Seminary, BD, 1962
ordained: 1962
charges: Aylmer, ON, 1962-66; Wallaceburg, ON, 1966-69; Hebron, Whitby, ON, 1969-74; First, Toronto, ON, 1974-85; First, Kingston, ON, 1985-90
retired: 1990

Ubels, Engbert
b. 09/18/1920, Ripon, CA
training: Calvin Theological Seminary, BD, 1945
ordained: 1945
charges: Alamosa, CO, 1945-49; Delavan, WI, 1949-53; Rochester, NY, 1953-54
d. 05/01/1954, Alamosa, CO

Uittenbosch, Hans
b. 05/20/1932, Haarlem, Noord Holland, Netherlands
training: Calvin Theological Seminary, BD, 1957
ordained: 1957
charges: Renfrew, ON, 1957-60; Kingston, ON, 1960-65; Minister for evangelism and harbor chaplain, Eastern Ontario at Dollard Des Ormeaux, QC, 1965-92; Action International Seafarer's Ministry, Montreal, QC, 1992-

Uitvlugt, Jacob William
b. 09/05/1928, Chatham, ON
training: Calvin Theological Seminary, BD, 1955; MDiv, 1978
ordained: 1955
charges: Bauer, MI, 1955-59; Calvary, Wyoming, MI, 1959-63; Second, Edmonton, AB, 1963-66; Creston, Grand Rapids, MI, 1966-71; Beverly, Wyoming, MI, 1971-81; Central Ave., Holland, MI, 1981-90; Beaverdam, MI, 1990-94
retired: 1994

Uken, Charles Donald
b. 02/06/1942, Mason City, IA
training: Calvin Theological Seminary, BD, 1967
ordained: 1967
charges: Missionary to Brazil, 1967-85; Eligible for call, 1985-86; Newman Chapel, Hesperia, MI, 1986-

Uken, Robert Herman
b. 03/05/1943, Belmont, CA
training: Calvin Theological Seminary, BD, 1968; MDiv, 1977
ordained: 1968
charges: Wisconsin Rapids, WI, 1968-75; Missionary to St. Cloud, MN, 1975-76; Clinical pastoral education, Pine Rest Christian Hospital, Cutlerville, MI, 1976-77; Chaplain/ Coordinator clinical pastoral education, Pine Rest Christian Hospital, Cutlerville, MI, 1977-

Vaandrager, Bruce John
b. 11/29/1967, Grand Rapids, MI
training: Calvin Theological Seminary, MDiv, 1996
ordained: 1996
charges: Morrison, IL, 1996-

Van Andel, Adrian
b. 04/06/1922, Oude Wettering, Zuid Holland, Netherlands
training: Calvin Theological Seminary, BD, 1953; Westminster Theological Seminary-PA, 1959
ordained: 1953

charges: Chaplain, United States Navy, 1953–57; Service pastor, Norfolk, VA, 1957–58; Associate pastor of evangelism, Grace, Inver Grove Heights, MN, 1959–66; Veterans Administration Chaplain, Marion, IN, 1966–75; Veterans Administration Chaplain, Palo Alto, CA, 1975–85
retired: 1985
d. 07/18/2002, Roseville, CA

Van Andel, Henry (Hendrikus)
b. 05/08/1907, Utrecht, Utrecht, Netherlands
training: Vrije Universiteit, Amsterdam, diploma, 1932
ordained: 1932
charges: GKN: Krommenie, 1932–39; Soest, 1939–41; Arnhem, 1941–46; Den Haag, 1946–54; CRC: New Westminster, BC, 1954–65; Maranatha, Bowmanville, ON, 1965
retired: 1965
d. 11/12/1984, Burnaby, BC

Van Antwerpen, Berton
b. 08/02/1937, Grand Rapids, MI
training: Calvin Theological Seminary, BD, 1962
ordained: 1962
charges: Emden, Renville, MN, 1962–66; Sheldon, IA, 1966–69; Immanuel, Hudsonville, MI, 1969–73; Cadillac, MI, 1973–78; Avery St., South Windsor, ON, 1978–89; Napa Valley, Napa, CA, 1989–93; Princeton, Kentwood, MI, 1993–2002
retired: 2002

Van Antwerpen, Russell J.
b. 07/30/1954, Rochester, NY
training: Calvin Theological Seminary, MDiv, 1982
ordained: 1982
charges: Missionary, American Indian Chapel, Chicago, IL, 1982–87; Leave, 1987–88; Church planter, Philippines, 1988–97; Faith Community, Zillah, WA, 1997–

Van Antwerpen, Willard
b. 03/15/1926, Grand Rapids, MI
training: Calvin Theological Seminary, ThB, 1951; MDiv, 1984
ordained: 1951
charges: East Palmyra, NY, 1951–57; Northside, Clifton, NJ, 1957–66; Prinsburg, MN, 1966–71; Calvary, Wyoming, MI, 1971–81; Bethel, Fulton, IL, 1981–91
retired: 1991

Van Arragon, George John
b. 08/14/1942, Zuidwolde, Drenthe, Netherlands
training: Theologische Universiteit, Kampen, di-

ploma, 1977; Calvin Theological Seminary, Special Program for Ministerial Candidacy, 1979
ordained: 1979
charges: Alliston, ON, 1979–83; Leave, 1983–84; Maranatha, St. Catharines, ON, 1984–85; Eligible for call, 1985–90; Chaplain, Oshawa General Hospital, Oshawa, ON, 1990–96; Chaplain, Shalom Manor, Grimsby, ON, 1996–

Van Baak, Edward Anthony
b. 05/25/1926, Detroit, MI
training: Calvin Theological Seminary, ThB, 1948
ordained: 1948
charges: Missionary to China, 1948–50; Bauer, MI, 1950–51; Missionary to Japan, (furlough, 1956) 1951–70; Asian area secretary, Board of World Missions, Grand Rapids, MI, 1971–87; Overseas Chinese Ministries, World Missions Committee, Hong Kong, 1987–91
retired: 1991

Van Baalen, Jan Karel
b. 04/08/1890, Den Haag, Zuid Holland, Netherlands
training: Theologische Universiteit, Kampen, diploma, 1914; Princeton Seminary, 1916
ordained: 1916
charges: Ada, MI, 1916–20; Munster, IN, 1920–26; Pease, MN, 1926–29; Twelfth St., Grand Rapids, MI, 1929–43; Mt. Vernon, WA, 1943–50; First, Edmonton, AB, 1950–55
retired: 1955
d. 06/27/1968, Lynden, WA

Van Beek, Donald J.
b. 08/06/1937, Chicago, IL
training: Calvin Theological Seminary, BD, 1962
ordained: 1962
charges: Peoria, IA, 1962–66; Missionary, South Grove, South St. Paul, MN, 1966–72; Allen Ave., Muskegon, MI, 1972–83; Creston, Grand Rapids, MI, 1983–98
retired: 1998

Van Beek, Johannes
b. 10/24/1884, Amersfoort, Utrecht, Netherlands
training: Calvin Theological Seminary, diploma, 1920; Princeton Seminary, ThM, 1922; University of Chicago, AM, 1923
ordained: 1923
charges: Oak Lawn, IL, 1923–45; Harrison, SD, 1945–52
retired: 1952
d. 08/09/1961, Grand Rapids, MI

Van Bruggen, Jacob

b. 10/23/1904, Chicago, IL
training: Calvin Theological Seminary, BD, 1932
ordained: 1933
charges: Preakness, Wayne, NJ, 1933-38; Missionary, Crownpoint, NM, 1938-58; Missionary/teacher, Cook Christian Training School, Phoenix, AZ, 1958-70
retired: 1970
d. 08/08/1997, Glendale, AZ

Vance, Robert William

b. 06/04/1949, Detroit, MI
training: Calvin Theological Seminary, MDiv, 1981
ordained: 1982
charges: Kelloggsville, Grand Rapids, MI, 1982-86; Brookside, Grand Rapids, MI, 1986-97; Hillcrest, Hudsonville, MI, 1997-

Van Daalen, Siebren Albert

b. 09/07/1946, Veenhuizen, Drenthe, Netherlands
training: Calvin Theological Seminary, BD, 1972; MDiv, 1974
ordained: 1972
charges: Forest, ON, 1972-77; Terrace, BC, 1977-84; First, Taber, AB, 1984-89; Holland Marsh, Newmarket, ON, 1989-

Van Dalen, Derek George

b. 11/10/1967, York, ON
training: Regent College, MDiv, 1998; Calvin Theological Seminary, Special Program for Ministerial Candidacy, 2000
ordained: 2000
charges: Community, Syracuse, NY, 2000-

Van Dalfsen, Cecil Nathan

b. 04/12/1935, Everett, WA
training: Calvin Theological Seminary, ThB, 1965
ordained: 1965
charges: Coopersville, MI, 1965-69; Calvary, Holland, MI, 1969-75; Trinity, North Haledon, NJ, 1975-82; Leave, 1982-92; released from denomination, 1992

Van Dam, Gerry Glenn

b. 02/25/1956, Slayton, MN
training: Calvin Theological Seminary, MDiv, 1994
ordained: 1995
charges: North Austin Community, Austin, TX, 1994-95; Leave, 1995-97; Maranatha, Farmington, NM, 1997-

Van Dam, Harry Andrew

b. 12/13/1931, Lake Wilson, MN

training: Calvin Theological Seminary, ThB, 1965
ordained: 1965
charges: Home missionary, Albuquerque, NM, 1965-69; Cook Christian Training School, Tempe, AZ, 1969-77; Denver Christian Indian Center, Denver, CO, 1977-84; Chaplain, Calvary Rehabilitation Center, Phoenix, AZ, 1984-96
retired: 1996

Van de Creek, Larry

b. 02/23/1938, Marion, MI
training: Calvin Theological Seminary, BD, 1963
ordained: 1963
charges: CRC: Chaplain, Topeka State Hospital, Topeka, KS, 1963-64; Chaplain in training, Columbia Theological Seminary, 1964-65; Hancock, MN, 1965-69; Indiana University Medical Center, Indianapolis, IN, 1969-75; Chaplain and Pastoral counselor, Department of Family Medicine, Ohio State University, Columbus, OH, 1975-94; PCUSA: Chaplain and Pastoral counselor, Department of Family Medicine, Ohio State University, Columbus, OH, 1994

Van Deelen, Henry C.

b. 07/23/1906, Waupun, WI
training: Western Theological Seminary, BD, 1936
ordained: 1936
charges: PC: Aberdeen, ID, 1936-38; Omro, WI, 1938-40; RCA: Oostburg, WI, 1940-45; Grace, Grand Rapids, MI, 1945-49; First, Rock Valley, IA, 1949-52; CRC: Hull, IA, 1952-60; First, Ripon, CA, 1960-65; Bethany, Holland, MI, 1966-68
retired: 1968
d. 09/05/1968, Grand Rapids, MI

Van De Griend, Kenneth Dwaine

b. 04/11/1944, Hull, IA
training: Calvin Theological Seminary, BD, 1969; MDiv, 1979
ordained: 1969
charges: Missionary to Taiwan, 1969-74; Ackley, IA, 1974-77; Peace, Cedar Rapids, IA, 1977-83; Shawnee Park, Grand Rapids, MI, 1983-89; Wilmar, MN, 1989-96; The Bible League, South Holland, IL, 1996-2001; First, Waupun, WI, 2001-

Van De Hoef, Jacob (Jack) Maurice

b. 08/23/1959, St. Thomas, ON
training: Calvin Theological Seminary, MDiv, 1985
ordained: 1985
charges: Iron Springs, AB, 1985-91; Westmount, Strathroy, ON, 1991-99; First, Guelph, ON, 1999-

Vande Kieft, Henry D.

b. 01/03/1896, Utrecht, Utrecht, Netherlands
training: Calvin Theological Seminary, BD, 1926
ordained: 1927
charges: Coopersville, MI and Hope, Grandville, MI, 1927-34; Coopersville, MI, 1934-43; Chaplain, United States Army, 1943-47
retired: 1947
d. 03/08/1971, St. Petersburg, FL

Vande Kieft, John M.

b. 05/05/1890, Elst, Utrecht, Netherlands
training: Calvin Theological Seminary, diploma, 1914; Princeton Theological Seminary, 1917
ordained: 1915
charges: Platte, SD, 1915-18; Among soldiers, 1918-19; Prairie City, IA, 1919-21; Fourteenth St., Holland, MI, 1921-25; Oakdale Park, Grand Rapids, MI, 1925-32; Bethel, Paterson, NJ, 1932-43; Service pastor, 1943-46; Home missionary at large, 1946-56
retired: 1956
d. 08/25/1959, Grand Rapids, MI

Vande Kieft, Joseph

b. 02/23/1892, Elst, Gelderland, Netherlands
training: Calvin Theological Seminary, BB, 1927, ThM, 1934
ordained: 1927
charges: Aetna, MI, 1927-31; Dutton, MI, 1931-43; Service pastor, 1943-46; First, Wellsburg, IA, 1946-51; Aylmer, ON, 1951-58
retired: 1958
d. 11/20/1980, Grand Rapids, MI

Van de Kieft, Reyer

b. 09/21/1861, Lunteren, Gelderland, Netherlands
training: with G. Vos and Kater H. Bode
ordained: 1899
charges: GKN: Evangelist Elst bij Rhenen, 1889-95; CRC: Teaching elder Second, Pella, IA, 1895-98; Second, Pella, IA, 1898-1907; Grant, MI, 1907-11; West Olive, MI, 1911-14; Alto, WI, 1914-15; Tracy, IA, 1915-22
retired: 1922
d. 05/23/1934, Grand Rapids, MI

Vande Kieft, Richard John

b. 09/22/1928, Grand Rapids, MI
training: Calvin Theological Seminary, BD, 1955
ordained: 1956
charges: Portland, MI, 1955-59; Dorr, MI, 1959-65; Alamo Ave., Kalamazoo, MI, 1965-76; Calvary, Lowell, MI, 1976-84; New Era, MI, 1984-94
retired: 1994

d. 01/08/2002, Middleville, MI

Vande Kieft, William

b. 02/18/1896, Netherlands
training: Calvin Theological Seminary, BD, 1930
ordained: 1930
charges: Rusk, MI, 1930-39; Bigelow, MN, 1939-43; Modesto, CA, 1943-49; Hull, ND, 1949-51; Colton, SD, 1951-54; Prairie City, IA, 1954-60; Portland, MI, 1960-62
retired: 1962
d. 05/14/1982, Modesto, CA

Van de Kolk, William

b. 10/31/1917, Netherlands
ordained: 1946
charges: GKN: Dronrijp, 1946-50; Beilen, 1950-56; Coevorden, 1961-74; CRC: Ingersoll, ON, 1956-59; Kitchener, ON, 1959-61

Van Dellen, Alfred John

b. 11/20/1953, Chicago, IL
training: Calvin Theological Seminary, MDiv, 1986
ordained: 1987
charges: Prairie Lane, Omaha, NE, 1987-89; Corsica, SD, 1989-96; Willmar, MN, 1996-

Van Dellen, Idzerd

b. 01/31/1871, Sassenheim, Noord Holland, Netherlands
training: Theologische Universiteit, Kampen; Calvin Theological Seminary, diploma, 1895
ordained: 1895
charges: Maxwell, NM, 1895-1902; Luctor, KS, 1902-03; Orange City, IA, 1903-07; First, Denver, CO, 1907-40
retired: 1940
d. 10/07/1965, Denver, CO

Van Dellen, Lubbert

b. 05/17/1842, Burum, Friesland, Netherlands
training: Theologische Universiteit, Kampen, diploma, 1868
ordained: 1868
charges: GKN: Sassenheim, 1868-71; Z.H. Hoogkerk, 1871-74; Veenwoudsterwal, 1874-76; Kollum, 1876-80; Nieuwe Pekela, 1880-94; CRC: First Englewood, Chicago, IL, 1894-1907; Middleburg, IA, 1907-08; South Holland, IL, 1908-14
retired: 1914
d. 09/05/1919, Chicago, IL

Van Dellen, Lubbertus W.

b. 12/29/1915, Chicago, IL

training: Western Theological Seminary, BD, 1951
ordained: 1951
charges: RCA: Worthington, MN, 1951-56; Racine, WI, 1956-60; CRC: St. Thomas, ON, 1960-64; Hammond, IN, 1964-69; Springdale, ON, 1969-73; West Evergreen, Evergreen Park, IL, 1973-74; Wisconsin Rapids, WI, 1975-81
retired: 1981

Vande Lune, James Lee
b. 03/21/1946, Oskaloosa, IA
training: Calvin Theological Seminary, MDiv, 1980
ordained: 1980
charges: Chaplain, United States Air Force, 1980-81; Sun Valley, Denver, CO, 1981-88; Farmington, NM, 1988-96; Immanuel, Wappingers Falls, NY, 1996-

Vande Lune, John G.
b. 01/09/1887, Pella, IA
training: Calvin Theological Seminary, diploma, 1913
ordained: 1913
charges: Firth, NE, 1913-16; Corsica, SD, 1916-20; Pease, MN, 1920-26; Sanborn, IA, 1926-30; Carnes, IA, 1930-37; Colton, SD, 1937-45; Hills, MN, 1945-53
retired: 1953
d. 12/19/1973, Orange City, IA

Vanden Akker, Andrew
b. 07/13/1954, Niuwehorne, Friesland, Netherlands
training: Calvin Theological Seminary, MDiv, 1987
ordained: 1988
charges: Stated supply, Cochrane, ON, 1980-82; Coordinator of evangelism, Grandville Ave., Grand Rapids, MI, 1982-88; First, Muskegon, MI, 1988-91; Trinity, Artesia, CA, 1991-

Vanden Akker, Joseph
b. 01/27/1959, Worchester, MA
training: Calvin Theological Seminary, ThM, 1984
ordained: 1984
charges: Hancock, MN, 1984-88; Grant, MI, 1988-96; Providence, Cutlerville, MI, 1996-

Vanden Berg, Arie
b. 03/08/1930, Schipluiden, Zuid Holland, Netherlands
training: Calvin Theological Seminary, BD, 1962
ordained: 1962
charges: Wyoming, ON, 1962-66; Rehoboth, Bowmanville, ON, 1966-72; Essex, ON, 1972-76;

Clinton, ON, 1976-83; Maranatha, Edmonton, AB, 1983-89; First, Port Alberni, BC, 1989-95
retired: 1995

Van Den Berg, Gerald William
b. 05/20/1924, Battle Creek, MI
training: Calvin Theological Seminary, BD, 1953
ordained: 1953
charges: Pine Creek, MI, 1953-58; Nobleford, AB, 1958-62; Bethel, Tucson, AZ, 1962-65; Hospers, IA, 1965-71; Bethel, Manhattan, MT, 1971-78; Prinsburg, MN, 1978-84; First, Waupun, WI, 1984-90
retired: 1990

Vanden Berg, Richard Dale
b. 10/15/1948, Grand Haven, MI
training: Theologische Universiteit, Kampen, ThD, 1977; Calvin Theological Seminary, Special Program for Ministerial Candidacy, 1978
ordained: 1978
charges: Forest, ON, 1978-82; Waterloo, ON, 1982-89; Chaplain, Ontario Correctional Institute, Brampton, ON, 1989-94; Chaplain, Coordinator of pastoral services Grand River Hospital, Kitchener, ON, 1994-

Vanden Berge, Ebenezer
b. 01/01/1855, Albany, NY
training: United Presbyterian Seminary, Xenia, OH; Calvin Theological Seminary, diploma, 1888
ordained: 1888
charges: Summer St., Passaic, NJ, 1888-91; First, Orange City, IA, 1891-93; South Olive, MI, 1893-96; Englewood, NJ, 1896-99; West Sayville, NY, 1899-1903; Dispatch, KS, 1903-04; Rotterdam KS, 1904-05; Firth, NE, 1905-07; Second, Pella, IA, 1908-11; RCA: Galesburg, IA and Killduff, IA, 1911-15; Muscatine, IA, 1915-17; UPCNA: Muscatine, IA, 1924-39
d. 04/24/1939, Muscatine, IA

Vanden Bos, William
b. 06/09/1928, Platte, SD
training: Calvin Theological Seminary, BD, 1973; MDiv, 1983
ordained: 1973
charges: Sumas, WA, 1973-84; Newton, IA, 1984-90; Bemis, SD, 1990-93
retired: 1993

Van Den Bosch, Koenraad
b. 02/19/1818, Wolvega, Friesland, Netherlands
training: with Frederik Alberts Kok, and esp. Wolter Alberts Kok

ordained: 1847
charges: GKN: Elburg, 1847–48; Het Loo, 1848–
54; Noordeloos, 1854–56; RCA: Noordeloos, MI,
1856–57; CRC: Noordeloos, MI, 1857–69, First,
Zeeland, MI, 1862–64; First, Grand Haven, MI,
1869–78; First, Chicago, IL, 1878–81
retired: 1881
d. 11/12/1897, Grand Haven, MI

Vanden Bosch, Thomas
b. 11/16/1922, Rock Valley, IA
training: Calvin Theological Seminary, BD, 1957;
Chaplain training, Pine Rest Christian Hospital,
Cutlerville, MI, 1965
ordained: 1958
charges: Home missionary, Waterloo, IA, 1958–
61; Hammond, IN, 1961–63; Chaplain in training,
Pine Rest Christian Hospital, Grand Rapids, MI,
1963–65; Chaplain, Sierra Conservation Center,
Jamestown, CA, 1965–71; Chaplain, Veterans Administration Hospital, Sioux Falls, SD, 1971–88
retired: 1988

Vanden Bosch, Thomas (Tamme) Melle
b. 08/03/1843, Nijensleek, Drenthe, Netherlands
training: Calvin Theological Seminary, diploma,
1879
ordained: 1879
charges: Home missionary, Zeeland, MI, 1879–82;
First, Chicago, IL, 1882–83; New Holland, SD,
1883–85; Harrison, SD, 1885–86; Jenison, MI,
1886–88; Vriesland, MI, 1888–89; Missionary to
Indians, 1889–90; Home missionary, Vriesland, MI;
Overisel, MI; and East Side, Cleveland, OH, 1890–
94; RCA: Rehoboth, Lucas, MI, 1894–97; De
Motte, IN and Koster, St. Anne, IL, 1897–1904;
stated supply, North Blendon, MI; North Blendon,
MI and Three Oaks, MI, 1908–10; Chicago Tract
Society, agent, 1910
d. 08/19/1913, Kalamazoo, MI

Vanden Bosch, William
b. 04/07/1947, Zeeland, MI
training: Calvin Theological Seminary, MDiv, 1872
ordained: 1972
charges: Lake City, MI, 1972–79; Oakdale Park,
Grand Rapids, MI, 1979–

Vanden Brink, Bert
b. 07/25/1893, Holland, MI
training: Calvin Theological Seminary, BD, 1930
ordained: 1930
charges: Oostburg, WI, 1930–31; Sibley, IA,
1933–43; Wright, IA, 1943–50; Bemis, SD, 1950–
53; Hawarden, IA, 1953–58

retired: 1931
d. 10/15/1975, Artesia, CA

Vanden Brink, Ronald Albert
b. 11/23/1959, Edmonton, AB
training: Calvin Theological Seminary, MDiv, 1994
ordained: 1994
charges: Salmon Arm, BC, 1994–

Vanden Einde, Harlan Gerald
b. 03/16/1939, Renville, MN
training: Calvin Theological Seminary, BD, 1964
ordained: 1964
charges: Newton, IA, 1964–68; Calvin,
Sheboygan, WI, 1968–74; Oakdale Park, Grand
Rapids, MI, 1974–79; Riverside, Grand Rapids, MI,
1979–87; Borculo, MI, 1988–2001
retired: 2001

Vanden Ende, Anthonie
b. 12/17/1926, Katwijk a/d Rijn, Zuid Holland,
Netherlands
training: Vrije Universiteit, Amsterdam, diploma,
1954
ordained: 1954
charges: GKN: Munnekeburen, 1954–59; CRC:
Brooks, AB, 1959–63; Welland Junction, ON,
1963–69; Fredericton, NB, 1969–77; Westmount,
Strathroy, ON, 1977–85; Immanuel, Brampton, ON,
1985–91
retired: 1992

Vanden Heuvel, Arie J
b. 08/17/1854, Werkendam, Noord Brabant, Netherlands
training: Calvin Theological Seminary, diploma,
1890
ordained: 1890
charges: CRC: Zutphen, MI, 1890–92; Dispatch,
KS, 1893–95; East Side and West Side, Cleveland,
OH, 1895–1901; Hospers, IA, 1902–03; Le Mars,
IA, 1904; Rochester, NY, 1904–07; North Side,
Passaic, NJ, 1907–12; RCA: Fourth, Passaic, NJ,
1912–14; Atwood, MI, 1914–17; Beverly, MI, 1917–
20; Twin Lakes, MI, 1920–22
retired: 1922
d. 03/09/1924, Clifton, NJ

Vanden Heuvel, Christian
b. 08/30/1906, Nieuw Vennep, Noord Holland,
Netherlands
training: Calvin Theological Seminary, ThB, 1935
ordained: 1937
charges: Hancock, MN, 1937–40; New Holland,
SD, 1940–45; Borculo, MI, 1945–49; West Leon-

ard, Grand Rapids, MI, 1949-58; Immanuel, Grand Rapids, MI, 1958-64; Trinity; Fremont, MI, 1964-70; Lamont, MI, 1970-72
retired: 1972
d. 02/02/1993, Grand Rapids, MI

Vanden Heuvel, Henry B.
b. 07/03/1937, Grand Rapids, MI
training: Calvin Theological Seminary, BD, 1962
ordained: 1962
charges: Lamont, MI, 1962-65; Princeton, Grand Rapids, MI, 1965-70; Bethel, Sioux Center, IA, 1970-79; Bethel, Zeeland, MI, 1979-91; First, Oak Lawn, IL, 1991-2000
retired: 2000

Vanden Heuvel, Jack
b. 04/05/1947, Zeeland, MI
training: Calvin Theological Seminary, BD, 1972
ordained: 1972
charges: Minister of evangelism, Faith, Holland, MI and Kibbie Chapel, South Haven, MI, 1972-82; Rolling Acres, Mason City, IA, 1982-

Vanden Heuvel, Thomas C.
b. 04/05/1936, Grand Rapids, MI
training: Calvin Theological Seminary, BD, 1961; MDiv, 1976
ordained: 1961
charges: CRC: Bethel, Waupun, WI, 1961-64; Milwaukee, WI, 1964-67; Central Ave., Holland, MI, 1967-75; First, Chino, CA, 1975-79; First, Orange City, IA, 1979-85; First, Byron Center, MI, 1985-97; PCA: Covenant Presbyterian, Holland, MI, 1997

Vanden Hoek, John B. Sr.
b. 10/23/1868, Chicago, IL
training: Calvin Theological Seminary, diploma, 1905
ordained: 1905
charges: Galesburg, IA, 1905-08; Carnes, IA, 1908-14; Volga, SD, 1914-18; Hills, MN, 1920-24
retired: 1918
d. 10/14/1937, Hull, IA

Vanden Hoek, John B. Jr.
b. 03/10/1891, Harrison, SD
training: Calvin Theological Seminary, diploma, 1920
ordained: 1921
charges: Vesper, WI, 1920-25; missionary Classis Orange City at Winnipeg, MB, 1925-29; Everett, WA, 1929-43; Service pastor for Pacific Northwest, 1943-44; Grangeville, ID, 1944-46; Mountain Lake, MN, 1946-49; Luverne, MN, 1949-57

retired: 1957
d. 04/03/1969, Alameda, CA

Vanden Hoek, Julius John
b. 06/24/1923, Vesper, WI
training: Calvin Theological Seminary, ThB, 1952
ordained: 1952
charges: Woden, IA, 1952-57; Missionary, Fairbanks, AK, 1957-61; Home missionary, Boulder, CO, 1961-65; Pompton Plains, NJ, 1965-71; Trinity, Fremont, MI, 1971-78; Missionary, Gaylord, MI, 1978-81; Immanuel, Salt Lake City, UT, 1981-83; Calvin, Spokane, WA, 1983-85
retired: 1985
d. 05/02/2002, Grandville, MI

Vanden Pol, Albert John
b. 09/08/1925, Nijmegen, Gelderland, Netherlands
training: Theologische Universiteit, Apeldoorn, diploma, 1949
ordained: 1949
charges: CGKN: Thesinge, 1949-53; Chaplain, Dutch Army, 1953-55; CRC: Rocky Mountain House, AB, 1955-57; Drayton, ON, 1957-61; Second, Sarnia, ON, 1961-63; Dunnville, ON, 1963-67; Georgetown, ON, 1967-73; Grace, Cobourg, ON, 1973-79; Surrey, BC, 1979-90
retired: 1990

Vanderaa, Harry J.
b. 08/06/1922, Lansing, IL
training: Calvin Theological Seminary, ThB, 1949
ordained: 1949
charges: Mountain Lake, MN, 1949-55; Lucas, MI, 1955-60; Missionary to Nigeria, 1960-69; Volga, SD, 1969-81; Parkersburg, IA, 1981-87
retired: 1987
d. 07/24/1991, Sioux Center, IA

Vander Ark, Clifford
b. 11/21/1911, Manhattan, MT
training: Calvin Theological Seminary, ThB, 1939
ordained: 1939
charges: Western Springs, IL, 1939-42; Chaplain, USA, 1942-46; Ocheyedan, IA, 1946-50; Everett, WA, 1950-55; Sanborn, IA, 1955-62; Delavan, WI, 1962-66; Overisel, MI, 1966-69
retired: 1969
d. 07/15/1981, Hudsonville, MI

Vander Ark, Harry G.
b. 08/02/1914, Ellsworth, MI
training: Calvin Theological Seminary, BD, 1948
ordained: 1948
charges: Missionary, Hope, Muskegon, MI, 1948-

52; Holland Heights, Holland, MI, 1952-62; First,
Fremont, MI, 1962-69; Millbrook, Grand Rapids,
MI, 1969-74
retired: 1974
d. 03/20/1980, Jenison, MI

Vander Ark, Jay Calvin
b. 04/10/1931, Manhattan, MT
training: Calvin Theological Seminary, BD, 1956;
MDiv, 1983
ordained: 1956
charges: Chaplain, United States Army, 1956-60;
Home missionary, Hayward, CA, 1960-66; Missionary, Crestview, Boulder, CO, 1966-74; Flanders Valley, NJ, 1974-81; Pleasant Valley,
Longmont, CO, 1981-93
retired: 1993
d. 05/10/2001, Manhattan, MT

Vander Ark, Tiede
b. 01/11/1868, Blija, Friesland, Netherlands
training: Calvin Theological Seminary, diploma,
1897
ordained: 1897
charges: Borculo, MI, 1897-1900; First, Grand
Rapids, MI, 1900-05; First, Pella, IA, 1905-10;
Drenthe, MI, 1910-16; Manhattan, MT, 1916-22;
Edgerton, MN, 1922-30; Harderwyk, MI, 1930-35
retired: 1935
d. 01/13/1937, Zeeland, MI

Vander Beek, Henry
b. 01/19/1946, Sauwerd, Groningen, Netherlands
training: Reformed Bible College, BRE, 1979;
Westminster Theological Seminary-PA, MDiv,
1983; Calvin Theological Seminary, Special Program for Ministerial Candidacy, 1985
ordained: 1985
charges: First, Edmonton, AB, 1985-92; Iron
Springs, AB, 1992-96; Smithville, ON, 1996-2002;
First, Thunder Bay, ON, 2002

Vanderbeek, Herbert Anthony
b. 04/02/1961, Hamilton, ON
training: Calvin Theological Seminary, MDiv, 2001
ordained: 2001
charges: First, Munster, IN, 1999-2001; Immanuel, Cornwall, ON, 2001-

Vander Beek, Peter Louis
b. 06/23/1957, Brooks, AB
training: Calvin Theological Seminary, MDiv, 1995
ordained: 1996
charges: Forest, ON, 1996-

Vander Beek, Samuel I.
b. 12/04/1848
training: with John Y. De Baun
ordained: 1875
charges: True Protestant Dutch Reformed:
Ramsey, NY, 1875-85; Paramus, NJ, 1886-88;
Ramsey, NJ, 1889; CRC: New York, NY, 1890-91;
Passaic/ Paterson, NJ, 1892; LaGrave Ave., Grand
Rapids, MI, 1992-98; no congregation, 1898-
1906; Leonia, NJ, 1906-08; True Reformed Dutch
Church: Leonia, NJ, 1908-11; Supplied vacant pulpits, 1911-19
retired: 1919
d. 08/12/1924, Ramsey, NJ

Vander Beek, William L.
b. 06/06/1928, Rotterdam, Zuid Holland, Netherlands
training: Vrije Universiteit, Amsterdam, 1952; Calvin Theological Seminary, BD, 1954
ordained: 1955
charges: Brooks, AB, 1955-58; Richmond, BC,
1958-63; Transcona, Winnipeg, AB, 1963-66;
Leave, 1966-69; Immanuel, Hamilton, ON, 1969-
75; First, New Westminster, BC, 1975-83; First,
Red Deer, AB, 1983-90; Salmon Arm, BC, 1990-
94
retired: 1994; released from ministry, 2001

Vander Berg, Edward (Epke)
b. 02/22/1942, Harkema, Friesland, Netherlands
training: Calvin Theological Seminary, BD, 1973;
MDiv, 1977; ThM, 1988
ordained: 1973
charges: Missionary to Brazil, 1973-74; Missionary to the Philippines, 1974-81; Missionary to Jordan, 1981-89; Leave, 1989-92; Director, Mission
India, 1998-99; CRC Refugee Ministries Coordinator, Grand Rapids, MI, 2000-

Vander Berg, Fred (Alfred)
b. 06/01/1952, St. Catharines, ON
training: Calvin Theological Seminary, MDiv, 1992
ordained: 1992
charges: Hebron, Renfrew, ON, 1992-2001;
Westmount, Strathroy, ON, 2001-

Vander Bilt, Maas
b. 06/08/1924, Garden Grove, CA
training: Calvin Theological Seminary, BD, 1954
ordained: 1954
charges: Kennedy School of Missions, 1954-55;
Missionary to Japan, 1955-79; Missionary to the
Philippines, 1979-89
retired: 1989

Van der Bok, Abram Van der Velde
see: Van der Velde VanderBok, Abraham

Vander Borgh, R. John
b. 01/02/1942, Oude Pekela, Groningen, Netherlands
training: Calvin Theological Seminary, BD, 1970; ThM, 1971
ordained: 1971
charges: CRC: East Palmyra, NY, 1971–73; Dorr, MI, 1973–76; Missionary to Nicaragua, 1976–81; Maranatha, Woodstock, ON, 1992–98; Momence, IL, 1998–2001; Resurrection Life Church: Missionary, Central America, 1982–86; Missionary, Mexico, 1987–92

VanderBrug, Duane Edward
b. 04/03/1935, Detroit, MI
training: Calvin Theological Seminary, BD, 1960
ordained: 1962
charges: Home missionary, Richton Park, IL, 1962–66; Missionary, Lawndale, Chicago, IL, 1966–69; Assistant field secretary of Home Missions, 1969–75; Director of personnel, Board of Home Missions, Grand Rapids, MI, 1975–91; Director, Established Church Development, Grand Rapids, MI, 1991–97; Church development specialist and regional director, Eastern Region, Grand Rapids, MI, 1997–98; CRC Ministry Plan Implementation Team, Grand Rapids, MI, 1998–2000; Home Missions Conferences Coordinator, Grand Rapids, MI, 2000–

VanderGiessen Likkel, Lynn Ann
b. 03/21/1946, Bellingham, WA
training: Fuller Theological Seminary, MDiv, 2000; Calvin Theological Seminary, Special Program for Ministerial Candidacy, 2000
ordained: 2000
charges: Director of worship, Christ Community, Nanaimo, BC, 1990–91; Community, Mill Creek, WA, 2000–

Vander Griend, Alvin James
b. 07/27/1936, Bellingham, WA
training: Calvin Theological Seminary, BD, 1961
ordained: 1963
charges: Atwood, MI, 1963–66; Peace, South Holland, IL, 1966–74; Alger Park, Grand Rapids, MI, 1974–82; Minister of evangelism, Board of Home Missions, Grand Rapids, MI, 1982–96; Mission India, Director, Houses of Prayer, Grand Rapids, MI, 1996–2001; Lighthouse Ministries, Mission America, 2001
retired: 2001

Vander Griend, Ronald Gene
b. 05/25/1954, Sheldon, IA
training: Calvin Theological Seminary, MDiv, 1981
ordained: 1981
charges: Missionary, Philippines, 1981–88; Leave, 1988–92; Asia Director, The Bible League, South Holland, IL, 1992–

Vander Haak, William
b. 09/15/1914, Sioux County, IA
training: Calvin Theological Seminary, ThB, 1941
ordained: 1941
charges: Sioux Falls, SD, 1941–44; Godwin Heights, Grand Rapids, MI, 1944–49; Midland Park, NJ, 1949–54; Third, Kalamazoo, MI, 1954–62; Director Education, Board of Publications, Grand Rapids, MI, 1962–72; Prospect Park, Holland, MI, 1972–79
retired: 1979
d. 03/28/2000, Holland, MI

Vander Hart, Archie Lee
b. 03/19/1950, Pella, IA
training: Calvin Theological Seminary, MDiv, 1982
ordained: 1984
charges: Colton, SD, 1984–88; Fuller Ave., Grand Rapids, MI, 1988–98; Leave, 1998; Hope, Grandville, MI, 1999–

Vander Hart, Mark Dean
b. 12/30/1952, Oskaloosa, IA
training: Calvin Theological Seminary, MDiv, 1980
ordained: 1980
charges: CRC: Grande Prairie-La Glace, AB, 1980–83; Faculty, Mid America Reformed Seminary, Orange City, IA, 1983–90; Leave, 1990–92; Faculty, Mid America Reformed Seminary, Dyer, IN, 1992–97; United Reformed Churches: Oak Glenn Covenant, Lansing, IL, 1997

Van der Heide, Hilbrent
training: declared eligible on the basis of exceptional gifts, 2001
ordained: 2001
charges: Houston, BC, 2000–

Van Der Heide, John William
b. 08/12/1952, Goshen, NY
training: Calvin Theological Seminary, MDiv, 1980
ordained: 1980
charges: Hawarden, IA, 1980–84; Calvary, Plainwell, MI, 1984–88; Highland, MI, 1988–94; Manhattan, MT, 1995–2000; Niekerk, Holland, MI, 2000–

Vander Heide, Kenneth
b. 07/13/1931, McBain, MI
training: Calvin Theological Seminary, BD, 1968
ordained: 1969
charges: Lakeview, Valentine, NE, 1969-73; Holland Center, SD, 1973-78; Terra Ceia, NC, 1978-82; Leave, 1982-84; Chaplain, West Mesa Hospital, Albuquerque, NM, 1984-93
retired: 1993

Vander Heide, Lloyd
b. 04/11/1929, Twijzeler, Friesland, Netherlands
training: Calvin Theological Seminary, BD, 1960
ordained: 1960
charges: Collingwood, ON, 1960-62; Pentecostal: Richmond, ON, 1999-2001
d. 07/06/2001, Holland Centre, ON

Van Der Heide, Meine
b. 12/27/1868, Lutten, Overijsel, Netherlands
training: Calvin Theological Seminary, diploma, 1904
ordained: 1904
charges: Platte, SD, 1904-08; Sully, IA, 1908-10; Hospers, IA, 1910-25
d. 04/25/1925, Hospers, IA

Vander Heide, Sjoerd S.
b. 12/03/1869, Ferwerd, Friesland, Netherlands
training: Calvin Theological Seminary, diploma, 1899
ordained: 1899
charges: First, Cutlerville, MI, 1899-1902; Beaverdam, MI, 1902-04; First, Grand Haven, MI, 1904-09; First, Chicago, IL, 1909-18; Northside, Passaic, NJ, 1918-29
retired: 1929
d. 09/11/1929, Passaic, NJ

Vanderhill, George Dale
b. 05/05/1920, Holland, MI
training: Calvin Theological Seminary, ThB, 1945
ordained: 1945
charges: Bluffton Chapel, Muskegon, MI, 1945-51; Dearborn, MI, 1951-68; Wheaton, IL, 1968-88
retired: 1988

Vander Hoek, Gerard Wayne
b. 10/26/1955, Des Moines, IA
training: Calvin Theological Seminary, MDiv, 1981; ThM, 1982
ordained: 1989
charges: Faculty, Dordt College, Sioux Center, IA, 1988-91; Leave, 1991-93; Pine Grove, Howard City, MI, 1993-98; Pease, MN, 1998-

Vanderhooft, Jeffrey Clifford
b. 04/11/1966, Winnipeg, MB
training: Calvin Theological Seminary, MDiv, 1996
ordained: 1996
charges: Cadillac, MI, 1996-98; Emden, Renville, MN, 1999-

Vander Horst, Everett James
b. 05/31/1968, Sarnia, ON
training: Calvin Theological Seminary, MDiv, 1996
ordained: 1996
charges: Telkwa, BC, 1996-2001; Shawnee Park, Grand Rapids, MI, 2001-

Vander Horst, Kenneth Mark
b. 10/28/1971, Sarnia, ON
training: Calvin Theological Seminary, MDiv, 2002
ordained: 2002
charges: Youth, Seymour, Grand Rapids, MI, 1998-2001; Imlay City, MI, 2002-

Vander Hoven, William Fred
b. 10/08/1920, Grand Rapids, MI
training: Calvin Theological Seminary, ThB, 1945; ThM, 1983
ordained: 1945
charges: Noordeloos, MI, 1945-48; Bethel, Edgerton, MN, 1948-52; Wyoming Park, Grand Rapids, MI, 1952-57; Pleasant St., Whitinsville, MA, 1957-62; Fuller Ave., Grand Rapids, MI, 1962-71; Westview, Grand Rapids, MI, 1974-82; East Coast interim home missionary, 1982-85
retired: 1985

Vande Riet, Garrett H.
b. 07/26/1913, Cleveland, OH
training: Calvin Theological Seminary, ThB, 1941
ordained: 1941
charges: Bejou, MN, 1941-44; Sioux Falls, SD, 1944-49; Parchment, MI, 1949-56; First, Edmonton, AB, 1956-60; Hospital pastor, Bethesda, Denver, CO, 1960-64; Baldwin, WI, 1964-76; Telkwa, BC, 1976-78
retired: 1978

Vande Riet, Gerrit John
b. 06/05/1883, Dispatch, KS
training: Calvin Theological Seminary, diploma, 1911
ordained: 1911
charges: East Side, Cleveland, OH, 1911-20; Overisel, MI, 1920-45
retired: 1945
d. 11/06/1952, Holland, MI

Vander Jagt, Samuel
b. 02/08/1918, Grand Rapids, MI
training: Calvin Theological Seminary, ThB, 1952;
MDiv, 1979
ordained: 1952
charges: Battle Creek, MI, 1952-56; Detroit, MI,
1956-60; Home missionary, Sacramento, CA,
1960-65; Kimberly Village, Davenport, IA, 1965-
79; Chaplain, Mercy Hospital, Davenport, IA,
1979-88
retired: 1988

Vander Kam, Henry
b. 11/08/1917, Houwerzijl, Groningen, Netherlands
training: Calvin Theological Seminary, ThB, 1945
ordained: 1945
charges: Prosper, MI, 1945-50; Second, Pella, IA,
1950-55; Twelfth Ave., Jenison, MI, 1955-65;
Grace, Kalamazoo, MI, 1965-78; Lake Worth, FL,
1978-79; Doon, IA, 1979-82
retired: 1982; affiliated with Independent Reformed Churches, Kalamazoo, MI, 1992
d. 01/11/1996, Kalamazoo, MI

Vander Klay, Hiram
b. 11/21/1904, Spring Lake, MI
training: Calvin Theological Seminary, BD, 1932
ordained: 1932
charges: Vesper, MI, 1932-40; Hancock, MN,
1940-44; Goshen, IN, 1944-49; Leighton, IA,
1949-52; Owen Sound, ON, 1952-61; West
Sayville, NY, 1961-67; Ferrisburg, VT, 1967-71
retired: 1971
d. 06/19/1991, Grand Rapids, MI

Vander Klay, Paul Henry
b. 07/24/1963, Paterson, NJ
training: Calvin Theological Seminary, MDiv, 1991
ordained: 1991
charges: Missionary, Dominican Republic, 1991-
97; Sacramento, CA, 1997-

Vander Klay, Stanley Jay
b. 05/12/1935, Wisconsin Rapids, WI
training: Calvin Theological Seminary, BD, 1960
ordained: 1960
charges: Home missionary, Northside Chapel,
Paterson, NJ, 1960-73; Northside Chapel, Paterson, NJ, 1973-96; Community, Syracuse, NY,
1996-2000
retired: 2000

Vander Kooi, George
b. 10/31/1909, Paterson, NJ
training: Calvin Theological Seminary, ThB, 1935

ordained: 1939
charges: Stated supply, Newton, IA, 1935-39;
Sioux City, IA, 1939-43; Chaplain, United States
Army, 1943-46; East Muskegon, MI, 1946-53;
Milwood, Kalamazoo, MI, 1953-57; Associate pas-
tor at Milwood and Chaplain at Kalamazoo State
Hospital, Kalamazoo, MI, 1957-67
d. 01/21/1967, Kalamazoo, MI

Vander Kooi, Joel Alan
b. 11/01/1960, Zeeland, MI
training: Calvin Theological Seminary, MDiv, 1986
ordained: 1986
charges: CRC: Bethel, Listowel, ON, 1986-92;
Walker, Grand Rapids, MI, 1992-97; United Reformed Churches: Walker, MI, 1997-

Vander Kooij, H. Raymond
b. 05/13/1966, Newmarket, ON
training: Calvin Theological Seminary, MDiv, 1994
ordained: 1994
charges: Immanuel, Simcoe, ON, 1994-

Vanderkooy, Paul Richard
b. 04/04/1962, Toronto, ON
training: Calvin Theological Seminary, MDiv, 2001
ordained: 2001
charges: Faith Community, Milford, NS, 2001-

Vander Kwaak, Nicholas
b. 02/02/1937, Leiden, Zuid Holland, Netherlands
training: Calvin Theological Seminary, BD, 1966;
MDiv, 1977; ThM, 1980
ordained: 1966
charges: Maranatha, York, ON, 1966-71; Emmanuel, Calgary, AB, 1971-76; Chaplain, Pine Rest
Christian Hospital, Cutlerville, MI, 1976-2002
retired: 2002

Vander Laan, Betty Joyce Deckinga
b. 01/25/1948, Chicago, IL
training: Chicago Theological Seminary, MDiv,
1996
ordained: 2001
charges: Chaplain, St. Catherine Hospital, East
Chicago, IN, 2001-

Vander Laan, Jack Lee
b. 08/16/1934, Jenison, MI
training: Calvin Theological Seminary, MDiv, 1977
ordained: 1958
charges: Leighton, IA, 1958-62; First, Cutlerville,
MI, 1962-67; First, Denver, CO, 1967-75; New Life
Fellowship, Denver, CO, 1975-76; Fort Lauderdale,
FL, 1976-81; Chaplain, Waste Management, Inc.,

Fort Lauderdale, FL, 1981-87; Chaplain, Waste Management, Inc., Oak Brook, IL, 1987-92; Chaplain, Waste Management, Inc. South, Fort Lauderdale, FL, 1992-94; Chaplain, Huizenga Holdings, Inc., Fort Lauderdale, FL, 1994-95; Chaplain, Auto Nation, Fort Lauderdale, FL, 1995-2001
retired: 2001

Vanderlaan, James Lee
b. 03/26/1938, Grand Rapids, MI
training: Calvin Theological Seminary, BD, 1963
ordained: 1971
charges: Bigelow, MN, 1971-76; Webster, NY, 1976-84; Parchment, Kalamazoo, MI, 1984-91; Clinical pastoral education, Pine Rest Christian Hospital/Hope Network, Grand Rapids, MI, 1991-92; Director, Committee on Disability Concerns for CRPM, Grand Rapids, MI, 1992-

Vander Laan, Raynard
b. 03/04/1951, Grand Rapids, MI
training: Westminster Theological Seminary-PA, MDiv, 1977; Yeshiva University, PhD, 1999
ordained: 1983
charges: Midland Park, NJ, 1983-90; Faculty, Eastern Christian High School, Midland Park, NJ, 1983-85, 1987-90; Faculty, Holland Christian High School, Holland, MI, 1990-

Vander Lee, Paul Gilbert
b. 07/21/1943, Spring Lake, MI
training: Calvin Theological Seminary, BD, 1968
ordained: 1968
charges: CRC: Chaplain, Texas Medical Center, Houston, TX, 1968-70; UPCUSA: Woodland, Houston, TX, 1970-72; St. Thomas, Houston, TX, 1972-75; unclassified, 1975-89; Non-ministerial vocation, Concord, MA, 1989

Vander Leek, Andrew George
b. 06/25/1958, Rocky Mountain House, AB
training: Calvin Theological Seminary, MDiv, 1986
ordained: 1986
charges: Edson-Peers, Edson, AB, 1986-90; Prince George, BC, 1990-95; Emmanuel, Calgary, AB, 1995-

Vander Ley, Rodney
b. 06/12/1943, Sioux Center, IA
training: Calvin Theological Seminary, BD, 1969
ordained: 1969
charges: Hammond, IN, 1969-73; Community, Tacoma, WA, 1973-

Vanderlip, Gilbert Gerrit
b. 02/05/1922, Cleveland, OH
training: Calvin Theological Seminary, BD, 1960
ordained: 1960
charges: CRC: Lucas, MI, 1960-65; Knollwood, Kalamazoo, MI, 1965-73; Minister, Kalamazoo, MI, 1973

Vander Lugt, Eliot
b. 01/03/1966, Salt Lake City, UT
training: Calvin Theological Seminary, MDiv, 1994
ordained: 1994
charges: Stephenville, TX, 1994-98; First, Ripon, CA, 1998-

Vander Lugt, John
b. 04/18/1926, Strasburg, ND
training: Calvin Theological Seminary, BD, 1963
ordained: 1963
charges: Hope, Muskegon, MI, 1963-65; Second, Byron Center, MI, 1965-70; Palos Heights, IL, 1970-81; Bunde, MN, 1981-91
retired: 1991

Van der Meer, John
b. 02/25/1903, Groningen, Groningen, Netherlands
training: Calvin Theological Seminary, BD, 1934
ordained: 1935
charges: Stated supply, Tracy, IA, 1934-35; Tracy, IA, 1935-38; Hollandale, MN, 1938-41; Missionary at Star Lake, NM, 1941-43; Chaplain, US Army, 1943-46; Holland Marsh, ON, 1946-51; Home missionary at Cochrane, ON, 1951-55; Barrie, ON, 1955-58; Essex, ON, 1958-62
d. 06/25/1962, Essex, ON

Vander Meer, Lewis Ray
b. 03/29/1941, Grand Rapids, MI
training: Calvin Theological Seminary, BD, 1966
ordained: 1969
charges: CRC: Minister of evangelism, Sunshine Chapel, Grand Rapids, MI, 1969-72; Sunshine, Grand Rapids, MI, 1972-91; Independent: New Community Church, Grand Rapids, MI, 1991

Vander Meer, Sieds
b. 03/17/1935, Koudum, Friesland, Netherlands
training: Calvin Theological Seminary, BD, 1971
ordained: 1971
charges: Wallaceburg, ON, 1971-75; Bethel, Newmarket, ON, 1975-82; Grace, Welland, ON, 1982-91; Exeter, ON, 1991-94
d. 08/22/1994, Exeter, ON

Vander Meulen, Derrick John

b. 08/24/1963, Bellflower, CA
training: Westminster Theological Seminary-CA,
MDiv, 1989; Calvin Theological Seminary, Special
Program for Ministerial Candidacy, 1990
ordained: 1991
charges: CRC: Director of youth ministries,
Christ's Community, San Diego, CA, 1989-90;
Eastmanville, MI, 1991-93; United Reformed
Churches: Bethel, Jenison, MI, 1993

Vander Mey, John

b. 02/26/1869, Holwerd, Friesland, Netherlands
training: Calvin Theological Seminary, diploma,
1894
ordained: 1894
charges: Lucas, MI, 1894-96; Cincinnati, OH,
1896-98; Sully, IA, 1898-1904: Hospers, IA,
1904-08; Manhattan, MT, 1908-13; Educational
Secretary Calvin College and Seminary, 1913-32
retired: 1932
d. 05/13/1933, Grand Rapids, MI

Vander Meyden, Calvin Dale

b. 05/23/1941, Harvey, IL
training: Calvin Theological Seminary, BD, 1966
ordained: 1966
charges: Monsey, NY, 1966-69; Missionary,
Flanders Valley, NJ, 1969-74; Jamestown, MI,
1974-79; Drenthe, MI, 1979-86; Pillar, Holland, MI,
1986-90; Cutlerville East, Cutlerville, MI, 1990-
97; Rusk, MI, 1997-

Vandermolen, Geoffrey Alan

b. 07/20/1970, Hamilton, ON
training: Calvin Theological Seminary, MDiv, 1996
ordained: 1996
charges: First, London, ON, 1996-2000; Hillside,
Calgary, AB, 2001-

Vandermolen, Vic

b. 07/21/1948, Hoogeveen, Drenthe, Netherlands
training: declared eligible on the basis of exceptional gifts, 1999
ordained: 1999
charges: Mount Brydges, ON, 1999-

Vander Neut, Clair

b. 10/11/1944, Rotterdam, Zuid Holland, Netherlands
training: Calvin Theological Seminary, BD, 1973
ordained: 1973
charges: Visalia, CA, 1973-74; Chelwood Community, Albuquerque, NM, 1974-80; Bethel, Princeton, MN, 1980-86; First, Modesto, CA, 1986-93;

Alamosa, CO, 1993-2000; Fellowship, Greeley, CO,
2000-2002; Unity, Prospect Park, NJ, 2002

Vander Plaat, Hilbert

b. 01/24/1928, Haarlem, Noord Holland, Netherlands
training: Vrije Universiteit, Amsterdam, diploma,
1952, Drs, 1968; McMaster University, PhD, 1983
ordained: 1952
charges: GKN: Oudega (Wijnbr), 1952-55; Dieren,
1955-59; CRC: Williamsburg, ON, 1959-63; East
Strathroy, Strathroy, ON, 1963-69; Kentville, NS,
1969-73; Mountainview, Grimsby, ON, 1973-85;
Providence, Beamsville, ON, 1985-93
retired: 1993

Vander Plaats, Gerrit

b. 06/29/1916, Holland, MN
training: Calvin Theological Seminary, ThB, 1949
ordained: 1949
charges: Bigelow, MN, 1949-52; New Holland,
SD, 1952-57; Calvin, Holland, MI, 1957-62; Bible
teacher, Western Christian High School, Hull, IA,
1962-70; First, Oskaloosa, IA, 1970-78; Momence,
IL, 1978-81
retired: 1981

Vander Plate, Clarence

b. 06/30/1919, Glen Ridge, NJ
training: Westminster Theological Seminary-PA,
MDiv, 1956; Calvin Theological Seminary, Special
Program for Ministerial Candidacy, 1957
ordained: 1957
charges: Doon, IA, 1957-60; Bethel, Sioux Center,
IA, 1960-65; First, Artesia, CA, 1965-81
retired: 1981
d. 07/17/1998, Redlands, CA

Vander Plate, Jack

b. 05/14/1946, Paterson, NJ
training: Calvin Theological Seminary, BD, 1971;
MDiv, 1981
ordained: 1972
charges: Iowa Falls, IA, 1971-75; First, Miami, FL,
1975-81; East Saugatuck, MI, 1981-88; Trinity,
Fremont, MI, 1988-2000; Bethel, Zeeland, MI,
2000-

Vander Ploeg, Colin

b. 04/05/1964, Sarnia, ON
training: Calvin Theological Seminary, MDiv, 1997
ordained: 1997
charges: Trinity, Edmonton, AB, 1997-2002; Living Hope, Abbotsford, BC, 2002-

Van der Ploeg, Dirk
b. 09/02/1866, Dantumawoude, Friesland, Netherlands
training: Calvin Theological Seminary, diploma, 1896
ordained: 1898
charges: Home missionary, Otley, IA, 1898–99; Middleburg, IA, 1899–1902; Hope Ave., Passaic, NJ, 1902–09; Home missions for Classis Illinois at Racine, WI, 1909–11; Kelloggsville, MI, 1911–15; Home missionary Classis Pacific at Shepherd, MT, 1915–18; Shepherd, MT, 1918–19
d. 11/26/1919, Shepherd, MT

Vander Ploeg, Herman Matthew
b. 10/24/1868, Pieterszyl, Groningen, Netherlands
training: Calvin Theological Seminary, diploma, 1899
ordained: 1899
charges: Alto, WI, 1899–1901; Oakdale Park, Grand Rapids, MI, 1901–03; Lafayette, IN, 1903–11; Sioux Center, IA, 1911–18; Second, Muskegon, MI, 1920–23; East Saugatuck, MI, 1923–34
retired: 1934
d. 03/02/1934, East Saugatuck, MI

Vanderploeg, John
b. 10/18/1902, Grand Rapids, MI
training: Calvin Theological Seminary, ThB, 1930
ordained: 1930
charges: East Paris, MI, 1930–39; First, Pella, IA, 1939–45; Lansing, IL, 1945–50; Grace, Kalamazoo, MI, 1950–56; editor, *The Banner*, 1956–70
retired: 1970
d. 09/24/1983, Zeeland, MI

Vander Pol, Allen Paul
b. 05/16/1951, Mt. Vernon, WA
training: Westminster Theological Seminary-PA, MDiv, 1976; Calvin Theological Seminary, Special Program for Ministerial Candidacy, 1977
ordained: 1979
charges: CRC: Holland, MN, 1980–86; on loan to Reformed Church, Nelson, New Zealand, 1986–90; First, Minneapolis, MN, 1990–97; United Reformed Churches: Trinity Reformed, Cape Coral, FL, 1997

Vander Pol, Mike (Marinus)
b. 06/07/1936, Zwijndrecht, Zuid Holland, Netherlands
training: Calvin Theological Seminary, BD, 1965
ordained: 1965
charges: Taiwan: Missionary, 1966–69; Church planting, 1969–72; Church planting and radio

work, 1972–77; Taipei International Church, 1977–86; Golden Gate, San Francisco, CA, 1986–93; World Missions, Manila, Philippines, 1993–2001
retired: 2001

Vander Roest, Robert John
b. 09/01/1953, Kalamazoo, MI
training: Calvin Theological Seminary, MDiv, 1979
ordained: 1979
charges: CRC: Jackson, MI, 1980–84; First, Des Plaines, IL, 1984–93; Leave, 1993–96; released from denomination, 1996

Vander Schaaf, James
b. 11/12/1942, Damwoude, Friesland, Netherlands
training: Calvin Theological Seminary, MDiv, 1974
ordained: 1975
charges: Agassiz, BC, 1975–77; Chaplain-intern, Bethesda Hospital, Denver, CO, 1977–80; Director, Criminal Justice Chaplaincy, Grand Rapids, MI, 1980–

Vander Slik, James Allen
b. 02/17/1945, Kalamazoo, MI
training: Calvin Theological Seminary, MDiv, 1987
ordained: 1987
charges: Kedvale Ave., Oak Lawn, IL, 1987–90; Sunlight Community, Port St. Lucie, FL, 1990–

VanderSluis, Harold
b. 03/21/1962, Toronto, ON
training: Ontario Bible College, MDiv, 1989; Calvin Theological Seminary, Special Program for Ministerial Candidacy, 1990
ordained: 1991
charges: Rimbey, AB, 1991–94; Zion, Pembroke, ON, 1994–

Vander Stelt, John Cornelis
b. 04/05/1934, Dussen, Noord Brabant, Netherlands
training: Calvin Theological Seminary, BD, 1965
ordained: 1965
charges: Newmarket, ON, 1965–67; Leave, 1967–68; Non-ministerial vocation: Faculty, Dordt College, Sioux Center, IA, 1968–99; Covenant, Sioux Center, IA, 1999
retired: 1999

Vander Stoep, Floris
b. 05/03/1903, Oak Harbor, WA
training: Calvin Theological Seminary, BD, 1935
ordained: 1935
charges: Ocheyedan, IA, 1935–40; Missionary at

Two Wells, NM, 1940-42; Missionary, Shiprock,
NM, 1942-68
retired: 1968
d. 08/22/1996, Grand Rapids, MI

Vander Stoep, John Andrew
b. 11/11/1965, Burlington, ON
training: Reformed Bible College, BRE, 1996; Calvin Theological Seminary, MDiv, 2000
ordained: 2000
charges: Seymour, Grand Rapids, MI, 2000-

Vander Top, Verlyn Dale
b. 03/27/1952, Pipestone, MN
training: Calvin Theological Seminary, MDiv, 1982
ordained: 1982
charges: CRC: Britt, IA, 1982-88; Calvary,
Loveland, CO, 1988-90; Eligible for call, 1990-95;
released from the denomination, 1995

VanderVaart, Richard Theodore
b. 04/20/1963, Hamilton, ON
training: Calvin Theological Seminary, MDiv, 1993
ordained: 1993
charges: Bethel, Saskatoon, SK, 1993-98;
Wallaceburg, ON, 1998-

Vander Veen, Dale Warren
b. 03/01/1943, Chicago, IL
training: Calvin Theological Seminary, BD, 1967
ordained: 1969
charges: Campus Crusade, Southern California,
1969-73; Calvary, Seattle, WA, 1973-78;
Brookside, Grand Rapids, MI, 1978-92; Bethany,
Bellflower, CA, 1992-2001; Georgetown,
Hudsonville, MI, 2002-

Vander Veer, Jack Edward
b. 05/12/1961, Cornwall, ON
training: Calvin Theological Seminary, MDiv, 1989
ordained: 1991
charges: On loan to Associate Reformed Presbyterian Church, Pakistan, 1991-99; Grace,
Cobourg, ON, 1999-

Vander Velde Vander Bok, Adam
b. 10/06/1846, Stad aan 't Haringvliet, Zuid Holland, Netherlands
training: Calvin Theological Seminary, diploma,
1896
ordained: 1897
charges: Rock Valley, IA, 1897-1904; Ebenezer,
SD, 1904-05
retired: 1905
d. 08/17/1914, Rock Valley, IA

Vander Vliet, Marvin J.
b. 12/26/1944, Grand Rapids, MI
training: Calvin Theological Seminary, BD, 1972
ThM, 1975
ordained: 1973
charges: Ellsworth, MI, 1973-76; Hillside Community, Cutlerville, MI, 1976-85; Hawarden, IA,
1985-94; First, Jenison, MI, 1994-

van der Vorst, Dick Burghart Jr.
b. 03/11/1963, Den Helder, Noord Holland, Netherlands
training: Calvin Theological Seminary, Special
Program for Ministerial Candidacy
ordained: 1994
charges: Missionary, Dominican Republic, 1994-
2000; Chaplain Intern, North Suburban Medical
Center, Denver, CO, 2000; Chaplain, Denver Health
Medical Center, Denver, CO, 2001-

Vander Vries, Edward (Eppe)
b. 09/25/1844, Zuidhorn, Groningen, Netherlands
training: with D.J. Vander Werp, 1874
ordained: 1874
charges: First, Kalamazoo, MI, 1874-79; First,
Grand Haven, MI 1879-83; First, Paterson, NJ,
1883-86; Central Ave., Holland, MI, 1886-96;
Dennis Ave., Grand Rapids, MI, 1896-1903; First,
Cutlerville, MI, 1903-06; Non-ministerial vocation,
1908
d. 07/17/1923, Grand Rapids, MI

Vanderwal, Kenneth John
b. 05/02/1941, Oudeschoot, Friesland, Netherlands
training: Calvin Theological Seminary, MDiv, 1984
ordained: 1984
charges: Blenheim, ON, 1984-92; Missionary,
Central America, 1992-

Vanderwal, Richard Todd
b. 04/21/1963, Hamilton, ON
training: Calvin Theological Seminary, MDiv, 1990
ordained: 1990
charges: Assistant to pastor, Twelfth Ave.,
Jenison, MI, 1987-90; Calvin, McBain, MI, 1990-
95; Second, Fremont, MI, 1995-

Vander Wall, Douglas Ray
b. 12/15/1929, Munster, IN
training: Calvin Theological Seminary, BD, 1953
ordained: 1959
charges: Peoria, IA, 1959-62; Phoenix, AZ, 1962-
67; Modesto, CA, 1967-75; Shawnee Park, Grand
Rapids, MI, 1975-81; Missionary, Summitview,

Yakima, WA, 1981-90; Avery Street, South Windsor, CT, 1990-95
retired: 1995

Vander Wall, Kenneth Jay
b. 11/25/1942, Hammond, IN
training: Calvin Theological Seminary, BSLD, 1964; BD, 1968
ordained: 1968
charges: Fairview, Denver, CO, 1968-72; Campus minister, IVCF, Northern New Jersey, 1972-

Vander Weide, Peter
b. 03/07/1928, Hines, CA
training: Calvin Theological Seminary, ThB, 1952
ordained: 1952
charges: Lebanon, IA, 1952-56; Baldwin, WI, 1956-63; Sanborn, IA, 1963-69; First, Jenison, MI, 1969-80; First, Oskaloosa, IA, 1980-87; Champlain Valley, Vergennes, VT, 1987-92
retired: 1992

Vander Weit, George Frederick
b. 08/05/1942, Chicago, IL
training: Calvin Theological Seminary, BD, 1968; MDiv, 1975
ordained: 1968
charges: Wayland, MI, 1968-71; East Side, Cleveland, OH, 1971-89; North Hills, Troy, MI, 1989-2000; Fuller Ave., Grand Rapids, MI, 2000-

Van Der Wekken, Denis
b. 10/18/1945, Rigny-Le-Perron, Aube, France
training: Calvin Theological Seminary, BD, 1971; MDiv, 1979
ordained: 1979
charges: Barrhead and Westlock, AB, 1979-83; Leave, 1983-86; Chaplain, Grey Nuns, Edmonton, AB, 1986-

Vanderwell, Howard Dale
b. 04/08/1937, Muskegon, MI
training: Calvin Theological Seminary, BD, 1962; MDiv, 1976; ThM, 1985
ordained: 1962
charges: Lebanon, IA, 1962-66; Trinity, Jenison, MI, 1966-72; Bethel, Lansing, IL, 1972-78; Hillcrest, Hudsonville, MI, 1978-2002
retired: 2002

Vanderwell, Ronald Dale
b. 04/20/1963, Sioux Center, IA
training: Calvin Theological Seminary, MDiv, 1990
ordained: 1990

charges: Southern Heights, Kalamazoo, MI, 1990-2000; The Gathering, Sacramento, CA, 2000-

Vanderwerf, Walter Henry
b. 02/22/1963, Brockville, ON
training: Calvin Theological Seminary, MDiv, 1991
ordained: 1991
charges: Edson-Peers, ON, 1991-96; Maranatha, St. Catharines, ON, 1996-

Van der Werp, Douwe Johannes
b. 04/13/1811, Groningen, Groningen, Netherlands
training: with Hendrik De Cock and Tamme Foppe DeHaan
ordained: 1844
charges: Kerken onder 't Kruis: Zwolle, 1840-41; GKN: Leeuwarden, 1844-52; Ferwerd, 1852-55; Lioessens, 1855-57; Broek op Langedijk, 1857-59; Den Helder, 1859-61; Burum, 1858-64; CRC: Graafschap, MI, 1864-72; First, Muskegon, MI, 1872-75
retired: 1875
d. 04/01/1876, Muskegon, MI

Van der Werp, Henry (Hendrik)
b. 03/20/1846, Bedum, Groningen, Netherlands
training: Theologische Universiteit, Kampen, diploma, 1878
ordained: 1879
charges: GKN: Beverswijk, 1879-81; CRC: Noordeloos, MI, 1882-83; Drenthe, MI, 1883-86; First Roseland, Chicago, IL, 1886-92; Fremont, MI, 1892-99; Cincinnati, OH, 1899-1905; Harrison, SD, 1905-08; Zutphen, MI, 1908-13
retired: 1913
d. 03/29/1918, Grand Rapids, MI

Van der Werp, Johannes B.
b. 05/29/1852, High Falls, NY
training: Calvin Theological Seminary, diploma, 1884
ordained: 1884
charges: CRC: Overisel, MI, 1884-87; South Olive, MI, 1888-89; First Englewood, Chicago, IL, 1889-92; Allendale, MI, 1893-94; Home missionary, 1894-95; New Era, MI, 1895-98; No congregation, 1898-1902; Falmouth, MI, 1902-09; Cincinnati, OH, 1909-11; Luctor, KS, 1911-14; Affiliated with Berean Reformed in Muskegon, MI and later Calvary Undenominational, Grand Rapids, MI
d. 12/20/1939, Wyoming, MI

Vanderwerp, Marvin John
b. 08/29/1902, Grand Haven, MI

training: Calvin Theological Seminary, ThB, 1928
ordained: 1928
charges: Peoria, IA, 1928-32; Prinsburg, MN, 1932-35; Second, Orange City, IA, 1935-40; First, Jenison, MI, 1940-44; Warren Park, Cicero, IL, 1944-48; Second, Fremont, MI, 1948-52; Ninth St., Holland, MI, 1952-58; Delavan, WI, 1958-62; Spring Lake, MI, 1962-67
retired: 1967
d. 12/29/1976, Holland, MI

Vander Werp, Vincent G.
b. 09/12/1936, Orange City, IA
training: Calvin Theological Seminary, BD, 1960
ordained: 1960
charges: Saginaw, MI, 1960-63; Haven, Zeeland, MI, 1963
d. 12/08/1963, Zeeland, MI

Vanderwerp, William D.
b. 07/13/1870, Graafschap, MI
training: Calvin Theological Seminary, diploma, 1897
ordained: 1897
charges: Monsey, NY, 1897-99; First, Grand Haven, MI, 1899-1903; Franklin St., Grand Rapids, MI, 1903-06; First, Zeeland, MI, 1906-11; East Saugatuck, MI, 1911-13; Maple Ave., Holland, MI, 1913-16; Drenthe, MI, 1916-25; Allendale, MI, 1925-27; Prairie City, IA, 1927-32; New Era, MI, 1932-37
retired: 1937
d. 02/27/1952, Cutlerville, MI

Van Der Wiele, David Lee
b. 08/02/1959, Grand Rapids, MI
training: Calvin Theological Seminary, MDiv, 1987
ordained: 1987
charges: Ivanrest, Grandville, MI, 1987-92; Saugatuck, MI, 1992-

Vander Windt, Harry Adrian
b. 03/16/1936, Schipluiden, Zuid Holland, Netherlands
training: Calvin Theological Seminary, MDiv, 1978
ordained: 1978
charges: Lindsay, ON, 1978-82; Bethel, Dunnville, ON, 1982-89; First, Owen Sound, ON, 1989-92; Fruitland, Stoney Creek, ON, 1992-99
retired: 1999

van der Woerd, Everett Alan
b. 08/10/1957, Vancouver, BC
training: Regent College, MDiv, 1987, ThM, 1991;

Calvin Theological Seminary, Special Program for Ministerial Candidacy, 1992
ordained: 1992
charges: Church developer, Seminario Reformado de Mexico, Mexico City, 1992-

Vander Woude, Eelco
b. 07/25/1943, Wieringen, Noord Holland, Netherlands
training: Calvin Theological Seminary, BD, 1970; Vrije Universiteit, Amsterdam, 1978
ordained: 1978
charges: Edson and Peers, AB, 1978-84; Edson-Peers, AB, 1984-85; Salmon Arm, BC, 1985-90
retired: 1990
d. 05/04/1997, Surrey, BC

Vander Woude, Harm
b. 02/16/1876, Niezijl, Groningen, Netherlands
training: Calvin Theological Seminary, diploma, 1921
ordained: 1921
charges: Cutlerville, MI, 1921-23; Edmonton, AB, 1923-27; Hoboken, NJ, 1927-29; Neerlandia, AB, 1929-41
retired: 1941
d. 02/01/1950, Chicago, IL

Vander Zee, Leonard John
b. 03/17/1945, Rochester, NY
training: Calvin Theological Seminary, MDiv, 1970
ordained: 1970
charges: Des Moines, IA, 1970-73; West Sayville, NY, 1973-78; Trinity, Iowa City, IA, 1978-83; Eastern Ave., Grand Rapids, MI, 1983-90; South Bend, IN, 1990-

Vanderzee, Nelson
b. 10/29/1921, Hawthorne, NJ
training: Calvin Theological Seminary, ThB, 1952
ordained: 1952
charges: Hope, Muskegon, MI, 1952-55; Minster of evangelism, Whitinsville, MA, 1955-60; Framingham, MA, 1960-63; Home missionary for the East Coast, at Hawthorne, NJ, 1963-64; Field Secretary, Board of Home Missions, 1964-72; Eastern Ave., Grand Rapids, MI, 1972-76; Bakersfield, CA, 1976-80; Rehoboth, NM, 1980-85
retired: 1985
d. 10/09/2001, Grand Rapids, MI

Vander Zee, Vernon Glenn
b. 10/27/1942, South Holland, IL
training: Calvin Theological Seminary, BD, 1967; MDiv, 1977

ordained: 1968

charges: Minister of evangelism, First, Los Angeles, CA, 1968-73; Hayward, CA, 1973-89; Lombard, IL, 1989-2000; South Kendall Community, Miami, FL, 2000-

Vander Ziel, Gerrit John

b. 11/09/1903, Haarlem, Noord Holland, Netherlands

training: Calvin Theological Seminary, BD, 1933

ordained: 1933

charges: Mountain Lake, MN, 1933-38; Rock Rapids, IA, 1938-43; Purewater, SD, 1943-47; Chatham, ON, 1947-53; Home missionary, Saskatoon, SK, 1953-59; Vesper, WI, 1960-64; Granum, AB, 1964-69

retired: 1969

d. 12/08/1992, Grand Rapids, MI

Vander Ziel, Thomas Henry

b. 11/22/1946, Valentine, NE

training: Calvin Theological Seminary, MDiv, 1974

ordained: 1974

charges: Hartley, IA, 1974-81; Missionary to Puerto Rico, 1981-85; Missionary, Dominican Republic, 1985-89; Leave, 1989-91; Grangeville, ID, 1991-97; Colton, SD, 1997-2001; First, Salt Lake City, UT, 2001-

Vander Zwaag, Marinus

b. 11/27/1908, Spring Lake, MI

training: Calvin Theological Seminary, BD, 1934

ordained: 1935

charges: Stated supply, Battle Creek, MI, 1934-35; Luctor, KS, 1935-38; Lamont, MI, 1938-43; Central Ave., Holland, MI, 1943-49; Bethany, Bellflower, CA, 1949-53; Grandville Ave., Grand Rapids, MI, 1953-59; Oak Glen, Lansing, IL, 1959

d. 12/25/1959, Lansing, IL

Vande Steeg, Marinus G. Jr.

b. 12/27/1945, Ede, Gelderland, Netherlands

training: Calvin Theological Seminary, MDiv, 1974

ordained: 1974

charges: Platte, SD, 1974-76; New Life Fellowship, Denver, CO, 1976-79; Chaplain, United States Army, 1979-81; Eligible for call, 1982; Chaplain, United States Air Force, 1983-

Vande Zande, Mark Allan

b. 12/07/1972, Fond du Lac, WI

training: Calvin Theological Seminary, MDiv, 2000

ordained: 2000

charges: Noordeloos, MI, 2000-

Van Donk, John William

b. 03/10/1954, Den Haag, Zuid Holland, Netherlands

training: Fuller Theological Seminary, MDiv, 1980; Calvin Theological Seminary, Special Program for Ministerial Candidacy, 1981

ordained: 1981

charges: Hayward, CA, 1981-83; Bay Area Industrial Chaplain, 1983-84; People-at-work, Life Enrichment Resources, Inc., Fremont, CA, 1984-87; North End, Halifax, NS, 1987-88; Covenant, Lansing, MI, 1988-89; Eligible for call, 1989-93; Nonministerial vocation, 1993

Van Donselaar, Marvin Lee

b. 02/16/1941, Mahaska County, IA

training: Calvin Theological Seminary, BD, 1966

ordained: 1966

charges: North Blendon, MI, 1966-70; Kanawha, IA, 1970-76; Ocheyedan, IA, 1976-89; Eligible for call, 1989-90; Calvin, Dundas, ON, 1990-

Van Drunen, Leonard Jr.

b. 07/21/1924, South Holland, IL

training: Calvin Theological Seminary, ThB, 1952

ordained: 1952

charges: Eastmanville, MI, 1952-58; Pine Creek, MI, 1958-65; First, Rock Valley, IA, 1965-72; South Grandville, Grandville, MI, 1972-90

retired: 1990

d. 11/14/1998, Grand Rapids, MI

Van Drunen, Peter

b. 06/27/1935, Steenwijk, Noord Brabant, Netherlands

training: Calvin Theological Seminary, ThB, 1965

ordained: 1965

charges: Ocheyedan, IA, 1965-70; Neerlandia, AB, 1970-73; Peoria, IA, 1973-77; Leave, 1977-78; Peoria, IA, 1978-82; Delavan, WI, 1982-85; Doon, IA, 1985-92

retired: 1997

Van Drunen, Seymour W.

b. 12/09/1923, South Holland, IL

training: Calvin Theological Seminary, BD, 1960

ordained: 1960

charges: Hamilton, MI, 1960-64

d. 07/24/1964, Spider Lake, Grand Traverse County, MI

Van Duyne, Elias A.

b. 01/20/1831, Morris County, NJ

training: with John Y. De Baun

ordained: 1889

charges: TPRD; Home missionary to vacant congregations, 1889-90; CRC: Home missionary in Classis Hackensack to vacant congregations, 1896-1901; Home missionary, Boonton NJ, 1901-08; Independent, 1908
d. 10/11/1916, Montville, NJ

Van Dyk, Casper
b. 11/09/1902, Little Falls, NJ
training: Calvin Theological Seminary, BD, 1931
ordained: 1932
charges: Glendale, CA, 1932-36; Leave, 1936-38; Non-ministerial vocation, 1938
d. 04/1976, Alameda, CA

Van Dyk, Frederick James
b. 02/28/1934, Fremont, MI
training: Calvin Theological Seminary, BD, 1960
ordained: 1960
charges: Home missionary, El Paso, TX, 1960-63; Burdett, AB, 1965-69; Highland, MI, 1969-78; Missionary, Paw Paw, MI, 1978-82; Faculty, Smith Memorial Bible College, Baissa, Nigeria, 1982-89; Eligible for call, 1989-90; Hollandale, MN, 1990-95; Pioneer, Cedar Springs, MI, 1995-99
retired: 1963-65, 1999

Van Dyk, Jerry
b. 07/19/1952, Netherlands
training: Westminster Theological Seminary-PA, MDiv, 1979; Calvin Theological Seminary, Special Program for Ministerial Candidacy, 1980
ordained: 1980
charges: CRC: Champlain Valley, Vergennes, VT, 1980-86; Wyoming, ON, 1986-91; Alliance of Reformed Churches: Covenant, Wyoming, ON, 1991-95; United Reformed Churches: Covenant Christian, Wyoming, ON, 1995-97; Bethel, Aylmer, ON, 1997-2000

Van Dyk, John (Jan)
b. 07/04/1925, Epe, Gelderland, Netherlands
training: Calvin Theological Seminary, BD, 1956
ordained: 1956
charges: Burlington, ON, 1956-59; Kentville, NS, 1959-62; Duncan, BC, 1962-65; Barrie, ON, 1965-69; Terrace, BC, 1969-73; Bethel, Listowel, ON, 1973-77; College Ave., Winnipeg, MB, 1977-80; Leave, 1980-82; Chaplain, Holland Christian Homes, Brampton, ON, 1982-85; Second, Brampton, ON, 1983-85; Covenant, Barrie, ON, 1985-89
retired: 1989

Van Dyk, Maarten H.
b. 05/22/1893, Zalk, Overijsel, Netherlands
training: Calvin Theological Seminary, diploma, 1925
ordained: 1925
charges: Hills, MN, 1925-29; GKN: Nieuweroord, 1929-46
retired: 1946
d. 08/15/1973, Hattem, Gelderland, Netherlands

Vandyk, Michael John
b. 10/10/1959, Kentville, NS
training: Calvin Theological Seminary, MDiv, 1993
ordained: 1993
charges: Bethel, Dunnville, ON, 1993-98; First, Taber, AB, 1998-

Van Dyk, Peter
b. 09/09/1885, Leens, Groningen, Netherlands
training: Calvin Theological Seminary, diploma, 1915
ordained: 1915
charges: Alto, WI, 1915-18; Peoria, IA, 1918-21; South Holland, IL, 1921-27; Prospect Park, Paterson, NJ, 1927-47; Conrad, MN, 1947-49; Nobleford, AB, 1949-52
retired: 1952
d. 08/20/1967, Manhattan, MT

Van Dyk, Wesley
b. 10/07/1945, Paterson, NJ
training: Calvin Theological Seminary, BD, 1970
ordained: 1970
charges: Cedar, IA, 1970-74; Hamilton, MI, 1974-83; Trinity, Iowa City, IA, 1983-91; Leave, 1991-93; Faith Community, Wyckoff, NJ, 1993-

Van Dyk, Wiebe
b. 02/28/1909, Surhuizum, Friesland, Netherlands
training: Vrije Universiteit, Amsterdam, diploma, 1935
ordained: 1936
charges: GKN: Zevenhoven and Noorden, 1938-42; Oudewater, 1942-47; Nijmegen, 1947-53; Gouda, 1953; CRC: St. Catharines, ON, 1953-59; Bible teacher, Hamilton (ON) District Christian High School, 1959-64; Acton, ON, 1964-67; Orillia, ON, 1967-73
d. 06/15/1973, Orillia, ON

Van Dyk, Wilbert M.
b. 04/15/1930, North Haledon, NJ
training: Calvin Theological Seminary, BD, 1955; ThM, 1976
ordained: 1955

charges: Fourth Roseland, Chicago, IL, 1955–59; Lake Worth, FL, 1959–64; Plymouth Heights, Grand Rapids, MI, 1964–86; Faculty, Calvin Theological Seminary, Grand Rapids, MI, 1986–95
retired: 1995

Van Dyke, Jacob Raymond
b. 05/30/1894, Rinsumageest, Friesland, Netherlands
training: Calvin Theological Seminary, diploma, 1921
ordained: 1921
charges: Plainfield, MI, 1921–25; Corsica, SD, 1925–29; Ireton, IA, 1929–45; Oak Harbor, WA, 1945–54; Ladner, BC, 1954–57; Langley, BC, 1954–57; Grangeville, ID, 1957–61
retired: 1961
d. 09/11/1979, Oak Harbor, WA

Van Dyke, Joel
b. 11/09/1966, Grand Rapids, MI
training: Westminster Theological Seminary-PA, MDiv, 1995
ordained: 1997
charges: Bethel Temple Community Bible Church, Philadelphia, PA, 1988–99; CRC: Bethel Temple Community Bible Church, Philadelphia, PA, 1999–

Van Dyke, John G.
b. 07/15/1893, Amsterdam, Noord Holland, Netherlands
training: Calvin Theological Seminary, BD, 1927; ThM, 1934; Pike's Peak Theological Seminary, ThD, 1938
ordained: 1927
charges: Bigelow, MN, 1927–31; First, Grand Haven, MI, 1931–40; East Leonard, Grand Rapids, MI, 1940–51; Home missionary in Michigan 1951; Home missionary in Chicago, IL, 1951–59
retired: 1959
d. 11/11/1969, Grand Rapids, MI

Van Dyke, Leslie Dale
b. 10/03/1966, Sioux Center, IA
training: Calvin Theological Seminary, MDiv, 1993
ordained: 1993
charges: Reeman, MI, 1993–

Van Dyke, Martin
b. 02/22/1893, Paterson, NJ
training: Calvin Theological Seminary, diploma, 1920; Princeton University, 1921; Columbia University, ThM, 1922; Princeton Seminary, PhD, 1924
ordained: 1924
charges: Inwood, IA, 1924–27; Sherman St.,

Grand Rapids, MI, 1927–31; Highland, IN, 1931–50; Missionary at Essex, ON, 1950–51
d. 11/03/1951, Essex, ON

Van Dyken, Albert
b. 03/20/1895, Muskegon, MI
training: Calvin Theological Seminary, ThB, 1926
ordained: 1926
charges: East Paris, MI, 1926–30; Wyoming Park, MI, 1930–39; Third, Lynden, WA, 1939–48
d. 11/24/1948, Lynden, WA

Van Dyken, Harry
b. 07/26/1917, Manhattan, MT
training: Calvin Theological Seminary, BD, 1954
ordained: 1954
charges: CRC: Second, Redlands, CA, 1954–57; Neerlandia, AB, 1957–62; Winnipeg, MB, 1962–67; Woodbridge-Maranatha, Toronto, ON, 1967–73; First, Mount Vernon, WA, 1973–77; Bethel, Listowel, ON, 1977–79; Independent: Orthodox Christian Reformed Church, Toronto, ON, 1979–85
d. 12/14/1985, Toronto, ON

Van Dyken, Jack Sr.
b. 11/05/1918, Edmonton, AB
training: Western Theological Seminary, BD, 1951; Calvin Theological Seminary, ThM, 1960
ordained: 1951
charges: RCA: Forest Grove, MI, 1951–58; Remembrance, Grand Rapids, MI, 1958–61; Chaplain, United States Army, 1961–78; CRC: Almond Valley, Ripon, CA, 1978–83
retired: 1984

Van Dyken, Jack Jan Jr.
b. 09/13/1952, Zeeland, MI
training: Calvin Theological Seminary, MDiv, 1978
ordained: 1979
charges: First, Oakdale, CA, 1979–82; Chaplain, United States Army, 1982–

Van Dyken, Paul John Jr.
b. 12/24/1954, Modesto, CA
training: Fuller Theological Seminary, MDiv, 1998; Calvin Theological Seminary, Special Program for Ministerial Candidacy, 1999
ordained: 1999
charges: Palm Lane, Scottsdale, AZ, 1999–

Van Dyken, Seymour
b. 06/17/1921, Grand Rapids, MI
training: Calvin Theological Seminary, ThB, 1946; Princeton Theological Seminary, ThD, 1962
ordained: 1946

charges: CRC: Bauer, MI, 1946-49; Northside, Passaic, NJ, 1949-52; Ridgewood, NJ, 1952-60; Lafayette, IN, 1960-64; Neland Ave., Grand Rapids, MI, 1964-70; Lecturer, Calvin Theological Seminary, 1970-72; Congregational Church: East Congregational, Grand Rapids, MI, 1972-86
retired: 1986

Van Dyken, William Dennis
b. 11/04/1945, Bellingham, WA
training: Calvin Theological Seminary, MDiv, 1983
ordained: 1983
charges: Hope, Hull, IA, 1983-87; Eligible for call, 1987-88; Chaplain, Religious Service Coordinator, Hope Haven, Rock Valley, IA, 1988-

Van Eck, Stephan Randall
b. 12/09/1953, Chicago, IL
training: Westminster Theological Seminary-PA, MDiv, 1980
ordained: 1982
charges: Bible Fellowship Church: Sunbury, PA, 1980-83; Denville, NJ, 1983-88; CRC: Iowa Falls, IA, 1988-91; Sunnyslope, Salem, OR, 1991-95; East Martin, MI, 1995-2001; Second, Highland, IN, 2001-

Van Ee, Bernard John
b. 10/16/1950, Oskaloosa, IA
training: Calvin Theological Seminary, MDiv, 1976
ordained: 1976
charges: Woden, IA, 1976-80; Hope, Hull, IA, 1980-83; Trinity, Anchorage, AK, 1983-92; Gallatin Gateway Community, Bozeman, MT, 1992-

Van Ee, Jan
b. 08/22/1947, Barneveld, Gelderland, Netherlands
training: Calvin Theological Seminary, MDiv, 1979
ordained: 1980
charges: Missionary to Mexico, 1980-

Van Ee, Verlan Gene
b. 06/08/1958, Oskaloosa, IA
training: Calvin Theological Seminary, MDiv, 1984
ordained: 1984
charges: Minister of youth and evangelism, Cascade, Grand Rapids, MI, 1984-86; Missionary, Hi-Desert, Barstow, CA, 1986-88; Pastor of outreach, Emmanuel, Sauk Village, IL, 1988-91; Interim, Webster, NY, 1991-92; Webster, NY, 1992-

Van Eek, Arie Gideon
b. 05/10/1932, Anna Paulowna, Noord Holland, Netherlands

training: Calvin Theological Seminary, BD, 1957; MDiv 1977; Westminster Theological Seminary-PA, 1958
ordained: 1958
charges: Exeter, ON, 1958-62; Fort William, ON, 1962-66; First, Calgary, AB, 1966-70; Kildonan, Winnipeg, MB, 1970-78; Executive secretary, Council for CRC in Canada, 1978-98
retired: 1998

Van Eerden, Thomas
b. 01/27/1908, Grand Rapids, MI
training: Calvin Theological Seminary, ThB, 1939; New York University, MA, 1953
ordained: 1939
charges: Plainfield, MI, 1939-42; First, Muskegon, MI, 1942-46; Broadway Ave., Grand Rapids, MI, 1946-51; Wyckoff, NJ, 1951-55; First Roseland, Chicago, IL, 1955-64; First, Fulton, IL, 1964-66; Devington, Indianapolis, IN, 1966-71; Immanuel, Muskegon, MI, 1971-73
retired: 1973
d. 04/12/1985, Grand Rapids, MI

Van Egmond, Peter
b. 03/15/1931, Rijnsburg, Zuid Holland, Netherlands
training: Calvin Theological Seminary, BD, 1957
ordained: 1957
charges: Iron Springs, AB, 1957-60; Wellandport, ON, 1960-65; Kingston, ON, 1965-69; First, Abbotsford, BC, 1969-80; Rehoboth, Toronto, ON, 1980-87; Chaplain, Holland Christian Home, Brampton, ON, 1987-

Van Elderen, Bastiaan Jr.
b. 12/29/1924, Ripon, CA
training: University of California, MA, 1955; Calvin Theological Seminary, BD, 1959; Pacific School of Religion, ThD, 1961
ordained: 1959
charges: Faculty, Calvin Theological Seminary, Grand Rapids, MI, 1959-72; Director, American Center of Oriental Research, Amman, Jordan, 1972-74; Faculty, Calvin Theological Seminary, Grand Rapids, MI, 1974-84; Faculty, Vrije Universiteit, Netherlands, 1984-90
retired: 1990

Van Elderen, Peter J. Jr.
b. 03/07/1950, Modesto, CA
training: Calvin Theological Seminary, MDiv, 1988
ordained: 1988
charges: Plymouth Heights, Grand Rapids, MI, 1988-97; Horizon Community, Denver, CO, 1997-

Van Enk, Gordon Lee
b. 05/11/1940, Grand Rapids, MI
training: Calvin Theological Seminary, MDiv, 1965
ordained: 1966
charges: Atwood, MI, 1966-69; Madison, WI, 1969-79; Crenshaw, Los Angeles, CA, 1979-91; Clinical pastoral education, 1991-92; Eligible for call, 1992-93; Chaplain, VITAS (Innovative Hospice Care), Los Angeles, CA, 1993-

Van Ens, Clarence
b. 09/25/1919, Moline, MI
training: Calvin Theological Seminary, BD, 1946
ordained: 1947
charges: Prospect St., Passaic, NJ, 1947-52; Missionary to Ceylon, 1952-66; Campus pastor, Western Michigan University, 1966-74; Orlando, FL, 1974-82; On loan to Box Hill Reformed Church, Victoria, Australia, 1982-84
retired: 1984

Van Ens, John
b. 09/25/1919, Moline, MI
training: Calvin Theological Seminary, ThB, 1952
ordained: 1952
charges: Missionary to Ceylon, 1952-68; First, Los Angeles, CA, 1968-73; University of South Dakota, 1973-77; Cypress Gardens-Winter Haven, FL, 1977-80; Missionary, Faith Presbyterian Reformed Church, Agana, Guam, 1980-83
retired: 1983

Van Essen, Clarence
b. 09/30/1927, Edgerton, MN
training: Calvin Theological Seminary, BD, 1956
ordained: 1956
charges: Cedar, IA, 1956-60; McBain, MI, 1960-65; Platte, SD, 1965-72; First, Fulton, IL, 1972-80; Maple Heights, Cleveland, OH, 1980-84; Harrison, SD, 1984-92
retired: 1992

Van Essen, Douglas Jay
b. 05/25/1954, Grand Rapids, MI
training: Calvin Theological Seminary, MDiv, 1980
ordained: 1980
charges: Minister of education and evangelism, Covenant, Cutlerville, MI, 1980-84; Bethany, Muskegon, MI, 1984-

Van Essen, Larry Eugene
b. 02/18/1944, Edgerton, MN vicinity
training: Calvin Theological Seminary, BD, 1969
ordained: 1969
charges: Missionary, Immanuel, Fort Collins, CO,

1969-77; Riverside, CA, 1977-89; Madison, WI, 1989-2001; First, Visalia, CA, 2001-

Van Essen, Lester Wayne
b. 07/25/1935, Rock County, MN
training: San Francisco Theological Seminary, 1961; Kennedy School of Missions, 1961; Calvin Theological Seminary, MDiv, 1985;
ordained: 1961
charges: Missionary to Nigeria, 1961-82; Immanuel, Burbank, IL, 1982-93; First, Lansing, IL, 1993-2002
retired: 2002

Van Eyk, Bart
b. 11/23/1948, Rotterdam, Zuid Holland, Netherlands
training: Calvin Theological Seminary, MDiv, 1976
ordained: 1976
charges: Fairlawn, Whitinsville, MA, 1976-82; First, Modesto, CA, 1982-85; Hope, Port Perry, ON, 1985-91; San Diego, CA, 1991-97; Covenant, North Haledon, NJ, 1997-99; Charlottetown, PE, 1999-

Van Farowe, Edward R.
b. 07/16/1894, Allendale, MI
training: Calvin Theological Seminary, diploma, 1922
ordained: 1922
charges: CRC: Wright, IA, 1922-26; Ireton, IA, 1926-28; Prinsburg, MN, 1928-31; Leave, 1931-32; RCA: Clifton, NJ, 1932-34
d. 04/11/1934, Clifton, NJ

Vang, Kou
training: declared eligible on the basis of exceptional gifts, 1999
ordained: 2001
charges: Hmong, Wisconsin Rapids, WI, 1994-99; Hmong, Sheboygan, WI 1999-

Van Geest, Adrian Arnold
b. 09/13/1936, Naaldwijk, Zuid Holland, Netherlands
training: Calvin Theological Seminary, BD, 1963
ordained: 1963
charges: Blenheim, ON, 1963-66; Maranatha, Calgary, AB, 1966-72; Drayton, ON, 1972-77; Ebenezer, Trenton, ON, 1977-84; Mountainview, Grimsby, ON, 1984-94; Blyth, ON, 1994-2001
retired: 2001

Van Gelder, Craig E.
b. 02/22/1945, Sibley, IA

training: Reformed Theological Seminary, MDiv, 1978; Southwestern Baptist Theological Seminary, PhD, 1982; University of Texas at Arlington, PhD, 1985
ordained: 1984
charges: PC(USA): Staff consultant, Presbytery of Mississippi, 1984–88; Faculty, Calvin Theological Seminary, Grand Rapids, MI, 1988–90; CRC: Faculty, Calvin Theological Seminary, Grand Rapids, MI, 1990–98; Faculty, Luther Seminary, St. Paul, MN, 1998–

Van Gelder, David Wayne
b. 05/31/1951, Orange City, IA
training: Calvin Theological Seminary, MDiv, 1976; ThM, 1978
ordained: 1977
charges: Chaplain, Pine Rest, Christian Hospital, Grand Rapids, MI, 1977–78; Leave, 1978–80; Faculty, Erskine Theological Seminary, Due West, SC, 1980–89; Executive director, Bethesda Christian Counseling Service, Denver, CO, 1989–94; Director, Behavioral Health, Centura-Porter Health Systems, Denver, CO, 1994–2001
d. 02/10/2001, Denver, CO

Van Gent, Donald Wilbur
b. 06/09/1928, Pella, IA
training: Calvin Theological Seminary, BD, 1958
ordained: 1958
charges: Atwood, MI, 1958–62; South Olive, MI, 1962–66; Missionary, Immanuel, Salt Lake City, UT, 1966–69; Tacoma, WA, 1969–72; Lincoln Center, IA, 1972–76; Anaheim, CA, 1976–81; Gallatin Gateway, MT, 1981–83
retired: 1983

Van Giessen, Adrian Gary
b. 01/15/1959, Chatham, ON
training: Calvin Theological Seminary, MDiv, 1986
ordained: 1986
charges: Penticton, BC, 1986–91; Bethel, Acton, ON, 1991–94; Crossroads Community, Ajax, ON, 1994–

Van Goor, Kornelis
b. 11/16/1848, Smilde, Drenthe, Netherlands
training: Theologische Universiteit, Kampen, diploma, 1872
ordained: 1872
charges: GKN: Veenwoudsterwal, 1872–74; Broek-op-Langedijk, 1987–76; Leeuwarden, 1876–79; Assen, 1879–83; Nieuwendijk bij Almkerk, 1883–89; Schiedam, 1889–91; Gorinchem, 1891–93;

CRC: Ninth Street, Holland, MI, 1893–1902; Second, Paterson, NJ, 1902–14
d. 02/26/1914, Paterson, NJ

Van Groningen, Gerard Sr.
b. 03/25/1921, Leota, MN
training: Calvin Theological Seminary, BD, 1954; Westminster Theological Seminary, ThM, 1955; University of Melbourne, MA, 1967; PhD, 1970
ordained: 1955
charges: Borculo, MI, 1955–58; Missionary, Australia, 1958–71; Faculty, Dordt College, 1971–73; Faculty, Reformed Theological Seminary, Jackson, MS, 1973–80; President, Trinity Christian College, Palos Heights, IL, 1980–84
retired: 1984

Van Groningen, Gerard Jr.
b. 12/26/1951, Grand Rapids, MI
training: Reformed Theological Seminary, MDiv, 1977; Calvin Theological Seminary, Special Program for Ministerial Candidacy, 1979
ordained: 1979
charges: Beaverdam, MI, 1979–85; Calvin, Rock Valley, IA, 1985–91; Bethel, Lynden, WA, 1991–2001; Baldwin Street, Jenison, MI, 2001–

Van Groningen, Willis Dean
b. 01/24/1956, Zeeland, MI
training: Western Kentucky University, MA, 1979; University of Missouri-Columbia, PhD, 1982
ordained: 1988
charges: Geneva Fellowship, Queens University, and Home Missions Campus Ministry Director, Kingston, ON, 1982–97; Director, Home Missions Campus Ministry, Ann Arbor, MI, 1997–

Van Haitsma, Lambert
b. 05/13/1888, Vriesland, MI
training: Calvin Theological Seminary, diploma, 1919; Princeton Seminary, 1920
ordained: 1920
charges: Rudyard, MI, 1920–24; First, Cutlerville, MI, 1924–29; Portland, MI, 1929–43
retired: 1943
d. 12/30/1976, Zeeland, MI

Van Haitsma, Mark Alan
b. 11/04/1962, Holland, MI
training: Calvin Theological Seminary, MDiv, 1990
ordained: 1990
charges: Paw Paw, MI, 1990–96; Olympia, WA, 1996–

Van Hal, William Gysbert
b. 12/06/1943, Oskaloosa, IA
training: Calvin Theological Seminary, BD, 1969
ordained: 1973
charges: CRC: Pipestone, MN, 1974–78;
Knollwood, Kalamazoo, MI, 1978–80; Holland, IA,
1980–84; Zillah, WA, 1984–89; Sibley, IA, 1989–
95; Alliance of Reformed Churches: Independent
Reformed, Woodstock, ON, 1995–96; United Reformed Churches: Bethel, Woodstock, ON, 1996

Van Halsema, Clark Gerard
b. 01/14/1953, Paterson, NJ
training: Calvin Theological Seminary, MDiv, 1981
ordained: 1981
charges: CRC: Missionary, Jackson, MS, 1981–
84; Cottage Grove, South Holland, IL, 1984–87;
Covenant, Appleton, WI, 1987–91; On loan: Christ
Church, Oak Brook, IL, 1991–92; Bible teacher,
Unity Christian High School, Hudsonville, MI,
1992–98; Resigned from denomination, 1998

Van Halsema, Dick Lucas
b. 06/19/1922, Grand Rapids, MI
training: Calvin Theological Seminary, ThB, 1949
ordained: 1949
charges: Home missionary at Monsey, NY, 1949–
56; Miami, FL, 1956–57; Home missionary at
large, 1957–59; Denominational minister of evangelism, 1959–63; Central Ave., Holland, MI, 1963–
66; President, Reformed Bible College, Grand
Rapids, MI, 1966–87
retired: 1987

Van Halsema, Emo Folkert Johan
b. 12/02/1890, Kampen, Overijsel, Netherlands
training: Calvin Theological Seminary, BD, 1921;
Union Theological Seminary, ThM, 1933
ordained: 1921
charges: East Paris, MI, 1921–25; Fuller Ave.,
Grand Rapids, MI, 1925–30; Northside, Passaic,
NJ, 1930–48; First, Hudsonville, MI, 1948–55; editor, *De Wachter*, 1955–61; Lecturer, Calvin College, 1955
retired: 1961
d. 03/09/1964, Grand Rapids, MI

Van Harmelen, John J.
b. 04/04/1901, Den Haag, Zuid Holland, Netherlands
training: Vrije Universiteit, Amsterdam, diploma,
1936
ordained: 1936
charges: GKN: Harkstede, 1936–39; Marrum,
1939–43; Amstelveen, 1943–46; Garijp, 1946–49;

Assen, 1949–53; CRC: Brampton, ON, 1953–58;
Hebron, Whitby, ON, 1958–69; Bethel, London,
ON, 1969–73; First, Woodstock, ON, 1973–76
retired: 1976
d. 10/25/1991, Whitby, ON

Van Harn, Karl John
b. 04/30/1957, Grand Rapids, MI
training: Calvin Theological Seminary, MDiv, 1985
ordained: 1986
charges: Assistant to pastor, Ridgeview Hills,
Denver, CO, 1985–86; Ridgeview Hills, Denver, CO,
1986–89; Chaplain, Presbyterian Hospital/St.
Luke's Medical Center, Denver, CO, 1989–92; Clinical pastoral education Supervisor/Chaplain, Santa
Rosa Memorial Hospital, Santa Rosa, CA, 1992–
94; Coordinator, Chaplain Services/Chaplain,
Wedgwood Christian Youth and Family Services,
Grand Rapids, MI, 1994–

Van Harn, Roger Earl
b. 09/30/1932, Grand Rapids, MI
training: Calvin Theological Seminary, BD, 1957
ordained: 1957
charges: Cottage Grove, South Holland, IL, 1957–
61; Home missionary, Eau Gallie, FL, 1961–66;
Olentangy, Columbus, OH, 1966–70; Campus minister, Ohio State, Columbus, OH, 1970–76; Grace,
Grand Rapids, MI, 1976–98
retired: 1998

Van Harten, David Ralph
b. 05/27/1960, St. Thomas, ON
training: Ontario Bible College, BRE, 1993; Calvin
Theological Seminary, MDiv, 2000
ordained: 2000
charges: Pioneer, Cedar Springs, MI, 2000–

Van Heest, Steven Jay
b. 04/29/1953, Grand Rapids, MI
training: Calvin Theological Seminary, MDiv, 1979
ordained: 1979
charges: Alamosa, CO, 1979–83; Irving Park, Midland Park, NJ, 1983–90; Clinical pastoral education, Kalamazoo, MI, 1990–92; Westwood,
Kalamazoo, MI, 1992–99; Chaplain, Spectrum
Health, Grand Rapids, MI, 1999–

Van Hemert, John
b. 08/31/1936, Oudewater, Zuid Holland, Netherlands
training: Calvin Theological Seminary, ThB, 1965
ordained: 1965
charges: Edson, AB, 1965–68; Langley, BC,
1968–80; Calvin, Pinellas Park, FL, 1980–84; The

King's Church, Port St. Lucie, FL, 1984-87; Faith Community, Lantana, FL, 1987-91; Stephenville, TX, 1992-93; Leave, 1993-94; First, Vancouver, BC, 1994-99; Good News Community, Kent, WA, 1999-2001; Hope in Christ, Bellingham, WA, 2002
retired: 2002

Van het Loo, Theodorus W.R.

see: Van Loo, Theodorus W.R.

Van Heyst, Adrian

b. 08/30/1944, Hapert, Noord Brabant, Netherlands
training: Calvin Theological Seminary, BD, 1969
ordained: 1969
charges: CRC: Austinville, IA, 1969-73; Immanuel, Salt Lake City, UT, 1973-76; Leave, 1976-80; available for call, 1980-82; Resigned from denomination, pastor, Murray, UT

Van Hoff, Herbert Aubrey

b. 12/07/1934, Maredone, Sri Lanka
training: Calvin Theological Seminary, BD, 1962; ThM, 1969
ordained: 1963
charges: Dutch Reformed Church: Ceylon, 1963-76; CRC: Transcona, Winnipeg, MB, 1976-80; Second, Abbotsford, BC, 1980-89; Covenant, Barrie, ON, 1989-97; Tillsonburg, ON, 1997-2000
retired: 2000

Van Hofwegen, Michael Henry

b. 06/04/1954, Upland, CA
training: Calvin Theological Seminary, MDiv, 1982
ordained: 1982
charges: Missionary, Costa Rica, 1982-88; South Kendall Community, Miami, FL, 1988-99; Burnaby, BC, 1999-

Van Hofwegen, Robert Eugene

b. 01/08/1950, Upland, CA
training: Calvin Theological Seminary, BD, 1974; MDiv, 1980
ordained: 1975
charges: Hawarden, IA, 1975-80; First, Hanford, CA, 1980-85; San Jose, CA, 1985-95; Fort Lauderdale, FL, 1995-

Van Hoogen, Hendrik

b. 02/18/1836, Midwolde, Groningen, Netherlands
training: Theologische Universiteit, Kampen, diploma, 1865
ordained: 1865
charges: GKN: Gees, 1865-67; Burum, 1867-73; Niezijl, 1873-75; Hoogeveen, 1875-79;

Wildervank, 1879-94; CRC: Second Roseland, Chicago, IL, 1894-95; Central Ave., Holland, MI, 1895-1903; Prospect Park, Paterson, NJ, 1903-07
d. 01/05/1907, Prospect Park, NJ

Van Houten, Abram

b. 08/20/1828, New York, NY
training: with James G. Brinkerhoff
ordained: 1852
charges: True Protestant Dutch Reformed: Nanuet, NY (also supplied pulpits in Paramus, 1857-61, and Hempstead, 1861), 1852-61; Schraalenburg, NJ, 1861-66; New York, NY, 1866-78; Leonia, NJ, 1878-84 and Ridgewood, NJ, 1878-88; Englewood, NJ, 1888-90; CRC: Englewood, NJ, 1890-92; Third, Paterson, NJ, 1892-95
d. 09/18/1895, Paterson, NJ

Van Houten, Charles Nicholas

b. 1856, Nanuet, NY
training: with Abram Van Houten
ordained: 1885
charges: PCUSA: East Hanford, 1885-88; Georgetown, KY, 1889-91; Manchester, 1891-1906; Bergenfield, NJ, 1911-1937; CRC: Bergenfield, NJ, 1906-08; True Reformed Dutch Church: Bergenfield, NJ, 1908-11
d. 11/08/1937, Bergenfield, NJ

Van Houten, Frederick William

b. 11/08/1913, Cascade Township, Kent County, MI
training: Calvin Theological Seminary, ThB, 1938; Northern Baptist Theological Seminary
ordained: 1938
charges: Otley, IA, 1938-43; Chaplain, United States Army, 1943-46; Oskaloosa, IA, 1946-50; Sherman St., Grand Rapids, MI, 1950-53; Third, Lynden, WA, 1953-57; Wyoming Park, Grand Rapids, MI, 1957-62; Warren Park, Cicero, IL, 1962-70; Ninth St., Holland, MI, 1970-74; Sully, IA, 1974-78; Orangewood, Phoenix, AZ, 1978-82; Orland Park, IL, 1982-86;
retired: 1986
d. 02/22/1994, Orland Park, IL

Van Houten, James Forrester

b. 01/04/1868, New York, NY
training: with Harvey Iserman and Abram Van Houten
ordained: 1894
charges: Monsey, NY, 1892-93; Paramus, NJ, 1893-1896; Prospect Street, Passaic, NJ, 1896-1909

d. 03/23/1910, Passaic, NJ

Van Houten, Mark Elwyn

b. 08/05/1958, Modesto, CA
training: Calvin Theological Seminary, MDiv, 1985
ordained: 1988
charges: CRC: Street minister, Northside Ecumenical Night Ministry Chicago, IL, 1988-90; Manhattan, NY, 1990-91; Eligible for call, 1991-93; Released from denomination, 1993

Van Houten, Myron Paul

b. 08/03/1936, Grand Rapids, MI
training: Calvin Theological Seminary, BD, 1960
ordained: 1960
charges: CRC: Hull, ND, 1960-65; Missionary pastor, Rapid City, SD, 1965-74; Resigned from denomination, pastor, Rapid City, SD

Van Houten, Siebert Andrew

b. 03/17/1947, Leeuwarden, Friesland, Netherlands
training: Calvin Theological Seminary, BD, 1972; MDiv, 1976; ThM, 1979
ordained: 1973
charges: First, Orillia, ON, 1973-77; Graduate studies and Clinical pastoral education, Pine Rest Christian Hospital, Cutlerville, MI, 1977-79; Chaplain, Hamilton Psychopathic Hospital, Hamilton, ON, 1979-84; Regional coordinator of chaplaincy, Hamilton, ON, 1984-95; Canadian chaplains director, Ancaster, ON, 1995-

Van Katwijk, Peter Louren

b. 03/25/1938, Rotterdam, Zuid Holland, Netherlands
training: Calvin Theological Seminary, BD, 1965; ThM, 1975
ordained: 1965
charges: CRC: Stratford, ON, 1965-68; First, Kitchener, ON, 1968-73; Leave, 1973-76; Director, Cambridge Interfaith Pastoral Counseling Centre, Cambridge, ON, 1976-85; Director of Training, Kitchener Interfaith Pastoral Counseling Centre, Kitchener, ON, 1985-91; Non-ministerial vocation, higher education, 1991

Van Kley, Byron Edward

b. 10/13/1966, Chicago Heights, IL
training: Calvin Theological Seminary, MDiv, 2000
ordained: 2000
charges: Bethany, Holland, MI, 2000-2001; River Rock, Vancouver, WA, 2001-

Van Klompenberg, Sherwin Royce

b. 07/20/1945, Jamestown, MI
training: Calvin Theological Seminary, BD, 1970; MDiv, 1976
ordained: 1971
charges: Pullman, Chicago, IL, 1970-71; Portland, MI, 1974-77; Non-ministerial vocation, 1977

Van Kooten, Jeff

b. 06/12/1963, Denver, CO
training: Denver Theological Seminary, MDiv, 1992
ordained: 1998
charges: The Outpost, Denver, CO, 1998-2002; Non-ministerial vocation, 2002

Van Kooten, Tenis C.

b. 12/14/1908, Prairie View, KS
training: Calvin Theological Seminary, BD, 1939; ThB, 1944
ordained: 1939
charges: Four Corners, Teec Nos Pos, AZ, 1939; Volga, SD, 1939-43; Western Springs, IL, 1943-47; New Holland, SD, 1947-51; Hamilton, ON, 1951-60; Second, Edmonton, AB, 1960-62; Fourteenth St., Holland, MI, 1962-73
retired: 1973
d. 09/18/2001, Lynden, WA

Van Korlaar, Evert

b. 11/26/1864, Putten, Gelderland, Netherlands
training: Calvin Theological Seminary, diploma, 1899
ordained: 1899
charges: Spring Lake, MI, 1899-1902; Caldwell, MI, 1902-05; Baldwin, WI, 1905-12; Vesper, WI, 1912-16; West Branch, MI, 1916-20
retired: 1920
d. 11/05/1938, Grand Rapids, MI

Van Laar, Gerard

b. 07/31/1895, Zwolle, Overijsel, Netherlands
training: Calvin Theological Seminary, BD, 1934
ordained: 1934
charges: Willard, OH, 1934-43; New Era, MI, 1943-47; Chandler, MN, 1947-50; Home missionary, Red Deer/Rocky Mountain House, AB, 1950-53, Missionary, Smithers/Telkwa/Terrace/Prince George, BC, 1953-58; Zillah, WA, 1958-62
retired: 1962
d. 10/27/1984, Willard, OH

Van Laar, Lambertus

b. 06/20/1894, Zwolle, Overijsel, Netherlands

training: Calvin Theological Seminary, diploma, 1923
ordained: 1923
charges: Leota, MN, 1923-26; Prospect Park, Holland, MI, 1926-39; Whitinsville, MA, 1939-45; Second, Kalamazoo, MI, 1945-52; Brockville, ON, 1952-56; Second, Pella, IA, 1956-61
retired: 1961
d. 11/15/1984, Grand Rapids, MI

van Leeuwen, Gerald (Gary) Thomas
b. 03/20/1968, Listowel, ON
training: Calvin Theological Seminary, MDiv, 2000
ordained: 2000
charges: Athens, ON, 1999-

Van Leeuwen, Raymond Cornelius
b. 10/02/1948, Artesia, CA
training: University of Toronto, MA, 1974; Calvin Theological Seminary, BD, 1976; University of St. Michael's College, PhD, 1984
ordained: 1986
charges: Faculty, Calvin Theological Seminary, Grand Rapids, MI, 1981-82, 1985-90; Faculty, Calvin College, Grand Rapids, MI, 1982-85, 1990-94; Interim, First, Brandon, MB, 1987-88; Faculty, Eastern College, St. Davids, PA, 1994-

Van Leeuwen, Wilhelmus Hein
b. 10/22/1807, Ten Boer, Groningen, Netherlands
training: declared eligible on the basis of exceptional gifts, 1845
ordained: 1845
charges: Kerken onder 't Kruis: Woerden and Linschoten, 1845-56; Den Helder, 1846-52 (merged with GKN); GKN: Den Helder, 1852-58; Werkendam, 1859-63; CRC: First, Grand Rapids, MI, 1863-67; First, Paterson, NJ, 1867-72; East Saugatuck, MI, 1875-80
retired: 1880
d. 10/08/1882, Grand Rapids, MI

Van Lonkhuyzen, John (Jan)
b. 06/15/1873, Kesteren, Brabant, Netherlands
training: Vrije Universiteit, Amsterdam, diploma, 1897; PhD, 1905
ordained: 1899
charges: GKN: Wilnis, 1899-02; Aarlanderveen, 1902-08; Missionary, Argentina, 1908; Rijswijk, 1909-11; Zierikzee, 1928-39; CRC: Alpine Ave., Grand Rapids, MI, 1911-18; First, Chicago, IL, 1918-28
retired: 1939
d. 12/29/1942, Grand Rapids, MI

Van Loo, Duane Jay
b. 03/25/1947, Bellingham, WA
training: Calvin Theological Seminary, BD, 1972; MDiv, 1975
ordained: 1973
charges: Minister of youth and evangelism, Munster, IN, 1973-76; Community, Saginaw, MI, 1976-83; Messiah, Hudsonville, MI, 1983-93; Kedvale, Oak Lawn, IL, 1993-

Van Loo, Theodorus W.R.
b. 05/16/1869, Sliedrecht, Zuid Holland, Netherlands
training: Calvin Theological Seminary, diploma, 1897
ordained: 1898
charges: Fulton, IL, 1898-1901; Firth, NE, 1901-03; Otley, IA, 1903-06; Vogel Center, MI, 1906-18
retired: 1918
d. 03/14/1945, Grand Rapids, MI

Van Marion, Jack
b. 01/25/1951, Barendrecht, Zuid Holland, Netherlands
training: Calvin Theological Seminary, MDiv, 1981
ordained: 1982
charges: North Blendon, MI, 1982-88; Des Moines, IA, 1988-95; Beamsville, ON, 1995-

Van Milligen, Thomas Jeffrey
b. 07/27/1963, Kitchener, ON
training: Calvin Theological Seminary, MDiv, 1991
ordained: 1991
charges: Telkwa, ON, 1991-95; North Hills, Troy, ON, 1995-1999; Crosspoint, Cincinnati, OH, 1999-

Van Muyen, Andrew
b. 06/17/1956, St. Mary's, ON
training: Calvin Theological Seminary, MDiv, 1988
ordained: 1989
charges: Immanuel, Cornwall, ON, 1989-93; Vernon, BC, 1993-97; Sonrise, Ponoka, AB, 1997-2002

Van Niejenhuis, Cecil
b. 06/11/1955, Edmonton, AB
training: Calvin Theological Seminary, MDiv, 1981
ordained: 1981
charges: Ancaster, ON, 1981-85; First, Lacombe, AB, 1985-91; First, Kitchener, ON, 1991-93; First, Edmonton, AB, 1993-

Van Niejenhuis, Herman
b. 02/28/1949, Bierum, Groningen, Netherlands
training: Calvin Theological Seminary, BD, 1974

ordained: 1975

charges: Maranatha, Lethbridge, AB, 1975-79; First, Kingston, ON, 1979-84; Bethel, Saskatoon, SK, 1985-88; Leave, 1988-89; Willowdale, Toronto, ON, 1989-2000; Covenant, Sioux Center, IA, 2000-

Van Osdol, Randall
b. 07/15/1954, Burlington, IA
training: Reformed Presbyterian Theological Seminary, MDiv, 1980
ordained: 1980
charges: Reformed Presbyterian Church NA: Sharon, Morning Sun, IA, 1980-84; Adelphi, MD, 1984-97; CRC: Hope, Rapid City, SD, 1997-

Van Oyen, Durant T.
b. 09/22/1934, Chicago Heights, IL
training: Calvin Theological Seminary, BD, 1959; Garrett Evangelical Seminary, 1960
ordained: 1960
charges: Calvin, Rock Valley, IA, 1960-65; Fairlawn, Whitinsville, MA, 1965-72; Missionary, Fellowship, Greeley, CO, 1972-80; Cascade, Grand Rapids, MI, 1980-88; Church planting, Minneapolis, MN, 1988-89
d. 09/20/1989, Maple Grove, MN

Van Oyen, Gerald Frederick
b. 09/30/1932, Chicago Heights, IL
training: Calvin Theological Seminary, BD, 1957; MDiv, 1979
ordained: 1957
charges: Hills, MN, 1957-60; Calvary, Pella, IA, 1960-64; Twelfth St., Grand Rapids, MI, 1964-70; Missionary to Mexico, 1970-73; Covenant, Cutlerville, MI, 1973-88; Pinegate Community, Cutlerville, MI, 1988-93; Caledonia, MI, 1993-94
retired: 1994

Van Peursem, William
b. 08/26/1901, Orange City, IA vicinity
training: Princeton Theological Seminary, BD, 1927; Calvin Theological Seminary, Special Program for Ministerial Candidacy, 1928
ordained: 1928
charges: Zutphen, MI, 1928-32; Sherman St., Grand Rapids, MI, 1932-40; First, Denver, CO, 1940-45; Fourteenth St., Holland, MI, 1945-51; Lee St., Grand Rapids, MI, 1951-58; Third, Bellflower, CA, 1958-67; Highland Ave., Redlands, CA, 1967-70
retired: 1970
d. 11/16/1999, Ontario, CA

Van Reenen, Cornelius
b. 05/01/1888, Driebruggen, Utrecht, Netherlands
training: Calvin Theological Seminary, diploma, 1922
ordained: 1922
charges: CRC: Home missionary, Bigelow, MN, 1922-26 and Sibley, IA, 1922-25; GKN: Woerden, 1927-56
retired: 1956
d. 06/17/1976, Hilversum, Utrecht, Netherlands

Van Rees, William L.
b. 05/18/1907, Sully, IA
training: Calvin Theological Seminary, 1932
ordained: 1932
charges: Bigelow, MN, 1932-39; Sanborn, IA, 1939-44; Second Roseland, Chicago, IL, 1944-51; First, Grand Rapids, MI, 1951-60; East Paris, Grand Rapids, MI, 1960-70; Rusk, MI, 1970-74
retired: 1974
d. 12/25/1990, Grand Rapids, MI

Van Regenmorter, John David
b. 04/19/1948, Grand Rapids, MI
training: Calvin Theological Seminary, MDiv, 1974
ordained: 1974
charges: Northside, Clifton, NJ, 1974-79; Shalom, Sioux Falls, SD, 1979-88; First, Denver, CO, 1988-97; Bethany Christian Services, Grand Rapids, MI, 1997-

Van Reken, Calvin Paul
b. 04/21/1949, Grand Rapids, MI
training: University of Chicago, MA, 1972; PhD, 1986; Calvin Theological Seminary, MDiv, 1981
ordained: 1982
charges: Momence, IL, 1982-86; Peace, South Holland, IL, 1986-91; Faculty, Calvin Theological Seminary, Grand Rapids, MI, 1991-

Van Ryn, John George
b. 09/23/1931, Chicago, IL
training: Calvin Theological Seminary, BD, 1956; MDiv, 1978
ordained: 1956
charges: Lakewood, CA, 1956-61; Second, Paterson, NJ, 1961-66; First, South Holland, IL, 1966-74; Executive Secretary, Board of Home Missions, Grand Rapids, MI, 1974-87; Fellowship, Big Rapids, MI, 1987-94; Providence, Cutlerville, MI, 1994-96
retired: 1996

Van Schelven, Kenneth Marinus B.
b. 03/19/1947, Glasgow, Scotland

training: Reformed Bible College, BRE, 1985; Calvin Theological Seminary, MDiv, 1991
ordained: 1992
charges: Hope, Port Perry, ON, 1992-96; Leave, 1996-98; Knollbrook, Corvallis, OR, 1998-

Van Schepen, John
b. 10/05/1946, Surhuizum, Friesland, Netherlands
training: Calvin Theological Seminary, BD, 1969; MDiv, 1978
ordained: 1972
charges: Missionary, Beaver Dam, WI, 1972-78; Community, Roselawn, IN, 1978-83; Sunnyslope, Salem, OR, 1983-90; First, Bellflower, CA, 1990-2002; Bethel, Lynden, WA, 2002-

Van Schouwen, Andrew Joseph
b. 08/12/1931, Harvey, IL
training: Calvin Theological Seminary, BD, 1958
ordained: 1958
charges: Hawarden, IA, 1958-63; Chandler, MN, 1963-68; Oakland, MI, 1968-79; Grace, Kalamazoo, MI, 1979-83; Leave, 1983; Hartley, IA and Spencer, IA, 1983-86; Hartley, IA, 1986-92; Ackley, IA, 1992-95
retired: 1995; affiliated with Messiah Independent Ref. Church, Holland, MI, 1998

Van Schouwen, Cornelius J.
b. 04/16/1903, Rotterdam, Zuid Holland, Netherlands
training: Calvin Theological Seminary, BD, 1931; Indiana University, MA; Winona Lake School of Theology, MA
ordained: 1931
charges: Archer Ave., Chicago, IL, 1931-37; De Motte, IN, 1937-42; Chaplain, United States Army, 1942-46; Bible teacher Western Christian High School, Hull, IA, 1946-54; Faculty, Dordt College, Sioux Center, IA, 1954-68
retired: 1968
d. 03/02/1994, Sioux Center, IA

Van Slooten, Clarence
b. 08/21/1917, Goshen, IN
training: Calvin Theological Seminary, BD, 1954
ordained: 1954
charges: San Diego, CA, 1954-63; First, Salt Lake City, UT, 1963-79
retired: 1979
d. 01/17/1993, Salt Lake City, UT

Van Smeerdyk, Gerald Peter
b. 06/22/1961, North Vancouver, BC
training: Calvin Theological Seminary, MDiv, 1995

ordained: 1995
charges: Emo, ON, 1995-2001; Bethel, Dunnville, ON, 2001-

Van Someren, Bernard Alvin
b. 11/28/1921, Baldwin, WI
training: Calvin Theological Seminary, ThB, 1952
ordained: 1952
charges: Ada, MI, 1952-55; Oostburg, WI, 1955-62; Sully, IA, 1962-67; Second, Paterson, NJ, 1967-86
retired: 1986

Van Someren, Bernardus
b. 11/28/1899, Asperen, Gelderland, Netherlands
training: Calvin Theological Seminary, diploma, 1925
ordained: 1925
charges: Hull, ND, 1925-30; Sanborn, IA, 1930-38; Second, Kalamazoo, MI, 1938-45; First, South Holland, IL, 1945-52; Second Roseland, Chicago, IL, 1952-58; De Motte, IN, 1958-65
retired: 1965
d. 06/16/1988, South Holland, IL

Van Staalduinen, Leonard Jr.
b. 04/06/1929, s'-Gravenzande, Zuid Holland, Netherlands
training: Calvin Theological Seminary, BD, 1957
ordained: 1957
charges: CRC: Edson, AB, 1957-60; Regina, SK, 1960-63; Leighton, IA, 1963-68; Lodi, NJ, 1968-75; Lucknow, ON, 1975-80; GKN: Daarle, 1980-91
retired: 1991

Van Stempvoort, John William
b. 02/10/1929, Warren, MI
training: Calvin Theological Seminary, BD, 1953
ordained: 1953
charges: Nobleford, AB, 1953-57; First, Randolph, WI, 1957-63; Springdale, ON, 1963-69; Lucknow, ON, 1969-75; Ebenezer, Leota, MN, 1975-80; Woodbridge-Maranatha, Toronto, ON, 1980-93
retired: 1993

Van't Hof, Mark Roger
b. 01/18/1961, Grand Rapids, MI
training: Calvin Theological Seminary, MDiv, 1988
ordained: 1989
charges: Westwood, Kalamazoo, MI, 1989-98; First, Denver, CO, 1998-

Van Tholen, James Robert
b. 12/16/1964, Oak Park, IL

training: Calvin Theological Seminary, MDiv, 1991
ordained: 1992
charges: Sacramento, CA, 1992-96; Rochester, NY, 1996-2000
retired: 2000
d. 01/22/2001, Rochester, NY

Van Tielen, John Leonard
b. 03/19/1874, Cincinnati, OH
training: Calvin Theological Seminary, diploma, 1900
ordained: 1900
charges: South Olive, MI, 1900-02; Spring Lake, MI, 1902-06; Hackensack, NJ, 1906-08; Sherman St., Grand Rapids, MI, 1908-11; Lamont, MI, 1911-15; Third, Muskegon, MI, 1915-21; West Sayville, NY, 1921-30; Hoboken, NJ, 1930-34
d. 07/30/1934, Hoboken, NJ

Van Til, Cornelius
b. 05/03/1895, Grootegast, Groningen, Netherlands
training: Princeton Theological Seminary, ThB, 1924; ThM, 1925; Princeton University, MA, 1927; University of Debrecen, PhD, 1938; Potchefstroom University, DD, 1983
ordained: 1927
charges: CRC: Spring Lake, MI, 1927-29; Faculty, Princeton Theological Seminary, 1929; Faculty, Westminster Theological Seminary, Philadelphia, PA, 1929-36; OPC: Faculty, Westminster Theological Seminary, Philadelphia, PA, 1933-1976
retired: 1976
d. 04/27/1987, Philadelphia, PA

Van Til, Henry R.
b. 12/23/1906, Griffith, IN
training: Westminster Theological Seminary-PA, 1936; Calvin Theological Seminary, ThB, 1937; Westminster Seminary, ThM, 1938; Vrije Universiteit, Amsterdam, diploma, 1940; University of Chicago Divinity School, 1946
ordained: 1940
charges: Sumas, WA, 1940-43; Chaplain, United States Army, 1943-46; Faculty, Calvin College, 1946-61
d. 09/28/1961, Grand Rapids, MI

Van Til, John
b. 01/14/1935, Oegstgeest, Zuid Holland, Netherlands
training: Calvin Theological Seminary, BD, 1964; MDiv, 1979
ordained: 1964
charges: Missionary pastor, Big Rapids, MI,

1964-70; Campus minister, University of Western Ontario, London, ON, 1970-75; Regional director, Central and Eastern Canada, Board of Home Missions, London, ON, 1975-2001
retired: 2001

Van Til, Kent A.
b. 11/05/1958, Highland, IN
training: Calvin Theological Seminary, MDiv, 1988
ordained: 1989
charges: Missionary, Costa Rica, 1989-97; Eligible for call, 1997-

Van't Land, Thomas John
b. 08/03/1946, Artesia, CA
training: Calvin Theological Seminary, BD, 1971
ordained: 1973
charges: Associate minister, First, Chino, CA, 1973-75; Campus minister, Purdue University, West Lafayette, IN, 1975-80; Trinity, Vancouver, WA, 1980-85; Eligible for call, 1985-

Van Tol, William
b. 12/26/1941, Inwood, IA
training: Calvin Theological Seminary, BD, 1967; MDiv, 1990
ordained: 1967
charges: Missionary, Serti, Nigeria, 1967-75; Nigerian field secretary, Board of World Missions, 1973-76; Africa area secretary, Board of World Missions, Grand Rapids, MI, 1976-85; Acting executive secretary, Board of World Missions, Grand Rapids, MI, 1985-86; Director, World Missions International, Grand Rapids, MI, 1986-97; Field director-Leadership Training, World Missions, Mexico, 1997-

Van Tuinen, Peter
b. 06/26/1909, Highland Township, Osceola, County, MI
training: Calvin Theological Seminary, ThB, 1936; Harvard Divinity School, MTh
ordained: 1941
charges: Arlene, MI, 1940-44; Pine Creek, MI, 1944-49; Leota, MN, 1949-54; Trinity, Artesia, CA, 1954-70; Granum, AB, 1970-74
retired: 1974
d. 02/15/2002, Modesto, CA

Van Vessem, Marinus
b. 04/10/1866, Cleveland, OH
training: Calvin Theological Seminary, diploma, 1887
ordained: 1887
charges: Clymer, NY, 1887-88; Home Missionary,

1888-90; Cincinnati, OH, 1890-95; Fulton, IL, 1895-97; Overisel, MI, 1897-1903; Drenthe, MI, 1903-10; Graafschap, MI, 1910-15; First, Zeeland, MI, 1915-26; Comstock, MI, 1926-28; Pastor, Pine Rest Christian Hospital, Cutlerville, MI, 1928-37
retired: 1938
d. 11/21/1945, Cutlerville, MI

Van Vlaanderen, Peter
b. 08/27/1850, Oost Souburg, Zeeland, Netherlands
training: Theologische Universiteit, Kampen, diploma, 1879
ordained: 1879
charges: GKN: Westmaas, 1879-83; Yerseke, 1883-89; CRC: First, Paterson, NJ, 1889-1904
retired: 1904
d. 10/30/1908, Rochester, NY

Van Vliet, Peter
b. 12/23/1859, Hallum, Friesland, Netherlands
training: Calvin Theological Seminary, diploma, 1888
ordained: 1888
charges: Lucas, MI, 1888-92; Munster, IN, 1892-1906; Home missionary, Doon, IA, 1906-08; Home missionary Classis Orange City, 1908-10; Ireton, IA, 1910; Bemis, SD, 1910-14; Home missionary Classis Sioux Center, 1914-17; Inwood, IA, 1917-18
d. 08/30/1918, Inwood, IA

Van Vliet, Peter D.
b. 09/14/1879, Ferwerd, Friesland, Netherlands
training: Calvin Theological Seminary, diploma, 1904
ordained: 1904
charges: Ellsworth, MI, 1904-07; Second, Grand Haven, MI, 1907-12; Lucas, MI, 1912-19; First Englewood, Chicago, IL, 1919-23; South Olive, MI, 1923-44
retired: 1944
d. 06/25/1963, Muskegon, MI

Van Weelden, James William
b. 05/17/1922, Oskaloosa, IA
training: Protestant Reformed Theological Seminary, diploma, 1944
ordained: 1945
charges: PRC: Sioux Center, IA, 1945-55; CRC: Sioux City, IA, 1955-60; Red Deer, AB, 1960-66; First, Chatham, ON, 1966-73; Mountainview, Grimsby, ON, 1973-84
retired: 1984

Van Wesep, Hermanus
b. 01/01/1858, Amsterdam, Noord Holland, Netherlands
training: declared eligible on the basis of exceptional gifts, 1895
ordained: 1895
charges: GKN: Hulpprediker Amsterdam, 1883-94; CRC: Teaching elder, Le Mars, IA, 1894-95; Le Mars IA, 1895-96; Wright, IA, 1896-1907; Noordeloos, MI, 1907-18
retired: 1918
d. 09/23/1929, Grand Rapids, MI.

Van Winkle, Clyde K.
b. 06/18/1935, Everett, WA
training: Calvin Theological Seminary, BD, 1963
ordained: 1963
charges: Holland, IA, 1963-66; Cottage Grove, South Holland, IL, 1966-71; Honolulu, HI, 1971-75; St. Joseph, MI, 1975-80
d. 11/04/1980, St. Joseph, MI

Van Wolde, Arthur John
b. 03/06/1966, Chicago, IL
training: Calvin Theological Seminary, MDiv, 1998
ordained: 1998
charges: Bunde, MN, 1998-

Van Wyhe, Arthur Lee
b. 12/05/1942, Hull, IA
training: Calvin Theological Seminary, BD, 1968
ordained: 1968
charges: Missionary, Kansas City, MO, 1968-73; Washington, PA, 1973-78; Second, Allendale, MI, 1978-86; Calvin, Spokane, WA, 1986-90; Dorr, MI, 1990-2000; Montello Park, Holland, MI, 2000-

Van Wyk, Case Gilbert
b. 10/21/1943, Hoofddorp, Noord Holland, Netherlands
training: Reformed Bible College, BRE, 1988; Calvin Theological Seminary, MDiv, 1991
ordained: 1991
charges: Missionary, Nigeria, 1991-97; Eligible for call, 1997-98; Grant, MI, 1998-

Van Wyk, Henry Cornelius Jr.
b. 10/27/1923, Grand Rapids, MI
training: Calvin Theological Seminary, BD, 1957
ordained: 1957
charges: Luverne, MN, 1957-61; Fourth Roseland, Chicago, IL, 1961-64; Hillcrest, Hudsonville, MI, 1964-71; Drenthe, MI, 1971-79; Lee St., Wyoming, MI, 1979-89
retired: 1989

Van Wyk, Kenneth E.
b. 04/15/1947, Otley, IA
training: Calvin Theological Seminary, BD, 1972
ordained: 1972
charges: McBain, MI, 1972-79; Haven, Zeeland, MI, 1979-96; First, Cutlerville, MI, 1996-

Van Wyk, William (Willem) Peter
b. 12/03/1874, Haarlemmermeer, Noord Holland, Netherlands
training: Calvin Theological Seminary, diploma, 1902
ordained: 1902
charges: New Holland, SD, 1902-04; Sioux Center, IA, 1904-11; Oakdale Park, Grand Rapids, MI, 1911-22; Second, Orange City, IA, 1922-25; Eastern Ave., Grand Rapids, MI, 1925-41
retired: 1941
d. 06/28/1943, Cutlerville, MI

Van Zalen, Timothy E.
b. 07/21/1958, Grand Rapids, MI
training: Calvin Theological Seminary, MDiv, 1994
ordained: 1995
charges: Hawarden, IA, 1995-98; Cascade Fellowship, Grand Rapids, MI, 1998-

Van Zanen, Steven James
b. 06/08/1960, Lakewood, CA
training: Calvin Theological Seminary, MDiv, 1990; ThM, 1991
ordained: 1990
charges: Raymond, MN, 1990-97; Faculty, Babes-Bolyai University, Missionary, Romania, 1997-99; Faculty, Lithuania Christian College, Klaipeda, Lithuania, 1999-

Van Zanten, Anthony
b. 11/11/1938, Rock Valley, IA
training: Calvin Theological Seminary, ThB, 1965
ordained: 1965
charges: Madison Ave., Paterson, NJ, 1965-76; Roseland Christian Ministries, Chicago, IL, 1976-

Van Zee, Cornelius L.
b. 09/11/1914, Jasper County, IA
training: Calvin Theological Seminary, BD, 1945
ordained: 1945
charges: CRC: Associate pastor, LaGrave Ave., Grand Rapids, MI, 1945-46; Hancock, MN, (loaned to Chaplaincy Corps, USN, 1945-46) 1946-60; Non-ministerial vocation, 1960
d. 01/17/1991, Renville, MN

Van Zomeren, Ronald L.
b. 06/17/1940, Pella, IA
training: Calvin Theological Seminary, BD, 1972
ordained: 1973
charges: Oak Harbor, WA, 1973-77; Hollandale, MN, 1977-83; Lexington Green, Kalamazoo, MI, 1983-87; Non-ministerial vocation, 1987

Varela, Gilbert
b. 12/10/1960, Heredia, Costa Rica
training: National Presbyterian Theological Seminary, Mexico, BTh, 1986; International Theological Seminary, ThM, 1988; Calvin Theological Seminary, ThM, 1989
ordained: 1987
charges: National Presbyterian Church of Mexico: Pastor, 1982-87; Faculty, Evangelical Methodist Theological Seminary, Costa Rica, 1990-92; Pastor and Faculty, Gonzalo Baez Camargo Theological Seminary, Mexico, 1992-94; CRC: Sol del Valle, Sun Valley, CA, 1995-

Varga, Ferenc
b. 11/02/1955, Satoraljaujhely, Hungary
training: Calvin Theological Seminary, MDiv, 1992
ordained: 1993
charges: Tracy, IA, 1993-96; Hope Community, Indianapolis, IN, 1996-2001, on loan to Hungarian Reformed, Allen Park, MI, 2001-

Vasquez, Hector
training: declared eligible on the basis of exceptional gifts, 2002
ordained: 2002
charges: Spirit and Truth Fellowship, Philadelphia, PA, 1990-

Veenema, Michael
b. 06/27/1953, Lunenburg, NS
training: Calvin Theological Seminary, MDiv, 1989
ordained: 1989
charges: Bethel, Newmarket, ON, 1989-92; Fredericton, NB, 1992-95; Campus ministry, University of Western Ontario and Fanshaw College, London, ON, 1995-

Veeneman, Gerrit Johannes
b. 10/21/1948, Lacombe, AB
training: Calvin Theological Seminary, MDiv, 1980
ordained: 1980
charges: Bethel, Listowel, ON, 1980-86; Fruitland, ON, 1986-92; Trinity, Abbotsford, BC, 1992-97
retired: 1997

Veeneman, Ryan Walter

b. 07/17/1953, Grand Haven, MI
training: Calvin Theological Seminary, MDiv, 1983
ordained: 1983
charges: Missionary, Dominican Republic, 1983-88; Eligible for call, 1988-90; Chaplain, Alcohol Outpatient Service-PROST, Fremont, MI, 1990-2000; New Hope Church, Grand Rapids, MI, 2000-

Veenstra, Alvin Paul

b. 02/12/1931, Moline, MI
training: Calvin Theological Seminary, BD, 1955
ordained: 1955
charges: CRC: Hamilton, MI, 1955-60; Chula Vista, CA, 1960-78; Independent: Chula Vista, CA, 1978-81; RCA: Community, Chula Vista, CA, 1981-2000
retired: 2000

Veenstra, Anson

b. 12/01/1960, Oskaloosa, IA
training: Calvin Theological Seminary, MDiv, 1993
ordained: 1993
charges: Wisconsin Rapids, WI, 1993-2000; Des Moines, IA, 2000-

Veenstra, Conrad R.

b. 03/02/1898, Grand Rapids, MI
training: Calvin Theological Seminary, ThB, 1930
ordained: 1930
charges: Waupun, WI, 1930-40, Grant, MI, 1940-46; Alameda, CA, 1946-51; First, Oskaloosa, IA, 1951-57; Hospers, IA, 1957-65
retired: 1965
d. 10/04/1969, Sioux City, IA

Veenstra, Gerrit Paul Jr.

b. 06/05/1946, Grand Rapids, MI
training: Calvin Theological Seminary, BD, 1973; MDiv, 1978
ordained: 1973
charges: Lamont, MI, 1973-78; Westwood, Kalamazoo, MI, 1978-85; Maple Heights, Cleveland, OH, 1985-92; Bethel, Zeeland, MI, 1992-99; Bethel, Lansing, IL, 1999-

Veenstra, John

b. 12/21/1941, Alkmaar, Noord Holland, Netherlands
training: Calvin Theological Seminary, BD, 1968
ordained: 1970
charges: John Calvin, Truro, NS, 1970-74; Campus Worship Community, Toronto, ON, 1974-80;

New Life, Pickering, ON, 1997-98; eligible for call, 1998-99; Zion, Oshawa, ON, 1999-

Veenstra, Paul Jay

b. 11/12/1925, Atwood, MI
training: Calvin Theological Seminary, ThB, 1952
ordained: 1952
charges: Rock Rapids, IA, 1952-61; Comstock Park, MI, 1961-75; Ogilvie, MN, 1975-87
retired: 1987

Veenstra, Ralph John

b. 05/05/1966, Bedum, Groningen, Netherlands
training: Calvin Theological Seminary, MDiv, 1992; ThM, 1994
ordained: 1995
charges: CRC: Director of evangelism and member assimilation, Caledonia, MI, 1990-91; Missionary, Dominican Republic, 1995-2000; RCA: New Life Community, Artesia, CA, 2000-

Veenstra, Rolf Lindemulder

b. 05/20/1913, Grand Rapids, MI
training: Calvin Theological Seminary, ThB, 1939
ordained: 1939
charges: Hope, Grandville, MI, 1939-41; East Muskegon, MI, 1941-46; Bethel, Grand Rapids, MI, 1946-52; First, Cicero, IL, 1952-57; Missionary to Nigeria, 1957-64; Faculty, Reformed Bible College, Grand Rapids, MI, 1964-69; Rehoboth, NM, 1969-79
retired: 1979
d. 12/29/1990, Rehoboth, NM

Veenstra, Willem

b. 09/25/1868, Paterson, NJ
training: Calvin Theological Seminary, diploma, 1901
ordained: 1901
charges: Zutphen, 1901-02
d. 04/05/1902, Zutphen, MI

Veenstra, William Cecil

b. 08/25/1951, Ureterp, Friesland, Netherlands
training: Calvin Theological Seminary, MDiv, 1977
ordained: 1977
charges: Ingersoll, ON, 1977-82; Clarkston, Mississauga, ON, 1982-92; Maple Ridge, BC, 1992-2001; Canadian Ministries Director, Burlington, ON, 2001-

Veldman, Harold Edward

b. 01/02/1959, Grand Rapids, MI
training: Calvin Theological Seminary, MDiv, 1990
ordained: 1990

charges: Godwin Heights, Grand Rapids, MI, 1990-97; Oak Harbor, WA, 1997-

Veldman, Richard (originally only R.)
b. 04/16/1889, Groningen, Groningen, Netherlands
training: Calvin Theological Seminary, diploma, 1914; Princeton Seminary, BD, 1917; University of Chicago, AM, 1918
ordained: 1918
charges: Prospect Park, Holland, MI, 1918-20; Prospect Park, Paterson, NJ, 1920-27; West Leonard, Grand Rapids, MI, 1927-48; Estelline, SD, 1949-58
retired: 1958
d. 02/26/1975, Volga, SD

Veldman, Richard J.
b. 11/11/1905, Chicago, IL
training: Protestant Reformed Theological Seminary, diploma, 1929
ordained: 1930
charges: PRC: Sioux Center, IA, 1930-37; Roosevelt Park, Grand Rapids, MI, 1937-39; First, Grand Rapids, MI, 1939-44; Fourth, Grand Rapids, MI, 1944-62; CRC: First, Oak Lawn, IL, 1962-70
retired: 1970; affiliated with Beverly Independent Church, 1993
d. 03/05/1994, Grand Rapids, MI

Vellekoop, Martin John
b. 08/12/1960, Peterborough, ON
training: Calvin Theological Seminary, MDiv, 1987
ordained: 1987
charges: Missionary, Japan, 1987-89; Eligible for call, 1989-90; Zion, Pembroke, ON, 1990-94; Millbrook, Grand Rapids, MI, 1994-2001; Maple Ridge, BC, 2001-

Vellinga, Henry Raimond
b. 05/25/1936, Chatham, ON
training: Calvin Theological Seminary, BD, 1961
ordained: 1961
charges: CRC: Minster of evangelism, Hope, Oak Forest, IL, 1961-64; Hope, Oak Forest, IL, 1964-82; left the denomination

Velthoen, Adrianas
b. 12/19/1927, Rotterdam, Zuid Holland, Netherlands
training: Calvin Theological Seminary, BD, 1969
ordained: 1969
charges: CRC: Hebron, Renfrew, ON, 1969-74; GKN: Augustinusga and Surhuizum, 1974-81; Gramsbergen, 1981-89

retired: 1989

Velthuizen, Barton Peter
b. 08/22/1957, Edmonton, AB
training: Calvin Theological Seminary, MDiv, 1985
ordained: 1985
charges: Hebron, Renfrew, ON, 1985-92; Hagersville Community, Hagersville, ON, 1992-

Velthuizen, Dirk
b. 05/12/1930, Doorn, Utrecht, Netherlands
training: Calvin Theological Seminary, BD, 1969
ordained: 1969
charges: Telkwa, BC, 1969-73; Brooks and Vauxhall, BC, 1973-78; Drayton, ON, 1978-88; First, Kemptville, ON, 1988-95
retired: 1995

Veltkamp, Albert James
b. 07/10/1925, Bozeman, MT
training: Calvin Theological Seminary, ThB, 1851; MDiv, 1977
ordained: 1951
charges: Luctor, KS, 1951-55; Home missionary at Calvin, Spokane, WA, 1955-70; Fellowship, Albuquerque, NM, 1970-90
retired: 1990

Veltkamp, Lambertus
b. 01/28/1876, Burum, Friesland, Netherlands
training: Calvin Theological Seminary, diploma, 1901
ordained: 1901
charges: Lamont, MI, 1901-04; Second, Grand Haven, MI, 1904-06; Franklin St., Grand Rapids, MI 1906-18; Coldbrook Ave., Grand Rapids, MI, 1918-25; Central Ave., Holland, MI, 1925-37; Drenthe, MI, 1937-42
retired: 1942
d. 02/06/1952, Drenthe, MI

Veltkamp, Lawrence Edward
b. 02/17/1913, Grand Rapids, MI
training: Calvin Theological Seminary, BD, 1938
ordained: 1938
charges: Dorr, MI, 1938-42; Montello Park, Holland, MI, 1942-46; Sherman St., Grand Rapids, MI, 1946-49; Bethany, Muskegon, MI, 1949-62; Shawnee Park, Grand Rapids, MI, 1962-74; Harderwyk, Holland, MI, 1977-79; Independent: Christ Church, Oak Brook, IL, 1974-77 (while on leave)
retired: 1979
d. 10/14/1984, Holland, MI

Veltman, Johannes (Joe)
b. 07/23/1948, Blija, Friesland, Netherlands
training: Calvin Theological Seminary, MDiv, 1975
ordained: 1975
charges: CRC: Hebron, Renfrew, ON, 1975-79;
Brooks, AB, 1979-86; Riverside, Wellandport, ON,
1986-89; RCA: Community, Maitland, ON, 1989

Veltman, Nelson Lantinga
b. 09/01/1912, Eastmanville, MI
training: Calvin Theological Seminary, ThB, 1938
ordained: 1938
charges: Prairie City, IA, 1938-43; Drenthe, MI,
1943-47; Whitinsville, MA, 1948-53; Boston
Square, Grand Rapids, MI, 1953-62; Highland
Hills, Grand Rapids, MI, 1962-67; Third,
Kalamazoo, MI, 1967-73; Walnut Creek, CA,
1973-77
retired: 1977
d. 07/06/1989, Zeeland, MI

Veltman, Peter
b. 01/11/1945, Blija, Friesland, Netherlands
training: Calvin Theological Seminary, BD, 1972
ordained: 1974
charges: Raymond, MN, 1974-81; Lake City, MI,
1981-83; Eligible for call, 1983-85; Emo, ON,
1985-94; Faith, Burlington, ON, 1994-97;
Cochrane, ON, 1997-2000
retired: 2000

Venegas, Dante A.
b. 10/05/1933, New York, NY
training: declared eligible on the basis of exceptional gifts, 1981
ordained: 1981
charges: Madison Square, Grand Rapids, MI,
1978-96; Director, Chaplaincy Service, Alternative
Directions, Grand Rapids, MI, 1996-99; City Hope,
Grand Rapids, MI, 1999-2002
retired: 2002

Venegas, Hugo
b. 09/24/1964, San Jose, Costa Rica
training: Denver Theological Seminary, MDiv,
1992
ordained: 1998
charges: Ewa Beach, HI, 1999-

Venema, Alvin Harold
b. 10/15/1926, Granville, IA
training: Calvin Theological Seminary, BD, 1954
ordained: 1955
charges: Kitchener, ON, 1955-58; St. Catharines,
ON, 1958-63; Richmond, BC, 1963-69; First,

Manhattan, MT, 1969-72; First, Brantford, ON,
1972-78; Shalom, Brantford, ON, 1978; West End,
Edmonton, AB, 1978-79; Covenant, Edmonton, AB,
1979-86
retired: 1986

Venema, Cornelis Paul
b. 04/25/1954, Sioux Center, IA
training: Calvin Theological Seminary, BD, 1978;
Princeton Theological Seminary, ThD, 1982
ordained: 1982
charges: Ontario, CA, 1982-88; Faculty, Mid
America Reformed Seminary, Dyer, IN, 1988-

Venema, Henry Albert
b. 11/28/1921, Hospers, IA
training: Westminster Theological Seminary-PA,
ThM, 1948
ordained: 1948
charges: Immanuel, Grand Rapids, MI, 1948-52;
First, Sarnia, ON, 1952-55; Second, Toronto, ON,
1955-64; West End, Edmonton, AB, 1964-68;
Rogers Heights, Grand Rapids, MI, 1968-70; Second, Sarnia, ON, 1970-72
d. 01/31/1972, Sarnia, ON

Venema, Richard James
b. 04/15/1922, Granville, IA
training: Calvin Theological Seminary, BD, 1954;
Northern Baptist Theological Seminary, DMin,
1981
ordained: 1954
charges: Bethel, Sioux Center, IA, 1954-58; Missionary to New Zeeland, 1958-64; Harderwyk,
Holland, MI, 1964-66; Missionary, Friendship
House, San Francisco, CA, 1966-70; First, Pella,
IA, 1970-75; First, South Holland, IL, 1975-80;
First, Chino, CA, 1980-86
retired: 1986; affiliated with United Reformed
Churches, 1995

Venhuizen, Steven Wayne
b. 04/05/1962, Beaver Dam, WI
training: Calvin Theological Seminary, MTS, 1993;
MDiv, 1998
ordained: 1999
charges: Grace, Grand Rapids, MI, 1999-2002

Verboon, Arthur Lenard
b. 09/12/1962, Brantford, ON
training: Calvin Theological Seminary, MDiv, 1997
ordained: 1997
charges: Maranatha, Edmonton, AB, 1997-

Verbrugge, John Cornelius

b. 09/03/1909, Chandler, MN
training: Westminster Theological Seminary-PA, 1935; Calvin College, Special Program for Ministerial Candidacy 1936
ordained: 1937
charges: Sioux Falls, SD, 1936-40; First, Grand Haven, MI, 1940-43; Chaplain, USA, 1943-46; First, Lynden, WA, 1946-51; Second, Edmonton, AB, 1951-55; Chatham, ON, 1955-60; Bowmanville, ON, 1960-66; Rochester, NY, 1966-70; Second, Randolph, WI, 1970-74
retired: 1974
d. 11/29/1984, Grand Rapids, MI

Verbrugge, Verlyn David

b. 09/04/1942, Grand Haven, MI
training: Calvin Theological Seminary, BD, 1968; ThM, 1979
ordained: 1968
charges: Leighton, IA, 1968-72; Southern Heights, Kalamazoo, MI, 1972-85; Leave, 1985-89; Theological editor, Zondervan Corp., Grand Rapids, MI, 1989-

Verbruggen, Mark Neil

b. 03/09/1969, Brockville, ON
training: Calvin Theological Seminary, MDiv, 1995
ordained: 1995
charges: Georgetown, ON, 1995-

Ver Burg, Alvin Percy

b. 11/11/1933, Inwood, IA
training: Calvin Theological Seminary, BD, 1961
ordained: 1961
charges: CRC: Edson, AB, 1961-64; Orangewood, Phoenix, AZ, 1964-68; Missionary, Calvary, Vermillion, SD, 1968-72; Pastor, Hills, MN, 1997

Verburg, Arthur John

b. 09/02/1927, Grand Rapids, MI
training: Calvin Theological Seminary, BD, 1952
ordained: 1952
charges: Hartley, IA, 1952-56; Ada, MI, 1956-65; Jamestown, MI, 1965-71; Oak Glen, Lansing, IL, 1971-93
retired: 1993, affiliated with United Reformed Churches, 1996

Verduin, Henry

b. 04/25/1889, New Holland, SD
training: Calvin Theological Seminary, diploma, 1918; Princeton, 1919
ordained: 1919
charges: Purewater SD, 1919-21; Detroit, MI,

1921-26; Creston, Grand Rapids, MI, 1926-46; Overisel, MI, 1946-53; Peoria, IA, 1953-59
retired: 1959
d. 02/16/1971, Youngstown, AZ

Verduin, Leonard

b. 03/09/1897, South Holland, IL
training: Calvin Theological Seminary, ThB, 1929
ordained: 1930
charges: Corsica, SD, 1929-41; Chapel, Ann Arbor, MI, 1941-62
retired: 1962
d. 11/10/1999, Payson, AZ

Ver Heul, Stanley Eugene

b. 05/14/1944, Oskaloosa, IA
training: Calvin Theological Seminary, BD, 1970; MDiv, 1977
ordained: 1971
charges: Dispatch, KS, 1971-73; IVCF minister, Univ. of Colorado and Colorado State University, 1973-80; Community, Los Angeles, CA, 1980-

Verhey, Allen Dale

b. 05/14/1945, Grand Rapids, MI
training: Calvin Theological Seminary, Special Program for Ministerial Candidacy
ordained: 1975
charges: CRC: Faculty, Hope College, Holland, MI, 1975-92; Director, Institute of Religion, Texas Medical Center, Houston, TX, 1992-94; Faculty, Hope College, Holland, MI, 1994-95; RCA: Faculty, Hope College, Holland, MI, 1995

Verhoef, William (Willem)

b. 07/16/1943, Amsterdam, Noord Holland, Netherlands
training: Calvin Theological Seminary, BD, 1972
ordained: 1973
charges: Corsica, SD, 1973-77; Parkview Heights, Cincinnati, OH, 1977-82; Highland Ave., Redlands, CA, 1982-90; Second, Denver, CO, 1990-2002; The River, Redlands, CA, 2002-

Verhulst, Eric Brant

b. 07/18/1964, Grand Rapids, MI
training: Calvin Theological Seminary, MDiv, 1991
ordained: 1991
charges: Hull, ND, 1991-95; Chaplain, United States Navy, 1995-

Verhulst, Kenneth J.

b. 09/26/1940, Chicago, IL
training: Calvin Theological Seminary, BD, 1966
ordained: 1966

charges: Nobleford, AB, 1966-71; Lighthouse, Inner city ministry, Toronto, ON, 1971-77; Peace Community, Calgary, AB, 1977-85: Christ Community, East Islip, NY, 1985-

Verhulst, Peter T.
b. 01/26/1964, Sheboygan, WI
training: Calvin Theological Seminary, MDiv, 1991
ordained: 1991
charges: Youth director, Mayfair, Grand Rapids, MI, 1989-90; Mayfair, Grand Rapids, MI, 1991-98; Brookfield, WI, 1998-

Verhulst, Theodore Peter
b. 06/07/1906, Sheboygan, WI
training: Calvin Theological Seminary, BD, 1934
ordained: 1934
charges: Hollandale, MN, 1934-38; Archer Ave., Chicago, IL, 1938-43; Second, Pella, IA, 1943-48; Graafschap, MI, 1948-52; Bethel, Lynden, WA, 1952-55
d. 03/23/1955, Sheboygan, WI

Verkaik, Richard Henry
b. 07/28/1951, Grand Rapids, MI
training: Calvin Theological Seminary, MCE, 1979; Western Theological Seminary, MDiv, 1989
ordained: 1989
charges: CRC: Director of youth and evangelism, Hillcrest, Hudsonville, MI, 1984-89; Friendship Chapel, Jenison, MI, 1995-2002; RCA: Clinical pastoral education Internship, Pine Rest Christian Hospital, Cutlerville, MI, 1989-90; North Atlanta Community, Roswell, GA, 1990-91; Hudsonville, MI, 1991-95

Vermaat, Peter Edward
b. 09/02/1935, Grand Rapids, MI
training: Calvin Theological Seminary, BD, 1960
ordained: 1960
charges: Home missionary, Bellingham, WA, 1960-64; Valley, Binghamton, NY, 1964-84; Nonministerial vocation, 1984

Vermaire, Mark Donald
b. 05/27/1953, Grand Rapids, MI
training: Fuller Theological Seminary, MDiv, 1982; Calvin Theological Seminary, ThM, 1988
ordained: 1984
charges: Sherman St., Grand Rapids, MI, 1984-99; Crossroads, San Marcos, CA, 1999-

Vermaire, Paul Louis
b. 03/15/1925, Grand Rapids, MI
training: Calvin Theological Seminary, BD, 1959

ordained: 1959
charges: Zutphen, MI, 1959-63; Westview, Grand Rapids, MI, 1963-73; Regional Home Missionary for Mideast, Board of Home Missions, 1973-90
retired: 1990
d. 01/18/1991, Grand Rapids, MI

Vermeer, John Anthony
b. 01/24/1961, Bellflower, CA
training: Westminster Theological Seminary-CA, MDiv, 1989; Calvin Theological Seminary, Special Program for Ministerial Candidacy, 1990
ordained: 1990
charges: CRC: Dispatch, KS, 1990-95; First, Sheldon, IA, 1995-2002; Resigned from the denomination

Vermeer, Robert Bruce
b. 12/31/1927, Alameda, CA
training: Calvin Theological Seminary, BD, 1953
ordained: 1953
charges: Delavan WI, 1953-58; First, Denver, CO, 1958-66; Maple Ave., Holland, MI, 1966-73; Bethel, Lynden, WA, 1973-81; Bakersfield, CA, 1981-85; Wright, Kanawha, IA, 1985-93
retired: 1993
d. 01/05/1999, Lynden, WA

Ver Meer, Wilbur (Bud)
b. 01/07/1922, Pella, IA
training: Calvin Theological Seminary, BD, 1962
ordained: 1962
charges: Bethel, Fulton, IL, 1962-64; Archer Ave., Chicago, IL, 1964-69; Colton, SD, 1969-72; Trinity, Sparta, MI, 1972-74; Pioneer, Cedar Springs, MI, 1974-76
retired: 1976
d. 11/08/1985, Pella, IA

Verseput, Theodore
b. 07/12/1927, Calhoun County, MI
training: Calvin Theological Seminary, BD, 1953
ordained: 1953
charges: Park Lane, Evergreen Park, IL, 1953-57; Miami, FL, 1957-62; Hillcrest, Denver, CO, 1962-68; East Muskegon, MI, 1968-85; Director of pastoral service, Hope Rehabilitation Network, Grand Rapids, MI, 1985-86; Director, Committee on Disability Concerns, Grand Rapids, MI, 1986-92
retired: 1992

Versfelt, John
b. 03/16/1924, Rotterdam, Zuid Holland, Netherlands
training: Calvin Theological Seminary, BD, 1967

ordained: 1967
charges: CRC: Missionary, Prince George, BC, 1967–70; Penticton, BC, 1970–74; High River, AB, 1974–75; Resigned from denomination, 1981; Pastor, Chase, BC

Versluys, James Edward
b. 06/16/1932, Grand Rapids, MI
training: Calvin Theological Seminary, BD, 1957; MDiv, 1985
ordained: 1957
charges: Missionary at Jackson, MI, 1957–63; Des Moines, IA, 1963–67; Bakersfield, CA, 1967–75; Trinity, Denver, CO, 1975–83; Trinity, Mount Pleasant, MI, 1983–93; West Olive, MI, 1993–96
retired: 1996

Versluys, William II
b. 03/10/1946, Grand Rapids, MI
training: Calvin Theological Seminary, MDiv, 1981
ordained: 1981
charges: Missionary, Molo, Iloilo City, Philippines, 1981–85; Jackson, MI, 1985–90; Community, Saginaw, MI, 1990–97; Bethel, Princeton, MN, 1997–2000; eligible for call, 2000–2002; Interim, Hancock, MN, 2002–

Versteeg, William
b. 10/20/1955, Edmonton, AB
training: Calvin Theological Seminary, MDiv, 1987
ordained: 1988
charges: Bethel, Saskatoon, SK, 1988–93; Bethlehem, Thunder Bay, ON, 1993–2002; Immanuel, Langley, BC, 2002–

Verwolf, William
b. 07/22/1906, Manhattan, MT
training: Calvin Theological Seminary, BD, 1932
ordained: 1933
charges: CPC: Pictou, NS, 1932–37; Summerside, PE, 1937–42; CRC: Milwaukee, WI, 1942–46; Des Moines, IA, 1946–49; Sumas, WA, 1949–57; Park Lane, Evergreen Park, IL, 1957–66; Rock Rapids, IA, 1966–69; Missionary, Fairbanks, AK, 1969–72
retired: 1972
d. 03/04/1996, Lynden, WA

Vigh, Julius Jr.
b. 06/14/1934, Budapest, Hungary
training: Calvin Theological Seminary, BD, 1964
ordained: 1964
charges: Bethel, Redlands, CA, 1964–70; Fresno, CA, 1970–78; Portland, MI, 1978–81; Portland, MI and Dildine Community, Ionia, MI, 1981–84; New Life, Ionia, MI, 1984–91; Leave, 1991–95

retired: 1995

Vilaylack, Sysay
b. 07/07/1957, Laos
training: declared eligible on the basis of exceptional gifts, 1991
ordained: 1991
charges: Life in Christ: Fountain Valley, CA, 1984–87, Huntington Beach, CA, 1987–88 Moreno Valley, CA, 1988–89; Vientiane Laotian, Westminster, CA, 1989–90; CRC: Vientiane Laotian, Moreno Valley, CA, 1989–

Villanueva, Milton
b. 07/25/1950, Arecibo, Puerto Rico
training: Seminario Biblico Alianza, Guayaquil, Ecuador, BA, 1970
ordained: 1997
charges: PCA: Iglesia Alianza Cristian y Misionera, Cruce Davilla, Barceloneto, Puerto Rico, 1972–76; Villa Pameras, Sanurce, Peurto Rico, 1976–88; Tampa, FL, 1988–90; Iglesia Unidia, Tampa, FL, 1990–93; Iglesia Presbiterianna, Tampa, FL, 1993–96; CRC: Comunidad de Cristo, Hialeah, FL, 1997–99; Hialeah Comunidad Christiana, Hialeah, FL, 1999–2001; Itinerant preacher, Puerto Rico, 2001–

Vink, Case Herman
b. 11/12/1950, Harmelen, Utrecht, Netherlands
training: Calvin Theological Seminary, MDiv, 1979
ordained: 1980
charges: Fellowship, Brighton, ON, 1980–83; Evergreen, Fort McMurray, AB, 1983–90; Leave, 1990–91; Special Pastoral Education, Royal Alexandria Hospital, Edmonton, AB, 1991–92; Ottewell, Edmonton, AB, 1992–95; Coordinator of training, Royal Alexandra Hospital, Edmonton, AB, 1995–

Vink, George Goris
b. 10/25/1944, Zaandam, Noord Holland, Netherlands
training: Calvin Theological Seminary, MDiv, 1975
ordained: 1975
charges: Vernon, BC, 1975–80; First, Manhattan, MT, 1980–86; Ivanrest, Grandville, MI, 1986–93; First, Visalia, CA, 1993–

Vis, Kenneth Wayne
b. 07/11/1942, Rock Valley, IA
training: Calvin Theological Seminary, BD, 1967
ordained: 1967
charges: Hawarden, IA, 1967–71; 36th St., Wyoming, MI, 1971–79; Trinity, Fremont, MI, 1979–84; Spring Lake, MI, 1984–97; Eligible for call, 1997–

Vis, Peter W.

b. 11/19/1912, Hull, IA
training: Protestant Reformed Theological Seminary, diploma, 1939
ordained: 1939
charges: PRC: Rock Valley, IA, 1939-48; Manhattan, MT, 1948-58; Oskaloosa, IA, 1958-61; CRC: Raymond, MN, 1961-70; First, Randolph, WI, 1970-77
retired: 1977
d. 10/18/1984, Grand Rapids, MI

Vis, William Dean

b. 04/15/1945, Orange City, IA
training: Reformed Theological Seminary, MDiv, 1980; Calvin Theological Seminary, Special Program for Ministerial Candidacy, 1982
ordained: 1982
charges: Hills, MN, 1982-84; Gallatin Gateway, Bozeman, MT, 1984-91; Enumclaw, WA, 1991-95; Granum, AB, 1995-2002; Colton, SD, 2002-

Vis, William Garret

b. 06/07/1952, Pipestone, MN
training: Calvin Theological Seminary, MDiv, 1979
ordained: 1979
charges: Bethel, Marion, SD, 1979-83; Archer Ave., Chicago, IL, 1983-87; Ft. Lauderdale, FL, 1987-93; Pleasant St., Whitinsville, MA, 1993-

Visker, Nathan Alan

b. 05/25/1974, Grand Rapids, MI
training: Calvin Theological Seminary, MDiv, 2002
charges: The River, Durham, NC, 2003-

Visker, Roger Jay

b. 03/30/1954, Kalamazoo, MI
training: Calvin Theological Seminary, MDiv, 1996
ordained: 1996
charges: Blythefield, Rockford, MI, 1996-2002; Valley Community, Napa, CA, 2002-

Viss, Simon Jr.

b. 12/02/1907, Oak Harbor, WA
training: Calvin Theological Seminary, ThB, 1947
ordained: 1947
charges: Luctor, KS, 1947-50; Prinsburg, MN, 1950-57; New Era, MI, 1957-62; Houston, BC, 1962-67; Transcona, Winnipeg, MB, 1967-72
retired: 1973
d. 08/30/1999, Ripon, CA

Visscher, Bernard E.

b. 12/05/1906, Fremont, MI
training: Calvin Theological Seminary, BD, 1935

ordained: 1935
charges: Ackley, IA, 1935-40; Vogel Center, MI, 1940-48; Calvin, Wyckoff, NJ, 1948-50; Ocheyedan, IA, 1950-56; First, Wellsburg, IA, 1956-65; Alamosa, CO, 1965-72
retired: 1972
d. 01/28/1988, Alamosa, CO

Visscher, Henry

b. 12/31/1930, Platte, SD
training: Calvin Theological Seminary, BD, 1955
ordained: 1955
charges: Dispatch, KS, 1955-59; Westwood, Kalamazoo, MI, 1959-64; Walnut Creek, CA, 1964-73; Non-ministerial vocation, 1973

Visser, Dale William

b. 12/12/1960, Upland, CA
training: Calvin Theological Seminary, MDiv, 1991
ordained: 1991
charges: Lebanon, IA, 1991-98; Raymond, MN, 1998-

Visser, Duane A.

b. 03/19/1941, Doon, IA
training: Calvin Theological Seminary, ThB, 1965
ordained: 1966
charges: Fresno, CA, 1966-70; Chaplain, Calvary Rehabilitation Center, Phoenix, AZ, 1970-73; Chaplain, Pine Rest Christian Hospital, Cutlerville, MI, 1973-85; Department Chair and Clinical pastoral education Supervisor, Pine Rest Christian Hospital, Cutlerville, MI, 1985-92; Chaplain, Loyola University Medical Center, Maywood, IL, 1992-95; Director, Pastor Church Relations, Grand Rapids, MI, 1995-

Visser, Edward Charles

b. 02/02/1960, Grand Rapids, MI
training: Calvin Theological Seminary, MDiv, 1987
ordained: 1987
charges: Calvin, Le Mars, IA, 1987-95; Fellowship, Big Rapids, MI, 1995-

Visser, Edward Fred

b. 02/24/1904, Holland, MI
training: Calvin Theological Seminary, ThB, 1935
ordained: 1935
charges: Hills, MN, 1936-38; Doon, IA, 1938-42; First, Grand Rapids, MI, 1942-51; First, Highland, IN, 1951-56; First, Hudsonville, MI, 1956-62; Wayland, MI, 1962-68; Bethel, Edgerton, MN, 1968-71
retired: 1971
d. 04/16/1981, Jenison, MI

Visser, Edward Wieger
b. 11/15/1950, Dunnville, ON
training: Calvin Theological Seminary, MDiv, 1981
ordained: 1981
charges: First, Regina, SK, 1981-88; Ebenezer,
Trenton, ON, 1988-96; Westside Fellowship,
Kingston, ON, 1996-

Visser, John
b. 11/11/1947, 's-Gravendeel, Zuid Holland, Netherlands
training: Calvin Theological Seminary, BD, 1972
ordained: 1972
charges: Barrhead-Westlock, AB, 1972-79;
Kentville, NS, 1979-85; Maranatha, Belleville, ON,
1985-

Visser, John William
b. 04/18/1917, Hull, IA
training: Calvin Theological Seminary, BD, 1943
ordained: 1943
charges: Otley, IA, 1943-47; Zutphen, MI, 1947-
52; First, Ripon, CA, 1952-55; East Leonard,
Grand Rapids, MI, 1955-61; Non-ministerial vocation: social work, Grand Rapids, MI, 1962-92, retired

Visser, Norman James
b. 07/18/1961, Guelph, ON
training: Calvin Theological Seminary, MDiv, 1989
ordained: 1989
charges: Colton, SD, 1989-97; Kentville, NS,
1997-

Vissia, Jacob A.
b. 12/16/1880, Heerenveen, Friesland,
Netherlands
training: Calvin Theological Seminary, diploma,
1911
ordained: 1911
charges: Prairie City, IA, 1911-15; Redlands, CA,
1915-19
retired: 1919
d. 09/11/1924, Santa Ana Canyon, CA

Vlaardingerbroek, Hank F.
b. 03/01/1944, Den Haag, Zuid Holland, Netherlands
training: Calvin Theological Seminary, MDiv, 1981
ordained: 1981
charges: East Palmyra, NY, 1981-86; Drenthe, MI,
1986-97; West 44th St., Wyoming, MI, 1997-

Vogelzang, Nicholas
b. 02/13/1919, Holland, MI

training: Calvin Theological Seminary, BD, 1955
ordained: 1955
charges: Home missionary, Salt Lake City, UT,
1955-60; Ogden, UT, 1959-61; Home missionary
at Immanuel, Salt Lake City, UT, 1961-64; First,
Lansing, IL, 1964-70; First, Sheldon, IA, 1970-76;
Bellevue, WA, 1976-81; Newton, IA, 1981-84
retired: 1984

Volbeda, Kurt Klaas Jr.
b. 08/27/1955, Sneek, Friesland, Netherlands
training: Calvin Theological Seminary, Special
Program for Ministerial Candidacy
ordained: 1989
charges: CRC: Green Meadow, Helena, MT, 1989-
90; Eligible for call, 1990-95; Independent:
Lakeshore Community, Holland, MI, 1995

Volbeda, Samuel (Sietse)
b. 10/14/1881, Winsum, Friesland, Netherlands
training: Calvin Theological Seminary, diploma,
1904; Vrije Universiteit, Amsterdam, ThD, 1914
ordained: 1904
charges: Beaverdam, MI, 1904-05; Alpine Ave.,
Grand Rapids, MI, 1905-11; Faculty, Calvin Theological Seminary, 1914-52 (President, 1944-52)
retired: 1952
d. 05/16/1953, Willard, OH

Voorhees, Jeffrey Douglas
b. 02/21/1971, Omaha, NE
training: Calvin Theological Seminary, MDiv, 2000
ordained: 2000
charges: Pine Creek, Holland, MI, 2000-

Voorhis, John Calvin
b. 04/17/1843, Hackensack, NJ vicinity
training: with John Y. De Baun
ordained: 1875
charges: True Protestant Dutch Reformed:
Englewood, NJ, 1874-86; Hackensack, NJ, 1887-
90; CRC: Hackensack, NJ, 1890-1906 Monsey, NY,
1906-08; True Reformed Dutch Church: Monsey,
NY, 1908-09; New York, NY, 1909-22
d. 10/23/1922, New York, NY

Voortman, John Marinus
b. 07/01/1878, Aalst, Gelderland, Netherlands
training: Calvin Theological Seminary, diploma,
1909
ordained: 1909
charges: Middleburg, IA, 1909-12; Moline, MI,
1912-13; Sheldon, IA, 1913-21; Leighton, IA,
1921-25; Randolph, WI, 1925-30; Wright, IA,
1930-42

retired: 1942
d. 09/20/1954, Cincinnati, OH

Voortman, Syburn Marten
b. 12/05/1923, Leighton, IA
training: Calvin Theological Seminary, BD, 1954
ordained: 1954
charges: Parkview Heights, Cincinnati, OH, 1954-57; Corsica, SD, 1957-61; Racine, WI, 1961-66; Walker, Grand Rapids, MI, 1966-71; First, Oak Lawn, IL, 1971-76; Dorr, MI, 1976-89
retired: 1989; affiliated with United Reformed Churches, 1992

Vorst, Cornelis
b. 05/ ?/1825, Zaandam, Noord Holland, Netherlands
training: with S. Van Velzen in Netherlands, D.J. Van der Werp and Calvin Theological Seminary
ordained: 1877
charges: Netherlands Reformed Church: First, Grand Rapids, MI, 1877-91; CRC: Lodi, NJ, 1891-95
retired: 1895
d. 05/20/1898, Holland, MI

Vos, Clarence John
b. 08/15/1920, Pella, IA
training: Calvin Theological Seminary, ThB, 1950; Vrije Universiteit, ThD, 1968
ordained: 1951
charges: Monroe, WA, 1951-54; Bethel, Paterson, NJ, 1954-61; Faculty, Calvin College, Grand Rapids, MI, 1961-85
retired: 1985

Vos, Jacob (Jack) B.
b. 09/21/1933, Baflo, Groningen, Netherlands
training: Calvin Theological Seminary, BD, 1960
ordained: 1962
charges: Stratford, ON, 1962-65; Grace, Chatham, ON, 1965-71; Grace, Scarborough, ON, 1971-83; Covenant, St. Catharines, ON, 1983-94; First, Barrie, ON, 1994-99
retired: 1999

Vos, Jan Hindrik
b. 03/18/1826, Oosterwold, Bentheim, Germany
training: with Wolter Alberts Kok, Jan Bavinck, Theologische Universiteit Kampen, diploma, 1858
ordained: 1858
charges: Altreformierte Kirche: Uelsen, Germany, 1858-60; GKN Heerenveen, 1860-65; Katwijk aan Zee, 1865-70; Lutten, 1870-74; Pernis, 1874-78;

Ommen, 1878-81; CRC: First, Grand Rapids, MI, 1881-1900
retired: 1900
d. 02/17/1913, Graafschap, MI

Vos, John O.
b. 09/04/1862, Westernieland, Groningen, Netherlands
training: declared eligible on the basis of exceptional gifts, 1909
ordained: 1909
charges: Fulton, IL, 1909-12; Summit, IL, 1912-17; Douglas Park, Chicago, IL, 1917-26; Kenosha, WI, 1926-34
retired: 1934
d. 12/20/1937, Cicero, IL

Vos, Kristin Jay
b. 12/09/1965, Pella, IA
training: Calvin Theological Seminary, MDiv, 1993
ordained: 1993
charges: Crossroads Community, St. John, IN, 1993-

Vos, Louis A.
b. 05/24/1936, Grand Rapids, MI
training: Calvin Theological Seminary, BD, 1961; Vrije Universiteit, Amsterdam, ThD, 1965
ordained: 1965
charges: Faculty, Calvin College, Grand Rapids, MI, 1965-95
d. 03/09/1995, Grand Rapids, MI

Vos, Peter
b. 10/02/1901, Kelloggsville, MI
training: Calvin Theological Seminary, BD, 1928; ThB, 1931
ordained: 1928
charges: Walker, MI, 1928-47; Holland Center, SD, 1947-50; Bejou, MN, 1950-53; Non-ministerial vocation, 1953
d. 11/14/1996, Grand Rapids, MI

Vos, Thomas Jay
b. 06/14/1953, Grand Rapids, MI
training: Calvin Theological Seminary, MDiv, 1979
ordained: 1979
charges: Luctor, KS, 1979-87; First, Wellsburg, IA, 1987-

Voskuil, Louis Frederick
b. 02/10/1906, Baldwin, WI
training: Calvin Theological Seminary, BD, 1933
ordained: 1933
charges: Holland, IA (and Grundy Center, IA,

1933-36), 1933-37; First, Wellsburg, IA, 1937-46; Montello Park, Holland, MI, 1946-52; First, Lynden, WA, 1952-55; Escalon, CA, 1955-71
retired: 1971
d. 01/23/1990, Visalia, CA

Voss, Albert Bernard
b. 04/25/1886, Fillmore, MI
training: Calvin Theological Seminary, diploma, 1919
ordained: 1919
charges: Bemis, SD, 1919-23; Manhattan, MT, 1923-27; Hospers, IA, 1927-36
d. 02/18/1936, Hospers, IA

Voss, Keith John
b. 05/08/1955, Holland, MI
training: Calvin Theological Seminary, MDiv, 1986
ordained: 1986
charges: CRC: Grace, Muskegon, MI, 1986-91; Central Coast, Arroyo Grande, CA, 1991-96; Eligible for call, 1996-98; Resigned from denomination

Vosteen, James Peter
b. 03/18/1931, Buffalo, NY
training: Westminster Theological Seminary-PA, BD/MDiv, 1956
ordained: 1956
charges: UPCNA: Lisbon, NY, 1956-58; OPC: Lisbon, NY, 1958-59; Lynnwood, WA, 1995-; CRC: Emo, ON, 1959-62; First, Minneapolis, MN, 1962-66; Smithers, BC, 1966-70; Pleasant St., Whitinsville, MA, 1970-75; First, Paterson, NJ, 1975-83; Cloverdale, Boise, ID, 1983-89; New Life Fellowship, Lynnwood, WA, 1989-93; Independent: Lynnwood, WA, 1993-95

Vredeveld, Ronald Clare
b. 01/18/1945, Grand Rapids, MI
training: Calvin Theological Seminary, BD, 1971; MDiv, 1980
ordained: 1971
charges: East Islip, NY, 1971-72; Chaplain intern, Pine Rest Christian Hospital, Cutlerville, MI, 1972-73; Maple Heights, Cleveland, OH, 1973-79; Coordinator, Association for Inter-faith Ministries to Developmentally Disabled, Mt. Pleasant, MI, 1979-

Vreeman, Jerry (Gerrit)
b. 05/05/1950, Sioux Center, IA
training: Calvin Theological Seminary, MDiv, 1976
ordained: 1977
charges: Minister of broadcasting, Back to God Hour, 1977-83; Multi-Media Ministries Interna-

tional, Lansing, IL, 1983-1998; Crossroads Community, Schererville, IN, 2001-

Vrieland, Douglas Jack
b. 12/24/1956, Grand Rapids, MI
training: Calvin Theological Seminary, MDiv, 1982
ordained: 1983
charges: Corsica, SD, 1983-89; Overisel, MI, 1989-93; Trinity Oaks, Arlington, TX, 1993-95; Eligible for call, 1995-96; Chaplain, United States Navy, 1996-

Vrieling, William H.
see: Frieling, William H.

Vriend, Cornelius
b. 06/05/1932, Andijk, Noord Holland, Netherlands
training: Calvin Theological Seminary, BD, 1962
ordained: 1962
charges: Emo, ON, 1962-65; First, Hamilton, ON, 1965-68; Bethel, Lacombe, AB, 1968-74; Neerlandia, AB, 1974-91; Barrhead, AB, 1991-97
retired: 1997

Vriend, Harry
b. 06/30/1941, Medemblik, Noord Holland, Netherlands
training: Calvin Theological Seminary, BD, 1970; MDiv, 1975
ordained: 1970
charges: Grande Prairie-La Glace, AB, 1970-76; John Calvin, Truro, NS, 1976-81; Trinity, Goderich, ON, 1981-91; Ebenezer, Leduc, AB, 1991-2001; Chaplain, Alberta Hospital, Edmonton, AB, 2001-

Vriend, John
b. 03/10/1925, Andijk, Noord Holland, Netherlands
training: University of Michigan, MA, 1952; Vrije Universitiet, ThM, 1956
ordained: 1956
charges: Montreal, QC, 1956-60; Simcoe, ON, 1960-64; Lethbridge, AB, 1964-70; First, Edmonton, AB, 1970-74; Church of the Servant, Grand Rapids, MI, 1974-83; Non-ministerial vocation, 1983
d. 02/10/2002, Grand Rapids, MI

Vriesman, Cornelius
b. 03/16/1878, Fremont, MI
training: Calvin Theological Seminary, diploma, 1908
ordained: 1908
charges: East Paris, Grand Rapids, MI, 1908-11; Zillah WA, 1911-16; Missionary for Classis Pacific

at Everett, WA, 1916-20; Everett, WA, 1920-25; Resigned from ministry
d. 03/23/1925, Muskegon, MI

Vrieze, Maarten
b. 08/12/1922, Den Haag, Zuid Holland, Netherlands
training: Theologische Universiteit, Kampen, diploma, 1946; Vrije Universiteit, Amsterdam; University of Port Elizabeth, South Africa
ordained: 1946
charges: GKN: Rotterdam, 1946-48; Heemstede, 1948-53; Chaplain, Royal Dutch Army, 1953-55; CRC: Oshawa, ON, 1955-58; Emmanuel, Calgary, AB, 1958-61; Minister of evangelism, Greater Edmonton, AB, 1961-66; Faculty, Trinity Christian College, Palos Heights, IL, 1966-86
d. 10/19/1986, Palos Heights, IL

Vroege, David Anthony
b. 01/15/1973, Vanderhoof, BC
training: Calvin Theological Seminary, MDiv, 2001
ordained: 2001
charges: All Nations, Halifax, NS, 2001-

Vroon, Simon
b. 08/22/1903, Dinteloord, Noord Brabant, Netherlands
training: Calvin Theological Seminary, ThB, 1932
ordained: 1932
charges: Zutphen, MI, 1932-39; Bethany, South Holland, IL, 1939-42; Chaplain, United States Army, 1942-45; First, Pella, IA, 1945-52; East Saugatuck, MI, 1952-59; Calvin, Oak Lawn, Il, 1959-68
retired: 1968
d. 08/14/1993, Holland, MI

Vruwink, Paul Harold
b. 07/27/1931, Oostburg, WI
training: Calvin Theological Seminary, BD, 1958
ordained: 1958
charges: Chaplain, United States Army, 1958-61; Wright, Kanawha, IA, 1961-64; Chaplain, United States Army, 1964-82; Thirty-Sixth St., Wyoming, MI, 1982-89; Missionary, Philippines, 1989-90
retired: 1990; resigned from denomination, 1998

Vryhof, Kevin John
b. 06/06/1961, Hanford, CA
training: Calvin Theological Seminary, MDiv, 1988
ordained: 1988
charges: Ogilvie, MN, 1988-95; Chandler, MN, 1995-2002; High River, AB, 2002

Vugteveen, Howard John
b. 10/24/1944, Grand Rapids, MI
training: Calvin Theological Seminary, BDm 1971; ThM, 1987
ordained: 1971
charges: Chapel, Lake Odessa, MI, 1970-73; Lake Odessa, MI, 1973-75; Immanuel, Hudsonville, MI, 1975-81; Faith Community, Wyckoff, NJ, 1981-95; New Life Ministries, Midland Park, NJ, 1995-

Vugteveen, Jochem
b. 06/28/1933, Borne, Overijsel, Netherlands
training: Calvin Theological Seminary, BD, 1962
ordained: 1962
charges: Birnamwood, WI, 1962-66; Winfield, IL, 1966-70; Westmount, Strathroy, ON, 1970-76; Trinity, Philadelphia, PA, 1976-94; Unity, Prospect Park, NJ, 1994-98
retired: 1998

Vugteveen, Marvin Lloyd
b. 05/06/1933, Doon, IA
training: Reformed Bible College, 1958; Calvin Theological Seminary, BD, 1967
ordained: 1967
charges: Lay evangelist, Shiprock, NM, 1958-61; Neighborhood evangelist, Seymour Square, Grand Rapids, MI, 1961-62; Ionia Avenue Chapel, Grand Rapids, MI, 1962-63; Neighborhood evangelist, First, Grand Rapids, MI, 1963-64; Missionary to Puerto Rico, 1967-75
d. 04/25/1975, Puerto Rico

Vunderink, Ralph (Roelof) Willem
b. 01/07/1939, Amsterdam, Noord Holland, Netherlands
training: Calvin Theological Seminary, BD, 1963
ordained: 1985
charges: Faculty, Winebrenner Theological Seminary, Findlay, OH, 1985-87; Eligible for call, 1987-93; Non-ministerial vocation, 1993

Wagenmaker, Todd Vincent
b. 05/25/1967, Cincinnati, OH
training: Westminster Theological Seminary-CA, MDiv, 1993; Calvin Theological Seminary, Special Program for Ministerial Candidacy, 1997
ordained: 1997
charges: Trinity, St. Louis, MO, 1997-2001; First, Oak Lawn, IL, 2001-

Wagenmaker, Tyler Jon
b. 10/20/1973, Grand Rapids, MI
training: Calvin Theological Seminary, MDiv, 2000
ordained: 2000

charges: Beaverdam, MI, 2000–

Wagenveld, Louis Wendell
b. 02/24/1940, Holland, MI
training: Calvin Theological Seminary, BD, 1967
ordained: 1967
charges: Missionary to Argentina, 1967–81; Sol del Valle, Sun Valley, CA, 1981–93; Regional director, Christian Reformed World Missions, Sol de Valle Community Center, Sun Valley, CA, 1993–94; Leave, 1994–95; Missionary, El Salvador, 1995–2000; Missionary, Mexico, 2000–
retired: 2002

Walcott, Alfred
b. 04/29/1911, Allendale, MI
training: Calvin Theological Seminary, BD, 1948
ordained: 1948
charges: Noordeloos, MI, 1948–51; Reeman, MI, 1951–58; Home missionary for Classis Holland, 1958–63; Missionary pastor, New Richmond, MI, 1963–64, Home missionary for Classis Holland 1964–65; Bethel, Waupun, WI, 1965–76
retired: 1976
d. 09/06/1982, Mackinaw City, MI vicinity

Walcott, Thomas James
b. 05/13/1958, Muskegon, MI
training: Calvin Theological Seminary, MDiv, 1984
ordained: 1984
charges: Missionary, Dominican Republic, 1984–91; Baymeadows Community, Jacksonville, FL, 1991–96; Chaplain, United States Navy, 1996–

Walhof, Frederick James
b. 11/30/1938, Edgerton, MN
training: Calvin Theological Seminary, BD, 1963
ordained: 1963
charges: Community, Saginaw, MI, 1963–68; Ames, IA, 1968–81 and Campus pastor, Iowa State University, Ames, IA, 1968–86; Hope Community, Flagstaff, AZ, 1986–

Walhout, Edwin
b. 05/14/1926, Muskegon, MI
training: Calvin Theological Seminary, ThB, 1952
ordained: 1961
charges: Holland, MN, 1961–65; Webster, NY, 1965–71; Framingham, MA, 1971–76; Adult education, Board of Publications, Grand Rapids, MI, 1976–81; Stated supply, Jackson, MI, 1984–85
retired: 1989

Walker, Trent Dee
b. 02/26/1966, Americus, GA

training: declared eligible on the basis of exceptional gifts, 1998
ordained: 1998
charges: Elmhurst, IL, 1988–91; Harderwyk, Holland, MI, 1991–99; Watershed, Holland, MI, 1999–

Walkotten, Henry
b. 03/21/1864, Georgsdorf, Bentheim, Germany
training: Calvin Theological Seminary, diploma, 1893
ordained: 1893
charges: First, Wellsburg, IA, 1893–95; Third, Muskegon, MI, 1895–99; First, Fremont, MI, 1899–1907; First, Wellsburg, IA, 1907–08; Oakland, MI, 1908–11; Hudsonville, MI, 1911–21; Second, Pella, IA, 1921–25
d. 05/17/1925, Pella, IA

Walkotten, John (Jan)
b. 07/27/1869, Georgsdorf, Bentheim, Germany
training: Calvin Theological Seminary, diploma, 1903
ordained: 1903
charges: Vogel Center, MI, 1903–05; Second, Muskegon, MI, 1905–10; First Roseland, Chicago, IL, 1910–14; Sixteenth St., Holland, MI, 1914–19; First, Paterson, NJ, 1919–43
retired: 1943
d. 12/11/1955, Paterson, NJ

Walma, Albert
b. 03/29/1922, Grand Rapids, MI
training: Calvin Theological Seminary, BD, 1953
ordained: 1953
charges: Chaplain, USA, 1953–56; Hull, ND, 1956–59; Tyler, MN, 1959–64; Austinville, IA, 1964–68; Morrison, IL, 1968–80
retired: 1981
d. 09/26/1986, Grand Rapids, MI

Walter, Robert Jr.
b. 09/09/1942, Paterson, NJ
training: Calvin Theological Seminary, BD, 1970; MDiv, 1975; ThM, 1979
ordained: 1970
charges: Monsey, NY, 1970–75; Gibson, Holland, MI, 1975–79; McBain, MI, 1979–84; Milwood, Kalamazoo, MI, 1984–93; First, Zeeland, MI, 1993–1999; Interim, Covenant, North Haledon, NJ, 1999–2001; Christ's Community, Chandler, AZ, 2001–2002; Interim, Bethany, Bellflower, CA, 2002–

Walters, Curtis Alan
b. 11/09/1964, Zeeland, MI

training: Calvin Theological Seminary, MDiv, 1991
ordained: 1991
charges: Hope, Grandville, MI, 1991-97; Covenant, Cutlerville, MI, 1997-

Walters, Dick Henry
b. 12/11/1907, Borculo, MI
training: Calvin Theological Seminary, ThB, 1933
ordained: 1933
charges: Prairie City, IA, 1933-38; Central Ave., Holland, MI, 1938-43; President, Reformed Bible College, 1943-67
d. 12/24/1967, Grand Rapids, MI

Walton, Charles
b. 12/12/1959, Bethesda, MD
training: Columbia International University, MDiv, 1989
ordained: 1997
charges: PCA: Bucks Central, Newtown, PA, 1989-95; Westminster, Lancaster, PA, 1995-2000; CRC: Wright, Kanawha, IA, 2000-

Wamala, Gideon E.
b. 11/14/1861, Nairobi, Kenya
training: Calvin Theological Seminary, MDiv, 2002
ordained: 2002
charges: Stephenville, TX, 2002-

Wanders, John Marvin
b. 06/21/1945, Oskaloosa, IA
training: Calvin Theological Seminary, MDiv, 1978
ordained: 1978
charges: Cascade, Marysville, WA, 1978-82; Community, Fountain Valley, CA, 1982-92; Bozeman, MT, 1992-99; Desert Harbor, Las Vegas, NV, 1999-

Warners, Douglas Arthur
b. 07/02/1941, Grand Rapids, MI
training: Calvin Theological Seminary, BD, 1967; MDiv, 1978
ordained: 1967
charges: Bible teacher, Kalamazoo (MI) Christian High School, 1967-74; Teacher, Denver (CO) Christian High School, 1974-76; First, Detroit, MI, 1976-82; First, Artesia, CA, 1982-94; Leave, 1994-95; East Leonard, Grand Rapids, MI, 1995-2001

Wassink, Albert
b. 05/05/1883, Arnhem, Gelderland, Netherlands
training: Calvin Theological Seminary, diploma, 1915
ordained: 1915

charges: Ocheyedan, IA, 1915-17; Carnes, IA, 1917-20; Brooten, MN, 1920-22; Worthington, MN, 1922-29; Inwood, IA, 1929-46; Duvall, WA, 1946-50
d. 06/12/1950, Duvall, WA

Wassink, Brent Allyn
b. 12/15/1960, Holland, MI
training: Calvin Theological Seminary, MDiv, 1988
ordained: 1989
charges: Britt, IA, 1989-96; Long Beach, CA, 1996-

Watson, David Kuyper
b. 09/21/1960, Lower Merion, PA
training: Calvin Theological Seminary, MDiv, 1998
ordained: 1998
charges: Terra Ceia, NC, 1998-2001; Good News Community, Kent, WA, 2002-

Weaver, Philip Harvey Guise
b. 03/24/1957, Farnborough, Kent, England
training: Calvin Theological Seminary, MDiv, 1987
ordained: 1989
charges: Vanastra Community, Vanastra, ON, 1989-92; Chaplain, Lakeland Psychiatric Hospital, Thunder Bay, ON, 1992-

Webenga, John
see: Wiebenga, John

Weber, William D.
b. 10/23/1956, Columbus, NE
training: Trinity Evangelical Divinity School, MDiv, 1994; Calvin Theological Seminary, Special Program for Ministerial Candidacy, 1999
ordained: 1999
charges: Peace, Menno, SD, 1999-

Weeber, George Gerald
b. 11/28/1903, Garijp, Friesland, Netherlands
training: Calvin Theological Seminary, ThB, 1935
ordained: 1935
charges: Superintendent, Helping Hand Mission, Chicago, IL, 1935-38; Edmonton, AB, 1938-40; Non-ministerial vocation, 1940-44; Lay preacher, First, Paterson, NJ, 1944-46; PCUSA: McBain/Lake City, MI, 1947-49; RCA: Fellowship, Muskegon, MI, 1949-51; First, Philadelphia, PA, 1954-56; Stated supply and visitation, Grand Rapids, MI area, 1963-80; OPC: Pilgrim, Bangor, ME, 1959-61; Available for call, 1961-63
retired: 1963
d. 03/13/1997, Grand Rapids, MI

Weeda, Jacob Cornelius

b. 06/01/1945, Naaldwijk, Zuid Holland, Netherlands
training: Calvin Theological Seminary, MDiv, 1974
ordained: 1974
charges: New Era, MI, 1974–83; Granum, AB, 1983–91; Bethel, Manhattan, MT, 1991–

Weeldreyer, Meindert M.

b. 09/28/1888, Stapemooreheide, Ostfriesland, Germany
training: Dubuque (IA) Presbyterian Seminary, diploma, 1918
ordained: 1918
charges: Presbyterian Church USA: Waukon, IA, 1918–19; CRC: Lincoln Center, IA, 1919–27; RCA: Bethany, Clara City, MN, 1927–53; Trinity, Allison, IA, 1953–56
retired: 1956
d. 03/29/1972, Kalamazoo, MI

Weemhoff, David John

b. 06/13/1954, Grand Rapids, MI
training: Calvin Theological Seminary, MDiv, 1981
ordained: 1981
charges: Prosper, Falmouth, MI, 1981–85; Beaverdam, MI, 1985–88; John Calvin, Truro, NS, 1988–92; Ellsworth, MI, 1992–2001; First, Sarnia, ON, 2002–

Weersing, Jacob J.

b. 09/27/1879, Graafschap, MI
training: Calvin Theological Seminary, diploma, 1909
ordained: 1909
charges: West Park, Cleveland, OH, 1909–12; Sherman St., Grand Rapids, MI, 1912–16; Peoria, IA, 1916–18; Hull, IA, 1918–24; First, Cicero, IL, 1924–32; First, Kalamazoo, MI, 1932–38; Glendale, CA, 1938–49; stated supply Escalon, CA, 1949–51
retired: 1949
d. 01/21/1976, Ripon, CA

Weerstra, Hans

b. 04/08/1936, IJlst, Friesland, Netherlands
training: Calvin Theological Seminary, ThB, 1964
ordained: 1964
charges: Missionary to Mexico, 1964–71; Leave, 1971–72; Missionary to Mexico, 1972–85; Nonministerial vocation, 1985

Weidenaar, Dirk

b. 04/23/1888, Niawier, Friesland, Netherlands

training: Calvin Theological Seminary, diploma, 1917
ordained: 1917
charges: Vesper WI, 1917–20; Home missionary at Plover, WI, 1920–26
retired: 1926
d. 08/22/1933, Cutlerville, MI

Weidenaar, Harry John

b. 12/10/1944, Evergreen Park, IL
training: Westminster Theological Seminary-PA, MDiv, 1969
ordained: 1975
charges: Atwood, MI, 1975–80; Morrison, IL, 1980–84; West Leonard, Grand Rapids, MI, 1984–88; Covenant, Sioux Center, IA, 1988–92; Calvin, Oak Lawn, IL, 1992–98; First, Seattle, WA, 1998–

Weidenaar, John

b. 09/20/1898, Chicago, IL
training: Calvin Theological Seminary, ThB, 1929; Princeton Seminary, ThM, 1944; Vrije Universiteit, Amsterdam, MTh, 1953
ordained: 1929
charges: Worthington, MN, 1929–32; Peoria, IA, 1932–36; Dennis Ave., Grand Rapids, MI, 1936–43; Fuller Ave., Grand Rapids, MI, 1942–49; Faculty, Calvin College and Associate pastor, Fuller Ave., Grand Rapids, MI, 1949–64
retired: 1964
d. 02/15/1977, Grand Rapids, MI

Weiland, Klaas Berend

b. 10/13/1830, Rysum, Hanover, Germany
training: Veldhausen Seminary, diploma, 1867
ordained: 1867
charges: Altreformierde Kirche: Neermoor, German, 1867–68; CRC: Ridott, IL, 1868–70; RCA: Third, Pella, IA, 1870–75; Parkersburg, IA, 1880–83; Lennox, SD, 1884–86; Sheldon, IA, 1886; Presbyterian Church USA: Fort Dodge, IA; Sioux Center, IA; Hospers, IA; Britt, IA; LeMars, IA
d. 01/11/1917, LeMars, IA

Weima, Jeffrey Alan David

b. 07/16/1960, Brockville, ON
training: Calvin Theological Seminary, MDiv, 1986, ThM, 1987; Wycliffe College, University of Toronto, PhD, 1992
ordained: 1993
charges: Faculty, Calvin Theological Seminary, Grand Rapids, MI, 1993–

Weland, Klaas Berend

see: Weiland, Klaas Berend

Welandt, Frank (Frans)

b. 02/05/1850, Leek, Groningen, Netherlands
training: Theologische Universiteit, Kampen and Calvin Theological Seminary, diploma, 1883
ordained: 1883
charges: West Side, Cleveland, OH, 1883-85; First, Kalamazoo, 1885-89; Niekerk, Holland, MI, 1889-99; Douglas Park, Chicago IL, 1899-1905; Sheboygan, WI, 1905-10; Lodi NJ, 1910-23
retired: 1923
d. 12/28/1937, Kalamazoo, MI

Werkema, Clarence George

b. 07/07/1920, Grand Rapids, MI
training: Westminster Theological Seminary, MDiv, 1954
ordained: 1954
charges: RCA: Hope, Clifton, NJ, 1954-59; CRC: Holland Center, SD, 1959-63; Monroe, WA, 1963-66; First, Waupun, WI, 1966-71; Walker, Grand Rapids, MI, 1971-78; Bethany, South Holland, IL, 1978-83
retired: 1983
d. 10/02/2002, Grand Rapids, MI

Werkema, Sidney Andrew

b. 08/01/1908, Grand Rapids, MI
training: Calvin Theological Seminary, BD, 1936
ordained: 1936
charges: Arlene, MI, 1936-40; Zutphen, MI, 1940-47; Home missionary at Iowa Falls, IA, 1947-50; at Willmar, MN, 1950-53; Home missionary in Chicago, IL, 1953-54; Thirty-Sixth St., Grand Rapids, MI, 1954-60; Hospital chaplain for evangelism, Grand Rapids, MI, 1960-62; Ideal Park, Grand Rapids, MI, 1962-67
retired: 1967
d. 01/17/1988, Cutlerville, MI

Werkman, Joseph (Johannes) J.

b. 08/15/1889, Muskegon, MI
training: Calvin Theological Seminary, diploma, 1918
ordained: 1918
charges: CRC: Volga, SD, 1918-23; Oak Harbor, WA, 1923-28; First, Bellflower, CA, 1928-34; RCA: Bethel, Bellflower, CA, 1935-42
d. 02/03/1967, Long Beach, CA

Wesseling, Jay Allan

b. 06/27/1927, Grand Rapids, MI
training: Calvin Theological Seminary, BD, 1953
ordained: 1953
charges: Holland, IA, 1953-57; Sully, IA, 1957-61; Baldwin St., Jenison, MI, 1961-70; First, Seattle,

WA, 1970-76; Third, Zeeland, MI, 1976-86; Walker, Grand Rapids, MI, 1986-91; First, Sheldon, IA, 1991-94
retired: 1994; affiliated with United Reformed Churches, 1995

Westenberg, Gerrit

b. 04/13/1867, Nevenhaus, Bentheim, Germany
training: Calvin Theological Seminary, diploma, 1897
ordained: 1897
charges: Peoria, IA, 1897-1901; New Era, MI, 1901-04; Fourth, Paterson, NJ, 1904-09; Summer St., Passaic, NJ, 1909-14; Jenison, MI, 1914-21; East Side, Cleveland, OH 1921-27; Home missionary at Holland, IA, 1927-28; Parkersburg, IA, 1928-35
retired: 1935
d. 04/08/1945, Grand Rapids, MI

Westenbroek, Robert Lee

b. 01/13/1940, Zeeland, MI
training: Calvin Theological Seminary, BD, 1966
ordained: 1966
charges: Faith, Kalamazoo, MI, 1964-65, 1966-69; Campus minister, University of Wisconsin, Madison, WI, 1969-75; Crestview, Boulder, CO, 1975-80; Lake Worth, FL, 1980-90; Peace Community, Houston, TX, 1990-

Westerhof, Jack

b. 04/01/1938, Niawier, Friesland, Netherlands
training: Calvin Theological Seminary, BD, 1964
ordained: 1967
charges: Lindsay, ON, 1967-71; Student pastor, First, Lacombe, AB, 1971-76; Campus minister, Western Ontario University, London, ON, 1977-81; Willowdale, Toronto, ON, 1981-88; Inglewood, Edmonton, AB, 1988-93; Palmerston, ON, 1993-2001; Interim, Redeemer, Sarnia, ON, 2001-

Westerhuis, (Pieter) Albert Adriaan

b. 06/05/1950, Zwartsluis, Overijsel, Netherlands
training: Calvin Theological Seminary, MDiv, 1984
ordained: 1985
charges: Prince George, BC, 1985-90; Surrey, BC, 1990-

Westervelt, John A.

b. 06/27/1857, New York, NY
training: with John Y. De Baun, 1880; Princeton Theological Seminary, 1896
ordained: 1880
charges: True Protestant Dutch Reformed: New York, NY, 1880-88; Ridgewood, NJ, 1888-90;

CRC: Ridgewood, NJ, 1890-92; Home missionary, Flat River, NY, 1892-93; Leave, 1893-96; Third, Paterson, NJ, 1896-1927
retired: 1927
d. 12/01/1951, Paterson, NJ

Westra, Erick Dean
b. 04/02/1970, Orange, CA
training: Calvin Theological Seminary, MDiv, 1998
ordained: 1999
charges: Missionary, Philippines, 1999-

Westra, Harold John
b. 06/06/1943, Bozeman, MT
training: Calvin Theological Seminary, MDiv, 1973
ordained: 1973
charges: Lakeview, Valentine, NE, 1973-78; Wright, Kanawha, IA, 1978-84; Calvin, McBain, MI, 1984-89; Volga, SD, 1989-98; Interim, Holland, MN, 1998-2000; Holland, MN, 2000-

Westra, Isaac
b. 10/28/1886, Tzummarum, Friesland, Netherlands
training: Calvin Theological Seminary, diploma, 1917
ordained: 1917
charges: Winnipeg, MB, 1917-19; Middleburg, IA, 1919-23; First Englewood, Chicago, IL, 1923-29; First, Lynden, WA, 1929-33; First, South Holland, IL, 1934-44
retired: 1933
d. 09/28/1944, South Holland, IL

Westra, Jonathan Dewey
b. 09/12/1959, Waupun, WI
training: Calvin Theological Seminary, MDiv, 1988
ordained: 1988
charges: East Side, Cleveland, OH, 1988-93; Celebration Community, Phoenix, AZ, 1993-2002; Faith Community Fellowship, Mount Vernon, WA, 2002-

Westveer, Rodney William
b. 03/31/1931, Grand Rapids, MI
training: Calvin Theological Seminary, BD, 1955
ordained: 1955
charges: CRC: Cutlerville East, Grand Rapids, MI, 1955-60; Lodi, NJ, 1960-62; Holland Heights, Holland, MI, 1962-68; Campus minister, Grand Valley State University, Allendale, MI, 1968-78; UPCUSA: John Knox, Grand Rapids, MI, 1981-95
retired: 1995

Wetselaar, Thomas David
b. 09/20/1958, Hamilton, ON
training: Calvin Theological Seminary, MDiv, 1987
ordained: 1987
charges: CRC: Prairie City, IA, 1987-91; Sumas, WA, 1991-94; Bethel, De Motte, IN, 1994-95; Alliance of Reformed Churches: Immanuel, De Motte, IN, 1995-97; United Reformed Churches: Immanuel, DeMotte, IN, 1997

Wevers, Franklin Theodore
b. 12/16/1952, Baldwin, MI
training: Calvin Theological Seminary, MDiv, 1975
ordained: 1978
charges: Highland, MI, 1978-82; Baymeadows Community, Jacksonville, FL, 1982-90; Calvary, Holland, MI, 1990-

Wevers, Theodore
b. 10/15/1923, Baldwin, WI
training: Calvin Theological Seminary, BD, 1960
ordained: 1960
charges: Prairie City, IA, 1960-64; Wyoming Park, Wyoming, MI, 1964-71; Prinsburg, MN, 1971-77; Immanuel, Ripon, CA, 1977-81; First, Oostburg, WI, 1981-87
retired: 1987

Wezeman, Frederick H.
b. 07/04/1892, Oak Park, IL
training: Calvin Theological Seminary, diploma, 1921
ordained: 1925
charges: Faculty, Grundy College, 1921-25; College Church, Grundy Center, IA, 1925-27; Principal, Bible teacher, Chicago (IL) Christian High School; 1927-51 (associate minister Fourth, Chicago, IL, 1937-51); Non-ministerial vocation, educator, 1951
d. 05/25/1968, Oak Lawn, IL

Wezeman, Kenneth Reni
b. 04/04/1945, Kansas City, MO
training: Calvin Theological Seminary, BD, 1971; MDiv, 1976
ordained: 1971
charges: CRC: Chaplain, Whitesburg Appalachian Regional Hospital, 1971-72; Chaplain, Morgan County Appalachian Regional Hospital, 1972-74; Muskegon Heights, MI, 1974-81; Chaplain-director, Dept. of Pastoral Care, South Bend Osteopathic Hospital, South Bend, IN, 1981-86; Chaplain, St. Joseph Hospital, Mishawaka, IN, 1986-92; released from denomination, 1992

0

Wezemen, Richard H.
b. 05/04/1904, Chicago, IL
training: Calvin Theological Seminary, ThB, 1933
ordained: 1934
charges: Coster, IA, 1933-36; Ridott, IL, 1936-42; Chaplain, United States Army, 1942-46, Lucas, MI, 1946-51; Volga, SD, 1951-54; Beverly, Wyoming, MI, 1954-61; Home missionary, Fairbanks, AK, 1961-66; Orlando, FL, 1966-69
retired: 1969

Whatley, Stephen
b. 08/20/1951, Ozona, TX
training: Western Conservative Baptist Seminary, MA, 1983; Faith Evangelical Lutheran Seminary, DMin, 1993; Trinity Theological Seminary, PhD studies
ordained: 1984
charges: Independent: Micronesian Institute of Biblical Studies, Chuuk, Micronesia, 1984-93; CRC: Missionary/Theological educator, Institute for Leaders and Pastors, Manila, Philippines, 1993-97; Faculty, Asian Theological Seminary, Bacolod, Philippines, 1997-

White, James Bliese
b. 07/08/1940, New York, NY
training: Westminster Theological Seminary-PA, BD, 1967
ordained: 1969
charges: Manhattan, New York, NY, 1969-78; Faculty, Trinity Christian College, Palos Heights, IL, 1978-81; Faculty, Calvin College, Grand Rapids, MI, 1981-85; Leave, 1985-93; Non-ministerial vocation, Administration Grand Rapids Public Schools, 1993

Whyte, George Willard
b. 04/29/1954, Sydney Mines, NS
training: Westminster Theological Seminary-PA, MDiv, 1975; Calvin Theological Seminary, Special Program for Ministerial Candidacy, 1979
ordained: 1981
charges: Missionary, Islam in Africa Project, Africa, 1981-84; Missionary, Guinea, West Africa, 1984-94; Non-ministerial vocation, 1994
d. 12/16/1996, Grand Rapids, MI

Wiebenga, John (Jan) W.
b. 07/30/1864, Netherlands
training: Calvin Theological Seminary, diploma, 1897
ordained: 1897
charges: CRC: Home missionary, Oak Harbor, WA, 1897; East Side, Cleveland OH, 1901-02; UPC:

Oak Harbor, WA, 1898-1901; RCA: Galesburg and Killduff, IA, 1903-05; Wichert, IL, 1905-09; Stated supply, Ada, MI, 1909-10; Lucas, MI, 1911-17; Atwood, MI, 1917-20; Hope, Clifton, NJ, 1920-26; Ireton, IA, 1926-33
retired: 1933
d. 04/01/1953, Maurice, IA

Wiebenga, Robert Lloyd
b. 09/26/1932, Wyoming Township, Kent County, MI
training: Calvin Theological Seminary, BD, 1958; MDiv, 1975
ordained: 1958
charges: Decatur, MI, 1958-61; Terra Ceia, NC, 1961-66; Calvin, McBain, MI, 1966-78; available for call, 1978-81; Non-ministerial vocation, 1979

Wiegers, John J.
b. 09/06/1938, Grootegast, Groningen, Netherlands
training: Calvin Theological Seminary, BD, 1963
ordained: 1963
charges: Hawarden, IA, 1963-67; Third, Bellflower, CA, 1967-71; Cottonwood Heights, Jenison, MI, 1971-79; Cragmor, Colorado Springs, CO, 1979-84; Pleasant St., Whitinsville, MA, 1984-92; Fox Valley, Crystal Lake, IL, 1992-99; Pine Grove, Howard City, MI, 1999-2003
retired: 2003

Wierenga, Henry
b. 09/11/1890, Grand Rapids, MI
training: Calvin Theological Seminary, diploma, 1920
ordained: 1920
charges: Jamestown, MI, 1920-25; Non-ministerial vocation, 1925
d. 03/17/1978, Grand Haven, MI

Wierenga, Herman
b. 11/23/1896, Grand Rapids, MI
training: Calvin Theological Seminary, BD, 1926
ordained: 1927
charges: Wright, IA, 1927-30; Winnipeg, MB, 1930-38; Missionary, Minneapolis, MN, 1938-39; Missionary, Sarnia, ON, 1939-50
retired: 1950
d. 01/15/1958, Grand Rapids, MI

Wieringa, John (Jan)
b. 05/11/1930, Ten Boer, Groningen, Netherlands
training: Calvin Theological Seminary, BD, 1966
ordained: 1966

charges: CRC: Wyoming, ON, 1966–71; GKN: 't Zandt, 1971–77; Heerde, 1977–95
retired: 1995

Wiersum, James Clyde
b. 09/28/1949, Racine, WI
training: Calvin Theological Seminary, MDiv, 1982
ordained: 1983
charges: High River, AB, 1983–88; First, Everett, WA, 1988–

Wiersum, Karl Jay
b. 09/11/1951, Grand Rapids, MI
training: Calvin Theological Seminary, MDiv, 1976
ordained: 1976
charges: Holland, IA, 1976–80; First, Des Plaines, IL, 1980–83; Enumclaw, WA, 1983–86; Chaplain, United States Air Force, 1986–

Wigboldus, Ralph Simon
b. 08/08/1962, Hamilton, ON
training: Calvin Theological Seminary, MDiv, 1999
ordained: 1999
charges: Second, Sarnia, ON, 1999–

Wigboldy, Homer John
b. 12/23/1932, Chicago, IL
training: Calvin Theological Seminary, BD, 1966
ordained: 1966
charges: Everson, WA, 1966–70; Immanuel, Ripon, CA, 1970–77; First, Fremont, MI, 1977–84; Second, Byron Center, MI, 1984–91; Bethel, Lansing, IL, 1992–98
retired: 1998

Wilandt, Frank
see: Welandt, Frank

Wilczewski, John Walter
b. 07/27/1966, Chicago, IL
training: Calvin Theological Seminary, MDiv, 1996
ordained: 1997
charges: Sunshine Community, Grand Rapids, MI, 1997–98; Bolingbrook, IL, 1998–99; The Peak Ministries, Oswego, IL, 1999–

Wildeboer, Henry
b. 07/06/1939, Den Hulst, Overijsel, Netherlands
training: Calvin Theological Seminary, BD, 1965; MDiv, 1975
ordained: 1965
charges: Sunnyside, WA, 1965–71; First, Calgary AB, 1971–84; Zion, Oshawa, ON, 1984–98; Regional director, Central and Eastern Canada, Home Missions/Director, Tyndale Seminary, Toronto, ON, 1998–

Wildschut, Ralph
b. 10/09/1914, Gaastmeer, Friesland, Netherlands
training: Calvin Theological Seminary, ThB, 1943
ordained: 1943
charges: Sullivan, MI, 1943–45; Granum and Burdett, AB, 1945–47; Granum, AB, 1947–50; Prosper, MI, 1950–53; Springdale, ON, 1953–59; Bethel, Lansing, IL, 1959–66; Goshen, NY, 1966–80
retired: 1980
d. 11/02/1998, Middletown, NY

Williams, Michael James
b. 08/22/1956, Tampa, FL
training: Westminster Theological Seminary-PA, MAR, 1987; University of Pennsylvania, PhD, 1999
ordained: 2000
charges: Faculty, Calvin Theological Seminary, 1994–

Williams, Richard Emanuel
b. 08/05/1944, Ancon, Canal Zone, Panama
training: Fuller Theological Seminary, MDiv, 1978; Calvin Theological Seminary, Special Program for Ministerial Candidacy, 1981
ordained: 1981
charges: Pastor's assistant, First, Los Angeles, CA, 1977–79; Pullman, Chicago, IL, 1981–

Willoughby, Karl Kendall
b. 02/07/1941, Owosso, MI
training: Calvin Theological Seminary, MDiv, 1975
ordained: 1975
charges: Chaplain, United States Army, 1975–2001; Chaplain, Covenant Hospice, Pensacola, FL, 2001–

Wilson, Jack
b. 11/06/1950
training: Northeastern Bible College, BRE, 1972; Biblical Theological Seminary, MDiv, 1975; Drew University, MPhil, 1981, PhD, 1989
ordained: 1975
charges: Baptist: Englewood Temple, Englewood, NJ, 1975–80; Evangelical Free (Calvary Church, NJ), 1980–94; Faculty, Eastern Christian High School, 1995–2000; CRC: Faculty, Eastern Christian High School, 2000; Faith Community, Wyckoff, NJ, 2000–

Wilton, William Samuel
b. 06/22/1965, Port Huron, MI

training: Calvin Theological Seminary, MDiv, 1999
ordained: 2000
charges: East Leonard, Grand Rapids, MI, 1999–2000; Sunrise, McMinnville, OR, 2001–

Winkle, Peter Donald
b. 07/20/1941, Grand Rapids, MI
training: Calvin Theological Seminary, BD, 1973; MDiv, 1977
ordained: 1973
charges: Second minister, LaGrave Ave., Grand Rapids, MI, 1973–77; Chaplain, Rehoboth Christian Hospital, Rehoboth, NM, 1977–86; Providence, Holland, MI, 1986–88; Prospect Park, Holland, MI, 1991–2000; LaGrave Ave., Grand Rapids, MI, 2000–2002; Non-ministerial vocation, 2002

Winnowski, Michael Gerard
b. 06/16/1956, Pittsburgh, PA
training: Calvin Theological Seminary, MDiv, 1988
ordained: 1990
charges: Assistant minister for congregational life, Church of the Servant, Grand Rapids, MI, 1987–88; Calvary Ministries, Vermillion, SD, 1990–93; Director, Ministry to Seafarers, Montreal, QC, 1993–97; Waterloo, ON, 1997–

Winter, Harold Andrew
b. 01/10/1974, Brantford, ON
training: McMaster Divinity College, MDiv, 2001; Calvin Theological Seminary, Special Program for Ministerial Candidacy, 2002
ordained: 2002
charges: Trinity, St. Catharines, ON, 2002–

Winters, Harry Raymond Jr.
b. 10/20/1958, Grand Rapids, MI
training: Calvin Theological Seminary, MDiv, 1986
ordained: 1987
charges: Holland, MN, 1987–92; Akron, OH, 1992–

Wisse, Donald Peter
b. 12/08/1930, Passaic, NJ
training: Calvin Theological Seminary, BD, 1957; MDiv, 1974
ordained: 1957
charges: Wayland, MI, 1956–61; Home missionary, Ogden, UT, 1961–65; Lake Worth, FL, 1965–70; Midland Park, NJ, 1970–96
retired: 1996

Witt, Cornelius
b. 09/10/1903, Broek op Langedijk, Noord Holland, Netherlands

training: Calvin Theological Seminary, ThB, 1929
ordained: 1929
charges: Leighton, IA, 1929–37; Hull, ND, 1937–41; Harderwyk, Holland, MI, 1941–50; Ebenezer, Trenton, ON, 1950–58; Flint, MI, 1958–63; East Palmyra, NY, 1963–68
retired: 1968
d. 12/08/1983, Holland, MI

Witte, Wilmer Roy
b. 02/02/1928, Midland Park, NJ
training: Calvin Theological Seminary, ThB, 1951
ordained: 1951
charges: Ackley, IA, 1951–54; Walker, Grand Rapids, MI, 1954–58; Ninth St., Holland, MI, 1958–65; Western Springs, IL, 1965–76; Mayfair, Grand Rapids, MI, 1976–93
retired: 1993

Witten, Clarence Henry
b. 07/30/1957, Edmonton, AB
training: Calvin Theological Seminary, MDiv, 1984
ordained: 1985
charges: Faith, Milford, NS, 1985–2001; Community of Matilda Township, Dixon's Corners, ON, 2001–

Wittenbosch, Hans
see: Uittenbosch, Hans

Witteveen, Frederick John
b. 05/05/1963, Duncan, BC
training: Calvin Theological Seminary, MDiv, 1990
ordained: 1991
charges: Friendship Community, Toronto, ON, 1991–

Witvliet, John Lyle
b. 01/10/1942, Highland, IN
training: Calvin Theological Seminary, BD, 1967
ordained: 1967
charges: Holland, MN, 1967–71; East Martin, MI, 1971–76; Central Ave., Holland, MI, 1976–81; First, Jenison, MI, 1981–93; First, Sioux Center, IA, 1993–

Wolf, Norberto Edmundo
b. 09/30/1937, Comodoro Rivadavia, Argentina
training: Northwestern Seminary, BD, 1954
ordained: 1967
charges: Reformed Church in Argentina: Tandil, 1967–71; Mar del Plata, 1972–76; Interdenominational Seminary (ISEDET), Buenos Aires, 1977–91; Florida, Buenos Aires, 1981–82; Comodoro Rivadavia, 1982–90; The Bible League, South

Holland, IL, 1990-91; CRC: Migrant Mission, New Era, MI, 1964-65, 1966-67; West Coast Regional Director for Race Relations, CRC-Pastoral Ministries, Bellflower, CA, 1991-

Wolfert, Simon
b. 05/04/1935, Marienberg, Overijsel, Netherlands
training: Calvin Theological Seminary, BD, 1965
ordained: 1968
charges: Missionary to Brazil, 1968-85; Grace, Scarborough, Toronto, ON, 1985-93; Harbour chaplain, Ministry to Seafarers, Vancouver, BC, 1993-2000
retired: 2000

Wolff, James Earl
b. 11/13/1953, Washington, DC
training: Calvin Theological Seminary, MDiv, 1978; ThM, 1979
ordained: 1981
charges: Lawndale, Chicago, IL, 1981-

Wolmarans, Nicolaas "Nic" Marthinus
b. 10/18/1953, Transvaal, South Africa
training: University of Pretoria, BD, 1979
ordained: 1979
charges: Nederduitch Hervormde Kerk van Africa: 1979-2001; CRC: Covenant, Rocky Mountain House, AB, 2001-

Wolters, Daniel Robert
b. 03/11/1971, Grand Rapids, MI
training: Calvin Theological Seminary, MDiv, 1999
ordained: 1999
charges: (interim) South Kendall Community, Miami, FL, 1999-2000; New Hope Community, Kincheloe, MI, 2000-

Wolters, Lloyd Jay
b. 10/29/1929, Holland, MI
training: Calvin Theological Seminary, BD, 1957
ordained: 1957
charges: Missionary for South Bend, IN, 1957-60; Missionary, Beacon Light Chapel, Sheboygan, WI, 1960-62; Waterloo, IA, 1962-65; Bethel, Fulton, IL, 1965-69; First, Des Plaines, IL, 1969-79; Lamont, MI, 1979-86; Saugatuck, MI, 1986-91
retired: 1991

Wolthuis, Thomas Ray
b. 06/05/1956, Kalamazoo, MI
training: Calvin Theological Seminary, MDiv, 1981; ThM, 1983; Duke University, PhD, 1987
ordained: 1987
charges: Princeton, Grand Rapids, MI, 1986-91;

Eligible for call, 1991-92; Pathway Ministries, Byron Center, MI, 1992-2000; Faculty, Calvin College, Grand Rapids, MI, 2000-01; Interim, Chapel, Ann Arbor, MI, 2001-

Won, Chun S.
b. 03/22/1947, Ham Nam, Korea
training: Western Reformed Seminary, MDiv, 1986
ordained: 1993
charges: Presbyterian: Korean New Life, Tacoma, WA, 1993-94; Zion Korean, Beaverton, OR, 1994-95; CRC: Zion Korean, Beaverton, OR, 1995-97; Gig Harbor, WA, 1997-2002; Church planter, Puyallup, WA, 2002-

Won, Paul W.
b. 10/23/1941
ordained: 1976
charges: Korean Presb. Church: Hap Dong Presb., 1976-84; CRC: Yang Moon, Bellflower, CA, 1984-90; Leave, 1990-91
retired: 1991

Won, Timothy Sang-Joon
b. 07/27/1969, Seoul, South Korea
training: Calvin Theological Seminary, MDiv, 1998
ordained: 2000
charges: Garden of Grace, Westminster, CA, 1999-2002; Chaplain, United States Army, 2002-

Wong, Kinfun
b. 06/23/1955, Hong Kong, China
training: Chinese University of Hong Kong, MDiv, 1986; Calvin Theological Seminary, Special Program for Ministerial Candidacy, 1988
ordained: 1988
charges: Hyde Park, Chicago, IL, 1987-99; Friendship Agape, San Jose, CA, 1999-

Workman, Stanley James
b. 04/11/1944, Muskegon, MI
training: Calvin Theological Seminary, BD, 1969
ordained: 1969
charges: Northern Heights, Kalamazoo, MI, 1969-74; Evergreen, Olympia, WA, 1974-83; Eligible for call, 1983-84; Oasis Community, Orlando, FL, 1984-

Worster, Paul Clarance III
b. 08/22/1963, Grand Rapids, MI
training: Calvin Theological Seminary, MDiv, 2002
ordained: 2002
charges: New church planting, Grand Rapids, MI, 2002-

Woudstra, Marten Hendrik

b. 07/23/1922, Bergum, Friesland, Netherlands
training: Theologische Hogeschool van de Gereformeerde Kerken in Nederland, Kampen, diploma, 1946; Westminster Theological Seminary-PA, 1948; Dropsie College for Hebrew and Cognate Languages, 1952; Vrije Universiteit,
ordained: 1953
charges: Third, Edmonton, AB, 1953–55; Faculty, Calvin Theological Seminary, (On loan to Reformed Theological College, Geelong, Australia, 1972), 1955–79
retired: 1979
d. 10/03/1991, Kentwood, MI

Woudstra, Sierd M.

b. 02/04/1928, Doniaburen, Friesland, Netherlands
training: Calvin Theological Seminary, BD, 1958; Westminster Theological Seminary-PA, ThM, 1961; ThD, 1963
ordained: 1961
charges: Ottawa, ON, 1961–65; Faculty, Dordt College, 1965–67; Faculty, Calvin Theological Seminary, 1967–72, On loan to Reformed Theological Seminary, Geelong, Australia, 1972–75; on loan from Foreign Mission to Hobart, Tasmania, Australia, 1975–77; Faculty, Calvin College, 1977–82; Eligible for call, 1982–88 (Editor, *De Wachter*, 1984–85); Kelloggsville, Grand Rapids, MI, 1988–91; Princeton, Grand Rapids, MI, 1991–93
retired: 1993

Wu, Ping C. (Philip)

b. 05/10/1939, Tainan City, Taiwan
training: Northern Baptist Seminary, MDiv
ordained: 1999
charges: Hyde Park, Chicago, IL, 1999–

Wyckoff, James

b. 01/16/1839, Lodi, NJ
training: New Brunswick Theological Seminary, diploma, 1864
ordained: 1864
charges: RCA: Queens, NY, 1864–71; Bushnell, IL, 1871–74; Germantown, NY, 1875–83; Presbyterian USA: Pine Plaines, NY, 1883–96; Leonia, NJ, 1899–1905; CRC: Leonia, NJ, 1896–99
d. 01/03/1905, Leonia, NJ

Wyenberg, Donald John

b. 03/14/1947, Winnipeg, MB
training: Calvin Theological Seminary, MDiv, 1980
ordained: 1980
charges: Hull, ND, 1980–85; Otay Mesa Community, San Diego, CA, 1985–93; Trinity, Vancouver, WA, 1993–1999; Home missions, Community Life, Houston, TX, 1999–2001; Community Life, Houston, TX, 2001–

Wyngaarden, Jacob

b. 02/20/1865, Vriesland, MI
training: Calvin Theological Seminary, diploma, 1890
ordained: 1890
charges: Oostburg, WI, 1890–93; Firth, NE, 1893–98; Harrison, SD, 1898–1904; New Era, MI, 1904–11; South Olive, MI, 1911–15; Eastmanville, MI, 1915–18; Walker, MI (Pastor, Camp Custer, 1918), 1918–28
retired: 1928
d. 06/03/1936, Grand Rapids, MI

Wyngaarden, Martin Jacob

b. 07/04/1891, Oostburg, WI
training: Calvin Theological Seminary, diploma, 1918; Princeton Theological Seminary, BD, 1919; Princeton University, AM, 1920; University of Pennsylvania, PhD, 1922; Yale University, 1923
ordained: 1923
charges: Tracy, IA, 1923–24; Faculty, Calvin Theological Seminary, 1924–61
retired: 1961
d. 08/11/1978, Grand Rapids, MI

Wynia, Richard Alan

b. 12/03/1958, St. Catharines, ON
training: Theological College of the Canadian Reformed Church, MDiv, 1986; Calvin Theological Seminary, Special Program for Ministerial Candidacy, 1987
ordained: 1987
charges: CRC: Aylmer, ON, 1987–91; Maranatha, Calgary, AB, 1991–92; Alliance of Reformed Churches: Bethel Independent, Calgary, AB, 1992–95; United Reformed Churches: Bethel Independent, Calgary, AB, 1995–98; Covenant Christian, Wyoming, ON, 1998

Yang, Chou Houa

see: Yang, Houa

Yang, David W.

b. 03/28/1936
ordained: 1980
charges: Gideon Presbyterian: Faculty, Korean Theological Seminary, Seoul, Korea, 1977–80; Pastor, Han Sung School Mission, 1978–80; Galilee Presbyterian, 1981–92; CRC: Galilee, Los Angeles, CA, 1992–2002

retired: 2002

Yang, Houa (Chou Houa)
b. 09/06/1964, Xieng Khoung, Laos
training: Reformed Bible College, BRE, 1988; Calvin Theological Seminary, MDiv, 1992
ordained: 1993
charges: CRC: Evangelist to Hmong, Lansing, MI, 1987–91; Missionary-at-large, Hmong, Sheboygan, WI, 1993–96; Eligible for call, 1996–99; Resigned from denomination, 1999

Yang, James C.
ordained: 1990
charges: CRC: Immanuel, Richmond, BC, 1990–92; Baptist: Chinese Baptist Church, El Paso, TX, 1992

Yang, Paul Chunkil
b. 07/31/1956, Seoul, South Korea
training: Princeton Theological Seminary, MDiv, 1987.
ordained: 1988
charges: Young Nok Presbyterian, Los Angeles, CA, 1987–92; CRC: Orange Korean, Fullerton, CA, 1992–97; Pilgrim Church, Clifton, NJ, 1997–99; PCUSA: congregation in New Jersey, 1999

Yang, Peter Sing Sui
b. 07/28/1936, Swaton, China
ordained: 1964
charges: Home missionary to Chinese, Los Angeles, CA, 1963–65; Home missionary, Golden Gate, San Francisco, CA, 1965–89; Leave, 1989–90; Overseas Chinese Mission, New York City, NY, 1990–91; Golden Gate, San Francisco, CA, 1991–2001
retired: 2001

Yang, William M.
b. 08/03/1942, Taegu-Shi, Korea
training: Southern California Theological Seminary, MDiv, 1986; ThM, 1988
ordained: 1992
charges: Pyung, Kang Church of Hawaii, Honolulu, HI, 1991–94; CRC: True Light Church, Honolulu, HI, 1994–

Yang, Xay Xue
b. 06/02/1951
training: declared eligible on the basis of exceptional gifts, 1987
ordained: 1987
charges: Hmong, Sheboygan, WI, 1987–98; Eligible for call, 1998–

Yao, Peter Hengki
b. 03/14/1950, Taipei, Taiwan
training: Taiwan Theological Seminary, MDiv, 1974; Drew University, MA, 1981; Calvin Theological Seminary, Special Program for Ministerial Candidacy, 1983
ordained: 1983
charges: Southern Baptist: Taiwanese Community, Ann Arbor and Detroit, MI, 1983–85; CRC: Hyde Park, Chicago, IL, 1985–86; Resigned from denomination, 1986

Yassa, Nasser Mansour
b. 05/23/1962, Assiut, Egypt
training: International Theological Seminary, MATS, 1989; Reformed Theological Seminary, MDiv, 1989
ordained: 1991
charges: Church planter, Good Land, Santa Monica, CA, 1991–93; The Back to God Hour, Chicago, IL, 1993–96; Eligible for call, 1996–2001; Non-ministerial vocation, 2001

Yazzie, Sampson T.
b. 12/20/1922, Burnham, NM vicinity
training: Calvin Theological Seminary, BD, 1965
ordained: 1965
charges: Shiprock, NM, 1950–65; Farmington, NM, 1965–86
retired: 1986

Yeo, Raymond (Tae-Hoo)
b. 07/13/1957, Ha-Dong, South Korea
training: Calvin Theological Semianry, MDiv, 1992; ThM, 2000
ordained: 1992
charges: Korean, Tacoma, WA, 1992–93; Chang-Ang (Central) Presbyterian, Phoenix, AZ, 1993–97; Boulder Korean, Boulder, CO, 1997–

Yeo, Woon Se
b. 10/07/1936, Pung Chun, Korea
training: General Assembly Theological Seminary, MDiv, 1959, ThM, 1964; Central Theological Seminary, ThM, 1971; Faith Theological Seminary, DMin, 1980; California Graduate School, PhD, 1989
ordained: 1963
charges: USPCA: Albany, NY, 1972–74; Southern Baptist Conference: Washington, DC, 1974–82; CRC: Orange Korean, Fullerton, CA, 1983–85; Eligible for call, 1987–88; Messiah Korean, Buena Park, CA, 1988–95; On loan: Presbyterian Church of Korea: Missionary, Chunan University, 1995–2001

retired: 2001

Yff, George
b. 07/21/1901, Amsterdam, Noord Holland, Netherlands
training: Calvin Theological Seminary, BD, 1932
ordained: 1935
charges: Vocational school, Fort Wingate, NM, 1932-35; Sioux City, IA, 1935-38; Missionary at Zuni, NM, 1938-44; Oakland, MI, 1944-48; Rehoboth, NM, 1948-57; Tohlakai, NM, 1948-57; City missionary for Kalamazoo Board of Missions, Kalamazoo, MI, 1957-60; East Martin, MI, 1960-65; Missionary pastor, Belding, MI, 1965-67
retired: 1967
d. 09/14/1995, Grand Rapids, MI

Yff, Peter John
b. 10/17/1893, Amsterdam, Noord Holland, Netherlands
training: Calvin Theological Seminary, diploma, 1919; Princeton Seminary, 1920
ordained: 1920
charges: Rochester, NY, 1920-23; Lodi, NJ, 1923-25
retired: 1925
d. 03/29/1926, Grand Rapids, MI

Yff, Thomas
b. 10/31/1905, Amsterdam, Noord Holland, Netherlands
training: Calvin Theological Seminary, ThB, 1930
ordained: 1930
charges: North Blendon, MI, 1930-36; Coldbrook Ave., Grand Rapids, MI, 1936-43; Hudsonville, MI, 1943-47; Ninth St., Holland, MI, 1947-52; Bethel, Grand Rapids, MI, 1952-56; Grace, Kalamazoo, MI, 1956-64; Kelloggsville, Grand Rapids, MI, 1964-72
retired: 1972
d. 03/08/1987, Grand Rapids, MI

Yi, Andrew Yongil
b. 09/08/1962, Kang Neung, Korea
training: Golden Gate Baptist Theological Seminary, MDiv, 1992; Calvin Theological Seminary, Special Program for Ministerial Candidacy, 1997
ordained: 1997
charges: Central Korean, 1988-90; Tigard Hope, 1990-94; Hebron, Fife, WA, 1994-

Yi, Dong Kwan
ordained: 2000
charges: PCA: Sah-Lang Church, Madison, WA, -

2000; CRC: Lynnwood Korean, Lynnwood, WA, 2000-2002

Yoo, Sang Ok
b. 12/22/1946
training: Westminster Theological Seminary-PA, MDiv
ordained: 1981
charges: General Association Presbyterian Church in Korea: Philadelphia, PA, 1981-87; Korean Presbyterian Church United States: Spokane, WA, 1987-89; CRC: Korean Grace, Spokane, WA, 1989-93; Korean Myung Sung, Portland, OR, 1993-94; withdrew from denomination, 1994

Yoo, Yin So
b. 09/30/1962, Chung Nam, Korea
training: Korean Presbyterian Seminary, MDiv
ordained: 1993
charges: Presbyterian Church of Korea: Onnuri Church, Korea, 1993-95; Director, Tyrannus International, 1994-97; All Nations Church, Los Angeles, CA, 1996-2002; CRC: All Nations, Los Angeles, CA, 2002-

Yoon, Chong Dae
b. 10/15/1948, Kyong Nam Keo Jae-Gun, Korea
training: Presbyterian General Assembly Theological Seminary, MDiv, 1980; Pacific University, MDiv, 1995
ordained: 1979
charges: Bu Cheon Dong Bu Presbyterian Church, 1974-80; CRC: Valley Dong San, Northridge, CA, 1989-

Yoon, Seung W.
b. 11/06/1941, Kyong Buk Kyong San-Gu, Korea
training: Presbyterian General Assembly Theological Seminary, MDiv, 1967
ordained: 1970
charges: Jang Choong Presbyterian Church, Seoul, Korea, 1965-70; Dong Do, Seoul, Korea, 1970-72; Ae Il, Seoul, Korea, 1972-83; Dae Gil, Seoul, Korea, 1983-88; CRC: Korean American, Orange County, CA, 1988-93; Leave, 1993; Orange Han Min, Garden Grove, CA, 1993-

Young, George Ross
b. 10/16/1947, New York, NY
training: Westminster Theological Seminary-PA, MDiv, 1975; Calvin Theological Seminary, Special Program for Ministerial Candidacy, 1977
ordained: 1979
charges: Missionary, Immanuel, Kalamazoo, MI, 1979-82; Missionary to Japan, 1982-

Young, Randal Kwok

b. 12/26/1957, San Francisco, CA
training: Calvin Theological Seminary, MDiv, 1988
ordained: 1988
charges: Church planting residency, Chino, CA, 1988-92; Friendship Community Church, Rancho Cucamonga/Fontana, CA, 1992-

Youngs, George Roderick

b. 01/06/1911, Grand Haven, MI
training: Calvin Theological Seminary, ThB, 1935
ordained: 1935
charges: Comstock Park Mission, Grand Rapids, MI, 1934-35; Stated supply, Lansing, MI, 1936-39; Lansing, MI, 1939-40; PCUSA: Evangelist, counselor, educator, administrator, 1940-79; RCA: 1979
retired: 1979
d. 02/17/1990, Spring Lake, MI

Ypma, Benjamin

b. 02/05/1919, Farmington, IA
training: Calvin Theological Seminary, ThB, 1952
ordained: 1952
charges: Missionary to South India, 1952-54; First, Grand Haven, MI, 1954-61; Missionary to Japan, 1961-65; Bauer, MI, 1965-72; Leave, 1972-74; On loan: Koinonia Medical Center, Grand Haven, MI, 1974-84
retired: 1984

Ypma, Jacob

b. 07/28/1948, Netherlands
training: Gordon-Conwell Theological Seminary, MDiv, 1973; Calvin Theological Seminary, Special Program for Ministerial Candidacy, 1976
ordained: 1976
charges: CRC: Penticton, BC, 1976-80; Leave, 1980-81; First, Calgary, AB, 1982; Rocky Mountain House, AB, 1982-85; pastor, Salmon Arm, BC

Ypma, Lambert

b. 04/27/1867, Holwerd, Friesland, Netherlands
training: Calvin Theological Seminary, diploma, 1904
ordained: 1904
charges: Lamont, MI, 1904-07; Bemis, SD, 1907-09; Prinsburg, MN, 1909-17; Worthington, MN, 1918-21; Second, Sioux Center, IA, 1921-34
retired: 1934
d. 03/18/1943, Grand Rapids, MI

Yu, Paul (Ki Cheol)

b. 08/07/1967, Pusan, Korea
training: Calvin Theological Seminary, MDiv, 1998
ordained: 2000
charges: First, Allendale, MI, 1999-

Yun, Sung Tae

ordained: 1981
charges: Korean Presbyterian Church, 1981-93; CRC: Boca Raton Korean, Boca Raton, FL, 1993-96; Resigned from denomination, 1996

Zandstra, Benjamin H.

b. 05/26/1953, Chicago, IL
training: Calvin Theological Seminary, MDiv, 1984
ordained: 1981
charges: Otay Mesa Community, CA, San Diego, CA, 1981-84; Non-ministerial vocation, 1984

Zandstra, David George

b. 05/28/1930, Grove City, PA
training: Calvin Theological Seminary, ThB, 1964; MDiv, 1975
ordained: 1965
charges: Home missionary, Flanders Valley, NJ, 1965-69; Trinity, Philadelphia, PA, 1969-76; Dallas, TX, 1976-83; San Diego, CA, 1983-90; Fairfield, CA, 1990-

Zandstra, Gerald L.

b. 05/20/1964, Hammond, IN
training: Calvin Theological Seminary, MDiv, 1990; ThM, 1993
ordained: 1991
charges: Midland Park, NJ, 1991-93; Seymour, Grand Rapids, MI, 1993-2000; Leave, 2000-01; Hillside, Cutlerville, MI, 2001-

Zandstra, Jack

b. 05/06/1904, Highland, IN
training: Westminster Theological Seminary-PA, ThB, 1934
ordained: 1934
charges: PCUSA: Alexandria, SD, 1934-36; OPC: Alexandria and Bridgewater, SD, 1936-39; Harrisville, PA, 1939-40; Missionary at Omaha, NE, 1940-42; Knox Church, Philadelphia, PA, 1942-43; Nathanael Institute, Chicago, IL, 1943-46; CRC: Nathanael Institute, Chicago, IL, 1946-49; Missionary-pastor, Sioux City, IA, 1949-55; Itinerant home missionary, 1955-65, at Columbus, OH, 1957-58; at Indianapolis, IN, 1958-62; at Salt Lake City, UT, 1964-65; Home missionary for Classis California South at Lakewood, CA, 1965-66; at Norwalk, CA, 1966-69; Missionary, Kettering, Dayton, OH, 1969; Missionary, Wanamassa, NJ, 1969-70
retired: 1970

d. 12/21/1984, Boca Raton, FL

Zandstra, Jerry Allen
b. 05/12/1939, Highland, IN
training: Calvin Theological Seminary, ThB, 1964;
Chapman College, MA, 1973
ordained: 1965
charges: CRC: Minister of evangelism for Madison
Ave., Paterson, NJ, 1965–67; Chaplain, United
States Navy, 1967–73; Chula Vista, CA, 1973–78;
RCA: Chula Vista, CA, 1978–85; Missionary, Ku-
wait, 1985–

Zantingh, Andrew
b. 10/01/1971, Dunnville, ON
training: Calvin Theological Seminary, MDiv, 2000
ordained: 2000
charges: First, Hamilton, ON, 2000–

Zantingh, Harry Douglas
b. 05/15/1958, Grimsby, ON
training: Calvin Theological Seminary, MDiv, 1989
ordained: 1989
charges: First, Taber, AB, 1989–94; Alliston, ON,
1994–

Zantingh, John
b. 08/16/1933, Hoogeveen, Drenthe, Netherlands
training: Calvin Theological Seminary, BD, 1961;
MDiv, 1986
ordained: 1961
charges: Bloomfield, ON, 1961–65; Woodstock,
ON, 1965–69; Richmond, BC, 1969–73; Calvin,
Dundas, ON, 1973–83; Maranatha, Bowmanville,
ON, 1983–90; Immanuel, Hamilton, ON, 1990–98
retired: 1998

Zeeuw, John J.
b. 10/09/1893, Paterson, NJ
training: Calvin Theological Seminary, diploma,
1922
ordained: 1922
charges: CRC: Noordeloos, Holland, MI, 1922–25;
First, Kalamazoo, MI, 1925–32; Oakdale Park,
Grand Rapids, MI, 1932–35; Non-ministerial vocation, education, 1935–52, Saginaw, MI; PCUSA:
Vasser, MI, 1942–52; Covenant, Bay City, MI,
1953–66
retired: 1966
d. 01/24/1972, Des Moines, IA

Zeilstra, William Don
b. 07/21/1954, Oak Park, IL
training: Calvin Theological Seminary, MDiv, 1982
ordained: 1987

charges: Grangeville, ID, 1987–91; Almond Valley,
Ripon, CA, 1991–95; Second, Pella, IA, 1995–

Zetterholm, Earl Ellis
b. 05/25/1912, Oak Park, IL
training: Westminster Theological Seminary-PA,
ThB and BD, 1948
ordained: 1948
charges: OPC: Seattle, WA, 1948–54; Stated supply, Grace Chapel, Lansing, MI, 1983–84; CRC:
First, Muskegon, MI, 1954–58; Non-ministerial vocation, high school educator, 1958–81
retired: 1981

Zevalking, John Garet
b. 11/26/1954, Lansing, MI
training: Calvin Theological Seminary, MDiv, 1990
ordained: 1990
charges: Coordinator of evangelism, Alpine Ave.,
Grand Rapids, MI, 1989–90; Cincinnati, OH, 1990–
98; Hillside Community, Cutlerville, MI, 1998–
2000; Non-ministerial vocation, 2000

Zimmerman, Douglas Roy
b. 12/06/1951, Grand Rapids, MI
training: Calvin Theological Seminary, MDiv, 1983
ordained: 1983
charges: Calvin, Wyckoff, NJ, 1983–89; North
Blendon, MI, 1989–95; Lee St., Wyoming, MI,
1995–98; Resigned from ministry, 1999

Zinkand, John
b. 03/08/1927, Hempstead, NY
training: Westminster Theological Seminary-PA,
BD, 1954; ThM, 1955; Brandeis University, PhD,
1958
ordained: 1965
charges: RCA: Faculty, Westminster Theological
Seminary, 1965–69; Faculty, Dordt College, Sioux
Center, IA, 1969–83; CRC: Faculty, Dordt College,
Sioux Center, IA, 1983–86; Faculty, Reformed
Theological College of Nigeria, Nigeria, 1986–90;
Faculty, Theological College of Northern Nigeria,
1990–91
retired: 1991

Zoerhof, Laryn Gene
b. 05/26/1946, Hamilton, MI
training: Calvin Theological Seminary, BD, 1971
ordained: 1971
charges: Worthington, MN, 1971–76; Sunnyside,
WA, 1976–84; First, Highland, IN, 1984–98;
Twelfth Ave., Jenison, MI, 1998–

Zomermaand, Robert Dean

b. 04/17/1952, Sioux Center, IA
training: Calvin Theological Seminary, MDiv, 1978
ordained: 1978
charges: Chandler, MN, 1978-84; First, Paterson, NJ, 1984-90; Lafayette, IN, 1990-96; Sunrise, Lafayette, IN, 1996-2002; First, Sheboygan, WI, 2002-

Zondervan, James Dale

b. 11/01/1953, Willmar, MN
training: Calvin Theological Seminary, MDiv, 1980
ordained: 1980
charges: Seminary intern, Oakdale Park, Grand Rapids, MI, 1978-79; Missionary-pastor, Olavarrma, Reformed Church of Argentina, 1980-86; Brooten, MN, 1986-91; Nobleford, AB, 1991-97; High River, AB, 1997-2002; Granum, AB, 2002-

Zuidema, Joel Wayne

b. 01/22/1963, Muskegon, MI
training: Calvin Theological Seminary, MDiv, 1973
ordained: 1992
charges: Director of youth, Midland Park, NJ, 1990-91 Church developer, Austin, TX, 1992-93; North Austin Community, Austin, TX, 1993-94; McBain, MI, 1994-98; Community, Roselawn, IN, 1998-

Zuidema, Todd Michael

b. 09/08/1969, Pella, IA
training: Calvin Theological Seminary, MDiv, 1999
ordained: 1999
charges: Mayfair, Grand Rapids, MI, 1999-

Zwaagman, Benjamin

b. 12/30/1877, Chicago, IL
training: Calvin Theological Seminary, diploma, 1911
ordained: 1911
charges: Sullivan, MI, 1911-15; Spring Lake, MI, 1915-17; Highland MI, 1917-24; Bauer, MI, 1924-27; Leave, 1927-28; Rock Rapids, IA, 1928-31
retired: 1931
d. 10/13/1933, Grand Rapids, MI

Zwaanstra, Henry

b. 07/27/1895, Chicago, IL
training: Calvin Theological Seminary, BD, 1932
ordained: 1933
charges: Worthington, MN, 1932-40; Lincoln Center, IA, 1940-54; Ellsworth, MI, 1954-62
retired: 1962
d. 11/26/1968, Grand Rapids, MI

Zwaanstra, Henry

b. 01/01/1936, Grangeville, ID
training: Calvin Theological Seminary, BD, 1961; Vrije Universiteit, Amsterdam, ThD, 1973
ordained: 1966
charges: Faculty, Calvin Theological Seminary, 1965-2001
retired: 2001

Zwaanstra, John

b. 04/16/1903, Chicago, IL
training: Calvin Theological Seminary, BD, 1932
ordained: 1933
charges: Grangeville, ID, 1933-38; Modesto, CA, 1938-42; Platte, SD, 1942-53; Third, Denver, CO, 1953-64; Burnaby, BC, 1964-68
retired: 1968
d. 08/04/1995, Denver, CO

Zwart, Andrew

b. 06/01/1934, Buitenpost, Friesland, Netherlands
training: Calvin Theological Seminary, BD, 1964
ordained: 1964
charges: Pioneer, Cedar Springs, MI, 1964-67; Calvin, Holland, MI, 1967-70; Non-ministerial vocation, 1970

Zwart, Steven A.

b. 04/19/1968, Hawarden, IA
training: Calvin Theological Seminary, MDiv, 1996
ordained: 1996
charges: Woodland Creek Community, Maple Grove, MN, 1996-98; Unity Prinsburg, MN, 1998-

Zwier, Daniel

b. 12/08/1879, Opperdoes, Noord Holland, Netherlands
training: Calvin Theological Seminary, diploma, 1911
ordained: 1911
charges: Oostburg, WI, 1911-14; Munster, IN, 1914-20; Maple Ave., Holland, MI, 1920-46; Chatham, ON, 1946
d. 06/17/1946, Holland, MI

Zylstra, Andrew

b. 12/17/1926, Buitenpost, Friesland, Netherlands
training: Calvin Theological Seminary, BD, 1953
ordained: 1953
charges: Rusk, MI, 1953-58; Bethel, Lynden, WA, 1958-65; Second, Pella, IA, 1965-70; First, Kalamazoo, MI, 1970-74; Spring Lake, MI, 1974-83; Cedar, IA, 1983-88
retired: 1988

Zylstra, Carl Eugene
b. 05/23/1948, Grand Rapids, MI
training: Calvin Theological Seminary, BD, 1973;
MDiv, 1978
ordained: 1973
charges: Hammond, IN, 1973–79; Leave at
Princeton, 1979–83; Immanuel, Orange City, IA,
1983–96; President, Dordt College, Sioux Center,
IA, 1996–

Zylstra, David Arthur
b. 04/07/1948, Chicago, IL
training: Calvin Theological Seminary, BD, 1973;
MDiv, 1987
ordained: 1974
charges: Archer Ave., Chicago, IL, 1974–81;
Baldwin, WI, 1981–92; Parkersburg, IA, 1992–99;
First, Prinsburg, MN, 1999–

Zylstra, Gerben
b. 09/18/1895, Knoxville, IA vicinity
training: Calvin Theological Seminary, diploma,
MA, 1923; Princeton Seminary, 1924
ordained: 1925
charges: Alamosa, CO, 1925–41; Middleburg, IA,
1941–49; Des Plaines, IL, 1949–62
retired: 1962
d. 03/14/1981, Grand Rapids, MI

Zylstra, Martin Gene
b. 12/18/1921, Lynnville, IA
training: Calvin Theological Seminary, ThB, 1952
ordained: 1952
charges: Clara City, MN, 1952–56; Milwaukee,
WI, 1956–63; Arcadia, Grand Rapids, MI, 1963–70;
Highland Ave., Redlands, CA, 1971–81; Volga, SD,
1981–88
retired: 1988

Zylstra, Paul Calvin
b. 12/18/1921, East Grand Rapids, MI
training: Calvin Theological Seminary, ThB, 1952;
ThM, 1985
ordained: 1952
charges: Aetna, MI, 1952–56; South Grandville,
Grand Rapids, MI, 1956–64; San Diego, CA, 1964–
70; Ferrysburg, MI, 1970–76; Preakness, Wayne,
NJ, 1976–81; Palm Lane, Scottsdale, AZ, 1981–87
retired: 1987

CHAPLAINS

Clinical Supervisors
Brander, William, 1980-95
Brummel, Robert L., 1983-
De Boer, Cornelius, 2002-
Dyk, W. Dean, 1998-
Evans, A. Dirk, 1972-2001
Jansen, John, 1986-
Kok, James R., 1969-
Uken, Robert, 1985 -
Van Harn, Karl J., 1994-
Vink, Case, 1995-
Visser, Duane A., 1972-95

Commercial/Industrial
Bultman, Stanley, 2001-
De Haan, Peter, 2001-
Klimp, Ronald A., 199-
Menninga, Arlan D., 1981-83
Rietema, Fred D., 1981-90
Steenhoek, Donald J., 1987-95
Vander Laan, Jack L., 1981-
Van Donk, John, 1983-87

Corrections
Beerens, A. Gene, 1988-95
Boersma, J. Karel, 1983-84
Bouma, Henry, 1986-97
Brander, William, 1990-96
de Vries, John Jr., 1975-79; 2001-02
Dykstra, William J., 1978-90; 1998-
Faber, Harry, 2001
Holtrop, Elton J., 1947-66
Hoogewind, Allen J., 1989-90
Huizenga, Thomas H., 1992-97
Keegstra, Carroll E., 1994-
Lamsma, John H., 1978-
Mantel, Peter, 1974-1978
Sikkema, Paul D., 1995-2001
Smidstra, Henry H., 1991-
Swierenga, Raymond C., 1983-
Vanden Berg, Richard D., 1989-94

Vander Schaaf, James, 1980-

Developmentally Disabled
Baker, Ronald D., 1999-
Bierling, William A., 1985-2000
Hoogewind, Allen J., 1990-
Klaasen, Thomas G., 2001-
Lenters, William R., 1973-81
Oosterveen, Gerald A., 1981-84
Van Dyken, William D., 1988-
Vredeveld, Ronald C., 1979-

Hospice
Bultman, Stanley J., 1995-
De Vries, Stanley J, 1996-
De Young, Ronald W., 1991-
Einfeld, Douglas J., 1997-
Evenhuis, Eric F., 2001
Flietstra, Carol, 1996-
Frens, Gerald W., 1991-
Greidanus, Janet, 1997
Hommes, Edward R., 2001
Hommes, Raymond E., 1997-
Kamper, Dennis, 1999-
Koornneef, Robert, 1990-97
Moxey, William J., 1995-
Van Enk, Gordon, 1993-
van Eyk, Bart, 1997
Willoughby, Karl K., 2001

Hospital
Baker, Louis F., 1979-85
Brummel, Robert L., 1979-
Bultman, Stanley J., 1986-
De Boer, Cornelius, 1999-2002
De Boer, Nell, 1991-
De Jong, Harold T., 1978-92
De Ruiter, Lydia, 1996-2000
De Vries, Gary A., 1993-
De Vries Jr., John, 2002-
De Vries, John W., 2001-

De Young, Roger, 1981–85
De Young, Ronald W., 1993–96
Deckinga, Mark D., 1998–
Dekker, Erika, 2001–
Dekker, Margriet, 2000–
Den Otter, Sini, 1988–98
Diemer, Fred, 1999–
Dyk, W. Dean, 1990–98
Dykstra, Edwin J., 1978–82
Dykstra, Jerry, 1972–80
Evans, A. Dirk, 1970–72
Evenhuis, Eric F., 1982–93
Flikkema, Melvin D., 1983–88
Frens, Gerald W., 1985–91
Friend, Jan, 1977–1987
Hommes, Edward R., 1993–2000; 2001–
Kaemingk, Franklin, 1964–76
Kieft, Gordon J., 1970–87
Klompeen, Donald J., 1983–89
Koning, Frederic J., 1998–
Koster, Philip J., 1975–99
Kranenberg, Peter, 1988–94
Kroeze, Gloria, 1998–
Kuperus, Harry, 1992–93
Mans, Peter J., 1979–83
Mueller, Ralph, 2001–
Mulder, Bernard, 1999–
Natelborg, John, 2001–
Pierre, Linda, 1999–2000
Poot, Arie, 1984–90
Post, Henry R., 1977–1991
Rietema, Fred D., 1990–
Rignalda, Gerard, 1987–95
Roelofs, Curt G., 1979–2001
Romeyn, Ruth, 1999–
Schaal, John, 1972–2000
Schipper, Allen H., 1988–
Sikkema, Paul D., 1997–
Smits, Lee R., 1999–
Sponholz, Howard D., 1976–95
Stoel, James, 1996–
Stroo, William A., 1969–70
Timmer, Wes, 1998–2001
Van Arragon, George J., 1990–96
Vande Creek, Larry, 1963–94
Van Dellen, Idzerd, 1907–65
VandenBerg, Richard D., 1994–
Vander Heide, Kenneth, 1984–93
Vande Riet, Garrett H., 1960–64
Vander Jagt, Samuel, 1979–94
Vander Laan, Betty, 2001
Vander Lee, Paul G., 1968–70
Vander Schaaf, James, 1977–80
van der Vorst, Dirk, 2001–
Vander Wekken, Denis, 1986–

Van Gelder, David W., 1994–2001
Van Harn, Karl J., 1992–94
Van Heest, Steven J., 1999–
Vink, Case, 1988–95
Visser, Duane A., 1992–95
Werkman, Sindney A., 1960–62
Wezeman, Kenneth R., 1971–74; 1981–92
Winkle, Peter D., 1977–86

Long Term Care

Bultman, Stanley, 1986–
De Bruyne, Peter W., 1992–96
De Jong, Harold T., 1992–95
De Young, Ronald W., 1992–93
Eising, Henry, 1992–
Geurkink, Vernon F., 1992–
Hubers, Wick, 2002–
Kiekover, Harvey A., 1994–
Klaasen, Thomas G., 2000–
Kok, James A., 1993–
Meppelink, John L., 1986–94
Persenaire, Clarence, 1997 –
Post, Henry R., 1991–2001
Praasma, Herman, 1998–
Reyneveld, Clarence, 1998–
Stoel, James, 2000
Van Arragon, George J., 1996–
Van Dyk, Jan, 1982–85
Van Egmond, Peter, 1987–
Zylstra, Andrew, 1995–

Mental Health Center

Alferink, Jerry L., 1985–87
Bruins, Rozanne Meyer, 1999–
de Vries, John Jr., 1986–88
Evenhuis, Eric F., 1978–82
Heerema, Jacob P., 1988–91
Heynen, Ralph, 1944–72
Hommes, Raymond E., 1969–70
Jabay, Earl, 1960–62
Jansma, Theodore J., 1962–74
Kieft, Gordon J., 1967–68
Kok, James R., 1969–84
Lise, Markus J., 1986–
Mans, Peter J. Jr., 1970–71; 1978–89
Mantel, Peter, 1973–74
Niewiek, Peter J., 1982–85
Post, Henry R., 1975–77
Uken, Robert H., 1977–85
Vanden Bosch, Thomas, 1963–65
Vander Kooi, George, 1957–67
Vander Kwaak, Nicholas, 1976–2002
Van Harn, Karl J., 1994–
Van Houten, Siebert A., 1979–84
Verseput, Theodore, 1985–86

Visser, Duane A., 1973-92
Weaver, Philip, 1992-

Military
Canadian Armed Forces Reserve
van Eyk, Bart, 1995-
Civil Air Patrol
De Young, James C., 1989-96, 1999-
Elder, Allen, 1999-2000
Friend, Jan, 1963-1965
Klimp, Ronald, 1999-
Slager, Kenneth R., 1979-
Vander Ziel, Thomas, 1997-2000
Zeilstra, William D., 1989-91
U.S. Air Force
Bode, Harold, 1962-74
Bronkema, Ralph W., 1966-86
Cornelisse, Charles R., 1991-
Dokter, Gerrit B., 1956-60
Guikema, Henry, 1962-80; 1983-85
Hartwell, Richard M. Jr., 1981-
Klaasen, Thomas G., 1986-97
Kok, Louis E., 1962-88
Menninga, Arlan D., 1968-74
Tadema, Rits, 1968-70
Vande Steeg, Marinus G., 1983-
Wiersum, Karl J., 1986-
U.S. Air Force Reserve
Aupperlee, J. George, 1982-
Bode, Harold, 1974-94
Bronkema, Ralph W., 1959-66
Cornelisse, Charles, 1986-91
Kammeraad, Carl, 1981-
Menninga, Arlan D., 1974-83
Rienstra, Andrew, 1973-82
Vande Lune, James, 1987-
Vander Ark, Jay C., 1960-89
Wisse, Donald P., 1979-90
U.S. Air National Guard
Klaasen, Thomas G., 98-
Sikkema, Lambert, 1989-
U.S. Army
Begay, Anthony, 1978-82
Brander, William, 1968-84
De Vries, Nicholas, 1943-46
Dusseljee, Aldrich, 1943-46
Ellens, Dale D., 1983-95
Ellens, Jay H., 1956-1961; 1983-95
Friend, Jan, 1962-77
Gho, InSoon, 1998-
Goote, Marinus, 1943-46
Hemple, Bruce C., 1959-69
Hoitenga, Dewey J., 1943-46
Holtrop, Corneal, 1943-45
Honderd, Peter, 1942-45

Hoogland, John J., 1959-89
Keizer, Herman Jr., 1968-2002
Kikkert, Timothy J., 1985-98
Konynenbelt, Marvin, 1965-93
Oldenburg, Cornelius, 1940-42
Oostenink, Dick J. Jr., 1945-146, 1947-57
Ouwinga, Harvey A., 1962-69
Rienstra, Andrew R., 1959-62
Rietkerk, Timothy L., 1996-
Schoolland, Cornelius M., 1943-46
Smit, Harvey A., 1956-59
Stob, George, 1943-1946
Terpstra, Gordon A., 1989-92
Touw, Philip R., 1977-95
Trap, Leonard, 1917-19
Vande Kieft, Henry D., 1943-47
Vander Ark, Clifford, 1942-46
Vander Ark, Jay C., 1956-60
Vander Kooi, George, 1943-46
Vander Meer, John, 1943-45
Vande Steeg, Marinus G., 1979-81
Van Dyken, Jack Jr., 1982-
Van Houten, Frederick W., 1943-46
Van Schouwen, Cornelius J., 1942-46
Van Til, Henry R., 1943-46
Verbrugge, John C., 1943-46
Vroon, Simon, 1942-45
Vruwink, Paul H., 1958-61; 1964-82
Wagenmaker, Tyler, 1998-
Wezeman, Richard H., 1942-46
Willoughby, Karl K., 1975-2001
Won, Timothy, 2002-
U.S. Army Reserve
Almarez, Joseph E., 1995-2000
Begay, Anthony, 1982-98
Bierenga, Robert L., 1991-
Brown, Norman, 1981-83
Dykstra, Thomas R., 1986-
Ellens, Dale D., 1981-83; 1995-
Ellens, J. Harold, 1979-83
Flikkema, Melvin J., 1985-
Friend, Jan, 1978-1991
Hensen, William C., 1989-
Koeman, Kenneth D., 1979-81
Koeman, Scott, 2002-
Mans, Peter J. Jr., 1979-85
Meyer, Galen, 1974-98
Oldenburg, Cornelius, 1937-40
Oostenink, Dick J. Jr., 1947-83
Ouwinga, Harvey, 1969-96
Pruim, Jay R., 1970-2000
Rietkerk, Timothy L., 1991-96
Schaal, John H., 1940-41
Shuart, Esler L., 1979-90
Spriensma, Audred T., 1989-93

Terpstra, Gordon A., 1993–
Van Dyken, Jack Jr., 1979–82
Verseput, Theodore, 1979–88

U.S. Coast Guard
Cooper, George D., 1983–86
Vrieland, Douglas J., 1999–
Walcott, Thomas J., 1998–

U.S. Coast Guard Reserve
Mans, Peter, 1982–1985

U.S. Navy
Anderson, Bruce M., 1987–
Belanus, Donald G., 1979–2000
Bergsma, Herbert L., 1966–91
Beversluis, Nicholas H., 1944–47
Boer, Harry R., 1942–46
Boertje, Paul A., 1945–46
Bouma, Roger L., 1992–
Brown, Norman F., 1983–
Brummel, Robert L., 1966–79
Cooper, George D., 1980–
Dahm, Arlo J., 1958–67
De Jong, Peter, 1944–46
Dekker, Harold, 1943–46
den Dulk, Donald E., 1975–83
Holtrop, Elton J., 1943–47
Kosten, William, 1955–58
Mans, Peter J., 1967–70
Meyer, Galen H., 1966–69
Roon, Albert J., 1966–92
Silveira, Richard J., 1985–
Swierenga, Raymond C., 1960–83
Van Andel, Adrian, 1953–57
Verhulst, Eric B., 1995–
Vrieland, Douglas J., 1996–
Walcott, Thomas J., 1996–
Zandstra, Jerry A., 1967–73

U.S. Naval Reserve
Almarez, Joseph E., 1995–2000
Belanus, Donald G., 1971–79
Brown, Norman, 1981–83
Cooper, George D., 1978–80
Dykstra, Thomas R., 1986–
Mans, Peter J. Jr., 1972–85
Meyer, Galen H., 1969–74
Shuart, Esler L., 1979–90
Walcott, Thomas J., 1994–96

Pastoral Counselers
Boer, H. Hendrik, 1998–
Brander, William, 1985–90
Byker, Donald A., 1989–94
Cho, John, 1996–
Compaan, Arlo D., 1979–
Dadson, Michael, 2001–
De Jong, Harold T., 1996–2000

DeLange, Karl J., 1999–
de Vries, John Jr., 1988–2000
De Young, Ronald W., 1989–91
Draayer, Sidney, 1978–99
Dreise, Albert, 1989–
Dykstra, Edwin J., 1975–78
Ellens, Dale D., 1995–
Evenhuis, Eric F., 1995–
Fondse, Charles H., 1996–99
Friend, Jan, 1978–94
Geelhoed, Robert K., 1990–
Gorter, Andrew, 2002–
Grevengoed, Richard O., 1983–
Haan, Tom, 2001–
Habermehl, Dirk N., 1985–93
Hager, Terry A., 1978–90
Helder, Albert, 1968–69
Hogan, Orlin J., 1989–91
Holtrop, Elton J., 1967–68
Holwerda, James A., 1997–
Hommes, Raymond E., 1992–97
Hoogewind, Allen J., 1979–1989; 2001–
Hoogland, Marvin P., 1976–2000
Jansen, John K., 1986–
Jansma, Theodore J., 1962–74
Kieft, Gordon J., 1969–70; 1987–93
Klompeen, Donald J., 1974–76; 1989–98; 1999–
Kok, James R., 1963–1964
Konynenbelt, Marvin, 1993–96
Lenters, William R., 1966–68; 1999–2000
Lieverdink, Dirk J.M., 1968–73
Mans, Peter J., 1970–71
Mantel, Peter, 1983–84; 1987–93
Nydam, Ronald J., 1984–98
Oosterveen, Gerald A., 1974–81
Peterson, Ronald L., 1994–
Piersma, Elton J., 1975–189
Pool, Melle, 1990–95
Steenhoek, Donald J., 1995–97
Stroo, William A., 1989–
Teitsma, Herman J., 1982–87
Van Dam, Harry, 1984–96
Vanden Bosch, Thomas, 1965–71
Van Gelder, David W., 1989–
Van Houten, Siebert A., 1984–
Van Katwijk, Peter L., 1976–91
Van Regenmorter, John D., 1997–
Veeneman, Ryan W., 1990–
Venegas, Dante, 1996–99
Visser, Duane A., 1966–70
Ypma, Benjamin, 1974–84

Service Pastors
Bratt, Albert H., 1918–19; 1943–45
Dekker, Harold, 1942–43

Dykstra, Harry A., 1941–46
Dykstra, Simon A., 1942–43
Moes, Herman, 1943–46
Schaal, John H., 1941
Van Andel, Adrian, 1957–58
Vande Kieft, John M., 1918–19; 1943–46
Vande Kieft, Joseph, 1943–46
U.S. Army
Pousma, Richard H., 1918
U.S. Army/YMCA
DeKorne, John C., 1918

Department of Veterans Affairs
Cok, Ronald H., 1992–
Dekker, Margriet, 1999–2000
Hemple, Ronald W., 1980–90
Hommes, Edward R., 2001
Kuperus, Harry, 1993–
Rietema, Fred D., 1990–
Robinson, Carol, 2001–
Swierenga, William, 1960–76
Van Andel, Adrian, 1966–85
Vanden Bosch, Thomas, 1971–88

Evangelists

Aardema, Onie
Horseshoe Gospel Chapel, Grand Junction, MI, 1947-58; Milgrove Chapel, Allegan, MI, 1958-59

Aardsma, Dirk
Hammond City Mission, Hammond, IN, 1946-58; Immanuel Chapel, Oak Lawn, IL, 1958-74; Chicagoland CR Missions, 1974-78; Trinity Chapel, Oak Lawn, IL, 1978-80

Aardsma, Walter
Roseland Back to God Chapel, Chicago, IL, 1950-55; Pullman Gospel Center, Pullman, IL, 1955-63

Adema, Bert
Indian Metis Christian Fellowship, Regina, SK, 1996-

Adema, James
Dildine, Ionia, MI, 1976-77

Ahrens, Nick
Bridge Community, Frankfort, IL, 2001-

Alderink, Wayne
Ionia Ave. Chapel, Grand Rapids, MI, 1954-55; Bowen Mills Chapel, Middleville, MI, 1955-59; Back to God Chapel, Paterson, NJ, 1959-60

Alfaro, Orlando
Nueva Comunidad, Compton, CA, 1998-2001

Altena, Hans
Stated supply, High River, AB, 1974; Youth minister, First Calgary, AB, 1974-76; Program coordinator, Young Calvinist Federation, 1976-77

Andries, J.
Cambodian, Stockton, CA, 1984-89; Christian Evangelical Chapel, Stockton, CA, 1984-85

Apostol, Vince
Missionary, Philippines, 1963-96

Arevalo, Edwin R.
Jersey City Mission, Jersey City, NJ, 1990-2001

Arthur, Salim
Asian Christian Church, Hamilton, IN, 2001-

Baccam, Khay
Faith, Sioux Center, IA, 1994-

Bailey, Arthur
Abundant Life Ministries, Grand Rapids, MI, 1999-

Bakker, Frank A.
Indian missions, Salt Lake City, UT, 1961-65; Allegan Chapel, Allegan, MI, 1965-71; American Indian Center, Los Angeles, CA, 1971-75; Cypress Gardens, Winter Haven, FL, 1975-76; Forgotten Man Mission, Grand Rapids, MI, 1976-77; Neighborhood evangelist, Godwin Heights and Coordinator of evangelism, Alpine Ave., Grand Rapids, MI, 1977-80

Baldwin, James L.
New Hope Community Church, Inez, KY, 1990-98; First Crookston/Grand Forks Community, Crookston/Grand Forks, MN, 1998-

Bandstra, Alvin
Tracy, IA, 1995-

Barber, Max
Back to God Chapel, Marion, MI, 1963-65; Guiding Light Mission, Grand Rapids, MI, 1968-69; Lakeside Community Church, Alto, MI, 1969-74

Battjes, Peter N.
Millgrove, Allegan, MI, 1978-87

Baudequin, Yannick
Eglise Chretienne Reformee St. Paul, Ottawa, ON, 1985-

Baylor, Nathan P.
Parish evangelism, Godwin Heights, Grand Rapids, MI, 1957-59; Back to God Chapel, Gallatin Gateway, MT, 1959-64; Hillcrest Chapel, Grand Rapids, MI, 1964-66; Horseshoe Chapel, Grand Junction, MI, 1966-70

Becenti, Alfred
San Antone, NM, 1964-77; Crownpoint, NM, 1977-80

Begay, Cato
Red Rock Mission, Shiprock, NM, 1966-72

Begay, Howard
Farmington, NM, 1962-63; Tohatchi, NM, 1969-72; Crownpoint, NM, 1972-82; Red Valley, AZ, 1982-92; emeritus

Benally, Bert
Shiprock, NM, 1972-80

Berghoef, Gerald
Livingston Chapel, Grand Rapids, MI, 1967-68, 1971-79; Windfall Chapel, Grant, MI, 1976-77

Berkompas, D.
Grass Lake, CA, 1981-82

Boehm, Henry
Palmer Chapel, Reeman, MI, 1958-60; Calvary Chapel, Hamilton, ON, 1960-65; Pine Grove, Howard City, MI and Windfall Chapel, Grant, MI, 1965-70; Marion, MI, 1970-75; Community, River Drive Park, ON, 1975-76; Marion, MI, 1976-77; Faith, Shubenacadie, NS, 1981-85; Pinegate Community, Cutlerville, MI, 1985-88; Cochrane, ON, 1988-97; John Calvin, Truro, NS, 1997-

Boetsma, Alvern G.
Good News Chapel, Oskaloosa, IA, 1965-

Boeve, Joseph
Reach, Inc., 1978-81; Missionary, Philippines, 1993-92; Reach Ministries International, Philippines, 1998-

Bol, Jack
Second Christian Reformed Gospel Chapel, Denver, CO, 1950-58; Way of Life Gospel Center, Den-

ver, CO, 1952-57; Bethesda Sanitarium, Denver, CO, 1958-60

Borrego, Ramon
see list of ordained ministers

Bouwkamp, Ronald
Back to God Chapel, Tawatinaw, AB, 1964-66; Back to God Chapel, Stauffer, AB, 1965-66; Alger Gospel Chapel, Alger, WA, 1966-71

Bouwman, Roger
see list of ordained ministers

Boyd, Bobby
Toadlena and Newcomb, NM, 1987-96; Bethlehem, Tohlakai, NM, 1996-

Boyd, David C.
Navajo Indian Fields, Carisso, NM, 1945-50; Calvary and Bravo Chapels, Holland, MI, 1950-55; Christian Reformed Church of Albuquerque, NM, 1955-58

Braaksma, Richard J.
Intern, New Life, Abbotsford, BC, 2000-01; The Talking Stick, Santa Monica, CA, 2000-

Braunius, James P.
Midland Park, NJ, 1995-

Brink, Daniel J.
see list of ordained ministers

Brinks, Harold
Ivanrest Chapel, Grandville, MI, 1948-50; Godwin Gospel, Chapel, 1950-54; Sunshine Back to God Chapel, Grand Rapids, MI, 1954-56; Lake Odessa, MI, 1962-63

Brummel, Corwin J.
Teec Nos Pos, NM, 1961-70; Shiprock, NM, 1970-77; Naschitti, Tohatchi, NM, 1977-88; Church Rock, NM, 1988-97; emeritus

Brummel, Foster
Spruce Ave. and Bravo Chapels, 1953-58, Bravo Chapel, Holland, MI, 1956-63; Woodville Chapel, White Cloud, MI, 1963-92; Palmer Chapel, Reeman, MI, 1970-71

Buikema, Henry
Star Lake Mission, Crown Point, NM, 1945-47; Arcadia Chapel, Grand Rapids, MI, 1947-58; Calvary Chapel, Lowell, MI, 1958-68; Belding Christian

Reformed Church, Belding, MI, 1968-69; Minister
of Evangelism, Bethel, Grand Rapids, WI, 1973-76

Buist, Clarence
Lawndale Gospel Chapel, Comstock, MI, 1953-63;
Beacon Light Chapel, Sheboygan, WI, 1963-66

Burton, Jerome
see list of ordained ministers

Byl, Ken
Sardis, BC, 1991-94; Hope Community, Surrey,
BC, 1991-94; Heartland Fellowship, Chillliwack,
BC, 1994-

Bytwork, Albert W.
Caledonia, Chapel, Caledonia, MI, 1954-62; Charlotte, MI, 1962-73; Portage, MI, 1973-78; Stated
supply, Portage, MI, 1978-79; Pinegate Community, Cutlerville, MI, 1979-85; Unity, Paw Paw, MI,
1985-90; Cutlerville East, Cutlerville, MI, 1990-

Calix, Denis R.
Bayonne, NJ, 1999-

Campbell, David
Missionary, Guinea, West Africa, 1989-

Canche, Pablo
Missionary, Honduras, 1984-86; El Salvador,
1986-89; Church planting, Honduras, 1989-

Caraballo, Edwin
Grace and Peace Fellowship, Chicago, IL, 2000-

Carter, O'Niel
Prison ministry, Lansing, IL, 1997-2000

Center, Bradley
First Christian Church, Muir, MI, 1991-96; Aetna,
Falmouth, MI, 1996-

Chan, Timothy K.
see list of ordained ministers

Chavez, Merlin
Church Rock, NM, 1945-71

Chee, Norman
Toadlena, NM, 2000-

Chimoni, Rex
Zuni, NM, 1966-96

Choh, Andrew H.
Youth pastor, Korean, Long Beach, CA, 1989-90,
Heaven Bound Ministries, Cerritos, CA, 1994-

Clement, Michael G.
Lasting Connections, Eugene, OR, 1996-

Cooper, Lester
North Park Chapel, Grand Rapids, MI, 1956-60;
Community Chapel, Gowen, MI, 1962-63

Cooper, Russel
North Park Chapel, Grand Rapids, MI, 1959-60;
Community Chapel, Gowen, MI, 1962-63

Cordillo, Leo
Bentheim Spanish Mission, Hamilton, MI, 1975-82

Crump, David
Immanuel, Salt Lake City, UT, 1988-99

Curley, Frank
Sanostee, NM, 1968-86

Dams, Lester
Comstock Park Chapel, Grand Rapids, MI, 1945-
49; Diamond and Milgrove Chapels, Classis
Zeeland, 1950-59; Supt. San de Fuca and Dewey
Sunday Schools, Oak Harbor, WA, 1959-64;
Anacortes, WA, 1964-70; Rehoboth mission,
Rehoboth, NM, 1970-73; Crookston, MN, 1973-80

Davies, John W.
Calvary Chapel, Willard, OH, 1963-67

Davis, George
Oakdale Park, Grand Rapids, MI, 2000-

DeBlois, Jean Guy
Eglise Réformée de la Rive-Sud, Quebec, QC,
1990-98

De Boer, Ben
Naschitti Mission, NM, 1937-44; West Olive Cha-
pel, West Olive, MI, 1944-50, 1958-63; Grace
Chapel, Bellflower, CA, 1950-55; Calvary Chapel,
Holland, 1955-58

De Boer, John
Campus ministry, Muskegon, MI, 1970-71; Minister of education, Calvin, Muskegon, MI, 1976-77

De Boer, Terry
Campus minister, Grand Valley State University,
Allendale, MI, 1978-80

Deckinga, Mark
Christian Indian Center, Denver, CO, 1985–89

Dedthanou, Sone
Laotian, Bigelow, MN, 1995–99; Lao, Worthington, MN, 1999–

De Jong, Andrew
see list of ordained ministers

del Rosario, Fernando
Christian Fellowship, Philippines, 1990–93; Dagupan, Pangasian, Philippines, 1993–95; Living Faith Fellowship-Filipino, Union City, CA, 1995–

De Nooyer, Norman
Coordinator of evangelism and education, Shawnee Park, Grand Rapids, MI, 1977–80; Alger Park, Grand Rapids, MI, 1980–89

De Ruiter, Walter
Williamsburg, ON, 1986–90; Hanover, ON, 1990–95

Deters, Allen Klein
New Life, Grand Junction, CO, 2001–

Deur, Earl
McCallum Church, Freemont, MI, 1967–68, 1974–75

De Vries, Jay
Horseshoe Chapel, Grand Junction, MI, 1962–66; Little Farms Chapel, Coopersville, MI, 1966–71

De Vries, Lester
McCallum Church, Freemont, MI, 1971–74

De Vries, Thomas
see list of ordained ministers

De Vries, Thomas D.
Richfield, Clifton, NJ, 1976–79

De Waard, Willard
Hanley, Grandville, MI, 1952–53; Immanuel Chapel, Roseville, MI, 1953–60; Lake City Chapel, Lake City, MI, 1960–62; Spruce Ave. Chapel, Holland, MI, 1962–64

DeWitt, John
Big Springs, Montague, CA, 1985–88

De Young, Greg
Sun Valley, CA, 1999–2000

Dillender, Charles
River Rock, Folsom, CA, 1998–

Disselkoen, Clarence
Beacon Light Chapel, Grand Rapids, MI, 1952–54; Woodville Christian Reformed Chapel, Woodville, MI, 1954–62; Saugatuck Chapel, Saugatuck, MI, 1962–69

Doot, Peter
Way of Life Chapel, Grand Rapids, MI 1944–48; Bethel Back to God Chapel, Grand Rapids, MI, 1949–55; Rogers Heights Christian Reformed Chapel, Grand Rapids, MI, 1955–58; Chapel, Belding, MI, 1958–64; Gold Ave. Chapel, Grand Rapids, MI, 1964–75; Windfall Chapel, Grant, MI, 1975–76; Chaplain, St. Mary's Hospital, Grand Rapids, MI, 1975–77

Draugelis, Mark
Ministry Team, LaGrave Ave., Grand Rapids, MI, 1979–80

Drenthe, Gerrit John
Vance Church, Ellsworth, MI, 1961–74

Drenthe, Henty
Vance Chapel, East Jordan, MI, 1977–80

Dryfout, Karl
Calvary Community, Redding, CA, 1982

Dube, Guy
L'Eglise Chretienne Reformee, Ste. Croix, QC, 1984–86; University of Montreal and Montreal Island, QC, 1986–90

Du Bois, Phil
Calvary, Chino, CA, 1999–2001; Friendship Community, Fontana, CA, 2001–

Dykman, Gerrit
New Richmond, MI, at Mack's Landing, 1937–46, at Bravo, MI, 1946–49; Fennville, MI, 1940–44, 1949–55

Dykshoorn, Jean
Home Missions Regional Representative, 1986–1996; Small group coordinator, New Life, Abbotsford, BC, 1997–

Dykstra, Bruce M.
Lakeside, Alto, MI, 1991–94; Congregational life, Pleasant St., Whitinsville, MA, 1995–

Dykstra, Elias J.
Roseland Back to God Chapel, 1944-50; Pullman, Chicago, IL, 1950-51; Gold Ave. Back to God Chapel, Grand Rapids, MI, 1951-64

Elder, Allen W.
Pleasant Valley, Longmont, CO, 1994-97

Ericks, Roger W.
First Christian Reformed Gospel Chapel, Denver, CO, 1954-57; Bravo Chapel, Fennville, MI, 1963-66

Esparza, Jesse
Bentheim Spanish Mission, Hamilton, MI, 1983-93

Faber, Harry
Assistant chaplain, Montana State Prison, Manhattan, MT, 1989-

Fakkema, Douglas
Director, Junior High Ministries, First Baptist, Salem, OR, 1985-89; Youth and Children, First Baptist, Minneapolis, MN, 1989-93; CRC: Youth and education, Oak Harbor, WA, 1993-97; Anacortes, WA, 1999-

Fauble, Douglas
see list of ordained ministers

Fikkert, John
North Park Chapel, Grand Rapids, MI, 1955-56; Beacon Light Chapel, Sheboygan, WI, 1967-72; Assistant to pastor, Second, Kalamazoo, MI, 1989-90

Fisher, Ronald
Hillcrest Chapel, Grand Rapids, MI, 1963-64

Fryling, Larry M.
see list of ordained ministers

Garnanez, Boyd
Red Rock Mission, Shiprock, NM, 1969-79; Church Rock, NM, 1979-89; Red Valley, AZ, 1982-92; White Horse Lake Mission, Crownpoint, NM, 1989-90

Geurink, Gordon A.
Faith, Kalamazoo, MI, 1962-63, Calvary Chapel, Plainwell, MI, 1963-73; Unity, Paw Paw, MI, 1973-77; Bravo, Fennville, MI, 1977-81

Gimenez, R.M.
Bentheim Spanish Mission, Hamilton, MI, 1974-75

Glewen, Arlyn
Church planter, Philippines, 1984-

Golon, Francisco G.
Church of God: Open Bible, Guatemala City, Guatemala, 1988-93; CRC: Iglesia Berea, Artesia, CA, 1993-98; Latin America, Anaheim, CA, 1996-

Gonzales, Antonio
Mustard Seed Fellowship, Chicago, IL, 1988-89

Gonzales, Rudy
Moreno Valley, CA, 2001-

Grey, Charley
White Horse Lake Mission, Shiprock, NM, 1960-74; Bethlehem, Tolakai, NM, 1971-74; Bethlehem, Gallup, NM, 1974-78; Window Rock, AZ, 1978-86; Bethany, Gallup, NM, 1989-91; Chinle, AZ, 1991-92

Haas, La Vern
Oakdale and Guiding Light Mission, Grand Rapids, MI, 1964-66; Bravo Chapel, Fennville, MI 1966-70; Windfall Chapel, Grant, MI, 1970-71, 1973-74; Pine Grove Chapel, Howard City, MI, 1971-82; Little Farms, Marne, MI, 1982-86; Coit Community, Grand Rapids, MI and Little Farms, Marne, MI, 1986-87; Chaplain, Kent Community Hospital, Grand Rapids, MI, 1987-92

Hamberg, Howard
Diamond Gospel Center, Hamilton, MI, 1948-49; Back to God Chapel, Lake Andes, SD, 1949-53; Grant Chapel, Grant, MI, 1953-58; Little Farms Chapel, Marne, MI, 1958-66

Harberts, Marinus
Lowell, MI, 1956-58; Shiprock, NM, 1958-60; Naschitti Mission, Tohatchi, NM, 1960-76; Tohlakai, NM, 1976-80

Harvey, Johnny
Ft. Wingate, NM, 1994-

Henry, Edward
see list of ordained ministers

Hoekstra, Henry
Ferrysburg, MI, 1952-53; Hanley Chapel, Grandville, MI, 1953-61; Stated supply, Hanley Church, Grandville, MI, 1961-62; Trinity Chapel, Sparta, MI, 1962-71; Allegan, MI, 1971-76; Superintendent, Mel Trotter Mission, Grand Rapids, MI, 1976-78

Hogan, Joel
Church planter, Philippines, 1984-98; Field director, Christian Reformed World Missions, Philippines, 1998-2001; Director of resources, training and education, World Missions, Grand Rapids, MI, 2001-

Hogue, Ty
RCA: Emmanuel, Paramount, CA, 1994-96; Long Beach, CA, 1996-98; CRC: Calvary, Pella, IA, 1998-2001; Youth, Harderwyk Ministries, Holland, MI, 2001-

Hugen, Rodney
New church developer, Tucson, AZ, 1997-

Huisjen, Albert
Chicago Helping Hand Mission, Chicago, IL, 1920-24; Nathaneal Institute (Jewish Mission), Chicago, IL, 1924-51; Field missionary, Jewish Evangelism, 1951-58

Huisman, Alvin
Pullman Gospel Center, Chicago, IL, 1963-69; Gibson CRC, Holland, MI, 1969-74

Huizenga, Rudy
Mona Lake Chapel, Muskegon Heights, MI, 1950-53; Beacon Light Chapel, Sheboygan, WI, 1953-58; Community Evangelism, Highland, IN, 1958-64; Back to God Gospel Center, Chicago, IL, 1965-80

Humphreys, Mark
Heartland, Tracy, CA, 1998-

Ingeneri, Paul
see list of ordained ministers

Jabaay, Donald L.
Calvary Chapel, Willard, OH, 1969-90; Calvary Evangelical Presbyterian, Flint, MI, 1990-93; First, Crookston, MN and Community, East Grand Forks, MN, 1993-97; Cedar, IA, 1997-

Jager, Henry C.
Classis Zeeland Mission, Allegan, MI, 1945-47; Helping Hand Mission, Chicago, IL, 1947-53; Good News Chapel, Oskaloosa, IA, 1953-56

Joling, Ronald
Hope, Coquille, OR, 1989-96

Jonkman, Norman
Indian Christian Center, Salt Lake City, UT, 1972-80

Jung, Stephen Moe
see list of ordained ministers

Kalsbeek, Wilhelmina
China 1922-49

Kamerman, John
Grace, Scarborough, Toronto, ON, 1992-

Katsma, David
Discipleship/Outreach, Faith Community, Beaver Dam, WI, 1993-98; New church ministry, Marshview, Horicon, WI, 1998-

Keuning, John
West Olive, MI, 1949-53

Keuning, Martin
Knollwood, Kalamazoo, MI, 1949-50; West Olive, MI, 1956-57; Kibbie Chapel, South Haven, MI, 1961-68, 1970-72; Lakeside Community, Alto, MI, 1974-80; Friendship Chapel, Jenison, MI, 1981-88

Kieu, Nathan (Nam) T.
see list of ordained ministers

Kim, Charles
Campus Ministry, Long Beach, CA, 2000- ; UCLA Campus Ministry, Long Beach, CA, 2001-

Kim, Hai Joon
Harvest Valley International, 2001-

Kim, John
Khmer, Denver, CO, 1994-

Kim, Sang-Su
Hope, Seattle, WA, 1991-

Kim, Sun M.
Greater Love Mission, Minneapolis, MN, 1991-

Kim, Yohn-Taek
see list of ordained ministers

Kleine Deters, Allen
Student life coordinator, Redeemer College, Ancaster, ON, 1985-87; Youth/Education/Evangelism, Cephas, Peterborough, ON, 1987-91; Youth, First, Calgary, AB, 1994-97; Youth, New life, Grand Junction, CO, 1997-

Klok, Henry
Forth Creek, AB, 1965-66; Back to God Chapel,
Tawatinaw, AB, 1966-68

Klunder, John
Alger Gospel Chapel, Mt. Vernon, WA, 1958-64;
Garfield Chapel, Chicago, IL, 1965-67

Kok, Ronald
Living Hope Community, Randolph, WI, 1997-
2000; East City Community, Orleans, ON, 2000-

Kooreman, Peter
Coit Community, Grand Rapids, MI, 1977-85,
1988-90; Three Rivers, MI, 1985-88

Kostelyk, John
Fort Wingate, NM, 1994-95; Church Rock, NM,
1996-2001; Tohatchi, NM, 2001-

Kramer, Herbert
Knollwood, Kalamazoo, MI, 1949-50; Western
Michigan University Campus Ministry, Kalamazoo,
MI, 1950-52; Griggs St. Chapel, Grand Rapids, MI,
1958-75

Krol, Kenneth
Trinity, Richfield Springs, NY, 2001-

Kuiper, David
Crosspoint, Anchorage, AK, 2000-

Kuipers, Gordon
Richfield, Clifton, NJ, 1995-99; Cedar Hill,
Wyckoff, NJ, 1999-

Laning, Clarence
Ivanrest Chapel, Grand Rapids, MI, 1951-52;
Helping Hand Mission, Chicago, IL, 1952-80

Laning, Peter
Helping Hand Mission, Chicago, IL, 1954-56; Cal-
vary Chapel, Celeryville, OH, 1959-62; Immanuel
Chapel, Kalamazoo, MI, 1962-65

Lanting, Frank
Anacortes, WA, 1985-93

Lauber, Peter
Adult ministries, River Terrace, East Lansing, MI,
1994-

Le, Vinh
see list of ordained ministers

Lee, Jung Hae
Rehoboth Korean, Los Angeles, CA, 1991-

Leung, David W. Y.
Bethel Chinese, Mississauga, ON, 1989-2000

Levering, Julius J.
Lakeview, Valentine, NE, 1966-68; Stated supply,
Hartley, IA, 1968-70; Stated supply, Hills, MN,
1970-71

Lewis, Robert
Church of the Way, Apple Valley, CA, 1993-

Likkel, Eric
Youth pastor, East Side, Cleveland, OH, 1994-95;
Intern, Oregon Community, Eugene, OR, 1995-96;
Emmaus Road, Seattle, WA, 1997-

Lim, James Ho
Director of education, Korean, Los Angeles, CA,
1978-80

Lineweaver, Jerry
Indian Christian Center, Salt Lake City, UT, 1970-
71; Brigham City, UT, 1970-73

Liu, Tony
Chinese Church, Iowa City, IA, 1999-

Lodewyk, Robert
Gifford Community Chapel, Matsqui, BC, 1983-86

Lopez, Florencio
Christian Reformed Church, El Salvador, 1979-85;
Community of the King, El Salvador, 1986-88;
Iglesia Hispana, Holland, MI 1992-96; Iglesia
Hispana/Calvary, Holland, MI, 1995-97; Church
planter, Mision Discipular del Rey Jesus, Holland,
MI, 1997-

Lopez, Marcos
Amor Viviente, El Monte, CA, 1999-

Maat, Daniel
Rhythm Ministries, Darien, IL, 1998-2000; Education, Harderwyk, Holland, MI, 2001-

Mac Donald, Karen
Evangelist assistant, Christian Ministry Center, Lafayette, IN, 1975-76

Malda, Gerben
CRC: Chapel on Wheels, Vinecroft Trailer Camp,
Grand Rapids, MI, 1955-56; Bristol Ave. Chapel,

Grand Rapids, MI, 1956-66; Portage, MI, 1966-73; Indep: Christian Reformation Church, Holland, MI, 1973. RCA: Friendship Chapel, 1979-87

Mannes, Gerald
Bravo CRC, Fennville, MI, 1971-77

Marcus, Abe
Millgrove Chapel, Allegan, MI, 1959-60; Mexican Boat Mission, Mexico, 1960-69; Mexico City evangelism, 1969-77; Missions, Baja, CA, 1977-78; Missions, Mexico, 1978-91

Marlowe, Jeff
South Shore, Montreal, QC, 1989-92

McGinn, Marty
Church planting, Virginia, 2001-

Meyer, Larry L.
see list of ordained ministers

Meyer, Ronald
see list of ordained ministers

Meyer, Wendell
Evangelism, music and youth, Pease, MN, 1978-80

Miguel, Lorenzo
Spanish ministry, Oakdale Park, Grand Rapids, MI, 1999-

Miranda, Gilbert
Evangelist, Primera Iglesia Christiana Reformada, Chino, CA, 1992-

Moua, Daniel
Home missionary, Free Will Baptist Church, NC, 1982-87; Bible School Director, Lao Evangelistic Church, CA, 1987-91; Hmong Community, Lansing, MI, 1991-95; Hmong, Fresno, CA, 1995-

Moua, Treu W.
Mong, Santa, Ana, CA, 1996-2001

Mould, Jon
Missionary, Guinea, West Africa, 1992-

Mulder, Albert
Beacon Light Chapel, Grand Rapids, MI, 1949-51; Christian Servicemen's Home, Alameda, CA, 1944-46, 1951-55; Godwin Heights Gospel Chapel, Grand Rapids, MI, 1955-61

Mulder, Dan
Norfolk Hospitality House, Norfolk, VA, 1985-94; Ocean View Shepherding Ministries, Norfolk, VA, 1995-96; Ocean View, Norfolk, VA, 1996-

Mulder, Gerry B.
Amor Viviene, El Monte, CA, 1989-99; Iglesia Evangelica, Sunnyside, WA, 1999-

Munro, Alex
Missionary, Philippines, 1977-95; Missionary, Ukraine, 1995-96; Missionary, Eastern Europe, 1995-

Na, Socheth
Cambodian Church, Denver, CO, 1983-91; Cambodian Fellowship, Holland, MI, 1991-

Navis, Kenneth
Ionia Ave. Chapel, Grand Rapids, MI, 1955-58; West 44th St. Chapel, Grand Rapids, MI, 1958-75; Director of Marketplace Ministries, Eastbrook Mall, Grand Rapids, MI, 1975-76

Nhem, Peter Phon
Cambodian, Stockton, CA, 1987-

Nibbelink, Gary
Intern, Holland, IA, 1994-98; Holland, IA, 1998-

Nieuwsma, D.
Sonshine Fellowship, Marshall, MN, 1984-85

Nikkel, Beckie
Director, Norfolk Service Home, Norfolk, VA, 1995-96

Nyenhuis, Ron
Muskegon, MI, 2001-

Oosterhouse, Edward W.
Dildine Chapel, Belding, MI, 1963-72; Guiding Light Mission, Grand Rapids, MI, 1972-84

Oppenhuizen, George
Tohatchi Mission, Tohatchi, NM, 1925-26; Nachitty Mission, Tohatchi, NM, 1926-37; San Antone Mission, Thoreau, NM, 1937-43; Allen Road and Ivanrest Chapels, Grand Rapids, MI and Hanley Chapel, Grandville, MI, 1943-46; Allen Road and Ivanrest Chapels, Grand Rapids, MI, 1946-48; Allen Road Chapel, Grand Rapids, MI, 1948-53; Good News Chapel, Oskaloosa, IA, 1953-54; West 44th St. Gospel Chapel, (plus Lee St. Church, 1958-60) Grand Rapids, MI, 1954-60

Owens, Joseph
Theological editor, Independent Bassa Churches, Liberia, 1981–91; Church planter/Theological Education Missionary, San Jose, Costa Rica, 1991–

Pak, Soon Hee
Faith, South Gate, CA, 1991–

Phim, Charlie (Chenglee)
Cambodian, Salt Lake City, UT, 1984–

Poel, Jay
Christian Reformed Chapel, Woodville, MI, 1949–54; Beacon Light Chapel, Gary, IN, 1954–57; Chapel, Middleville, MI, 1957–62

Pollema, Robert L. Jr.
Desert Streams, Las Vegas, NV, 2001–

Poot, Arie
see list of ordained ministers

Postma, Edward
Kalamazoo Board of Mission, 1944–48; Front Ave. Chapel, Grand Rapids, MI, 1948–52; Ideal Park Chapel, Grand Rapids, MI, 1952–58

Prol, Kenneth
Trinity, Richfield Springs, NY, 2001–

Rasasak, Rawat James
Lao Community, Holland, MI, 1997–

Redhouse, Howard
Four Corners, Teec Nos Pos, AZ, 1960–65; Assistant evangelist, Tohatchi, NM, 1973–80

Ribbens, William D.
see list of ordained ministers

Ridley, William M.
Cape Coral, FL, 1975–77; Horseshoe, Grand Junction, MI, 1977–82; Gold Ave., Grand Rapids, MI, 1982–91

Roeda, Mark
Kent State University, Akron, OH, 1985–96

Romero, Domingo
see list of ordained ministers

Ruthven, William
Classis Zeeland Diaconal Committee, 1996–97; His Harvest Stand, Zeeland, MI, 1997–99; Training

in evangelism, Classis Zeeland, 1999–2001; Evangelist, Hudsonville, MI, 2001–

Sandoval, Jerome
Naschitti, NM, 1988–93; Church planting, Kayenta, AZ, 1993–

Schaap, Verlyn
Sunnyslope, WA, 1977–82; Friendship, Gaylord, MI, 1982–93; Big Springs, Montague, CA, 1993–2000; Friendship Community, Sioux City, IA, 2000–

Schut, Louis
Good News Chapel, Oskaloosa, IA, 1959–65; teacher, Southwest Minnesota Christian High School, 1965–71; Windfall Chapel, Grant, MI, 1971–73

Shim, Jai-Sung
Evangelist, Presbyterian Korean, Saginaw, MI, 1992–93

Siebersma, Stanley
Evangelism, Oakdale Park, Grand Rapids, MI, 1958–59; Ionia Ave. Chapel, Grand Rapids, MI, 1958–60; Diamond and Horseshoe Chapels, Hamilton, MI, 1960–61; Allegan Chapel, Allegan, MI, 1960–65; Sunshine Chapel, Grand Rapids, MI 1965–68; Home Missions, Fort Wingate, NM, 1968–77; Missionary, Navajo, NM, 1977–80; Maranatha Community, Mesa, AZ, 1999–2001

Sikma, Roderic
Evangelist, for Fairlawn Ave. and Pleasant St., Whitinsville, MA, 1975–80

Silakhom, Ranong
Lao Community, Holland, MI, 1991–96; St. Petersburg, Laotian, St. Petersburg, FL, 1996–

Slim, Ray
see list of ordained ministers

Slofstra, Bert
see list of ordained ministers

Spriensma, Audred
see list of ordained ministers

Suarez, Xavier
Lake Worth, FL, 2001

Suk, William
see ordained ministers

Tak, Monineth
Cambodian, Salt lake City, UT, 1985-91

Talley, John
Church Rock, AZ area, 1963-65; Teec Nos Pos, NM, 1965-74; Assistant White Horse Lake Mission, Crownpoint, NM, 1974-75; Beclabito, Teec Nos Pos, AZ, 1975-92

Tanis, Miner
Lamar Plat Chapel, Grand Rapids, MI, 1941-46; Hillcrest Chapel, Grand Rapids, MI, 1946-55; Grace Chapel, Bellflower, CA, 1955-61; Calvary Chapel, Chino, CA, 1961-69; Home mission work for Classis California South, 1969-71; Third, Bellflower, CA, 1971-85; Minister of visitation, Rosewood, Bellflower, CA, 1985-90

Tapia-Ruano, Carlos
see list of ordained ministers

Tebben, Kasjen
Pinegate Community Church, Cutlerville, MI, 1967-79

Tebsen, J.
Cochrane, ON, 1967-68

Timmer, Willis
Ivanrest Chapel, Grandville, MI, 1952-61; Hillcrest Chapel, Battle Creek, MI, 1955-59; Godwin Gospel Chapel, Grand Rapids, MI, 1961-69

Tjapkes, R.H.
New Life, Ionia, MI, 1977-78

Toering, Louis K.
Hillcrest Community, Grand Rapids, MI, 1976-96

Tso, Tom
Evangelist, Navajo, NM, 1982-91

Tucker, Joe Alvin
Mission, Fennville, MI, 1950-54; Sunshine Chapel, Grand Rapids, MI, 1957-60; Mexican Boat Mission, Mexico, 1960-64

Uzel, P.K.
Marshalltown, IA, 1982-83

Valstar, Harry
Evergreen, Fort McMurray, AB, 1992-

Vanden Brink, Everett
Spruce Ave. Chapel, Holland, MI, 1952-58; Evangelist to Spanish-speaking people, 1958-65

Vanderaa, Larry
Switzerland, 1982-84; Mali, West Africa, 1984-

Vander Ark, W.
Vance Chapel, East Jordan, MI, 1974-75

Vander Berg, Richard
Stated supply, Forrest, ON, 1977-78

Vander Bilt, Henry
Hillcrest Chapel, Grand Rapids, MI, 1960-63; Northwood Chapel, Kalamazoo, MI, 1963-65; Lawndale Chapel, Kalamazoo, MI, 1965-69; Eastern Hills, Kalamazoo, MI, 1969-71

Vander Hart, Stephen
Grandville Avenue, Grand Rapids, MI, 1991-94; Sunshine, Grand Rapids, MI, 1994-2001; Youth, Calvary, Chino, CA, 2001-

Van Der Kamp, Peter
Beacon Light Chapel, Gary, IN, 1948-54; Griggs St. Gospel Chapel, Grand Rapids, MI, 1954-58; Emmanuel Chapel, Sauk Village, IL, 1958-64; West Olive Chapel, West Olive, MI, 1964-69; Minister of evangelism, Central Ave., Holland, MI, 1969-70; Saugatuck Chapel, 1970-73; Horseshoe Mission, Grand Junction, MI, 1973-76, 1982-83

Vander Kwaak, Mike
New Life, Abbotsford, BS, 1993-96; Ministry coordinator, Surrey, BC, 1996-98; The Bridge Community, Frankfort, IL, 1998-2000; Rosewood, Bellflower, CA, 2000-

Vander Vaart, P.
Community Sunday School, Munster, IN, 1952-56

Vander Veen, Art
Church, Dallas, TX, 1973-74

Vander Veer, Andrew
Missionary for Classis Holland, 1933-42; Mission, West Olive, MI, 1942-44; West Fulton Mission, Grand Rapids, MI, 1944-51; Bowens Mills, Middleville, MI, 1954-55; Wayland, MI, 1955-56; Guiding Light Mission, Grand Rapids, MI, 1956-57; Superintendent, Guiding Light Mission, Grand Rapids, MI, 1957-66

Vander Wagen, Andrew
Navajo field, 1896-1953

Vander Woud, Sid
Hope Community, Surrey, BC, 1989-

Vande Water, John
Evangelism, Holland, MI, 1912-15; Helping Hand Missions, Chicago, IL, 1915-29; Mission Industrial Store, Grand Rapids, MI, 1929-45; Comstock Park, MI, 1936-37; Northside Community Chapel, Paterson, NJ, 1945-53

Van Drongelen, John
Redwood Community, Surrey, BC, 1995-96; Red River Christian Fellowship, Winnipeg, MB, 1996-

Vang, Neng Houa
Hmong Community, Grand Ledge, MI, 1998-

Vang, Ku
Hmong, Wisconsin Rapids, WI, 1994-1999; Hmong, Sheboygan, WI, 1999-2001

Vanga, Jose Edwin
Iglesia Cristiana Reformada Hispanic, Boston, MA, 1984-89

Van Hofwegen, Robert
see list of ordained ministers

Van Klompenberg, Sherwin
see list of ordained ministers

Van Manen, Robert
Little Farms, Coopersville, MI, 1990-98

van Milligen, Leslie
North Hills, Troy, MI, 1995-1999; Crosspoint, West Chester, OH, 1999-

Van Sloten, John
New Hope, Calgary, AB, 1996-

Van Til, Henry
Little Farms, Coopersville, MI, 1957-58; Chapel, Hamilton, ON, 1959-60; Bowen Mills Chapel. Middleville, MI, 1960-64, 1970-72

Van Zee, Larry
Missionary, Nigeria, 1976-

Veen, Albert
Bethel Chapel, Grand Rapids, MI, 1940-49; Buckley St. Chapel, Grand Rapids, MI, 1949-62;

evangelist, Sherman Street Grand Rapids, MI, 1962-66

Veenstra, George J.
Comstock Park Chapel, Grand Rapids, MI, 1937-45; First Christian Reformed Gospel Chapel, Denver, CO, 1945-53; Beacon Light Chapel, Racine, WI, 1953-64; Alger Gospel Chapel, Bellingham, WA, 1964-65

Veenstra, John
John Calvin, Truro, NS, 1970-74; First, Toronto, ON, 1974-78; New Life Community, Pickering, ON, 1997-1999

Veilleux, Mario
L'Eglise Chretienne Reformee, Ste. Croix, QC, 1986-90

Veltkamp, Martin
Back to God Chapel, Edmonton, AB, 1947-50; Paramus Chapel, Midland Park, NJ, 1950-53; Back to God Chapel, Lake Andes, SD, 1953-58; Rapid City, SD, 1958-60; Chapel, Beaver Dam, WI, 1960-65; Spec Lake Chapel, Allegan, MI, 1965-68; Director of evangelism, Mayfair, Grand Rapids, MI, 1979-80

Venegas, Dante
see list of ordained ministers

Verhage, Isaac E.
Neighborhood evangelist, Grandville Ave., Grand Rapids, MI, 1970-74; Faith Chapel, Shubenacadie, Truro, NS, 1974-76; Gaylord, MI, 1976-77

Verkaik, Richard
see list of ordained ministers

Vermaas, Lee
Eastside Gospel Chapel, Clifton, NJ, 1946-58, 1959-64; Comstock Chapel, Kalamazoo, MI, 1958-59

Vielleuz, M.
L'Eglise Chretienne Reformee, Ste. Croix, QC, 1986-90

Visscher, Edwin
Sunshine Chapel, Grand Rapids, MI, 1960-65; Beacon Light Chapel, Racine, WI, 1965-72; Saugatuck, MI, 1972-81; Calvary Ministries, Vermillion, SD, 1981-89; Charlotte, MI, 1989-93; Kibbie, South Haven, MI, 1993-98

Visser, James
Vanastra, Clinton, ON, 1981–89; Missionary, Costa Rica, 1989–96

Visser, Robert
Good News Fellowship Ministries, Winnipeg, MB, 1996–

Vredevoogd, Jacob
Godwin Mission, Grand Rapids, MI, 1944–46; Director, Guiding Light Mission, Grand Rapids, MI, 1968–72

Ward, Bill
Congregational life, Rosewood, Bellflower, CA, 1995–

Warren, Clay M.
Youth, Community, Tacoma, WA, 2001–

Weenink, Bill
Faith Fellowship, Fairview, AB, 1991–2000; La Glace, AB, 2000–

Wildeboer, John
Crossroads Community, Ajax, ON, 2001–

Williams, Richard E.
see list of ordained ministers

Willink, Willard R.
Hillcrest Chapel, Battle Creek, MI, 1953–54; Windfall Chapel, Grant, MI, 1955–57; Pioneer Chapel, Kent City, MI, 1955–57, 1960–61; Pine Grove Chapel, Howard City, MI, 1955–62; Back to God Chapel, Paterson, NJ, 1962–66; Millgrove Chapel, Allegan, MI, 1966–77; Horseshoe Chapel, Grand Junction, MI, 1975–77; Chapel of Christ, Grand Haven, MI, 1977–85

Wind, John
Evangelism/Education, Calvary, Chino, CA, 1976–77; Missionary, Mexico, 1977–79; Missionary, Honduras, 1979–99; Missionary, Mexico, 1999–

Wissink, Michael
Campus ministry, Fellowship, Big Rapids, MI, 1995–

Wunderink, Steven
Friendship chapel, Allendale, MI, 1995–98; Grace Valley, Henderson, NV, 1998–

Yang, Cherhoua
Hmong, Grand Ledge, MI, 1987–

Yazzie, Jackson
Indian Christian Center, Salt Lake City, UT, 1957–61, 1970–71; Indian Center, Riverside, CA, 1961–62; Zia, Gallup, NM, 1968–70; Bethlehem, Tohlaki, NM, 1969–70; Christian Indian Center, Denver, CO, 1971–76

Zandstra, Patricia
Wycliffe Bible Translators, 1973–74; Intervarsity Christian Fellowship, 1974–76; Michigan State University, 1974–96; Spiritual director, Michigan State University, East Lansing, MI, 1996–97; River Terrace, East Lansing, MI, 1998–

Zayas, John
Evangelism/Youth, Grace and Peace Fellowship, Chicago, IL, 2000–

Zondervan, James
see list of ordained ministers

Home Missions

Appalachia
Boldenow, James, 1976–80
Doesburg, Janna, 1976–77
Laack, James E., 1975–96
Limburg, Rev/Mrs Timothy C., 1977–84
Van Denend, Bob, 1978
Willink, Del, 1977–82
Zeilstra, Don, 1978–84
Zeilstra, Janna, 1978

Arizona
Begay, Cato, 1968–1971
Belin, Paul, 1959–67
Brummel, Corwin, 1961–71
Fryling, Herman, 1897–98
Fryling, Herman/Jennie, 1898–1905
Fryling, Herman/Katie, 1896–97
Hayenga, Calvin G., 1925–60
Heeringa, John, 1996–98
Laack, James E., 1977
Redhouse, Paul, 1943, 1950–63
Sandoval, Jerome/Lolita, 1989–96
Stuit, Gordon A., 1988–93
Timmer, Riena, 1974–75
Vander Wagen, Andrew/Effie, 1896–97
Wiersma, Sadie, 1943–58

Chicago, IL
Schaap, Arthur, 1967–76

City Missions
Vande Water, John, 1962

Grand Rapids, MI
Schaap, Arthur, 1977–80

Kentucky
Kaldeway, Mary, 1969–72

Miami, FL
Boersma, Carol, 1971–72

Infante, Ileana J., 1973
Izquierdo, Mrs Bessie Vander Valk, 1967–68
Limburg, Peter A., 1968
Magally, M., 1967
Menchaca, Sara, 1969–73
Palma, Roberto, 1967–70
Ruano, Omelia, 1967–72
Sandall, N.J., 1967
Tuinstra, James M., 1969–72
Turk, Mrs. C, 1971–72
Van Arragon, G., 1969–70
Vega, T., 1967–72

Mississippi
Evans, Susie, 1976–92
Spoelstra, Elvinah, 1976–88

New Mexico
Aardsma, Alice, 1913–18
Alwynse, Gertrude, 1924–27
Anama, Janet, 1967
Anderson, Chee, 1949–56
Apol, Marvin, 1979–81
Apol, Mr/Mrs Marvin, 1970–79
Arviso, Janice, 1934–42
Atkinson, Thomas, 1922
Baas, Mr/Mrs Julian, 1970–76
Baas, Marvin, 1967
Baas, Mary, 1972–75
Baas, Ralph David, 1972–75
Bainbridge, Hudson, 1907–16, 1920–23
Baker, Marilyn, 1972
Baker, Nellie, 1916–25, 1927–32
Bambacht, Wilma, 1954–65
Bangma, Lois, 1950–51
Bartels, Johanna, 1908–09
Barton, Stewart, 1949–63
Barton, Stewart Jr, 1966–73
Bates, Rena, 1939–56
Baxter, Chris, 1979–80

New Mexico, continued

Becenti, Alfred, 1941-51, 1955-83
Becenti, Edward, 1914, 1921-30
Becenti, Fanni, 1914-18
Becenti, Ferne, 1901, 1940-41
Becenti, Grace, 1943
Becenti, Miss N., 1938
Beech, Thomas, 1966-67
Beekman, Hattie, 1912-24
Beernink, Ernest H., 1921-74
Begay, Cato, 1972
Begay, Evelyn, 1975-78
Begay, Fred, 1960
Begay, George, 1960-61
Begay, Helen, 1954
Begay, Howard/Ruth, 1964-91
Begay, Leo Tso, 1931-35
Begay, Mattie, 1941-42
Begay, Stella, 1950
Beldman, Nellie, 1979-80
Benally, A., 1985
Benally, Bert, 1973-1982
Benally, Bertha, 1946
Benally, Betty, 1965
Benally, Ernest P., 1961-62, 1966-68
Benally, Evelyn, 1978-79
Benally, Lena, 1953-54, 1958-63
Benally, Lolita, 1959-64, 1969-72
Benally, Willie, 1971-78
Bennet, Alice (nee Arviso), 1934-36, 1939-42
Berghuis, Bernice, 1978-86
Beringa, Clara, 1951-56
Berkompas, Edward, 1948-73
Betone, Helena, 1966
Bierenga, Clara, 1951-55
Bierma, Gretta, 1971-73
Bierma, Mildred, 1968-69
Bileen, Jimmie, 1952-56
Bitsie, Grace, 1963-66
Bitsilli, Tom, 1961-62
Bitsy, Walter, 1929-32
Bloomfield, Fern, 25
Bode, Aliene, 1926-31
Bode, Anthony, 1926, 1929-40
Bode, Grace A., 1926-35
Bode, Helen M., 1925-26
Bode, Lillian, 1950-52
Bol, Jacob, 1950-62
Bolt, Jacob, 1914-40
Boogman, Janet, 1956-62
Boomstra, Gertruda, 1924-26
Boone, Archie, 1941-42
Boone, Verena, 1984-86
Boot, Eugene, 1968-75
Boot, Mary, 1969-75

Boot, William, 1975
Bos, Louis H., 1946-61
Bosch, Alice, 1920
Bosscher, Arthur, 1946-82
Bosscher, Beatrice, 1930-31, 1933-35
Bosscher, Jacob H., 1904-52
Bosscher, Kathy, 2000-01
Bosscher, Robert, 1947
Bosscher, Robert, 1983-84
Bouma, Mark/Anna, 1907-26, 1931-41
Bouma, Mary, 1922-24
Bouma, Winnie, 1918-21
Bowman, Alfred, 1925, 1930
Boyd, Ann, 1969-84
Boyd, Bobby, 1988-2001
Boyd, Harry, 1928-31
Branderhorst, Cora, 1934-35
Brandt, Cora, 1926-32
Brink, Dena, 1918-19, 1939-40
Brink, John W., 1912-25, 1930--38
Brink, Leonard P. Jr., 1950-55
Brink, Rev/Mrs Leonard P., 1900-13, 1915-136
Brink, Marie (Mrs. R. Ebbert), 1925, 1931-34
Brink, Wilhelmina, 1924-26
Broersma, Delmar, 1958-59
Brouwer, Andrew, 1967-71
Brown, Paul H., 1943
Brummel, Corwin/Esther, 1972-96
Brummeler, Mr/Mrs J.D., 1919-20
Bruxvoort, Gilbert, 1975-79
Buining, Roger, 1953-68
Bulthuis, Lena, 1952-61
Burmania, Wilhemina, 1936-38
Bush, Alice, 1921-22
Buus, Beulah, 1953-57
Bylsma, Etta, 1965-66
Bylsma, Jessie, 1951-52
Bysterveld, Brenda, 1963-64
Cambridge, Miss L., 1938
Capitan, Rose, 1938-40
Cell, C.W., 1926
Chamberlain, Ethel, 1938-59
Charles, John, 1956-67
Charles, Theodore, 1970-79
Chavez, Melvin, 1945-70
Chavez, Verna, 1991-92
Chee, Debbie/Norman, 1999-2001
Chee, Norman, 1991-93
Cheschilly, Alice, 1949
Chimoni, Nina, 1982-92
Chimoni, Rex, 1956-63, 1966-78
Chimoni, Rex/Betty, 1983-96
Chimoni, Sam, 1980-92
Clahchischilli, Sylvia, 1980-87
Clark, Guy, 1929-30

New Mexico, continued

Cook, James A., 1961–62
Cooke, Edward, 1963–73
Curley, Frank, 1963–86
Dalton, Karletta, 1957–60
Damon, Charley, 1931–33
Damon, Nettie, 1953–57
Dams, Mr/Mrs Lester, 1971–73
Das, Mary, 1906–07
Davey, Julia, 1982–84
De Boer, Ben, 1937–53
De Boer, Jeannette, 1941–43
De Boer, Jennie, 1955
De Groot, Mr/Mrs James E., 1897–1900
De Haan, Kathleen, 1958–61
De Jong, Andrew, 1979–82
De Jong, Lois, 1979
De Jong, Margaret, 1952–56
De Jong, Marla, 1970–73
De Jong, Nellie, 1908–21
De Kleine, Nora, 1971–84
De Korne, James, 1975–84
De Kryger, Joann, 1962–64
De Lange, Helen, 1942–55
De Lange, Marie, 1945
De Mik, Nellie, 1961
De Ruyter, Margaret (Mrs. Van Hulsen), 1912–16
De Velder, Gary, 1970–74
De Vos, Lawrence, 1946–51
De Vries, Ann, 1955–65
De Vries, George, 1976–77
De Vries, Nicholas, 1937–43
De Vries, Sarah, 1973–74
De Witt, Cornelia, 1944–56
De Witt, Susie, 1951–55
De Young, Gayle, 1977–86
De Young, Michael, 1979–84
De Young, Ronald, 1965–67
Deckinga, Jennette, 1937–39
Deeking, Jeanne, 1937–19
Deemter, Jane, 1953
Dekker, Trena, 1970–72
Den Bleyker, Julius, 1950–93
Den Hartog, Don, 1953–54
Denetdele, Alice, 1953
Denetdele, Hugh, 1915–16, 1920–25
Denetdele, Irene, 1951–53
Denetsone, Bessie, 1949
Dennison, Esther, 1942–43
Dennison, George, 1918–24
Derks, Anna, 1905–16
Dieleman, Susanna, 1906–12
Diephuis, Henrietta, 1947–60
Disselkden, Madelyn, 1935–37
Dobben, Aileen, 1916–31, 1934–40

Dobbs, Carol, 1963
Dobbs, Kenneth, 1961–68
Donkersloot, Ronald, 1981–84
Doornbos, Debra, 1980
Doyle, David M., 1966–69
Duiker, Rob, 1998
Dwarshuis, Tina Beth, 1951–52
Dykema, Clarence, 1946–51
Dykema, Earl, 1958–64
Dykhuizen, Dorothy, 1938–51
Dyksterhuis, Lois, 1972–73
Dykstra, Clarence, 1948
Ebbers, John T., 1952–57
Ederveen, Catherine, 1925–27
Eelkema, Bess, 1968–69
Eldridge, Wilson, 1929–32
Engbers, Bernard/Niecia, 1986–90
Ensink, Julia, 1947–83
Eskeets, Dixie/Fritz, 1988–2000
Ethart, Cora, 1922–23
Faber, Kenneth, 1975–87
Fauble, Gloria, 1969–70
Feenstra, Lori, 1980
Fennema, Ida, 1932–40
Feyen, Mary, 1971–85
Fik, Margeurite, 1940–52
Fikkert, John, 1955–59
Flikweert, Peter, 1989
Folkert, Marlene, 1968–69
Frank, Floyd/Katheryn, 1971–87
Frazier, Ann, 1984
Fridsma, Hilda, 1953–57
Fryling, Herman/Jennie, 1906–26
Fryling, Sophia, 1918–22
Garnenez, Boyd/Anna Nae, 1958–88
Geba, Manuleto, 1931
Gelder, Alvern, 1969–74
George, John, 1958–69
Gonzales, Mr/Mrs James, 1977–84
Gonzales, Mr/Mrs Santiago, 1977–84
Gordy, Nona, 1920
Goudberg, Anna, 1923–25
Goudberg, William, 1926–54
Goudzwaard, Peter, 1981–84
Gough, Jocelyn, 1977–80
Gray, Charlie, 1957
Gray, Mary, 1965–66
Green, Mattie, 1919–20
Grevengoed, Hattie, 1943–53
Grey, Charles/Ann, 1962–92
Grit, Elaine, 1952–56
Gritter, Winabelle, 1955–60
Groen, Watson, 1926–27, 1967
Hale, Mr/Mrs Frank, 1979
Hamilton, Alice D., 1954–66

New Mexico, continued

Hamming, Nellie, 1926-32
Hampton, Garland, 1959
Harberts, Jacoba, 1978-89
Harberts, Marinus, 1958-82
Harkema, Justin, 1974-78
Harlan, Nelson, 1957
Harris, Julia, 1940-41
Hart, Douglas, 1978-80
Harthoorn, Sharon, 1965-66
Hartman, Annie, 1942-43
Hartog, Cocia, 1906-11
Harvey, John, 1997-98
Harvey, Lois, 1977-2000
Harvey, Lucy, 1962-70
Haveman, Alyce, 1941-52
Haven, Bernard, 1949-62
Haverhals, Adeline, 1953-58
Havinga, Anna, 1921-24
Heil Benally, Ruth, 1996-98
Heiman, Melissa, 1980-82
Hekman, Elsie, 1941-142
Hekman, Paul, 1958-70
Helland, Luella, 1968-1980, 1984-91
Helmus, Mr/Mrs Thomas, 1962-64
Hendricks, Betty, 1967-73
Hendricks, Mr/Mrs Glenn, 1980-84
Henry, Albert, 1956, 1972-87
Henry, Ben, 1949-69
Henry, Grace, 1956-?
Henry, Marian, 1953-57
Henry, Rev/Mrs Edward, 1941-42, 1946-69
Henry, Violet, 1963-84
Heronimus, Lillian, 1953-66
Heusinkveld, G., 1911-15
Heusinkveld, Mrs. G., 1914
Heyns, Herman, 1915-19
Hielkema, Gladys, 1969
Hirdes, Mr/Mrs Steve, 1981-83
Hoekstra, Marie, 1948-66
Hoekstra, William, 1947-84
Hoff, Patricia, 1960-63
Hofman, John Jr., 1965-68
Hofstra, Dora, 1937-74
Hogue, Benjamin, 1957
Holtgeerts, Josie, 1954-68
Holtrop, Brenda, 1966
Holtrop, Deborah, 1964-65
Honaker, Robin/Lavaine, 1994-95
Hood, Alice, 1931-32, 1938-40
Hood, Christina Belz, 1912-17
Hood, Velma, 1939-40
Hoogezand, Peter/Lena, 1915-18, 1935-37
Hoogstra, Calvin, 1974
Houseman, Court D., 1924-39

Houseman, Donald Esko, 1948-60
Houseman, Elmira, 1927-31
Huizenga, Lee S., 1913-18
Huizingh, Edward, 1975-77
Huizingh, Mr/Mrs Evert, 1974
Huizingh, Paulette, 1975-77
Hunt, Helen, 1962-63
Jacobs, John, 1973-74
Jager, Barbara, 1968-71
James, Tullie, 1934-69
Jansen, Hermina, 1947-54
Jasperse, Joel, 1975-78
Jelgerhuis, Leanne, 1980-92
Jergens, Mr/Mrs Lloyd, 1969
Jim, Alfred, 1979-82
Jipping, Robert, 1962-65
Joe, Bessie, 1953-58
Johnson, Gloria, 1973-74
Johnson, Mr/Mrs Albert, 1982-84
Jones, Paul, 1915-16
Jonkman, Bev, 1989-93
Julian, Lily, 1914
Kaemingk, Janet, 1980-84
Kamps, Betty, 1968-69
Kamps, Edwin, 1956
Kamps, Gordon/Ruth, 1983-90, 1997-99
Kamps, Helen, 1930-31
Kamps, J., 1966
Kamps, Jacob R, 1928-63
Kamps, Jeff, 1977
Kamps, Mr/Mrs Roland, 1976-84
Kamps, Roland, 1949-68
Kass, Jessie, 1957-59
Kats, Janie, 1927-30
Kerr, Robert, 1975-84
Klay, Mary, 1981
Klein, John, 1965-70
Klompeen, D., 1970
Kloosterman, Carl D., 1972-89
Kloosterman, Frieda, 1970
Klumpenhower, Gary, 1969-86
Knoll, Genevieve, 1937-38
Kobes, Jacob C., 1926-63
Kok, Egbert, 1963
Kollis, Clara, 1942-64
Kollis, Elizabeth, 1942-66
Koning, Faye, 1954-57
Koning, Marla, 1978-80
Koning, Stanley, 1953-63
Koolhas, Abram W., 1969-89
Koops, Bernard, 1950-68, 1974
Koops, Jean, 1964
Koops, Mrs Bernard, 1959
Kortman, Bertha, 1932-33
Kostelyk, John, 1999-2001

New Mexico, continued

Koster, Maude, 1919-20, 1927-32
Kromminga, Emily, 1935-37
Kruis, Beth, 1984
Kruis, Brian, 1986-96
Kruis, Mary Jean, 1949-62
Kruis, Richard, 1945-68
Kruis, Sally, 1973-74
Krygsheld, Mr/Mrs Burt, 1974-76
Kuik, Mary J., 1944-74
Kuik, Perle, 1952-53
Kuipers, Albertha, 1960-65
Kuipers, Arlene, 1966-67
Kuipers, Cornelius, 1927-55
Kuipers, Keith, 1967-84
Kurley, Floyd, 1982-85
Kurley, Melanie, 1986-87
Kurley, Winfred, 1974-80
Lam, Jeanette, 1920-25
Lam, Nellie, 1921-59
Lamberts, Jack, 1941
Landheer, Lois, 1972-76
LaPlante, Lorena, 1949
Largo, Jimmie, 1943
Largo, Levi, 1959, 1963-64
Lasiloo, Genevieve, 1959
Lay, Simon A., 1926
Lee, Alice Mae, 1961-66
Lee, John, 1964-65
Lee, Mr/Mrs John, 1974-84
Lee, Sally, 1961
Leekity, Colleen, 1984-85
Lefler, Ilene, 1928-32
Lewis, Anna, 1970
Lineweaver, Mr/Mrs Jerry, 1980-84
Long, Sarah, 1959-62
Lopez, Tom, 1941-42
Lucas, Cornelius, 1923-27
Lucht, Gordon, 1951-54
Lyttle, Madge, 1947
Mahke, Fannie, 1939-39
Manuelito, Elizabeth, 1949-55
Manuleto, Gebba, 1932
Mariano, Jane, 1966
Martin, Geronimo, 1943-44, 1949, 1952, 1968-70
Martin, Mrs Robert, 1944
Martinus, Mr/Mrs William, 1972-73
Masselink, Barbara, 1974-76
Matthysse, Wayne, 1977-78
Memmelaar, Jennie, 1927-31
Meyer, Mary, 1946
Meyer, Peter, 1944-53
Mierop, Jessica, 1930-32
Mierop, Mrs. William, 1928-33
Mierop, William, 1920-28

Moblard, Ruth, 1965-66
Mokma, Ethel, 1965-66
Mokma, Laura, 1926
Moore, C.J. K., 1919
Moore, Dorothea, 1952
Morgan, Jacob C., 1926-37
Morgan, Jack, 1946
Mulder, J.D., 1917-22
Muyskens, Derk H., 1912-13
Nabahi, Jean, 1960-62
Nashapoo, Nathaniel, 1945
Natachu, Dena, 1982-92
Natani, Morris, 1930-32
Natelborg, Evelyn, 1966
Natewa, Neil, 1965-73
Natewa, Rex, 1938-66
Nederveld, Gary, 1973-74
Neuman, Bessie, 1953-55
Newmeyer, Marie R., 1960-62
Nez, Clara Mae, 1958
Nez, Louise, 1955-56
Nez, Sidney, 1940-43, 1946-68
Nibbelink, Mathilda, 1957-59
Nieuwsma, Angie, 1943-57
Noort, Dorothea, 1952-53
Norton, Miss, 1924
Nyenhuis, Jane, 1914-16
Nyenhuis, Johanna, 1919
Nyhof, Ethel, 1975-76
Nyhof, Gerald, 1970-72
Nyhof, Hermina, 1967-84
Nyhof, Joan, 1972-73
Onderlinde, Robert, 1974-78
Oppenhuizen, Edward, 1964-82
Oppenhuizen, Hessel, 1938-40
Oranje, Gertrude, 1946-62, 1965-66
Orille, Fern, 1965-66
Ottens, Lois, 1979
Overeem, Gertrude, 1935-38
Pars, Garrett D., 1946-51
Penning, Olive, 1948-56
Peshlakai, Dora, 1946-57
Peshlakai, Frank, 1937-40
Peshlakai, Marie, 1949-65
Peshlakai, Wallace, 1929-37
Petersen, Don, 1976
Peterson, Miss E., 1937-38
Peterson, Grace, 1951-52
Pettigrew, Jennie, 1959-60
Pierson, Clarissa, 1914-18
Pikaart, Grace, 1974-98
Pikaart, Stanley, 1974-98
Pikaart, Tim, 1990-92
Pinto, Amy Rose, 1958-66
Ploeg, Deanetta, 1942-43

New Mexico, continued

Plummer, Narcissa, 1942
Plummer, Pearl, 1945
Poel, Abel, 1926-57
Polinder, Mr/Mrs Ron, 1973-80
Polinder, Ron, 1978-82
Pontier, Margaret, 1952
Poppen, Kathrine, 1938-40
Post, Eunice, 1956-76
Posthuma, Rev/Mrs Roger, 1961-67
Postuma, Ruth, 1978-82
Pousma, Richard H., 1927-41
Prince, Louise, 1940-41
Punt, Cora, 1936
Redhouse, Anna Mae, 1963
Redhouse, Howard, 1949-65, 1973-80
Redhouse, Joan, 1964
Redhouse, John, 1944-59
Redhouse, Louise, 1956-61
Redhouse, Scott, 1959, 1962-15
Renkema, Gary, 1949
Rhebergen, Anita, 1958-61
Riemersma, Fanny, 1989-91
Rikkers, Henry, 1936-41
Roedema, Mary, 1969-70
Roelefs, Johanna, 1966
Roeters, Dorothy, 1951-52
Romeyn, John, 1925-29
Roon, Wendy, 1980-84
Rooze, Ruth, 1959-62
Rosbach, Bertha, 1909-19
Rosbach, Katherine, 1905-36
Rotman, Vera, 1949-53
Rozeboom, Mr/Mrs Garrett, 1943-55
Ruiter, Gertrude, 1945-52
Rus, Aletta, 1936-65
Russell, Peggy, 1942-43
Sandovel, Julian, 1946
Sautter, Carolyn, 1978-79
Savino, Karen, 1979-84
Schaefer, Gertrude, 1922-25
Schans, Cornelius, 1920-21
Schaver, Gertrude, 1922-25
Schooland, Thelma, 1953-55
Schoon, Winnie, 1918-22
Schouten, Audrey, 1972-73
Schram, Henry, 1906-07
Schripsema, Herman J., 1943-65
Schuurman, Audrey, 1973
Seciwa, Chalotte, 1986-92
Shaver, Gertrude, 1922-25
Sheche, Myron, 1978-90
Sheeres, Maribeth, 1985-88
Shorthair, Jessie, 1962
Shorty, Bernice, 1954-62

Siebersma, Mr/Mrs Robert, 1976-78
Siebersma, Stan/Heidi, 1969-90
Sikkema, Hermina, 1956-58
Simmelink, Bertha, 1912-13
Singer, Rena, 1962
Sipe, Mr/Mrs Wilbur, 1910-12
Skeets, Annie, 1963-64
Slager, Rena, 1961
Smit, Wilma, 1959-62
Smith, Loren, 1956-58
Smitter, Mr/Mrs Russell, 1959-60
Spoelhof, Carolyn, 1952-59
Spoelstra, Eleanor, 1971
Sprik, Bert, 1921-34
Spyker, John, 1911-25
Stam, Gerrit, 1946-55
Start, Clarence, 1957-64
Stevens, Egbert, 1922
Stevens, Hendrika, 1919-20
Stevens, John, 1976-80
Stijf, Mary, 1912-15
Stob, Gertrude, 1921
Stob, Renzina, 1916-65
Stroven, Kathy, 1980
Struik, Johanna, 1946-55
Stuit, Gordon, 1957-64
Stuit, Gordon A., 1974-88
Stultz, Linda, 1979-86
Styf, Mary, 1912-15
Sutter, Carolyn, 1979
Suwyn, Mr/Mrs Richard, 1973
Suwyn, Richard, 1973-74
Swart, Mr/Mrs Marvin, 1966-72
Swets, John H., 1922
Swierenga, John B., 1936-58
Swierenga, Marilyn, 1963-67
Talley, John/Gladys, 1951-88
Talley, Molly, 1951-53
Tamminga, Don, 1977
Tamminga, Donald/Jenny, 1985-94
Ten Houten, Carrie, 1911-21
Ter Molen, Miss A., 1916-18
Thomas, Herbert, 1960
Thomas, Mary, 1945
Tibboel, Margaret, 1951-53
Tibboel, Nellie, 1946-53
Tibboel, Ted, 1952-84
Tiemeyer, Lena Francis, 1940-42
Tigchon, Ann, 1927-52
Tjoelker, Bessie, 1938-68
Toeset, Theodore, 1939-41
Toledo, Jack, 1953-67
Tommelly, J.O., 1922
Tso, Billy, 1938, 1940
Tso, John, 1959, 1963-69

New Mexico, continued

Tso, Sena, 1945
Tso, Tom/Louise, 1983-87
Tsosie, Clarence, 1960-66
Tsossi, Anita, 1942
Tsossi, John, 1941-42
Van Andel, Dennis/Ruth, 1977-2001
Van Andel, Gerrit, 1969
Van Boven, Bessie, 1954-69
Van Boven, Cornelius, 1969-71
Van Boven, Ella, 1951-52, 1969-70
Van Bree, Bessie, 1955
Van Bree, Mrs Arie, 1918-19
Van Bruggen, Rev/Mrs Jacob, 1938-70
Van Dam, Wilma, 1954-68
VanDellen, Idzerd, 1944
Vanden Bosch, M.P., 1966
Vanden Bosch, Thelma, 1965-76
Vanden Burg, Henry, 1927-28
Vanden Hoek, Helen, 1938-39
Vander Ark, Henry, 1919-22
Vander Ark, John D., 1962-68
Vander Ark, Mr/Mrs John D., 1960-62
Vander Beek, H., 1916-19
Vander Beek, Meindert, 1914-25
Vander Hart, Cornelius B., 1940-51
VanderHeide, Joyce, 1978-79
Vander Hoven, William, 1972-78
Vander Kodde, Catherine, 1922-30
Vander Kodde, Joan, 1921-26
Vander Laan, Keith, 1978-92
Vander Laan, Lori, 1981-84
Van Der Meer, John, 1941-43
Vander Meulen, Miss G., 1932
Vander Meulen, Garret, 1941-43
Vander Meulen, Gerrit, 1939-51
Vander Meulen, Ida, 1941
Vander Molen, Jennie, 1923-25
Vander Molen, Scott, 1978-84
Vander Riet, Anna, 1912-13
Vander Slik, Jennie, 1923-26
Vandersloot, Mary, 1980
Vander Sluis, Merle, 1968-89
Vander Stoep, Floris, 1936-63
Vander Veen, Jennie, 1910-14
Vander Veer, Lenora, 1940-57
Vander Ven, Thelma, 1957-62, 1966-72
Vander Wagen, Andrew/Effa, 1897-34
Vander Wagen, Dick, 1955
Vander Wagen, Dick/Nellie Noordhof, 1903-05
Vander Wagen, Ed, 1932-34
Vander Wagen, Marie Brink, 1925-26
Vander Wall, Fanny, 1922-27
Vander Weide, Marie, 1920-64
Vander Werp, Jeanette, 1920-22

Vander Woude, Rena, 1950-83
Vander Wulp, Sharon, 1980-81
Van Deursem, Nettie, 1911
Vande Werken, Angeline, 1925-27
Van Doorne, Rena, 1952-57
Van Dyk, Hermina, 1952-53
Van Dyken, Dinah, 1938-59
Van Dyken, Joan, 1923-26
Van Dyken, Matilda, 1905-06
Van Dyken, Rick, 1991
Van Dyken, Sadie, 1940-42, 1946-62
Van Engen, Rita, 1963-66
Van Farrowe, Emalene, 88
Van Haitsma, Gertrude, 1946-60
Van Houw, Theresa, 1952-66
Van Hoven, Bessie, 1956
Van Iwaarden, Adrian, 1947-53
Van Klompenberg, Wanda, 1963-83, 2000-01
Van Koevering, Cora, 1920
Van Kooten, Tenis C., 1938-39
Van Laar, Gerard, 1951
Van Meekeren, Beth, 1983
Van Mersbergen, Nellie, 1957-60
Van Otterloo, Alice, 1938-41
Van Otterloo, Dorothy (Mrs. Ray Ras), 1941-42
Van Til, Estelle, 1940-41
Van't Land, John, 1970-75, 1979-84
Van Voorthuisjen, Lorrie, 1977
Van Voorthuisjen, Ted, 1977
Van Westenbrugge, William, 1929
Van Zanten, Cora, 1921-36
Van Zanten, Jacoba, 1915-21
Van Zytveld, Catherine, 1926
Vedders, Alice, 1933-42
Veenstra, James, 1972
Veenstra, Lynn, 1970-76
Veenstra, Rolf, 1979-84
Veltkamp, James, 1970-72
Veltkamp, Jean, 1970-72
Venema, Jeanne, 1968-71
Venema, Katherine, 1914-16
Venhuizen, Alice, 1927-43
Vennegerts, Jennie, 1926-31
VerBeek, Wanda, 1974
Verduin, Lorraine, 1945-51
Verhulst, Glen, 1976-79
Vermeulen, Gertrude, 1930-34
Versprille, Martha, 1939-43
Veurink, Anna, 1919-20
Veurink, Hattie, 1944-66
Veurink, Johanna (Mrs. C. Schans), 1919-20
Vis, Sharon, 1969-71
Visocky, Pat, 1994-95
Visser, Andrew, 1974-75
Visser, Jennie, 1946-69

New Mexico, continued

Visser, Sharon, 1968
Visser, Theodore, 1951–59
Vlietstra, Edward, 1964–70
Vlietstra, Thelma, 1966–67
Vogel, Cora, 1948–56
Vos, Erma, 1971–81
Vos, Marie, 1926–59
Vos, Martha, 1938–42
Voss, Sena, 1914–18
Vugteveen, Marvin, 1958–61
Walstra, Rosemary, 1980
Warner, Violet, 1950–62
Weeda, Thomas, 1966–90
Wegman, Anna, 1925–26, 1932–35
Weidenmeier, Linda, 1972–73
Westenburg, Lena Ruth, 1931–35
Westendorp, Lucille, 1950–53
Westendorp, Sylvia, 1951–53
Whipple, Christine, 1912–17
Whipple, Mrs. H., 1919
Whitehorse, Boyd, 1967–72
Whitehorse, Ken, 1972–74
Wiedenmeier, Linda, 1973
Wierenga, Donald, 1970, 1972–73
Wiers, Ann, 1975–76
Wilderom, Rena, 1931–40
Wilson, Ruth, 1944
Witteveen, Mr/Mrs Fred, 1984
Woody, Anna Mae, 1959–60
Workman, Angelyn, 1927
Woudenberg, Christine, 1924–25
Wybenga, Evelyn, 1952–53
Wybenga, Marian, 1952–56
Yazzie, Elmer, 1976–84
Yazzie, Emma Jean, 1965–66
Yazzie, George, 1961–62
Yazzie, Jackson, 1968–71
Yazzie, Sally, 1956
Yazzie, Sampson, 1951–57, 1961–86
Yff, George, 1932–57
Yonker, Sandy, 1984
Youngsma, Gertrude, 1969–74
Yzenbaard, Richard, 1978
Yzenbaard, Richard/Jan, 1985–88
Zandstra, Gertrude, 1915–19
Zimmer, Beverly, 1956–58
Zwiers, Alyda, 1931–35

WORLD MISSIONS

Africa
Zagers, Bertha, 1935-37

Argentina
Amsing, Mr/Mrs Bert, 1987
Arkema, Alan A., 1961-66
Berkompas, Lillian, 1977-78
Boonstra, Juan S., 1948-61
Borrego, Rev/Mrs Ramon C., 1973-78
Brinks, Rev/Mrs Raymond G., 1958-80
Bruxvoort, Brandt, 1930-35
Bulthuis, Linda, 1972
De Vries, Rev/Mrs William Thomas, 1957-78
Dokter, Rev/Mrs G. Bernard, 1964-72
Drenth, Cecelia, 1969-75, 1978-79
Eldrenkamp, Ruth, 1999-2000
Gimenez, Mr/Mrs Raul, 1978-82
Hutt, Rev/Mrs John, 1971-82
Huttinga, Rev/Mrs Jack, 1974-82
Jipping, Robert L., 1969-74
Kallemyn, Sylvia, 1974-77
Kimm, Eunice, 1982-83
Lim, Eunice, 1980
Lindemulder, Janet, 1975-77
MacLeod, Angus, 1958-67
Medendorp, John, 1979-80
Meyer, Edward, 1958-76
Pott, Rev/Mrs J. Jerry, 1938-59
Renkema, William John/Teresa, 1977
Ritsema, Ken/Gayle, 1980-81
Rooy, Sidney H./Mae, 1965-91
Rumph, Rev/Mrs Arnold, 1956-73
Sonneveldt, A.C., 1926-51
Stob, Rev/Mrs Harvey, 1972-84
Van Antwerpen, Willard, 1956-58
Vander Roest, Robert, 1972-73
Vander Velde, J., 1951
Wagenveld, Rev/Mrs Louis W., 1967-81
Walcott, Virginia, 1977-78
Zondervan, Rev/Mrs James, 1980-86

Australia
Houseward, Rev/Mrs John, 1978-83
Morren, John, 1960-70
Senneker, Jan, 1960-66
Van Ens, Rev/Mrs Clarence, 1982-84
Van Groningen, Rev/Mrs Gerard, 1958-86
Woudstra, Sierd, 1971-77

Bahamas
Spee, George, 1984-91

Bangladesh
Berkenbosch, Roy, 1991-92
Bos, Jeffrey/Melissa, 2001-
Brink, Paul, 1981-86
Brouwer, John, 1976-78
Byler, Dan, 2001
Daring, Kohima, 1998-2001
De Graaf, Rick, 1983-90
De Graff, Rick, 1976-77
De Vries, Marve, 1978-80
Deelstra, John, 1977-18
Haarsma, Valerie, 1995-96
Hamstra, Albert A./Mindy, 1980-89
Morrow, John/Lynn, 2001-
Mostert, Martin, 1980-82
Myers, Shelly, 1995-96
Poppe, Kees, 1978-81
Postma, William, 1993-98
Prins, Ronald, 1976-78
Ryskamp, Andrew, 76
Seebeck, Douglas, 1980-81
Spee, Jim, 1981-82
Ten Broek, Nancy, 1988-2001
Vanderkooy, Olive, 1984-85
Vanderkooy, Peter, 1982-88
Vander Meulen, Peter, 1978-82
Van Der Puy, Dave, 1977-78
Walker, Rebbeca, 1993-94
Ysselstein, Peter, 1984-86

Belize

De Jong, Dawn, 1990-91
De Vries, Helen, 1981-82
Hamstra, John, 1986-90
Meyer, Dorothy, 1981-
Post, Tom, 1986-90, 1992-97
Roldan, Elisabeth, 1987-90
Schout, Debra, 1990-91
Zantingh, Albert, 1988-92

Brazil

Bosma, Carl J./Anneke, 1973-90
Dekker, Rev/Mrs James C., 1977-78
Dirksen, Rev/Mrs Willem, 1969-80
Muller, William V., 1935-79
Oldenkamp, Rev/Mrs Bernard, 1967-78
Uken, Rev/Mrs Charles D., 1967-85
Vander Berg, Edward, 1973-74
Wolfert, Simon, 1968-82

Cambodia

Arensen, Lisa, 2001
Chann, Navy/Ly Chhay, 1999-2001
Fennema, Mike, 1997-98
Jost, Shanti, 1999-2001
Meyer, Ben/Judy, 2001
Van Wyke, Elizabeth, 1998-2000
Wilson, Deb/Mark Schneider, 1996-98

Canada (fieldmen)

Aasman, Casey, 1952
Andre, Garret, 1948-60
Betten, Joseph, 1951-54
Bos, Ralph J., 1948-59
Brondsema, Samuel G., 1940-43, 1948-56
Cruson, P.J., 1956-59
DeGraaf, Rick, 1998-
De Jager, Anthony, 1952
De Jong, Arnold, 1949-60
De Jong, E., 1948
de Jong, Jacob, 1949-52
De Jong, John, 1948-56
De Jonge, A., 1952-60
De Koekoek, Paul, 1949-56
De Vos, Martin, 1952
De Walle, Sam, 1956-60
Disselkoen, Arie, 1953-58
Dornbush, Menzo, 1950-66; 1962-68
Gritter, John, 1948-58
Hanenburg, John, 1950-59
Hoekstra, Peter J., 1949-62
Immink, J., 1952
Jongbloed, Remmelbert A., 1951-54
Kampjes, G.John, 1956-61
Kool, Leonard, 1949

Kooy, Peter, 1951-52
Lam, Herman J., 1953-61
Laninga, E., 1954-61
Looy, A.J., 1956-60
Maat, D.J., 1951-62
Mast, Carl, 1947-48
Meyer, William, 1929-41
Moes, Herman, 1949-60
Mol, Marinus, 1969-61
Mussche, J., 1958-61
Niebor, Bernard, 1948-61
Nieman, Henk, 1956-61
Noordam, A.H., 1960-62
Persenaire, Adam, 1948-61
Polet, Tom, 1952-57
Prins, Jacob, 1948-59
Reitsma, Ted, 1956-61
Rientjes, Gerrit H., 1952-55
Rubing, John, 1948-58
Schenkel, H., 1952
Smit, Albert H., 1950-57
Spoelhof, Charles, 1948-62
Steenhof, Christopher, 1952-61
Ten Hove, Harm Jan, 1947-60
Togtema, K.G., 1953
Turkstra, Peter, 1949-51
Van den Berg, Luke, 1950-55
Van Der Meer, John, 1951-55
Vander Vliet, John, 1949-66
Vander Ziel, Gerrit J., 1953-59
Vander Zouwen, Nick, 1956-61
Van Dyke, Martin, 1950-51
Van Laar, Gerard, 1950-58
Vellinga, John, 1947-55
Vos, Tom E., 1958-62
Wierenga, Herman A., 1948-14
Wyenberg, J.J.A., 1929-32
Zoethout, H., 1959-61

Central America

Diemer, Rev/Mrs Fred, 1983-93

Ceylon

De Jong, Peter Y., 1952-53
De Ridder, Richard, 1946-73
De Ridder, Richard R., 1956-60
Greenway, Roger, 1958-63
Perara, Ananda, 1959-67

China

Alons, Monique, 1994
Arkema, James, 1989
Auperlee, Tim/Renee, 1998-
Baker, Christopher, 2002

China, continued

Bancroft, Peter, 1992
Behm, Justin/Sarah, 2002
Besteman, Carolee, 1990
Blankespoor, Harvey/Marlene, 1997–99
Bos, Rachel, 2001
Bouman, Nellie, 1992
Bouwsma, David/Cathleen, 2002
Branderhorst, John/Kendra, 1993
Brasser, Jana, 1996–
Bunce, Steve, 1993
Buunk, Laura, 1988
Campo, Karin, 1991–93
Chao, David/Bess, 1994–95
Chei, Han Ku/Stella, 1994–96
Dam, Tim/Rena, 2002
Dekker, Joyce, 1989
De Korne, John C., 1920–35
De Roos, Erin, 1996–97
De Vries, Nicholas, 1926–28
De Vries, Sarah, 2002
Dykstra, Harry Andrew, 1920–41
Dykstra, Simon (Sam) Andrew Rev., 1921–51
Ebens, Selina, 1990, 1995–1997
Gabrielse, Abigail, 2001–
Geiger, Peter/Sandra, 1995–97
Godeke, Carry, 2001
Groen, Mike, 1991
Haan, Angie, 1924–26
Haarsma, Valerie, 1992
Hamstra, Albert A./Mindy, 1991–97
Hanna, John/Gwen, 1992–93
Heetderks, Jeanne, 1929–1932
Helmus, Mike, 1988
Holtrop, Philip/Marie, 2000–
Holwerda, Karla, 1989
Hoover, Brent/Julie, 1996–97
Hordijk, Roelof/Jennifer, 1999
Huddleston, Billie Jo, 1995
Huizenga, Myrtle, 1937–40, 1947
Huizenga, Tena A., 1931–40
Hulst, Craig, 1996–2000
Ibeling, Darrel, 1989–90
Jasperse, George/nancy, 1992
Jensen, Kieth/Laura, 1991–
Kamps, Jacob R, 1926–28
Klein, Robert, 2001–
Klein-Horsman, Joycegina, 1990
Klompien, Mark, 1998–99
Koetje, Sarah, 2002
Konyenbelt, Roslalie, 1998–
Konynenbelt, Rose, 1992
Kreisel, Renè, 1993–97
Kroeze, Angie, 2001
Kroll, Dennis/Rosemari, 1991–

Kuiper, Bruce, 1992–94
Kuiper, Bruce/Monique, 1999–
Laarman, Alice, 1989–
Lubben, Verna, 1992
McGuire, Charlotte, 2001
Netz, Heidi, 2002
Nikkel, Trixanna, 2002
Oliver, Paul/Katherine, 1990–91, 1995–97
Orlebeke, Clifton/Barb, 1993, 1996
Ochsner, Lisa, 2002
Patterson, Selina/Mark, 1999–
Peetsma, Brenda, 1993–94
Perry, Samuel/Sandra, 2001–
Persenaire, Ardell, 1992–93
Petersen, Keith/Yolande, 1988–92
Pousma, Richard H., 1924–27
Powell, Susan, 1990
Prince, Robert/Mary, 1988
Romeyn, Kimberly, 2000
Rupke, Dan/Lynda, 1993
Schaaf, Kristi, 2001–
Schouten, Kevin/Elizabeth, 2002
Selles, Kurt D./Vicki, 1993–
Smalligan, Hustin, 2002
Smid, Jackie, 1992–93
Spykman, EveLynn, 1989–90
Steenbergen, Evert, 1992
Steensma, John/Juliana, 1988
Stegink, Larry/Harlean, 1992–
Stevens, Richard/Janice, 1988–89
Stienstra, Mike, 1992
Van Baak, Edward A./Fran, 1987–91
van Belle, Christine, 1993–94
Van Bruggen, Jay/Arlene, 2002
Van Dam, Bill/Ena, 1992–96
Vander Ark, Julie, 1992–93
Vanderstoel, Robbert, 2001–
Vander Tuin, Gwenellyn, 1988–91
Vander Werf, Alice, 1999–
Van Kley, Mike, 1992
Van Prooyen, Michelle, 1992–95
Van Schooneveld, Ethel, 1945
Van Steenbergen, Evert, 1990–93
Veldkamp, Arnold/Helen, 1997–
Veltma, John, 1995–97, 2001
Verboon, Art, 1992
Verhoef, Monique, 1992–93
Watson, David, 1989–90
Wierenga, Ralph, 1993–97
Young, Betty Jo, 1994
Zuidhof, Marilyn, 1990–91

Costa Rica

Barrett, Robert, 1982–83
Bergsma, Paul J./Barbara, 1983–

Costa Rica, continued

Boldenow, James, 1981–89
De Voogd, Stan, 1981–86
De Vries, Helen, 1983
De Vries, Steven/Lori, 1988
Drenth, Cecelia, 1985–
Duthler, Patricia, 1976
Gietema, Gertie, 1976–77
Green, William P. III/Aletha, 1984–97
Grit, Nelson, 1983–84
Kater, Hans/Joanne, 1999–
Klaasen, Rev/Mrs Thomas G., 1984–85
Koning, Rev/Mrs Gerald A., 1985–87
Korevaar, Lori, 1986–87
Laarman, Bob/Laurie, 1989–91
Ludema, Jim, 1984–90
Maatman, Rebecca, 1989–90
Martin, Gregg, 1998–
Mortensen, Darryl, 1977
Owens, Joseph/Mary, 1991–97
Pennings, Eric/Carla, 1986–94
Ravensbergen, Ronald D./Michelle, 1990–94
Rienstra, Robert J./Heidi, 1988–98
Schipper, Rev/Mrs Gary, 1977–80, 1987–88
Schrotenboer, Rachel, 99
Smith, Everdine, 1986–87
Soerens, Rev/Mrs Thomas G., 1983–91; 2000–
Spamen, Jennifer, 1999
Stam, Jeffrey/Denise, 1984–91
Strong, Mr/Mrs Joseph, 1984
Teja, Gary/Jackie, 1983–90
Theule, Paul/Laurie, 1994–97
Van Den Berge, Marinus/Karen, 1985–91
Vanderwall, Ken/Sally, 1993
Van Hofwegen, Michael H./Lynn, 1982–88
Van Lopik, Bill/Sue, 1987
Van Til, Kent A./Kathy, 1989–97
Visser, James/Hilda, 1991–96
Walcott, John/Kathy, 1989
Wunderink, Don/Mae, 1996–98

Côte d'Ivoire

Foster, Brabara, 1999
Huibregtse, Melissa, 1997–98
Knapper, Pamela, 1995
Kuipers, Myron/Jenny, 2000–
Langelaar, Winnie, 1995–96
Ledeboer, Rod/Julis, 1996

Cuba

Garcia, Mr/Mrs Erelio Martinez, 1974–87
Izquierdo, Vicente B., 1957–62
Martinez, Erelio, 1969–73
Nyenhuis, Clarence, 1958–60

Dominica

Geleynse, Greg, 1983–84
Oosterhouse, Mr/Mrs Kenneth, 1983–85

Dominican Republic

Abma, Beverly, 1983–84
Bazuin, George/Shryl, 1995
Besteman-Estrella, Diane, 1992–99
Biel, Kristen, 1995–96
Billin, Troy/Sarah, 2002
Bossenbroek, Tim/Roxann, 1995–96
Brauning, Steven/Sandra, 1991–
Brinks, Raymond G./Gladys, 1980–96
Broersma, Dean/Sharla, 1998–
Davelaar, Kathy, 1997–2000
De Jong, Jeffrey/Kathleen, 1984–98
De Jong, Mark, 2002
Den Bleyker, Lynette, 1999–
De Ruiter, Richard J./Marcia, 1987–94
Deters, James/Mary Lou, 1997–99
De Vries, Steven J./Lori, 1988–2002
De Young, Michelle, 1995–98
De Young, Rev/Mrs Wayne R., 1978–86
Duimstra, Cheryl, 1983–85
Dyk, Lynn, 1993–94
Geerdes, Cynthia, 1984
Geerts, Linda, 1997–99
Geisterfer, Caspar, 1986–95
Geisterfer, Leanne, 1983–93
Genzink, Marcia, 1990–92
Gritter, Katie, 2001–
Haglund, Jeanette/Lloyd, 1990–92
Hegeman, Neal/Sandra, 1978–93
Hernandez, Michelle/Guillermo, 2000–
Hubers, Barbara, 1997–
Jager, Trudy, 1994–95
Kimm, Eunice, 1989–92
Kornelje, Sheryl, 1986–91
Laarman, Robert/Laurie, 1986
Martinez, Rev/Mrs Jose, 1982–86
Mc Cullough, Jane, 1985–87
Medendorp, John C./Susan, 1991–2001
Meyer, Dawn, 1986–88
Miedema, Scott, 1997–
Noorloos, Arley-Ann, 1987
Oostendorp, Derk/Nancy, 1984–88
Oudbier, Joel/Diona, 1997
Overweg, Timothy/Lori, 1993–95
Roeda, Daniel J./Janette, 1986–90
Runia, Mavis, 1995–1998
Scholma, Elizabeth, 2002–
Slachter, Eric, 1990
Thonus, Rebecca, 1998–99
Tubergen, Roger/Sharla, 1991–92
Vanderburg, Roland, 1990–91

Dominican Republic, continued

Vander Klay, Paul/Beth, 1991-97
Vander Meulen, Peter, 1983-87
Vander Sluis, Karen, 1990
van der Vorst, Dick/Carolyn, 1995-2000
Vander Ziel, Thomas H./Judy, 1985-89
Van Dragt, Geoff, 2001-
Van Oord, Julia, 2000-
Van Til, Max/Kina, 1994-
Van Veen, Gary/Pamela, 1991-
Veeneman, Ryan W./Julie, 1983-88
Veenstra, Ralph/Beth, 1995-2000
Vermeet, Melinda, 1983
Versluys, Julie, 2000
Visser, Mindy, 1998-2000
Walcott, John/Kathy, 1988-94
Walcott, Thomas J./Jaci, 1984-91
Walhof, Tammy, 1990-91
Wunderink, Donald/Mae, 2001-
Wybenga, John/Helen, 1994-97
Zwier, Joel/Patti, 1983-2001

Eastern Europe

Munro, Alex/Renona, 1996-

Ecuador

Eldrenkamp, Neal/Ruth, 1994-97
Eldrenkamp, Ruth, 1998
Lanning, Heide, 1994
Lopez, Alba, 1998
Rikkers-DeBorst, Jim/Jeanne, 1998
Roldan, Betty, 1993-97
Tinholt, Susan, 1994
Van Dam, Howard/Ruth, 1994
Vanden Hoek, Daniel/Patricia, 1994
Van Haitsma, Doug/Yvonne, 1995
Van Wyhe, Brian, 1994
Wiersma, Mark/Eileen, 1994
Wood, Betty/Robert Roldan, 1998-2001

Egypt

Jellema, David, 1990-91

El Salvador

Canche, Pablo/Sheryl, 1987-89
de Voogd, Stan, 1987
Padilla-DeBorst, Jim, 1999-
Padilla-DeBorst, Ruth Eldrenkamp, 2001-
Haut, Iris, 1989
Klaasen, Rev/Mrs Thomas G., 1977-1980
Koning, Gerald A./Laura, 1987-1989
Lopez, Alba, 1999-2001
Martinez, Rev/Mrs Jose, 1979-80
Michmerhuizen, Steve/Jan, 2001
Rikkers-DeBorst, Jim/Jeanne, 1993-97

Schipper, Mr/Mrs Gary, 1979-80
Van Haitsma, Doug/Yvonne, 1996-97
Van Lopik, Bill/Sue, 1988-92
Vugteveen, Dan, 1979
Wagenveld, Louis W., 1995-2000
Walcott, Peter/Birgit, 1989

England

Vander Laan, Julie, 1971-72

France

Kallemeyn, Harold/Elsbeth, 1989-
Post, Susan, 2000

Francophone Africa

Vanderaa, Mr/Mrs Larry, 1981-85
Whyte, Rev/Mrs George, 1982-84

Gambia

Koops, Robert/Esther, 1997-

Guam

Allen, David/Louise, 1999-2001
Bode, Bruce, 1974-1976-80
Boer, Jim/Wilma, 1999
Bonnema, Amber, 2002
Bouma, Ray/Barbara, 2001
Bowater, George/Marie, 2001-
Bruxvoort, Calvin, 1968-72
Cooper, George, 1977-81
Cooper, Rev/Mrs George D., 1977-80
Culbertson, E. Neil/Janie-Lou, 1983-
De Boer, Christine, 2001-
De Vries, Hendrik/Judy, 1991-
Douma, Mr/Mrs Conrad, 1965-82
Dykema, Rev/Mrs Henry, 1965-77
Essenberg, Michael/Kim, 1996
Hagedorn, Joshua/Cassandra, 2002
Hofman, John Jr., 1960-62
Hummel, Philip/Johanna, 2000-
Kaptein, Amy, 2001
Koning, Ann, 1970-71
Kuiper, James/Beth, 2001
Kuiper, Julius/Arlene, 1986-92
Meyer, Rev/Mrs Norman, 1983
Norman, Mr/Mrs Sidney, 1983-85
Poel, Jay, 1962-70
Schepel, Ken, 1970-71
Schuring, Rev/Mrs John, 1950-80
Steulpnagel, Julie, 2002
Teerman, Dan/Sherry, 2001
Van Biert, Pauline, 2001
Van Ens, Rev/Mrs John, 1980-82
Van Staalduinen, Holly, 2002
Visbeen, Adrian/Ruth, 1996-97

Guam, continued

Vogel, Cora, 1998-2000
Whitney, Mr/Mrs David, 1977
Wilgenburg, Ed/Elizabeth, 1994-95

Guatemala

Baas, Julie, 1991-92
Colop, Moises, 1998-2001
Dekker, Rev/Mrs James C., 1979-84
Kapenga, Mark, 1977
Limburg, Peter A., 1979-80
Meyer, Mary Anne, 1991
Rikkers-DeBorst, James, 1991-92
Rumph, Rev/Mrs Arnold, 1977-81
Van Tongeren, Ellen/Paul, 2001
Van Tongeren, Paul, 1994

Guinea

Bolt, Robert D./Mary, 1986-96
Bosch, Lydia/Chris, 1997
Campbell, David/Joyce, 1990-
de Jong, Cheryl, 1994-
De Young, Julia, 1994-95
Doane, Linda, 1991-92
Evans, J. Barrie/Nancy, 1986-96
Groenewold, Wiena, 1989
Hofland, Calvin/Jamie, 1995-2001
Markus, Jill, 1995-96
Mohle, Ken/Margreet, 2001-
Mould, Mary/Jon, 1992-
Ooms, Amy, 2001-
Pruim, Jenifer, 1998
Span, John/Ann, 2000-
Spyksma, Kristie, 1996-97
Steele, William O./Diana, 1996-
Temmimck, Evert, 1997-98
Tolsma, Laura, 2000
Vander Schuur, Brenda, 1990-
Vogel, Cora, 1993-95
Whyte, George/Rhonda, 1984-94
Wierda, David, 1987-97
Wierda, David/Slimatou, 1998-2000
Wigboldy, Valerie, 2001
Ypma, Mary Ann, 1996
Zylstra, Marie, 1998-2000

Haiti

Beelen, Sandy, 1977-80
Both, Dick, 1978-86
Brink, Paul, 1988-90
Brower, Jaclyn, 2002
Buma, Michael, 2002
Danford, Cloe Ann, 1980
Dening, Edwin/Sylvia, 1997-2000
De Vries, Marvin, 1984-87

De Yager, Bridget, 2002
De Young, Wayne R./Sandra, 1986-93
Diephuis, Bill/Karen, 1997-98
Dykstra, Linda, 2001
Eising, Adrian/Rosanne, 1986-89
Fazier, Julie, 1981-83
Franje, Pat, 1981-86
Geisterfer, Leanne/Caspar, 1996-2001
Geleynse, Nick, 1981-86
Genzink, David, 1976-80
Gerrits, Jacqueline, 2002
Hill, JoLynn, 1987
Hof, Monica, 1999
Holtrop, Steven/Kimberley, 2002
Hunse, Hank, 1985-87
Jeanty, Edner, 2001
Jongejan, Rick/Ruth, 1997
Kobes, Dave, 1980-1982
Kroeze, Jon/Laura, 1998-99
Koorn, Trisha, 2002
Orkar, Patsy, 1997-98
Ten Napel, Sherra, 1999
Tinklenberg, Lavon, 1980-88
Van Dam, Howard/Ruth, 1993-
Vanden Hoek, Daniel/Patricia, 1990-
Vanderkooy, Tricia, 2001
Vander Wees, Mark/Nancy, 1992-2001
Vander Zaag, Ray/Jayne, 1985-93
vanDonkersgoed, Albert, 1999
Van Whye, Brian, 1993
Verhulst, Cairn, 1997-98
Vugteveen, Sara, 1997
Wiersma, Mark/Eileen, 1991-
Wright, Charlotte, 1994-95
Zylstra, James, 1980-83

Honduras

Apoll, Tracy, 2001
Bathel, Bob/Barbara, 1997
Bergsma, Rev/Mrs Paul J., 1977-83
Boersma, Carol, 1975-77
Botting, Lori, 1983
Canche, Pablo/Sheryl, 1985-86, 1990-
De Jonge,Jason, 2002
Dekker, Rev/Mrs James C., 1978-79
De Murillo, Irene, 1998-2001
De Rose, Mariann, 1992-93
De Vries, Helen, 1984-86
De Vries, Thomas, 1974
De Young, Rev/Mrs Wayne, 1977-78
Diemer, Fred/Betty, 1983-93
Doepp, George/Davina, 1995-96
Dokter, Rev/Mrs G. Bernard, 1972-79
Estrada, Matthew R., 1992-99
Fast, Janelle, 1985-86

Honduras, continued

Feikema, Mr/Mrs Roger, 1985-86
Flikweert, Helen/Peter, 1987-88
Harris, Kathleen, 1989-90
Heeringa, Mr/Mrs Sam, 1983-85
Hekman, Laura, 1981
Helmus, Sidney/Elaine, 1984-85, 1991-95
Huls, Kim, 1990
Jasperse, Mr/Mrs Dick, 1985-87
Jeltema, David/Roberta, 1998
Jones, Dr/Mrs Bryn, 1984-1987
Kamps, Matthew, 2001-
Kater, Hans/Joanne, 1996-98
Kern, Greg/Christine, 2001
Kerssies, Heide, 2000
Klaasen, Rev/Mrs Thomas G., 1980-84
Koene, Coba, 1980-83
Konynenbelt, Glenda, 1983-86
Kooi, Veryl, 1980-82
Korevaar, Lori, 1984
Kruize, Grace, 1983-86
Kuipers, Arla, 1983-86
Laarman, Robert/Laurie, 1987
Langendoen, Ernest/Betsy, 1990-94
Lundell, Mark/Dawn, 1994-95
Meyer, Janet, 1987-1990
Miedema, Don, 1992-99
Miedema, Don/Eva, 2000-
Mortensen, Darryl, 1978-82
Mostert, Peter/Betty, 1997-98
Mulder, Peter/Birgit, 1981-92
Oppewall, Linda, 1990
Overzet, Lisa, 1998
Pennings, Mr/Mrs Eric, 1983
Persenaire, Rev/Mrs Cornelius A., 1971-76
Petersen, Eunice, 1985-88
Pierik, Gordon/Belinda, 2001
Pippel, John/Darlene, 1995-98
Post, Thomas, 1975-77
Renkema, William John/Teresa, 1979-89
Rienstra, Robert/Heidi, 1988
Robbins, Scott/Vicky, 2002
Roldan, Elizabeth, 1976-86
Sawyer, Frank/Aria, 1985-92
Schepel, Rachel, 1999-2000
Schipper, Rev/Mrs Gary, 1981-85
Sneller, Norman/Kathy, 1996
Soerens, Thomas G./Cheryl, 1984-97
Strong, Joseph/Nellie, 1985-93
Strong, Mr/Mrs Joseph, 1980
Theule, Paul/Laurie, 1993
Theule, Shaelyn, 1997
Timinskis, Deborah, 1992
Van Beek, Brad, 1996-2000
Vander Goot, Cathy, 1981-83

Vandermeet, Timothy/Laura, 1999-2000
Vander Wal, Jane, 1982-83
Vanderwal, Kenneth/Sally, 1992, 1995-
Van Ess, Carol, 1976-1978
Van Staalduinen, Jan, 1995-98
Van Woerden, Ed/Angela, 1997
Veeneman, Mr/Mrs Ryan, 1977-78
VerBeek, Kurt/JoAnn, 1988-92
Visser, John/Hilda, 1990
Vreugdenhil, Lori-Ann, 1998
Vriend, James/Jennifer, 2001
Vugteveen, Debra, 1979-80
Wind, John/Shirley, 1982-99
Wind, Mr/Mrs John, 1979-80
Wunderink, Don/Mae, 1999
Zwart, Monika, 1997
Zwier, Joel, 1979-82
Zwiers, Richard/Carol, 1997

Hong Kong

Roest, Rev/Mrs Gary, 1979-84
Van Houten, Dr/Mrs Richard, 1983-86

Hospital Christian Fellowship

Kaldeway, Mary, 1998-

Hungary

Craven, Lois, 1993-
De Haan, Sue, 1997-2001
De Vries, Tom R./Mary, 1995-96
De Vuyst, George/Sarah, 1996, 98-
Enserink, Steve/Shirley, 1998-99
Geerlings, Jon/Janet, 1991-92
Greydanus, Sam/Elsie, 1991
Heeringa, Jon, 1994
Heyink, Brenda, 2000-01
Kmecz, Anita, 1997-1998
Kreeft, Kimberly, 1997-99
Kuipers, Myron/Jenny, 1992-93
Lachniet, Melinda, 1994
LaGrand, Ann, 1996-97
Ludema, Karen, 1993
Meyer, Debra, 1995-96
Reitsma, JoAnnita, 2000
Sawyer, Rev/Mrs Frank, 1992-
Schut, Kevin/Kristen, 1998-2000
Sliedrecht, Timothy/Angela, 2002
Sytsma, Angela, 1997
Vandermeer, Jenny, 2001
van der Pol, Kristine, 1997-98
Van Der Weele, Stephen/Viola, 1994
Van Zanen, Steve/Christine, 1997-99
Veenstra, Ted/Tina, 2000
Wassenaar, Cheryl, 1996
Wisse, Alice, 1992

Hungary, continued
Yeazel, Jennifer, 1997

India
Bosch, Anna C., 1952-54
Ramiah, Arthur V., 1951-65

Indonesia
Armstrong, Nick/Laura, 1997-2001
Brink, Paul/Priscilla, 1990-2000
Lamigo, José, 1986-1992
Saher, Iskandar, 2001
Talstra, Eric, 1999-2000
Yoder, Greg, 1989

Israel
Mennenga, Harry, 1988-91

Japan
Bergwell, Grace, 1997
Boerman, Mary, 1985
Boersma, Mr/Mrs Jack, 1985
Boswell, Ted J./Josie, 1990-
Bouma, Pamela, 1983
Bruinooge, Rev/Mrs Henry, 1951-83
Bruxvoort, Mr/Mrs Carl, 1977-78
De Berdt, Michiel/Trudy, 1962-95
Deelstra, Doreen, 1987-
De Hoog, John Jr., 1969-74
De Jonge, Rev/Mrs Philip V., 1972-88
De Koekkoek, Ryan, 2002
Dengerink-Van Til, Daniel/Lara, 1998
Den Ouden, Gary/Wendi, 1993
De Young, Ronald, 1971-74
Dykhouse, Sandra, 1993-
Dykstra, Scott/Lori, 1994-95
Engel, Twyla, 1993-95
Essenburg, Martin, 1959-73
Essenburg, Martin/Barbara, 1999-2000
Essenburg, Michael/Kim, 1997-
Fedders, Roger, 1986
Fennema, Amy, 1989-91
Fennema, Beth, 1986-
Fennema, Dawn, 1992-94
Fennema-Dion, Dawn, 2001-
Ferwerda, Martin/Bernice, 1993
Gho, Jeong Seok/MiSook, 1995-
Groenwold, Wiena, 1986
Hekman, Bruce/Ruth, 1987-94
Hemple, Rev/Mrs Ronald W., 1970-78
Herweyer, Al/Judy, 1978-87
Hommes, Raymond/Sharon, 1970-89
Hong, Charles, 2000-01
Huizenga, John, 1965
Jones, Mr/Mrs Jack, 1973-82

Koedoot, Rev/Mrs Gerrit, 1966-81, 1997-2000
Koets, Magdalena, 1952-56
Kooiker, John Jr., 1972-73
Kort, Lori, 1985
Kress, Arnold S./Lorraine, 1979-92, 2000-01
Kwants, Rev/Mrs Dick J., 1960-80
La Fleur, William, 1963-69
Lee, Ken/Jeannie, 1999-2001
Leigh, Wayne E./Barbara, 1984-90
Meyer, Marvin W., 1973-74
Mobach, Martin T./Sandra, 2001
Navis, Dave/Darlene, 1994
Norman, Mr/Mrs Sidney, 1978-82
Ouwinga, John, 1971-72
Palsrok, Carin, 1999
Park, James J./Young, 1990-2001
Pettinga, Tom, 1970-71
Postema, Thomas/Michele, 1987-89, 1994-
Roest, Gary, 1977
Schurman, Jennifer, 2000
Siebenga, Norma, 1973
Smit, Dr/Mrs Harvey, 1958-77
Spalink, Lawrence K./Ruth, 1980-
Stob, Rev/Mrs William J., 1966-82
Stulp, Keith, 1984
Sutton, Robert, 1952-66
Sweetman, Leonard, 1954-61
Sytsma, Rev/Mrs Richard D., 1952-84
Sytsma, Richard E./Sandra, 1968-2001
Sytsma, Tina, 1998
Tabak, Daniel, 2001
Terpstra, Harold, 1965-70
Theule, Paul/Laurie, 1984-92
Theule, Shaelyn, 1999
Timmer, John, 1959-74
Tinkenberg, Keith/Beverly, 1991-93
Van Baak, Edward A./Fran, 1951-70
Vander Bilt, Corinne, 1973-74
Vander Bilt, Rev/Mrs Maas, 1953-80
Van Farrowe, John, 2001
Van Wyk, Allison, 2001-
Veenstra, Linda, 1986-87
Vellekoop, Martin/Cynthia, 1986-89
Vellinga, Jame, 1986
Viss, Carol, 1982
Woodworth, Patricia, 1996-97
Young, George R./Ruth, 1982-
Ypma, Benjamin, 1961-65

Jordan
Bosch, Robert, 1979
De Jonge, Rev/Mrs Philip V., 1979-82
De Vries, Bert, 1973
Haan, Robert, 1979-80
Kok, Paul, 1973-77

Jordan, continued

Slager, Larry, 1977–78
Vander Baan, Lee, 1975–76
Vander Berg, Rev/Mrs Edward, 1981–87
Vander Vliet, Dave, 1978–79

Kenya

Addink, Roxanne, 1990
Berends, Willem/Henny, 1990–91
Booy, Dirk, 1989
Bruinooge, Michael, 1984
Buwalda, Anja, 1996–
De Haan, Greg, 1992–94
De Vries, Brian, 1993
Disselkoen, Keith, 1992–98
Hooyer, John, 1985
Ipema, Rev/Mrs Peter, 1977–79
Ippel, Jotham, 1998–2000
Janz, Janet, 1999–
Kaldeway, Mary, 1987–97
Kuperis, Peter, 1991–96
Muthoka, Francis, 1999–
Post, Tom/Melva, 1998–2000
Ritskes, Janne, 1989–91
Seebeck, Douglas, 1984–85, 1989–96
Tazelaar, Grace, 1985
Vliegenthart, Janet, 1990
Vreeken, Ary, 1984
Wraith, Steve/Sandi, 2001

Korea

Boelens, Peter, 1961–68
Byma, Sidney, 1970–73
Faber, Robert G., 1969–72
Feddema, Peter, 1967–68
Hekman, Calvin, 1969–71
Hubers, Henry J., 1967–68
Lim, Sook Kyung, 1967
Mulder, D.J., 1967–71
Spoelstra, Elvinah, 1967–71
Ten Have, Ralph, 1961–63
Vander Sloot, Charles L., 1969–73
Venhuizen, Kenneth, 1972–73

Kosovo

Disselkoen, Keith, 2001

Latin America

Boldenow, James, 1990–96
Gritter, Winabelle, 1983–2001
Roldan, Betty, 1991
Stam, Jeffrey/Denise, 1992–93

Liberia

Anderson, Mark, 1988
Blankespoor, Gilbert/Janice, 1987
Bloemsma, Mr/Mrs Terry, 1986
Bosserman, Mr/Mrs Ronald, 1980
Broekhuizen, Rensselaer O./Janice, 1983–91
Bruinooge, Michael, 1985–87
Cruise, Connie, 1990
De Boer, Mr/Mrs Peter, 1983–84
Enter, Margarent, 1978–86
Fennema, Amy, 1988
Haan, Katie, 1985
Haveman, Louis, 1982–83
Hekstra, Mr/Mrs Mike, 1982
Hubers, Mr/Mrs Mark, 1984–85
Ipema, Rev/Mrs Peter, 1972–79
Ippel, Paul, 1983–87
Kraker, Roger H./Yvonne, 1985–90
Lemcke, William, 1989
Lotze, Kenneth/Jerri, 1983–91
Nieuwsma, Duane/Barbara, 1989
Noteboom, Peter, 1992–93
Owens, Joseph/Mary, 1982–90
Rikkers-DeBorst, James, 1990
Scheffers, Mark A./Patricia, 1979–91
Scholten, Herman, 1967–76
Slager, Donald J./Marty, 1978–98
Slager, Tim/Diane, 1983–91
Stehouwer, Richard, 1982–86
Tinklenberg, Perry/Kathy, 1981–91
Van Biert, Pauline, 1990
Van Haitsma, Gertrude, 1986
Vanderaa, Mr/Mrs Larry, 1977–81
Vreeken, Ary, 1985–86

Lithuania

Ochsner, Brandie, 2002
Stab, Reuben/Janneke, 2002
Van Zanen, Steven/Christine, 2000–

Malawi

Bengelink, Jonathan/Kendra, 1996–97
Gunnison, John, 1993
McAuley, Larry/Linda, 1999–2001
Ott, Michael, 1993
Van Es, Rowland Jr./Jane, 1991–96

Mali

Admiraal, Ellen, 1999–2000
Budding, Renne, 1998
Colyn, Darren/Treena, 1997
Crickmore, Mary/Scott, 1986–2001
de Ruiter, Tom/Debra, 1998–
Dykhuis, Bill/Nell, 1981–86
Elgersma, Grace, 1991–2000

Mali, continued

Geffrard, Willys/Suzètte, 2001
Gunnison, John/Linda, 1990-92
Hunse, Henrietta, 1989-98
Lagerwey, Sandra, 1998
Lyzenga, Bonnie, 1995-97
Michelson, Eugene/Dawn, 1988-
Monsma, George/Ellen, 1989-90
Orkar, Patsy, 1999-2001
Postmas, William, 1986
Rustenberg, Tania, 1995-96
Sinclair, Greg/Nelly, 1993-2001
Smith, Everdine, 1991-
Syler, Keith, 1993-95
Vanderaa, Larry/Ann, 1986-
Westra, Brian, 1993

Mexico

Aulie, Mr/Mrs Ed, 1980-83
Bajema, Duane, 1972-76
Bergsma, Rev/Mrs Paul J., 1969-77
Berkenbosch, Roy, 1972
Block, Bert, 1971
Block, Mr/Mrs Bert, 1977
Boersma, Fred, 1972-73
Brook, Richard, 1986-87
Buurma, Bruce, 1972-76
Buurman, Loren, 1977-79
Clousing, Wayne, 1971-74
De Boer, Clarence, 1970-82
De Vries, Nathan, 1994
De Waal, Sidney C.J., 1967-70
De Wolf, Willem, 1965-72
De Young, John, 1972-73
De Young, John/Jerre, 1978-
De Young, Wayne, 1970
Doornbos, Roger, 1992-
Doyle, Rev/Mrs David M., 1974-78
Faber, Henry, 1967-68
Ferwerda, Martin/Bernice, 1990
Geurink, Daniel/Jean, 1982-89
Geurink, Scott/Marcia, 1993-
Green, Larry/Muriel, 1980
Greenway, Roger, 1963-70
Gritter, Winnabelle, 1977-81
Groen, John G., 1971-74
Hamstra, John, 1982-85
Hogan, Rev/Mrs Orlin, 1973-75
Holwerda, David, 1962-63
Kass, David, 1967-69
Koetje, John, 1979
Korf, Mr/Mrs Louis, 1979-82
Kroeze, Mr/Mrs Nick, 1974-81
Kuiper, Daniel R./Jeananne, 1981-93
Lagerway, Rev/Mrs Donald, 1972-75

Leder, Arie C./Olga, 1985-87
Lee, Abraham/Elaine, 2000-
Limburg, Peter A., 1969
Lubbers, Cal, 1970-1977
Maatman, Rebecca, 1987
Marcus, Abe, 1966-74
Marcus, Abe/Doris, 1977-91
Medendorp, Jacob, 1969-71
Mellema, Paul, 1969
Mortensen, Darryl, 1993-96
Nyenhuis, Gerald/Francisca, 1962-94
Oostendorp, Derk/Nancy, 1977-80, 1990-98
Poll, Shirley J., 1969-72
Post, Melva, 1984-85
Post, Tom, 1982-85
Postuma, Duane, 1976-78
Pott, Rev/Mrs J. Jerry, 1963-75
Redondo, William/Marry, 1984-89
Roberts, Mr/Mrs John P., 1978-84
Roberts, Rev/Mrs J. Larry, 1964-84
Roeda, Mr/Mrs Jack, 1967-80
Ruis, Rev/Mrs Robert, 1956-81
Rumph, Rev/Mrs Arnold, 1982-84
Sanchez, Esperalza Garnido, 1964-67
Schemper, Chester M., 1964-73
Silva, Catharine Marcus, 1974
Silva, Cathy, 1973-77
Swier, Loren, 1974-86
Thompson, Richard/Lynn, 1990
Tuinstra, John, 1969-71
Vander Ende, Sam, 1979-82
Vander Klippe, Bill, 1980-85
Vander Klippe, Hilda, 1984
Vanderploeg, Kenneth J./Patricia, 1987-
Vander Schuur, David, 1972-73
Vander Woerd, Alan/Eileen, 1992-
Van Ee, Jan/Darlene, 1980-
Van Ee, John, 1971-74
Van Oyen, Gerald, 1971-73
Van Tol, William/Laura, 1997-
Visser, Mr/Mrs James, 1980
Wagenveld, Louis/MaryAnne, 2001
Walstra, Richard, 1972-73
Weerstra, Dr/Mrs Hans, 1964-85
Wind, John/Shirley, 2000-

Mkar

Lett, Ronald, 1977-79

Mozambique

Boven, Greg/Ruth, 1996-97
Miedema, Wayne/Judy, 1994-95

The Netherlands

de Blois, Kees/Janneke, 1995-

The Netherlands, continued
Guter, Frank/Hilary, 1995

New Guinea
De Vries, Mr/Mrs Nelson, 1982–83
De Vries, Rev/Mrs Thomas, 1979–83
Roosma, Gary, 1987–89
Schering, Rev/Mrs Erik, 1979–86

New Zealand
Cooper, Sidney, 1960–68, 1984–87
Stadt, Rev/Mrs Paul D., 1980–83
Van Dam, Peter, 1966
Vander Pol, Allen P./Marcia, 1986–90
Venema, Richard J., 1958–65

Nicaragua
Bot, Elicia, 2000
Duthler, Patricia, 1975
Flikweert, Peter/Helen, 2002
Fortna, Steven, 2002
Hoksbergen, Roland, 1996–97
Hubers, Rhomda, 2001–
Huyser, Joel/Jeannie, 1996–
Kamphouse, Joan, 1977–82
Kuipers, Kelly, 2000–01
Laarman, Bob/Laurie, 1988
Lee, John, 2002
Limburg, Peter A., 1973–78
MacLeod, Peggy, 1975
Martinez, Rev/Mrs Jose, 1978
Meyer, Ben/Amy, 1998–99
Mortensen, Darryl/Donna Jean, 1998–
Pausma, Jasen, 2000
Prins, Shawna, 2001–
Schipper, Rev/Mrs Gary W., 1977–84
Starkenburg, Liam, 2001–
Suwyn, Rob, 2001
Teja, Gary/Jackie, 1977–82
Van Der Borgh, Rev/Mrs R. John, 1976–81
Vander Wier, Nathan/Hannah, 2000–01
Van Straten, Barbara, 1998–
Veltkamp, David, 1975
Walhof, Tammy, 1992–94
Zwier, Joel, 1977–78

Niger
De Wilde, John/Pam, 1995–96
Disselkoen, Jan, 1998–2001
Dotinga, Judy, 1976–77
Franje, Pat, 1982
Frei, Markus, 1976–80
Nikkel, Steve, 1976
Noteboom, Peter, 1994–96
Syler, Keith, 1996–98

Vreeken, Ary/Joanna, 2001

Nigeria
Achterhoff, Betty, 1995–99
Achtyes, Daniel, 1972–74
Ali, Bulus/Rifkatu, 1998–2001
Anderson, Sidney/Louise, 1977–88
Arends, Gerald, 1981–85
Aukeman, Owen, 1964
Baas, Mr/Mrs LeRoy, 1965–84
Bahnson, Dr/Mrs Fred, 1985–87
Baker, Mr/Mrs Reed, 1985
Baker, Ralph/Verna, 1952–89
Bakker, Fred/Theresa, 1986–90
Bakker, Mr/Mrs Frank, 1983
Bandstra, John, 1976, 1978
Beeksma, Jack/Mary, 1986–93
Beelen, Laura, 1957–72
Berends, Willem/Henny, 1977–89
Berg, Nellie, 1979
Bergsma, Harold, 1954–67
Bergsma, Stuart K. Jr., 1954–62
Bestman, Gerrit, 1987
Bierling, Albert/Kay, 1963–90
Bierma, William, 1959–65
Bliek, Peggy, 1976–80
Boer, Ella, 1958–1968
Boer, Harry, 1947–50, 1955–78
Boer, John/Fran, 1966–69, 1976–96
Boot, Diana, 1979–81
Bos, Patricia, 1998–99
Bosma, Fred/Nancy, 1990
Bosscher, Dr/Mrs David, 1977–79
Bosserman, Mr/Mrs Ronald, 1977–79
Bouma, Reanard (Ray), 1964–72
Branderhorst, Donald, 1966–70
Branderhorst, Joyce, 1954–56
Brandsen, Mr/Mrs Preston, 1961–64
Bratt, Harvey/Fran, 1964–78
Bredell, Aleda Vander Vaart, 1952–61
Bremer, Donald/Jean, 1969–1980
Breukleman, Fred/Doreen, 1998
Brinks, Mr/Mrs Gordon, 1968–79
Broersma, Mr/Mrs James, 1982–85
Broersma, Tom, 1966
Bronger, Ruth, 1991–94
Brouwer, Bonnie, 1980–83
Brouwer, Mr/Mrs Norman, 1982
Brouwer, Norman, 1962–74
Brouwer, Rev/Mrs Wayne A., 1985–86
Browneye, Raymond, 1955–78
Bulthuis, Peter, 1951–71
Burma, Bruce, 1973
Buys, Gordon, 1964–83
Byker, Kevin, 1986–88

Nigeria, continued

Camburn, Jan, 1995–
Channer, Dr/Mrs John, 1969–77
Chapel, Nancy, 1959–78
Chomock, Zakka, 2001
Coetzee, Jacoba, 1964
Cok, Mr/Mrs Ralph, 1958–83
Cremer, Mr/Mrs Gerald, 1979–85
Daining, David, 1970–74
Danford, Cloe Ann, 1965–71
Davis, Roy Dr., 1951, 1953
De Boer, Arthur, 1961–64
De Boer, Mr/Mrs Warren, 1976–79
De Boer, Warren, 1972–74
De Bruyn, Margrieta, 1976–80
Decking, Bruce, 1969
De Groot, Harold, 1955–70
De Groot, Janet, 1971–72
De Groot, Terry, 1975–76
De Haan, Joyce, 1949–60
De Haan, Robert/Cheryl, 1986–89
De Jager, Mr/Mrs John, 1974–83
De Jong, Fred, 1972–75
De Jong, Harold, 1969–74, 1983–87
De Jong, Jessie, 1959–70
De Jong, Mike/Deanne, 1987–88
De Jong, William, 1968–75
De Jonge, Anne, 1988–92
de Jonge, Harold/Joanne, 1983–91
Dekker, Harold, 1966–67
Dekker, Peter, 1945–70
Den Besten, Lawrence, 1957–74
De Ruyter, Grace, 1979–80
Deters, Ellis E., 1964–66
De Vries, Mr/Mrs Richard, 1965–72
De Vries, Neva, 1953–76
De Vries, Stanely, 1969–70
De Young, Rev/Mrs Roger, 1981–85
Dik, Ralph, 1955–65
Disselkoen, Kieth/Georgiann, 1989
Distler, John Allen, 1975–77
Dolislager, Donna Mae, 1970–72
Driesenga, Mr/Mrs Henry, 1957–62
Duyst, Emily, 1961–73
Dykgraaf, David/Janice, 1968–
Dykhuis, William, 1977–82
Dykstra, Donald, 1983–85
Dykstra, Margaret, 1945–80
Dykstra, Meredith, 1998–2001
Dykstra, Sheila, 2001–
Eldrenkamp, Neal, 1983–84
Elgersma, Marlene, 1986
Ellens, Gene/Jane, 1992–94
Ellens, Sy/Janice, 1977–80
Evenhouse, Aldrich, 1967–76

Evenhouse, Mr/Mrs William, 1966–80, 1984–93
Faber, Mr/Mrs Harry, 1968–79
Feikema, Mr/Mrs Fred, 1967–77
Fliestra, Allen, 1967–74
Franz, Marjorie Ann, 1962–77
Frei, Markus, 1975
Freswick, Mr/Mrs David, 1985–87
Friend, Nancy, 1964–65, 1968–74
Fynewever, Kim, 1996–97
Gabrielse, Leonard J., 1967–74
Geels, Mr/Mrs Robert, 1977–78
Geerlings, Mr/Mrs Mark, 1981–86
Geerlings, Mr/Mrs Ronald, 1981–87
Geleynse, Geraldine, 1958–72
Gerryts, W.D., 1963–68
Gezon, Mr/Mrs John, 1975–83
Gils, Ganette, 2000–01
Gray, Dr/Mrs Herman, 1953–88
Greidanus, Dr/Mrs Peter, 1971–80
Greydanus, Mr/Mrs Stuart, 1977–78
Grissen, Raymond, 1952–68
Groen, G. Paul, 1964–73
Groen, Maxine Ohlmann, 1961–73
Groenwold, Wilma, 1987, 1991–2001
Haak, Ann, 1984
Haak, Clarence/Diane, 1986–88
Haarsma, Ruth, 1965–72
Hammink, Terry, 1966–68
Hart, William/Alie, 1980–97
Haspels, Arie A., 1960–67
Havemen, Louis J., 1968–82
Hekstra, Fred, 1964–65
Helleman, Adrian/Wendy, 2001–
Heyboer, Marvin W., 1967–68
Hiemstra, Marc/Joanna, 1975–78
Hoekman, Mark, 1975–85
Hoekstra, Mark, 1981–83
Hoekstra, Robert, 1967–69
Holkeboer, Gilbert, 1949–55, 1958–67
Holwerda, Harry L., 1965–73
Hogeterp, Gerald/Jackie, 2001–
Hoogewind, Allen J., 1967–68
Hoogstra, Calvin, 1958–61
Hoolsema, Angie, 1956–82
Horlings, Andy/Linda, 1977–
Huisken, Steven, 1982–86
Huizenga, Tena A., 1940–54
Hutt, John, 1969–70
Ipema, Peter/Tina, 1948–72, 1991
Jameson, Steven/Karen, 1985–90
Jansen, Charles, 1961–74
Kaldeway, Mary, 1972–81, 1989
Kanzler, Richard W., 1963–67
Karnemaat, Frances, 1967–87
Kass, Connie, 1985–86

Nigeria, continued

Kass, Frank C., 1969-76
Keegstra, Jennie, 1963-69
Kiekover, Mike, 1992-
Kiekover, Rev/Mrs Harvey, 1962-84
Kingma, Dr/Mrs Stuart, 1961-77
Kirkman, Noel E., 1960-64
Knoester, John, 1997-98
Koetje, Mr/Mrs Dave, 1976-79
Kok, Bena, 1953-72
Kok, Ralph, 1961, 64
Kok, Suzanne, 1964-68
Koning, Tako/Henrietta, 95
Kooiman, Dennis/Kathy, 1981-86, 1991-93
Kooiman, Margaret, 1953-80
Kooistra, Gordon, 1956-72
Koop, Mr/Mrs Thomas, 1979-85
Koops, Mr/Mrs Robert, 1966-96
Korhorn, Mr/Mrs Cornelius, 1962-85
Kortenhoven, Paul, 1966-67, 1972-75
Koster, Janice, 1968-73
Kotze, Gwaie, 1964
Kotze, Mr/Mrs Johannes W., 1964-78
Kredit, Carolyn, 1964-67
Kremer, Dr. Truus, 1984
Kuik, Gordon, 1961-72
Kuiper, James, 1968-76
Kuiper, Menno, 1973-76
Kuipers, Alie, 1977-82
Kuipers, Gordon, 1962-70
Lambers, Stephen, 1954-79
Lamingo, José, 1994-97
Lemcke, Mr/Mrs William, 1956-81
Lensink, Sharon, 1961-62
Leodolff, M., 1964
Lett, Dr/Mrs Ronald, 1978-79
Lindquist, Janet, 1968-76
Llwellyn, Neal Nelson, 1964
Lobdell, Lawrence/Linda, 1984-89, 1990-92
Lodewyk, Bauke, 1967-74
Lodewyk, Bob/Ineke, 1987, 1990-98
Lootsma, Anna, 1962-66
Lovelace, David/Chris, 1988-91
Mabee, Thomas, 1973
Manuel, Jane, 2000
Mast, Mae Jerene, 1952-79
Medenblik, Susan, 1999-2000
Meinhardt-Hoekma, Dr Ginny, 1977-85
Meyer, Harry, 1967-71
Meyer, Mr/Mrs Barry, 1974-80
Monsma, Timothy, 1962-74
Moolman, Rachie, 1946-73
Mulder, Dennis, 1967-68
Mulder, Tom, 1985-86
Nelson, Rev/Mrs Timothy L., 1978-83

Niemeyer, Elzo, 1960-72
Niessink, Peter/Ineke, 1980-88
Nikkel, Steve, 1978-1980, 1982-85
Nobel, Faith, 1969-71
Noble, Kathryn R., 1984-85
Ohlmann, Maxine, 1962-65
Oosterhouse, Kenneth, 1969-73
Oosterhuis, Dr/Mrs Koen, 1983-84
Oosterhuis, Thomas, 1965-66
Oosthuizen, Peter, 1963-64
Opperwall, Nola, 1978
Orffer, J.F., 1962-63
Orkar, John/Esther, 1984-2001
Ottens, Henry, 1968-72
Ouwerkerk, Gerrit, 1972-73
Paauw, Donald, 1978
Padding, Harold, 1957-72
Palmer, Timothy/Wilma, 1985-
Palsrok, Russell/Sherrill, 1987-89
Peerbolt, Dr/Mrs Dale, 1977-79
Persenaire, Allan/Jacie, 1979-
Persenaire, Cornelius A., 1955-62, 1965-71
Persenaire-Hogeterp, Ardell/Henry, 1996-
Plagerman, Mr/Mrs Peter, 1982
Plate, Keith/Carol, 1962-89
Poel, Harvey, 1957-1968
Porter, Susan, 1985-1993
Posthumus, Jessie, 1958-77
Posthumus, Mr/Mrs Thomas, 1968-77
Pothoven, Lois, 1968-74
Prins, Dr/Mrs Ray, 1969-77
Quist, Brian/Kristy, 1993
Ragagni-Bratt, Mary, 1983-86
Reberg, Alan, 1967-73
Recker, Robert, 1949-70
Reedyk, Dr/Mrs Martin, 1969-79
Regnerus, Mr/Mrs Louis, 1977-78
Renzema, Robert, 1971
Ribbens, Michael/Megan, 2001-
Rienstra, John, 1972
Ritter, Jim/Sue, 1979-83, 1988-92
Roos, Christine, 1968-
Rouw, Mr/Mrs Otto, 1973-86
Rubingh, Eugene, 1955-86
Rumph, Mr/Mrs Albert, 1984-86
Salomons, Jo Ann, 1970-71
Salomons, Ruth, 1966-80
Schemper, Mr/Mrs Kenneth, 1980-84
Schepel, Dennis, 1979-82
Scholten, Herman, 1964-70
Schoonveld, Evertt, 1966-69
Schutt, George, 1967-74
Seinen, Dick/Margaret, 1972-
Shaarda, Josh/Mandy, 2001-
Sikkema, Donald, 1960-67

Nigeria, continued

Sjaardema, Mr/Mrs John, 1976-82
Sjardsma, Sandra, 1981
Smit, Henry M., 1960-69
Smith, Rev/Mrs Edgar H., 1940-69
Spee, Rev/Mrs George, 1974-83
Stehouwer, Mr/Mrs Edward, 1958-84
Stel, Phillip, 1974-77
Stelpstra, acob/Donna, 1986-88
Sterken, John, 1967-70
Stielstra, Jennie, 1939-67
Strydhorst, Albert/Carolyn, 1993-
Suh, Gil/Joyce, 1999-
Suk, Ethel, 1982-84
Swartz, Mr/Mrs Marvin, 1959-61, 1965-66
Sytsma, Dorothy, 1954-81
Tadema, Ritz, 1955-58
te Nyenhuis, Leny, 1978-84
Termorshuizen, Mr/Mrs Willem, 1972-79, 1983-86
Terpstra, Gerard, 1952-79
Terpstra, Philip, 1983-85
Theule, Mr/Mrs Paul, 1974-81
Thirion, Maria Aletta, 1964-69
Thornburg, William/Sandra, 1986-
Tiemersma, John, 1971-73
Tiemstra, Nellie, 1988
Tigchelaar, Mr/Mrs Arnold, 1977-78
Tinklenberg, Mr/Mrs Keith, 1982-85
Triezenberg, Jim, 2001-
Triezenberg, Mr/Mrs Ryer, 1969
Tyokighir, David, 1998-2001
Ubels, Mr/Mrs Engbert, 1970-78
Ubels, Roelf, 1970-79
Van Andel, Dick/Ruth, 1989
Van Beek, Jean, 1959-76
Van Biert, Pauline, 1989-91
Van Den Berg, Betty, 1944-75
Vanden Berg, Elizabeth, 1946-54
Vanden Berg, Geraldine, 1951-89
Vanden Berg, Jerry, 1954-68
VandenBerge, Betty, 1958-60
Vander Aa, Harry, 1953-71
Vanderaa, Mr/Mrs Leland, 1981
Vander Ark, Nolan, 1967-76
Vander Bie, Gordon, 1960-72
Vanderbrug, Elsie, 1955-66
Van Der Dyke, Mike/Victoria, 1979-
Vander Griend, Mr/Mrs Howard, 1986-87
Vanderkloet, Kathleen, 1989-
Vander Kooy, Dr/Mrs John, 1969-77
Vander Laan, Julie, 1973-81
Vander Leest, Case/Elaine, 1986-90
Vander Merve, D.T., 1963-64
Vander Meulen, Ruth, 1955-80
Vander Ploeg, Scott/Andrea, 2001-

Vander Pol, Allen, 1978-79
Vander Steen, John/Irene, 1983-88
Vander Steen, Mr/Mrs Richard, 1966-79
Vander Steen, Wilma, 1980-87
Vander Stel, Kathy, 1996
Vander Vaart, Aleda, 1953-54
Vander Vlis, Bernhard, 1994-
Vander Weide, Mr/Mrs Ronald, 1979-81
Vander Zwaag, Frances, 1955-88
Van Dorp, Dr/Mrs John, 1979-84
Van Dussen, Jeffrey/Mary, 1989-90
Van Duyvendyk, Jeremy, 1979
Van Dyk, Frederick J./Bette, 1982-89
Van Dyken, Richard/Susan, 1984-89
Van Ee, Miriam, 2001-
Van Essen, Rev/Mrs Lester, 1961-82
Van Haitsma, Gertrude, 1960-74, 1980, 1984
Van Heukelum, Margaret, 1961-76
Van Ieperen, Leonard, 1955-70
Van Kley, James, 1984
Van Kooten, Dan/Andrea, 1994-97
Van Korlaar, Lois, 1962-63
Van Leeuwen, Leanne, 1976-80
Vannette, Avert, 1962-72
Van Reken, Donald, 1949-58
Van Staalduinen, Tina, 1962-90
Van Tol, William/Laura, 1967-75
Van Tongeren, Warren, 1960-73
Van Vugt, Mr/Mrs Gerrit, 1962-70
Van Wyk, Case/Gremar, 1992-97
Van Wyk, Mr/Mrs Cornelius, 1973-87
Van Zee, Larry/Rose, 1977-
Veenstra, Dr Fred/Dr Hazel, 1978-84
Veenstra, Rolf, 1956-71
Veltkamp, Ruth, 1969-95
Verbrugge, Verlyn, 1966-67
Verdun, Marina, 1968-76
Verhoef, Daniel/Lois, 1985-88
Vermeer, Stanley, 1965
Vermeer, Stanley, 1969-79
Viss, Mr/Mrs Norman, 1977-87
Visser, Dr/Mrs Hendrik, 1980-85
Visser, Mr/Mrs Henry, 1961-72
Visser, Thomas, 1964-73
Vissia, Anita A., 1941-79
Volkema, Frederick, 1952-78
Vredevoogd, Evelyn, 1950-75
Vreeke, Abe, 1969-84
Vreeke, Abe/Carol, 1994-2000
Vreeke, James/Kristin, 1996-2001
Vreeman, Betty, 1968-1970, 1977-78
Vroon, John, 1958-66
Walcott, Tom, 1982
Warsen, Phyllis, 1977-80
Winkle, Peter, 1965-69

Nigeria, continued

Wybenga, Anna, 1966–71
Zaagman, Mr/Mrs Leonard, 1978
Zeilenga, Donald, 1973–76
Zeilstra, Mr/Mrs William, 1980–81
Zinkand, John/Mary, 1986–91
Zoet, Ronald, 1972–74
Zuidema, John, 1967–70
Zuiderveen, Mr/Mrs Steve, 1982–83

Pakistan

Vander Veer, Jack/Anita, 1994–98

Philippines

Adema, Bruce G./Joanne, 1997–
Afman, Carl J./Jan, 1991–
Apostol, Vincente/Lucy, 1963–96
Baas, Lee/Carolyn, 1991–98
Bekker, Rev/Mrs Gary J., 1977–84
Blankers, Rev/Mrs Barry, 1965–77
Boeve, Jospeh/Kate, 1984–92
Boldenow, Peter/Tanya, 2002
Bouma, Dick C./Evelyn, 1968–75, 1984–93
Brouwer, Edward, 1988–97
Bulthuis, Rev/Mrs W. Keith, 1973–76
De Kam, Ivan, 1975–94
De Vries, Dan/LaDonna, 1987–97
De Vries, Mr/Mrs Richard, 1984
De Vries, Mr/Mrs Steven, 1987
De Vries, Rev/Mrs Henry, 1971–83
De Vries, Rev/Mrs Robert W., 1972–79
De Vries, Robert, 1972–1979
De Vries, Thomas J./Yvonne, 1992–2001
De Young, James/Mary Ann, 1989–96
Dewey, Melissa, 2002
Doezema, Lambert/Joanne, 1988
Elzinga, Mr/Mrs Steven, 1982
Fernhout, Mr/Mrs William, 1975–86
Fox, Mr/Mrs Joseph, 1980–85
Glewen, Arlyn/Lois, 1984–95
Haan, Eleanor, 1978–80
Harris, Robert/Patricia, 1998–
Helleman, Rev/Mrs Adrian A., 1977–87
Hofman, Mr/Mrs Marvin, 1980–81
Hogan, Joel/Patty, 1984–2001
Holwerda, Timothy/Tammy, 1993–
Howerzyl, Debra, 1999–2000
Johnson, Scott/Brenda, 1993–94
Klaassens, Anne, 1987
Knoper, Mark J./Ruth, 1979–94
Koedoet, Gerrit/Ruth, 1981–97
Kruis, Stanley/Bessie, 1985–
Kwants, Dick J./Anne, 1980–
Lamingo, Joe/Arlyn, 1998–2001
Lubbers, Karen, 2002

Luchtenburg, Paul, 1990
Mobach, Mr/Mrs Martin, 1986
Moret, Randy, 1992
Munro, Alex/Renona, 1977–95
Navis, David/Darlene, 1985–92
Nikkel, Steve, 1977
Oppelaar, Rev/Mrs William, 1984
Persenaire, Rev/Mrs Cornelius, 1982–83
Ritskes, Janne, 1981–88
Romeyn, Tony, 1984–87
Rupke, Lynda/Dan, 99
Ryskamp, Andrew, 1980–81
Schaap, Aljean, 1989
Schuld, Fred, 1970–73
Smidstra, Rev/Mrs Henry H., 1977–85
Steen, Henry/Joan, 1984–95
Stravers, Rev/Mrs Dave, 1976–86
Tangelder, Johan D., 1976–78
Tanis, Lauren, 1990
Thielke, Dwayne F./Gladys, 1990–
Van Antwerpen, Russell/Patricia, 1988–97
Vander Berg, Edward/Nita, 1974–88
Vander Bilt, Maas/Eloise, 1980–89
Vander Griend, Mr/Mrs Ronald, 1978–87
Vander Hoven, William, 1988–90
Vander Pol, Mike/Lois, 1993–2001
Vander Vliet, Joyce, 1985
van der Vorst, Dirk/Varolyn, 1994
Van Hemert, James, 1988–92
van Leeuwen, Gary, 1999
Van Regenmorter, John, 1973–74
Van't Land, John, 1983–84
Veenstra, Mr/Mrs David, 1980–85
Veenstra, Ralph, 1992
Vellenga, Peter, 1975–80
Vellenga, William, 1975
Versluys, Rev/Mrs William, 1981–85
Visser, Ed/Jean, 1979–1980
Vruwink, Paul H./Gwen, 1989–90
Werder, Joy, 2000
Westerhof, Karl, 1988–91
Westra, Erik, 2000–
Whatley, Stephen/Lorrie, 1993–
Winkle, Steven, 1985, 1996–98
Zylstra, James/Marilyn, 1995–98

Puerto Rico

Bolt, Jane, 1983–1984
De Vries, William Thomas, 1978–85
Den Bleyker, Rev/Mrs Merle, 1972–82
Gritter, Winabelle, 1981–83
Leder, Arie C./Olga, 1977–85
Pott, Rev/Mrs Frank E., 1976–80
Renkema, Rev/Mrs W. John, 1979–94
Rottschafer, Esther, 1983–84

Puerto Rico, continued

Rumph, Rev/Mrs Arnold, 1973-77
Sawyer, Rev/Mrs Frank, 1983-85
Sprik, Rev/Mrs Ronald R., 1967-85
Vander Ziel, Rev/Mrs Thomas H., 1981-85
Vugteveen, Marvin L., 1967-75
Wagenveld, John/Angela, 1994-2001

Romania

Achim, Gabi, 2001
Balla, Zsuzsa, 2001
Bandstra, Alvin, 1995
Daray, Atilla, 2001
De Haan, Sue, 2002
Dykema, Tim, 2001
Elenbaas, Dawn, 2001
Henry, Glennis, 2001
Van Tol, Rockland/Jennifer Ryder, 1995-96
Vandermeer, Jenny, 2002

Russia

Bultman, James A., 1993
Busscher, Jeff/Natasha, 1995-2000
Dik, Ralph/Celia, 1993
Helleman, Adrian/Wendy, 1996-2001
Hendriksen, Daniel/Shirley, 1993
Munro, Alex/Renona, 1996-2001
Postma, Edward/Norma, 1993
Schraa, Raymond/Wilma, 1993
Stevens, Richard/Janice, 1993
Timmerman, Gary, 2001-
Van Der Weele, Steven/Viola, 1993
Vander Hart, Gary, 1993
Veenstra, Marvin/Marilyn, 1993
Wilson, Nathaniel/Emily, 2002
Wisse, Donald P./Ethel, 1993

Saipan

Schemper, Lynn, 2001
Stuelpnagel, Juli, 2001

Senegal

Abma, Bev, 1995-97
Hasselblad, Wyva, 1995-2001
Nederveld, Anne, 1995-96
Vander Meulen, Peter, 1987-95

Sierra Leone

Adema, Bert, 1985-90
Baker, Norman, 1985-90
Bokma, Alice, 1989
Booy, Dirk, 1982-1988
Bosch, Bob, 1980-83
Brothers, Ruth/Jack, 1991-93
De Haan, Greg, 1991

De Kuiper, William/Jacki, 1983-89
De Ruiter, Jennifer, 1989-90
De Vries, Patricia, 1982-87
Disselkoen, Janet, 1984-97
Drenth, Stanley/Barbara, 1977-88
Hanstra, Beth, 1991
Hiemstra, Mark, 1981-83
Hoolsema, Angie, 1981-90
Hoots, Belinda, 1985
Jawara, Robert, 1998-2000
Kortenhoven, Paul/Mary, 1980-2001
Kraker, Rev/Mrs Roger H., 1980-85, 1990-98
Kraker, Yvonne, 1984-85
Laarman, Robert/Laurie, 1985
Meyer, Barry, 1981-85
Mortensen, Darryl/DonnaJean, 1990-92
Nikkel, Steven/Carol, 1986-92
Oldham, Joy, 1982
Pohler, Kenneth, 1983
Prins, Ronald, 1981-85
Smit, Kathy, 1988-91
Spaling, Harry, 1982-88
Temminck, Evert, 1993
Tensen, Annette, 1988-91
Thompson, Sharon, 1990-91
Vander Schuur, Brenda, 1983-87
Vander Vate, Joyce, 1988
Vander Velde, Daniel/Sara, 1987-88
Van Ens, Roland, 1986-87
Van Gilst, Jacki, 1989-91
Van Haitsma, Gertrude, 1988
Zandstra, Dan, 1991-92

South Africa

Haveman, Lou/Jan, 1999-
Spee, George, 1955-73

South India

Ypma, Benjamin, 1952-54

Sri Lanka

Schuringa, John O., 1948-52; 1957-63
Van Ens, Clarence, 1952-66
Van Ens, Rev/Mrs John, 1952-68

Taiwan

Afman, Rev/Mrs Carl J, 1975-86
Bieber, Ken/Carla, 2000-
Bode, Lillian, 1953-67
Gritter, Winabelle, 1960-67
Jen, Isaac, 1952-1973
Knoper, Mark J./Ruth, 1994-2001
Kosten, William, 1955-76
Kuipers, Marjorie, 1984
Machiela, Al/Mary, 1969-77

Taiwan, continued

Mulder, Dennis, 1969-77
Peng, Frank, 1948-56
Reilly, Rev Thomas H., 1983-87
Roest, Rev/Mrs Gary, 1980-82, 1984-99
Selles, Kurt D./Vicki, 1987-93
Stevens, Dick/Jan, 1990
Swier, Mr/Mrs Loren, 1987
Tong, Peter/Freda, 1965-98
Van de Griend, Kenneth, 1969-73
Vander Pol, Rev/Mrs Mike, 1966-86
Van Houten, Dr/Mrs Richard, 1987

Tanzania

Booy, Dirk, 1990-94
Bulten, Tom/Lisa, 1991
Buwalda, Bill/Anja, 1994-95
De Vries, Jack, 1991-92
Hodgson, Dwayne, 1999-
Moini, Moses, 2001
Njuguna, Margaret, 1999-
Sennema, Greg/Christy, 2000
Timmerman, Peter/Catherine, 1995-97
Untema, Stanley/Lynelle, 1993
Warners, David, 1991-92
Wind, Tricia, 1999-
Woudstra, Brian/Marie, 1991-98
Yntema, Stanley/Lynelle, 1994

Thailand

Hamstra, Albert A./Mindy, 1989-91
Schneider, Deb, 1995

Uganda

Bulten, Tom/Lisa, 1992-97
De Boer, Rod/Barb, 1999-2000
De Kam, Ivan, 1995-97
Hooyer, John, 1986-90
Kaastra-Mutoigo, Ida, 1986-94
Lyzenga, Bonnie, 1998-2000
Melles, Brenda/Mike, 2001
Mutoigo, Ida/James, 2001
Seebeck, Douglas, 1986-89
Snoeyink, Laura, 1994-97
Tazelaar, Grace, 1986-91
Timmerman, Peter/Catherine, 1998-2001
van der Meijden, Rene, 1992-97
Zylstra, Jim, 2001

Ukraine

Gorter, Rodney D./Lydia, 1997-
Munro, Alex/Renona, 1995-96

Utah

Baas, Le Roy, 1959-63

Klumpenhower, Gerrit, 1963-64
Kuipers, Cornelius, 1955-68
Lineweaver, Jerry, 1970-73
Van Westenbrugge, William, 1918

Venezuela

Dekker, Rev/Mrs James C., 1984-86

Zambia

Baker, Norm, 1991-94
Bootsma, Tim/Andrea, 1999-2001
de Jong, Harold/Joanne, 1991-95
Dice, David/Susan, 1995-2001
Van Tongeren, Warren/Marian, 1993

CHRISTIAN REFORMED WORLD RELIEF COMMITTEE

* Dates approximate, based on yearbook entries.

Bangladesh
Berkenbosch, Roy, 1990-92
Brink, Paul/Priscilla, 1980-85
Brouwer, John, 1976-78
Byler, Dan, 2001-
Daring, Kohima, 1998-*
Deelstra, John, 1976-79
De Graaf, Rick, 1976-77, 1983-90
De Vries, Marvin, 1977-84
Haarsma, Valerie, 1994-96
Mostert, Martin, 1980-83
Myers, Shelly, 1994-96
Poppe, Kees, 1977-81
Postma, William, 1985-86, 1992-98
Postma, Rebbeca Walker, 1993-94*
Prins, Ronald, 1976-81
Ryskamp, Andrew, 1976-80
Seebeck, Douglas, 1978-81
Spee, Jim, 1980-83
Ten Broek, Nancy, 1988-*
Vanderkooy, Olive, 1984-85
Vanderkooy, Peter, 1981-89
Vander Meulen, Peter, 1978-82
Van Der Puy, Dave, 1976-79
Vander Zaag, Peter, 1973-75
Van Dijk, Conrad, 1973-74
Ysselstein, Peter, 1983-86

Belize
De Jong Brouwers, Dawn, 1989-91
Hamstra, John, 1986-91
Post, Tom, 1985-97*
Roldan, Elisabeth, 1987-90*
Schout, Debra, 1989-91
Zantingh, Albert, 1987-92

Cambodia
Arensen, Lisa, 2001-*
Chann-Chhay, Navy/Ly, 1999-*

Jost, Shanti, 1997-2001
Schneider Wilson, Deb/Mark, 1995-98
Van Wyke Cooper, Elizabeth, 1997-2000

Canada
DeGraaf, Rick, 1998-2001*

Costa Rica
Boldenow, James, 1981-90
De Voogd, Stan, 1981-87
Duthler, Patricia, 1975-76
Fictorie Gietema, Gertie, 1976-77
Grit, Nelson, 1982-85
Laarman, Bob/Laurie, 1986-87, 1989-92
Ludema, Jim, 1983-90
Mortensen, Darryl, 1977-78*
Van Lopik, Bill/Sue, 1986-92
van Til, Kathy, 1990-92
VerBeek, Kurt/JoAnn, 1987-88

Dominica
Geleynse, Greg, 1982-84

Dominican Republic
Abma, Beverly, 1982-85
Bossenbroek, Tim/Roxann, 1994-96
Geisterfer, Caspar, 1986-95*
Geisterfer, Leanne, 1983-93*
Kornelje Santos, Sheryl, 1986-91
Laarman, Robert/Laurie, 1986-89*
Meyer, Dawn, 1985-89
Vanderburg, Roland, 1989-90
Vander Meulen, Peter, 1982-87
Vander Sluis, Karen, 1989-90
Visser, Mindy, 1997-99
Walhof, Tammy, 1989-92
Zwier, Joel/Patti, 1983-*

Ecuador

Lopez, Alba, 1998-99*
Rikkers-DeBorst, Jim, 1998-99*
Roldan, Betty, 1993-97*
Van Haitsma, Doug/Yvonne, 1994-96*
Wood, Betty/Robert Roldan, 1998-*

Egypt

Jellema, David, 1989-91

El Salvador

DeBorst, Jim, 1999-2000*
De Voogd, Stan, 1987-88
Lopez, Alba, 1999-*
Michmerhuizen, Steve/Jan, 2001-*
Musch, Glenn/Cindy, 1998-2000
Rikkers-DeBorst, Jim, 1993-97
Vanderburg, Roland, 1990-91
Van Haitsma, Doug/Yvonne, 1996-97
Van Lopik, Bill/Sue, 1988-92

Guatemala

Baas DeHaan, Julie/Joel, 1990-92*
Colop, Moises, 1998-
Kapenga, Mark, 1977-78
Limburg, Peter A., 1979-80*
Meyer, Mary Anne, 1990-91
Rikkers-DeBorst, James, 1991-92
Van Tongeren, Paul, 1994-2001*

Guinea

Markus Feikema, Jill, 1994-96
Wierda, David, 1986-98
Wierda, David/Slimatou, 1998-2000

Haiti

Beelen, Sandy, 1976-79
Both, Dick, 1977-86
Brink, Paul/Priscilla, 1988-90
Danford, Cloe Ann, 1979-81
Dening, Edwin/Sylvia, 1996-99
De Vries, Marvin, 1984-87
De Vries, Marvin, 1984-87
Diephuis, Bill/Karen, 1996-98
Dykstra, Linda, 2001-
Franje, Pat, 1981-86
Frazier, Julie, 1981-84
Geisterfer, Leanne/Caspar, 1996-*
Geleynse, Nick, 1981-86
Genzink, David, 1975-80
Hill, JoLynn, 1986-87
Hunse, Hank, 1985-88
Jeanty, Edner, 2001-*
Kobes, Dave, 1978-81
Orkar, Patsy, 1997-98*

Tinklenberg Hasan, Lavon, 1980-88
Vanderkooy, Tricia, 2001-*
Vander Wees, Mark/Nancy, 1992-*
Vander Zaag, Ray/Jayne, 1985-93
Verhulst, Cairn, 1996-98
Wright, Charlotte, 1993-96
Zylstra, James, 1980-83*

Honduras

Apoll, Tracy, 2001-02*
Barrett, Bob, 1995-98
Boersma, Carol, 1973-77
de Murillo, Irene, 1998-
Laarman, Robert/Laurie, 1987-88
Miedema, Don, 1992-99*
Miedema, Don/Eva, 1999-*
Mortensen, Darryl, 1978-82*
Pierik, Gordon/Belinda, 2001-02*
Post, Thomas, 1975-77
Roldan, Elizabeth, 1976-86*
Timinskis, Deborah, 1990-92
Van Ess, Carol, 1975-76
VerBeek, Kurt/JoAnn, 1988-92
Zwier, Joel, 1979-83*

Indonesia

Armstrong, Nick/Laura, 1997-*
Brink, Paul/Priscilla, 1990-2000
Lamigo, José, 1986-92*
Saher, Iskandar, 2001-*
Talstra, Eric, 1998-2000
Yoder, Kay, 1988-89

Jordan

Bosch, Robert, 1978-80
De Vries, Bert, 1972-74
Haan, Robert, 1978-81
Kok, Paul, 1973-77
Slager, Larry, 1977-78
Vander Baan, Lee, 1974-76
Vander Vliet, Dave, 1977-79

Kenya

Addink, Roxanne, 1989-91
Addink DeGraaf, Roxanne/Brent, 1993
Booy, Dirk, 1989-2001
Bruinooge, Michael, 1984-85
Buwalda, Bill/Anja, 1996-*
De Haan, Greg, 1992-94*
De Vries, Brian, 1992-93
Disselkoen, Keith, 1991-98, 2001-02
Hooyer, John, 1985-86*
Ippel, Jotham, 1997-2000
Janz, Janet, 1999-*

Kenya, continued

Kuperis, Peter, 1991-96
Lutz, Stephan, 2001-*
Muthoka, Francis, 1999-*
Omanyo, Davis, 2001-*
Post, Tom/Melva, 1997-2001
Ritskes, Janne, 1988-1991
Seebeck, Douglas, 1980-86, 1989-96*
Tazelaar, Grace, 1985-2001*
Vliegenthart, Janet, 1990-91*
Vreeken, Ary, 1984-85*
Wraith, Steve/Sandi, 2001-*
Zents, Alicia, 2001-*

Korea

Byma, Sidney, 1970-73
Faber, Robert G., 1969-72
Feddema, Peter, 1967-68
Hekman, Calvin, 1969-71
Hubers, Henry J., 1967-68
Lim, Sook Kyung, 1967-68*
Mulder, D.J., 1967-71
Spoolstra Zwier, Elvinah, 1967-71
Vander Sloot, Charles L., 1969-76
Venhuizen, Kenneth, 1972-76

Kosovo

Disselkoen, Keith, 2000-01*

Laos

Armstrong, Nick/Laura, 2001-*
Cruz, Ken/Jomil, 2001-*

Latin America

Boldenow, James, 1990-96
Roldan, Betty, 1991-2001*

Liberia

Bruinooge, Michael, 1985-88
Haveman, Louis, 1982-83*
Ippel, Paul, 1982-88
Kuipers, Lynne, 1987-88
Lemcke, William, 1989-91*
Noteboom, Peter, 1991-93
Rikkers-DeBorst, James, 1989-91
Vreeken, Ary, 1985-86*

Malawi

Bengelink, Jonathan/Kendra, 1995-98
Gunnison, John, 1993-94*
McAuley, Larry/Linda, 1999-*
Ott, Michael, 1993-94*
Van Es, Rowland Jr./Jane, 1990-96

Mali

Admiraal, Ellen, 1998-2000
Budding, Renee, 1997-99
Crickmore, Mary/Scott, 1986-*
Geffrard, Willys/Suzètte, 1991-2002
Hunse, Henrietta, 1988-99
Lagerwey, Sandra, 1998-2001*
Lyzenga, Bonnie, 1994-98
Michelson, Josie, 2001-*
Monsma, George/Ellen, 1988-91
Orkar, Patsy, 1999-*
Postma, William, 1986-87*
Rustenberg, Tania, 1994-96
Syler, Keith, 1992-95
Westra, Brian, 1992-94

Mexico

Bajema, Duane, 1974-76
Buurma, Bruce, 1974-76
Buurma, Loren, 1976-79
De Boer, Clarence, 1976-81
Hamstra, John, 1982-86
Koetje, John, 1979-80
Limburg, Peter A., 1969-73*
Lubbers, Cal, 1969-76
Mortensen, Darryl, 1993-96*
Post, Melva, 1984-85*
Post, Tom, 1982-85
Postuma, Duane, 1977-79
Vander Ende, Sam, 1978-84
Vander Klippe, Bill, 1979-85
Vander Klippe, Hilda, 1984-85

Mozambique

Boven, Greg/Ruth, 1996-98
Miedema, Wayne/Judy, 1993-95

Nicaragua

Boldenow, Emily, 2001-*
Duthler, Patricia, 1973-75
Hoekwater, Jim/Chris, 1973-74
Hoksbergen, Roland, 1995-97
Laarman, Bob/Laurie, 1988-89
Limburg, Peter A., 1974-77
MacLeod, Peggy, 1975-76*
Mortensen, Darryl/Donna Jean, 1998-*
Vander Meulen, Peter, 1973-75
Veltkamp, David, 1973-76
VerBeek, Kurt/JoAnn, 1986-87
Walhof, Tammy, 1992-94
Zwier, Joel, 1977-79

Niger

De Wilde, John/Pam, 1994-96
Disselkoen, Janet, 1998-*

Niger, continued

Dotinga, Judy, 1976-77*
Franje, Pat, 1977-81
Frei, Markus, 1975-81
Nikkel, Steve, 1976-77*
Noteboom, Peter, 1993-96
Syler, Keith, 1996-98
Vreeken, Ary/Joanna, 2001-*

Nigeria

Ali, Bulus/Rifkatu, 1998-*
Burma, Bruce, 1973-74*
Chomock, Zakka, 2001-*
Havemen, Louis J., 1968-82
Kool, David, 1987
Lamigo, José, 1994-98
Mulder, Tom, 1984-86
Nikkel, Steve, 1976-83
Orkar, John/Esther, 1984-*
Tyokighir, David, 1998-*

Philippines

Brouwer, Edward, 1987-97
De Kam, Ivan, 1973-95
De Vries, Dan/LaDonna, 1986-97
Fernhout, William/Dorothy, 1972-86
Haan, Eleanor, 1976-79
Johnson, Scott/Brenda, 1992-94
Lamigo, Joe/Arlyn, 1998-2001*
Luchtenburg, Paul, 1989-90
Nikkel, Steve, 1977-78*
Ritskes, Janne, 1980-88
Romeyn, Tony, 1984-88
Ryskamp, Andrew, 1980-83
Schuld, Fred, 1970-73
Van Hemert, James, 1987-92
Veenstra, David/Cindy, 1980-85
Vellenga, Peter, 1974-80
Vellenga, William, 1975-76
Westerhof, Karl, 1986-97*

Romania

Achim, Gabi, 2001-*
Balla, Zsuzsa, 2001-02*
Daray, Atilla, 2001-*
Dykema, Tim, 2001-*
Elenbaas, Dawn, 1999-2001
Henry, Glennis, 2001-*
Kozma, Noemi, 2001-*
Menning, Mike, 2001-*

Rwanda

Barker, Stephen/Liz, 2001-*
Syler, Keith, 1995-96

Senegal

Abma, Beverly, 1994-97
Hasselblad, Wyva, 1995-*
Nederveld, Anne, 1994-96
Vander Meulen, Peter, 1987-95
Van Geest de Groot, Matt/Esther, 1999-2001
Wood, Siri, 1994-97

Sierra Leone

Adema, Bert/Ruth, 1984-90
Baker, Norman, 1984-89
Booy, Dirk, 1981-87
Bosch, Bob, 1980-85
Brothers, Ruth/Jack, 1990-93
De Haan, Greg, 1990-91
De Haan, Jeff, 1983-84
De Vries, Patricia, 1982-88
Dekker Tensen, Annette, 1987-91*
Disselkoen, Janet, 1984-97*
Drenth, Stanley/Barbara, 1977-88*
Hiemstra, Mark, 1981-84
Hoolsema, Angie, 1981-90
Hoots Wharton, Belinda, 1984-85
Jawara, Robert, 1998-2000*
Kortenhoven, Paul/Mary, 1980-*
Kraker, Yvonne, 1984-86
Laarman, Robert/Laurie, 1984-86*
Lemcke, William, 1988-89
Meyer, Barry, 1980-85
Mortensen, Darryl/Donna Jean, 1990-92*
Nikkel, Steven/Carol, 1985-92
Oldham, Joy, 1982-83*
Prins, Ronald, 1981-85*
Spaling, Harry, 1982-89
Thompson, Sharon, 1990-91*
Vander Schuur, Brenda, 1982-87
Van Ens, Roland, 1986-87
Van Es, Rowland Jr./Jane, 1986-87*
Van Gilst, Jacque, 1989-91
Zandstra, Dan, 1990-92

South Africa

Haveman, Lou/Jan, 1999-*

Sudan

Vaalburh, Klasien, 1990

Tanzania

Booy, Dirk, 1989-95
Bulten, Tom/Lisa, 1991-92*
Buwalda, Bill/Anja, 1994-95*
De Vries, Jack, 1991-93
Hodgson, Dwayne, 1999-*
Moini, Moses, 2000-02
Njuguna, Margaret, 1999-*

Tanzania, continued
Sennema, Greg/Christy, 1997–99
Timmerman, Peter/Catherine, 1995–97*
Untema, Stanley/Lynelle, 1993–94*
Warners, David, 1991–192
Wind, Tricia, 1999–*
Woudstra, Brian/Marie, 1990–98
Yntema, Stanley/Lynelle, 1992–95

Thailand
Schneider, Deb, 1995–96*

Uganda
Bulten, Tom/Lisa, 1990–97
De Boer, Rod/Barb, 1998–2000
De Kam, Ivan, 1995–97
Hooyer, Ihla, 1984–90
Kaastra-Mutoigo, Ida, 1986–94*
Lyzenga, Bonnie, 1998–99
Melles, Brenda/Mike, 2001–*
Mutoigo, Ida/James, 2001–*
Seebeck, Douglas, 1986–89*
Snoeyink Musoke, Laura, 1993–97
Tazelaar, Grace, 1985–1991
Timmerman, Peter/Catherine, 1998–*
van der Meijden, Rene, 1991–97*
Zylstra, Jim, 2001–

United States
Begay, Mitzie, 2001–*
Boldenow, James, 1976–81
Boersma, Carol, 1971–72*
DeVries, Dan, 2001–*
Diephouse, Greg, 1999–2001
Doesburg, Janna, 1976–78*
Douma, Vera, 1999–2001
Evans, Susie, 1976–90
Friesen, Dan, 1998–*
Gonzales, Lorena G., 2001–*
Gonzalez, Rudy, 1998–*
Hinken, Brian, 1989–96
Howell, Lyman, 1998–*
Infante, Ileana J., 1973–74*
Izquierdo, Mrs Y., 1967–68*
Jacobs, John, 1973–74*
Kornelje Santos, Sheryl, 1997–2001
Laack, James E., 1975–77
Limburg, Peter A., 1968–69*
Littlejohn, Jeff, 2001–*
Magally, M., 1967–68*
Menchaca, Sara, 1969–73*
Menning, Mike, 1998–2001*
Musch, Glen/Cindy, 2000–*
Nikkel, Steve, 2001–*
Palma, Roberto, 1967–10*

Rodriguez, Joe, 1983–93
Ruano, Omelia, 1967–72*
Sandall, N.J., 1967–1968*
Schaap, Arthur, 1967–80*
Spoolstra Zwier, Elvinah, 1977–88
Turk, Mrs. C, 1971–72*
Van Arragon, G., 1969–70*
Van Denend, Bob, 1977–80
Van Dyken, Ken, 1985–95
Van Groningen, Jay, 1998–*
Vega, T., 1967–72*
Verwys, Ryan/Rachel, 2001–*
Vo, Thu, 2001–*
Willink, Del, 1976–82
Zeilstra, Don/Janna Doesburg, 1978–84

Zambia
Baker, Norman, 1991–94
Bootsma, Tim/Andrea, 1999–*
Dice, David/Susan, 1995–*
Mol, Sue, 1994–95
Van Tongeren, Warren/Marian, 1993–

SPECIALIZED MINISTERS

Aardema, Thelma
Millgrove, Allegan, MI, 1951–52

Aasman, Joann
Evangelism/Outreach, Roosevelt Community, Grand Rapids, MI, 1995–2000

Aboyue, Kim
Youth, Lombard, IL, 2001–

Abma, Rick
Houston, BC, 1992–93; Oakhills Presbyterian, Grand Rapids, MI, 1993–1994, 1994–95; Maranatha, Woodstock, ON, 1994; Youth, Woodynook, Lacombe, AB, 1995–

Ackerman, Dan
see list of ordained ministers

Ackerson, Joe
Youth, First, Langley, BC, 2001–

Adamy, Mark
Music, New Life Ministries, Franklin Lakes, NJ, 1999–

Afman, Thomas
Madison Square, Grand Rapids, MI, 1940–48; Blodgett Home, Grand Rapids, MI, 1944–48; Grace Chapel, Bellflower, CA, 1950–51; Beacon Light Chapel, Racine, WI, 1952–53

Afman, Dennis
Youth and Education director, Second, Lynden, WA, 1985–88

Alderink, Albert
Sunshine Chapel, Grand Rapids, MI, 1940–45

Alderink, Douglas
Youth minister, Third, Lynden, WA, 1976–77

Alderink, Wayne
Ionia Ave. Chapel, Grand Rapids, MI, 1954–55
Bowen Mills Chapel, Middleville, MI, 1955–59

Alexander, Joyce
Director of youth ministries, Madison Ave., Paterson, NJ, 1987–90

Algera, John
Director of community outreach, Madison Ave., Paterson, NJ, 1978–79

Algra, Bart
Youth, The Burlington, Burlington, ON, 1994–2001

Alles, Mike
Youth, Caledonia, MI, 1995–

Altena, Ben
East End, Holland, MI, 1946–48; Spruce Ave. Chapel, Holland, MI, 1948–52

Altena, Louis
Calvary, Holland, MI, 1952–53

Ammerman, Robb
Education/Children/Youth, Willmar, MN, 2001–

Anderson, C.
Back to God Chapel, Edmonton, AB, 1953–54

Anderson, Marvin P.
Minister of youth and evangelism, Utah ministries Committee and IVCF, UT, 1977–82; Director of education and evangelism, Dearborn, MI, 1982–91; Education/evangelism, Sunnyside, WA, 1991–2000; Evangelism, First Hanford, CA, 2000–

Anderson, Zachary
see list of ordained ministers

445

Andriese, Jack
Missionary to Hmong, Stockton, CA, 1985–87

Annis, Paula
Administrator, Rosewood, Bellflower, CA, 1991–98

Antonides, Mary
see list of ordained ministers

Apol, E.
Seaman's/Immigrant home, Hoboken, NJ, 1932–42

Apol, Ruth
Director of ministries, Madison Square, Grand Rapids, MI, 1982–90

Arevalo, Edwin R.
see list of ordained ministers

Armstrong, David
see list of ordained ministers

Assink, Brent
Minister of music, Calvary, Minneapolis, MN, 1982–90

Atkins, Jan
Director of Rainbow Children's Center, New Hope Community, Kincheloe, MI, 1985–86

Avila, Marco
see list of ordained ministers

Baar, William
Beverly Mission, Evergreen Park, IL, 1953–56

Baarman, Kryn
Allen Rd. Chapel, Grand Rapids, MI, 1944–49

Baarsma, T.G.
Killarney Chapel and Sunday School, Vancouver, BC, 1961–64

Baas, Jeffrey
Worship, Southern Heights, Kalamazoo, MI, 1992–

Baas, LeRoy W.
Brigham City, UT, 1959–63; Friendship House, San Francisco, CA, 1965–66

Baas, Marvin
Indian Center, Riverside, CA, 1962–63, 1964–65; Indian Christian Center, Salt Lake City, UT, 1963–64; Friendship House, San Francisco, CA, 1965–66

Baas, Ralph
Mary Free Bed Hospital, Grand Rapids, MI, 1955–60

Bailey, Robyn
Youth pastor, First, Taber, AB, 1999–

Bajema, Clifford E.
see list of ordained ministers

Bajema, Donna
Director of worship, Sonlight Community, Lynden, WA, 1990–91

Baker, David
Minister of youth and evangelism, First, Redlands, CA, 1985–86

Baker, Ed
Director of education, North Blendon, MI, 1990–91

Baker, Edward
Director of education and evangelism, First, Zeeland, MI, 1975–76

Baker, Frank
Oakdale Park, Grand Rapids, MI, 1959–60

Baker, Kenneth A.
West End, Edmonton, AB, 1977–78

Baker, M.
Indian Center, Riverside, CA, 1966–70

Bakker, Betty
Ministry coordinator, Crossroads Community, St. John, IN, 1998–2001

Bakker, Peter
Christian Indian Center, Denver, CO, 1964–71

Bakker, Pamela
Minister of education, Richfield, Clifton, NJ, 1979–80

Bales, Walt
Youth, Fairfield, CA, 1997–

Ballard, Ron
Nardin Park Community, Detroit, MI, 1976–77

Banazak, Lori
Administration, Madison Square, Grand Rapids, MI, 1992–95

Banga, David
Music, South Bend, IN, 2000–

Bannink, Daniel
Youth, River Terrace, East Lansing, MI, 1999–

Barber, Henry
Comstock Park, Grand Rapids, MI, 1944–47

Barber, Robert
Youth minister, Northside, Paterson, NJ, 1975–78

Bareman, Vern
Cottage Grove, South Holland, IL, 1981–85; Adult education, Sunshine, Grand Rapids, MI, 1985–

Barendrecht, Cor
Evan. Resource Center, Grand Rapids, MI, 1984–87

Barton, Stewart
Bethany, Gallup, NM, 1949–63

Bates, Francis
Minister of visitation, Bethlehem, Tohlakai, NM, 1986–87

Batts, J.
Calvary Community, Dayton, OH, 1960

Baudequin, Yannick
Evangelist, Calvin, Ottawa, ON, 1989–90

Bauer, Herbert H.
Ministries coordinator, Community, Tacoma, WA, 1978–88

Bé, Sylvia
Pastoral assistant, Sherman St., Grand Rapids, MI, 1993–94

Becenti, Alfred
Four Corners, Teec Nos Pos, AZ, 1951–52; San Antone Mission, Thoreau, NM, 1962–77

Beelen, Joan R.
Coalition of Christian Outreach, 1983–89; Campus Pastor, Trinity, Mount Pleasant, MI, 1989–91; Education/Youth, First, Victoria, BC, 1991–95; Ministry coordinator, Sherman St., Grand Rapids, MI, 1996–

Beem, Anita
Education/Evangelism, North Hills, Troy, MI, 2001–

Begay, Stella
Star Lake, NM, 1950–51

Belin, S.
Iglesia El Buen Samaritano, Miami, FL, 1967–69

Benally, Lolita
Brigham City, UT, 1959–64

Benton, Luther
Director of community ministries, Lawndale, Chicago, IL, 1990–93

Berens, Norma
Administrator, Sunshine, Grand Rapids, MI, 1990–91

Berg, Darrin
Youth, East Strathroy, ON, 2001–

Bergman, Carl W.
see list of ordained ministers

Berkenbosch, Roy
see list of ordained ministers

Berkhout, P.G.
Jewish Mission, Paterson, NJ, 1952–56

Berlanga, Juan
Mexican Mission, Chicago, IL, 1960–64

Bero, Tim
Campus pastor, Western Michigan University, Kalamazoo, MI, 1975–77

Beversluis, Claudia
Director of congregational life, Church of the Servant, Grand Rapids, MI, 1989–90

Beyer, Dan
Youth pastor, Calvin, Holland, MI, 1989–90

Bezuyen, Al
Pastoral assistant, Trinity, St. Catharines, ON, 1990–91

Bielema, Howard L.
North Park Chapel, Grand Rapids, MI, 1960–64; American Indian Chapel, Chicago, IL, 1964–83; Indian Christian Center, Salt Lake City, UT, 1983–86

Bierlink, Henry
Ministries coordinator, First, Lynden, WA, 1986-88

Biesheuvel, Barend
Youth pastor, First, Calgary, AB, 1976-79; Director, One-Way House, Sunshine, Grand Rapids, MI, 1979-81; Maranatha, Bellville, ON, 1981-83; First, Thunder Bay, ON, 1983-86; Assistant harbour chaplain, Montreal Board of seaway ministries, Classes Eastern Canada and Quinte, 1986-94

Bigej, Lisa
Youth administration ministries, First, Seattle, WA, 1997-99

Bileen, Jimmie
Four Corners, Teec Nos Pos, AZ, 1952-56

Bishop, Colleen and David
Hospitality House co-directors, Pacific Community, Honolulu, HI, 1985-88

Black, Jeffrey
Stated supply, Washington, PA, 1985-87

Blacketer, Gracia (Sandy)
Youth director, Alger Park, Grand Rapids, MI, 1991-93; Education/Youth, Second, Grand Haven, MI, 1993-95; Youth Discipleship, Hillside Community, Cutlerville, MI, 1995-2000; Youth, Neerlandia, AB, 2000-2002

Blair, Kevin
Ministry development, Granite Springs, Rocklin, CA, 2001-

Blair, Shelly
Youth advisor, Faith, New Brighton, MN, 1989-90

Blom, Kel
Director of youth and outreach, Third, Lynden, WA, 1985-90; Director of youth, Orland Park, IL, 1990-94; Youth, Calvary, Holland, MI, 1994-2001; Youth Unlimited, Grand Rapids, MI, 2001-

Bode, Lillian
Way of Life Chapel, Grand Rapids, MI, 1941-44; Sixth St. Chapel, Grand Rapids, MI, 1944-45; Bridge St. Chapel, Grand Rapids, MI, 1945-47

Boden, Marine
Judyville Mission, Kalamazoo, MI, 1951-53

Boelkins, W.
Green Creek, Muskegon, MI, 1953-54

Boer, James
see list of ordained ministers

Boer, William
Bravo Community, Fennville, MI, 1941-43

Boersma, Carol
Iglesia El Buen Samaritano, Miami, FL, 1965-69

Boersma, Harry
Lowell Chapel, Lowell, MI 1953-56

Boersma, Steven
Youth director, 36th Street, Wyoming, MI, 1985-86

Bogaard, Jamie
Youth, Second, Highland, IN, 1997-1999; Youth, Second, Fremont, MI, 2000-

Bokhout, Bill
Ministry coordinator, Beckwith Hills, Grand Rapids, MI, 1997-

Bol, Jacob
San Antone Mission, Thoreau, NM, 1957-62

Bol, Ken
Director of youth ministries, Ridgewood, Jenison, MI, 1986-87

Bonnema, Mary
Sixth St., Chapel, Grand Rapids, MI, 1943-44; Bethany Christian Home, Grand Rapids, MI, 1944-53

Bonnema, Micki
Director of music, Christ Community, Virginia Beach, VA, 1990-91

Bonnema, Nancy
Minister of music, Third, Kalamazoo, MI, 1989-90

Boonstra, Ingrid
Ministry coordinator, Living Hope, Peterborough, ON, 2001-

Boomsma, Shirley
Minister of music, Calvin, Grand Rapids, MI, 1989-91

Boonstra, Wally
Youth leader, Bethel, Waterdown, ON, 1986-87

Bootsma, Michael
see list of ordained ministers

Borduin, Jean
Minister of music, Unity, Prospect park, NJ, 1989–90

Borgdorff, Patricia
Children's ministry, Sunshine Ministries, Grand Rapids, MI, 1991–2000

Borger, Joyce
Youth director, Covenant, Winnipeg, MB, 1996–2000

Borgering, E.
Mona Lake Mission, Muskegon, MI, 1955–56

Bos, Daniel
Adult ministries, Millbrook, Grand Rapids, MI, 2001–

Bos, Gertrude
Roseland Community Gospel Mission, Chicago, IL, 1940–49, 1952–53

Bos, Michael
Ministry coordinator, Sunshine Ministries, Grand Rapids, MI, 1991–95

Bosma, Louis
Clinton, ON, 1991–96; Pastor of congregational life, Aylmer, ON, 1996–

Bosscher, A. Douglas
see list of ordained ministers

Bossenbroek, Eunice
Service ministry coordinator, River Terrace, East Lansing, MI, 1984–

Botma, Menno
Community Chapel, Lansing, IL, 1953–71; Community Sunday School, Highland, IN, 1963–64

Bouma, Mark/Anna
Mission, Hoboken, NJ, 1910; Tohatchi, NM, 1915–25; San Antone Mission, Thoreau, NM, 1932–34, 1935–36; Two Wells Station, NM, 1932–36

Bouma, Mary
Director of children's ministries, Sunshine, Grand Rapids, MI, 1983–87; Director of children's ministries, Seymour, Grand Rapids, MI, 1987–90

Bouma, Mary-Lee
see list of ordained ministers

Bouwers, John
see list of ordained ministers

Bouwkamp, T.
Ivanrest Chapel, Grand Rapids, MI, 1934–43

Boyd, Harry
San Antone Mission, Thoreau, NM, 1929–32

Brandenstein, Bill
Director of music, Rosewood, Bellflower, CA, 1990–91

Branderhorst, John
Children/Youth, Granite Springs, Rocklin, CA, 1994–

Brands, Michael
see list of ordained ministers

Brands, Pamela
Minister of music and evangelism, Arcadia, CA, 1985–86

Bandsma, Paul
Youth, Second, Abbotsford, BC, 2001–

Bratt, Albertha
New Richmond, MI, 1941–54; Bravo Community, Fennville, MI, 1946–48

Brawdy, Bruce
Ministry staff, Ramona, CA, 1987–88

Bregman, Henry
Jewish Mission, Paterson, NJ, 1917–22

Breuker, John
Lakewood/Wakazoo, Holland, MI, 1945–50; North Shore Mission, Holland, MI, 1949–50

Brink, Peter E.
Grand Rapids Community, Grand Rapids, MI, 1976–83

Brink, Peter L.
Pioneer Chapel, Kent City, MI, 1957–60

Brinks, Joe
Allen Rd., Chapel, Grand Rapids, MI, 1936–37

Brock, John
Lamar Plat Outreach, Grand Rapids, MI, 1946–48

Broekhuizen, Marius J.
Seaman's/Immigrant home, Hoboken, NJ, 1923, 1927-32

Broer, Linie
Pastoral assistant, Campus Ministry, McMaster University, Hamilton, ON, 1990-91

Broersma, Marie
Church secretary, Zion Oshawa, ON, 1980-2001

Brott, Anita
Outreach coordinator, Creston, Grand Rapids, MI, 1985-89

Brouwer, B.
Monterey, Allegan, MI, 1941-44

Brouwer, Esther
Community outreach worker, Maple Ave., Holland, MI, 1986-90

Brouwer, Mark
Sunrise, Austin, TX, 1991-92

Brouwer, Randall
Oakdale Park, Grand Rapids, MI, 1977-78

Brouwers, Gary
Pastoral assistant, Blythefield, Rockford, MI, 1990-99

Brower, Katie
Beacon Light Chapel, Grand Rapids, MI, 1944-46

Brown, Martha
Music director, Community, Los Angeles, CA, 1987-90

Bruinkool, Henry
Sunshine Chapel, Grand Rapids, MI, 1937-40

Bruinsma, Rick
Ancaster, ON, 1993-97; Ministry director, Covenant, St. Catharines, ON, 1997-99; Youth, Community, Kitchener, ON, 1999-

Bruinsma, Walter
Guiding Light Mission, Grand Rapids, MI, 1959-60

Brummel, Robert
Comstock Chapel, Kalamazoo, MI, 1964-65

Brummels, Henry
Burton Heights Mission, Grand Rapids, MI, 1945-50

Bruxvoort, J.
Good News Chapel, Oskaloosa, IA, 1949-50

Butler-Systsma, Jeaninne
Director of youth ministries, Garfield, Chicago, IL, 1979-84; Director of outreach, Immanuel, Kalamazoo, MI, 1984-87

Buckhout, Mrs. Thomas
Campus ministry assistant, West Lafayette, IN, 1977-78

Buffinga, Jay C.
Hillcrest Chapel, Battle Creek, MI, 1952-53, 1954-57, 1961-62

Buis, Dan
Minister of youth, Long Beach, CA, 1989-91

Buist, Keith
Outreach/Worship, Evergreen Park, IL, 2001-

Bultje, H.S.
Lawndale, Chicago, IL, 1961-62

Burgos, Elias
see list of ordained ministers

Burton, Jerome
Evangelism/Outreach, Coit Community, Grand Rapids, MI, 1994-97

Buwalda, Beckie
Evangelism/Outreach, Lake City, MI, 1993-97

Buys, Keith
Youth director, Trinity, Philadelphia, PA, 1989-90

Byker, Kevin
Director of youth and adult education, First, Denver, CO, 1989-90

Byl, Catherine
Administrative assistant, Immanuel, Hamilton, ON, 1989-90

Byma, Peter
see list of ordained ministers

Capen, Todd
Youth, Sunshine Community, Grand Rapids, MI, 1993–97

Cappendyk, Gordon
Horseshoe Chapel, Grand Junction, MI, 1970–72

Carberry, Jim
Congregational life, Second, Lynden, WA, 1996–

Carmer, Karen
Outreach coordinator, Community, Grand Rapids, MI, 1989–90

Carpenter, Laura
Director, Teen ministries, Madison Square, Grand Rapids, MI, 1996–

Cascio, Carla
Day care ministry, Ft. Lauderdale, FL, 1984–

Castillo, Henry, Jr.
Youth/Young adults pastor, Palm Lane, Scottsdale, AZ, 1996–2001

Caverly, Mrs. R.
Hope Centre, Winnipeg, MB, 1974–77

Cell, C.W.
Indian Center, Riverside, CA, 1926–27

Center, Bradley
Evangelist, First Christian Church, Muir, MI, 1991–96; Evangelist, Aetna, Falmouth, MI, 1996–99

Chamberlain, Ethel
Bethel, Shiprock, NM, 1949–50

Chamberlin, John
Director of music, Immanuel, Kalamazoo, MI, 1990–91

Chang, Diane T.
Church secretary, Golden Gate, San Francisco, CA, 1995–

Chase, Stephanie
Calvary Baptist, Garland, TX, 1994–97; Day care ministry, Second, Denver, CO, 1997–

Chavez, Jerry
Minister of youth, Sun Valley Community, Denver, CO, 1989–90

Chavez, Melvin
Two Wells Station, NM, 1950–61

Cheng, Ping On
Youth minister, Immanuel, Richmond, BC, 1986–87

Chey, Victor
Minister of youth, Korean, Long Beach, CA, 1987–88

Cho, Nam-Soo
Minister for Christian education, Orange Korean, Fountain Valley, CA, 1978–80

Choi, Byung Nam
Korean, Grand Rapids, MI, 1984–87

Choi, Tai Eun
Minister of youth, Cerritos Central, Artesia, CA, 1987–90

Chong, Chol
Education/youth, West Bethel Korean, Los Angeles, CA, 1991–94

Chong, Kong P.
Korean American Central Presbyterian, Los Angeles, CA, 1999–

Chong, Paul K.
Evangelist to youth, Immanuel, Hacienda Heights, CA, 1987–90

Chu, Ronald I.
Orange Korean, Fullerton, CA, 2001–

Chung, Peter Joongjin
Minister of youth, Orange Korean, Fullerton, CA, 1987–88

Chung, Yang Bae
Director of education, Korean, Chicago, IL, 1989–90

Chupp, John
Palmer Chapel, Reeman, MI, 1960–63

Clachischilli, Sylvia
Minister for students, Fort Wingate, NM, 1980–87; Minister of evangelism, Arcadia, CA, 1989–90

Clark, Roy A.
Evangelism/Youth, Ridgewood, Jenison, MI, 1993–

Clarke, Cale
Ministry, Grace, Scarborough, Toronto, ON, 2001–

Clayton, Barbara
Director of religious education, Lawndale, IL, 1974–80

Clousing, Jeff
Director of youth and evangelism, Calvin, Oak Lawn, IL, 1985–86

Cody, Teresa
Day care ministry, Spirit and Truth Fellowship, Philadelphia, PA, 1991–94

Coe, Forrest
Director of music, Sunshine, Grand Rapids, MI, 1985–86

Colenbrander, Sarah H.
Field director of youth evangelism, 1970–71

Collins, Carolyn
Day care ministry, Fellowship, Traverse City, MI, 1993–95

Contant, Martin J.
see list of ordained ministers

Cook, O.
Bethel Mission, Grand Rapids, MI, 1934–40

Cooper, Liz Baker
Degage Ministries, Grand Rapids, MI, 1986–88

Cornelisse, Minna
Director of music, Maranatha, Edmonton, AB, 1990–91

Corsten, David
Youth, Covenant Life, Grand Haven, MI, 2001–

Cregan, Douglas C.
Education/Youth, First, Bellflower, CA, 1997–2000

Cremmer, Menno
Calvary Chapel, Willard, OH, 1970–74

Crute, Allen
Minister of youth, Christ Community, Virginia Beach, VA, 1989–90

Curley, Frank, Sr.
Sanostee Rural Station, Shiprock, NM, 1963–86

Curnow, William
Assistant minister of pastoral care, Sunshine, Grand Rapids, MI, 1982–90

Dahm, John J.
Seaman's/Immigrant home, Hoboken, NJ, 1942–62

Damon, Angie
Director, Bethany Day Care Center, Bethany, Gallup, NM, 1989–90

Damon, Charlie
San Antone Mission, Thoreau, NM, 1931–34

Darnall, Lanell
Rosewood, Bellfower, CA, 1998–2000

Datema, Robert
Youth pastor, Calvin, Ottawa, ON, 1989–91; Education/Youth, Maranatha, Woodstock, ON, 1995–

Davis, Craig
Campus ministry, Pittsburgh, PA, 1987–90; Youth, Tri-Cities, Kennewick, WA, 1993–99

De Boer, Cornelius
see list of ordained ministers

de Boer, Hank
Pastoral assistant, First, Kitchener, ON, 1993–95

De Boer, Harry
Roseland Community Gospel Mission, Chicago, IL, 1932–41

De Boer, James
South Christian High School, Cutlerville, MI, 1978–80; Zeeland High School, Zeeland, MI, 1980–88; Church administrator and minister of music, Providence, Holland, MI, 1988–

De Boer, Joel
Young adult leader, Alger Park, Grand Rapids, MI, 1989–90

De Boer, Nell
Chaplain, Wellesley/Princess Margaret, North York General Hospital, 1991–94; Coordinator, Chaplaincy Service, United Church of Canada, 1994–1998; Hospital chaplain, Toronto, ON, 1995–

De Boer, Mary
West Fulton Chapel, Grand Rapids, MI, 1943–45;

Bethany Christian Home, Grand Rapids, MI, 1944–56

de Boom, Mike
Minister of youth, First, Chino, CA. 1989–90

De Bruin, Marie
Nathaneal Institute, Chicago, IL, 1942–46

De Bruyn, Henk
see list of ordained ministers

Deckinga, Mark D.
see list of ordained ministers

De Groot, Norlan
Bethel, Lansing, Il, 1986–87; Youth director, Mayfair, Grand Rapids, MI, 1987–88; Education, Messiah, Hudsonville, MI, 1992–93

De Groot, Patrick
Youth, Bethel, Fulton, IL, 2001–

De Groot, Robert
Minister of outreach, Tri-Cities, Kennewick, WA, 1987–91; Youth, Third, Lynden, WA, 1991–99

De Haan, Adrianus
Comstock Chapel, Kalamazoo, MI, 1966–68

De Haan, Mary
Director of outreach, Fort Lauderdale, FL, 1990–91

De Hoog, Walter
Baxter St. Mission, Grand Rapids, MI, 1935–37

De Jager, Mary
Family of Christ, Maple Grove, MN, 1991–94; Youth, Orland Park, IL, 1994–

De Jong, Andrew
see list of ordained ministers

de Jong, David
Youth, New Life Reformed, 1989–91; Host couple, Ministry to Seafarers, 1991–93; Education/Evangelism/Youth, Rogers Heights, Wyoming, MI, 1993–96

De Jonge, Nell
Kalamazoo Mission Board, Lawndale Chapel, Northwood Chapel, Kalamazoo, MI, 1953–64; Local Mission Worker and Deaconess, Third, Kalamazoo, MI, 1964–69

De Jonge, Philip V.
Minister of education and mission, Harderwyk, Holland, MI, 1975–76; Friendship, Jenison, MI, 1987–94

Dekker, Laurie
Director of music and children's ministries, Bethany, Holland, MI, 1990–92

Dekker, Linda
Administration, Crossroads Community, Schererville, IN, 2000–

Dekker, Margriet
Congregational life/Youth, Third, Kalamazoo, MI, 1997–99

De Koekoek, Joel
Youth for Christ, Battle Creek, MI, 1992–96; Youth, Grace, Kalamazoo, MI, 1996–

De Koekkoek, John
see list of ordained ministers

De Korte, Bert
Ionia Ave. Mission, Grand Rapids, MI, 1945–55

De Koster, Harry
North End Gospel Hall, Holland, MI, 1949–50; Calvary, Holland, MI, 1953–54

De Kruyter, Lois
Fairmont Hospital/Pine Crest State Hospital, Kalamazoo, MI, 1952–53

De Lange, Karl
see list of ordained ministers

De Lange, Richard
see list of ordained ministers

De Lange, Robert
Charlotte, MI, 1973–77

Delis, Miss T.
Nathaneal Institute, Chicago, IL, 1928–42

Del Vecchio, Abel
Way of Life Chapel, Grand Rapids, MI, 1917–20

De Mey, Neal
Minister of outreach, LaGrave Ave., Grand Rapids, MI, 1985–90

Den Haan, Edward
see list of ordained ministers

Den Haan, Martin
Director of counseling ministry, Christ Community, Nanaimo, BC, 1987-88

De Nooyer, Norman
Youth, Shawnee Park, Grand Rapids, MI, 1977-80; Evangelism, Alger Park, Grand Rapids, MI, 1980-

Den Otter, Sini
see list of chaplains

De Ridder, David R.
Youth Evangelsim Service, Toronto, ON, 1972-76; Minister of youth and evangelism, First, Munster, IN, 1976-80; First, Visalia, CA, 1980-86; Director of education and evangelism, First, Bellflower, CA, 1986-92; Education/Evangelism, Third, Denver, CO, 1992-

De Ruiter, Walter
see list of ordained ministers

De Ruyter, Herb
see list of ordained ministers

Deters, Ellis
Eastern Ave., Grand Rapids, MI; Home Missions; Director of adult ministries, Alger Park, Grand Rapids, MI, 1990-91

Deters, Jerome
Contact person, Lao Community, Holland, MI, 1987-88

De Vos, F.
Boston St. Mission, Grand Rapids, MI, 1934-35

De Vries, Brenda
Music/Worship, Ivanrest, Grandville, MI, 2001-

De Vries, Dick
Windfall Chapel, Grant, MI, 1958-60

De Vries, Dirk
Director of youth and adult education, First, Denver, CO, 1982-87

De Vries, Fred
Glad Tidings Center, Edmonton, AB, 1970-77; Community, River Drive Park, ON, 1977-85; Pastoral assistant, East Strathroy, ON, 1985-86

De Vries, Gary
see list of ordained ministers

DeVries, George
Horseshoe Chapel, Grand Junction, MI, 1942-43

De Vries, Gerald
Living Waters Chapel, Queenston, ON, 1969-72, 1974-77

De Vries, James
Spec Lake Chapel, Allegan, MI, 1960-61; Comstock Chapel, Kalamazoo, MI, 1961-63; Horseshoe Chapel, Grand Junction, MI, 1963-66; Little Farms, Coopersville, MI, 1966-71

De Vries, Judy
Coordinator of outreach, Prairie Lane, Omaha, NE, 1985-86

De Vries, Robert C.
Comstock Chapel, Kalamazoo, MI, 1964-65

De Vries, Rudy
Youth leader, First, Lethbridge, AB, 1974-79

De Vries, Tom
Missions and outreach administrator, Sunshine, Grand Rapids, MI, 1989-90

De Vries, William
Campus ministry, Detroit, MI, 1970-72

de Waal Malefyt, Norma
Director of music, Hillcrest, Hudsonville, MI, 1988-

De Wit, Melody
Minister of music, First, Chino, CA, 1989-91

De Wys, A.
Millgrove, Allegan, MI, 1949-50

De Young, Fred S.
Youth, Second, Kalamazoo, MI, 1993-

De Young, Jeff
Evangelism/Youth, Drenthe, Zeeland, MI, 2001-

De Young, Marge
Pastoral care administrator, Sunshine, Grand Rapids, MI, 1983-90

De Young, Marinus
Mona Lake Mission, Muskegon, MI, 1941-51

Dibben, Shelly
Administration, New Life Fellowship, Red Deer, AB, 1989-2001

Diemer, Mrs. Frank
Oakdale Park, Grand Rapids, MI, 1954-58

Dik, Jack B,
Director of education and evangelism, Spring Lake, MI, 1978-83; Minister of outreach and education, Third, Kalamazoo, MI, 1983-94

Di Maggio, Joe
Ionia Ave. Mission, Grand Rapids, MI, 1963-64

Dirkse, Robert D.
Director of youth education, Korean Church of Orange Co., Buena Park, CA, 1987-89

Disselkoen, DeNella
Millgrove, Allegan, MI, 1943-47

Dixon, Delores
Manhattan, New York, NY, 1958-60

Dolislager, James
Director of youth and evangelism, Neland, Ave., Grand Rapids, MI, 1976-78

Doll, Jeff
Associate pastor, Borculo, MI, 1995-

Doornbos, Clarence
Director of music, Fuller, Ave., Grand Rapids, MI, 1989-90

Doornbos, Keith
Evangelism coordinator, East Leonard, Grand Rapids, MI, 1978-80

Doornbos, Ross
Little Farms, Coopersville, MI, 1954-57

Dragt, Bruce
Ministry coordinator, North Austin Community, Austin, TX, 1994-97

Dreyer, A.C.
Englewood Community Mission, Chicago, IL, 1950-53

Dubois, Lori
Administration, Madison Square, Grand Rapids, MI, 1991-92

Dunnewold, Grace
Director of music and fine arts, First, Calgary, AB, 1990-91

Duong, Lap
Minister, Vietnamese Christian Reformed, Kentwood, MI, 1999-

Dyk, John J.
Diamond Gospel Center, Hamilton, MI, 1950-52

Dyk, Simon
Director of music, Third, Edmonton, AB, 1985-86

Dykehouse, Bernard
Juvenile Home, Kalamazoo, MI, 1951-56; County Infirmary, Kalamazoo, MI, 1952-56

Dykema, Charles
Livingston, Grand Rapids, MI, 1967-69

Dykema, Clarence
Bethel, Shiprock, NM, 1951-52

Dykshoorn, Jan G.
Ministry, East Martin, MI, 1992-95

Dykstra, Darwin
Assistant to pastor, First, Chino, CA, 1985-86

Dykstra, Elias J.
Bridge Street Mission, Grand Rapids, MI, 1950-51; Gold Ave., Grand Rapids, MI, 1951-63

Dykstra, Gerard
see list of ordained ministers

Dykstra, Jeanette C.
Horseshoe Chapel, Grand Junction, MI, 1946-50

Dykstra, M. Elias
Roseland Community Gospel Mission, Chicago, IL, 1946-49

Dykstra, Miss
Beacon Light Chapel, Grand Rapids, MI, 1942-43

Dykstra, Richard P.
Education/Youth, Second, Highland, IN, 1995-96; Youth, First, Munster, IN, 2000-

Dykstra, Virginia
Nathaneal Institute, Chicago, IL, 1928

Ebbelink, Bertha
Lamar Plat Mission, Grand Rapids, MI, 1949-52

Ebenstein, Lance
Sunshine Community, Grand Rapids, MI, 2001-

Eckardt, Robert W.
Minister of calling, Pleasant St., Whitinsville, MA, 1984-88

Eenigenburg, Matthew
Oak Glen, Lansing, IL, 1990-92; Sunshine Ministries, Grand Rapids, MI, 1992-94; Youth, Faith, New Brighton, MN, 1994-

Elgersma, Scott
Christ's Community, Hayward, CA, 1994-96; Youth pastor, First, Visalia, CA, 1996-

Elhart, Cora
Nathaneal Institute, Chicago, IL, 1929-33

Ellens, G.J.
City mission, Hammond, IN, 1922-47

Ellestad, Laura K.
Administrative assistant, Geneva Chapel, Madison, WI, 1989-90

Elsenbroek, Jim
Grand Rapids Deacons Conference, 1974-75

Elve, Anthony
Ionia Ave. Mission, Grand Rapids, MI, 1943-44

Elzinga, Alice
Youth evangelist, Paramaribo, Dutch Guiana, 1944-54; Neighborhood Missionary, Summer St. Sunday School, Passaic, NJ, 1954-56; Neighborhood missionary, Summer St., Christian Reformed Church, Passaic, NJ, 1956-61

Elzinga, Vance
Third Reformed, Pella, IA, 1983-87; Director of youth, education and outreach, Harderwyk, Holland, MI, 1987-90

Engbers, Jan
Ministries coordinator, Eastern Hills Community, Aurora, CO, 1990-

Engelsman, Lois
Staff worker, Tri-Cities, Kennewick, WA, 1977-80

Eppinga, Stu
Director of Music, Walnut Creek, CA, 1990-91

Eriks, R.
Gospel Chapel, Denver, CO, 1955-57

Essenberg, Benjamin
Vance Chapel, East Jordan, MI, 1961-67

Estrade, David
Mexican work Classis Holland, 1956-57

Evenhouse, Dale
Degage Ministries, Grand Rapids, MI, 1970-72; Youth director, Bradenton, FL, 1973-76; Pastoral assistant, Maranatha, Belleville, ON, 1989-99; Youth, Trinity, Grandville, MI, 1999-

Evenhouse, Ruth
Director of children's ministries, Fourteenth St., Holland, MI, 1987-90

Faber, Ann
Baxter Clinic, Grand Rapids, MI, 1985-87

Faber, Harry
Boston Square Neighborhood evangelism, Grand Rapids, MI, 1948-52

Fallon, Michael
Campus ministry, Hamilton, ON, 1998-

Farrand, Chad
Education/Youth, Westview, Grand Rapids, MI, 1999-

Feddes, David
see list of ordained ministers

Feenstra, Wiebe
Northside Community Chapel, Paterson, NJ, 1952-58

Fennema, Jim/Dawn
Coordinators of evangelism and assimilation, Hayward, CA, 1989-90

Fennema, S.
Lamar Plat Gospel Mission, Grand Rapids, MI, 1936-39

Fernhout, Bill
Congregational Life, Westwood, Kalamazoo, MI 2001-

Fledderus, Bill
Pastoral assistant, Ministry to Seafarers, Montreal, QC, 1995-96

Flokstra, Henry
Madison Square Chapel, Grand Rapids, MI, 1934-40; Sunshine Chapel, Grand Rapids, MI, 1945-53

Flooryp, Mrs. J.
Community, River Drive Park, ON, 1974-76

Flores, Juan
see list of ordained ministers

Folgers, Virginia
Director of music, Lombard, IL, 1989-90

Folkerts, Kari
Youth, Faith, Elmhurst, IL, 2001-

Fongers, James
Director of counseling, Sunshine, Grand Rapids, MI, 1985-

Foster, Barry
Executive Director, Christian Service Club, 1966-68; Development Secretary, RBC, 1968-72; Program Director, United Evangelism Association, 1972-76; Director of education and evangelism, Cragmor, Colorado Springs, CO, 1976-79

Foster, Linda
Director of ministries, Valley, Binghamton, NY, 1990-91

Foster, Ronald
Minister of church education and music, Northside Community Chapel, Paterson, NJ, 1985-88

Francken, Ann
Iglesia El Buen Samaritano, Miami, FL, 1968-69

Frank, Floyd
Evangelist, Toadlena, NM, 1971-87

Frans, Ron
Administration, New Life, Abbotsford, BC, 2001-

Frens, Bruce/Marty
Service home, Norfolk, VA, 1978-82

Fridsma, Hilda
Bethel, Shiprock, NM, 1953-57

Fryling, Herman
Sparta Chapel, 1937-39

Gabrielse, Edward
Campus ministry, Cedar Falls, IA, 1969-70

Gebben, Debi
Education/evangelism, Park Lane, Evergreen Park, IL, 1991-92

Geelhoed, William
Way of Life Chapel, Grand Rapids, MI, 1928-46

Geels, Donald
Youth minister, Oak Hills, Portland, OR, 1974-75; Youth pastor, Director of education, El Paso, TX, 1975-76

Geels, John
Chapel, Beaver Dam, WI, 1966-69

Geerts, A.
Millgrove, Allegan, MI, 1946-47

Geers, Henry
Pine Grove, Howard City, MI, 1957-59

Geers, Jeff
Trinity Presbyterian, Seattle, WA, 1990-92; CRC: Youth and campus ministries, River Terrace, East Lansing, MI, 1992-2001

Geisterfer, Aren P.
Campus ministry, Hamilton, ON, 1980-98

George, John
Four Corners, Teec Nos Pos, AZ, 1957-60; Skeets, Chapel, Vanderwagen, NM, 1965-66; Bethlehem Chapel, Gallup, NM, 1970-71

Gibson, Christopher E.
Director of youth and outreach, Oak Hills, Portland, OR, 1989-95; Youth, Battle Creek, MI, 1995-

Giesbrecht-Segger, Marnie
Director of music, Third, Edmonton, AB, 1986-88

Gill, Joyce
Parish worker, Madison Ave., Paterson, NJ, 1976-87

Gipson, Frank
Pastoral assistant, Sherman Street, Grand Rapids, MI, 1989-90

Giusto, Donna
Church secretary, First, Munster, IN, 2001–

Goe, Alberta
Christian service worker, Emmanuel, Sauk Village, IL, 1984–87

Goedhart, Pieter
Director of music, Anaheim, CA, 1990–91

Goeman, Nancy
Director of Christian education, Faith, Nashville, TN, 1985–86

Gonzalez, Antonio
Minister of youth, Grace and Peace Fellowship, Chicago, IL, 1989; Minister, Mustard Seed Fellowship, Chicago, IL, 1989–90; Director of youth, Grace and Peace Fellowship, Chicago, IL, 1990–94

Goodyear, Francine
Administrator, Community of Meadowvale, Mississauga, ON, 1989–90

Goossen, Esther
West Fulton Chapel, Grand Rapids, MI, 1945–51

Gordon, Peter
Coordinator of evangelism, Grandville Ave., Grand Rapids, MI, 1989–90

Gossman, Lori
Pastoral assistant, Hope Community, Santa Rosa, CA, 1993–95

Grasley, Monika
Administration, Gateway Community, Merced, CA, 2001–

Grasman, D.
Seaman's/Immigrant home, Hoboken, NJ, 1948–50

Grassman, Bess
Service home, Norfolk, VA, 1963–65

Grassmid, Jud
Coordinator for youth and evangelism, East Paris, Grand Rapids, MI, 1986–87; Degage Ministries, Grand Rapids, MI, 1988–89

Greenfield, Bernard
Mid-Harlem Community Parish, 1957–60

Gremmer, Menno
Calvary Chapel, Willard, OH, 1972–74

Greenfield, Bernard
Manhattan, New York, NY, 1958–60

Grevengoed, Charles
North River Mission, Holland, MI, 1947–49; Kibbie, South Haven, MI, 1960–61

Greydanus, Betty
Director of outreach ministries and Sunday school, First, Chino, CA, 1985–86

Griffen, John
Beacon Light Mission, Grand Rapids, MI, 1943–48

Griffioen, Donald
Missionary at large, Grand Rapids, MI, 1971–89

Griffioen, Martheen
Director of education and evangelism, Fuller Ave., Grand Rapids, MI, 1980–91

Groendyk, Marion
Millgrove, Allegan, MI, 1963–69

Groeneveld, A.
Millgrove, Allegan, MI, 1947–47

Gronski, Joseph
West Leonard St. Gospel Mission, Grand Rapids, MI, 1942–48; Front St. Mission, Grand Rapids, MI, 1948–89

Groothuis, Agnes
Ivanrest Chapel, Grand Rapids, MI, 1936–37

Groothuis, Dick
Back to God Chapel, Huntington, BC, 1965–71; Back to God CRC, Abbotsford, BC, 1972–76

Grotenhuis, Judith
Iglesia El Buen Samaritano, Miami, FL, 1962–65

Grussing, Robert
Director of youth and evangelism, First, Zeeland, MI, 1977–79; Director of youth and evangelism, Brookside, Grand Rapids, MI, 1979–85; Minister of youth and education, LaGrave Ave., Grand Rapids, MI, 1985–

Guerrin, David M.
Kedvale Ave., Oak Lawn, IL, 1979–80; Eastern Christian High School, Lynwood, IL, 1980–86; Di-

rector of ministries, Bethel, Lansing, IL, 1986-92; Ministry, Providence, Holland, MI, 1992-2001

Guikema, Henry
Minister of youth, education and evangelism, Seymour, Grand Rapids, MI, 1987-88

Guillaume, Susanne
Ministry coordinator, Hope Centre, Winnipeg, MB, 1993-94

Guter, Frank
see list of ordained ministers

Haagsma, A.
Ann Arbor, MI, 1968-69

Haan, Jim
Youth leader, Alger Park, Grand Rapids, MI, 1989-90

Haan, Leonard R.
Gospel Chapel, Denver, CO, 1949-50

Haan, P.J.
Kent County Home, Grand Rapids, MI, 1940-47

Haas, Dale
Fine Arts/Music, Horizon Community, Lombard, IL, 2000-

Habers, Mildred
Horseshoe Chapel, Grand Junction, MI, 1946-47

Hamming, Dick
Kent County Home, Grand Rapids, MI, 1947-51

Hammond, Don
Minister of youth and education, Chula Vista, CA, 1975-78

Hamstra, Devon
Administrative assistant, Madison Square, Grand Rapids, MI, 2001-

Han, Ki Won
Minister of education, Korean Church of Orange Co., Buena Park, CA, 1987-90

Hanstra, Anna
Helping Hand Mission, Chicago, IL, 1919-27; Star of Hope Mission, Paterson, NJ, 1927-46; Grace Chapel, Bellflower, CA, 1946-51; Good News Chapel, Oskaloosa, IA, 1951-54; Community Sunday School, Lansing, IL, 1954-55

Harnden, Harrison F.
see list of ordained ministers

Harris, Robert
see list of ordained ministers

Harrison, Emmett
see list of ordained ministers

Hart, Jim
Director of education and evangelism, Cragmor, Colorado Springs, CO, 1979-80; Director of discipleship and outreach, Maranatha, Holland, MI, 1986-90

Harts, Ethel L.
Administrative assistant, Roseland Christian Ministries Center, Chicago, IL, 1987-88

Hashimoto, Don
Hospitality House ministry director, Pacific Community, Honolulu, HI, 1989-90

Haswood, Jerry
Indian Christian Center, Salt Lake City, UT, 1992-

Haswood, Shirley
Community worker, Christian Indian Center, Salt Lake City, UT, 1979-87

Hays, David Vance
see list of ordained ministers

Heetderks, H.
Lakewood/Waukazoo, Holland, MI, 1943-45

Heerema, Evan
see list of ordained ministers

Heerschap, Margaret
Northside Community Chapel, Paterson, NJ, 1950-51

Heezen, Rudy
Minister of evangelism, Zion, Oshawa, ON, 1986-87

Heilman, David
see list of ordained ministers

Heinrich, Otto E.
Way of Life Chapel, Grand Rapids, MI, 1941-48

Heitke, Rick
Director of congregational life, Pease, MN, 1996–99

Helder, Cathy
Minister of youth/music, Rosewood, Bellflower, CA, 1984–87

Helder, Robert A.
Minister of youth/music, Rosewood, Bellflower, CA, 1984–87; Third Reformed, Grand Rapids, MI, 1987–89; Director of youth group ministries, Sunshine, Grand Rapids, MI, 1989–91; Crystal Cathedral, Garden Grove, CA, 1991–94; Education/Youth, Providence, Holland, MI, 1994–99

Helder, S.
Allen Road Chapel, Grand Rapids, MI, 1937–40

Helleman, Katherine
Beacon Light Chapel, Grand Rapids, MI, 1944–45

Helmus, Bernard
Spruce Ave. Chapel, Holland, MI, 1960–62

Hendriksen, Sue
Day care ministry, Cottonwood Heights, Jenison, MI, 1997–

Hendrikson, John
Fairmont Hospital, Kalamazoo, MI, 1953–54

Henion, Tom
Teen minister, Madison Ave., Paterson, NJ, 1989–90

Henry, Edward
see list of ordained ministers

Hermann, Kenneth
Director of campus ministry, Akron, OH, 1980–91

Hernandez, Vicente
Iglesia El Buen Samaritano, Miami, FL, 1963–69

Hess, Anna
Star of Hope Mission, Paterson, NJ, 1906–10

Hesselink, Derwin
Southside Community Chapel, Chicago, IL, 1951–55

Hesselink, Keith
Ministry coordinator, Faith, Tinley Park, IL, 2001–

Hesselink, Sue
Director of church education and youth ministries, Rochester, NY, 1997–

Heuss, Carl A.
see list of ordained ministers

Hewitt, Greg
Director of music, Sunshine, Grand Rapids, MI, 1986–88; Director of fine arts, Hillside Community, Cutlerville, MI, 1990–92

Hewitt, Mark
Evangelism coordinator, Hayward, CA, 1986–87

Hewitt, Michael
Youth, Elmhurst, IL, 1996–

Hickman, Robert
Director of counseling, Midland Park, NJ, 1985–87

Higdon, Dianna
Administration, Calvary, Chino, CA, 1997–2001

Hitchcock, Nathan
Young adults, Heartland Community, Sioux Falls, SD, 2001–

Hitziger, Debra
Education/evangelism, Lake Worth, FL, 1994–97

Hoag, Michael S.
Minister of youth and evangelism, West Park, Cleveland, OH, 1985–86

Hodges, Victoria
Outreach, First, Grand Rapids, MI, 1990–91

Hoeksema, Alvin
Director of youth, education and evangelism, Bradenton, FL, 1978–80

Hoeksema, Henry
Baxter Street Mission, Grand Rapids, MI, 1937–39

Hoezee, Scott
see list of ordained ministers

Hofland, Calvin T.
Director of youth, Cascade, Marysville, WA, 1990–94; Evangelist, Christian Reformed World Missions, Guinea, West Africa, 1994–

Hofman, Mary Lou
Church secretary, Kelloggsville, Kentwood, MI, 1993-

Hofman, Ruth
see list of ordained ministers

Hogenes, Yvonne
Music director, First, Langley, BC, 1987-88

Hogeterp, Peter
see list of ordained ministers

Hoisington, Michael
Willow Creek Community, South Barrington, IL, 1989-94; Ministries coordinator, Sunshine Ministries, Grand Rapids, MI, 1995-

Holkeboer, Earl
Middleville, MI, 1956-57

Holkeboer, Gertrude
Way of Life Mission, Grand Rapids, MI, 1928-45; North End Mission, Holland, MI, 1942-46; Madison Square Chapel, Grand Rapids, MI, 1945-59

Holmes, Sheila
see list of ordained ministers

Holt, Tammy
Small children's ministry, Oakdale Park, Grand Rapids, MI, 1989-90

Holtrop, Cindy
see list of ordained ministers

Holwerda, Robert
Hillcrest Chapel, Grand Rapids, MI, 1956-60

Holwerda, Tim
see list of ordained ministers

Hommes, Kendal
Ministry, Trinity, Artesia, CA, 1997-2001; Senior High, Eastern Hills, Aurora, CO, 2001-

Honaker, Robin E.
Bethlehem, Tohlakai, NM, 1993-95

Hong, Jin-Sook
Director of music, Korean, Boca Raton, FL, 1988-90

Hoogendoorn, Simon
Back to God Chapel, Abbotsford, BC, 1971-72

Hopp, Roy
Director of music, Hillcrest, Denver, CO, 1985-86

Horner, George
Calvary, Vermillion, SD, 1994-96

Hosmar, Ron
Youth, Second/First/Redeemer, Sarnia, ON, 1995-

Hough, Lynnsey
Administration, Christ Community, Nanaimo, BC, 1995-

Hough, Robert S.
Director of education and evangelism, Bethany, Muskegon, MI, 1972-77

House, Karl
see list of ordained ministers

Houston, Daniel
Youth/Outreach, Second, Grand Haven, MI, 2001-

Houting, Gloria
Church secretary, VictoryPoint Ministries, Holland, MI, 1997-2001

Hoven, Clarence
Good News Chapel, Oskaloosa, IA, 1956-59; Stated supply, Bellevue, WA, 1979-80

Hubers, Sylvan
Oakdale Park Evangelism, Grand Rapids, MI, 1958-60

Huff, John
Minister of education, evangelism and youth, Visalia, CA, 1977-79

Huissen, Jerry
Mission Thrift Store, Grand Rapids, MI, 1985-89

Huizenga, Jonathan L.
see list of ordained ministers

Huizenga, Martin
Northside Community Chapel, Paterson, NJ, 1949-50

Huizenga, Rudy
Community evangelism, Highland, IN, 1960-64; Back to God Chapel, Chicago, IL, 1964-80

Huizenga, Sam
Director of education and evangelism, Arcadia-Plainfield, Grand Rapids, MI, 1985–86

Huizenga, Thomas Henry
see list of ordained ministers

Huleatt, Jim
Director of youth, Sonlight Community, Lynden, WA, 1990–91

Hull, Tim
see list of ordained ministers

Hulst, Henry
Hazen Street Chapel, Grand Rapids, MI, 1935–36, 1937–39

Hulst, John B.
Beacon Light Mission, Grand Rapids, MI, 1944–48

Hulst, Sharon
Director of ministries, Holland Heights, Holland, MI, 1987–

Hutchings, Dave
Administration, Sunshine Community, Grand Rapids, MI, 1994–

Hwang, Shin Jae
Hawaii, 1997–2001

Hybels, Harold
Fair Oaks State Hospital, Kalamazoo, MI, 1959–60

Hyma, Helen
Griggs St., Chapel, Grand Rapids, MI, 1958–65

Hyun, Soo Il
see list of ordained ministers

Ickes, Arlene
Guiding Light Mission, Grand Rapids, MI, 1957–58

Im, Si Hyuk
Director of music, Korean, Long Beach, CA, 1986–88

Ipema, Ron
Ministry coordinator, First, Denver, CO, 1998–

Ipema, William B.
Campau Lake Chapel, Alto, MI, 1967–68

Ipson, Eric
Evangelism/Youth, Eastern Hills Community, Aurora, CO, 1992–

Ireland, Bruce
Director of education, Orland Park, IL, 1990–91

Jaarsma, C.J.
Grant St. Mission, Grand Rapids, MI, 1917–19

Jackson, James K.
Education/Evangelism/Youth, Madison Ave., Paterson, NJ, 1993–

Jacobs, John
Friendship House, Gallup, NM, 1973–74

Jager, Henry G.
Horseshoe Chapel, Grand Junction, MI, 1946–47; Diamond Gospel Center, Hamilton, MI, 1947–48; Helping Hand, Chicago, IL, 1948–49

James, Earl
Ministry coordinator, Madison Square, Grand Rapids, MI, 1994–2001

Jannsens, Glen
Administrative assistant, Ministry to Seafarers, Montreal, QC, 1989–90

Jansen, H.
Back to God Chapel, Abbotsford, BC, 1970–71

Jansen, Henry
Director, Gifford, Matsqui, BC, 1972–76

Jansen, Mark
Director of youth, Covenant, Cutlerville, MI, 1990–92

Jasperse, Jan
Director of education, Georgetown, Hudsonville, MI, 1985–90

Jasperse, Neil
see list of ordained ministers

Jasperse, Sher
Beacon Light, Gary, IN, 1973–75

Jenkins-Rice, Winky
Director, Rainbow Children's Center, New Hope Community, Kincheloe, MI, 1986–87

Jennings, Deborah
Ministry coordinator, Faith, Tinley Park, IL, 1996–2001

Johnson, Arlene
Millgrove, Allegan, MI, 1951–52

Johnson, David
Co-pastor, Maple Ave., Holland, MI, 1994–97

Johnson, James E.
Pastor of youth, education and evangelism, Second, Highland, IN, 1989–91

Johnson, Robert
Director of music, Bethany, Bellflower, CA, 1990–91

Joling, Ronald
Lay leader, Hope, Coquille, OR, 1989–90

Jolman, David
see list of ordained ministers

Jones, John
Music coordinator, Atlantic Community, Jacksonville, FL, 1989–90

Jones, Patricia
Director of discipleship, Covenant, North Haledon, NJ, 1987–88

Jongbloed, T.
Seaman's/Immigrant home, Hoboken, NJ, 1919–23

Jongsma, Arthur E.
American Indian Chapel, Chicago, IL, 1960–64

Jongsma, Daniel
see list of ordained ministers

Jonker, Peter
see list of ordained ministers

Jordan, G.
Goodwell Community Sunday School, Freemont, MI, 1941–42

Kaemingk, Alida
Ionia Ave. Mission, Grand Rapids, MI, 1944–45

Kahler, Mitch
Youth, Calvary, Holland, MI, 2001–

Kammer, Bobby
Millbrae Bible Church, Millbrae, CA, 1991–93; Community Bible Church, Mountain View, CA, 1993–94; Worship, New Life Ministries, Franklin Lakes, NJ, 1995–97

Kamps, Jacob R.
see list of ordained ministers

Kamrath, Roswell
North Park Chapel, Grand Rapids, MI, 1966–68

Kang, Soon Yung
Director of education, Cerritos Central, Artesia, CA, 1987–90

Kang, Young Suk
Korean, Grand Rapids, MI, 1981–83

Kapteyn, Ann Plantinga
Education/Evangelism/Youth, Fuller, Ave., Grand Rapids, MI, 1993–96

Karsten, Elizabeth
Horseshoe Chapel, Grand Junction, MI, 1951–52

Katsma, David
Evangelism/Outreach, Faith Community, Beaver Dam, WI, 1993–96

Kenbeck, Tona
Manhattan, New York, NY, 1958–60

Kennedy, Carolyn
Assistant director of evangelism, Ridgewood, Jenison, MI, 1989–90

Kennedy, Douglas
Evangelism/Youth, Hayward, CA, 1992–97

Khang, Vang
Hmong, Wisconsin Rapids, WI, 1991–94

Kiefer, Marty
Director of music ministries, Sunshine, Grand Rapids, MI, 1989–90

Kiekintveld, Joel
West End, Grand Rapids, MI, 1993–95; Youth, Trinity/Crosspoint, Anchorage, AK, 1995–2001; Ministry coordinator, Youth for Christ, Anchorage, AK, 2001–

Kiekintveld, Rick L.
Lay minister, Trinity Reformed, West New York,

NJ, 1973-75; Director of education, youth and evangelism, Lafayette, IN, 1975-78; Pastor of youth and community outreach, Graafschap, MI, 1979-87; Pastor of youth and evangelism, Millbrook, Grand Rapids, MI, 1987-99; Education/ Evangelism/Youth, Ada, MI, 1999

Kiel, Brian
Evangelism/Youth, Immanuel, Burbank, IL, 1991-95

Kim, Eui Kyum
Education/Evangelism/Youth, East Bay Korean, El Cerrito, CA, 1992-94

Kim, Hong D.
Director of education, Korean, Los Angeles, CA, 1989-90

Kim, Jae Sung
Assistant pastor, Korean, Los Angeles, CA, 1986-88

Kim, Keon-Yong
Director of education, Evergreen Korean, Los Angeles, CA, 1990-91

Kim, Kuk Sung
Youth teacher, Korean, Grand Rapids, MI, 1985-87

Kim, Paul C.
Minister of youth, Korean, Los Angeles, CA, 1989-90

Kim, Samuel
see list of ordained ministers

Kim, Young Min
Director of music, Korean, Chicago, IL, 1989-90

Kingma, Betsy
Director of Children's ministry, Sunshine, Grand Rapids, MI, 1987-90

Kirkpatrick, Allan
Youth/Evangelism, Clarkson, Mississauga, ON, 2000-

Kirrdlosa, Adell
Evangelism/Outreach, Dearborn, MI, 1996-99

Kitchings, Lynn
Child care director, Madison Ave., Paterson, NJ, 1989-90

Klaver, Dick
Marriage and family counselor, Calvary, Loveland, CO, 1984-87

Klein, Lois J.
Administration, First Bellflower, CA, 1993-99

Kleine-Deters, Allen
Student life coordinator, Redeemer College, Ancaster, ON, 1985-87; Director of youth, education, evangelism, Cephas, Peterborough, ON, 1987-91; Youth, First, Calgary, AB, 1991-2001

Klompeen, Kristin
Youth, First, Bellflower, CA, 1995-97

Klompien, David
Evangelism/Outreach, Ontario, CA, 1996-98

Klompien, Mark
Interim pastor, Sunnyside, WA, 2001

Klumpenhower, Gary
see list of ordained ministers

Klunder, Mr/Mrs Ray
Service home, Norfolk, VA, 1965-78

Klungel, Diana
Ministry coordinator, Calvary, Holland, MI, 2001-

Knaack, Robin K.
Ionia Ave. Chapel, Grand Rapids, MI, 1960-62; Gibson Chapel, Holland, MI, 1962-68

Knierim, Michael D.
Gold Ave., Grand Rapids, MI, 1975-86

Knoll, John Sr.
Mack's Landing, Fennville, MI, 1941-44

Ko, Keon Joo
Administration, Korean Church of Orange County, Buena Park, CA, 1995-

Koeman, Benita
Church secretary, Brookside, Grand Rapids, MI, 1995-2001

Koeman, Scott
Education/Evangelism, EverGreen Ministries, Hudsonville, MI, 2000-

Koeman, Ted
Director of youth and evangelism, Neland, Ave.,

Grand Rapids, MI, 1975-76; Minister of Youth, Ogden, UT, 1976-80

Koeman, Tricia
Education/Youth, Sunshine Community, Grand Rapids, MI, 1997-2001

Koetje, Jerry
Director of education, Ferrysburg, MI, 1987-88

Kok, Bena
Jewish Mission/Nathaneal Institute, Chicago, IL, 1947-49

Kok, Janette
Administration, Friendship Agape, San Jose, CA, 1994-

Kok, Thomas
see list of ordained ministers

Koning, Earl
State Hospital, Kalamazoo, MI, 1955-59

Koning, Herman
Guiding Light Mission, Grand Rapids, MI, 1984-89

Koning, Janet
Horseshoe Chapel, Grand Junction, MI, 1951-52

Koning, James
Director of music, Western Springs, IL, 1990-91

Koning, Ken
Director, Young people's society, Heritage, Byron Center, MI, 1986-87

Kooima, Troy
Youth pastor, First, Sioux Falls, SD, 1996-

Koopman, Doris
Director of music, Pleasant Street, Whitinsville, MA, 1989-90

Koopman, James
see list of ordained ministers

Koorneef, Robert
Belding, MI, 1970-76

Koot, Mike
Interim, Faith Christian Fellowship, Walnut Creek, CA, 2001-

Kooy, Steven
Youth, Ancaster, ON, 1997-

Kooyman, Jack
Degage Ministries, Grand Rapids, MI, 1985-87

Korf, Louis
see list of ordained ministers

Koster, Merwyn
Windfall Chapel, Grant, MI and Pine Grove Chapel, Howard City, MI, 1962-64

Krogman, Stewart
Education/Evangelism/Youth, New Life Fellowship, Red Deer, AB, 1994-2001

Kruis, John
see list of ordained ministers

Kruis, Mary Jane
Diamond Gospel Center, Hamilton, MI, 1949-50; Back to God Chapel, Edmonton, AB, 1951-52

Kruis, Richard
Creston Evangelism, Grand Rapids, MI, 1950-51; Bethel, Shiprock, NM, 1952-53; Four Corners, Teec Nos Pos, AZ, 1953-57; Bethlehem, Tohlaki, NM, 1957-60, 1962-68; Kibbie, South Haven, MI, 1968-70

Kuhl, Carol
Program administrator, Calvary, Chino, CA, 1987-90

Kuik, Daniel
Illiana Chritian High Shcool, 1981-86; Minister of youth, education and evangelism, First, Munster, IN, 1986-91; Education/youth, Haven, Zeeland, MI, 1991-92

Kuiper, Jo Ann
Community Chapel, Hammond, IN, 1956-58

Kuiper, Robert J.
Marion Chapel, Marion, MI, 1966-67; Cedar Rapids Chapel, Marion, IA, 1967-68; Lakeside Community Church, Alto, MI. 1968-69

Kuipers, Cornelius
Canyon Cito, NM, 1933-39

Kunnen, R.
Mona Lake Mission, Muskegon, MI, 1953-54

Kuperus, Harry
Director, Indian and Metis CRC Fellowship, Regina, SK, 1987–88

Kuperus, Tim
see list of ordained ministers

Laarman, Edward
see list of ordained ministers

Lageveen, G.
North River Mission, Holland, MI, 1934–35

Lago, Delfin
Spanish Bookstore, Grand Rapids, MI, 1977–79

Lam, Henriette
North River Mission, Holland, MI, 1941–42

Lange, Krista
Administration, Sonlight Community, Lynden, WA, 2001–

Langejans, Calvin P.
Director of music, Harderwyk, Holland, MI, 1990–91

Langejans, H.
Chapel, Fennville, MI, 1965–71

Laning, P.
Calvary Chapel, Willard, OH, 1959–62

Laninga, Bradley
Palos Heights, IL, 1993–99; Plymouth Heights, Grand Rapids, MI, 1999–

Larsen, Eric
Ministry, Spirit and Truth Fellowship, Philadelphia, PA, 1991–92

Last, Johanna
Beacon Light Mission, Grand Rapids, MI, 1947–52

Lau, Larry
see list of ordained ministers

Lazaroito, Carl
Calvary Temple, Winnipeg, MB, 1990–91; Broadway Church, Vancouver, BC, 1992–96; Education, Maple Ridge, BC, 2000–

Lee, J.J.
Director of evangelism, Korean, Los Angeles, CA, 1986–87

Lee, John
Two Wells Station, NM, 1963–65

Lee, Kee Duk
Ministry, West Bethel Korean, Los Angeles, CA, 1989–99

Lee, Kwanjik
Seongdo Presbyterian, 1985–89; Administrator, Valley, Arleta, CA, 1990–94

Lee, Woo-Ho
Director of education, Korean, Boca Raton, FL, 1987–90

Lee, Woo-Chun
see list of ordained ministers

Lee, Won-Kwan
Director of evangelism, Korean, Orange County, CA, 1986–87

Leese, Marvin J.
see list of ordained ministers

LeMahieu, Jean
Grand Rapids, MI, 1999–2001

LeMahieu, Tim
Director of youth, Oakdale Park, Grand Rapids, MI, 1990–91

Lengkeek, Henry
see list of ordained ministers

Lennips, William
Community, River Drive Park, ON, 1970–74

Lester, Cheryl
Director of music, Park, Holland, MI, 1989–90

Leugs, Timothy
Youth, Alger Park, Grand Rapids, MI, 1997–2001

Lew, Harry W.
see list of ordained ministers

Libolt, Clayton
see list of ordained ministers

Likkel, Lynn
see list of ordained ministers

Lim, Clifford
Education/Youth, Western Springs, IL, 2001–

Limburg, Timothy C.
see list of ordained ministers

Ling, Stephanie
Church secretary, Faith, New Brighton, MN, 2001–

Link, Ryan
Youth, Almond Valley, Ripon, CA, 2001–

Lo, Wayne
Pastoral assistant, Zion Chinese, Abbotsford, BC, 1996–

Loeks, Mary Carol F.
Director of Christian education, Church of the Servant, Grand Rapids, MI, 1986–90

Lolling, LaVonne
Director of music, Grace, Inver Grove Heights, MN, 1985–87

Looman, Arge
Palmer Chapel, Reeman, MI, 1964–65

Lopez, Florencio
Community of the King, El Salvador, 1986–88; Evangelist, Iglesia Hispana, Holland, MI, 1993–97

Loree, Ronald
Minister of music, Fruitport, MI, 1989–90

Lotterman, Dorius
Allen Road Chapel, Grand Rapids, MI, 1934–36; Godwin Chapel, Grand Rapids, MI, 1946–48

Lubber, George
Youth, Bethel, Newmarket, ON, 2001–

Luimes, Timothy
Education/Youth, Georgetown, ON, 1991–92

Lumkes, John
Director of youth, Alger Park, Grand Rapids, MI, 1990–91

Lycklama, David
Chapter director, Christian Service Club, Inc., 1973–75

Maatman, Rebecca
Administrative assistant, Eastern Ave., Grand Rapids, MI, 1982–87

Mac Donell, Todd
Youth director, Redlands, CA, 1996–2001

Machado, Frederico
see list of ordained ministers

MacNeil, Kirk
see list of ordained ministers

Male, Linda K.
Minister of youth and education, Plymouth, Grand Rapids, MI, 1989–92

Maliepaard, John
see list of ordained ministers

Man, Pat
Pastoral director, Sunrise Community, Austin, TX, 1989–90

Manning, Mark
Director of youth and eduaction, Willmar, MN, 1981–84; Minister of evangelism, Rapid City, SD, 1984–88

Marcusse, Edward
see list of ordained ministers

Maring, Paula R.
Director of church education, Calvin, Muskegon, MI, 1975–76

Mark, Mr/Mrs
Seaman's/Immigrant home, Hoboken, NJ, 1910–11

Martin, Arlene
Director of education, Crestview, Boulder, CO, 1986–90

Martin, Geronimo
Crownpoint, NM, 1954–75

Martin, Steve
Campus ministry, Halifax, NS, 2001–

Martinez, Albert
Sun Valley Community, Denver, CO, 1990–91

Mason, Eric
Youth, First, Highland, IN, 2001–

Mast, Carla
Director of music, Oakdale Park, Grand Rapids, MI, 1987–90

Mast, Richard
Youth director, Second Brampton, ON, 1992–98; Youth, West End, Edmonton, AB, 1998–

Matthysse, Wayne
Youth minister, Fort Wingate, NM, 1978–79

Mazurek, Susan
Director of enfolding ministry, Sunshine, Grand Rapids, MI, 1990–91

Mc Atee, Bret
Charlotte, MI, 1995–

McCabe, Matthew
Youth, Oak Hills, Beaverton, OR, 2001–

McDaniel, Joni
Ministry coordinator assistant, Gateway Community, Merced, CA, 2001–

Mc Kenzie, E.
Star Lake, NM, 1950–52

Mc Mahon, Lora
Administrative assistant, New Hope Community, Kincheloe, MI, 1985–87

McMann, Matthew
Lighthouse Community, Holland, MI, 1992–93; Celebrant division, VictoryPoint Ministries, Holland, MI, 1993–

Medendorp, John
see list of ordained ministers

Meekhof, Milton
Mission Industrial Store, Grand Rapids, MI, 1972–84

Meenen, Sherrill
Employment counselor, Madison Ave., Paterson, NJ, 1987–88

Meeter, M.
Community Chapel, Lansing, IL, 1949–53

Meinders, Erik
Evangelism/Youth, Mission Hills Community, Mission, BC, 2001–

Meinen, Andrew
Calvin Presbyterian, Abbotsford, AB, 1994–97; Youth, Goshen, NY, 1997–2001

Meiste, Gerald
Lawndale Chapel, Kalamazoo, MI, 1949–57, 1959–60

Melissen, John
Youth, Northern Lighthouse, Lincoln, NE, 1999–2001

Menchaca, Sara
Community missionary, Good Samaritan, Miami, FL, 1977–85; Iglesia El Redentor, Hialeah, FL and Good Samaritan, Miami, FL, 1985–87; Missionary, Iglesia El Redentor, Hialeah, FL, 1987–91

Metcalf, Fred
Assistant to the pastor, Gold Ave., Grand Rapids, MI, 1987–89; Minister of evangelism, Grandville Ave., Grand Rapids, MI, 1989–94

Meydrech, Lee F.
Lay Work Program, Sioux City, IA, 1957–62

Meyer, Reuben S.
Spec Lake Chapel, Allegan, MI, 1959–60

Meyers, Peter
Wiser Lake Chapel, Lynden, WA, 1972–73

Michael, Virgil L.
Director of evangelism, Sunnyside, WA, 1979–80

Middleton, J. Richard
InterVarsity Christian Fellowship, University of Guelph, Guelph, ON, 1981–86; Protestant Chapel Community, University of Rochester, Rochester, NY, 1986–89; Campus minister, Brock Christian Reformed Campus Ministry, St. Catharines, ON, 1989–91

Miedema, Barry
Assistant to pastor, Ontario, CA, 1985–87

Miedema, Gary
Campus ministry, Geneva Fellowship, Queen's University, Kingston, ON, 1997–99

Miedema, Robert K.
Coordinator of youth ministries, San Diego, CA, 1989–93; Education/Youth, First, New Westminster, BC, 1993–99

Miles, Gary
First Reformed, Lynden, WA, 1980–84; Hinsdale Baptist, Hinsdale, IL, 1984–86; Church planting, Linz, Austria, 1986–89; Family Bible Church, Oak Harbor, WA, 1989–93; Ministries coordinator, Sonlight Community, Lynden, WA, 1993–

Miller, Paul
Ministry coordinator, Covenant Life, Grand Haven, MI, 1997-

Moes, John M.
Cedar Bend Chapel, Waterloo, IA, 1955-57

Mogan, Carol
Administrator, Cadillac, MI, 1990-91

Molina, Samuel
Associate pastor, Sol de Valle, Sun Valley, CA, 1987-88

Monnahan, Pat
Youth director, Faith, New Brighton, MN, 1985-87

Monroe, Stan
Minister of music, Sunrise Community, Austin, TX, 1989-90

Monsma, William B.
Campus ministry, Minneapolis, MN, 1979-80

Moon, Chang Jae
Director of music, Korean, Chicago, IL, 1990-91

Moore, Bob D.
Evangelical Health Systems, Oak Brook, IL, 1976-89; South Coast Community Church, Irvine, CA, 1989-91; Administrator, St. Joseph, MI, 1991-94

Morbey, Graham E.
see list of ordained ministers

Morris, Mark
Third Reformed, Pella, IA, 1986-90; Director of youth, Elmhurst, IL, 1990-91

Muir, D.B.
Jewish Mission, Paterson, NJ, 1953-57

Mulder, Alan
Pastoral helper, Second, Brampton, ON, 1987-90

Mulder, Mr/Mrs Dan
Hospitality House hosts, Honolulu, HI, 1985-89; Service home, Norfolk, VA, 1989-95

Mulder, Ivan
Home missions, 1966-72; Pella Christian High School, Pella, IA, 1972-88; Director of education and evangelism, First, Pella, IA, 1988-94

Mulder, Laura
Coordinator of evangelism and assimilation, Hayward, CA, 1987-89 Director of outreach and education, Park Lane, Evergreen Park, IL, 1989-90

Mulder, Mara
Director of music, Covenant, North Haledon, NJ, 1990-91

Mulder, P.
McCallum Chapel, Fremont, MI, 1965-67, 1968-70

Mulder, Tim
First, Allendale, MI, 1991-92

Muyskens, Kevin
see list of ordained ministers

Nanninga, Henry Richard
see list of ordained ministers

Naugle, Chalmer
Ministry, Eastern Hills Community, Aurora, CO, 1996-

Nauta, Jelke
Helping Hand, Chicago, IL, 1949-53

Navis, William
North Christian Mission, Kalamazoo, MI, 1960-62; Madison Square Chapel, Grand Rapids, MI, 1962-68

Neerhof, Karl
Director of education, Hillcrest, Denver, CO, 1987-90

Negen, Allen
Minster of education, Cragmor, Colorado Springs, CO, 1973-76

Newman, Elias
Jewish Mission/Nathaneal Institute, Chicago, IL, 1920-24

Nibbelink, Donald W.
Campus ministry, Iowa City, IA, 1969-70

Niewenhuis, William D.
see list of ordained ministers

Nieuwsma, David
Minister of education and evangelism, First, Modesto, CA, 1979-82; Minister of evangelism, First, Pipestone, MN, 1982-85; Youth pastor, First,

Hanford, CA, 1985–90; Director of youth, Maple Ridge, BC, 1990–2001

Noh, John Jae Hwan
see list of ordained ministers

Noonon, David Jack
Director of evangelism, Creston, Grand Rapids, MI, 1979–80

Noordam, Joe
Judyville Mission, Kalamazoo, MI, 1952–54

Noordam, Ronald
Beacon Light Chapel, Grand Rapids, MI, 1962–63

Norgren, Cora
Day Care Ministries, Maple Ridge, BC, 2000–

Northouse, David
Neighborhood evangelism, Caledonia, MI, 1970–71

Nyenhuis, Gerald
Trinity, Sparta, MI, 1958–62

Nyenhuis, Joy
Youth, Sunshine Ministries, Grand Rapids, MI, 1991–92; Youth director, Immanuel, Fort Collins, CO, 1997–

Nyhof, Hermina
Assistant, Christian Education Office, Shiprock, NM, 1978–80

Nymeyer, Bradd
see list of ordained ministers

Nymeyer, Brent
Director of education, Rogers Heights, Wyoming, MI, 1989–90

Nyp, Cindy
Youth, Hope, Brantford, ON, 1995–96

Nyp, Scott
Willowdale, Toronto, ON, 1994–95; Youth, Community, Kitchener, ON, 1995–2001

Oh, Amos Eun Kyu
Assistant pastor, West Bethel Korean, Los Angeles, CA, 1987–90

Ok, Hae Kyung
Director of education, Korean, Chicago, IL, 1985–88

Olson, R.
Pinewood Chapel, New Brighton, MN, 1963–64

Olthoff, Nancy
Hospitality House Hostess, Norfolk, VA, 1985–87

Ondersma, Bernard
Mary Free Bed Hospital, Grand Rapids, MI, 1951–55

Onugha, George
Director of youth ministries, Northside Community Chapel, Paterson, NJ, 1978–80

Oosterhouse, J.
Campus ministry, Bellingham, WA, 1970–71

Oosterhouse, Rod
Education/Youth, First, Denver, CO, 1993–97

Oosthoek, Sharlene
Youth, Bethel, Waterdown, ON, 2001–

Orlie, Charlie
Visitation minister, Bethlehem, Tohlakai, NM, 1986–87

Orren, Todd
Education/Evangelism/Youth, Christ Community, Portland, OR, 1991–92; Education/Evangelism/Youth, First Ripon, CA, 1992–99

Ortiz-Vasquez, Debbie
Evangelism/Outreach, Ayuda Community Center, Philadelphia, PA, 1994–

Osborne, Tim
Youth, Cedar Hill, Wyckoff, NJ, 2001–

Otte, Marilyn
Secretary, Calvin, Sheboygan, WI, 2001–

Otto, Jeff
Fine arts/Music, Crossroads Community, Schererville, IN, 2001–

Ouwinga, John
Grand Rapids Community College, Grand Rapids, MI, 1973–78

Overway, Clarence
Horseshoe Chapel, Grand Junction, MI, 1951–52

Overzet, Harry
City Mission, Muskegon, MI, 1930–38

Overzet, John
Lawndale, Chicago, IL, 1952-53

Pacheco, Luis
Pastoral assistant, Servant of the Lord, Chula Vista, CA, 1990-91

Padro, Peter L.
La Iglesia Reformada Latino Americana, Carson, CA, 1987-91; First Spanish Evangelical Presbyterian (PCUSA), 1992-97; Church planter (PCA), 1998-99; Interim, Richfield, Clifton, NJ, 2001-

Pais, Mary
Director of outreach, Bethel, Grand Rapids, MI, 1990-91

Palma, Dorothy
Community work, Spring Lake, MI, 1961-62

Park, Clara
Day care ministry, Glory, Los Angeles, CA, 1995-

Park, Daniel
see list of ordained ministers

Park, Hee K.
Assistant minister, Korean, Los Angeles, CA, 1989-90

Park, W-Yong
Director of music, Korean, Chicago, IL, 1986-87

Parry, Steven
Minister to singles, River Terrace, East Lansing, MI, 1985-87

Parsons, Matthew
Youth, Ann Arbor, MI, 2001-

Paulina, N.
Madison Street Mission, Chicago, IL, 1940-41

Pawlak, Sue
Minister of music, Community Life, Lockport, IL, 1989-90

Penner, Glen
Assistant to pastor, Fresno, CA, 1985-88

Pereboom, Pieter
see list of ordained ministers

Perez, Abraham
music, Sol del Valle, Sun Valley, CA, 2001-

Perez, Amy
Ministry, Spirit and Truth Fellowship, Philadelphia, PA, 2001-

Perez, Henry
Coit Community, Grand Rapids, MI, 1991-94

Perez, Kate
Ministry, Spirit and Truth Fellowship, Philadelphia, PA, 2001-

Petersen, John
Assistant pastor, First, Modesto, CA, 1989-90

Peterson, P.B.
Sixth St. Mission, Grand Rapids, MI, 1941-45

Pettigrew, Jennie
Bethel, Shiprock, NM, 1958-60

Pettijohn, Carole
Ministry coordinator, Ivanrest, Grandville, MI, 1992-

Pettit, David
Youth, Valley, Binghampton, NY, 1996-

Petroelje, Katha
Music coordinator, Maple Ave., Holland, MI, 1989-90

Peuler, J.
Pine Grove, Howard City, MI, 1959-60

Pfarr, David (Mike)
Director of youth, Second, Kalamazoo, MI, 1990-91

Phaneuf, Janice
Administration, Madison Square, Grand Rapids, MI, 1995-2001

Plaggermeyer, Fred
Hanley Chapel, Grandville, MI, 1936-43; Mission, Fennville, MI, 1945-46

Plante, Jim
RCA: New Life, Artesia, CA, 1983-87; CRC: Minister of youth, Rosewood, Bellflower, CA, 1987-2001

Plate, Madell
Church secretary, Fresno, CA, 1995-96

Plug, Mr/Mrs C.
Southside Mission, Chicago, IL, 1949-51

Pluimer, Mark
Assistant, Unity, Prinsburg, MN, 2001-

Plum, Grace
Helping Hand, Chicago, IL, 1936-38

Poel, Barb
Director of education, Faith, Nashville, TN, 1989-90

Pohler, Robert
Director of Christian education and evangelism, Bethany, Muskegon, MI, 1978-80; Associate in ministry, Plymouth Heights, Grand Rapids, MI, 1980-86; Education/Youth, Faith, Holland, MI, 1986-

Polinder, Colleen
Administrative assistant, Sonlight Community, Lynden, WA, 1987-88

Polman, Bert
Director of music, Immanuel, Hamilton, ON, 1989-90

Pontier, Scott
Youth, EverGreen Ministries, Hudsonville, MI, 2001-

Poortinga, Cindy
Church secretary, First, Munster, IN, 1983-

Pops, Jans
Youth pastor, West End, Edmonton, AB, 1985-86

Posie, Denise L.
Baptist: Tabernacle Missionary Baptist, Detroit, MI; St. John Baptist and Bethel AME, Columbia, SC; CRC: Immanuel, Kalamazoo, MI, 1999-

Posthuma, Phil
Music, Providence, Holland, MI, 1991-92

Postma, Kay
Millgrove, Allegan, MI, 1949-51

Postma, Teresa
Youth ministries program director, Western Springs, IL, 1996-2001

Pot, Bernie/Donna
Evangelism/Outreach, Ministry to seafarers, Montreal, QC, 1995-96

Pott, H.
Comstock Chapel, Kalamazoo, MI, 1965-66

Pott, J. Jerry
see list of ordained ministers

Potter, Cory
Evangelism/Youth, East Saugatuck, MI, 2001-

Potts, Cathy
Director of music, Park, Holland, MI, 1990-91

Pratt, Edmund (Rip)
Prince of Peace Lutheran Church, Costa Mesa, CA, 1979-82; Youth director, Escondido, CA, 1986-

Prince, Wesley
Ivanrest Mission, Grand Rapids, MI, 1963-64

Pruiksma, Sadie
Northside Community Chapel, Paterson, NJ, 1946-47

Puuohau, Jo
Administration, Anuenue, Ewa Beach, HI, 2000-

Quist, Cornelius
Kent County Jail, Grand Rapids, MI, 1944-60

Quist, Jonathan
Youth, Alger Park, Grand Rapids, MI, 1996-97; Education/Youth, Keystone Community, Grand Rapids, MI, 1997-

Ratahnahk, Savann
Ministry coordinator, Mountain View, Lynden, WA, 1994-

Redhouse, Paul H.
Four Corners, Teec Nos Pos, AZ, 1950-51

Redondo, William
Love Song Community, Fresno, CA, 1995-

Reedyke, Jake
Community work, Lethbridge, AB, 1961-64

Reeves, Samuel B., Jr.
see list of ordained ministers

Reichert, Gene
Administrator of education, Immanuel, Hudsonville, MI, 1989-92

Reiffer, Minerd
Beacon Light Chapel, Grand Rapids, MI, 1959-62

Reitsma, A.
Lawndale, Chicago, IL, 1950-53

Renkema, Marcus
Congregational life/Outreach, First, Chino, CA, 1994-97

Renn, George
Big Springs, CA, 1990-91

Ribbens, Marjorie
Beacon Light Chapel, Grand Rapids, MI, 1940-41; Assistant, Ogden, UT, 1971-75

Ridley, William M.
Gold Avenue Chapel, Grand Rapids, MI, 1982-89

Riemersma, Leonard
Minister of youth and evangelism, Mayfair, Grand Rapids, MI, 1978-79; Minister of education and evangelism, Burton Heights, Grand Rapids, MI, 1979-80

Rietkerk, Eleanor
see list of ordained ministers

Rigg, Bill
Salt ministries, Jenison, MI, 19??; Grace Youth Camp, Mears, MI, 19??; Assistant minister to singles, Sunshine, Grand Rapids, MI, 1987-90

Ringelberg, John H.
Campus ministry, Mount Pleasant, MI, 1969-70

Rivera, Jose
Pastor, Spirit and Truth Fellowship, Chicago, IL, 1987-98

Roberts, Ann
Rainbow Children's Center director, New Hope Community, Kincheloe, MI, 1987-90

Roberts, Sheryl
Administration, First, London, ON, 1993-94

Robertson, Edie
Coordinator of assimilation, Baymeadows Community, Jacksonville, FL, 1989-90

Robison, Sherry
Ministry, Avery St., South Windsor, CT, 1993-

Roby, Mr/Mrs E.
Service home, San Diego, CA, 1967-69

Roeda, Jack H.
Missionary, CRWM, Mexico, 1967-80; Spanish media coordinator, Back to God Hour, Palos Heights, IL, 1980-87

Roelofs, C.
Campus ministry, Madison, WI, 1969-70

Roetman, Ron
Campus Crusade for Christ, 1980-89; Minister of congregational life, Calvary, Chino, CA, 1989-91; Administration, Harderwyk, Holland, MI, 1991-96

Romero, Domingo
Spanish, Grand Rapids, MI, 1973-89

Romero, Kimberly Huis
Education/Evangelism/Youth, Iglesia Hispana, Holland, MI, 1991-

Roorda, Aaron
Music/Youth, Trinity, Abbotsford, BC, 2001-

Roorda, Marjorie
Director of senior ministry, Washington, DC, 1986-87

Roorda, Nicholas
Charlotte, MI, 1979-82

Rop, Jan
Pastoral assistant for outreach, Immanuel, Roseville, MI, 1985-87

Rops, Kay L.
Youth, Ebenezer, Berwyn, IL, 1995-

Rosendale, John R.
Jewish Mission, Paterson, NJ, 1938-53

Rosendale, M.
Jewish Mission, Paterson, NJ, 1940-60

Rottenberg, David/Kathryn
Servicemen's Center, San Diego, CA, 1973-91

Rottenberg, J.
Jewish Mission/Nathaneal Institute, Chicago, IL, 1921-23

Roxburgh, Heather
Youth, Bellingham, WA, 1995-2001

Roseboom. Gysbert
Little Farms, Coopersville, MI, 1978–81

Rozema, Dave
Stated supply, Brigham City, UT, 1985–87

Rozema, W.J.
Campus ministry, Flagstaff, AZ, 1966–68

Rozendal, Martha
Paterson Hebrew Mission, Paterson, NJ, 1923–58

Rubingh, Linda
Prospect Presbyterian (PCUSA), Maplewood, NJ, 1991–92; Roschaven Ministry to women in prostitution, Grand Rapids, MI, 1992–94; Evangelism/Outreach, New City Church, Jersey City, NJ, 1994–

Rubio, Mr/Mrs A.
Migrant Mission, New Era, MI, 1961–64

Ruisch, Joel
Education/Youth, Third, Zeeland, MI, 2001–

Ruiter, Daniel
Fourth Reformed, Holland, MI, 1979–80; Palm Lane, Scottsdale, AZ, 1981–85; Haven Reformed, Kalamazoo, MI, 1986–90; Valley Christian High School, Cerritos, CA, 1990–94; Youth, Bethany, Bellflower, CA, 1994–97

Ruiz, Juan V.
Iglesia Cristiana Siervo del Senor, Chula Vista, CA, 1992–96

Runia, Lauren
Director of youth and music, Bethel, Manhattan, MT, 1990–91

Rutgers, Gerald
Pastoral assistant, First, Redlands, CA, 1977–79

Rylaarsdam, Merwin
see list of ordained ministers

Ryu, Roger, Y.
see list of ordained ministers

Sandoval, Jerome
Assistant in evangelism, Nachitti, NM, 1986–87

Santana, Manuel
Hoboken, NJ, 1965–66; Missionary to Spanish speaking, Paterson, NJ, 1967–73

Saunders, Nikki
Church secretary, North Hills, Troy, MI, 1995–96

Scamehorn, W.
Michigan Street Mission, Grand Rapids, MI, 1935–37

Schaaf, Kate
Ministry, Spirit and Truth, Philadelphia, PA, 1997–2001

Schaap, Ron
Director of evangelism, Grandville Ave., Grand Rapids, MI, 1975–78; Assistant pastor, First, Orange City, IA, 1978–80

Schachermeyer, Carol
Church secretary, North Hills, Troy, MI, 1996–2001

Schemper-Carlock, Marcia
Director of Music, New Life, Houston, TX, 1989–90

Schievink, Chris
Intern, Palmerston, ON, 2001–

Schinkel, Margot
Administration, Community, Kitchener, ON, 2000–

Schipper, Earl
Middleville, MI, 1963–68

Schipper, Jack C.
Beverly, Grand Rapids, MI, 1978–79; Grandville Ave., Grand Rapids, MI, 1979–82; Ministries coordinator, First, Seattle, WA, 1982–87; Director of youth and education, Westview, Grand Rapids, MI, 1987–91; Director of youth, education and evangelism, First, South Holland, IL, 1991–94

Scholten, H.
Lamar Plat Mission, Grand Rapids, MI, 1939–41

Scholten, Ruth
Ionia Avenue Chapel, Grand Rapids, MI, 1945–46

Scholtens, William
Congregational life administrator, Sunshine, Grand Rapids, MI, 1985–91; Ministry, Burton Heights, MI, 1991–96

Schonewill, Kevin
Arts ministries, Calvary, Holland, MI, 1997–

Schregardus, Jan
Director of education, youth and pastoral care, Woodlawn, Grand Rapids, MI, 1990-91

Schreur, George
Mack's Landing, Fennville, MI, 1946-49

Schripsema, Ken
Director of Youth/Young adults ministries, Kelloggsville, Kentwood, MI, 1993-

Schrotenboer, Paul
Godwin Heights Chapel, Grand Rapids, MI, 1948-49

Schultz, J.H.
Jewish Mission, Paterson, NJ, 1922-38

Schutt, Herman
Bowen Mills, Middleville, MI, 1968-72; Grand Rapids Community, Grand Rapids, MI, 1972-75

Schuurman, Peter
Brock Christian Reformed Campus Ministry, St. Catharines, ON, 1996-

Schuurman, Phylis
Minister of music, Northside, Clifton, NJ, 1989-90

Seciwa, Wilbert
Evangelism/Youth, Zuni, NM, 1995-

Segger, Joachim
Minister of music, West End, Edmonton, AB, 1989-90

Selles, Kurt
see list of ordained ministers

Senbouttarath, Pheuy
Lao Community, Holland, MI, 1994-97

Sennema, Norman
see list of ordained ministers

Sichterman, Chris
Knollwood, Kalamazoo, MI, 1950-54

Sikkenga, E.
Migrant Mission, New Era, MI, 1965-66

Silakhom, Ranong
Contact person, Lao Community, Holland, MI, 1987-88

Sinclair, Dean
Evangellism/Outreach, Sunshine Community, Grand Rapids, MI, 2001-

Sinkgraven, Richard
Director of youth and evangelism, First, Sioux Falls, SD, 1983-87

Sinnema, Donald W.
Campus minister, University of New Brunswick, Fredericton, NB, 1986-87

Slachter, Terry
see list of ordained ministers

Slager, J.
Mission, Fennville, MI, 1941-45

Slager, Kenneth Ray
Comstock Chapel, Kalamazoo, MI, 1956-59, 1960-62

Slenk, Dean
Director of worship, Providence, Holland, MI, 1999-

Slenk, Howard
Director of music, Woodlawn, Grand Rapids, MI, 1989-90

Sliekers, Hendrik
Director of education, Western Springs, IL, 1985-87

Slifer, Jim
Education/Youth, First, Denver, CO, 1991-92

Slofstra, Diane
Day care ministries, First, Langley, BC, 1993-99

Sloterbeek, John
Director, Greater Salt Lake Bible Academy, Salt Lake City, UT, 1978-79

Sluis, Arthur J.
Allegan, MI, 1976-81

Sluiter, Allison
Millgrove, Allegan, MI, 1951-52

Sluiter, Joyce
Director of education, North Street, Zeeland, MI, 1989-90

Smallman, Stephen
New City Fellowship, Chattanooga, TN, 1985–91; Ministry, Spirit and Truth Fellowship, Philadelphia, PA, 1991–92

Smeelink, Joe
Hazen Street Chapel, Grand Rapids, MI, 1936–37

Smid, Pamela
Cedar Hill, Wyckoff, NJ, 1992–93; Long Hill Chapel, Sussex, NJ, 1993–95; Youth, Covenant, North Haledon, NJ, 1995–

Smit, Kathy
Sierra Leone, West Africa, 1987–91; Administrator, New Life, Abbotsford, BC, 1991–92

Smit, Trude
Millgrove, Allegan, MI, 1949–50

Smith, Clayton
Youth, Bethel Community, Edmonton, AB, 2001–

Smith, David A.
Director of youth and outreach, Peace, South Holland, IL, 1990–91

Smith, Grace
Chapel activity coordinator, Campus Chapel, Ann Arbor, MI, 1987–88

Smith, Janice Boone
Administration, Sunshine Ministries, Grand Rapids, MI, 1991–

Smith, Larry
Pastoral assistant, Spirit and Truth Fellowship, Philadelphia, PA, 1993–94

Smitter, Elizabeth
Madison Square, Grand Rapids, MI, 1914–19; Blodgett Home, Grand Rapids, MI, 1935

Solle, Edward
Director of development, Sunshine, Grand Rapids, MI, 1985?-90

Sommerville, Jim
Evangelism/Outreach, Sunshine Ministries, Grand Rapids, MI, 1991–94

Son, Robert
Evangelist, Korean, Long Beach, CA, 1989–90

Song, In Ho
West Bethel Korean, Los Angeles, CA, 1990–95

Song Yeum, Young R.
Evangelism/Youth, Kent First Korean, Kent, WA, 1996–

Spalink, Benjamin
Ideal Park, Grand Rapids, MI, 1959–60

Spalink, Henry
Livingston, Grand Rapids, MI, 1966–67, 1969–70

Spiers, Minnie M.
Madison Street Mission, Chicago, IL, 1939–42

Spoelstra, Martin
Education/Evangelism/Youth, First, Fremont, MI, 1996–2000; Youth/Outreach, Twelfth Ave., Jenison, MI, 2000–

Spoelstra, Peter A.
Mission, Kalamazoo, MI, 1938–39; Knollwood, Kalamazoo, MI, 1941–44

Sprik, Al
Director of education, Immanuel, Salt Lake City, UT, 1975–80

Stam, Gerrit
Beacon Light Chapel, Grand Rapids, MI, 1955–58

Stam, Peter Sr.
Star of Hope Mission, Paterson, NJ, 1916–21

Stammis, Rita
Youth, Community, Richmond Hill, ON, 1995–96

Stamps, Mary D.
Ministry, Madison Square, Grand Rapids, MI, 1991–92

Start, Herb
Minister of Music, Burton Heights, Grand Rapids, MI, 1989–90

Stastny, James
see list of ordained ministers

Steen, Suzie
Graystone Presbyterian, Indiana, PA, 1981–85; Hope CRC, Framingham, MA, 1985–88; Haven Reformed, Hamilton, MI, 1988–92; Ministry coordinator, Park, Holland, MI, 1992–

Steenstra, George
Helping Hand, Chicago, IL, 1929-35

Steenwyk, Gerrit J.
Executive director, Christian Service Club, Inc., 1970-77

Stehouwer, Ellen
Education, River Terrace, East Lansing, MI, 1991-92

Steigenga, Joseph J.
Comstock Chapel, Kalamazoo, MI, 1965-66, Lawndale, Chicago, IL, 1968

Steinbach, Mark
Director of music, Webster, Rochester, NY, 1987-88

Stek, Henrietta
Nathaneal Institute, Chicago, IL, 1922-24

Stellingwerf, Ernest
Evangelism/Outreach, Bellevue, WA, 1991-92

Stellingwerff, John
Youth pastor, First, Hamilton, ON, 1987-90

Sterenberg, Fred S.
Administration, Eastern Avenue, Grand Rapids, MI, 2001-

Stevenson, W. Peck
Minister of music, Arcadia, CA, 1987-88

Strait, Brett
Reformed campus ministry, Trinity, Ames, IA, 1992-

Strak-Dykema, Lou Ann
Director of education and evangelism, Christ's Community, Grand Rapids, MI, 1985-86

Stremler, Chris (Catrienas)
Horseshoe Chapel, Grand Junction, MI, 1943-45; Community Chapel, Lynden, WA, 1945-

Stroobach, Erwin
Director of music, Grace, Cobourg, ON, 1987-88

Struyk, Robert J.
Seacrest Blvd. Presbyterian Church, 1988-91; Ministry, Sunshine Ministries, Grand Rapids, MI, 1991-92

Styf, Irene
Christian Group Home Director, Village of Hope, Fort Wingate, NM, 1979-80

Suh, Justin J.
Orange Korean, Fullerton, CA, 2001-

Sutton, Alco
Employment ministry, Madison Avenue, Paterson, NJ, 1991-

Suwyn, Lesli
Director of education, Woodlawn, Grand Rapids, MI, 1989-90

Suwyn, M.
Sun Valley Community, Denver, CO, 1966-68

Swets, Melvin
Director of education and youth, Cragmor, Colorado Springs, CO, 1975-76

Swierenga, Harry
Bridge Street Mission, Grand Rapids, MI, 1946-49

Swierenga, John B.
see list of ordained ministers

Swierenga, William
see list of ordained ministers

Sytsma, Dorothy
City Mission, Oskaloosa, IA, 1949-52

Sytsma, Jessie
Mission Industrial Store, Grand Rapids, MI, 1943-50; Back to God Chapel, Paterson, NJ, 1950-64

Sytsma, Steve
see list of ordained ministers

Syswerda, Frederick
Beacon Light Chapel, Grand Rapids, MI, 1963-64

Talley, John
Four Corners, Teec Nos Pos, AZ, 1956-57; 1965-70

Tamminga, Dale
Evangelism and Youth coordinator, East Leonard, Grand Rapids, MI, 1977-78

Tamminga, Donald
Director of Christian education, South Grandville, Grandville, MI, 1976-84; Classis Red Mesa Home

Leadership Training Coordinator, 1984–88; Fort Wingate, NM, 1988–94

Tamminga-Tebben, Glenda
Congregational life/Youth, Baldwin, Jenison, MI, 1997–

Tandayu, Joy
Church secretary, Grace Filipino, Bellflower, CA, 1997–

Tanis, Dennis
Palmer Chapel, Reeman, MI, 1965–67

Tanis, Edward J.
Ryerson Heights Mission, Muskegon, MI, 1952–54

Tanis, N.
Moore School, Allegan, MI, 1948

Tanis, P.
Peace River Chapel, Tawatinaw, AB, 1963–64

Tans, Mark S.
Evangelism/Youth, Cottonwood Heights, Jenison, MI, 1983–85; Youth director, Trinity, Philadelphia, PA, 1985–86; Pastor of youth and evangelism, Caledonia, MI, 1986–87; Minister of youth and evangelism, Midland Park, NJ, 1987–90; Director, Cross-Fire Adult Singles (Classical) Ministry, Grand Rapids, MI, 1990–

Taylor, Ty
PCA: North Coast Presbyterian, 1986–95; CRC: Evangelism/Outreach, Elmhurst, IL, 1997–99

Te Grootenhuis, Maleeta
Service workers, Emmanuel, Sauk Village, IL, 1977–80

Te Krony, Arian
Youth and outreach advisor, Faith, New Brighton, MN, 1989–90

Ten Brink, Harold
Pine Crest State Hospital, Kalamazoo, MI, 1955–56; Fair Oaks State Hospital, Kalamazoo, MI, 1957–58

Ten Harmsel, John
Hopkins, MI, 1941–44; Horseshoe Chapel, Grand Junction, MI, 1942; Bravo Community, Fennville, MI, 1949–50

Tensen, John
CRC, Cochrane, ON, 1968–73

Terborg, Ruth
City Mission, Hammond, IN, 1954–56

Terpstra, Simon
Ionia Avenue Chapel, Grand Rapids, MI, 1953–54

TeVelde, Annette
Sunshine Community, Grand Rapids, MI, 1994–95; Youth, Ebenezer, Leduc, AB, 1995–99

Theule-Van Dam, Chris
Youth, EverGreen Ministries, Hudsonville, MI, 1994–

Thomas, C.
Indian Center, Riverside, CA, 1964–65; Indian Christian Center, Salt Lake City, UT, 1965–66

Thomas, John
Director of youth, Madison Ave., Paterson, NJ, 1990–91

Thompson, NeeOdoi Edward
All Nations Grace, Allen, TX, 1994–98

Thornburg, William
Youth director, First, Allendale, MI, 1986–87

Tibboel, Ted
Bethany, Gallup, NM, 1955–57

Tibma, Jacoba S.
Jewish Mission/Nathaneal Institute, Chicago, IL, 1920–34

Tieman, Earl
Communication division, VictoryPoint Ministries, Holland, MI, 1997–

Tiemeyer, Alfred
Community evangelist, Caledonia, MI, 1989–90

Tigchelaar, Sylvia
Lamar Plat, Grand Rapids, MI, 1944–46

Timmer, Jackie
CRC Publications, Teacher training, Grand Rapids, MI, 1977–90; Director of education and evangelism, Shawnee Park, Grand Rapids, MI, 1982–

Timmer, Keith
Youth director, Hanford, CA, 1975–78

Timmer, Mark
see list of ordained ministers

Timmer, Rena
Tacoma, WA, 1964–73; Assistant, Elim in the Desert, Tucson, AZ, 1974–75; Executive director, Appalachia Reach Out, Inez, KY, 1975–80

Timmerman, Alice
Millgrove, Allegan, MI, 1942–44

Tinholt, Marvin
Mack's Landing, Fennville, MI, 1943–47

Tinklenberg, David
Director of evangelism, Green Meadow, Helena, MT, 1986–87

Tjapkes, Peter
Jolman Mission, Muskegon, MI, 1949–50

Tolsma, G.
Northside Community Chapel, Paterson, NJ, 1950–58

Tong, Joseph
Crenshaw, Los Angeles, CA, 1975–78

Toonstra, Martin
see list of ordained ministers

Top, Terry
Assistant to pastor, First, Pella, IA, 1978–79

Touw, Philip R.
see list of ordained ministers

Tran, Vinh Q.
Vietnamese Reformed Christian Church, Grand Rapids, MI, 1983–85

Trapp, Vann
Minister of youth and education, Ridgeview Hills, Denver, CO, 1989–90

Triezenberg, Paula
Congregational ministries, South Bend, IN, 1999–

Tripp, Nancy
Ministry coordinator, St. Joseph, MI, 1997–2001

Truong, Khiet Thanh
Vietnamese Reformed Christian Church, Grand Rapids, MI, 1978–82

Tubergen, Jeff
Youth, Cottonwood, Jenison, MI, 1998–

Tucker, J. Alvin
Sunshine Chapel, Grand Rapids, MI, 1957–60

Tucker, Lynn
Director of religious education, Lawndale, Chicago, Il, 1984–87

Tuininga, James
Pastor's assistant, West End, Edmonton, AB, 1976–77

Tuininga, William C.
see list of ordained ministers

Tuit, Wilhelmina
Bethel Mission, Grand Rapids, MI, 1940–43; Nathanael Institute, Chicago, IL, 1943–47; Jewish Mission, Paterson, NJ, 1947–56

Turkstra, John Richard
Spec Lake Chapel, Allegan, MI, 1958–65

Turpen, Blake
Youth, Prairie Lane, Omaha, NE, 2001–

Tyhuis, Brian
Youth, Oak Harbor, WA, 2001–

Umfleet, Randy
Calvary Reformed, Orland Park, IL, 1983–84; Moody Bible Institute, 1984–87; Fellowship Reformed, Lombard, IL, 1987–90; Director of Music and drama, Sunshine, Grand Rapids, MI, 1990–2001

Valk, John
Campus minister, University of New Brunswick, Fredericton, NB, 1987–

Van Dam, Michael
Music director, First, Langley, BC, 1989–90

Vande Berg, Theodore,
Director of youth/Young adults, Highland Hills, Grand Rapids, MI, 1989–90

Vande Guchte, Mary
Director of music, West Leonard, Grand Rapids, MI, 1989–90

Vanden Akker, Andy
see list of ordained ministers

Van Den Berg, Dewey
Director of education, Park, Holland, MI, 1990-91

Van Den Berg, Doug
Minister of music, Southern Heights, Kalamazoo, MI, 1989-90

Van Den Berg, Julie
Director of evangelism, Park, Holland, MI, 1990-91

Vanden Berg, Tony
State Hospital, Kalamazoo, MI, 1952-53

Vanden Berg, William
Gibson Chapel, Holland, MI, 1958-62

Vanden Berge, Anthony
Way of Life Chapel, Kalamazoo, MI, 1951-52

Vanden Bos, Arlan
Administrator, Calvary, Chino, CA, 2001-

VanDenend, Mary
Church secretary, Harderwyk, Holland, MI, 1989-

Vanden Heuvel, James
Tri-Cities Youth director, Ferrysburg, Spring Lake, First and Second Grand Haven, MI, 1996-

Vanden Heuvel, Jeremy
Education/Evangelism/Youth, Westview, Grand Rapids, MI, 1995-

Vander Ark, K.
Indian Center, Riverside, CA, 1963-64; Pinewood Chapel, New Brighton, MN, 1965-65

Vander Ark, Willard
Vance, Ellsworth, MI, 1974-75

Vander Beek, Herbert
Interim, First, Munster, IN, 1999-2001

Vander Beek, J.
Campus ministry, Corvallis, OR, 1966-69

Vander Berg, W.
Gibson, Holland, MI, 1960-62

Vanderburg, Herman
First, Calgary, AB, 1978-91; Counseling, Zion, Oshawa, ON, 1991-97

Vanderburg, Sandi
Administrative assistant, Calvary, Chino, CA, 1994-

Vander Graaf, Rick
Director of youth, Burnaby, BC, 1986-88

Vander Griend, M.D.
Wiser Lake Chapel, Lynden, WA, 1960-72

Vander Hart, Cornelius B.
Four Corners, Teec Nos Pos, AZ, 1942-43

Vander Hart, Stephen
Grandville Ave., Grand Rapids, MI, 1990-94; Youth, Sunshine Community, Grand Rapids, MI, 1994-2001

Van der Heide, Hilbrent
Houston, BC, 2000-

Vander Heide, Walter
Pastor of Christian growth, Lake City, MI, 1978-83; Director, Hospitality House, Pacific Community, Honolulu, HI, 1983-85; Ministries coordinator, Oakdale Park, Grand Rapids, MI, 1990-97

Vander Hoek, Hans
Pastoral assistant, First, Ripon, CA, 2001-

Vander Horst, Kurt
Youth director, First, Denver, CO, 1979-80

Vander Leest, Marcia
Director of congregational ministries, Community Life, Lockport, IL, 1989-90

Vander Ley, Mark
Education/Youth, First, Ripon, CA, 2001-

Vander Lugt, Gerald
Hillcrest Community Church, Grand Rapids, MI, 1966-75; Marion, MI, 1975-76

Vander Lugt, Herbert
Sparta, MI, 1941-44

Vander Mate, Betty
Nathaneal Institute, Chicago, IL, 1927

Vander Meer, David
Pastoral assistant, Trinity, Sparta, MI, 2001-

Vander Meer, Mark S.
Lake City, MI, 1998-2001

Vander Meer, Peter
Kent County Juvenile Home, Grand Rapids, MI, 1937-47, 1951-58

Vander Meulen, Derrick
see list of ordained ministers

Vander Meulen, Edith
Chicago Jewish Mission, Chicago, IL, 1923-34, 1943-71

Vander Meulen, Gerrit
San Antone Mission, Thoreau, NM, 1943-45

Vander Meulen, Rhine
Bravo Community, Fennville, MI, 1943-46, 1948-49, 1953-54

Vandermolen, Richard C.
Evangelism/Youth, First, Lansing, IL, 1991-92

Vander Ploeg, Elsie
Manhattan, New York, NY, 1956-57

Vander Ploeg, Jan
Outreach/Education, Park Lane, Evergreen Park, IL, 1992-2001

Vander Ploeg, Marcella
Peace Reformed, Middleville, MI, 1989-90; Director of education and youth, Ancaster, ON, 1990-91

Vander Ploeg, Tom
Youth, Westwood, Kalamazoo, MI, 2001-

Vander Pol, Bertha
Griggs Street, Grand Rapids, MI, 1944-45

Vander Poort, Margaret
Immanuel, Roseville, MI, 1958-59

Vander Roest, Lawrence
Lexington Green Community, Portage, MI, 1970-71

Vander Steen, Dirk
Minister of education and outreach, Third, Kalamazoo, MI, 1978-80

Vander Stel, Kathy
Ministries Coordinator, Friendship, Byron Center, MI, 1992-97

Vanderstelt, Curt
Youth pastor, Calvin, Muskegon, MI, 1996-2001

Vanderstelt, Jeff
Young Life, Chicago, IL, 1988-89; Olivet Evangelical Free Church, Muskegon, MI, 1989-90; Youth, First, Seattle, WA, 1991-97

Vander Stelt, Nathan John
Director of youth, First, Allendale, MI, 1990-91

Vander Til, Louis
Haney Chapel, Grandville, MI, 1946-53; Middleville, MI, 1952-56

Vander Veen, Daryl
Education/youth, First, Hanford, CA, 1991-92

Vander Veen, Kasey
Youth, Immanuel, Hamilton, ON, 1989-91; Pastoral counselor, Step by Step Ministries, Winnipeg, MB, 1992-96; Evangelism/Youth, Calvin, Holland, MI, 1999-

Vander Veer, John S.
Allen Road Chapel, Grand Rapids, MI, 1940-42

Vander Veer, Mrs. J.
Sunshine Chapel, Belmont, MI, 1936-37

Vander Velde, Alice
Coordinator of Asian ministry, Covenant, Lansing, MI, 1987-90

Vander Velden, Stewart
Education/Youth, Sunrise Community, Austin, TX, 1991-94

Vander Wal, Michelle
Youth, Second, Brampton, ON, 1998-

Vander Wal, Richard
see list of ordained ministers

Vander Wall, Albert
Palmer Chapel, Reeman, MI, 1967-70, 1971-72

Vander Wall, John
Calvary, Lowell, MI, 2001-

Vander Weide, Ida
Helping Hand, Chicago, IL, 1935-37, Roseland Community Gospel Mission, Chicago, IL, 1939-46

Vander Weit, Deborah
Education/Youth, Faith, Tinley Park, IL, 1996-99

Vander Woude, Rick
Director of music, West End, Edmonton, AB, 1986–88

Vander Woude, Sharon
Church secretary, Second, Highland, IN, 1988–

Vander Zee, Ruth
Minister of music, Hayward, CA, 1987–88

Vander Zwaag, Alice
Bridge Street Mission, Grand Rapids, MI, 1948–51; Wayland, MI, 1951–52; Gold Ave. Back to God Chapel, Grand Rapids, MI, 1951–59

Vanderzwan, Eileen
Director of music, Grace, Scarborough, Toronto, ON, 1989–90

Van Dijk, Alida
Ministry, Covenant, St. Catharines, ON, 1999–

Van Donselaar, Carolyn
Ministry-Preschool, Second, Denver, CO, 1991–97

Van Doorne, Martin
Bethel Mission, Grand Rapids, MI, 1944–45

Van Dop, Carmen
Day care ministry, Maple Ridge, BC, 2000–

Van Dyk, Mace
North Side Mission, Paterson, NJ, 1954–60

Van Dyke, Irving
Livingston Chapel, Grand Rapids, MI, 1970–71

Van Dyken, M. James
Ionia Avenue Mission, Grand Rapids, MI, 1934–45

Van Ee, Verlan
see list of ordained ministers

Van Eerden, Helen
Oakdale Park Evangelism, Grand Rapids, MI, 1948–54; Boston Square evangelism, Grand Rapids, MI, 1949–50

VanEk, Todd
Director of youth, Trinity, Grandville, MI, 1990–91

Van Engelhoven, C.
Cedar Rapids Chapel, Marion, IA, 1966–67

Van Ens, John
Minister of evangelism, Long Beach, CA, 1989–90

Van Eps, Mike
Director of youth, Willmar, MN, 1986–88

Van Ess, Mark
Evangelist, Hillcrest Community, Grand Rapids, MI, 1996–

Van Goch, Edwoud
Youth, First, London, ON, 1991–92

Vang, Kou
Evangelist, Covenant, Lansing, MI, 1989–90

Van Groningen, John
Director of music, Orland Park, IL, 1989–90

Van Groningen, Willis D.
see list of ordained ministers

Van Halteren-Stammis, Rita
Youth, Community, Richmond Hills, ON, 1995–99

Van Harn, Karl
see list of ordained ministers

Van Hill, Craig
Youth, Providence, Cutlerville, MI, 1996–99; Youth, Graafschap, Holland, MI, 2001–

Van Houten, Fred
Minister of calling, Orland Park, IL, 1989–90

Van Hoven, Bob
The Outpost, Denver, CO, 1998–

Van Hulsen, David
Music evangelist, 1971–83; Advent Christian Church, Haverhill, MA, 1990–95; Youth, Friendship Chapel, Jenison, MI, 1996–

Van Hulzen, Mary
Ministry coordinator. Church secretary, Third, Lynden, WA, 1990–

Van Kampen, Sharon
Administration, First, London, ON, 1994–2001

Van Kooten, Tenis C.
see list of ordained ministers

Van Laar, Richard
Lamar Plat Mission, Grand Rapids, MI, 1948–49;
Beacon Light Chapel, Grand Rapids, MI, 1962–63

Van Lant, Tim
Ministry coordinator, Community, Wyoming, MI,
2001–

Van Mersbergen, Nellie
Beacon Light Chapel, Grand Rapids, MI, 1944–45;
Oskaloosa, IA, 1946; Lawndale Gospel Chapel,
Chicago, IL, 1946–54; Nathaneal Institute, Chicago, IL, 1954–57; Bethel, Shiprock, NM, 1957–60

Van Netten, David
Youth ministry, 1985–87; Director of youth and
evangelism, Graafschap, MI, 1987–92

Van Ord, Melody
Program coordinator, Third, Edmonton, AB, 1989–91; Youth, First, Langley, BC, 1991–92

Van Someren, Marvin D.
Reformed church, Portage, MI; Director of youth
ministry, Ridgewood, Jenison, MI, 1987–93; Education/Evangelism/Youth, Bethel, Lansing, Il,
1993–94

Van Stelle, Paul
Director of youth, First, Richmond, BC, 1990–91

Van Til, Henry
Little Farms, Coopersville, MI, 1957–58; Bowen
Mills, Middleville, MI, 1960–64, 1966–68, 1970–72; Gibson, Holland, MI, 1968–69

Van Tol, Magdalene
Griggs Street Chapel, Grand Rapids, MI, 1948–53

Van't Riet, Cornelius
Kelloggsville Mission, Grand Rapids, MI, 1936–37;
Beacon Light Chapel, Grand Rapids, MI, 1937–41

Van Veen, Jan
Mission, Montreal, QC, 1964–65

Van Westenberg, William
Mission, Ogden, UT, 1918

Van Wieren, Donna
Director of education, Calvary, Holland, MI, 1986–87

Van Wieren, Larry
Director of education, Calvary, Holland, MI, 1986–87

Van Wolde, Arthur J.
Education/Youth, Dearborn, MI, 1993–94

Van Wyhe, Kevin
Evangelism/Youth, Cragmor, Colorado Springs, CO,
1994–98; Youth and education, Ivanrest,
Grandville, MI, 1998–

Van Wyke, Henry
Front Street Chapel, Grand Rapids, MI, 1952–57

Vasquez, Hector
Youth, Spirit and Truth Fellowship, Philadelphia,
PA, 1990–

Veenstra, Agnes
Madison Square, Grand Rapids, MI, 1937–39

Veenstra, George
Gospel Chapel, Denver, CO, 1946–52; Back to God
Chapel, Edmonton, AB, 1952–53; Beacon Light
Chapel, Racine, WI, 1953–64; Community, Alger,
WA, 1964–67

Veenstra, Johanna
Way of Life Mission, Grand Rapids, MI, 1916–17

Veenstra, Ralph
see list of ordained ministers

Veldhorst, David
Education/Evangelism/Youth, Second, Highland,
IN, 1991–94

Vellinga, Agnes
Jewish Mission, Paterson, NJ, 1942–48

Veltman, Joe
Evergreen, Olympia, WA, 1974–75

Veltman, Nelson
First, Zeeland, MI, 1989–90

Velzen, Jane/Bernard
Pastoral assistant for congregational care,
Woodlawn, Grand Rapids, MI, 1989–90

Venema, Trena
Millgrove, Allegan, MI, 1942–43

Venema, Tena
Director of programs/administration, New Life, Abbotsford, BC, 1989-90

Verboom, Andy
Faith Chapel, Shubenacadie, NS, 1979-80

Verhulst, Glen
Farmington, NM, 1978-79

Ver Meer, Bud
Trinity, Sparta, MI, 1961-62, 1972-74

Ver Merris, Don
Director of youth and fellowship, Beckwith Hills, Grand Rapids, MI, 1987-90

Vila, David
Migrant Mission, New Era, MI, 1957-59

Vis, Eudell
Minister of evangelism, Riverside, CA, 1978-79

Vis, William D.
Little Farms, Coopersville, MI, 1981-82

Visser, Dr. A.J.
Seaman's/Immigrant home, Hoboken, NJ, 1923-27

Visser, Andy
Zuni, NM, 1974-75

Visser, Arlene
Outreach director, Community of Meadowvale, Mississauga, ON, 1986-88

Visser, Marjorie
Harlem Negro Evangelism, Manhattan, NY, 1955-58

Visser, Michele
Youth, Good News Fellowship, Winnipeg, MB, 1991-

Vlasma, Hilbert
Mona Lake Mission, Muskegon, MI, 1955-56

Vogel, Cora
Bethel, Shiprock, NM, 1950-52

Vogel, Jane
Director of youth education, Bethany, Bellflower, CA, 1985?-87

Volkers, Bruce
Director of music, Fruitport, MI, 1990-91

Volkers, Lois
Lay worker, Fruitport, MI, 1971-73; 1990-91

Vos, Erma
Brigham City, UT, 1964-69; Assistant, Bethany, Gallup, NM, 1969-79; Director of Bethany Day Care Center, Gallup, NM, 1979-87

Vreeman, Steve
Youth director, Hanford, CA, 1978-80

Vugteveen, Daniel
Pastor of education and evangelism, Alger Park, Grand Rapids, MI, 1985-86

Vugteveen, Jonathan
Administration, Providence, Holland, MI, 1998-

Vugteveen, Marvin
Four Corners, Teec Nos Pos, AZ, 1958-61

Waalkes, Nancy
Church secretary, Covenant, Cutlerville, MI, 1989-

Wade, Michelle
Day care ministry, Maple Ridge, BC, 2000-

Wagenveld, Mary Anne
Administrative assistant, Sol de Valle, Sun Valley, CA, 1989-90

Walcott, Al
New Richmond, MI, 1963-64

Walcott, Elmer
Green Creek, Muskegon, MI, 1953-56

Walker, Cindy
Church secretary, Eastern Hills Community, Aurora, CO, 1996-

Walker, Odis
Director of education and evangelism, Christ's Community, Grand Rapids, MI, 1985-90

Walker, Trent
see list of ordained ministers

Walsh, Brian
Campus ministry, Toronto, ON, 2001-

Walstra, Sue
City mission, Hammond, IN, 1950-51

Ward, Bill
Congregational life, Rosewood, Bellflower, CA, 1995-99

Warfield, Deborah
Director of outreach, Immanuel, Kalamazoo, MI, 1987-90

Warners, William
Allen Road Chapel, Grand Rapids, MI, 1942-43

Wassenaar, Joe
Garfield, Chicago, IL, 1963-64

Wassenaar, Mary
Hope Center, Winnipeg, MB, 1973-74

Weeda, Thomas
Principal, Zuni Christian Reformed Mission School, Zuni, NM, 1966-70; teacher, Rehoboth Mission School, 1970-74; Director of Christian Education, Rehoboth, NM, 1974-80

Wellington, W.
Friendship House, San Francisco, CA, 1967-68

Welliver, Donna
Administration, Rosewood, Bellflower, CA, 1996-2001

Wessels, Laura
Education/Outreach, Park Lane, Evergreen Park, IL, 1990-91

Wessels, Todd & Cindy
Evangelism/Outreach, Park Lane, Evergreen Park, IL, 2001-

Westerhof, K.
Lawndale Chapel, Kalamazoo, MI, 1970-71

Westfield, Henry
Ivanrest Chapel, Grand Rapids, MI, 1950-51

Westhouse, Charles
Coordinator of evangelism and youth, Cottonwood Heights, Jenison, MI, 1982-83; Associate in ministry of youth, evangelism and education, First, Zeeland, MI, 1983-87

Westra, Henry
Back to God Chapel, Bozeman, MT, 1955-59

Westra, Miss J.
Ionia Avenue Chapel, Grand Rapids, MI, 1937-44

Westra, Karen
Minister of music, East Side, Cleveland, OH, 1989-90

Westra, Kenneth J.
Kentwood Community Church, Kentwood, MI, 1089-92; Gun Lake Community, Wayland, MI, 1994; Youth, Sunshine, Grand Rapids, MI, 1997-99

Westveer, Bob
Chapel activity coordinator, Campus Chapel, Ann Arbor, MI, 1987-88

White, Robert N.
Northside Community Chapel, Paterson, NJ, 1974-75

Whitehorse, Boyd
CRC, Farmington, NM, 1968-73

Wicker, Lloyd
Education/Evangelism/Youth, Bethel, Lansing, IL, 1997-2001

Wiener, Cliff
Music, Suburban Life Community, Darien, IL, 1995-

Wierenga, Harry
Bridge Street Mission, Grand Rapids, MI, 1946-49

Wiers, Grace
LaGrave Neighborhood Evangelism, Grand Rapids, MI, 1948-53; Wayland, MI, 1951-54; Creston Neighborhood Evangelism, Grand Rapids, MI, 1953-55

Wilcox, Amy
Ministry, Spirit and Truth Fellowship, Philadelphia, PA, 1995-2001

Wildeboer, John
Ajax/Pickering, ON, 2001-

Wildschut, John
Minister of youth, evangelism and education, First, Ripon, CA, 1983-92

Wilk, Karen
Director of youth ministry and outreach, West End, Edmonton, AB, 1986-92

Winnowski, Michael
see list of ordained ministers

Winter, Peter
Mission Industrial Stores, Grand Rapids, MI, 1944–72

Witte, Jane
Youth worker, First, New Westminster, BC, 1987–88

Witte, John/Mary
Co-director, Hospitality House, Honolulu, HI, 1979–80

Wobben, Bart
CRC, Bellvue, AB, 1969–76

Wolf, Noberto E.
see list of ordained ministers

Wolters, Cindy
Director of outreach and education, Christ's Community, Chandler, AZ, 1987-88

Wolthuis, Thomas
see list of ordained ministers

Won, Timothy S.
Assistant pastor, Garden of Grace, Westminster, CA, 2000–

Wong, Kinfun
see list of ordained ministers

Woods, John
Ministry, Community of Meadowvale, Mississauga, ON, 1989–99

Worster, Paul C. III
Volunteer ministries/New Members, Sunshine, Grand Rapids, MI, 1996–

Woudstra, Andrew
Minister of education and youth, Barrie, ON, 1978–79

Witvloed, George
Director of Ministries, Zion, Oshawa, ON, 1989–90

Wybenga, Thomas J.
Youth/Young Adults, First, Bellflower, CA, 1993–94

Wynia, Bonny
CRC Publications, Grand Rapids, MI, 1985–94; Di-

rector, Teen/Children's ministries, Madison Square, Grand Rapids, MI, 1994–2001

Wynstra, Carolyn
Director of evangelism, Sonlight Community, Lynden, WA, 1990–91

Yang, Houa
see list of ordained ministers

Yang, Kyung Sun
Ministry, West Bethel Korean, Los Angeles, CA, 1991–94

Yazzie, Sampson
Bethel, Shiprock, NM, 1951–57, 1960–65

Yett, Mr/Mrs L.
Service home, San Diego, CA, 1969–70

Ybarra, Jose
Monte Sion, San Diego, CA, 2000–

Yi, Andrew Y.
see list of ordained ministers

Yong, Greg
Bethel, Sun Valley, CA, 1999–

Yong, Woo Shik
Director of education and evangelism, Korean American of Orange County, Fountain Valley, CA, 1990–91

Yonker, Maleeta
Christian service worker, Emmanuel, Sauk Village, IL, 1985–86

Yonker, William
Jewish Mission/Nathaneal Institute, Chicago, IL, 1925–53

Youngs, George R.
see list of ordained ministers

Youngsma, N.
Helping Hand, Chicago, IL, 1939–48, Madison Street Mission, Chicago, IL, 1945–46

Yu, Danny Kwok Leung
Crenshaw, Los Angeles, CA, 1976–79

Zabiskie, Astrid M.
Administrator, Faith Community, Wycoff, NJ, 1990–91

Zandee, Rhea
Women's and children's ministry, Alger Park,
Grand Rapids, MI, 1989-90

Zandstra, Sharon
Long-term volunteer, First, Wellsburg, IA, 1978-80

Zapata, Hernan
Good Shepherd, Prospect Park, NJ, 1997-99;
Campus ministry, Paterson, NJ, 2001-

Zekuelo, Tony
Youth counselor, Marantha, Woodstock, ON, 1987-
88

Zevalking, John
see list of ordained ministers

Zierhof, David A.
The King's Church, Port St. Lucie, FL, 1987-88

Zubia, Lupe
Social worker, Sun Valley Community, Denver, CO,
1985-91

Zuidema, John
Fruitport, MI, 1944-51

Zuidema, Joel
see list of ordained ministers

Zuidema, John A./Catherine
Newman, New Era, MI, 1972-79; McCallum
Chapel, Fremont, MI, 1975-76; Christ Community
Chapel, North Muskegon, MI, 1979-80

Zylstra, David
Kent County Juvenile Home, Grand Rapids, MI,
1958-60

Zylstra, Ken
Youth leader, First, Artesia, CA, 1989-94; Youth,
First, Abbotsford, BC, 1994-

Zylstra, Wilbur
Brookmark Sunday School, Grand Rapids, MI,
1962-63

BACK TO GOD HOUR BROADCAST STAFF

Atallah, Victor, 1983–85
Atmarumeska, Junus, 1969–2001
Boonstra, Juan S., 1965–92
Bremer, Calvin L., 1996–
Bruinooge, Henry, 1974–91
De Boer, Wayne, 1987–90
Den Dulk, James, 1955–56
Dykstra, Don, 1949–79
Eldersveld, Peter H., 1946–65
Feddes, David J., 1990–
Ferreira, Wilson Carlos, 1976–80
Gama, Celsino, 1981–
Heringa, Lucile, 1956–79
Ishii, Shojiro, 1981–98
Jen, Isaac I.C., 1973–98
Kayayan, Aaron R., 1969–95
Kuiper, Alice, 1960–79
Kuiper, John, 1952–71
Kuyers, John A., 1994–2000
Lin, Jimmy T., 1991–
Madany, Bassam M., 1958–94
Mpindi, Paul Mbunga, 1999–
Nederhood, Joel H., 1960–96
Ongkowidjaja, Untung, 2001–
Rusticus, Roland, 1986
Serrano, Guillermo A., 1991–
Slagter, Ira A., 1982–87
Sossedkine, Serguei, 1997–
Van Milligan, Peter, 1963–79
Vander Meer, Harry J., 1978–80
Vander Ploeg, David, 1988–93
Vreeman, Jerry H., 1977–83
Yamashita, Masao, 1999–
Yassa, Nasser, 1993–1995

Calvin Theological Seminary

Administration

Brink, Emily, 1987–
Hart, Dirk J., 1987–
Kim, John-Taek, 1994–98
Veenhof, Jan, 1996–97
Witvliet, John D., 1997–

Faculty

Avila, Mariano, 2001–
Bandstra, Andrew J., 1964–92
Bekker, Gary J., 1995–2001
Berkhof, Louis, 1906–44
Beuker, Hendricus, 1894–1900
Bierma, Lyle D., 1996–
Boer, Geert E., 1876–1902
Boer, Harry R., 1951–52
Bolt, John, 1988–
Boonstra, Harry, 1989–2000
Bosma, Carl J., 1990–
Bouma, Clarence, 1924–52
Byker, Donald E., 1999–
Cooper, John W., 1985–
De Jong, Gabriel D., 1893–94, 1908–14
De Jong, James A., 1983–
De Jong, Peter Y., 1964–70
Dekker, Harold, 1956–87
De Moor, Henry, 1986–
Deppe, Dean B., 1990–91, 1998–
De Ridder, Richard R., 1973–86
De Vries, Robert C., 1987–
Engelhard, David H., 1970–94
Feenstra, Ronald J., 1992–
Fields, Paul W., 1990–
Gamble, Richard C., 1987–97
Greenway, Roger S., 1987–2001
Greidanus, Sidney, 1990–
Hemkes, Gerrit K., 1883–1908
Hendriksen, William, 1943–52
Heyns, William W., 1902–26
Hoekema, Anthony A., 1958–78
Holwerda, David E., 1984–98

Hugen, Melvin D., 1970–98
Janssen, Ralph, 1902–06, 1914–22
Kelderman, Duane K., 2001–
Klooster, Fred H., 1953–88
Kromminga, Carl G., 1954–90
Kromminga, Diedrich H., 1928–47
Kromminga, John H., 1952–83
Kuiper, Barend K., 1926–28
Kuiper, Herman, 1953–58
Kuiper, Rienk B., 1952–56
Leder, Arie C., 1987–
Minnema, Theodore, 1974–91
Monsma, Martin, 1953–64
Muller, Richard A., 1992–
Nydam, Ronald J., 1998–
Plantinga, Cornelius Jr., 1979–96, 2002–
Praamsma, Louis, 1962–63
Recker, Robert R., 1967–88
Rylaarsdam, David M., 2001–
Rutgers, William H., 1944–52
Schemper, Lugene L., 2000–
Schultze, Henry, 1926–40, 1951–59
Snapper, J. Marion, 1974–87
Stek, John H., 1961–91
Stob, George, 1948–52
Stob, Henry, 1952–75
Stob, Ralph, 1953–64
Sytsma, Richard E., 2000–
Tanis, Keith W., 1990–1999
Ten Hoor, Foppe M., 1900–24
Tucker, Ruth A., 2000–
Tuit, Pieter, 2000–
Vander Lugt, John, 1976–
Van Dyk, Wilbert M., 1985–95
Van Elderen, Bastiaan Jr., 1959–84
Van Gelder, Craig E., 1988–98
Van Leeuwen, Raymond C., 1985–90
Van Reken, Calvin P., 1989–
Volbeda, Samuel, 1914–52
Vos, Gerhardus, 1888–93
Weima, Jeffrey A.D., 1992–

Williams, Michael J., 1995–
Woudstra, Marten H., 1955–85
Wyngaarden, Martin J., 1924–61
Zwaanstra, Henry, 1965–2001

CALVIN COLLEGE

* Includes only full-year, full-time appointments

Administration

Alderink, Robert, 1987–
Anema, Joy (Marilyn E.) DeBoer, 1979–
Anema, Samuel, 1972–
Baas, Brian, 1979–
Baas, John M., 1993–
Baas, Kenneth J., 1991–94
Baker, Josephine, 1931–64
Bellows, Constance A., 1989–
Berg, Rhonda, 1989–2001
Berkhof, Robert A., 1987–
Bielema, John R., 2000–
Blanke, Emery, 1967–71
Blocksma, Douglas, 1955–58
Boender, Donald L., 1967–98
Boer, Warren J., 1969–2000
Boer, William J., 1987–91
Booker, Rhae-Ann, 1991–
Boonstra, Harry, 1989–99
Bootsma, Kenneth Bernard, 1974–77
Bos, Jodi R., 1998–
Brasser, Jane M., 1988–89
Brink, Arnold, 1947–53
Broene, Johannes, 1925–30, 1939–40
Bruinsma, Grace H., 1944–47
Bult, Conrad, 1965–99
Bush, Dawn C., 1986–
Buursma, Bruce, 1991–94
Buursma, Randall J., 1990–
Buurstra, Annette, 1953–68
Byker, Gaylen J., 1995–
Carpenter, Joel A., 1996–
Cooper, Dale, 1976–
Crow, C. Robert, 1987–89, 1998–
de Haan, Philip, 1988–
De Jong, Jeanette Bult, 1973–98
De Koster, Lester, 1959–68
De Mey, Kathleen L., 1999–
De Roo, Carlene G., 1961–62
DeVries, Henry E., 1996–
Diekema, Anthony J., 1976–95

Diephouse, Evelyn, 1980–94
Distelberg, Donald G., 1977–86
Doornbos, Robert J., 1982–96
Duyst, Johanna, 1977–96
Dykstra, Gladys May, 1962–63
Dykstra, Linda Hertel, 1968–71
Ellens, S. Dean, 1987–97
Ellens, Sharon T., 1989–
Emerson, Allen W., 1986–95
Eppinga, Judith, 1982–98
Eppinga, Richard J., 1979–84
Faber, Harry, 1967–77
Feldkamp, Mark R., 1992–96
Fetzer, Tamara, 1991–
Fields, Paul W., 1990–
Gamble, Richard C., 1987–97
Guikema, Dale J., 1991–97
Guthrie, David S., 1992–98
Harkema, Peter M., 1991–95
Harms, Richard H., 1998–
Heerspink, Janice B., 1981–
Heerspink, John C., 1980–91
Heffner, Gail, 1994–
Heffner, Kenneth W., 1993–
Hendriksma, Jane E., 1994–
Hiemenga, John J., 1919–25
Hoekenga, James P., 1965–79
Hollebeek, James M., 1980–88
Hoogstra, Shirley Vogelzang, 1999–
Hubers, Todd K., 1994–
Ippel, Lester, 1949–1987
Joosse, Anamarie L., 1978–
Kerestly, C. Edward, 1998–
Kok, Cynthia J., 2001–
Konyndyk, Lois J., 1967–68, 1991–
Kool, Preston, 1969–72
Kraai, James L., 1997–2000
Kuilema, Robert J., 1996–
Kuiper, Dale K., 1984–
Kuiper, Rienk B., 1930–33
Laarman, Joan R., 1976–78

Lambers, Stephen L., 1969-92
Lautenbach, Donald, 1965-91
Lewis, Francene L., 1992-
Lohman, Todd, 1988-
Lumpkins, Elias, 1972-76
MacKenzie, James A., 1995-
Male, Margaret A., 1998-
McWhertor, Thomas E., 1991-
Meyering, Darlene, 1991-
Monsma, Ellen B., 1998-
Monsma, Marjorie, 1953-56
Monsma, Marvin E., 1965-97
Morrison, Beverly H., 1979-
Mullins, Judith D., 1977-79
Myers, Robert L., 1996-
Nielsen, Cheryl L., 1991-97
Nieuwsma, Randall G., 1979-
Ornee, Nell, 1955-57
Pekelder, Bernard E., 1962-85
Pels, Grace, 1939-1944
Pluymert, Jeffrey A., 1994-
Prince, David J., 1989-92
Quist, James H., 1987-2001
Reed, Robert, 1985-2001
Regnerus, Mark D., 2001-
Remelts, Glenn A., 1990-
Rhoden, Sherry, 1988-91
Sammons, Dana L., 1996-2000
Schemper, Lugene L., 2000-
Schultze, Henry, 1940-51
Sennema, Gregory, 1999-
Sluiter, Barbara, 1951-92
Smartt, Rueben R., 1970-76
Spoelhoff, William, 1951-76
Steele, Gerald W., 1996-
Steenwyk, Annette, 1971-82
Steenwyk, Thomas L., 1989-
Stob, Jeffrey A., 1991-
Stob, Ralph, 1933-1939
Stob, William K., 1970-92
Strikwerda, Madge, 1968-90
Stronks, William J., 1993-97
Swets, Patricia, 1969-70
Timmer, Edward, 1978-92
Timmer, Jay, 1977-98
Timmer, Johanna, 1926-39
Trap, Ann Minnema, 1963-70
Triezenberg, Glenn E., 1988-
Twight, Willemina, 1953-55
Vande Guchte, Peter, 1963-97
Van Denend, Michael J., 1984-
Vander Ark, Mark, 1977-80
Vander Ploeg, Sally J., 1999-
Vander Pol, Diane D., 1992-
Vander Yacht, Douglas L., 1989-98

Van Eck, Thomas, 1998-
Van Laar, Myrtle, 1965-70
Van Opynen, Catherine W., 1947-72
VerMerris, Nancy, 1965-67, 1999-
Vertregt, Elizabeth, 1928-31
Verwolf, John W., 1979-93
Vredevoogd, Carolyn L. (RN), 1956-61
Wassink, Kurt L., 1997-2000
Williams, Eric, 1988-89
Wolthuis, Dawn M, 1989-96
Wolthuis, Randall L., 2000-
Youngsma, Sydney T., 1952-74
Zuiderveen, Gretchen, 1971-73
Zwart, Lavonne M., 1998-

Faculty

Aay, Henk, 1982-
Abadeer, Adel S., 1999-
Adams, Gerry A., 1983-87
Adams, Joel C., 1989-
Adams, John C., 1968-68
Afman, Gregg H., 1988-
Albers, Robert J., 1972-85
Allen, Henry L., 1987-91
Anderson, Michael, 1986-90
André, Calvin, 1952-55
Anker, Roy M, 1988-
Ankney, Rachelle M, 2001-
Aring, Kenneth, 1970-71
Ariza, Sandra K., 1975-83
Armstrong, Anton E., 1980-90
Arnoys, Eric J., 1999-
Attebury, Donald, 1997-
Bailey, Marcia L., 1988-90
Bailey, Michael E., 1997-98
Baker, Cynthia, 1988-91
Baker, Janice F., 1972-73
Baker, John H., 1964-65
Baker, Judith A., 1994-
Bakker, Conrad Q., 1996-2001
Bakker, Debra L., 1994-
Bakker, Martinus A., 1981-97
Baldwin Allan, Claude-Marie, 1971-83
Bandstra, Andrew, 1957-63
Banks, Betty S., 1993-96
Banstra, James, 1983-84
Baron, Henry J., 1968-97
Barret, Justin L., 1997-2000
Bascom, Johnathan, 2000-
Basney, Lionel, 1985-99
Basson, Andre F., 1996-97
Bays, Daniel H., 2000-
Beebe, John D., 1969-
Belleville, Linda L., 1986-89
Bendroth, Margaret Lamberts, 1998-

Bengelink, Henry, 1947-78
Bennink, Carl D., 1978-82
Benthem, James A., 1976-80
Berends, Kurt O., 1999-2000
Berghuis, Melvin E., 1948-81
Bergsma, Jerry G., 1996-
Bergwerff, Kenneth A., 2001-
Berkhof, Louis, 1906-25
Berkhout, Peter G., 1924-26
Besselsen, Gilbert, 1969-82
Beuker, Henricus, 1894-1900
Beversluis, Claudia D., 1991-
Beversluis, Eric H., 1980-83
Beversluis, John, 1961-62
Beversluis, Nicholas H., 1966-80
Bierling, Marilyn R., 1984-
Bijkerk, Roelof Jan, 1958-70
Billings, David A., 2000-
Blankespoor, Betty, 1966-67
Blankespoor, Curtis L., 1994-
Blankespoor, Ronald L., 1977-
Block, Wayne E., 1991-92
Blok, Kathryn, 1969-89
Blystra, Andrew R., 1994-99
Bobbitt, William R., 1980-81
Boer, Geert E., 1876-1902
Boersma, Clarence, 1948-74
Boesak, Allan A., 1980-81
Boevé, Edgar G., 1958-91
Boevé, Ervina Van Dyke, 1954-90
Bolt, Eunice, 1966-67
Bolt, John, 1980-82
Bolt, Martin, 1970-
Bolt, Robert, 1965-95
Bolt, T. Macyn, 1981-85
Bonnema, Joy D., 1997-
Bontekoe, Jon, 1970-71
Bonzelaar, Helen Joldersma, 1967-2001
Boomsma, Shirley Balk, 1950-55
Boonstra, Paul H., 1965-87
Bordewyk, Gordon L., 1980-83
Borst, Marilyn J., 1980-81
Bos, Bert P., 1961-71
Bos, John R., 1925-28
Boscaljon, Brian L., 1996-99
Bosma, Bette D., 1976-92
Bosma, Nelly J., 1966-70
Bosscher, James Peter, 1954-87
Bosscher, Robert A., 1966-72
Boss-Potts, Renae L., 2001-
Botha, Elaine M., 1978-79
Bouma, Donald H., 1946-60
Bouma, Hessel III, 1978-
Bradley, James, 1986-
Brandsen, Cheryl, 1989-

Brant, Dale E., 1995-96
Brashler, Lenore R., 1967-69
Bratt, Albertus D., 1958-98
Bratt, James D., 1987-
Bratt, John H., 1946-76
Bratt, Kenneth D., 1977-
Bratt, Wallace Henry, 1958-97
Braun, John E., 1966-68
Brink, Daryl M., 1974-
Brink, John H., 1974-
Brinks, Herbert J., 1962-95
Brinks, Steven M., 1992-93
Broene, Albert E., 1903-46
Broene, Herman H., 1956-84
Broene, Johannes, 1908-46
Brogan, John, 1995-97
Brooks, David C., 1979-80
Brothers, Jack E., 1983-88
Brouwer, Fred E., 1956-57
Brouwer, Helen H., 1956-57
Brouwer, Jeffrey E., 1997-98
Brouwer, Randall J., 1991-
Brouwer, Tony, 1957-1971
Brown, W. Dale, 1987-
Brownsen, James V., 1988-89
Bruinsma, Henry A., 1947-55
Bullock, Virginia, 1982-99
Bult, John C., 1945-52
Bultje, Marjorie J., 1981-83
Burden, Linda, 1990-91
Buter, Gordon, 1941-55
Butler, Robert C., 1999-2001
Buursma, Randall J., 1990-
Byam, Ynes M., 1975-93
Byker, Donald, 1962-66
Byker, Winnifred N., 1960-65
Bytwerk, Randall L., 1985-
Cannon, Joel W., 1989-92
Cardoso-Meekhof, Dinora Caridad, 1988-91
Carpenter, Joel A., 1976-77
Carvill, Barbara M., 1977-
Chadburn, Nancy L., 1979-80
Christians, Clifford G., 1983-84
Chumbley, Robert Emmett III, 1988-89
Clark, James A., 1982-97
Clark, Kelly J., 1989-
Class, Bradley M., 1977-85
Clevenger, Sandra K., 1975-
Cloete, Gerhard Daniel, 1984-85
Cook, David A., 1985-
Cooper, John W., 1980-85
Corcoran, Kevin J., 1997-
Cornelisse, Melanie Lynn Gesink, 2001-
Cornelisse, William, 1920-27, 1930-35
Cortina, Elsa, 1965-90

Cox, John D., 1983–84
Crump, David M., 1997–
Curry, Janel M., 1996–
Czanko, James, 1966–69
Dahm, John J. Jr., 1963–64
Daling, John T., 1945–74
Danford, Cloe A., 1982–86
Davis, Abraham K., 1987–88
Davis, William C., 1992–93
Davison, Scott A., 1993–94
De Beer, John L., 1948–77
De Bie, John, 1956–72
De Blaey, Gordon L., 1970–2001
De Boe, James B., 1985–86, 1995–97
De Boer, Cecil, 1950–55
De Boer, Jesse, 1935–38
De Boer, Lisa J., 1998–99
De Boer, Peter P., 1962–95
De Boer, Willis P., 1962–88
De Borst, James H., 1964–92
De Bruin, Robert L., 1967–69
De Graaf, Donald G., 1998–
de Groot, Christiana, 1979–80, 1988–
Dehaan, Laura G., 2001–
De Haan, Sander, 1976–79
De Heer, David H., 1985–
De Jong, Fred J., 1998–
De Jong, Gabriel D., 1908–14
De Jong, Jack C. Jr., 1978–80
De Jong, Peter Y., 1969–
De Jong, Richard G., 1987–
De Jong, Terrence M., 1973–74
De Jonge, James J., 1947–76
Dekker, Harold, 1941–46, 1954–56
Dekker, Harry G., 1921–58
De Kock, Roger L., 1976–
De Koster, Lester, 1951–59
De Lange, Leon W., 1978–86
Dengler, Mary J., 1995–97
Den Hartog, Anastasia, 1967–70
Den Hartog, Gerrit L., 1967–70
Dennison, William D., 1990–91
De Rooy, Leonard P., 1999–
Dersch, John A. Jr., 1980–83
De Torro, Berta, 1966–67
De Vos, Peter A., 1965–90
de Vries, Bert, 1967–
De Vries, Claudia L., 1974–75
De Vries, Herman J. Jr., 1997–
De Vries, John, 1939–67
De Vries, Rick E., 1994–
De Vries, Robert Lee, 1964–
De Vries, Tiemen, 1913–14
De Vries, Walter, 1955–56, 1959–62
De Wall, Marilou, 1962–64

De Wit, Henry, 1953–88
De Witt, Calvin, 1958–59
De Young, Derald D., 1978–
De Young, Gary W., 1994–95
De Young, Rebecca L. Konyndyk, 1998–
Diekema, Douglas S., 1985–86
Diephouse, David J., 1976–
Diepstra, Stephene A., 2001–
Dirkse, Steven P., 1994–95
Dirkse, Thedford P., 1947–80
Dodge, John W., 1980–92
Doezema, William R., 1990–91
Doorn, Arlene, 1955–56
Doornbos, Mary Molewyk, 1983–
Douma, Edward R., 1984–85
Dozeman, Thomas B., 1986–88
Dragt, Alexander J., 2001–
Driessenga, Esther F., 1978–82
Driscoll, Mariam C., 1994–96
Drost, Richard, 1939–61
Duimstra, Betty, 1955–58
Dunbar, David L., 1976–80
Dunch, Ryan F., 1996–98
Dunn, Susan, 1999–
Dykema, Eugene R., 1973–93
Dykema-VanderArk, Anthony M., 1999–
Dyksen, Wayne, 1982–84
Dykstra-Pruim, Pennylyn, 2000–
Ebels, Daniel M., 1977–83
Echeverria, Eduardo Jose, 1988–90
Ehlers, Vernon J., 1966–83
Eisch, Robert, 1998–
Engbers, Chad A., 2001–
Entingh, Daniel, 1968–69
Entingh, Thressa, 1968–69
Ericson, Edward E. Jr., 1977–
Ermer, Gayle E., 1994–
Escobar, Samuel, 1983–84
Eshelman, Mark, 1993–94
Etheridge, Sharon A., 1987–
Etter, Robert Terrance, 2000–
Evans, C. Stephen, 1994–
Evans, Jan E., 1994–
Eves, Terry L., 1985–92
Faber, J. Arthur, 1961–62, 1966–66
Faber, Jacob, 1962–63
Faber, Paul W., 1978–79
Faber, Richard G., 1995–96
Faber, Roger J., 1959–65
Fackler, Mark, 1998–
Farhadian, Charles, 2001–
Feenstra, Cheryl J., 1989–
Feikema, Brenda S., 1996–
Felch, Susan M., 1992–
Ferdinands, Ronald J., 1988–

Feringa, Harold W., 1962–63
Fessler, Paul R., 1997–98
Fetzer, Glenn W., 1987–
Fife, Earl D., 1988–
Fischer, Barrett II, 1987–88
Fleetham, Deborah L., 1997–2000
Flikkema, Eltjen J., 1968–70
Flikkema, Mary E., 1988–
Flokstra, Lambert J., 1927–65
Floyd, Shawn D., 1997–99
Fondse, Gerard Jr., 1999–
Fortner, Robert S., 1989–
Freeberg, Debra L., 1991–
Frens, Jeremy D., 2000–
Fridsma, Bernard, 1946–70
Fuentes, David R., 1998–
Gall, Kimerly, 1997–
Gallagher, Susan V., 1986–97
Gebben, Allen I., 1955–93
Geerdes, Harold, 1955–79
George, Ivy, 1987–88
George, Tamara, 1999–
Goetz, Margaret J., 1999–
Goi, Simona, 1997–
Gormas, Janice S., 1998–
Gray, Terry M., 1986–97
Greenway, Edna C., 1986–2001
Greidanus, Sidney, 1978–79
Greidanus-Probes, Anna, 1988–
Greydanus, Samuel, 1967–88
Griffioen, Arie J., 1992–
Griffioen, Roger D., 1961–99
Griffis, Nelson G., 1995–98
Gritter, Marianne, 1987–91
Groen, Gerrit D., 1964–66
Groenendyk, Kathi L., 1998–
Groenhout, Ruth E., 1996–
Gsell, Ray A., 1986–1986
Gunnoe, Charles D., 1996–99
Gunnoe, Marjorie L., 1996–
Gustafson, Mark T., 1995–
Haan, Sharon, 1966–1969
Haan, Stanley L., 1983–
Haarsma, Deborah B., 1999–
Haarsma, Loren D., 1999–
Hageman, Dolores, 1971–79
Hakkenberg, Michael A., 1988–90
Hamersma, John E., 1954–
Hamilton, Joseph, 1965–66
Hanisch, Mark R., 1998–
Harding, Karalee S., 1997–2000
Hardy, Lee P., 1981–
Hare, John E., 1989–
Harlow, Daniel C., 1999–
Harper, George Graham "Tom," 1952–89

Harper, Paul E., 2000–
Harris, George, 1959–95
Harwood, Morton H., 1985–86
Hasseler, Susan K., 1995–
Hegewald, Cornelius P., 1965–93
Heid, Christy A., 2000–01
Hekman, H. George, 1968–70
Hemkes, Gerrit K., 1883–1905
Hendricks, William C., 1963–79
Henry, Paul B., 1970–79
Hernández, Alannah A., 2001–
Herzberg, Lawrence R., 1989–
Hess, Deborah, 1966–67
Hesselink, Paul K., 1983–84
Hettinga, Donald R., 1984–
Hewitt, John D., 1997–99
Heynen, James, 1969–71
Heyns, William, 1901–25
Hietbrink, Mary, 1976–77
Hiskes, Mark S., 2000–01
Hoag, Jennifer Steensma, 1995–
Hodgkins, Christopher T., 1989–91
Hoekema, Anthony A., 1939–41, 1956–58
Hoekema, David A., 1974–75, 1992–
Hoekema, Gerald, 1981–82
Hoeks, Henry J., 1961–62, 1969–93
Hoeksema, Robert J., 1977–
Hoeksema, Thomas B., 1975–
Hoekstra, Dennis, 1964–73
Hoekstra, Peter, 1918–54
Hoitenga, Dewey, 1977–78
Hoksbergen, Roland G., 1983–
Holberg, Jennifer L., 1998–
Holkeboer, Winifred, 1957–76
Hollingsworth, Kerry J., 1985–89
Holquist, David J., 1966–96
Holstege, Henry, 1957–97
Holtrop, Philip C., 1977–99
Holwerda, David E., 1963–84
Honderd, Ralph John, 1966–
Hoogewerf, Arlene J., 2000–
Hook, Harmon D., 1967–74
Hoolsema, Daniel J., 1995–
Hotz, Kendra G., 1998–
House, Donald R., 1981–87
Houseman, Mark E., 1984–85
Houseman, Melvin R., 1926–27
Houskamp, Richard E., 1978–83
Houts, Margo C., 1996–98
Howard, Douglas A., 1988–
Howell, Elizabeth A., 1995–
Hubbard, Robert J., 1996–
Hubers, Kathleen A., 1979–80
Hugen, Beryl L., 1997–
Huisman, Carl J., 1967–

Huizenga, Gertrude A., 1964-98
Huizinga, Todd M., 1988-89
Hull, Nancy L., 1999-
Ibe, James G., 1990-91
Icenhower, Jonathan P., 1996-97
Ippel, Henry, 1951-84
Jaarsma, Cornelius, 1947-65
Jadrich, James R., 1992-
Jager, Thomas L., 1974-
Jalkanen, Karl J., 1996-97
Janssen, Ralph, 1901-04, 1914-21
Jelks, Randal M., 1992-
Jellema, Dirk W., 1961-82
Jellema, William Harry, 1920-35, 1948-63
Jensen, Robert A., 1964-95
Jeong, Yousceek, 1994-97
Johnson, Bruce A., 1986-87
Johnson, Jeffrey S., 1989-91
Johnson, Lloyd Carl, 1990-97
Joldersma, Clarence W., 1995-
Joldersma, Hermina, 1980-81
Joosse, Wayne G., 1972-
Kain, Patrick P., 1999-2000
Kaiser, Carl W., 1977-99
Karppinen, Richard T., 1987-96
Karsten, Martin, 1946-75
Kass, Corrine E., 1963-66, 1979-93
Katerberg, William H., 1999-
Katte, Richard, 1958-59
Keegstra, Phillip B., 1987-89
Keeley, Robert, 1997-
Kemeny, Paul C., 1996-99
Kennedy, Thomas D., 1982-84
Kielinen, Cynthia E., 1981-89
Kim, Hyesook, 1991-
Kim, Jong-Il, 1997-
Kim, Seyoon, 1985-86
Kingma, Jan William, 1949-65
Kistemaker, Simon, 1957-58
Klassen, Gene A., 1984-89
Kleinhuizen, Lloyd, 1957-59
Klooster, Beverly J., 1961-2000
Klooster, David J., 1978-79
Klooster, Fred, 1953-56
Knol, Thelma, 1961-79
Knoppers, Annelies, 1968-74, 1989-90
Knoppers, Sherry M., 1996-
Koch, Margaret L., 1989-90
Koetje, David S., 1998-
Koning, Harold, 1967-69
Konyndyk, Irene, 1992-
Konyndyk, Kenneth J., 1967-94
Konyndyk, Roger D., 1977-80
Koole, Robert B., 1991-92
Koop, Allen H., 1989-2001

Koop, Janice B., 1989-
Koopman, Douglas L., 1995-
Korf, James D., 1980-
Krähenbühl, Lee E., 1994-95
Krajenbrink, Dirk Joe, 1965-68
Kraker, Myra J., 1985-
Kreuzer, Bernard, 1960-77
Kroeckel-Kiekover, Deborah A., 1991-99
Kroese, Irvin B., 1968-87
Kromminga, Albion J., 1965-97
Kuiper, Barend K., 1900-18
Kuiper, Carol M., 1988-89
Kuiper, James A., 1978-83
Kuiper, Kenneth W., 1963-95
Kuipers, Jack, 1967-86
Kuipers, Kenneth J., 1973-93
Kuipers, Louis, 1964-68
Lagerwey, Walter, 1953-83
Lalani, Judy M., 1999-2000
Lamse, James L., 1969-2000
Lamse, Mary J., 1979-82
Langerak, Edward, 1985-86
Lanning, Gale L., 1985-86
Laverell, W. David, 1984-
Lawson, Daniel, 1997-99
Leder, Olga H., 1999-
Lederle, Henry I., 1980-81
Lee, D. John, 1987-96
Lee, Won W., 1996-
Leegwater, Arie, 1977-
Leestma, Sanford C., 1968-
Leigh, Patricia D., 1994-
Lesage, Jasper, 1978-80
Libolt, Clayton, 1977-78
Lillis, John R., 1981-82
Lindskoog, Donald P., 1978-79
Livingston, David N., 1989-90
Lopez-Gonzaga, Voleta, 1986-87
Lorio, E. Goerge, 1985-87
Louters, Laurence L., 1984-
Loyd-Paige, Michelle R., 1985-
Lubbers, Ronald J., 1968-71
Lucar, Diane K., 1988-90
Lucasse, Philip R., 1956-69, 1971-91
Lugo, Luis E., 1988-96
Lundin, Roger W., 1982-83
Luttikhuizen, Henry M., 1991-
Lyon, David, 1982-83
Lyzenga, David R., 1968-69
Maag, Karin, 1997-
Manweiler, Robert, 1977-80
Marsden, George M., 1965-86
Marsman, Pieter, 1970-71
Mason, John D., 1988-89
Masson, Margaret J., 1988-92

Prince, Clarence E., 1983-84
Prins, Philip R., 1984-88
Prins, Tunis, 1961-73
Pronk, Dorothea Ariette, 1998-2000
Pruim, Randall J., 1998-
Pruis, Donald E., 1957-93
Pyper, Marcie J., 2000-
Radius, William T., 1933-72
Railsback, Rick D., 1993-95
Ramaker, David, 1974-75
Ramsbottom, John D., 1986-87
Ramsbottom, Mary M., 1986-87
Ratajeski, Kent, 1999-2000
Ratzsch, Delvin L., 1979-
Read, Lois A., 1970-1971
Reber, Douglas C., 1980-82
Reiter, David D., 1994-97
Reynolds, Alfred J., 1965-90
Reynolds, Lewis E.L., 1998-99
Ribeiro, Paulo Fernando, 2000-
Rice, Rodger R., 1964-69, 1972-2001
Richeson, Joseph Scott, 1999-
Rienstra, Debra K., 1996-
Rienstra, M. Howard, 1957-86
Rietberg, Dale R., 1980-85
Rietberg, Dean E., 1984-85
Rinck, William, 1905-20
Ritsema, Beth E., 1990-91
Ritsema, Robert A., 2001-
Roberts, Frank C., 1969-2001
Rodrigúez, Maria N., 2000-
Roelofs, Matthew R., 1996-97
Roels, Shirley J., 1979-
Romanowski, William D., 1988-
Rooks, Albertus J., 1894-1942
Rooks, James Kevin, 2001-
Rosenboom, Hanna, 1965-66
Roskamp, Michael J., 2001-
Rottman, Ellen, 1957-59
Rottman, Theodore A., 1956-94
Rozendal, Sandra L., 1994-2001
Rubingh, Darlene G., 1983-87
Runner, H. Evan, 1950-81
Rus, Louis C., 1960-63
Rus, Ruth K., 1978-91
Rutgers, Marilyn J., 1959-60
Ryskamp, Henry, 1918-64
Sandberg, Stephanie L., 1996-
Sanderson, William Ashman, 1970-89
Saupe, Karen, 1994-
Sawyer, Charsie Randolph, 1996-
Schaefer, Kurt C., 1987-
Scheerhorn, Mary, 2001-
Schierbeek, Donald J., 1983-84
Schimmrich, Steven H., 1998-99

Schipper, Timothy H., 1982-83
Schmidt, Gary D., 1985-
Schneider, John R., 1986-
Schoolland, Marian M. 1939-44
Schoolland, Klaas, 1894-23
Schultze, Quentin J., 1982-
Schutte, Kelli J., 1995-
Schutten, Mary C., 1989-2001
Schutter, Catherine Gallouet, 1980-81, 1982-83
Schuurman, Douglas, 1984-86
Schuurman Jr., Henry J., 1975-76
Schwander, Lissa M., 1999-
Schwartz, K. Marion, 1985-86
Scofield, Thomas L., 2000-
Selles, Kurt D., 1999-
Selles, Otto H., 1997-
Semple, Rhonda A., 2001-
Settergren, Robert G., 1946-52
Sevensma, Elisha S., 1904-05
Shangkuan, Pearl, 1998-
Shoemaker, Allen L., 1988-
Siebring, Barton, 1967-77
Sietsma, Debra L., 1999-
Sikkema, Edna, 1961-62
Simpson, Robert W., 1987-91
Sinke, Carl J., 1956-91
Sinniah, S. Kumar, 1995-
Sjoerdsma, Ronald J., 1991-
Slager, Raymond L., 1982-
Slagter, Cynthia G., 1993-
Slenk, Howard J., 1960-95
Slingerland, Gertrude, 1946-70
Smalligan, Donald H., 1968-89
Smart, Robert P., 1994-95
Smedes, Lewis, 1957-70
Smidt, Corwin E., 1977-
Smit, J. William, 1967-96
Smit, Laura A., 1999-
Smith, Cynthia J., 1982-83
Smith, David I., 2000-
Smith, Paul E., 1960-63
Snapper, J. Marion, 1960-87
Snapper, John N., 1978-83
Snow, Robert E., 1984-85
Snuttjer, David M., 1976-82
Snyder, David C., 1985-87
Speyers, Franklin D., 1988-
Spoelhof, William, 1946-51
Spoelman, Linda, 1975-79
Spoelman, Ronald J., 1969-70
Spykman, Gordon J., 1959-91
Staal, Arie, 1964-65
Stapert, Calvin R., 1969-
Stark, Mary Ann, 2000-01
Stearley, Ralph, 1992-

Steen, Barney, 1952-82
Steen, Todd P., 2001-
Steenwyk, Steven D., 1988-
Stegink, LeRoy D., 1975-
Stegink, Steven J., 1988-2000
Stehouwer, R. Scott, 1978-
Sterk, Andrea L., 1994-95
Sterk, Helen M., 1979-80, 1997-
Stevenson, William R. Jr., 1989-
Stob, Michael J., 1981-
Stob, Ralph, 1917-53
Storkey, Alan, 1980-81
Storm, Kathleen H., 1990-92
Stouwie, Roger J., 1972-94
Strikwerda, Charles E., 1976-78, 1979-2001
Strikwerda, Earl U., 1946-79
Stronks, Gloria Goris, 1985-2001
Stuart, William, 1923-25
Sudduth, Michael L., 1996-97
Sunshine, Glenn, 1993-95
Sweetman, Leonard Jr., 1964-89
Sweetman, Robert S., 1988-91
Swets, Seymour, 1923-67
Swets, Thomas L., 1968-70
Swierenga, Robert P., 1961-62, 1965-68
Szto, Peter P., 1994-99
Tagle, José A, 1969-71
Talsma, Gary W., 1976-
Tanis, Reona, 1960-61
Te Brake, Wayne, 1976-78
Teitsma, Larry, 1971-81
Tellinghuisen, Donald J., 2000-
Ten Broek, Bernard, 1955-89
Ten Cate, James A., 1984-85
Ten Harmsel, Henrietta, 1957-85
Ten Hoor, Foppe M., 1900-13
Ten Huisen, Dwight, 1996-
Terborg, Robert H., 1968-
Ter Haar, Cornelis, 1968-69
TerHaar, Teresa M., 2000-
Ter Molen, Janna L., 1987-93
Terris, Walter, 1957-60
Thiselton, Anthony Charles, 1982-83
Thomasma, Timothy D., 1978-79
Thompson, Thomas R., 1992-
Thornton, Larry P., 1985-86
Tiemersma, Richard R., 1955-83
Tiemstra, John P., 1975-
Tigchelaar, Alisa J., 1999-
Tigchelaar, Peter V., 1975-
Timmer, David E., 1979-80
Timmer, James R., 1970-
Timmer, Karen L., 1966-71
Timmer, Kathleen Mae, 1966-68
Timmerman, John H., 1977-

Timmerman, John J., 1945-75
Timmermans, Barbara, 1992-
Timmermans, Steven R., 1989-
Topp, G. Dale, 1967-
Traas, Debora Van Iderstine, 1980-81, 1988-91
Trap, Leonard, 1914-15
Triplett, Paula E., 2001-02
Tuls, John H., 1946-73
Turner, James Michael, 1999-
Tuuk, David Bruce, 1952-88
Ubels, John L., 1995-
Van Andel, Glen E., 1980-
Van Andel, Henry J.G., 1915-53
Van Antwerp, Jennifer Jewett, 1999-
Van Antwerp, Jeremy G., 1999-
Van Baak, David A., 1980-
Van Bruggen, John A., 1953-69
VandeBrake, Timothy R., 1999-
Vande Guchte, Marten, 1954-55, 1957-93
Vande Kieft, Ruth, 1947-50
Vande Kopple, William J., 1980-
Van Dellen, Elzo L., 1905-09
Vanden Berg, Jack, 1961-62
Vanden Berg, John, 1947-82
Vanden Berg, Susan J., 1986-94
Vanden Berg, Todd M., 1996-
Vanden Berg-Blom, Patricia, 1986-94
Vanden Berge, James C., 1959-61
Vanden Bosch, Bryan K., 2000-
Vanden Bosch, Jacob G., 1900-46
Vanden Bosch, James, 1983-
Vander Ark, Gertrude, 1960-74
Vander Berg, Jenniete T. Van Dellen, 1962-63, 1966-73
Vander Brug, Gordon J., 1968-70
Vander Goot, Henry, 1976-92
Vander Goot, Mary P., 1976-87
Vander Hart, Archie L., 1978-81
Van Der Heide, Evert M., 1982-
Vanderhill, Matthew, 1974-75
van der Hoeven, Johannes, 1970-71
Vander Kooi, Kora L., 1998-2000
Vander Kooi, Ronald C., 1970-78
Vander Laan, Karen J., 2001-
VanderLeest, Steven H., 1988-
Vander Lei, Elizabeth A., 1997-
Vander Linde, Scott H., 1985-
Vander Linden, Keith N., 1996-
Vander Lugt, Garrett, 1968-70
Vander Lugt, Leonard A., 1955-71
Vander Meulen, David Lee, 1976-77
Vander Molen, Ronald K., 1966-68
Vander Nat, Peter J., 1976-77
Vanderploeg, William S., 1976-77
VanDer Slik, Jack R., 1972-73

Vander Stoep, Scott W., 1996-99
Vander Veen, Steven K., 1989-
Vander Veen, Thomas D., 1995-96
Vander Wal, Marvin, 1983-94
Vander Weele, Ray, 1970-71
Van Der Weele, Steve J., 1950-87
Van der Wekken, Léonard, 1969-71
Vander Woude, Judith, 1994-
Vande Streek, Kevin N., 1996-
Van Dijk, Deanna, 1999-
Van Doorne, William, 1966-2001
Van Dragt, Randall G., 1975-76, 1981-
Van Dyke, Christina J., 2001-
Van Ee, Yvonne H., 1985-
Van Eerden, Ann-Marie, 1988-89
Van Elderen, Bastiaan, 1952-56
Van Engen, John, 1976-77
Van Enk, Richard, 1979-80
Van Haitsma, John P., 1909-54
Van Halsema, Brenda, 1976-82
Van Halsema, Emo F.J., 1923-25
Van Harn, Barbara A., 1988-89
Van Harn, Gordon Lee, 1961-99
Van Heukelem, Raymond F., 1972-73
Van Hook, Jay M., 1977-79
Van Houten, David E., 1966-68
Van Houten, Richard L., 1979-80
Van Kley, Dale, 1969-97
Van Kley, Edwin J., 1961-95
Van Kley, Marlene R., 1959-61
Van Koevering, David B., 1983-84
Van Laar, Helen, 1947-64
Van Laar, Timothy J., 1977-81
Van Leeuwen, Mary Stewart, 1985-93
Van Leeuwen, Raymond C., 1982-85, 1990-94
van Liere, Frans A., 1998-
van Liere, Katherine Elliot, 1998-
Van Noord, Nancy Lynn, 1976-
Van Nuis, Hermine J., 1966-67
Van Opynen, Catherine, 1946-72
Van Poolen, Lambert J., 1968-
Van Reeuwyk, Jo-Ann P., 2001-
Van Solkema, Sherman, 1955-61
Van't Hof, Ellen R., 1976-
Van't Hul, Bernard, 1959-60, 1964-69
Van Til, Henry R., 1945-61
Van Till, Howard J., 1967-98
Van Vugt, Ernest, 1955-87
Van Vugt, William E., 1986-
Van Wyk, Lourens A., 1979-80
Van Zwalenberg, George, 1960-97
Van Zwoll, Cornelius, 1956-59
Van Zyl, Henry, 1923-53
Van Zytveld, John B., 1969-97
Veenstra, Jeffrey John, 2001-

Veldkamp, Arnold H., 1966-68
Vellenga, David B., 1996-98
Venema, Gerard, 1979-
Ver Beek, Kurt A., 1996-
Verbrugge, Rita M., 1983-86
Verhey, Allen, 1985-86
Vermeer, Margaret J. De Boer, 1966-69
VerMeulen, Carol Lamberts, 1990-92
Viehl, Marjorie Petzing, 1991-97
Vierzen Wierenga, Wilma, 1968-69, 1970-71, 1976-77
Vila, David W., 1957-75
Villalta, Pablo, 2000-01
Volbeda, Samuel, 1914-16, 1921-23
Vos, Arvin G., 1980-81
Vos, Clarence J., 1961-85
Vos, Claude-Marie Baldwin, 1968-97
Vos, Gerhardus, 1888-93
Vos, Louis A., 1965-95
Vos, May (Meintje) B., 1962-63
Vos, Nelvin, 1957-59
Vos-Camy, Jolene E., 1997-
Voskuil, Julie A., 2000-
Vredeveld, Lon M., 1978-80
Vredevoogd, Jene K., 1968-69
Vriend, David J., 1978-79
Vroon, Anthony D., 1959-97
Vryhof, Steven C., 1990-91
Wagstrom, Rikki Bryanna, 1999-
Wagstrom, Thor A., 1999-
Wahby, Wafeek S., 1996-98
Walhof, Darren R., 2000-01
Walhout, Clarence P., 1969-97
Walhout, Matthew S., 1996-
Walker, Frederic R., 1970-73
Wallace, Kay, 2001-
Walters, Keith A., 1999-
Walters, Mary A., 1962-2001
Walton, Julie A., 1999-
Ward, Dean A., 1987-
Warners, Amber L., 1996-
Warners, David P., 1997-
Warners, John D., 1984-85
Wassenaar, John D., 1977-78
Wassink, Harry J., 1931-65
Weaver, Glenn D., 1975-
Weeda, Thomas, 1990-92
Weidenaar, John, 1947-64
Wells, Ronald A., 1969-
Wentzheimer, W. Wayne, 1998-
Westmaas, Richard, 1957-64
Westmaas, Wesley V., 1985-86
Westra, Dorothy, 1967-84
Westra, Helen P., 1988-89
Westra, Johan G., 1958-97

Westra, Lois A., 1964–70
Wevers, Richard F., 1962–96
Wheeler, Margaret J., 1995–
White, James B., 1981–85
Whitekettle, Richard, 1994–
Wierenga, Edward R., 1975–76
Wiersma, Jack, 1968–97
Wiersma, Stanley, 1958–86
Wilkins, James D., 1989–97
Williams, Mark F., 1987–
Willms, N. Bradley, 1995–97
Wilson, Donald R., 1962–96
Wingard, John C. Jr., 1997–99
Winkle, Jeffrey T., 2000–
Winters, Carol J., 1986–89
Winzenz, David J., 1971–73
Witvliet, John D., 1997–
Wolinski, Jeffrey, 1996–99
Wolters, Karla Hoesch, 1974–87
Wolterstorff, Nicholas P., 1959–81
Wolthuis, Dawn M., 1980–82
Wolthuis, Enno, 1949–77
Wolthuis, Thomas R., 2000–01
Worst, John W., 1966–99
Woudstra, Sierd, 1959–60, 1978–79
Wykstra, Stephen J., 1984–
Wyngarden, Kathy, 2001–
Ye, Ziang-Dong, 1987–98
Yff, Esther, 1979–79
Young, Charles R. III, 1983–
Young, Davis A., 1978–
Youngs, G. Roderick, 1965–76
Zandee, Gail L., 1993–99
Zandstra, Dianne M., 1988–
Zegers, John E., 1960–62
Zimmerman, Laura L., 1979–80
Zoetewey, James, 1963–64
Zuidema, Doris J., 1963–96
Zuidema, Marvin A., 1961–
Zuidervaart, Lambert P., 1985–
Zwaanstra, Mary E., 1990–98
Zwart, John W., 1991–92
Zweir, Timothy S., 1983–88
Zwier, Paul J., 1960–95
Zylstra, Henry, 1938–56
Zylstra, Mildred R., 1962–76
Zylstra, Uko, 1976–

Synods

From 1857 to 1865 the highest governing body in the denomination was the classical assembly. Once a second classis was formed in 1865, a higher governing body, the general assembly, was formed to adjudicate questions beyond the scope of the classes. In 1880 the general assembly was renamed the synod. Below is a listing of the meeting of these governing bodies, the location of the meeting and the presiding officer. The classis met several times per year, while the general assembly/synod met annually or bi-annually.

February 1857
in Holland, MI
Hendrik Klijn presiding (No records extant)

October 1857
in Vriesland, MI
Koenraad Van den Bosch presiding

February 1858
in Grand Rapids, MI
Gijsbert Haan presiding

October 1858
in Noordeloos, MI
Koenraad Van den Bosch presiding

February 1859
in Grand Rapids, MI
Gijsbert Haan presiding

June 1859
in Vriesland, MI
H.W. Dam presiding

October 1859
in Graafschap, MI
Koenraad Van den Bosch presiding

February 1860
in Grand Rapids, MI
Koenraad Van den Bosch presiding

June 1860
in Vriesland, MI
Koenraad Van den Bosch presiding

October 1860
in Graafschap, MI
Koenraad Van den Bosch presiding

February 1861
in Grand Rapids, MI
Koenraad Van den Bosch presiding

April 1861
(special session), in Grand Rapids, MI
Koenraad Van den Bosch presiding

June 1861
in Vriesland, MI
Koenraad Van den Bosch presiding

February 1862
in Graafschap, MI
Koenraad Van den Bosch presiding

June 1862
  in Graafschap, MI
    Koenraad Van den Bosch presiding

October 1862
  in Grand Rapids, MI
    Koenraad Van den Bosch presiding

February 1863
  in Graafschap, MI
    Koenraad Van den Bosch presiding

July 1863
  in Zeeland, MI
    Wilhelmus H. Van Leeuwen presiding

October 1863
  in Grand Rapids, MI
    Koenraad Van den Bosch presiding

February 1864
  in Graafschap, MI
    Wilhelmus H. Van Leeuwen presiding

June 1864
  in Vriesland, MI
    Koenraad Van den Bosch presiding

August 1864
  in Noordeloos, MI
    Wilhelmus H. Van Leeuwen presiding

October 1864
  in Graafschap, MI
    Koenraad Van den Bosch presiding

January 1865
  in Zeeland, MI
    Douwe J. Van der Werp presiding

April 1865
  in Grand Rapids, MI
    Wilhelmus H. Van Leeuwen presiding

June 1865
  in Vriesland, MI
    Koenraad Van den Bosch presiding

1865
  in Graafschap, MI
    Douwe J. Van der Werp presiding

1866
  in Grand Rapids, MI
    Douwe J. Van der Werp presiding

1867
  in Grand Rapids, MI
    Douwe J. Van der Werp presiding

1868
  in Graafschap, MI
    Roelof Duiker presiding

1869
  in Chicago, IL
    Koenraad Van den Bosch presiding

1870
  in Chicago, IL
    Willem H. Frieling presiding

1871
  in Chicago, IL
    Roelof Duiker presiding

1872
  in Chicago, IL
    Douwe J. Van der Werp presiding

1873
  in Chicago, IL
    Koenraad Van den Bosch presiding

1874
  in Chicago, IL
    Douwe J. Van der Werp presiding

1875
  in Chicago, IL
    Willem H. Frieling presiding

1876
  in Chicago, IL
    Gerrit E. Boer presiding

1877
  in Chicago, IL
    Willem H. Frieling presiding

1878
  in Chicago, IL
    John Kremer presiding

1879
  in Chicago, IL
    Leenert Rietdijk presiding

1880
  in Chicago, IL
    Roelof T. Kuiper presiding

1881
in Grand Rapids, MI
Leenert Rietdijk presiding

1882
in Grand Rapids, MI
Willem H. Frieling presiding

1883
in Grand Rapids, MI
Jan H. Vos presiding

1884
in Grand Rapids, MI
Lammert J. Hulst presiding

1886
in Grand Rapids, MI
Leenert Rietdijk presiding

1888
in Grand Rapids, MI
Evert Bos presiding

1890
in Grand Rapids, MI
Lammert J. Hulst presiding

1892
in Grand Rapids, MI
Andrew Keizer presiding

1894
in Grand Rapids, MI
Klaas Kuiper presiding

1896
in Grand Rapids, MI
Andrew Keizer presiding

1898
in Grand Rapids, MI
Jacob Manni presiding

1900
in Grand Rapids, MI
Andrew Keizer presiding

1902
in Holland, MI
Gabriel D. De Jong presiding

1904
in Holland, MI
Evert Breen presiding

1906
in Holland, MI
Hendrik Van Hoogen presiding

1908
in Muskegon, MI
Jacob Manni presiding

1910
in Muskegon, MI
John W. Brink presiding

1912
in Chicago, IL
Andrew Keizer presiding

1914
in Chicago, IL
Jacob Manni presiding

1916
in Grand Rapids, MI
Andrew Keizer presiding

1918
in Grand Rapids, MI
Idzerd Van Dellen presiding

1920
in Grand Rapids, MI
William P. Van Wijk presiding

1922
in Orange City, IA
Jacob Manni presiding

1924
in Kalamazoo, MI
Idzerd Van Dellen presiding

1926
in Chicago, IL
William P. Van Wijk presiding

1928
in Holland, MI
Henry Keegstra presiding

1930
in Grand Rapids, MI
William P. Van Wijk presiding

1932
in Grand Rapids, MI
Idzerd Van Dellen presiding

1934
in Grand Rapids, MI
William P. Van Wijk presiding

1936
in Grand Rapids, MI
Henry J. Kuiper presiding

1937
in Grand Rapids, MI
Henry J. Kuiper presiding

1938
in Grand Rapids, MI
Idzerd Van Dellen presiding

1939
in Grand Rapids, MI
Watson Groen presiding

1940
in Grand Rapids, MI
Watson Groen presiding

1941
in Grand Rapids, MI
Nicholas J. Monsma presiding

1942
in Grand Rapids, MI
Herman Bel presiding

1943
in Grand Rapids, MI
Gerrit Hoeksema presiding

1944
in Grand Rapids, MI
Gerrit Hoeksema presiding

1945
in Grand Rapids, MI
Martin Monsma presiding

1946
in Grand Rapids, MI
Herman Kuiper presiding

1947
in Grand Rapids, MI
Emo F.J. Van Halsema presiding

1948
in Grand Rapids, MI
Henry Baker presiding

1949
in Grand Rapids, MI
Emo F.J. Van Halsema presiding

1950
in Grand Rapids, MI
Martin Monsma presiding

1951
in Grand Rapids, MI
Henry Baker presiding

1952
in Grand Rapids, MI
Herman Bel presiding

1953
in Grand Rapids, MI
Emo F.J. Van Halsema presiding

1954
in Grand Rapids, MI
Herman Bel presiding

1955
in Grand Rapids, MI
Henry Baker presiding

1956
in Grand Rapids, MI
Herman Bel presiding

1957
in Grand Rapids, MI
Nicholas J. Monsma presiding

1958
in Grand Rapids, MI
Tenis C. Van Kooten presiding

1959
in Grand Rapids, MI
John Gritter presiding

1960
in Grand Rapids, MI
Tenis C. Van Kooten presiding

1961
in Grand Rapids, MI
William Haverkamp presiding

1962
in Grand Rapids, MI
John C. Verbrugge presiding

1963
in Grand Rapids, MI
William Haverkamp presiding

1964
in Grand Rapids, MI
Peter Y. De Jong presiding

1965
in Sioux Center, IA
William Haverkamp presiding

1966
in Pella, IA
William P. Brink presiding

1967
in Grand Rapids, MI
William Haverkamp presiding

1968
in Grand Rapids, MI
John C. Verbrugge presiding

1969
in Grand Rapids, MI
William P. Brink presiding

1970
in Grand Rapids, MI
Henry De Mots presiding

1971
in Grand Rapids, MI
George Gritter presiding

1972
in Grand Rapids, MI
Clarence Boomsma presiding

1973
in Grand Rapids, MI
Leonard Greenway presiding

1974
in Grand Rapids, MI
George Gritter presiding

1975
in Grand Rapids, MI
Clarence Boomsma presiding

1976
in Grand Rapids, MI
Henry Vander Kam presiding

1977
in Grand Rapids, MI
Bastiaan Nederlof presiding

1978
in Grand Rapids, MI
Clarence Boomsma presiding

1979
in Grand Rapids, MI
Leonard J. Hofman presiding

1980
in Grand Rapids, MI
Jacob D. Eppinga presiding

1981
in Grand Rapids, MI
John A. De Kruyter presiding

1982
in Grand Rapids, MI
Clarence Boomsma presiding

1983
in Grand Rapids, MI
Jacob D. Eppinga presiding

1984
in Grand Rapids, MI
Roger E. Van Harn presiding

1985
in Grand Rapids, MI
Calvin Bolt presiding

1986
in Grand Rapids, MI
Jacob D. Eppinga presiding

1987
in Grand Rapids, MI
Calvin Bolt presiding

1988
in Grand Rapids, MI
Calvin Bolt presiding

1989
in Grand Rapids, MI
Calvin Bolt presiding

1990
in Grand Rapids, MI
Howard D. Vanderwell presiding

1991
  in Sioux Center, IA
    Calvin Bolt presiding

1992
  in Grand Rapids, MI
    Howard D. Vanderwell presiding

1993
  in Grand Rapids, MI
    Peter W. Brouwer presiding

1994
  in Grand Rapids, MI
    Calvin Bolt presiding

1995
  in Grand Rapids, MI
    Calvin Bolt presiding

1996
  in Grand Rapids, MI
    John Van Ryn presiding

1997
  in Grand Rapids, MI
    Michael De Vries presiding

1998
  in Grand Rapids, MI
    Howard D. Vanderwell presiding

1999
  in Ancaster, ON
    Wayne A. Brouwer presiding

2000
  in Grand Rapids, MI
    Michael De Vries presiding

2001
  in Grand Rapids, MI
    Morris N. Greidanus presiding

2002
  in Grand Rapids, MI
    Norman L. Meyer presiding

CLASSES

Alberta
organized: 11/27/1951, from Classis Pacific
Inactive: Divided into Classes Alberta North and
Alberta South, 1956

Alberta North
organized: 11/8/1956, from Classis Alberta
Active

Alberta South
name changed to Alberta South/Saskatchewan

Alberta South/Saskatchewan
organized: 12/4/1956, from Classis Alberta
Name changed from Alberta South, 1977-8
Active

Arizona
organized: 9/20/1988, from Classis Rocky Mountain
Active

Atlantic Northeast
organized: 9/28/1976, from Classis Hudson
Active

British Columbia
organized: 9/23/1958, from Classis Pacific
Inactive: 9/15/1985
Divided into Classes British Columbia North-West and British Columbia-South-East

British Columbia North-West
organized: 9/18/1985, from Classis British Columbia
Active

British Columbia South-East
organized: 9/18/1985, from Classis British Columbia
Active

Cadillac
Name changed to Northern Michigan, 1994-5

California
Name changed to California South, 1962

California South
Name changed from California, 1962
organized: ca.9/5/1925, from Classis Pella
Daughter Classes
Rocky Mountain, 1955 (with congregations from Classis Pella)
Central California, 1962
Greater Los Angeles, 1989
Pacific Hanmi, 1996 (with congregations from Classis California South)
Active

Central California
organized: 9/19/1962, from Classis California
Active

Chatham
organized: 12/3/1952, from Classis Ontario
Daughter Classis
Huron, 1967 (with churches from Classis Toronto)
Active

Chicago North
Name changed to Northern Illinois, 1978-9

Chicago South
organized: 9/16/1941, from Classis Illinois
Daughter Classis
Illiana, 1966
Active

Columbia
organized: 10/16/1969, from Classis Pacific Northwest

Daughter Classis
  Yellowstone, 1989 (with congregations from
  Classis Rocky Mountain)
  Active

Eastern Canada
  former name: Eastern Ontario until 1968–9
  organized: 12/6/1952, from Classis Ontario
  Daughter Classis
  Quinte, 1967
  Active

Eastern Ontario
  Name changed to Eastern Canada, 1968–9

Eastfriesland
  See: Ostrfriesland

Florida
  Name changed to Southeast US, 1998/9

Georgetown
  organized: 9/22/1988, from Classes Georgetown
  and Zeeland
  Active

Grand Rapids
  organized: 7/19/1882, from Classis Michigan
  Daughter Classis
  Muskegon, 1888
  Inactive: Divided into Classes Grand Rapids East
  and Grand Rapids West, 1898

Grand Rapids East
  organized: 9/16/1898, from division of Classis
  Grand Rapids
  Daughter Classes
  Grand Rapids South, 1938 (with congregations
  from Grand Rapids West)
  Kalamazoo, 1928 (with congregations from
  Grand Rapids West)
  Ontario, 1950
  Lake Erie, 1960
  Thornapple Valley, 1980
  Active

Grand Rapids North
  former name: Grand Rapids West until 1971–2
  organized: 9/16/1898, from division of Classis
  Grand Rapids
  Daughter Classes
  Grand Rapids South, 1938 (with congregations
  from Grand Rapids East)

Kalamazoo, 1928 (with congregations from
  Grand Rapids East)
  Active

Grand Rapids South
  organized: 1/12/1938
  From Classes Grand Rapids East and Grand
  Rapids West
  Daughter Classis
  Grandville, 1958
  Active

Grand Rapids West
  Name changed to Grand Rapids North, 1971–2

Grandville
  organized: 1/15/1958
  From Grand Rapids South, 1958
  Daughter Classis
  Georgetown, 1988 (with congregations from
  Classis Zeeland)
  Active

Greater Los Angeles
  organized: 9/21/1989, from Classis California
  South
  Daughter Classis
  Pacific Hanmi, 1996 (with congregations from
  Classis California South)
  Active

Hackensack
  organized: 4/15/1890
  Was True Reformed Dutch Church, 1824–1889
  Active

Hamilton
  organized: 12/3/1952, from Classis Ontario, 1952
  Daughter Classis
  Toronto, 1957 (with congregations from Classis
  Eastern Ontario)
  Active

Heartland
  former name: Orange City until 1994–5
  organized: 3/21/1905, from Classis Iowa
  Daughter Classes
  Sioux Center, 1912
  Pacific, 1910
  Minnesota, 1937
  Rocky Mountain, 1955
  Active

Holland
  organized: 7/19/1882

From Michigan
Daughter Classis
Zeeland, 1908
Active

Hudson
organized: 6/5/1878, from Classis Michigan
Active

Huron
organized: 9/20/1967, from Classes Chatham and Toronto
Active

Iakota
former name: Sioux Center
organized: 9/24/1912, from Classis Orange City
Active

Illiana
organized: 9/20/1966, from Classis Chicago South
Active

Illinois
organized: 10/7/1868, from Classis Michigan
Daughter Classis
Iowa, 1877
Inactive: Divided into Chicago North and Chicago South, 1941

Iowa
organized: 10/3/1877, from Classis Illinois
Daughter Classes
Ostfriesland, 1896
Pella, 1904
Inactive: Became Classis Sioux Center, 1912

Kalamazoo
organized: 1/12/1938, from Classes Grand Rapids East and Grand Rapids West
Daughter Classis
Lake Erie, 1960 (with congregations from Grand Rapids East)
Active

Lake Erie
organized: 9/30/1960, from Classes Kalamazoo and Grand Rapids East
Active

Lake Superior
organized: 8/28/1952
Divided from Minnesota

Name changed from: Minnesota North, 1997/8
Active

Michigan
organized: 8/1/1868
Daughter Classis
Hudson, 1878
Inactive: Divided into Classes Grand Rapids and Holland, 1882

Minnesota
organized: 9/28/1937, from Classis Orange City
Inactive: Divided into Classes Minnesota North and Minnesota South, 8/28/1952

Minnesota North
Name changed to Lake Superior

Minnesota South
Name changed to Minnkota, 1998/9

Minnkota
former name: Minnesota South
organized: 8/28/1952
Divided from Minnesota
Active

Muskegon
organized: 8/22/1888, from Classis Grand Rapids
Daughter Classis
Cadillac, 1955
Active

Niagara
organized: 9/24/1986, from Classis Hamilton
Active

Northcentral Iowa
organized: 10/15/1896, from Classis Iowa
Name changed from Ostfriesland, 1958
Also known as East Friesland
Active

Northern Illinois
former name: Chicago North until 1978-9
organized: 9/16/1941, from Classis Illinois
Active

Northern Michigan
former name: Cadillac until 1994-5
organized: 7/6/1955, from Classis Muskegon
Active

Ontario
organized: 12/6/1950, from Classis Grand Rapids
East
Inactive: Divided into Classes Eastern Ontario,
Hamilton, Chatham, 1952

Orange City
Name changed to Heartland, 1994/5

Ostfriesland
Name changed to Northcentral Iowa, 1958

Pacific
Name changed to Pacific Northwest, March 1963

Pacific Hanmi
organized: 9/30/1996, from Classes California
South and Greater Los Angeles
Active

Pacific Northwest
former name: Pacific until March 1963
organized: 10/12/1910, from Classis Orange City
Daughter Classes
Alberta, 1954
British Columbia, 1958
Columbia, 1969
Active

Pella
organized: 9/11/1904
From Classis Iowa
Daughter Classis
California South, 1925 (with congregations from
Classis California)
Rocky Mountain, 1955 (with congregations from
Classis California)
Active

Quinte
organized: 9/14/1967, from Classis Eastern
Canada
Active

Red Mesa
organized: 9/15/1982, from Classis Rocky
Mountain
Active

Rocky Mountain
organized: 10/19/1955, from congregations from
Classes Pella and California
Daughter Classis
Yellowstone, 1989 (with congregations from
Classis Columbia)
Active

Sioux Center
Name changed to Iakota, 1978/9

Southeast US
former name: Florida, 1965–98
organized: 9/15/1965, from Classis Hackensack
Active

Thornapple Valley
organized: 9/16/1980, from Classis Grand
Rapids East, 1980
Active

Toronto
organized: 9/12/1956, from congregations from
Classes Hamilton and Eastern Ontario
Active

Wisconsin
organized: 9/10/1924, from Classis Illinois
Active

Yellowstone
organized: 9/13/1989, from congregations from
Classes Columbia and Rocky Mountain
Active

Zeeland
organized: 8/11/1908, from Classis Holland
Active